❧ VOLUME 4 ❧

THE PAPERS OF JOSEPH HENRY

January 1838–December 1840
The Princeton Years

Joseph Henry (1797–1878), from a daguerreotype presumably taken in the early 1840s. Courtesy of the Division of Photographic History, National Museum of American History, Smithsonian Institution.

The Papers of
JOSEPH HENRY

Editor: Nathan Reingold
Associate Editor: Arthur P. Molella
Assistant Editor: Marc Rothenberg
Staff Historian: Kathleen Waldenfels
Research Assistant: Joan F. Steiner

VOLUME 4

January 1838–December 1840
The Princeton Years

SMITHSONIAN INSTITUTION PRESS
CITY OF WASHINGTON
1981

Published in the United States by the Smithsonian Institution Press.
Designed by Crimilda Pontes.
Produced in the United States by Heritage Printers, Inc.

ENDPAPERS: *A modern view of Nassau Hall—in Henry's day the center of college activities. Courtesy of the Princeton University Archives.*

Library of Congress Cataloging in Publication Data

Henry, Joseph, 1797–1878.
The papers of Joseph Henry.

Includes bibliographical references.

CONTENTS: *v. 1. December 1797–October 1832: the Albany years.*
          v. 2. November 1832–December 1835: the Princeton years.
          v. 3. January 1836–December 1837: the Princeton years.
          v. 4. January 1838–December 1840: the Princeton years.

1. Science—Collected works.
2. Science—History—United States—Collected works.
3. Smithsonian Institution—Collected works.
  I. Reingold, Nathan, ed.
QH113.H43   537'.092'4   72–2005
ISBN 0–87474–123–8 (V. 1)

❧ CONTENTS ❧

❧ ILLUSTRATIONS ❧

Frontispiece: Joseph Henry

Following page 222:

Asa Gray

Robert Hare

Letter from Joseph Henry to Alexander Dallas Bache,
January 3, 1839

William C. Redfield

James P. Espy

The Princeton campus

Philosophical Hall

John William Draper

Stephen Alexander

Antoine-César Becquerel

Charles Grafton Page

The closing years of the 1830s were filled with economic uncertainty, rising sectional conflict, disputes over the Canadian border, and harsh political debate. Joseph Henry was not immune from or uninterested in the effects of political controversy or economic downturns. Such affairs intruded into his life but were usually at the periphery of his thoughts. The dominant theme of this volume is Joseph Henry as scientist. With renewed enthusiasm generated from his experiences in Europe, the now forty-year-old Henry returned to the problems of the laboratory and the institutional and social structure of the American scientific community.

Although occasionally drawn into other areas of science by the arrival of a journal or the observation of a curious phenomenon, Henry's scientific preoccupations during the years 1838 through 1840 were electricity and magnetism. In April 1838 he conducted his first sustained experiments in nearly two years. Thereafter his work in the laboratory fell into a distinct pattern. Periods of intense activity during the spring and fall alternated with quiescent intervals in the summer and winter when he was immersed in teaching.

Henry's principal vehicle for professional dissemination of his work was the American Philosophical Society. Five times during these years he presented the results of his research in electromagnetism to a Society meeting. On November 2, 1838, "Contributions III" was read. "Contributions IV" was presented in two parts on June 19, 1840, and November 20, 1840. Shorter, less formal, letters were read at the meetings of May 4, 1838, and October 18, 1839. With the possible exception of the October 1839 communication (a very specific response to a conclusion Faraday had drawn in a recent publication), these presentations do not represent logical terminating points in a particular set of experiments. They are progress reports written at the end of a period of concentrated experimentation concluded by the college calendar, not choice. The letters grew out of Henry's fear of loss of priority in his continuing race with Faraday and others to describe and explicate the phenomena of electricity and magnetism. As published papers, their appearance was probably premature. In his haste to secure recognition of his work and establish priority, Henry sometimes presented research results which were still only half-digested. The haste involved in publishing "Contributions III" and "Contributions IV" is implicit in the disorganized nature of the publications. More explicitly, the two papers are peppered with reports of anomalous results not yet understood and requiring further research, or corrections of previous errors resulting from generalization upon insufficient data. Henry also left dangling certain threads of his research. Not until the experiments of 1841 and 1842 (to be presented in the next volume of *The Papers of Joseph Henry*), reported to the American Philosophical Society in "Contributions V," did Henry complete the phase of his research activity begun in April 1838.

When Henry resumed his research efforts in April 1838 his "primary object . . . was to discover, if possible, inductive actions in common electricity analogous to those found in galvanism."[1] During April his success with static electricity proved most exciting. But when he presented "Contributions III" on November 2, 1838, he spent less than a third of his time on static electricity. The major portion of the discussion centered on the phenomena of galvanic induction, which Henry had been studying at this time only as a preliminary step to his work on static electricity. Somewhat to his surprise, he made some extremely interesting discoveries with galvanic electricity.

There are six major sections to "Contributions III." The initial section examines the conditions which influence self-induction. Section two expands this study to secondary currents produced by galvanic induction. Henry was particularly interested in determining the necessary conditions for producing quantity or intensity currents. In the course of his experiments he found that an intensity current could induce one of quantity and, conversely, that quantity currents could induce those of intensity—the fundamental principle of the transformer. The following section contains Henry's discovery that secondary currents could be induced over great distances and through wooden partitions. In section four he expanded upon the latter discovery in an effort to generalize Humphry Davy's finding that one could not screen the magnetizing effect of electricity on steel needles. After considerable trial and error, Henry concluded that all conductors could shield galvanic induction, but nonconductors had no effect. He argued that the screening was produced by the induction of a current in the conducting substances, which in turn neutralized the primary; Davy's result was a special case due to the particular structure of the experiment. Henry viewed the neutralization of the primary by the screening current as a third-order effect and wondered if higher order induced currents could be isolated. In the fifth section he described his success at isolating higher order currents and identified their direction relative to the primary current.

---

[1] "Contributions III," paragraph 3.

At last, in the sixth and final section, Henry turned to static electricity. Having first confirmed the differences between lateral discharges and inductions from static electricity, Henry proceeded to show the various analogies between static and galvanic induction. He demonstrated induction at a distance, screening, and the existence of higher order inductions. At first he discovered anomalies in the direction of the higher order currents, but eventually was able to demonstrate that the direction was dependent upon the distances between conductors.

In "Contributions IV"—presented in two parts on June 19 and November 20, 1840—Henry continued to focus on galvanic induction. The prime object of study in "Contributions III" was the current induced at the sudden termination of a galvanic current, i.e., at the breaking of a circuit. Currents induced at the formation of a current, i.e., at the completion of the circuit, were too weak to discuss with much confidence. But by modifying the experimental set-up and utilizing a Daniell constant battery, Henry was now able to generate inductions at the formation of a galvanic current strong enough to compare with those created at the breaking of the circuit.

The first of the three major sections of "Contributions IV" is Henry's investigation of the conditions which influence the inductive action at the formation of the current, as well as a comparison of these inductions with those created at the termination of the current. He found that the two types exhibited similar properties. In both cases he was able to create higher order inductive currents with corresponding alternating directions. Both types of currents could be screened. The transformer effect could be produced with equal ease.

In the second section Henry expanded on a letter written to Alexander Dallas Bache on October 16, 1839,[2] and subsequently read to the American Philosophical Society. Much to Henry's surprise, Michael Faraday's pronouncements in his Fourteenth Series on screening by conducting bodies were in direct opposition to Henry's findings in "Contributions III." Faraday had concluded there was no screening. Confident that he could not have misinterpreted his own results, Henry reexamined his work, ultimately deciding that both men were half right. The secondary current appeared to consist of two parts of differing intensities and properties. The low-intensity part could only be screened by iron, while the high-intensity part was screenable by any conductor. Depending upon the arrangement of the apparatus, the experimenter could vary the part he was examining. Moreover, higher order inductive currents were almost exclusively high intensity and hence screenable.

---

[2] Printed below.

The final section of "Contributions IV" contains Henry's attempt to reduce all the induction phenomena to a few simple laws. Utilizing the work of Faraday[3] and Ohm's Law, Henry converted galvanic inductions to graphic representations. By qualitatively analyzing these graphs with particular concern for the relative intensity and quantity of the respective currents, Henry was able to show that all inductive phenomena were the result of the sometimes complex interactions of currents. In some cases inductive currents reinforced, while in others they neutralized. He fitted what had been seen as a diverse collection of facts into previously established theoretical models, creating a new framework for the understanding of galvanic and static induction.

Henry concluded "Contributions IV" with an announcement that he had conducted a series of experiments on induction from static electricity and felt that the same theoretical framework which explained galvanic induction would suffice for static. He refused to come to a definite conclusion, however, until further experiments had been attempted, foreshadowing "Contributions V."

On a superficial level "Contributions III" and "Contributions IV" received rapid and extensive recognition by the European scientific community. The articles were reprinted in a number of journals,[4] while selected results were incorporated into standard texts.[5] Everyone seemed interested in the existence of higher order inductive currents. Once again Henry had proven his mastery of electromagnetic apparatus. His manipulative skills and ability to bring his laboratory insights to fruition obviously impressed Europeans. And yet Faraday, whose scientific concerns had paralleled Henry's so often in the past, responded to these papers with at best mild interest. There is no evidence that Faraday was bothered by Henry's priority in the shielding experiments or the subsequent analysis of the apparent contradictions in the results of the two scientists. Faraday's interests were now centered on dielectrics, a subject Henry had barely touched.

---

[3] Specifically, *Experimental Researches in Electricity*, First Series, paragraph 26, which deals with the direction of induced currents, and Third Series, paragraph 366, which concludes that the deflecting force on a galvanometer needle is dependent upon the quantity and not the intensity of the electricity passing through. As L. Pearce Williams points out in his *Michael Faraday: A Biography* (New York, 1965), pp. 218–219, in the latter case Faraday was wrong generally but correct for specific conditions. Fortunately, Henry was concerned with the same conditions: a rapid discharge of relatively high voltage rather than a steady-state current.

[4] e.g., *The Annals of Electricity, Magnetism, and Chemistry*, 1839–1840, 4:281–310, and 1841, 7:21–56; *Annales de chimie et de physique*, 1841, 3d ser. 3:394–436; *Phil. Mag.*, 1840, 3d ser. 16:200–210, 254–265, 551–562, and 1841, 3d ser. 18:482–514.

[5] Two examples are J. Frederic Daniell, *An Introduction to the Study of Chemical Philosophy*, 2d ed. (London, 1843), pp. 590–591, and Antoine-César Becquerel, *Traité expérimental de l'électricité et du magnétisme*, 7 vols. (Paris, 1834–1840), 5, part 2:98–106.

Introduction

While grappling with the intricate experimental problems of "Contributions III" and "Contributions IV," Henry pursued collateral lines of research which run as subthemes through the Record of Experiments. Two were prospects for contemplated but never-realized publications: patterns of magnetization and electroacoustics. The former was a long-standing concern going back to his early years at Princeton. His interest was partially rekindled by publications of M. H. von Jacobi. Ampère's theoretical models continued to guide his thinking in magnetization.

By contrast, electroacoustics was a totally new phenomenon to Henry, first suggested to him by an article of Charles Grafton Page. It was Page who noticed that an iron bar under inductive influence gave forth a sonorous tone which he called galvanic music. Henry never accepted Page's molecular explanation of the effect. But his follow-up experiments on galvanic music and on the related effect of magneto-striction (the influence of magnetization on the dimensions of a body) failed to yield a satisfactory theoretical alternative, which probably explains the lack of a publication by Henry on these experiments.

There is a miscellany of other scientific interests represented in this volume. Electrochemistry in both its scientific (the sustaining battery) and technological aspects (the electrotyping of Jacobi) received sporadic attention. Optical polarization, a subject Henry picked up in Europe chiefly from Babinet and Brewster, caught his imagination for its possible links with electricity—an interrelationship which greatly concerned Faraday. An accidental observation in the laboratory gave rise to a different topic—the diffusion of mercury through lead by capillary action. Henry related the phenomenon to electricity and eventually to the theory of matter. This work later resulted in two publications. Having received some notoriety in London for manipulations of thermoelectricity, Henry made it the subject of occasional study in the period 1838–1840, redoing some experiments of J. D. Forbes, for example.

"Atmospheric" phenomena were a perennial side-interest. In response to a solicitation from Bache, he wrote an informal survey of meteorology for Bache's use in preparing a report to the British Association. He also found himself briefly in the middle of heated theoretical controversy between William Redfield and James P. Espy on the nature of cyclones. Henry continued to oblige fellow observers with late-night observations of meteor showers and the aurora borealis. And an equally beautiful phenomenon, a brilliant rainbow seen in Princeton, evoked from Henry a rare blend of objective description and aesthetic appreciation.

*   *   *   *   *

"I have now again got into my old track and things go on with me something after their usual fashion," Henry wrote Alexander Bache on August 9, 1838,[6] nine months after his European tour. His prodigious laboratory output was perhaps the best sign that life had begun to return to normal. He now had time to publish his results, to reflect upon some of the science he had learned abroad, and to reassume his active role in the scientific community. Despite the lure of other job offers, Henry had clearly decided to settle in at Princeton, where existence was made increasingly pleasant by inducements from the administration: a renovated Philosophical Hall, assistants for his laboratory, and a new house (in which the Henrys had their fourth and last child in 1839).

Yet life had not returned completely to normal. Henry's European experience profoundly affected his perceptions of himself and his American environment. What Henry saw from this new perspective was both gratifying and deeply disturbing to him.

Received as a peer by Europe's scientific elite, Henry felt he had arrived professionally. After returning to Princeton, he carefully nurtured his many European contacts. He initiated exchanges of books and reprints with Faraday, Becquerel, Pouillet, and other new European friends. His burgeoning correspondence with English and French colleagues brought him fully into the informal communications network that is so vital to the life of science. Formal channels of communication were also opened. For instance, Adolphe Quetelet, the Belgian astronomer and statistician, invited Henry to send contributions to his journal, the *Correspondance mathématique et physique*[7] (although Henry apparently did not oblige).

When European scientists sought American scientific cooperation, Henry was one of the first to be consulted. One such approach figures prominently in this volume: the attempt by British geophysicists to enlist American counterparts in a Magnetic Crusade. North American data was needed to fulfill Edward Sabine's dream of a global map of terrestrial magnetism. Americans were thus given a chance to participate in a great effort of worldwide data-gathering, one of the many cooperative scientific endeavors that were characteristic of the 1830s.[8] As matters turned out, lack of government support seriously curtailed U.S. involvement, but even the limited participation of American scientists was evidence of their enhanced visibility in the sciences.

Despite signs that science in America was coming of age, Henry's Euro-

[6] Printed below.
[7] Letter of Quetelet of July 29, 1838, below.
[8] As we were reminded by Walter F. Cannon, "History in Depth: The Early Victorian Period," *History of Science*, 1964, 3:21.

pean experience accentuated his fears of national inadequacy, fears that were widely shared among scientists of his generation. Henry had no reason to doubt the demonstrations of respect shown him abroad. Yet, he could still comment that the British held a "generally low opinion [of] American science and literature."[9] While shrugging off some of such criticisms as aristocratic snobbery, Henry believed that most of this prejudice had a factual basis. "When I first returned from England," he confessed to Bache in one of the most revealing letters of this volume, "I was much dissatisfied with many things both in reference to my own affairs and those of the public generally."[10] There followed a litany of complaints. Confronting Henry were inventors whose self-assurance was matched only by their cupidity, and fringe savants—well-meaning lay theorists, cranks of various degrees of eccentricity, and outright charlatans. To him they were part of a spectrum including the writers of the dreary mediocrity so often found even in U.S. journals publishing substantial contributions to knowledge.

Quacks and charlatans, to use the contemporary epithets, caused great anguish among Henry's inner circle. In Bache's apocalyptic phrase, science must "put down quackery or quackery will put down science." Henry called these charlatans a national disgrace and quietly voiced fears that Europeans would get wind of their mischief. Yet, when one noted British scientist was told of an embarrassing instance, he made nothing of it, at least not publicly. Such things also existed in Britain and France[11] but by and large scientists there could disregard them as the scientists were "established" and set the norms for "truth"; here the situation was problematic. Sharing Henry's fears of European exposure, John Torrey pleaded with him, "Why will you not use your influence in putting down this miserable spirit of quackery in our country?"[12] Torrey's faith in Henry's powers, naive in view of the dimensions of the issues involved, is another indication of how other scientists viewed the Professor of Natural Philosophy at the College of New Jersey.

Henry did act in the summer of 1838 in the case of Henry Hall Sherwood. An obscure New York physician with a bent for eccentric theorizing, Sherwood approached Congress with a new concept of terrestrial magnetism. What the New York doctor considered revolutionary, Henry considered sheer quackery. A Senate committee's favorable response moved Henry to publish a rejoinder in a Princeton journal. Sherwood, he felt, set a horrible

[9] Henry to Bache, August 9, 1838, below.
[10] Ibid.
[11] In France, theorists on the scientific fringe rose to challenge established scientific authority in the late eighteenth century. See Roger

Hahn, *The Anatomy of a Scientific Institution: The Paris Academy of Sciences, 1666–1803* (Berkeley, 1971), chapter 5.
[12] On August 2, 1838, below.

precedent for government science. In addition to criticizing the physician's magnetic theories, Henry addressed the deeper problem of public gullibility. He stressed the importance of intellectual standards and of deference to proper authority—in this case, expert knowledge of the electromagnetic physicist. He made light of the pro-Sherwood testimonials given by eminently respectable, but scientifically unqualified public figures. Henry reiterated these ideological points on the several other occasions when he exposed cases of charlatanism or scientific incompetence in the popular press.[13]

Henry also criticized fellow scientists for being too tolerant of unprofessional behavior. Noting, for example, a deterioration of editorial standards in the *American Journal of Science,* he admonished the senior Silliman to establish a panel of expert "collaborators" to assist him in refereeing articles outside his own areas of competence. A decade later, as President of the American Association for the Advancement of Science, Henry would attempt to urge upon the general scientific community a code of ethics designed in part to combat scientific fraud and incompetence.

Beset by quackery and public misunderstanding, Henry and his coterie regarded themselves as a small, beleaguered minority. They assumed the scientific community was properly theirs to control. Indicative of this attitude were Henry's remarks to Bache about some of the consequences of their European sojourn:

> An absence from a place for a single year makes many changes and you will probably find My Dear Bache that the two years you have been absent has made as great a change in the disposition of things which you once controlled as if you had been consigned to the grave during that period. Persons with whom you have associated and perhaps controlled have learned to do without you and measures and plans which you have laboured to advance are set aside for others not as good but carried into operation because the production of others and those on the spot.[14]

Unity was considered essential to effective action. Yet existing groups were extremely fragile. For example, the "club," the informal peer organization in Philadelphia to which Henry belonged, fell apart in 1840 as members pursued separate careers. There was a need felt for more permanent organizations, but only under proper conditions. In the period covered by this and the next volume, Henry and his scientific allies came out

---

[13] See his letter to the *Newark Daily Advertiser,* August 1, 1838, below.

[14] August 9, 1838, below.

against two proposals for national scientific organizations: the physician John Collins Warren's American Institution for the Cultivation of Science, modeled on the British Association, and Francis Markoe's National Institute, in Washington. The opposition of the Henry group had much to do with the failure of the former and the stunted life-history of the latter. The "promiscuous assemblies" of amateurs and professionals in the British Association aroused Henry's skepticism. Transferring that model to egalitarian America might lead to submersion of the scientifically talented in a sea of inferior scientists and well-intentioned but technically illiterate laymen—not to mention cranks and quacks.

Henry and his Philadelphia allies were, consequently, unimpressed with the Boston group supporting Warren's initiative. They were probably even less impressed with Markoe, the obscure State Department official behind the National Institute. Henry feared that the Washington-based organization would fall prey to amateurs and to partisan politics.

The late 1830s have been portrayed as a gestation period for national scientific organizations.[15] Although not opposed to national initiatives per se, Henry, Bache, and other leading scientists revealed other priorities—at least at that time. They may have considered their community of dedicated professionals as yet too small to warrant association on a national scale. Moreover, in Henry's opinion, the core professional group had more important goals:

> The real working men in the way of science in this country should make common cause and endeavour by every proper means unitedly to raise our scientific character, to make science more respected at home, to increase the facilities of scientific investigation and the inducements to scientific labours.[16]

Put another way, his objective was to improve the conditions for research in America. The motley representation of a large national body would likely dilute this research ideal. Henry preferred more specialized forums (but not so highly specialized as the disciplinary organizations that formed after the Civil War). He and others were also not averse to working with existing structures: examples are the rehabilitation of the American Philosophical Society, the infusion of a research ethos in others (such as the Franklin Institute),[17] and the invigoration of science in the colleges.

[15] Sally Gregory Kohlstedt, *The Foundation of the American Scientific Community: The American Association for the Advancement of Science, 1848–60* (Urbana, Chicago, London, 1976), chapter 2.

[16] Henry to Bache, August 9, 1838.

[17] For the scientists' strategy regarding the Franklin Institute, see Bruce Sinclair, *Philadelphia's Philosopher Mechanics: A History of the Franklin Institute, 1824–1865* (Baltimore and London, 1974).

Henry took a cautiously optimistic view of the increase of the governmental role in science. "There is a disposition on the part of our government to advance the cause [of science] if this were properly directed," he wrote Bache, but the Sherwood example and others made him wary: "at present . . . Charlatanism is much more likely to meet with attention and reward than true unpretending merit."[18] The remedy, in Henry's mind, was to place control of such matters in the hands of the scientists themselves, that is, those who possessed the necessary competence. Henry greatly admired the peer review process used by the British Association in allocating private funds for research and thought the same principle might be applied to the apportionment of research support in the United States. Up to that point, the federal government had a mixed record as a patron of research. The Wilkes Expedition, launched in August 1838, proved a great vexation to the scientists involved, like Asa Gray. The political infighting was horrendous. In one of the early attempts by a scientific organization to gain federal financial backing, the American Philosophical Society failed in its bid to procure a War Department subvention for U. S. participation in the British-led Magnetic Crusade. Yet, a sign of things to come, the Army's Topographical Bureau eventually awarded a small amount in support of Bache's magnetic observatory at Girard College.

Public indoctrination in the methods and values of science was a prerequisite for the implementation of Henry's views. Yet Henry and his research-oriented compeers expressed mixed feelings about taking part in such endeavors. Opportunities to instruct the layman were never lacking in America in the 1830s and 1840s, the heyday of the popular lecture. Some scientists like Silliman leaped wholeheartedly into the enterprise. Others like Torrey found it financially expedient but demeaning to play the "Great Magician."[19] Bache took a perverse pleasure and excelled at amusing and instructing an impressionable public, only complaining that it cost him "more labour than a hundred pages of my book & lasted one hour & 20 minutes! The effect perhaps less enduring."[20] Henry's reservations were well known. Still, in early 1839, he delivered six lectures on sound and electromagnetism to New York's Mercantile Library Association. He initially questioned the propriety of his involvement and, lacking the oratorical confidence of a practiced public lecturer, expressed some nervousness at performing experiments before a large assembly. Despite his lack of self-confidence, Henry had good market value as a lecturer. His six hundred dollar fee was at the higher end of the scale for nationally prominent

---

[18] Henry to Bache, August 9, 1838, below.
[19] Letter of January 15, 1840, below.

[20] Letter to Henry of February 13, 1840, below.

speakers in that period.[21] By Henry's account, his performance was well received by an audience of well over a thousand, which, incidentally, he could not resist chiding with "remarks on the subject of quackery in the City of New York."[22]

The question arose, could a scientist still be counted a serious investigator while active in broader educational contexts? Bache took slight umbrage at Henry's implication that his role as President of Girard College took away from his commitment to research. Using a popular contemporary phrase, he assured Henry his objective remained to "extend" not just to "diffuse" knowledge. Still, a research commitment did not preclude a deep interest in public instruction. Bache and Henry exchanged concerned letters about plans for Girard College and Bache's study of European primary and secondary education. An imperious note entered these discussions. As in their planning for the scientific community, Bache assumed that he and Henry should have a strong personal influence on American educational patterns. For instance, considering the adaptation of the German "Real Schools" to America, Bache looked for an "opportunity to urge them upon our non professional classes, ex cathedra."[23] Assumptions like this and their denouements over time will appear in later volumes.

Although there were important events in Henry's life during these three years, there were no abrupt transitions or major changes. Adjustment and steady evolution after the European experience were the keynotes—this was a process which continued into the mid-1840s. This volume, then, becomes, like Henry's publications, a progress report terminated by the calendar, rather than a logically self-contained unit. Research, family responsibilities, collegiate activities, participation in the institutional development of American science, and transatlantic associations are all themes which will continue into the remaining Princeton volumes.

*   *   *   *   *

The editorial work on this volume of *The Papers of Joseph Henry* was supported by the Smithsonian Institution. The National Historical Publications and Records Commission and the Peter C. Cornell Trust Fund provided welcome additional funding. Once again we wish to acknowledge the interest and concern of the Joint Committee of our sponsoring organizations.

A former staff member, Joel N. Bodansky, contributed to the early stages

---

[21] Donald M. Scott, "The Popular Lecture and the Creation of a Public in Mid-Nineteenth-Century America," *The Journal of American History*, 1980, 66:792–793.

[22] Henry to Harriet Henry, February 5–6, 1839, below.

[23] Letter of February 13, 1840, below.

of this volume. Beverly Jo Lepley, Administrative Officer of the project, not only prepared the typescript of this volume, but managed the daily activities of this office.

We continue to be indebted to a large number of historians, archivists, and librarians for all manner of assistance. They deserve much credit for the virtues of what follows. Our efforts were particularly aided by colleagues at the Smithsonian Institution Archives and the Smithsonian Institution Libraries. The contributions of our designer, Crimilda Pontes of the Smithsonian Institution Press, are self-evident and much appreciated by the staff of the Henry Papers.

We and our readers are also under a debt of gratitude to the holders of the originals who so graciously cooperated in our efforts. In addition to the Smithsonian Institution Archives, they are:

American Philosophical Society Library
Beinecke Library, Yale University
British Library
College of Physicians of Philadelphia
Duke University Library
Eisenhower Library, Johns Hopkins University
Gray Herbarium Library, Harvard University
Historical Society of Pennsylvania
Institution of Electrical Engineers, London
Library of Congress
National Archives and Records Service
New York Botanical Garden Library
New-York Historical Society
Pierpont Morgan Library
Princeton University Archives
Public Record Office, London
Royal Society of London
State Historical Society of Wisconsin

No volume in this endeavor can pass into print without mention of our very great indebtedness to the volunteers who transcribed the original manuscripts.

ON METHOD AND STYLE

Reprinted from the first volume of
The Papers of Joseph Henry.

Car rien ne supplée aux documents: pas de documents, pas d'histoire . . .
—Langlois and Seignobos,
Introduction aux études historiques,
2d ed. (Paris, 1899), p. 2.

Complete disclosure of working assumptions and operating techniques is not feasible, even with the best of intentions. The literature of history is strewn with examples of later disclosures of assumptions hidden not only from readers but even from their originators. And a detailed accounting of rationales, procedures, and techniques would soon weary even the most ardent lover of historical shop talk. What follows is an overview of our intentions and a succinct guide to necessary particulars of our practice.

Objectivity is widely ascribed to editing of documents by fellow historians and laymen alike. With the coming of the modern editorial projects associated with the program of the National Historical Publications Commission, this belief was undoubtedly reinforced. The sheer quality and quantity of the historical record thus made available has had considerable impact. We are most aware and appreciative of our great predecessors and contemporaries in historical editing. Writing footnotes on the shoulders of giants is not comfortable. While emulation animates us, so too does the consciousness of differences. And these differences, subtle and gross, arise partly from the three elements from which the objectivity of historical editing supposedly derives: the inclusiveness of the edited texts; their accuracy; and the impartial reliability of annotations.

Providing authentic historical source material is the ultimate justification for historical editing. Historical editors are predisposed to complete coverage of relevant documentation. After all, if presenting documentation is good, the more presented, the better. The importance of the subjects (e.g., Founding Fathers) often endows every scrap with an appreciable measure of value. Beyond these factors is the memory of a long, sad history of editions flawed by omissions due to incomplete research and arbitrary excisions. While the comprehensiveness of volumes in the National Historical Publications Commission's program has had most beneficial consequences, the implied goal of literal completeness has raised real problems. In practice, of course, literal completenesss is not attained, but rather inclusiveness within a carefully delimited domain. Even so, the size of the documentation plus the bulk of the editorial apparatus has generated editorial projects beyond a lifetime's capacity, perhaps even requiring several generations. If this is so for major figures of the eighteenth and early nineteenth centuries, the problems for the editors of the papers of later worthies are many times multiplied—in fact, multiplied in proportion to the increase in the numbers of surviving manuscripts.

One way out is simply to microfilm the originals, without annotations, avoiding not only the cost of printing but the burden of financing an editorial staff over a long time period. But only a few fellow specialists will look at manuscripts, filmed or original. Another strategy calls for selected editions in letterpress. Our solution is to combine the letterpress and the microfilm editions—but with one essential modification. Our printed volumes will constitute an interpretive select edition. The existence of the microfilm edition will amply discharge our obligation to present an exhaustive body of source materials, enabling the printed work to stand or fall on its merits as a history of a special kind. To aid our research and to produce a guide for the microfilm edition, we are describing and indexing the Henry documentation by means of a computer system.

Specifying fixed standards of selection is impossible for that implies foreknowledge of both the contents of all the manuscripts, even those yet ungathered, as well as complete assurance of what topics are preeminently important. Even with extensive preparation, this first volume is filled with surprising documents entailing unpredictable research. Rather than fixed standards, we operate by working resolutions. The first is to document Henry's research and professional career for an understanding of both science and the growth of the national scientific community. The second is to use the life of Joseph Henry as an occasion to present a broad documentary history of a period and a place, not merely a narrow recital of events in a career. The life becomes the thread upon which the beads of history are strung. We are impelled in this regard by the belief that science is not a foreign body embedded in the national culture but integrally part of it. Our aim is to merge imperceptibly the scientific work and the general background, to present few sharp edges between the "internal" life of science and the "external" milieu. Sharp edges occur more frequently in the literature than they do in reality. Third, we will make a deliberate attempt to include evidences of the routine of daily activities which define the texture of the past as much as, if not more than, the grand themes of the professional literature.

Still another viewpoint has influenced our editorial attitudes toward comprehensivness and selectivity. Justifications for the letterpress editions of eminent Americans rightly and understandably stress the value of the evidence for the study of the lives and works of their subjects. All too often the richness of information beyond the obvious is overlooked. Excluding cases where time destroyed most sources, the more interesting the personage, the wider the range of topics occurring in his papers. Merely to select for known, obvious themes would deprive readers of much knowledge while presenting a distorted view of the man. Our solution deliberately strives to exploit the unexpected subject-diversity of the sources. Science, education, and institutional histories will occur in these volumes; so too will economics, politics, and religion.

To these resolutions we must add a caveat. Our treatment is limited by the nature of the surviving evidence. Topics absent or nearly so get short shrift, no matter their importance. In this volume we have very little to say about Henry before his twenty-fifth year because so few manuscripts survive. His Albany work on electromagnetic induction is barely touched upon for the same reason. In our coverage of the years in Princeton, Henry's scientific work will receive incomparably better documentation. This caveat is not a sign of weakness. On the contrary, if our documentation did not disclose much that is fresh and valuable, we might have no other choice than to ruminate endlessly over the absent topics.

The second source of the belief in objectivity in historical editing is textual accuracy. Modern editions shine by comparison with the standard of most past efforts. The obvious care for detail in converting a manuscript to print here complements inclusiveness of the sources and the density of annotations. Some details of our practice are given in the next section. Our intention is to give the text as close to the original as print permits with only a few modifications required for the understanding of modern readers. And these few modifications are explained in footnotes, if not covered explicitly by our general remarks on style. Although undoubtedly the most objective aspect of historical editing, the process is hardly mechanical. Some manuscripts are physically messy; even very legible manuscripts may contain pen strokes which no longer communicate. Errors can occur despite great care. Legitimate differences of opinion are possible. While striving for perfection, the editors have recognized that goal as other-worldly and welcome any improved readings from friends and colleagues.

Perhaps the least objective aspect of editions of historical documents are the annotations. If editors blandly limit footnotes to matter-of-fact identifications of names and the like, the impression of objectivity is further strengthened. Two different problems are involved: what is selected for footnoting and the depths to which one probes in a footnote. There is no example of historical editing which does not silently omit footnotes others might regard as desirable. (Or conversely, the edition is vulnerable for singling out minor points.) There is no example of historical editing others cannot fault for too little (or too much) annotation of particular points. Even a decision simply to give the original texts with the barest of annotations says much about an editor. Inevitably, historical editing has an appreciable element of human art. A footnote is not an occasion for mere display of erudition, but an exercise in conveying meaningful content.

We are not squeamish about stating opinions frankly. If circumstances seem appropriate, we will expand the detail given in annotations, as well as in our commentary. Readers of this volume also will occasionally encounter fairly detailed explanations of our procedures, involving both successes and failures in research. Historians have an obligation to indicate the degree of certainty of facts and interpretations. More important, we feel that the steps in historical research and reasoning should remain visible to professionals and laymen alike in order to elucidate the nature of history as a research process.

This volume (and its successors) is best understood in cinematic terms. A time succession of documents passes before the eyes of the reader. The editors, conscientious drones assembling the frames of the film, want to help the viewer of the documents. Deliberately, they insert related film clips, sometimes before the document but usually in the course of the document. These take the form of footnotes. Sometimes, the editors simply scrap a document and appear on film themselves, explaining points in the plot. What must strike the eye of the intelligent reader is the role of time. If the manuscripts are the main story line—the time-present of the plot— then the editorial apparatus is not simply about that particular moment. Past and future times are mingled in the editors' inserted film clips. Rarely are they solely about the moment of the events penned by our cast of characters.

Unlike the author of a screenplay, the editor of historical documents does not create his cast and he cannot manipulate his characters in devising his plot. Footnotes reflect imperfect comprehensions of what preceded and incomplete apprehensions of what will follow. Neither reader nor editor will really know the plot until the end. Until then, surprise and, perhaps, pleasure should draw us forward to the next volume.

⇥{ NOTES ON STYLE }⇤

Our practices are generally similar to those of other editorial projects, particularly to those of the Adams Papers. The nature of our documents and our personal inclinations have resulted in a few departures from the style of that great project, and these are noted below. In preparing this volume we followed an expanded and revised version of the style manual prepared prior to the editing of volume one. Copies of the revised manual are available to scholars interested in the editing of historical documents. Here a few points necessary for the reader's understanding are presented.

Organization

Documents are given in chronological order. If a specific date is not given or is not ascribable, the document is placed at the end of the dated documents from the nearest unit of time to which it can be tied. For example, if only the year can be determined, the document will appear at the end of all the items of that year. If the month and year are available but not the day, the document will appear after the fully dated documents of that month and year. Where the year is in doubt, the item will normally appear in an appendix.

Preliminaries to the Documents

Preliminaries to the documents are title, provenance note, and (sometimes) an introductory headnote.

The title briefly signals what is to come. In the case of correspondence, if Henry is the author of the letter, we simply indicate to whom he is writing:

TO BENJAMIN SILLIMAN, SR.

or we note the name of the person writing to Joseph Henry:

FROM BENJAMIN SILLIMAN, SR.

If Henry is neither the author nor the recipient, both parties are specified:

BENJAMIN SILLIMAN, SR., TO ROBERT HARE

In the case of noncorrespondence items, we prefer using the titles given on the originals. If the title is lacking or if the given title is noncommunicative, the editors will devise a suitable title, usually with an explanatory footnote. "RECORD OF EXPERIMENTS" will be used for entries from Henry's three-volume laboratory notebook. Entries from his various reading and lecture notebooks will be titled HENRY NOTEBOOK ENTRY.

The provenance note, immediately following the title, briefly gives the location of the original and, if necessary, the nature of the document being published (i.e., "draft," "retained copy," etc.). If these matters are too complicated for the provenance note, we normally provide additional pertinent details in a footnote. In the provenance note and in footnotes, we will refer to Henry's lecture and reading notebooks by the numbers (enclosed in brackets) which were assigned when they were entered into the project's control system (e.g., notebook [7171]). The use of such traditional abbreviations as "ALS" and the like are avoided. When the particulars of authorship or handwriting are historically significant, these are elaborated in a footnote if not clear from the title and provenance note.

In a few instances an explanatory headnote, immediately after the provenance note, will introduce a document. Where important items are not suitable for publication in a work of this nature, the headnote, often expanded in size, stands in their stead.

Date and Place

Date and place are usually placed at the top, right-hand side preceding the body of the text, regardless of location in the original. Missing dates are supplied in brackets as an editorial insertion. If the place is lacking, it is only supplied or discussed in a footnote if of some historical significance. Where the dating is not obvious or hinges on a matter of moment, this too becomes the subject of a footnote.

Texts

Our general practice is to hew as close to the original as possible, so long as the meaning is reasonably clear to a modern reader. A few revisions, mostly specified below, are made silently in the interest of clarity. We prefer to retain the original and to aid the modern reader in this respect by means of our annotations: only rarely do we make changes or insertions indicated by using square brackets, [ ]. "Sic" does not appear in our texts; barring human error, a reader must assume that any strange usage in print is a faithful transcription of the original.

Mary Henry, our subject's daughter, bequeathed a nasty problem to this project. Shortly after her father's death Mary Henry began working toward the preparation of a biography. In her possession were most of Joseph Henry's personal papers. To this she added items gathered from friends and relatives, as well as documents culled from the official archives of the Smithsonian Institution. Mary Henry's efforts eventually progressed to the point where she had prepared a partial text which included original documents and transcriptions done by herself and her cohorts. Her text and its associated materials were largely the basis upon which Coulson based his biography of Joseph Henry. Although posterity owes Mary Henry thanks for efforts to preserve her father's literary remains, many of her actions resulted in irreparable damage to many Joseph Henry manuscripts. For example, in a number of cases she removed part of a book or transcribed a few pages, carelessly losing the entire volume. A neat trick of Mary's was to remove items from groups of documents and, in the process, to lose some and hopelessly disorder and scatter the remainder. The transcriptions she prepared for the contemplated biography are another vexation she inflicted on posterity. Almost invariably they omit an undisclosed amount of text, frequently passages of great interest. The transcribing is inaccurate at times and often corrects the language to conform with later standards, sometimes changing meanings. Unfortunately, many of the originals were lost, because, we think, of careless handling by Mary Henry and her aides. Many of these faulty, unique copies are quite important. We have decided to use them in our edition, signaling their nature by the expression "Mary Henry Copy" in the provenance note. From the numerous instances where both the copy and the original survive, we are convinced these are not fabrications, that the omissions were short-sighted but not acts of suppression, and that the surviving texts are reliable enough for use. Here and here alone, in the absence of any evidence to the contrary, we resolve textual uncertainties by opting for modern usage. There seems little point in trying to recapture Henry's archaisms.

Only in the few cases where the original paragraphing causes confusion in modern print have we made changes. Grammatical usage, punctuation, and spelling are usually faithfully preserved. The biggest exception is our decision to start each sentence with a capital letter and to end with appropriate punctuation. Punctuation that is obviously intrusive is removed; ubiquitous dashes are converted to modern commas and periods, and a few commas and periods are inserted silently where absolutely necessary for clear understanding. Only in a few egregious cases do we silently correct slips of the pen. Where the reading is doubtful or where meaning is otherwise unclear, we give an editorial insertion in square brackets, [ ]. Where these insertions are offered tentatively, we indicate our uncertainty by placing a question mark within the bracket. If the entire insertion is tentative, the question mark is placed immediately after the opening bracket, [? March 6, 1832]; if only one element is uncertain, the question mark is placed immediately afterward to indicate our doubt, [March 6?, 1832]. When the insertions arise from matters of moment, they will receive amplification in footnotes. A special case are entries from Henry's "Record of Experiments." The unique format of these entries called for special treatment which is explained in the headnote to the entry of August 15, 1834, in volume two.

In a number of documents there are interlineations, canceled matter, variant texts, marginalia, and even footnotes by the original author. The first are silently brought into line unless there is some point in their position. In that event we generally use a footnote to elucidate the significance, retaining the original position only in exceptional cases. If canceled matter or variant versions of expressions have historical, psychological, or stylistic significance, we place them immediately preceding the text in question in italics within angled brackets:

celebrated <*mathematical*> philosophical school at Alexandria.

Marginalia of significance are inserted into the text at the proper points with suitable comments in footnotes. Author's footnotes are given symbols other than arabic numerals which are reserved for editorial annotations.

Where one or two words are illegible or missing, we have so indicated by inserting suspension points enclosed in square brackets, [. . .]; if more than two words, we will, in addition, give an explanatory footnote, estimating, where possible, the number missing. Where a reasonable reconstruction is possible, we do so as an editorial insertion within square brackets.

Abbreviations occur frequently in the documents. If clear to the modern reader, they are retained. Otherwise the term is spelled out. The ampersand is used in place of the many variant forms occurring during Henry's lifetime. A particular problem to many readers unfamiliar with past usages is abbreviations involving raised letters, a practice quite common in Henry's generation and at least as far back as the seventeenth century. The writer would retain the first letter or letters of a word, giving the last letter or letters of the word in a raised position with or without a marking underneath:

Jany or Jan^{ry} for January

A reader aware of this practice should have no trouble understanding such abbreviations which we leave unchanged. Some raised letter abbreviations are likely to cause trouble. Sch^{dy} for Schenectady is not exactly obvious. In such cases we simply spell out the word without comment.

Signatures or initials at the close are given as in the original, usually without any commentary. Draft or retained copies generally lack these, as will our printed versions without any further notice. Where the recipient's name appears at the bottom left of the last page of an original letter, this is silently omitted as repeating information already given in the title. Dates at the end are also suppressed as redundant unless we silently shift their position to supply the missing dating at the start. We have retained closing matter of this nature only where meaning is conveyed. In the love letters exchanged by Joseph Henry and his wife Harriet, the closing salutations tell us something about the sentiments of the correspondents and are, therefore, given.

Editorial footnotes are numbered consecutively within each entry. We follow the citation form of the 12th edition of the *Manual of Style* of the University of Chicago Press with one important exception. We prefer the ISIS form in citing the periodical literature. Of less moment, perhaps, are two other preferences. The Editor does not relish the current tendency to suppress capitalization and to use the lower case in titles of officials, names of institutions, and publications. We capitalize. There is also an antipathy here against the tendency to run abbreviation-wild. We think readers should not have to approach each footnote as an exercise in decoding. Except for a few standard usages (e.g., n.d., ibid., etc.), everything is given in full or nearly so. The principal exceptions are the items below for which we consistently use short titles or standard abbreviations.

Academy Seventy-fifth Anniversary	*The Celebration of the Seventy-fifth Anniversary of the Founding of the Albany Academy, October 25, 1888* (Albany, 1889).
"Alexander Genealogy"	Unpublished Alexander Family Genealogy by Robert Gaylord Lester in the Henry Papers files.
Biographical Directory of the American Congress	*Biographical Directory of the American Congress, 1774–1949* (Washington, 1950).
Burke's Index	Edmund Burke, compiler, *List of Patents for Inventions and Designs Issued by the United States from 1790–1847, with the Patent Laws and Notes of Decisions of the Courts of the United States for the Same Period* (Washington, 1847).
Columbia Alumni	M. Halsey Thomas, compiler, *Columbia University Officers and Alumni, 1754–1857* (New York, 1936).
"Contributions I: Battery"	Joseph Henry, "Contributions to Electricity and Magnetism. No. I.—Description of a Galvanic Battery for Producing Electricity of Different Intensities," *Transactions of the American Philosophical Society*, 1837, n.s., 5:217–222.
"Contributions II: Spiral Conductor"	Joseph Henry, "Contributions to Electricity and Magnetism. No. II.—On the Influence of a Spiral Conductor in Increasing the Intensity of Electricity from a Galvanic Arrangement of a Single Pair, &c.," *Transactions of the American Philosophical Society*, 1837, n.s., 5:223–231.
"Contributions III: Electro-Dynamic Induction"	Joseph Henry, "Contributions to Electricity and Magnetism. No. III.—On Electro-Dynamic Induction," *Transactions of the American Philosophical Society*, 1839, n.s., 6:303–337.
"Contributions IV: Electro-Dynamic Induction"	Joseph Henry, "Contributions to Electricity and Magnetism. No. IV.—On Electro-Dynamic Induction," *Transactions of the American Philosophical Society*, 1843, n.s., 8:1–35.

"Contributions V: Induction from Ordinary Electricity; Oscillatory Discharge"	Joseph Henry, "Contributions to Electricity and Magnetism. No. V.—On Induction from Ordinary Electricity; And on the Oscillatory Discharge," *Proceedings of the American Philosophical Society*, January 1841–June 1843, 2:193–196.
Coulson	Thomas Coulson, *Joseph Henry: His Life and Work* (Princeton, 1950).
Cullum	G. W. Cullum, *Biographical Register of the Officers and Graduates of the United States Military Academy, at West Point, New York*, rev. ed., 2 vols. (New York, 1879).
DAB	*Dictionary of American Biography*
DNB	*Dictionary of National Biography*
DSB	*Dictionary of Scientific Biography*
Hageman	John F. Hageman, *History of Princeton and its Institutions*, 2d ed., 2 vols. (Philadelphia, 1879).
Henry Papers	Nathan Reingold, editor, *The Papers of Joseph Henry* (Washington, 1972–).
Herringshaw	Thomas William Herringshaw, *Encyclopedia of American Biography of the Nineteenth Century* (Chicago, 1905).
Howell and Tenney	George Rogers Howell and Jonathan Tenney, editors, *History of the County of Albany, N.Y., from 1609 to 1886* (New York, 1886).
Hun, "Albany Academy"	Henry Hun, "A Survey of the Activity of the Albany Academy" (unpublished manuscript, 1922–1935, Manuscript Division, New York State Library and Archives of the Albany Academy).
King	W. James King, "The Development of Electrical Technology in the 19th Century: 1. The Electrochemical Cell and the Electromagnet; 2. The Telegraph and the Telephone; 3. The Early Arc Light and Generator," *United States Museum Bulletin No. 228* (Washington, 1962), pp. 231–271, 273–332, 333–407.
Maclean	John Maclean, *History of the College of New Jersey, 1746–1854*, 2 vols. in 1 vol. (1877; reprint ed., New York, 1969).
Munsell, *Ann. Alb.*	Joel Munsell, compiler, *Annals of Albany*, 10 vols. (Albany, 1850–1859).

Munsell, *Coll. Alb.*   Joel Munsell, compiler, *Collections on the History of Albany, from Its Discovery to the Present Time, with Notices of Its Public Institutions and Biographical Sketches of Citizens Deceased*, 4 vols. (Albany, 1865–1871).

Nason   Henry B. Nason, editor, *Biographical Record of the Officers and Graduates of the Rensselaer Polytechnic Institute, 1824–1886* (Troy, 1887).

Phil. Mag.   The well-known London journal which began as *The Philosophical Magazine* in 1798 and appeared under various titles throughout Henry's life. See Henry Carrington Bolton, *A Catalogue of Scientific and Technical Periodicals, 1655–1895...*, 2nd ed. (Washington, 1897), pp. 445–446.

Phil. Trans.   *Philosophical Transactions of the Royal Society of London.*

Poggendorff   J. C. Poggendorff, compiler, *Biographisch-Literarisches Handwörterbuch Zur Geschichte Der Exacten Wissenschaften.*

Princeton Annual Catalogue   *Catalogue of the Officers and Students of the College of New-Jersey* (Princeton).

Princeton Catalogue   *General Catalogue of Princeton University, 1746–1906* (Princeton, 1908).

Roberts   Edward Howell Roberts, compiler, *Biographical Catalogue of the Princeton Theological Seminary, 1815–1932* (Princeton, 1933).

Silliman's Journal   Benjamin Silliman, editor, *American Journal of Science and Arts* (New Haven, 1818–   ).

Sprague, *Annals*   William Buell Sprague, *Annals of the American Pulpit*, 9 vols. (New York, 1857–1869).

Union Catalog   *Union University: Centennial Catalog, 1795–1895, of the Officers and Alumni of Union College in ... Schenectady, N.Y.* (Troy, 1895).

Weiner, "Joseph Henry's Lectures"   Charles Irwin Weiner, "Joseph Henry's Lectures on Natural Philosophy: Teaching and Research in Physics, 1832–1847" (Ph.D. dissertation, Case Institute of Technology, 1965).

Wertenbaker   Thomas Jefferson Wertenbaker, *Princeton, 1746–1896* (Princeton, 1946).

THE PAPERS OF JOSEPH HENRY

TO ROBERT M. PATTERSON

General Correspondence, Records of the United States Mint at Philadelphia,
Records of the Bureau of the Mint, RG 104, National Archives

Princeton Jany 13th 1838

My Dear Sir

I regret that I was obliged to leave Dr Emmet's paper[1] behind when I left the city. I gave it into the hands of Mr Vaughan on the evening of the meeting with the intention of calling for it on monday morning. The rail road cars however started so early that I was unable to call. I have not since been able to obtain it although I have requested several persons to call for it. Mr Vaughan is only to be found at the rooms of the society early in the morning or at night.

Dr. E. has written to me on the subject. I have not however answered his letter but intend to do so on saturday next. Before that time I will not have a moment to devote to the subject.

I am now doing double college duty and cannot possibly be in Phil[a] on next saturday but if you will send me the article by some opportunity within a few days I will devote my leisure moments to the study of it and be with you on the morning previous to the meeting after next,[2] inorder to arrange the affair of the report.

The whole affair is rather a disagreeable one. The Dr. is very ardent and sanguine and I fear will hardly be convinced of the fact that his theory is untenable.

The principal phenomenon given in his communication as explained to me in his letter is certainly a well known fact readily explicable on the admitted principles of Physical optics. I allude to the phenomenon of a black patch on a white ground.[3] It will however be a work of some labour to refer all the facts given in the communication to their proper places in the admitted theories of light—particularly if the mind has not been long occupied with the subject and all parts of the theories of vibration & emission perfectly familiar.

The Dr informs me that he has been engaged in making a series of experiments connected with the same subject and which he also intends to

---

[1] The American Philosophical Society had asked Henry, Patterson, and Henry Vethake to referee a paper submitted by John P. Emmet. For more information, see *Henry Papers*, 3:524–528.

[2] February 2 was the date of the meeting in question. Henry was not, however, able to meet this deadline. See below, Patterson to Henry, February 9, 1838.

[3] See *Henry Papers*, 3:526–527.

communicate to the society. Cannot he be prevailed on to publish a selection of his facts or even the whole of them without his theory and in this way neither jeopardize his own character or that of the society.

With much Respect
Yours &c
Joseph Henry

HENRY NOTEBOOK ENTRY

*Commonplace Book [10615], page 506, Henry Papers,
Smithsonian Archives*

[January] 1838

While in N. Y in Jany I made an observation on the transmission of Light through sirrup. When viewed by reflected light the article appears of a light yellow but by transmitted light through a thick stratum of a deep red.[1]

---

[1] There is a marginal notation to this entry, made, as explained below, between 1845 and 1852 or 1853. The notation reads "now called epipolic reflection."

The phenomenon that attracted Henry's attention—the different colors exhibited by a liquid or solution according to whether it was viewed in reflected or transmitted light—was first recorded by Nicolás Monardes, a Spanish physician in the New World, in 1574. A number of natural philosophers of the seventeenth and eighteenth centuries wrote accounts of the phenomenon. Among them were Robert Boyle (1664) and Isaac Newton (1672).

It was not until a few years after Henry jotted down his observation, however, that a satisfactory explanation of the changes in color was arrived at. In 1845 John F. W. Herschel published two papers ("On a Case of Superficial Colour Presented by a Homogeneous Liquid Internally Colourless," *Phil. Trans.*, 1845, pp. 143–145; "On the Epipolic Dispersion of Light, Being a Supplement to a Paper Entitled 'On a Case of Superficial Colour Presented by a Homogeneous Liquid Internally Colourless,'" *Phil. Trans.*, 1845, pp. 147–153) in which he described experiments he had made with a solution of sulphate of quinine in tartaric acid. This solution is usually colorless, but will appear blue under certain conditions of illumination. Because the blue hue appeared to be a surface phenomenon, Herschel called it epipolic dispersion, from the Greek, *epipole*, a surface. Seven years later George G. Stokes (1820–1903) published an extensive paper ("On the Change of Refrangibility of Light," *Phil. Trans.*, 1852, pp. 463–562) reinvestigating the work of Herschel and David Brewster in this area. Stokes's explanation, which won for him the Rumford Medal of the Royal Society, was that the incident light was absorbed by the solution, then reemitted at a longer wavelength. In a footnote to this paper he suggested the term fluorescence for the phenomenon, a suggestion he reconfirmed in his follow-up paper (*Phil. Trans.*, 1853, pp. 385–396). E. Newton Harvey, *A History of Luminescence From the Earliest Times Until 1900*, Memoirs of the American Philosophical Society, vol. 44 (Philadelphia, 1957), pp. 390–398.

Although fluorescence is usually thought of as a short duration form of phosphorescence (Harvey, *History of Luminescence*, pp. 390–391), there seems to be no direct connection between the observation made by Henry in 1838 and the experimental work he did on phosphorescence in 1843. The former is one of Henry's random observations of the world about him, while the latter, published as "On Phosphorogenic Emanation," *Proceedings of the American Philosophical Society*, 1843, 3:38–44, was the result of a sustained series of experiments in reaction to the published work of other scientists. Henry's experiments on phosphorescence will be discussed in detail in the next volume of the *Henry Papers*.

FROM ROBERT M. PATTERSON
Gratz Collection, State Historical Society of Wisconsin

Philadelphia, Feb. 9, 1838

Dear Sir,

I received, last week, a letter from Dr. Emmet, making anxious inquiry as to the disposition made of his paper on light. Our Society will meet on Friday evening next, (16th.) Can you not have a report ready for that meeting, and come down with it that day or the day before?[1]

Dr. Emmet requests me to state that he has found that "couloured shadows do not depend upon a deflection of light *at the surface of the opaque object*. That the penumbra, seen upon the surfaces of bodies held near the eye is the result of a double image upon the retina, in consequence, apparently, of a power which we possess of making the distance between the lens and retina *shorter* than the focal distance. That the appearance of differently coloured rays upon *opposite* sides of the focus of a double convex lens is no longer regarded as an evidence of the convertibility of colours into each other."

Dr. Emmet states that he wishes permission to make these corrections of his former opinions in a note, and that, as these opinions are now relinquished, the committee need not consider their merits.

It appears, then, that Dr. Emmets theories are not very firmly founded even in his own mind.

I am, dear Sir, very respectfully
and truly Your's
R.M. Patterson.

---

[1] Henry attended the February 16 meeting of the American Philosophical Society but presented no report on Emmet. It was announced at the March 16 meeting that Emmet had decided to withdraw his paper:

Dr Patterson communicated a request from Dr John P Emmet, for the withdrawal of the communication heretofore presented by him, on certain phenomena of light, and on motion of Profr Vethake, leave was given to Dr Emmet, to withdraw the communication.

APS Minutes, vol. 1834–1839, p. 195, APS Archives.

"RECORD OF EXPERIMENTS"
Henry Papers, Smithsonian Archives

[February 12, 1838]

View this evening, Feby 12th, the bright lines in the spectrum from the electric spark.[1] This needs no narrow slip. The lines are very distinct, also the dark spot in the middle of the spark

---

[1] Henry had previously examined the spectrum from an electric spark and discussed the phenomenon with Wheatstone. See *Henry Papers*, *3*:26, 216–217.

FROM JOHN TORREY
Mary Henry Copy, Memoir, Henry Papers, Smithsonian Archives

New York Feb 26. 1838

My dear Friend. I expect to leave here for Princeton on Thursday morning and to deliver my first lecture the following day. . . . My man or boy Friday I shall bring along. He is a rough diamond[1]. . . . You say bring on a lot of glass but without specifying what sorts. Find out what is needed in the chemical department. Sulphuric acid we can get in Princeton but if the nit. & mur. acids are out I will purchase here. How are we off for Platinum & tin foil. . . . I have been making quite a lot of *magnesium* a metal that has never been seen except by a few chemists & only in microscopic quantities. I prepare it by a new process and I hope to repeat it before you at Princeton. The burning of the metal in the open air over a spirit lamp is a splendid experiment[2]. . . .

I send you a prospectus of our "Society for the Diffusion of Useful Knowledge"[3]. . . . We wish to have some popular works on science prepared—fit

---

[1] This is C.B. Goodrich. When Torrey returned to New York, Goodrich remained at Princeton to assist Henry in his experiments. See below, Henry to Torrey, April 16, 1838.

[2] In 1831 A.–A.–B. Bussy reported the first preparation of magnesium. He heated magnesium chloride with metallic potassium and then washed out the potassium chloride to get magnesium in metallic form. Mary Elvira Weeks, *Discovery of the Elements*, 7th ed. (Easton, Pennsylvania, 1968), p. 500. We do not know what Torrey's method of preparation was. When heated as Torrey suggests the magnesium burns brilliantly and forms magnesia.

[3] The American Society for the Diffusion of Useful Knowledge was founded in New York City in 1836. The Society was largely the creation of Gorham D. Abbot (1807–1874, *DAB*), a Presbyterian clergyman and educator. Convinced of the power of printed works in achieving moral and intellectual development, Abbot surveyed societies in the United States and in England and conducted a subject survey of recent American publications before enlisting others in his attempts to found a society to promote his aims. The Society was formally organized on October 17, 1836. A constitution was adopted and officers were elected, including Stephen Van Rensselaer as President, Abbot as Secretary, and John Torrey as one of the Executive Committee. Following incorporation on May 16, 1837, the Executive Committee issued a lengthy prospectus describing the organization and goals of the Society. It included Abbot's survey of English institutions in which he reported on the Royal Society of London, the Royal Institution, and the British Association for the Advancement of Science in addition to such obvious possible models as the London Society for the Diffusion of Useful Knowledge.

In October 1837 the Society issued the *Prospectus of the American Library for Schools and Families* (New York, 1837). This was to be

for our academies. . . . I am commissioned to request you to prepare a work on some branch of Natural Philosophy—say on steam—or electricity—or whatever you please—a work of about 250 or 300 pages—popular and yet dignified and a proper introduction to something more profound. . . . Ever faithfully yours. John Torrey

P.S. Our Committee will meet in a few days and I would be glad to have your answer respecting the proposed work immediately.[4]

---

a systematic, comprehensive library covering all branches of useful knowledge. Although Torrey's solicitation of Henry indicates that the Society was commissioning new works, the fifty-volume library published by Harper & Brothers in May 1838 was composed of previously published works, mostly Harper & Brothers publications. The publication was rushed by the attempt to corner the market in New York State which in April 1838 had passed an act mandating and appropriating funds for the purchase of libraries by each district. An intensive effort to distribute the library culminated in a memorial to Congress on February 19, 1839 (*Senate Documents*, 25th Congress, 3d Session, No. 235). The memorial proposed two goals in addition to the library: the publication of a popular journal and of a set of textbooks.

The Society had counted heavily on the adoption of its library by New York State schools. When this failed to occur, the library project was abandoned for lack of funds. The popular journal was never published. The textbook program produced only two reports, two endorsements of texts, and a spelling book by Abbot. There is no record of the activities of the Society past 1843.

"The American Society for the Diffusion of Useful Knowledge," Henry Barnard, ed., *The American Journal of Education*, 1865, *15*:239–245.

[4] We have not located any response by Henry. It is unlikely he would have been interested in Torrey's offer. He had research problems in mind and was only waiting for the arrival of his apparatus from France to resume the investigations which resulted in "Contributions III: Electro-Dynamic Induction."

"RECORD OF EXPERIMENTS"
Henry Papers, Smithsonian Archives

Feby 1838[1]

    W Bullions made for me
1 a coil of fine wire (bottle wire) 1640 feet long (2 wires interspersed of about 70 each)[2]

---

[1] This notation about induction apparatus being prepared for "Contributions III: Electro-Dynamic Induction" appears on a page between May 14 and May 15, 1835.

[2] At the beginning of "Contributions III" Henry described his experimental apparatus. This coil appears to be that designated in the publication as helix no. 4, formed of 546 yards of wire, 1/49 of an inch in diameter, and insulated with cement. After several experiments, and in his article, Henry called his long wire coils "helices" to distinguish them from the flat coils of copper ribbon. William Bullions was Henry's lab assistant.

Coil No 1 Long N.B   This Coil was destroyed by a discharge from a Leyden jar[3]

2 <*Small*> 2nd coil of copper ribbon about one inch wide 60 feet long.

3 Coil of cotton wire varnished is about 1400 feet long. (coil No 2 Long)

[3] In "Contributions III," paragraphs 54, 55, and 75, Henry notes the destruction of insulation on the helix giving him some anomalous results. See also the "Record of Experiments" entry of April 13, 1838, below, experiment 3.

TO THOMAS HUN

Mary Henry Copy, Henry Papers, Smithsonian Archives

Princeton March 5th, 1838

My dear Dr.

The apparatus has not yet come to hand and I have heard nothing from Pixii, relative to the long delay. I begin to fear that some accident has happened to the package and that I am in danger of losing the whole amount of my purchase as no insurance was effected on them.

Prof. Vethake, my predecessor at Princeton and now of the University of Pennsylvania, has just published a work on political economy, in which the subject of the currency is ably discussed. His views are almost identical with those we adopted while in Paris and which I presume you have found no solid reason to change, notwithstanding all the hue and cry raised in reference to the importance of the Banking system of the United States. I am amused with the manner in which the Banks are spoken of in the papers as the established Institutions of our country.[1]

[1] Henry's agreement with Henry Vethake shows a preference for a hard-money position on the controversial issues of currency and banking. Vethake's *The Principles of Political Economy* (Philadelphia, 1838), his published economics lectures, was highly critical of the existing banking system as caretaker of the government's fiscal affairs and suggested instead a version of the "Sub-treasury scheme," whereby an independent Treasury would issue non-interest-bearing Treasury notes backed by specie (pp. 172 ff., 201). Although placing his ultimate faith in specie currency, Vethake saw virtues in a "mixed" currency consisting of a proportion of specie and of paper convertible into specie on demand (p. 198). A free-trader, Vethake's treatise has been described as the "closest of the period to the views of the Ricardian school in England." (Dorfman, 2:733). Proposed in the United States as early as 1834, the idea of a Sub-treasury system, breaking the alliance between the government and the banks (national or state), received a strong boost after the 1837 depression demonstrated to many the failure of banks as issuers and regulators of currency. A highly modified version of the plan was adopted in 1840. For a history of the emergence of the Sub-treasury scheme and for Vethake's role in it, see Joseph Dorfman, *The Economic Mind in American Civilization, 1606–1865*, 2 vols. (New York, 1966), 2:604, 611, 613, 617, 731–740.

Send on the advertisement of De La Rive and I will forward it to Prof. Silliman.[2]

I have a number of experiments on hand some of which promise a good harvest, but want of the proper apparatus and the difficulty of getting anything made in the mechanical line in this place is a great drawback.

Yours &c.
Joseph Henry

[2] The July 1838 issue of *Silliman's Journal* (vol. 33) contains two mentions of De La Rive's work: a listing of his "Researches into the Causes of Voltaic Electricity" in "Acknowl- edgements" of foreign articles (p. 7); and a report on his paper on "Electro-Magnetic Cur- rents" presented at the Liverpool meetings of the British Association (pp. 6–7).

TO CHARLES COQUEREL[1]
Miscellaneous Manuscripts Collection, Library,
American Philosophical Society

Princeton College of New Jersey
March 14th 1838

My Dear Sir

My Friend Dr Thomas Hun with whom you sent your kind letter[2] last autum and the very acceptable acompanying package returns to France in the Packet of the 16th of this month. I therefore embrace with much plea- sure the opportunity of sending you a few articles in the scientific line and also this letter expressing my warmest thanks for the many favours I re- ceived from you while in Paris and also for the package which evinces that I still live in your remembrance.

I hope you will pardon me for not before acknowledging the receipt of your letter by Dr Hun. I have however been so much ingaged in my college duties since my return from Europe that I have been obliged to defer all my own concerns until the end of my winter course of Lectures. I have now just finished and devote almost the first of my leisure to the kind Friends I met with in Europe. I regret to learn that you had not at the date of your letter received the numbers of the Library of Useful Knowledge you com- missioned me to purchase for you in London. As soon as I arrived in that city I delivered your memorandum and the money accompanying to my

[1] This letter is essentially an expansion of Henry's shipboard note to Coquerel of October 1, 1837 (*Henry Papers*, 3:510–513) discussing his itinerary after leaving Paris.
[2] Not found.

agent Mr. O. Rich No 12 Red Lion Square London and directed him to procure the books and send them to you to the care of the House you mentioned on your paper. Mr Rich is an american book seller; a very respectable man who informed me a few days after that the books had been sent according to the direction given. I have not the least doubt but that they were sent, as you directed, and that they have been delayed by the carlessness of the agents. I hope however that you have heared something about them before this time; since immediately after the receipt of your letter, I wrote to Mr. Rich and requested that he would inform you by letter to what House the articles were sent. I gave him your address and he has probably written to you although I have as yet received no answer to his letter.

There is I find great carelessness on the part of agents relative to the transmission of Packages between France & England. I was much vexed when I returned to London to learn that a box from America had been sent by the assistant secretary of the Royal society to the curator of the French Institute for me. The article must have been in Paris almost all the time I stoped in the city but I saw nothing of it nor perhaps ever will. I delivered the pamphlets you sent by me to England and America and I have just written to Professor Olmsted informing him that I will transmit any package he may wish to send to you and will probably find something from him when I go to New York. Dr. Sprague[3] was much gratified with the circumstance of my having made an acquaintance with you and was much pleased that you had sent him the autographs although I could not deliver them to him at the time we met since my articles were still on ship board. If he knows that Dr. Hun returns to Paris he will probably send you something in return.

I purchased a considerable amount of philosophical articles and several hundred dollars worth of books, and left them in the care of a person in Paris to be sent to America in September last but as yet I heave heared nothing about them—the delay has caused me much trouble. Dr Hun has kindly promised to attend to the affair when he gets to Paris.

After I left Paris I went to Brussels spent a few days there—then to Antwerp with the intention of visiting Holland but found that the stupid old *Dutch* King had forbiden all intercourse bettween his dominions and those of the King of Belgium. I therefore went directly to London, stoped a few days then sailed for Edinburgh—was much pleased with my visit to Scotland and particularly gratified with the result of a tour I made to see Sir David Brewster. He lives near Melrose about 40 miles from Edinburgh

---

[3] William Buell Sprague, Presbyterian clergyman and autograph collector; see *Henry Papers,* *1*:464n.

and within two miles of the residence of the late Sir Walter Scott. I paid a hurried visit to some of the Scotch Lakes and then journeyed to the south along the western coast of Scotland—passed through the birth place of the Scottish minstrel Burns—and arrived at Liverpool just in time for the meeting of the *Association*. I was much gratified by the reception I met with at this meeting and with the attention I received from some of the principal men of science.

I next visited Cambridge and spent 3 days very pleasantly in company with Professor Henslow who belongs to the University. I then returned to London—bid good bye to my Friends in that city—proceeded to Portsmouth to sail in the ship Toronto on the 1st day of October we however did not bid fare well to old England until the 2nd. After a very favourable passage of 26 days we landed in New York. I hastened to Albany to meet my family and had the pleasure to find all well. Nothing remarkable occurred during my voyage. I was as usual quite sea sick but did not suffer as much as when I went out. We had on one occasion quite rough weather accompanied with Thunder & lightening. All our masts and spars were tipped with the fire of St. Elmo. I regretted that sea sickness prevented my making any observations on this Electrical Phenominon which appears to be only an electrical discharge to or from the clouds from the pointed parts of the vessel. A child died a few days before, the body was put in a cask of spirits to be preserved until we should reach shore. The superstitious sailors were very uneasy at this and declared that the presance of the dead body was the cause of the storm.

Did you receive a copy of the London Atheneum containing the report of the British Association? Just before I left London I paid the publisher for two copies and directed him to send one to you and the other to Professor Babinet.[4] I would have sent them myself but only two of the four numbers which contained the article had been printed when I left London. I have now no copies of my papers in my possession and have been so much ingaged since my return that I have done as yet nothing in the way of experimenting. I promised to send you a copy of the report of the academies in the State of New York on meterology which is annually made to the Legislature but the article has not yet been published for the present year. It will be forwarded to you along with the copies to the Institute sometime during the spring. Give my respects to Melloni. I feel much indebted to you for the introduction you obtained for me to that distinguished and interesting individual. I was much pleased and instructed with his experiments. The account I took to England of the experiments of Thilorier on

[4] See below, Henry to [Babinet], March 1838.

the solidification of carbonic acid was received with much interest by Dr Faraday and Professor Daniel. They think that these experiments do not receive the attention they deserve. Have you not in Republican France a good deal of the aristocracy of science? And will the labours of Thilorier be received and aplauded with as much enthusiasm as if they came from a member of the Institute? Give my respects also to Thilorier.

I would be much pleased if you were to form the acquaintance of my Friend Dr Hun. He has resided several years in Paris and will stop in the city for a few months. You will find him a very intelligent and interesting person when you get fully acquainted with him. Let me hear from you soon —and permit me to subscribe myself with much respect

Your Friend   Joseph Henry

Do not forget my direction namely

Professor Henry College of New Jersey Princeton

TO JAMES HENRY

Family Correspondence, Henry Papers, Smithsonian Archives

Princeton March 22nd 1838

My Dear James

We have been looking for a letter from you with much anxiety for some time past. Our family are all anxious to hear something more relative to the death of Poor Susan.[1] I have been so much occupied during the winter with my college duties that I have been obliged to defer all most all the answers to the letters I have received. I have now however some leisure and am devoting it to writing up my correspondance.

All the children have been sick but are now better. We were quite alarmed with a fear that they had taken the varialoid.[2] A black man the brother of one of our servants stopped a few days in our kitchen, was there taken sick with what appeared to be the small pox. We sent him off to his sisters in the country. His brotherinlaw caught the small pox and died. Also the sister of the black man who lived with us caught the disease. Our children have only had the chicken pox, and as I said before are now nearly well. Mary is still not entirely recovered; she was the last taken sick. I went to New York last week to meet Dr Hun who is going to Paris.[3] I wished to

---

[1] Susannah Shankland, a longtime friend of the Henrys, died on March 6. *Henry Papers*, *1*: 284n; Munsell, *Ann. Alb.*, *10*:277.

[2] Varioloid is a mild form of smallpox.

[3] See above, Henry to Hun, March 5, 1838.

see him on account of the apparatus I purchased in Paris. The articles were to be sent by the first of October but I have as yet heared nothing of them. Dr Hun did not arrive; he was probably detained by the badness of the roads.

I have lately heard nothing of your paper.[4] Has the affair fallen through? If so I hope you are no sufferer by the project. I have not determined whether I will visit Albany this spring. Stephen and his wife will be up as soon as the term closes which will be in about 2 weeks or a little more from this time.

We now live in a house near the Theological Seminary[5] quite a pleasant situation but so far from the Philosophical Hall where my books are that it is very inconvenient for me.

Harriet wrote you immediatly after the receipt of your last letter but one which contained an account of Susan's being sent to the asylum. We also received your letter anouncing the death of Susan. Harriet's letter enclosed one for Mary Ann La Grange.[6] As nothing since has been received from Albany there is some fear that the letters have miscarried.

I hope all your affairs are in good condition and that you have done a fair business this past winter. The purchase of the House was under the circumstances of the case apparently a good one although it increases your expenditure and consequently will require increased activity of business to meet it. Stephen will call on you most probably relative to the notes of Mr Fasset. I think however it is not very probable that you have been able to collect anything these dull times.[7]

I send this letter by John Newland[8] who makes a visit of a few weeks to Albany. He is now a private Tutor in the Family of Dr. Hodge and is well liked. William Bullions is still with me and has been of much assistance during my course. He hopes to get the situation now occupied by William Mc Cammon[9] if that person should resign. There has been a rumour that Mc Cammon is going to take charge of the Furnace.

We saw in the papers an account of the murder of a person by the name of Shephard. Was he the son of Shephard the silversmith?[10]

---

[4] James Henry published *The Jeffersonian,* an Albany weekly which appeared from February 17, 1838, to February 9, 1839. It was edited by Horace Greeley. *DAB,* s.v. "Greeley."

[5] After their old house was torn down and while awaiting a new house, the Henrys needed to rent for several months. The Princeton Trustees appropriated up to $300 for the rent of a house. The Henrys moved into their new house in September 1838. Princeton Trustees Minutes, September 27, 1837, Princeton University Archives.

[6] Susan Shankland's sister (*Henry Papers,* 2:43n).

[7] A reference to family financial dealings, also mentioned in *Henry Papers,* 2:428, 489.

[8] See *Henry Papers,* 2:467n.

[9] For Bullions and McCammon see *Henry Papers,* 2:8n, 274n.

[10] Robert Shepherd (or Shepard), a young clerk in Albany, formerly of Buffalo, was murdered on March 10 by Thomas Rector, "the

Our old acquaintance Rens Van Rensselaer has rendered himself quite famous or rather infamous by his Canadian exploits.[11] What Van Rensselaer has now the charge of the paper? Have you seen Shankland lately or heard anything more about his accounts?[12] Henry James has been in Albany for some months past but is expected in Princeton in a few days. His boy will probably call on you before he leaves the city. If the reports of the Regents of the University have been published I wish you to send me a few copies.

Harriet sends her love to Caroline & Nancy also to Aunty Platt and the girls. I have heard indirectly that Eliza Selkirk[13] is shortely to be married to the Partener of Rachels Husband. I hope she may get a good husband.

As Ever Your Brother

P.S. Please to inform John Patterson[14] that the books I purchased for him have not yet arrived.

---

keeper of a house of ill fame." Rector smashed Shepherd's skull as Shepherd and two others attempted to enter Rector's establishment. *Howell and Tenney*, p. 305; *Daily Albany Argus*, March 12, 1838; *Albany Evening Journal* (same date). We cannot verify a relationship to the Thomas Shepherd, silver plater, who is listed in the Albany City Directories, 1831–1836.

[11] Rensselaer Van Rensselaer (ca. 1802–1850), son of General Solomon Van Vechten Van Rensselaer, conspired with the Canadian rebel William Mackenzie in a plan to liberate Canada. Attempting to pass himself off as his famous father, "General" Van Rensselaer set up headquarters on Navy Island, on the Canadian side of the border near Niagara Falls, and hired the steamer *Caroline* to convey supplies and munitions to the island. In December 1837, Canadian loyalists sank the *Caroline* in American waters. Although President Van Buren protested the sinking, he had Mackenzie and Van Rensselaer arrested for violating the neutrality laws of the United States. Van Rensselaer published a narrative of his exploits in the *Albany Advertiser*, March 30, 1838. The *Caroline* affair was an important event in the history of the "Canadian Rebellion" and British-American diplomacy. Florence Van Rensselaer, *The Van Rensselaers in Holland and America* (New York, 1956), p. 66. Samuel Eliot Morison, *The Oxford History of the American People*, 3 vols. (New York, 1972), 2:209–212.

[12] Possibly a reference to P. V. Shankland's handling of city funds as Albany City Chamberlain. See Reynolds, *Alb. Chron.*, p. 524.

[13] Probably a daughter of Henry's aunt, Elizabeth Selkirk.

[14] John Paterson was an obscure mathematical fringe figure who apparently knew Henry from Albany. He received an honorary A.M. from Union College in 1835 and, in 1850, published *Calculus of Operations* (Albany), an idiosyncratic foray into the philosophical foundations of mathematics which the Union College professor Isaac W. Jackson described as "peculiar and metaphysical." Jackson nevertheless considered Paterson a thinker of great merit and made valiant but unsuccessful attempts to find him a suitable position in science, including one with Henry at the Smithsonian in the late 1840s. By that time Paterson was impoverished and working at odd manual jobs. Although deeply committed to mathematics and natural philosophy, he apparently never found a position in keeping with his talents. For a time at least he worked as Albany's city weigher and measurer. E. A. Werner, *Civil List and Constitutional History of the Colony and State of New York* (Albany, 1889), p. 314. *Union Catalog*, p. 48. Jackson to Henry, February 18, 1847, January 6, 1851; and Paterson to Henry, May 30, 1848, December 3, 1849, Henry Papers, Smithsonian Archives.

TO [JACQUES BABINET][1]
Retained Copy, Henry Papers, Smithsonian Archives

[March 1838]

The report of the proceedings of the British association was published in a London weekly paper called the Atheneum. I thought a copy of the report would be interesting to you and therefore paid the publisher for two copies, one for you and the other for M. Coquerel and directed him to send them to you, as soon as they were published. I would have sent them myself before leaving the city but only two num[bers] had appeared previous to my sailing.

You will probably be interested in my visit to Sir David Brewster. He lives about 40 miles from Edinburgh near Melrose Abbey and within two miles of Abbotsford the residence of the late Scottish novelist, Sir Walter Scott. I had a letter to him and made the journey to his residence from Edinburgh for no other purpose than to make the acquaintance of this celebrated <person> man. He received me with much kindness and prevailed on me to remain with him for two days. He was then much occupied with the study of the dark lines of the spectrum, as seen through a glass tube filled with nitrous acid gas.[2] His method of showing the spectrum is the same as that discribed in Herchels work on Light. The tube of glass containing the nitrous acid gas is about ¾ of an inch in diameter and 6 or 7 inches long. It is filled with the acid gass and then hermetically sealed. The gas as you know only magnifies the lines without increasing their number or altering their position; Sir David is therefore using this agent for making a much larger and more accurate map of the spectrum than has yet been published. Sir David has not a very extensive apparatus, nor as good a collection of crystals as you have. He has however a few good instruments which he uses in various forms to suit the occasion.

He <also> showed me several extracts from some papers which have lately been found relative to the life of Sir Isaac Newton. These papers were collected and some of them written by a person who married a niece of Sir Isaac and were intended for publication. The person however suddenly died and the papers have lain for nearly a hundred years in some garret and have only within a short time been brought to light.

---

[1] Internal evidence and Henry's letter to Coquerel of March 14, 1838 (see above), have led us to conclude that this is a fragment of a retained copy of a letter to Jacques Babinet. Henry met the French physicist during his European tour (*Henry Papers*, 3:387–392).

[2] The following description of Brewster's investigation of the dark lines of the spectrum is more detailed than in any of Henry's previous letters or his notebook entry of August 19–21, 1837 (see *Henry Papers*, 3:482, especially footnote 41).

Sir David Brewster is shortely to publish a new life of Newton. I should have mentioned that amoung the papers there is an original love letter from Sir Isaac to a widow Lady which proves most conclusively that the great Philosopher was composed like other men of *flesh* and *blood*.

I have been so much occupied since my return to America with my lectures that I have as yet found no leisure for experimenting although I have several subjects relative to Electricity and magnetism under way. I have also been much annoyed on account of not having received the articles which I purchased in Paris. They were to have been sent by the Havre packet by the end of September last. It is now March & I have as yet heard nothing of them. All my books—The apparatus I purchased from Solile were left to be sent with the articles to be constructed by Pixii but none have come. I fear all is lost. My Friend Dr. Hun however has kindly undertaken to look after the articles and send them to me if they can be found.

Let me hear from you as soon after the receipt of this letter as convenient. When I was in Bermingham I had the little book in which you wrote your address stolen from me. You will therefore oblige me by giving in your first letter your title and address. You will reccollect to address your letters or packages to me thus

> Professor Joseph Henry
> College of New Jersey
> Prinston
> United States
> of
> America

You will find a good biographical sketch of Sir David Brewster in a work recently published in Paris the Biography Contemporain.[3] It was probably written by himself or some intimate friend and contains a list of his papers and discoveries. I send you a small piece of the singular substance described in the [. . .][4] of the Philosophical magazine a kind of artificial mother of pearl which possesses peculiar optical properties.[5] I also divide with you a small piece of *Tabesheer*[6] given me by Sir David Brewster. You however

---

[3] The sketch of Brewster is in the *Biographie Universelle et Portative des Contemporains ou Dictionnaire Historique*, 5 vols. (Paris, 1836), 5:77–81. The Henry Library contains this set which he purchased in Paris; a translation of the Brewster profile is in the Henry Papers, Smithsonian Archives.

[4] Word missing.

[5] For a discussion of this substance, a combination of lime, glue, and flour, discovered in a cotton mill, see *Henry Papers*, 3:481, footnote 37.

[6] A mass of silica found in the stems of bamboo and valued as medicine in the East Indies.

will not perhaps thank me for it as you may <*perhaps*> probably have a large supply of the article. I have very little news that will interest you. Our country for a year past has been labouring under great commertial difficulties. We got largely into debt a few years since to England for assistance in the construction of our rail roads and also for a <*great*> quantity of English articles of luxury which we were forced to purchase on account of the abundance of money and flourishing state of the whole country. We had been in the habit of paying for all our purchases <*of*> in England by the supplies of Cotton which we sent to her but last year the bank of England suddenly ceased to loan money to the English Houses which traded with America. These were required to pay their debts to the bank and therefore could not buye our *Cotton* but demanded from the merchants in America immediate payment of all debts in *Specie*. This could not be done and the consequence has been that most of the great Merchants of this country became bankrupt. All business has been been[7]

[7] The surviving text ends here. We assume that this fragment also lacks Henry's opening paragraphs.

"RECORD OF EXPERIMENTS"[1]
Henry Papers, Smithsonian Archives

April 6$\underline{th}$ 1838

1 Put tourmaline at one end of an iron tube and another at the other, magnetized the tube suddenly with a coil noted the effect on the polarized beam, could perceive no action. Also made the same arrangement with a ribbon coil—no effect—the tourmalines were so turned as to appear nearly opaque. Try the same with long coil so as to produce tension.[2]

[1] This is the first entry in Henry's lab notebook since December 1837 and the start of his first sustained series of experiments in nearly two years. The European trip seems to have been largely responsible for the hiatus.

[2] Henry reasoned that any visible change in the light passing through the tourmaline pair would indicate a rotation in the plane of polarization of the light beam. An undated experimental note ("Record of Experiments," vol. 2, p. 316, Henry Papers, Smithsonian Archives) shows Henry looking for the reciprocal effect—the ability of a polarized beam to induce magnetism: "Polarize a tolerably large beam of light, put needle of soft iron in this with magnetic filings—1st put the needle in the axis of the beam, next transversely to the same—note with magnifying glass the effect." We have omitted an accompanying illustration. Otherwise, Henry did not seriously pur-

Exp 2 Heated small bar of soft iron, presented it to compass needle, attraction took place when bar arrived near a black heat in the day light. When large magnet was presented attraction was evident at a higher temperature. Also the force did not appear to be developed suddenly, but by degrees[3]

Exp 3ᵈ The same piece of iron was heated to whiteness and then presented to the large compound magnet, attraction took place as soon as the iron became cherry red. It appears from this exp in connection with the last that a stronger magnet indicates attraction sooner than a weak one.

Exp 4 Put[4] electro magnet in *gas* pipe No 1. Slight indications of magnetism on the out side

Exp 5 Put helix of long wire wrapped around a glass rod into long gas pipe, which was magnetized. No shock from the helix from within

---

sue his investigation of magneto-optics, a phenomenon eagerly sought by Michael Faraday in his attempt to prove the existence of the "electrotonic state." In Henry's lab notebook entry for August 30, 1839, below, he refers to Faraday's (unsuccessful) attempt to demonstrate a magneto-optic effect with fluids. Faraday's eventual discovery of a relationship between light and electromagnetism is documented in L. P. Williams, *Michael Faraday* (New York, 1965), pp. 386–392.

[3] Henry heats up the iron bar and then checks for the magnetic effect as it cools down. The loss of magnetism by iron heated to whiteness was well known by this date, due to the work of Peter Barlow, author of "On the Anomalous Magnetic Action of Hot-Iron Between the White and Blood-Red Heat," *Phil. Trans.*, 1822, pp. 117–126; "Experiments on the Effect of Red-Hot Iron on the Compass," *Astronomische Nachrichten*, 1823, *1*: cols. 193–196.

[4] The remaining experiments of this day and the majority of lab notebook entries through October 1838 were destined for publication in "Contributions to Electricity and Magnetism. No. III. On Electro-Dynamic Induction," read to the American Philosophical Society in November. Although Henry initially intended the paper to be an investigation of induction from common electricity, he ended up includ-

ing a great deal of material on galvanic induction.

"Contributions III" has six main parts. Section one follows up his earlier work on self-induction. Section two examines the characteristics of secondary currents induced by galvanism, particularly the relationships between quantity and intensity (the principle of the transformer). In the third, Henry discovers that secondary currents can be induced over considerable distances. Section four concerns shielding and an explanation of the phenomenon in terms of neutralizing currents. Higher order inductions, up to the fifth, are the subject of the next section. Here a major problem arises of determining the sequence of directions of the higher order currents. The final section makes the comparison with induction of different orders from static electricity. By Henry's own admission, the results of "Contributions III" were not as complete as he would have wished. He lacked the time for more extensive investigation but wanted to get results into print as soon as possible. As later entries of his lab notebook will show, Henry's conclusions about the direction of higher order currents were particularly tentative. In fact, it was not until "Contributions IV," presented in 1840, that Henry resolved many of these problems to his own satisfaction.

Exp 6 Put round iron electro magnetic magnet into a hollow iron cylinder No 2—then Helix No 3 on the out side, contact with the battery at *a b*, magnetized the magnet within, very slight if any action on the needle of the galvanometer.[5] The hollow cylinder was next withdrawn, the magnet again magnetized. The current now appeared through the helix and galvanometer in the same direction—contrary to my supposition

(Try this again with other magnet)

Ex 7 Placed the same helix mentioned exp 6th in a helix of ribbon then strong shocks.

NB While engaged in the above experiments observed a singular interruption of the current as tested by the snaps. Sometimes they would be quite loud at other times almost entirely cease. Prob[ably] produced by Battery[6]

Remark It appears from exp 6 and 7 that iron screens the magneto electrical inductive action.

Will the same screening influence be exerted on the attraction and repulsion descovered by Ampere? Try the exp

[5] Vertically in the margin, "galvanometer not sensible."

[6] This last phrase looks as if it might have been added later. Henry elaborated on the cause in the margin: "Probably produced by a deposition of reduced copper on the wood which separates the metals of the battery."

"RECORD OF EXPERIMENTS"
Henry Papers, Smithsonian Archives

April 7th 1838

It is stated in the arcana of Science page 72 vol for 1828* that magnetized iron is a bad conductor of electricity.[1]

(* also stated in Phil Mag Vol 1 n.s. p 266)

[1] The article, "Lightning Rods and Compasses," *Arcana of Science and Art*, 1828, *1*:72, reported the opinions of Dr. J.W. Fischer who believed that iron became a poor conductor of static electricity when magnetized and that it should therefore not be used for lightning rods. Fischer recommended copper rods instead. Fischer's statements originally appeared in his article, "Ueber die Leitung der Elektricität durch magnetisirtes Eisen...," *Archiv für die gesammte Naturlehre*, 1824, *3*:421–424.

The *Arcana* article also gave the contrasting opinion of J.H. Abraham who asserted that conducting power was increased when iron was

To test this fact I placed a rasp in an electrical circuit excited by a thermo electrical battery exposed to a constant temperature. After the needle had taken a fixed position the rasp was magnetized by a powerful horseshoe magnet but no effect could be observed

Again the rasp was replaced by a cylinder of soft iron & when the needle was stationary the cylinder was magnetized by a coil of copper ribbon but no effect was produced

It would appear from these experiments that the assertion is not well founded[2]

---

magnetized and that therefore lightning rods should be made of magnetized iron. Abraham's observations in the *Arcana* were taken from his "New Phaenomena Caused by the Effect of Magnetic and Electric Influence and Suggestions for Ascertaining the Extent of the Terrestrial Magnetic Atmosphere," *Phil. Mag.*, 1827, 2d ser. *1*:266–271. In a notebook entry of May 5, 1835, Henry had written "Try the conducting power of a magnetic bar before & after magnetization," and cited the Abraham article (*Henry Papers*, 2:390).

[2] In an undated entry in his commonplace book (notebook [10615]), p. 100, Henry re-

ferred back to these experiments and wrote that he had "found no difference in the conduction." In an 1859 publication, Henry wrote that "the magnetization of a bar, so far as it has any effect, tends to cause the electrical discharge to revolve around it, and to render the iron very slightly, if anything, a less perfect conductor." "Meteorology in its Connection with Agriculture. Part V, Atmospheric Electricity," *Agricultural Report of the Commissioner of Patents, 1859* (Washington, 1860), p. 513. In the same article (p. 522), he recommended that lightning rods be made of iron.

"RECORD OF EXPERIMENTS"
Henry Papers, Smithsonian Archives

April 9th 1838

1 Exp with two coiles long one No 1, and the ribbon coil No 2 arranged so that the break might take place in the outer and inner coil at the same time. No effect no shock

Exp 2nd The same arrangement was next made as in the last with the exception of the ends of the reel and coil were seperated by a piece of insulating substance and the two bound together so that the breaking of contact would be simultaneous. With this arrange- ment a shock was given but not more intense than in the case of the arrangement without [closing] the circuit

"RECORD OF EXPERIMENTS"
Henry Papers, Smithsonian Archives

April 10th 1838

Exp 1 Attached to the inner long coil a magnetizing spiral (spiral containing needle).[1] Sent current through outer—no magnetism in needle. Repeated the exp several times always with the same result

Exp 2 Repeated the above experiment with the exception of substituting for the long coil a short ribbon coil. The needle was rendered magnetic in the <*inverse*> direction of the current of the outer coil several times repeated

Exp 3 Placed the needle in the centre of the concentric coils. Slightly magnetized in the direction of the outer current or the battery current

Exp 4 Sent small charge from jar through the spiral for magnetising needles (Exp 1). A needle was magnetized in the proper direction as indicated by the electromagnetic model.[2]

Exp 4 Placed coil No 2 (Ribbon) horizontally on the table and within this long helix No 2 (1500 feet) and within this again long helix No 1 (1640). Shock from Helix No 2 rather more intense than from helix No 1. Probably because helix No 2 is larger and therefore is everywhere nearer the outside coil & consequently is more acted on. But the most important result from this experiment is the fa[c]t that when the ends of the middle helix are seperated then the inner helix produces the shock without any dimmunition of intensity but when the ends of the middle helix are closed no shock can be produced from the inner coil.[3] The closing of the ends of the inner coil has no effect on the shock from the outer coil

---

[1] This magnetizing spiral, used to determine the direction of the induced currents, was a cylinder of thirty spires of copper wire just wide enough to admit a sewing needle. "Contributions III," paragraph 11.

[2] For a discussion of Ampère's electrodynamic molecule, see *Henry Papers*, 2:230n–232n. This experiment is merely to test the magnetizing spiral. For the next experiment, also numbered 4, we assume Henry switched back to a galvanic battery.

[3] In the margin Henry wrote "Exp of screening." He later used the neutralization caused by an interposed circuit to rule out interference as the cause of the screening. He finally explained the phenomenon according to the alternation in the direction of induced currents of higher orders.

> . . . when a third conductor is acted on at the same time by a primary and secondary current (unless it be very near the second wire) it will fall into the region of the *plus* influence of the former, and into that of the *minus* influence of the latter, and hence no induction will be produced.

"Contributions III," paragraphs 68–73, 94–96, and 130 (quotation).

5 Exp Used the 2nd & 1st long helices with the small shaker battery of 25 plates. Shock from this and the second coil about as intense as from the 1st helix with the copper ribbon[4]

6 Exp Placed <*coil N*> long helix No 1 within No 2, produced the inductive shock by sending current from small crookshank battery through <*coil*> helix No 2. Action nearly as great as induction from ribbon coil with battery of single element. In these experiments shock was only felt at breaking contact not on making

The intensity of the induced current is so great that 3 persons grasping hands felt the shock[5]

Note to exp 4. When the handles from both coils were grasped at the same time by two different persons then each receved a shock. The interposition of the hands partially retarded the action of the middle coil so as to let the action extend in part to the inner coil.

important

---

[4] Henry later added "See exp July 18th." In that entry (printed below) he also used the Shaker battery to test combinations of various helices and coils.

[5] In the margin Henry wrote "Important."

"RECORD OF EXPERIMENTS"
Henry Papers, Smithsonian Archives

April 11th 1838

Passed a current from small crookshank battery through long helix no 2. At the same time current through ribbon coil No 2 on the outside of the helix. No shock could be produced while the current was passing. This perhaps was caused by the current passing through the acid instead of the body. No difference in the result when the current was reversed.

"RECORD OF EXPERIMENTS"
Henry Papers, Smithsonian Archives

April 12 1838

1 Sent current through ribbon coil, then suddenly thrust into the centre of the same the long helix No 2 which was connected with the galvanometer, slight indication of a current at making & breaking contact

2 Substituted for the helix above mentioned the <*long*> ribbon cylindrical coil; the effect with this was considerably greater, the direction of the current was the same as that of the outer coil when the cylender was drawn out

Placed[1] long helix No 2 within ribbon No 2. Sent current from Thermo battery through outer, received slight shock from inner by placing one handle above the tongue the other beneath. Same exp repeated with a rasp in the one cup of mercury and the end of the coil drawn along this. The shock was now much more intense and could be felt to the wrists nearly; the spark is also much better shewn in this way—

By screwing the rasp to the wire, so as to make a better metallic contact & putting the battery into iced salt a much more powerful and disagreeable shock is produced which may be felt to nearly the elbows. This effect however was only produced when the iron was quite hot and the outer side of the battery immersed in a freezing mixture

[1] "Thermobattery shock—" appears in the margin.

"RECORD OF EXPERIMENTS"
Henry Papers, Smithsonian Archives

April 13th 1838

1 Placed large ribbon coil No 1 on the table. Sent current through it from two batteries, small cylendrical. Also placed long helix No 2 on the out side, shock perceptable when helix 4 inches without the circle. Next the helix was held over the circle in the direction of its axis, centre of helix more than a foot from centre of circle, the effect still perceptible, a motion of an inch or two upwards rendered the action imperceptible.[1]

2 With one battery the effect was greater than with both arranged as in the above experiment in which the two formed a compound battery. With one the distance above at which the shock was felt was about 16 inches

3 Tried long helix no 1 to produce shock inside of large coil, found no effect. No 2 placed in the same position gave powerful shocks. Can account for this on no other principle than that of having destroyed the insulation

[1] Henry's tests of distance effects in the production of secondary currents are summarized in Section III of "Contributions III: Electro-Dynamic Induction."

of no 1 by passing through it a shock from a small jar highly charged—I had placed this coil in contact with prime conductor & then sent sparks through it. They at first were quite pungent, but after the shock had been sent through the coil the effect appeared to cease.

N B The cause of the destruction of the helix is now more apparent. It appears to depend on the screening influence of the part of the coil cut off by the electricity passing through[2]

4th Attempted to generate a current in one coil and accelerate it by passing it through another. The ribbon coil no 2 was placed inside of No 1 & the ends of the former connected with the long helix no 2 placed without but no shock could be obtained, perhaps the intensity was not sufficiently great

5th The same arrangement with the difference of putting the long helix No 1 inside & the other long helix out side; the helix no 1 although injured gave a shock but not a very intense one with a small cercle

It appeared that no effect was produced with a single snap, but when the file was used to give a series of explosions then the effect was increased

6th Placed ribbon coil No 2 within coil No 1, observed spark from No 1 when No 2 was open & shut, *ie* when the ends were joined and open—no difference apparently in the result

---

[2] i.e., Henry concluded that the closed circuit due to the destruction of insulation screened the remaining part of the helix from the inductive influence, in keeping with the results of his second experiment 4, April 10, 1838, above. Henry discusses this experimental anomaly in paragraph 75 of "Contributions III."

"RECORD OF EXPERIMENTS"
Henry Papers, Smithsonian Archives

April 14th 1838

1 Placed the ribbon coil No 2 inside of No 1, & then placed the long helix No 2 inside of this. When the ends of no 2 ribbon were joined no shock could be felt from no 2 long helix. The snap at the same time was quite <*vivid and*> loud. When the long helix was placed on the outside then the shock was produced.

2 Small helix placed within No 2 which remained as in the last exp and its ends fastened so that the current in No 2 would circulate through the small helix, a needle placed in this became magnetic showing that although the current in the 2nd coil would not produce a [?current] in the long helix and appears to screen it from the action of the long ribbon without, still it produces magnetism in a needle. This effect is as yet quite inexplicable to me.

3 Placed one coil of thin wire around a glass tube within an other tube and 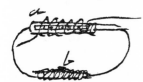 through the outer spiral or coil a discharge from the large jar was sent;[1] a needle within became of course—magnetic —The two ends of the inner spiral were next joined together, so as to make an arrangement like that in the previous experiment to test the principle of screening in common electricity. The needle in the inner spiral was magnetic as before but now appeared a little more intensely magnetized.

4 The last experiment gave indications of an inductive action although  none of screening. To test this action a second or rather 3rd spiral was placed on the out side as at *b*. The discharge from a large jar sent through outer spiral *a* and a needle placed in *b* became highly magnetic. The direction of the current was the same as that from the jar.
Good Experiment

5 As the above experiment developes an important principle it is highly important to be assured that the effect is produced by induction and not by a current passing around, for this purpose the jar which I had formerly coated inside and out with slips of tin foil was suspended horizontally from a silk ribbon[2] and great care taken that the effect should be produced soley by the action of the induced current. The experiment was then several times repeated and always with the same result.

6 The apparatus was arranged as in the last experiment with the exception of introducing between the charged jar and the jar with a spiral around it an other magnetizing spiral, needles of the same size being put into each of the helices;[3] after the discharge they were both found magnetic but the

---

[1] Here Henry begins to seek equivalent inductive effects from the passage of static electricity.

[2] To insulate the apparatus.

[3] Magnetizing spirals to test for current were connected to both the primary and secondary circuits.

one in the spiral of the induced current much the stronger. This was tried several times in succession with the same result. As some difference might possibly exist in the power of the two helices they were made to change places but the result was still the same. The needle in the induced or secondary current was still the stronger. This effect was produced when the induced current was on the out side

TO JOHN TORREY
Torrey Papers, Library, New York Botanical Garden

Princeton April Monday
16th 1838

My Dear Dr

Your letter[1] was received this morning. Mr. Goodrich[2] starts tomorrow morining at 4 o'clock. We are very sorry to learn that Mrs. Torrey has not yet recovered but hope she will not long be confined. She must have been very anxious to see you and it was well that you hurried off as soon as you did.

I have been very much engaged since you left in experimenting. It took me at first about a week to get started and I almost began to fear that I had lost the power of interrogating nature with any effect. I have since however found no cause of complaint on that account and have been as successfull as I could hope to be with the labour bestowed.

I have found Mr Goodrich a very excellent assistant. He possesses some good traits for a situation of this kind, intelligence sufficient to take a lively interest in the experiments and modesty enough to prevent all obtrusiveness. He appeared perfectly willing to do anything however humble it may be. I find it of great importance in experimenting to have some person with whom I can talk on the subject in the way of sharpening myself. In the act of communicating my half formed conceptions to others they insensibly take a more definite shape in my own mind. Mr G. will inform you con-

[1] Not found.

[2] A July 31, 1838, letter from Henry to Goodrich (printed below) is addressed to Fowler, a tiny community in far upstate St. Lawrence County, New York, but we have been unable to obtain any information about Goodrich's activities there. In another letter later that year Torrey informed Henry that Goodrich had gone west to seek his fortune, but again his whereabouts remain a mystery. The cata-logue of Columbia University alumni lists a C. B. Goodrich as a nongraduating student at the College of Physicians and Surgeons from 1839 to 1840 (*Columbia Alumni*, p. 256), and a Charles B. Goodrich turns up in the New York City Directory, 1842–1843, as a printer on 138 Fulton St. Aside from these scant details, however, we have not been able to secure any other information on Henry's former helper.

cerning our experiments which I intend immediately to place before the Phil. Society. Until they are published I do not wish them to be mentioned.

The college is not yet in funds but the Treasury will be replenished in a few days when I will attend to your money affairs as you directed.[3]

Saxton promised to visit me during the vacation.[4] If he does so I will reccollect the affair of the Gallery.[5]

Your Friend
Jos. Henry

P.S. I intend to write to Chilton in a few days, perhaps tomorrow, and will then request him to send the package you mention by some person I may find going to the city.   J.H.

[3] Torrey had not yet received his salary for teaching the senior class in chemistry during the 1837–1838 Winter Session. He was to wait another month before Henry could forward him a check.

[4] See the "Record of Experiments" entries of April 19, 20, and 21, 1838, below, for Saxton's work with Henry in Princeton.

[5] This may be a reference to Torrey's attempt to establish a gallery of science in New York City. In a January 23, 1839, letter to Harriet (printed below), Henry noted that Torrey was planning to apply for an act of incorporation. We do not know if this is related to the efforts of others. For example, on January 8, Rubens Peale, one of the sons of Charles Willson Peale, and others submitted a petition to the New York State Assembly requesting a bill of incorporation for a Museum of Natural History and Science in New York City. After con-sideration by the appropriate committee, the Senate on March 5 and the Assembly on March 21, 1839, passed the bill for the New-York Museum of Natural History and Science. *New York Senate Journal*, 62nd Session, January 1839, p. 188; *New York Assembly Journal*, 62nd Session, January 1839, pp. 69–70, 144, 471, 480, 491.

A summary of the original petition by Loring D. Chapin, an assemblyman from New York City, may be found in Document No. 71 in *New York Assembly Documents*, 62nd Session, 1839. The petitioners hoped that an act of incorporation would enable their institution to attract numerous private collections and individual donations for their public exhibits. In addition the museum was to provide facilities for scientific experiments and arrange public lectures by leading scientists.

TO STEPHEN ALEXANDER

Mary Henry Copy, Family Correspondence, Henry Papers, Smithsonian Archives

Princeton April 16th, 1838

My dear Stephen

All things have gone on as usual since you left. . . . The Trustees met on Tuesday at about four o'clock and adjourned the same evening. It was not a very full meeting, the members from New York were not present.[1] I know not what acts of wisdom or of importance were passed. The Doctor was

[1] Only fourteen of the twenty-three Trustees were present at the April 10, 1838, meeting. Minutes of the Trustees, *3*:342, Princeton University Archives.

ordered to borrow money to replenish the Treasury.[2] "I call spirits from the vasty deep, but will not come at my call."[3] The Doctor may call creditors for the college but will they come these moneyless times at his bid.

Mr. Goodrich, Dr. Torrey's rough diamond, leaves me tomorrow. I regret his departure since I have found him of much assistance, since Dr. James[4] left. Immediately after the examination, which was principally finished on Thursday, I commenced experimenting and have been much engaged since. It is just two years since I have attempted any thing of the kind and, at first, I made but little progress that I began to fear that the power of successfully interrogating Nature had departed from me. I however persevered and at length succeeded in eliciting from the ambiguous responses a number of truths which have an important bearing on the whole phenomena of electrical dynamic induction. I can now produce, in a very striking manner, secondary and tertiary lateral currents from the discharge of a Leyden Jar and have thus opened, as I conceive, a highly interesting field of inquiry on the subject of ordinary electricity, which as you know, has remained stationary for many years. I will devote myself assiduously, during the remainder of the vacation, to this subject and endeavour to get my paper published[5] within a few weeks. I hope Mr. Meads will have his organ in full tone by the time I next visit Albany and that I shall then have sufficient knowledge to appreciate its merits.[6] I am, as you know, if my ap-

---

[2] Princeton was facing a deficit of $4600. In addition, a note for $1500 was to come due on May 3. Dr. Carnahan was ordered to raise the needed $4600 "by loan or otherwise," as well as to renew the note. Minutes of the Trustees, 3:344.

[3] Henry has combined lines from two passages in Shakespeare's *Henry IV, Part I* into a single quotation. The actual dialogue, act 3, scene 1, lines 57–59, is as follows:

Glendower: I can call spirits from the vasty deep.

Hotspur: Why, so can I, or so can any man; But will they come when you do call for them?

[4] Perhaps a transcriber's error. None of the laboratory assistants which have been mentioned so far were called "Dr. James" by Henry.

[5] This is the first indication (along with a remark in Henry's letter to Torrey of the same date) that Henry had begun envisioning his "Contributions III: Electro-Dynamic Induction." Henry made a preliminary public announcement of his results in a letter to the American Philosophical Society dated May 4, 1838 (*Proceedings of the American Philosophical Society*, 1838–1840, *1*:14). The paper was not read, however, until November 2, 1838.

[6] The cabinetmaker John Meads (*Henry Papers*, *1*:63–64) patented his improvements in the arrangement and shape of the valves of an organ in November 1838. In the Fall of 1839 Henry forwarded a model of the organ to the London Society of Arts for evaluation. The subsequent investigation, which included the collating of reports by organists and organmakers on both sides of the Atlantic, concluded with a recommendation in April 1841 that the Society not endorse Meads's improvements because they represented no advantage in either the making or playing of organs. Indeed, most of the English artisans called to testify judged Meads's organ to be a step backwards in organ design.

Burke's Index, p. 324. Manuscript Minutes, Committee of Mechanics, Royal Society of Arts, January 23, 1840; February 6, 1840; April 30, 1840; March 11, 1841; April 1, 1841; and April 22, 1841. Henry to William Vaughan, October 18, 1839, and Henry to Petty Vaughan, March 30, 1840; both letters are printed below.

paratus arrives in good time, to lecture on sound the next session.[7] I intend to know more of the subject. It is now past twelve o'clock. . . .

[7] The summer session began during the third week in May. Henry's apparatus arrived after the beginning of the session but before its mid-August termination for seniors. The order, however, was incomplete. Neither Henry's notes nor his students' notebooks can be dated accurately enough to say whether he lectured on sound this session.

Acoustics was not, in any case, an important part of Henry's natural philosophy course. A survey of students' notebooks in the New York State Library, the Smithsonian Archives, and the Princeton University Library shows that of the eight sections of Henry's lecture course, sound was the smallest, taking up, at a maximum, just over 5% of the lectures.

On the other hand, Henry's interest in acoustics was growing. The amount of time he was spending on the subject in his course doubled during his years at Princeton. Moreover, as we shall see in later volumes of the *Henry Papers*, the phenomenon of sound became one of Henry's major research fields while at the Smithsonian.

"RECORD OF EXPERIMENTS"
Henry Papers, Smithsonian Archives

April monday 16th 1838

1 Adjusted the glass cylender or jar with the tinfoil coil with a tube in it so that there could be no possibility of contact at any point. Sent the discharge through. The needle in the magnetizing helix was affected as usual—the magnetism being stronger in the helix of the induced current than in the one connected with the direct discharge. This was repeated several times and always with the same result. From this it would appear that the <*magnetism of the*> induced current does not move as rapidly as the primary current.[1] It is possible that the great magnetic effects produced with the large jar, and described 2 years and more since are in part referable to some action of this kind[2]

2 Next arranged the apparatus so that the induced current should pass around a tube and thus give place to a current in a helix placed in this tube and then pass around another tube in which a needle was placed. Thus a secondary current would be detected if any were produced. The result was as anticipated, the needle became magnetic. The direction was in the same way as in the original current.

[1] Henry begins to investigate whether a quantity current can be induced from one of intensity. He achieved this capability on October 23, 1838, below. In "Contributions III," paragraph 42, Henry attempted to explain how "intensity and quantity may both be produced from the same induction"—the transformer effect. With intensity, a small quantity of fluid was set in rapid motion. Quantity resulted when a larger current was given a slower velocity. Were it not for the increased resistance of longer conductors, Henry hypothesized, the "quantity multiplied by the square of the velocity would be the same."

[2] Possibly the experiments of March 19, 1836, documented in *Henry Papers*, 3:29.

"RECORD OF EXPERIMENTS"
Henry Papers, Smithsonian Archives

Tuesday April 17th 1838

Placed 2nd ribbon coil on the outside of a glass jar and the long helix No 2 in the inside. Then sent a charge through the outer coil, got a strong shock from the inner coil by induction, in precisely the same manner as in the galvanic arrangement. The shock appeared very similar to that from the coil when charged by the battery.

No 2 Arranged the apparatus as in the last experiment. Sent through the outer coil charge from the small jar (pint) instead of the large jar, no shock. Again with the large jar a shock. It is probable that in [this] experiment that the insulation of the spires of the outer coil was not perfect & that some of the electricity cut across. Electricity of small jar more intense than large one

3 Made the same arran[gement] as before with the exception of the addition of a magnetizing spiral. Sent shock from large jar, no magnetism. Again sent shock which was so intense as to be felt by the finger which held the spiral yet no signs of magnetism could be perceived. This result is precisely analogous to that obtained by galvanism.

4 With a ribbon coil on the outside the spirals of which were placed at the distance of a tenth of an inch, the shock was less intense. With the apparatus of the spiral tinfoil no shock, properly so called, could be felt. The sensation appeared to be produced by the common lateral discharge.
N. Mr Goodrich my assistant left me so that I now cannot get on as fast as before

"RECORD OF EXPERIMENTS"
Henry Papers, Smithsonian Archives

Wednesday 18th april 1838

1 Put the large globe in contact with the prime conductor of the machine with the tinfoil coil arranged and connected with a magnetic helix. Passed spark, needle became slightly magnetic in same direction as the primary current. The lateral discharge was in this case quite sharp on the fingers which held the helix containing the needle. This fact in connection with the comparatively small magnetism of the needle would show that the magnetism does not depend on the free electricity[1]

Put up long conductor

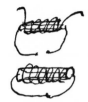

Placed one helix with needle within an other, the ends at first apart. Then with the projecting ends of the inner one in contact. The magnetism of the latter arrangement was much stronger than with the former. *This* would suggest a method of making strong magnets by an electrical discharge. Place several coils one within an other. Send the current through the outer, close the inner. *Try this*

Repeated an exp of Savarys.[2] Put needle into magnetising helix, first however inserted it into an extra glass tube, noted the magnetism which was quite intense. Next placed the needle into a piece of copper tube and this again into a piece of lead tube. When the same intensity of discharge was passed no magnetism

Try if a thick metal tube will screen action of current[3]

---

[1] Henry subscribed to the theory that lateral discharge was due to the action of "free electricity." See *Henry Papers*, 3:53n–54n.

[2] Félix Savary.

[3] Without attributing them specifically to Savary, P.M. Roget discusses similar screening experiments. Roget notes that when the metal shield is decreased in thickness, the magnetic effect becomes perceptible and, remarkably, when the thickness is reduced further, the needle becomes even more magnetic than without any shield at all. *Treatises on Electricity, Galvanism, Magnetism, and Electro-Magnetism* (London, 1832), "Electro-Magnetism," p. 57.

"RECORD OF EXPERIMENTS"

Henry Papers, Smithsonian Archives

Thursd, April 19th 1838

1 Placed the long helix No 2 with[in] a thin brass kettle and this again within the long ribbon. With No 1 thus arranged a slight shock was just perceptible. With the kettle out the shock was quite intense. Again kettle in, shock scarce perceptible. Out intense. If the kettle had been a litle thicker the result would have been more decisive

2 Put a hollow cylender of copper or rather bronze into the ribbon coil No 2 and within this a piece of round iron then transmitted the current. The iron became magnetic as if the hollow cylender of bronze was not present. Hence the cylender does not screen the magnetic property of the galvanic current

31

3ʳᵈ Placed cylinder of soft iron within ribbon No 1 and within this cylinder the long helix. No shock could be obtained and this was scarcely to be expected since when the broad spiral is put in, as long as the ends were not in contact the action passed through the copper. Hence we may infer that the effect is not due to any screening influence of the metal but to the circumstance of its producing or rather in having currents produced in it. That there are currents produced in it is shown by passing them through a spiral and magnetizing needle in one of the former experiments. The iron in the above experiment was about 1/30 of an inch thick.

4ᵗʰ Placed long ribbon coil horizontally then held long helix over it. Interposed plate of glass. Shock quite intense. Next iron no shock. Next large plate of zinc no effect. Again glass, shock as before.

5 Repeated the exp of shock with the thermo-pile. Ground the end of the rasp to make contact with mercury a little more intimate. Sparks very brilliant with coil N 2. Battery put on plate with salt and pounded ice. Action greatest at first, light beautiful green light on the rasp which can be seen over the whole room. Shock a thrilling censation. This exp was repeated to exhibit the action of the thermopile to My Friend Mr Saxton, who has come on from Phil⁴ according to previous agreement, to make some experiments with me. He was much gratified by the action of the thermo-pile.

Same evening used Mr Saxton's revolving mirror to seperate the brush into seperate sparks of electricity.[1] Effect striking and beautiful. Brush formed by a blunt wire put into the end of the conductor.

---

[1] This apparatus is best known in connection with Wheatstone's determination of the velocity of electricity. See *Henry Papers*, 2:492n. According to Henry, Saxton constructed the apparatus for Wheatstone's well known experiment. "Memoir of Joseph Saxton, 1799–1873," National Academy of Sciences, *Biographical Memoirs*, 1877, *1*:304.

"RECORD OF EXPERIMENTS"
Henry Papers, Smithsonian Archives

Friday april 20 1838
1 Spent the morning with Mr S in experiments on light &c.[1] Afternoon made 2 flat ribbon coils, one 50 feet and the other 60 long. Placed one on piece of glass, the other on it with glass interposed. Sent charge from large

---

[1] The nature of these experiments is unknown to us.

jar through the under coil, intense shock was take[n] from the upper. A magnet was also formed by the current from the upper. The experiment was tried several times and the direction was always contrary to that of the original current.[2]

2 At night used Mr Saxton's revolving mirror for an attempt to seperate the pulsations of galvanism when the points of charcoal are intensely ignited by the agent. The effect was negative. The light appeared like a continued ribbon perhaps with a greater motion the result sought might have been obtained. The mirror however revolved with sufficient rapidity to seperate the sparks of the elect brush. We have also concluded to make the experiment with burning hydrogen when it gives the musical sounds[3]

Saw with a small opera glass the difference between the light from a planet and a fixed star. In order to show this adjust well the focus then give a conical motion to the glass so as to make the object describe a circle or a line in the heavens. In the case of the fixed star the light is not perfectly continuous but is so in that of the planet.

---

[2] Henry's marginal notes reveal initial doubt —"(some mistake in this)"—and then a reconsideration—"No mistake, current changed by distance."

[3] In notebook [7169], p. 219, Henry describes this experiment in the following way:

To sh[o]w the musical tubes use the Phil. candle with acid much diluted. This gives a steady stream which does not go out as in the case of the bell glass. The tube may be of glass drawn out at the end. The hole may be enlarged to suit the purpose in-stantly by breaking off a part. The sounds in this way are very fine and may be varied by using tubes of different lengths.

Also by closing the upper end or the lower with the hand, similar to the stop of an organ pipe.

The philosophical candle, an apparatus for the slow burning of hydrogen, consisted of a glass flask fitted with a cork perforated to receive a narrow glass tube. Hydrogen was generated by a mixture of zinc or iron and sulphuric acid.

"RECORD OF EXPERIMENTS"
Henry Papers, Smithsonian Archives

Saturday April 21st 1838

1 Repeated or attempted to repeat the exp of Peltier of producing elect by scraping a piece of copper with an other piece of the same metal.[1]

No effect was produced. Mr S. thinks the results of Peltier were obtained by the heat from the friction giving rise to electrical currents.

---

[1] "Sur l'électricité dynamique engendrée par le frottement," *Comptes Rendus*, 1837, 4:172–173. Peltier placed one plate of copper in the magnetic meridian and rubbed it with an-other. Each plate was connected to one lead from a galvanometer, whose needle deflected during the act of rubbing.

2 Repeated the exp. of Dr Page[2] for producing musical sounds from a magnet. Best method of operating is to put the two fore fingers into the ears and suspend from these by a string the magnet which is made to straddle a flat spiral. When the contact is broken a ringing noise is produced. The effect is probably owing to the attraction of the spiral for each end of the magnet and attempts to draw them together, this produces a slight agitation[3]

3 While the battery was in operation last night for the exp on the charcoal points repeated the exp. with the long and short coil, also with the shock on breaking contact. The short coil did not increase the effect, with the long helix the effect was very intense both in burning and the *shock*

The shock on breaking contact was also quite perceptible and was thought to be produced by the action of the fluid in the battery on itself as well as the fluid in the body. It was found to increase by increasing the length of the circuit.

4 Placed one of the narrow spiral coils on the small stool with hole in the bottom, put large plate of glass over this and the other narrow coil on the glass. When shock was sent through lower coil intense shock felt from the upper but no signs of magnetism could be obtained; this was repeated several times and always with the same result which was different from that obtained yesterday when under apparently the same circumstances the needle was always magnetized in a direction contrary to that of the original current. I know not at present how to account for the result obtained yesterday.[4]

---

[2] The electrical experimentalist and inventor Charles Grafton Page (1812–1868). In the late 1830s, Page published extensively on electromagnetic induction. He devoted many years to an unsuccessful quest for a practical battery-powered motor. From 1842 Page was a principal Examiner of the Patent Office. Robert C. Post, *Physics, Patents, and Politics: A Biography of Charles Grafton Page* (New York, 1976).

[3] Page's discovery of what he called "galvanic music" contributed to the early history of telephony. He attributed the sound vibrations to a "molecular derangement" which allegedly occurred when the magnet expanded and contracted as the coil was energized and deenergized. See Page's "The Production of Galvanic Music," *Silliman's Journal*, 1837,

32:396–397. His work in electroacoustics is assessed by Robert C. Post, op. cit., pp. 18–19.

Two years later Henry conducted further experiments on electroacoustics. These are documented below, beginning on April 29, 1840. In experiments April 10 and May 8, 1840, Henry failed to find clear evidence of Page's assertion that magnetization affected the size of iron.

The end of the second volume of Henry's "Record of Experiments" contains a reading note on Félix Savart's article "Recherches sur les vibrations longitudinales," *Annales de chimie*, 1837, 65:337–408, which Henry stated he consulted "in connection with the expermts on the sound from magnet."

[4] See the preceding "Record of Experiments" entry, experiment 1.

5 The same arrangement remaining, the shock from the galvanic battery was sent through the lower coil, then a needle was made strongly magnetic (but no shock)

6 The long helix was next substituted for the narrow ribbon spiral and now no magnetism could be obtained but a shock too powerful to be taken through the body was sent through the <*arms*> one hand. It would appear from these exps that the action of the galvanic current and of the electrical one is almost identical, they differ somewhat in intensity, the snap of the long coil is nearly as intense as the electrical discharge and produces on a long wire an intensity much greater. The shock from the jar however is more intense for it gives a short or comparatively short wire the power by induction of giving shocks. It is important to remark that the power of giving shocks in both cases is unaccompanied by that of making magnets the analogy in this respect is complete.[5]

6 Next tried the effect of interposing plates of metal. When thin plate of copper was interposed the effect of the shock was much less but not interely obliterated. When a second sheet of copper was interposed no *shock* could be obtained. When the copper was withdrawen and its place supplied by a plate of glass of the same thickness the shock was very intense. There can be no doubt therefore of the screening influence of the conductors placed between the coils

7 Mr S suggested to me a simple method of making a helix by cutting a piece of copper plate into a spiral form, then slightly expanding the spires covering them with silk, forming an other covering it in the same manner and then soldering the several spires together

8. Commenced this afternoon to fit up the apparatus for attempting to get the spark from the magnetism of the earth.[6] For this purpose we (Mr S and myself) procured a piece 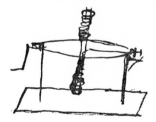 of round iron 1 inch in diameter and four feet long. This was mounted on a wooden axle and made to revolve with a crank. Around each end was rolled one of the narrow ribbon coiles, the ends joined at the middle so as to form one continued coil around the whole length of the bar, but a greater accumulation of the ribbon was made at each end.

[5] In the margin next to this experiment Henry wrote "Exam this expemt again Dec 1838." No record of this experimentation has been found.

[6] The initiative for this partially recorded experiment probably came from Saxton, since

The other two ends of this long coil were brought out at one of the axes and insulated from each other and furnished with points and a mercury cup for breaking contact

---

Henry attributes the plans for it to him in "Memoir of Joseph Saxton, 1799–1873," Na-

tional Academy of Sciences, *Biographical Memoirs*, 1877, *1*:303–304.

FROM ROBERT HARE
Henry Papers, Smithsonian Archives

Philad[a] April 21st 1838

Dear Sir

The wire requested in your letter of yesterday[1] will be forwarded this eve'g freight paid.

I [am] pleased to hear you are so well occupied. You will observe in the last number of the Philosophical Magazine Watkins does you justice as the original inventor of a machine for producing power by electromagnetism. In what he alleges I fully concur.[2]

I am engaged upon the gases as when you were here.[3]

Yours Sincerely
Rob[t] Hare

[1] Not found.

[2] Francis Watkins, "On Electro-magnetic Motive Machines," *Phil. Mag.*, 1838, 3d ser. *12*:190–196. Watkins described an electromagnetic motor of his own design that he applied to the operation of mechanical models. Watkins, who had met Henry in Europe, was extremely generous in crediting Henry with the original principle of the electric motor, even though subsequent improvers had substituted a rotary motion for Henry's reciprocating idea. Watkins modestly declined credit for any basic discovery, going so far as to write:

Henry's principle being universally adopted, it is clear that all those who attempted to carry out the idea of obtaining a motive power by this principle are only entitled to the credit of those modifications

of the arrangement which may emanate from their mechanical ingenuity, and to such credit only do I aspire in the present communication on my machines, which I will now describe.

(p. 191.) In light of his past frustrations in obtaining credit for the electromagnetic motive principle, Henry must have been deeply gratified by such expressions of deference. In fact, Watkins's wording makes one suspect that Henry had tutored him on these matters during their European encounter. Compare Watkins's words with earlier complaints by Henry in 1834. *Henry Papers*, 2:162.

[3] Experiments involving gases were the subject of some of Hare's publications from this period, but we are unable to specify what Henry may have witnessed on his last visit.

TO [THOMAS ROMNEY ROBINSON][1]
Mary Henry Copy, Memoir, Henry Papers, Smithsonian Archives

Princeton. April 28. 1838.

My dear Sir. I fear you will think me very remiss in not writing before this relative to the chronometer.[2] The truth is I have been so much engaged since my return from Europe in making up lee-way in my college duties that I have had little leisure for anything else. The chronometer has kept very good time and been of much use to me in making some magnetic observations. I do not think however I will be able to keep it unless an appropriation be made by the college for additional apparatus, a circumstance which is very doubtful, on account of the losses which the Institute has suffered by the stoppage of the banks and the commercial difficulties of the country. . . .

I shall always remember with much pleasure the night we passed together at Sir James South. The wonders of the Heavens shown us then are still vividly impressed on my memory. I was highly gratified in making the acquaintance of Sir James. I left England with very warm feelings and shall always retain the most lively recollections of the hospitality and kindness I everywhere received in your country.

I write this with the intention of sending it by the steamship [Sirius][3]

[1] Mary Henry omitted the name of the recipient in her copy of what apparently is a draft written by Henry. Since it was Thomas Romney Robinson who supplied Henry with an introduction to Sir James South (*Henry Papers*, 3:505), we assume that Robinson was the intended recipient.

[2] This reference to a chronometer leaves us a bit bewildered. We know of one chronometer purchased in Europe by Henry, but it was obtained from Arnold & Dent. A receipt of April 3, 1839, from E. & G. W. Blunt indicates it was not paid for until early 1839 (Folder of accounts with various European instrument- and apparatus-dealers, Joseph Henry for the College of New Jersey, 1837, Princeton University Archives). Perhaps Henry had promised Robinson a report on the performance of the Dent chronometer. Another possibility is that there was a second chronometer obtained in Europe, acquired either from or through Robinson, but not kept by Princeton for the reasons mentioned in the letter.

[3] The era of regular, steam-powered, transatlantic service began on the morning of April 23, 1838, when the *Sirius*, whose owners had sent her out from Cork on April 4 with the goal of being the first, arrived in New York harbor. That afternoon the *Great Western*, the first steamship built specifically for the transatlantic voyage, also arrived in New York, having set out from Bristol on April 8. These two voyages generated, as Henry indicates, great excitement and optimism.

The initial impact of the steamship was somewhat less than hoped. True, when everything was working, steamships made the passage of people and news between Europe and America much more rapid. During the first two years of service the steamships averaged sixteen to eighteen days traveling from Europe to the United States, depending upon the ship, and thirteen to seventeen days back. Sailing packets during the same period averaged thirty to thirty-six days to America, and twenty to twenty-four days to return. However, economic and technological problems dampened early enthusiasm. The undercapitalization of steamship companies, the great expenses of fuel and construction, and the perceived unreliability of engines all limited the efficiency of the steamship lines.

These problems were not quickly overcome. Sailing vessels remained the cheapest form of

which goes tomorrow. I hope you will receive it in the course of about two weeks.[4] The arrival of two steam vessels from across the great deep on the same day has caused a great sensation in our country and already several parties have been formed to visit England for the Coronation.[5] The result of the experiment must have an important influence on the state of Europe and America.

---

transporting cargo until at least 1860. Not until the post-Civil War immigrant boom was the economic survival of steamship lines not dependent upon government subsidies for carrying the mail. Engine reliability remained a question throughout the nineteenth century. It was 1899 before a steam liner was built without provision for the setting of canvas in case of engine breakdown.

We suspect that Henry obtained some personal satisfaction in the arrival of the *Sirius*. Dionysius Lardner and Henry previously clashed over the velocity of the Hudson River steamboats (*Henry Papers*, 3:508–510; Henry to Bache, August 9, 1838, below); in 1835 Lardner was quoted as equating the possibility of a direct steam voyage between Liverpool and New York with one from Liverpool to the moon. The alternative route proposed by Lardner was from Valentia, Ireland, to St. Johns, Newfoundland, a distance of only 1,900 miles, as compared to the 3,500 miles between New York and Liverpool. The former dis-

tance was safely within the range limitations of steam vessels as set by Lardner, approximately 2,550 miles. With the success of the *Sirius* and *Great Western*, Lardner was forced to admit his error at the 1838 meeting of the British Association.

David Budlong Tyler, *Steam Conquers the Atlantic* (New York, 1939); Edgar Charles Smith, *A Short History of Naval and Marine Engineering* (Cambridge, England, 1937), pp. 39–48; George Rogers Taylor, *The Transportation Revolution, 1815–1860* (New York, Evanston, and London, 1968), pp. 115–119.

[4] The *Sirius* left New York on May 1, 1838. She required seventeen days for the return voyage, two days more than the *Great Western*, which left on May 7. Tyler, *Steam Conquers the Atlantic*, p. 61; E. Keble Chatterton, *Steamships and Their Story* (London, New York, Toronto, and Melbourne, 1910), p. 100.

[5] Queen Victoria (1819–1901) was crowned on June 28, 1838.

TO LEWIS R. GIBBES[1]
Gibbes Papers, Library of Congress

Princeton April 28th 1838

My Dear Sir

Our text books in Natural Philosophy are Boucharlats mechanics,[2] Lardner on the Steam Engine,[3] Electricity, Magnetism, Electro-magnetism & Light from the Library of useful Knowledge.[4] Boucharlat is not the proper

---

[1] Apparently a reply to a Gibbes letter no longer existing. We have not located any letter to Henry earlier than 1843.

[2] This is the translation by E. H. Courtenay for which see *Henry Papers*, 2:32–33, et passim.

[3] Dionysius Lardner's popular book on the steam engine was a great success on both sides of the Atlantic. In fact, in 1836 two editions

appeared in the United States. The New York edition with additions by James Renwick, *The Steam Engine Familiarly Explained* . . . , is probably the work used by Henry.

[4] For the Library of Useful Knowledge, see *Henry Papers*, 2:84. The electricity and magnetism sections are by P. M. Roget; David Brewster authored the optics.

book for us. It has too little *physique* and I think of substituting for it Renwicks mechanics a work which contains more Physical facts than any other I am acquainted with in the English language. I do not like however the mathematical part and would probably substitute demonstrations selected from other sources.[5]

I have not yet given any lectures on Light since my return and therefore have not attempted to get up the experiments on polarization for exhibition to a class. I was formerly in the habit of giving some of the more simple phenomena but think much more may be done in the way of illustration on a large scale. You will probably be surprised when I inform you that I have as yet heard nothing from my apparatus since you left Paris. I wrote soon after your arrival but have received no answer. All my books and many other articles were in the boxes left with Pixii. Unless some good reason be given for the delay I now feal like publishing the affair from Georgia to Maine warning all americans to be ware of French dealers.

Our Friend Dr Hun sailed for Paris on the 24th of March. I expect a letter from him as soon as one can return which will give me the information required concerning my apparatus. Dr H. intends remaining in Paris during the summer and then to return for a perminent residence in America. He will probably settle in Albany.

I am now much engaged in a series of experiments on common electricity & have succeeded in developing some new and interesting results on the Phenomina of electricity in motion. I am much in want of the French articles for these experiments and must defer one part of the investigation until I can command some more powerful apparatus. I hope to be able to send you a copy of my memoir[6] in a few weeks.

With much Respect
Yours &c
Joseph Henry

May 3rd

We have just heard the melancholy intelligence that your city is nearly

---

[5] Prior to 1838–1839, the entry in the *Princeton Annual Catalogue* for junior year courses gave Boucharlat as the mechanics text. In that year appear the cryptic words, "Renwick's additions," most likely based upon *The Elements of Mechanics* (Philadelphia, 1832). This comment to Gibbes is indicative of Henry's attempts to define his place as a scientist which we can loosely equate with the transformation of natural philosophy into physics. In defining his interests to Princeton in 1832, Henry described them as "intermediate to pure Mathematics on the one hand and the more detailed parts of Chemistry . . ." (*Henry Papers*, *1*:435). Here he substitutes the physical specifics of Renwick for the more analytic mode of Boucharlat but then expresses a need for a better mathematical treatment.

[6] Gibbes is on the distribution list for "Contributions III: Electro-Dynamic Induction." Address book, p. [25], Box 17, Henry Papers, Smithsonian Archives.

destroyed by fire. I h[ope] that the accounts are exaggerated and that you and yours are not amoung the sufferers.[7]

Yours
J.H.

[7] The fire started in the evening of April 27. The *Charleston Courier* of May 1 estimated that 1,000 structures were destroyed.

"RECORD OF EXPERIMENTS"
Henry Papers, Smithsonian Archives

May 4[1] 1838

Cleaning Hall & cold weather has prevented my doing any thing since the last date except to have made 3 coils

Exp 1 Coils on flat boards one over the other with space for plates of different substances to be interposed. The distance of the two coils was 8 inches. When a plate of <*thin*> copper about 1/30 of an inch thick the screaning was perfect at this distance, was nearly perfect with a thin pece of copper, the screaning was not as perfect with a still thicker piece or two pieces each 1/30 of an inch; the shock could now be felt

Exp 2nd The metal was next varied in position, *ie* lowered and raised between the two coils but no apparent change produced in the screening effect

Exp 3rd Different metals were placed between the coils to determine if any difference exists in the power of screening. The screening effect of lead and mercury appeared to be much less then than that of copper and zinc.[2] A measure of the screening effect of different metals approximately was obtained by gradually increasing the distance of the coils and then noting when the shock became imperceptible with the different substances of equal thickness interposed. All the metals transmitted the principle when the upper coil was sufficiently near the lower one. A rather singular result show in the extreme case that the action was not perfect. A thin plate of iron acted about as well as copper

[1] Henry originally wrote "May 3rd," then wrote a 4 over the 3.
[2] In April 1840 Henry footnoted this result with the observation "This effect was found to be due to the greater superficial extent of the zinc and copper plates."

Exp 4 A Tub of quicksilver was then placed between the coils but the screening influence was not as great as that of copper or zinc. Next a tub of water was introduced, this appeared to have no effect scarcely beyond the mere effect of distance.

Exp 5 A flat spiral was introduced first with the ends seperate then with the ends in contact. The effect most striking when the ends were seperate, the shock was quite severe; when united not the least effect; even when the coils were all placed almost in contact the effect was very feeble and what effect was produced perhaps came from the circumstance that the galvanic coil or the one through which the original current was passed was a little larger than the other

Exp Placed the compound helices on the long coil and connected with this Faraday decomposing apparatus.[3] Decomposition readily produced but not magnetism. The best method of applying the paper is to put all things in th[eir] places, then moisten with water; the decomposition is best seen on the opposite side. With the same arrangement except that one of the narrow coils of 60[4] feet was substituted for the long compound helix and now magnetism was produced.

Screening takes place when the plate is not between the two but held on the upper side[5]

[3] A sensitive apparatus devised by Faraday to test electrochemical decomposition. Faraday wetted a piece of filter or litmus paper in the solution to be decomposed and then placed the paper under the electrodes. *Experimental Researches in Electricity*, Third Series, paragraphs 316 ff.
[4] Possibly "80."
[5] A slight variation in the hand suggests this sentence may have been added later.

"RECORD OF EXPERIMENTS"
Henry Papers, Smithsonian Archives

May 5th [1838] Saturday

Exp 1 Placed the compound helix on the coil No 1 formed into a plan[e] not a hoop and the coil No 2 around it on the out side so that the lower spiral was under the compound helix. The screening took place when the ends of the lower coil were joined. Shock in this case weak (some mistake).[1]

[1] In experiments 1 through 3, Henry is testing whether the screen necessarily had to be placed *between* the interacting induction coils to effectively block the inductive action.

Exp 2 Two flat coils were placed one on the other and the compound helix on these, shock felt as before scarcely any diminution although some was probably produced. Placed the flat <*spiral*> coil inside compound spiral and coil N 2 around this. The effect was not destroyed but somewhat weakened when the ends of the outer one were joined. Repeated exp 1 but not with the same effect when the battery was well charged.

With one of these exp the shock at making contact was very perceptable but intensity less than in breaking contact. While the shock at breaking contact agitated the whole, from that at making was scarcely perceptible. If a plate of metal be placed under the coil the effect on the helix above will be diminished.

Exp 3 Placed flat coil between two other flat coils, closed the ends of the outer ones. Spark from helices not quite so bright as when the ends were open. Still the effect not interely anihilated—as in the case of the two spirals wound together.

Exp 4

Placed coil No 2 (hoop) horizontally, within this long helix No 1, connected this with helix No 2 and with in this placed the flat spiral with the handles attached, with this arrangement a shock was felt but when the small spiral was taken from *b* and put within *a*, no effect could be perceived.[2] This is a very singular effect and perfectly analogous to that obtained with common electricity.

When both the outside spirals were placed within, then a slight effect was produced. This screening phenomenon is a very puzzling one. A current is produced in the screening and yet this in presence of the outer current produces no effect but when removed from the influence of the other its effect is sensible. This looks something like an interference.[3]

He finds in fact that screening is produced even when the screening conductor is placed below or around the induction coils. Henry hypothesized that screening was due to neutralizing currents induced in the screen. In paragraphs 66–73 of "Contributions III," he defends this hypothesis.

We are not sure why Henry felt he had made a mistake in the experiment. In experiment 2, below, he apparently repeats this experiment using a more powerfully charged battery and gets an unspecified but different result.

[2] Screening occurred when the small spiral was put within *a*. "Contributions III," paragraph 67, reveals the reasons for this arrangement: "the fact of the perfect neutralization of the primary current by a secondary, in the

interposed conductor, led me to conclude that if the latter could be drawn out, or separated from the influence of the former, it would itself be capable of producing a new induced current in a third conductor." Henry found this technique to be the key to producing what he termed higher order inductions.

"Important Result" appears as an annotation to this experiment in the left margin.

[3] This experiment is important as a test of the interference hypothesis as the cause of screening. Apparently helix no. 2 is placed within helix no. 1 and the small detecting spiral at the center. Henry is initially puzzled because, as he states in his publication (paragraph 67, "Contributions III"): "How does it happen that the two currents, both in

Exp 5 One of the flat coils was placed within hoop coil No 2, and the ends of this connected with the 2nd helix as in the last experiment, but no shock could be perceived. The current passed apparently through as if there were no action on it of the <*coil*> helix. The electricity produced by this arrangement was of course very low and not increased by passing through the long wire.[4] But when the compound spiral was [placed][5] on a second flat <*spir*> coil which then represented the 2nd helix in the last exp then shocks were obtained of about the same intensity as in the case of the helix used under the same circumstances. It would appear that the resistance of the long wire produces the same effect in this experiment as that of opening the circuit but when the short thick coil is used the electricity passes freely.

NB This experiment suggests the method of producing the greatest effect possible with the coil (perhaps) make a coil of two strands wound together then send this through another coil

Exp 6th

Made an arrangement for the production of tertiary currents. <*long helix on 2nd coil b*> flat <*spir*> coil in *a* long helix on *b* helix no 2 around helix no 3—shock perceptible by the tongue. Action appears due in some measure to the action of the spires not however in the way of reaction on itself but merely on account of the multiplication of the current

The large coil 90 feet placed under the 2nd helix did not produce as great effect as the smaller one

Exp 7 Attempted to produce decomposition by the <*tertiary*> 4th current but could not although the shock was disagreeable. The shocks to the elbows

---

the same direction, can neutralize each other?" The interference of periodic electrical vibrations from the two excited conductors was a possible explanation. In "Contributions III," paragraphs 67 and 73, Henry reveals why he had to reject the interference theory of screening: "If this were true the effect should depend on the length and other conditions of the current in the interposed conductor." However, he found that "the neutralization takes place with currents in the interposed or adjoining conductors of all lengths and intensities, and therefore cannot, as it appears to me, be referred to the interference of two systems of vibrations."

Despite the negative results of these experiments, Henry reveals an inclination toward the notion of electrical force as a periodic phenomenon in space.

[4] As a consequence of using the flat coil as the secondary circuit rather than the longer helix of experiment 4 above. The long second helix outside the induction coils failed to accelerate the secondary current by self-induction; rather its length only increased the resistance.

[5] One word obscured by ink blot.

Exp 8. Magnetized a needle by the tertiary current, found the direction the same as in the case of ordinary electricity namely in the direction of the battery current. Magnetism very marked but not intense.[6]

[6] Henry later annotated this experiment: "This a mistake, when the large battery was used needle more powerfully mag; direct op- posite. See July 19th." See, below, "Record of Experiments," July 19, 1838.

TO STEPHEN ALEXANDER
Family Correspondence, Henry Papers, Smithsonian Archives

Princeton May 6th 1838

Dear Stephen

I have intended to write to you for several days past but have been so much engaged that I have not found leisure. I have been going on with my experiments but since Mr Goodrich left me have been much pestered in getting a proper assistant. Besides this the weather has been so cold that I could not get along in the Hall without wood. I have however at length procured the services of Schmidt[1] the german wood sawyer. He is not much of an assistant but makes an admirable galvanometer. I give him many shocks in a day, and note as the result, his some what graphic descriptions. Did you feel that! Yes a *leetle* in de *thumb*. That one? Yes in the arm so so. That one, the *ne plus ultra*, ah! ah! over the whole body down *true* my toes, dat was pretty hard but it is better *as* sawing wood, *she* makes me feel spry all over. Although I have been much interrupted I have developed a number of new and interesting phenomena and amoung others have fallen on something which looks like electrical interferences and have also indirectly shown that electrical currents may be induced in a vacuum, consequently the electrical principle forms a *plenum*.[2]

Harriet and my self talked of going to New York last week but on account of the rain defered the jaunt; since then I have concluded to go to Philadelphia tomorrow or the next day to communicate my facts to the Philosophical Society for fear of anticipation abroad.[3]

[1] We have not identified Schmidt.

[2] The first mention of this in Henry's "Record of Experiments" does not occur until May 7. See the entry of that date, printed immediately below.

[3] Henry was not yet aware that Robert M. Patterson had already communicated his latest findings to the American Philosophical Society on May 4 (see Patterson's letter of May 8, below). Patterson's action made Henry's proposed trip less urgent and maybe unnecessary.

Perhaps only coincidentally, at the next meeting of the APS it was proposed that an abstract of the proceedings be published "from time to time." At the June 15 meet-

Harriet requests that you will purchase for us a barrel of brown sugar—that is if you can get it without the money. We will transmit the amount as soon as we know the sum. Also a quantity of tea, 8 or ten *lbs*. She says she can get good broken down lump shugar in Princeton for one shilling per *lb*.

Aunt[4] has gone back to your house to attend to the cleaning and making the garden. She stoped with us on sabbath but returned on monday.

We had a visit last week from Monday to Friday from Dr Cuyler[5] and one of his daughters. The Dr preached the sermon before the students[6]

---

ing the proposal was adopted, a move of obvious importance to Henry and others concerned about establishing priority. APS *Proceedings*, 1838–1840, *1*:16, 18.

[4] Nancy Connor.

[5] Cornelius C. Cuyler (*Henry Papers*, 2:267), a friend from Henry's Albany days.

[6] This is at the bottom of the second page of the letter, the remainder of which has apparently been lost.

"RECORD OF EXPERIMENTS"

Henry Papers, Smithsonian Archives

May 7th [1838] monday

Exp 1 Helix No 1 in coil no. 2 and connected with coil No 5 on the out side and with this helix No 2, no shock could be produced. The action of the induced current unless passing through a second coil produced no effect.[1] Hence the secondary current acts on its self—not necessarily[2]

Exp 2 To determine whether the screening effect existed between secondary currents when a conducting substance was 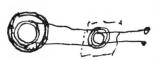 interposed. 2nd coil surround first helix, induced a current in 2nd helix, induced a current in 3rd helix, shock produced. Plate of zinc interposed—no shock. Hence, secondary currents of the same kind are susceptible of being screened.

Also currents from coil to helix *ie* induced by coil on helix screened in the same way as was shewn by substituting for the 2nd & [?3] helix, two ribbon coils—the effect was the same.

---

[1] Henry continues to investigate the properties of higher order inductions. A set-up similar to this experiment is considered in paragraph 89 of "Contributions III" where Henry concluded that the quantity of electricity induced in the helix is too small to produce an effect.

[2] "not necessarily" appears to be in a slightly different hand and therefore possibly a post-facto evaluation.

Exp 3rd The helix No 2 was placed in a jar over the plate of an air pump and the coil No 2 placed around it, then the effect was determined with the battery charged with sulphate of copper to produce a constant action. The air was next exhausted and the effect noted. The result appeared to be that the action[3] was greater when the air was in than when without. The effect was small but appeared to be in favour of the air within.

Could this fact be well established it would have an important bearing on the theories of electricity since it would tend to show that electricity fills all space and is probably identical with the luminiferous ether.[4] This exp is doubtful since the screening effect of water is very small.[5]

Exp 4 In reference to distance. Placed large coil (No 1) on top of board between t[w]o lamp supports. Sent through charge from small battery—shock perceptible from the 2nd helix—when the distance of the two coils was 28 inches. Afterwards coil no 2 was put within no 1 making one long coil of 150 feet, exterior diameter of which was about 20 inches. With this the effect did not appear to be sensibly increased above that of the single coil when a single battery was used but when the two small batteries were arranged so as to make one with two elements then the effect was greater—(Next see if there is any change of distance) With the compound helix felt the shock 30 inches.
Common electricity shock from large jar.

Exp 5 Put helix No 1 on glass stand, helix No 2 *<under this>* within this and one of the small flat coils within. Sent charge through under coil with compound, no effect—Sent charge through under coil with helix No 2, shock—sent shock through coil with helix No 1 shock a little greater than the last—with compound again no effect.—Inverted the inner coil and now a shock was produced—*very surprising result. The result explained.* The coil was placed within the

---

[3] i.e., the screening action.

[4] This along with the preceding letter to Stephen Alexander is one of the earliest known references by Henry to the plenum as the medium for transmitting electrical force. Henry did not adopt the plenum theory in print until 1842 in "Contributions V: Induction from Ordinary Electricity; Oscillatory Discharge." In "Joseph Henry's Lectures," pp. 173–180, Charles Weiner charts Henry's development of the hypothesis from this time until his 1857 reconciliation of the plenum with action at a distance.

[5] If we interpret Henry correctly, he assumes that the screening effect of air is less than water and therefore should not be so readily detectable as this experiment would seem to indicate.

outer one in the wrong direction at first as was shewn by the galvanic battery. I have been using these two coils in the experiments on distance in this way by mistake and hense got only differences of action. Now intend to repeat and shall probably get more intense results—but still there is something inexplicable in the action of the coil with common electricity—sometimes a shock is given and sometimes not.

Exp 6 Sent very small shock through the lower coil, made needle strongly magnetic, when with same arrangement a strong shock produced no magnetism. The last fact is an important one since I can now determine the direction of the current without the perplexity of results before obtained.

The effect may have been produced by the intensity of the discharge being too great to produce magnetism or by the electricity cutting across in the lower coil when a very heavy charge was sent through.

"RECORD OF EXPERIMENTS"
Henry Papers, Smithsonian Archives

May 8th 1838

Ex 1 The morning united the large jar and the battery of 8 jars[1]—gave small charge elect to about 18°. Needles in helix always magnet but in the reverse direction to that of the current from the jar, tried this repeatedly. Also gradually increased the distance between the two coils which were the same as those used last evening—magnetism still in same direction when coils were seperated to the distance of 6 inches.

Exp 2 Substituted for the lower flat coil in the above experiment the hoop ribbon coil no 2. Placed the inductive coil within then sent charge, magnet still in the contrary direction. While the apparatus remained the same sent shock from the battery, copper pole corresponding to the + pole of the jar. Now the result was the same as the battery current. A remarkable *fact* which must be worked out.

(This was worked out)

---

[1] This day's experimentation concentrates on the direction of induced currents, for Henry one of the most perplexing aspects of electromagnetic induction. He begins in experiment one with static discharges in the primary conductors, finding that the secondary current was induced in a contrary direction to the primary. He then compares these results with galvanic currents, finding that the secondary now had the same direction as the primary. Henry also factors in the effect of distance on the directions of induction.

Exp 3ʳᵈ Placed large hoop coil on table. Within this the flat coil no 3— needle still magnetic in the contrary direction to that of the current from the battery.[2] Next placed the <*needle*> spiral coil near one side and interposed a screen of copper so as partially to screen the inner coil. Needle still magnetized in the contrary direction.

Exp 4 Sent small discharge through two parallel wires every where about ½ an inch distant, needle magnetic showing current opposite to that of the jar. Again placed the same wires at the distance of 1½ inches, the same polarity as before—again at the distance of two inches the current was as before. Again at 4 inches the current continued in the same direction as the last.

Tried with a smaller jar the original experiment with the original apparatus April 14ᵗʰ.[3] Found that the charge was in the same direction with that of the jar as was originally determined.

Exp 5 Stretched two slips of tin foil parallel to each other with mica interposed. The current was in the direction of that of the jar. The slips of tin foil were about 1/50 of an inch apart. Again placed the slips at the distance of about the ⅛ᵗʰ of an inch. The direction was now reversed from that of the current. With a small[er] charge the direction was reversed. With a larger charge it was the same as the last.

At the distance of ¼ of an inch the current was in the adverse direction of the primative current

---

[2] We assume Henry has switched back to the Leyden jar battery of experiment 1.

[3] Possibly the set-up of experiment 4 of April 14, 1838, above.

FROM ROBERT M. PATTERSON

Henry Papers, Smithsonian Archives

Philadelphia, May 8th [18]38

Dear Sir,

I received, in good time, your letter of the 4th,[1] and had the notes of your very curious experiments inserted in the minutes of the meeting of the Philosophical Society, the same evening.[2] I consider your discovery the most

---

[1] Henry's original letter has not been located, but see footnote 2.

[2] Henry's May 4 letter was a preliminary notice of results which were reported in full

important made in common electricity for many years, and I hope you will communicate your experiments to the Society in detail at an early day. We shall not delay the printing longer than a fortnight, and you may have copies of the paper to send to your European correspondents.

You have many questions to answer. What is the effect of the length of the first and of the second coil on the induced shock? Will the second coil give off a spark, when its ends are near together? Is this spark longer or shorter than that from the jar? If the electricity passing through the second coil moves more slowly, giving a pungent pain like the shock through an imperfect conductor, try if it will not readily inflame gunpowder. Is the direction of the secondary current, the same as that of the first? Can you produce corresponding effects by the simple current of electricity from the machine, without the jar? *&c. &c.*

I am sorry that Dr. Emmet's paper has caused so much annoyance.[3] But it is the character of the doctor's mind, to be sanguine and confident, and I have no doubt that he sincerely thinks he has made important discoveries in optics, which we are too dull to comprehend, or too jealous to acknowledge. I will return his paper by the first opportunity. We have made him some amends by electing him into the Society.

Mitchell repeated, at our last meeting, the experiment of freezing carbonic acid, and with it freezing a quarter of a pound of mercury in half a minute. I have never witnessed a more interesting experiment.[4]

Let me know when you mean to print your paper? I hope you will show us some of the leading experiments at the same time.

With great regard,
Most truly yours,
R. M. Patterson

---

in November 1838 in "Contributions III: Electro-Dynamic Induction."

Dr. Patterson read a letter from Professor Henry, of Princeton, dated May 4, 1838, announcing that, in recent experiments, he has produced directly from ordinary electricity, currents by induction analogous to those obtained from galvanism; and that he has ascertained that these currents possess some peculiar properties, that they may be increased in intensity to an indefinite degree, so that if a discharge from a Leyden jar be sent through a good conductor, a shock may be obtained from a contiguous but perfectly insulated conductor, more intensely than one directly from the jar. Professor Henry remarks that he has also found that all conducting substances screen the inductive action, and that he has succeeded in referring this screening process to currents induced for a moment in the interposed body.

APS *Proceedings*, 1838–1840, *1*:14.

[3] See the exchanges between Patterson, Emmet, and Henry of December 4, 1837 (*Henry Papers, 3*:524–528), January 13, 1838, and February 9, 1838, above.

[4] John Kearsley Mitchell was repeating, in modified form, the recent experiments by Thilorier (for Henry's account of similar experiments see *Henry Papers, 3*:371–374). His results were published as "On the Liquefaction and Solidification of Carbonic Acid," *Journal of the Franklin Institute*, 1838, n.s. 22:289–295.

"RECORD OF EXPERIMENTS"
Henry Papers, Smithsonian Archives

May 9ᵗʰ 1838

Exp 1ˢᵗ Put coil No 2 within coil No 1 and within the former flat coil No 4. The ends apart of the intermediate spiral. Sent discharge through—needle magnetized in a direction the same as that of the current of the jar. This result is entirely different from all those obtained yesterday.[1] May it not be caused by the magnetizing helix used which in this instance was the long or thick one

Used the smaller magnetizing helix *and the result was the contrary.*

Placed another magnetizing helix precisely similar in length and size between the outer coil and the jar, the magnetism of the two was reversed. Repeated the exp. with the <*lon[g]*> thick helix but not with the same result, probably I was mistaken in the first result given above. It is however highly necssary to determine if such a result[2] may not affect the apparent direction of the current. Repeated the exp with the thick helix, the result the same as with the thin one, the direction of the current adverse to that of the battery.

Exp 2ⁿᵈ Joined the ends of the intermedial coil to observe the screening influence—no magnetism. Opened the circuit *ie* seperated the ends—needle magnetic. Determined by another discharge the direction of the <*magn*> current in the intermediate coil—found it contrary to that of the jar.
This would readily account for the screening influence in common electricity but not in galvanism[3]

Exp 3 On the change of the magnetizing helix[4] 1ˢᵗ with small single helix, magnetism always in the same direction with that of the current from the jar gradually increasing from 2 turns of the machine up to 80

---

[1] The intermediate circuit being opened, there was no screening. In the previous day's experiments, the secondary current ran contrary to the primary, a result which Henry duplicates below.

[2] Here, above the line, Henry inserted "the thickness of the tube &c."

[3] Henry reasoned that the oppositely directed primary and secondary currents from static electricity should cancel; not the case with galvanism where the two currents ostensibly ran in the same sense. However, directly below this sentence, Henry later interpolated the following correction: "Afterwards found precisely the same result in the 2ⁿᵈ current of galvanism."

[4] It is not clear in the following experiments whether Henry is running an induction or simply evaluating the effect of charge on the magnetizing helix, a test of the reliability of his detector.

2nd with thick or compound helix,[5] magnetism gradually increasing with the electricity of the jar from 2 turns up to 18, then no signes of magnetism. After this magnetism began to appear and gradually increased up to 80 turns. *The Jar used was the gallon* one

With the pint jar the results were somewhat different—the magnetism was always in the same direction but with 40 turns it was very small. The maxim[um] was about 30 turns, with 60 70 & 80 the magnet was scarcely perceptible but still in the same direction as the current from the jar[6]

With same jar and single magnetizing helix the magnetism constantly increased from 3 turns up to 90, very slowly at the last, magnetism always in the same direction as the jar.

With the large jar[7] magnetism constantly increased with the number of turns but very slowly always in the same direction with the current of the jar; these were made with the single helix

With the double helix large jar from one up to 40 turns <*stron*> gradually increasing and <*in*> the same direction as the jar which may be called +

> With 40 turns + strong
> 60 turns + slightly
> 70 turns + slightly
> 80 turns + tolerably strong
> 100   "   + strong
> 150   + not as strong
> 200   + slightly

Exp 4th Attempted to decompose by the induced current from common electricity with long <*coil*> helix not successful.

The same with galvanic battery decomposition current, as indicated by the deposition of iodine, in the same direction as the battery current.—Attempted with same current to produce magnetism did not suceed.

Exp 5  Placed flat coil on glass table and long compound helix on this. Made following observations

Compound helix on plate
Small jar[8]

---

[5] "Gallon Jar" was written in the left margin.
[6] Henry marked this paragraph by writing "Pint Jar" in the left margin.
[7] "Large jar" was also in the left margin.
[8] This experiment was incompletely recorded.

May 10, 1838

"RECORD OF EXPERIMENTS"
Henry Papers, Smithsonian Archives

May 10th [1838]

Exp 1 Placed two copper ribbons (flat coils no 3 & 4) on the floor and bound them together with silk between. Thus—put magne-tizing helix between the ends of the one, and battery[1] between those of the other. Needle magnetized in the [direction] of a current from the battery

Could not magnetize the needle with the long mag helix, but powerfully with the smallest one.

While the *<needle re>* ribbons remained in the same situation a shock from the large jar was sent through but now the magnetism indicated a current opposite to that of the jar. Bound a thick and thin wire together in contact, sent charge through thick wire, current in the other in opposite direction. This effect probably due to the direct passage of a part of the discharge through the ends of the smaller wire. The magnet[izin]g was very slight

[1] From the illustration, a galvanic battery.

TO JOHN TORREY
Torrey Papers, Library, New York Botanical Garden

Princeton May
18[th] 1838

My Dear Dr

I have been absent on a visit to Philadelphia and therefore did not answer your last letter but one. The last[1] came to hand yesterday and I would have sent you the above check immediately but the money could not be drawn until to day.

One of the New York Banks has lately declared a dividend otherwise we would not yet have been in funds. I have only to day drawn my own salary. The prospect of full classes is now as favourable as could be expected for the times but the great difficulty of getting money from the south will con-siderably affect the interest of the college during the present year.[2]

[1] Neither letter has been found.
[2] Fluctuating economic conditions followed the Panic of 1837. Changes in the market for cotton affected American financial resources,

Besides this the descision of the new school party of the church to seperate from the old will also probably some what lessen our numbers unless the Professors and directors of the Institution make some more vigorous efforts to raise and sustain the establishment.[3]

I did intend to spend some days with you in New York but was induced to go to Phil[d] inorder to repeat some of my experiments on Elect on a large scale with the machine & battery of Dr Hare. The Dr was very kind and I was fortunate enough to produce some interesting results.

I found that by sending a discharge from 32 gallon jars through a copper wire 80 feet long 1/10 of an inch in diameter that currents were produced on every side of it to such an extent that needles could be magnitised at t[he] distance of 12 feet. What is also very remarkable these currents change their directions with different distances and when discharges of different intensities are passed through the wire.[4] I will write you more at length soon. My love to the little ones and respects to Mrs. Torrey

In haste yours
Joseph Henry

Professor Maclean is one of the delegats to the general assembly and will probably take an active part in the debates.[5]

---

but whether this is the problem to which Henry alludes is impossible to determine.

[3] The Old School party, for various reasons, had expelled the New School Presbyterians at the General Assembly of 1837. See *Henry Papers*, 3:71.

Princeton Theological Seminary had historically taken a moderate position in Presbyterian theological controversies, resisting blanket condemnation of disputed views. When the split occurred in 1837 the Princeton party reluctantly sided with the Old School. George M. Marsden, *The Evangelical Mind and the New School Presbyterian Experience* (New Haven, 1970), pp. 42, 57, 69, 73. This position cost both the Seminary and College some students. Enrollment at the College, which had been 225 in 1838, and 250 in 1839, dropped to 216 in 1840. The Seminary went from a high of 134 students in 1838 to a low of 91 in 1840, in spite of a policy which called for trust money to be distributed to any needy and qualified student, regardless of affiliation with either faction of the Church. However, John Maclean, like Henry, attributed the decline in enrollment not only to the schism, but also to economic conditions. *Princeton Annual Catalogues*, 1838–1840; *Maclean*, 2: 308–309; *Minutes of the General Assembly*

of the Presbyterian Church in the United States of America, 1838 (Philadelphia, 1838), p. 56; *Minutes . . . , 1840* (Philadelphia, 1840), p. 314.

[4] Conducted in Philadelphia, this experiment does not appear in the "Record of Experiments." However, a more complete description of this series of experiments, with illustration, appears in paragraphs 121–123 of "Contributions III."

[5] The 1838 General Assembly of the Presbyterian Church convened in Philadelphia on May 17. Before the end of the first session, the New School faction, denied formal recognition by the Moderator, had left to form their own Assembly. John Maclean was later called to testify in a suit brought by New School members against Old School Assembly officials. Although he remained with the Old School Assembly, serving on several committees, Maclean objected to a report which described the New School delegates' departure as accompanied by "tumult and violence."

D. W. Lathrop, ed., *The Case of the General Assembly of the Presbyterian Church in the United States before the Supreme Court of the Commonwealth of Pennsylvania* (Philadelphia, 1839), pp. 241, 245.

TO CHARLES BABBAGE
Babbage Papers,[1] British Library

Princeton College of
New Jersey May 18th 1838

Dear Sir

I am induced by the kindness received from you while in London to take the liberty of introducing to your acquaintance my respected Friends Messrs Biddle[2] and Mc Ilvaine[3] of Philadelphia.

Mr. Biddle is, with us, an eminent member of the Legal Profession, and has devoted much time to the subject of Political Economy. Mr Mc Ilvaine was formerly the Cashier of the United States Bank but has now retired from Public office to amuse himself with the cultivation of general literature and Science.

I would hesitate to offer this letter to my Friends knowing that your time is much occupied were I not confident that the acquaintance of these gentlemen will be plesant to you; Although living in a distant country they have duely appreciated the value of your scientific labours and taken a lively interest in their results.

We may now hope to see you at no distant period in the United States since if I remember aright you promised to visit america should the steam ship project prove successful.

With the highest Respect
& Esteem I am your
obt servant
Joseph Henry

P.S. I have devoted my college vacation to a series of experiments on electrical induction, and have succeeded in producing secondary currents from *common* electricity, and these at a surprising distance. I find that if a discharge from a battery of 32, gallon, jars be sent through a thick copper wire 80 feet long, needles can be magnetized on all sides to the astonishing distance of 12 feet.

Also that the induced currents change their direction with a change in the intensity of the discharge, the thickness of the wire, & the distance from

---

[1] There is a retained copy in the Henry Papers. A note indicates that a similar letter was sent to J. A. F. Plateau of Brussels.

[2] Perhaps Clement Cornell Biddle (1784–1855), a fellow member of the American Philosophical Society. Although a lawyer, Biddle did not practice that profession. An ardent free trader, he translated and annotated Say's *Treatise on Political Economy* and was active in banking and insurance. *National Cyclopaedia of American Biography*, 5:504–505.

[3] William McIlvaine was Cashier of the second Bank of the United States from 1826 to 1832. Ralph C. H. Catterall, *The Second Bank of the United States* (Chicago, 1903), p. 105.

the conductor. Also that under certain curcumstances, all conductors of electricity produce a screening effect.

I have communicated a paper to the american Phil Socity on this subject and hope shortly to be able to send you a copy.[4]

J H

[4] Henry's address book shows that Babbage received a copy of "Contributions III."

"RECORD OF EXPERIMENTS"
Henry Papers, Smithsonian Archives

May 25th 1838

Mr. J Lock states Sillimans Journal April 1838[1] that he produces magneto elect currents by putting one end of a magnetic bar on one end of the

galvanometer wire and the other end of the same wire around the middle of the bar; by whirling the magnet around as on two pivots the galvanometer is affected.
This if true appears to be an important experiment since mere motion in this manner should not increase or diminish the intensity of action[2]

When one current is suddenly approximated to another the effect appears to be the same as if a new current were suddenly created or a current suddenly commenced but no such effect is produced in the above

Exp. 1 The currents in the magnet will revolve parallel to <*those in*> the wire or will cut the long part of the wire at right angles but in this last case no current should be produced

Exp— One coil perpendicular to the plain of another no shocks; when slightly inclined shocks commenced to be felt[3]

Exp 2 I received from Dr Goddard[4] while in Philadelphia a hank of very fine wire which he informed me would not produce shocks. Tried about

[1] John Locke, "Magneto-Electricity, and Electro-Magnetical Machines," *Silliman's Journal*, 1838, *34*:131–132.

[2] Locke described his ideas as only a restatement in more "convenient" form of generalizations previously obtained by Faraday, Henry, and other electricians. Under experiment 1, below, Henry explains that he is puzzled by the geometric arrangement of the magnet and the wires in Locke's experiment.

[3] Paragraph 46 of "Contributions III" is a summary of experiments on the effect of inclination on induction.

[4] Probably University of Pennsylvania physician and photography pioneer Paul Beck Goddard (1811–1866), *DAB*.

1500 feet[5] shock feeble in the 2nd ribbon coil. The screening effect could not be produced with it and I of course concluded that it is too fine for the induced current to be generated in it.[6] This fact is one of considerable consequence in the practical repetition of exp. of the kind. Since no doubt a very long wire of considerable thickness would produce a better effect than a thin one of the same length particularly in case of <*magn*> galvanic induction since the action is on all bodies at considerable distance.

Exp 3d. Gave the shock to Schmidt from the long helix on the flat coil No 3 and afterwards from the same helix placed within coil No 2. The feeling described was that in the first case the shock was felt higher up in the arms but in the second greater pain was produced.

Exp 4 Attached the small red magnet to the Thermo-battery with hot iron, salt and snow below; the magnet would support the small armature of the cast iron magnet but not the 7 lb armature of my 1st made magnet. Mr Watkins[7] of London has made magnets by Thermo-electricity

> N.B The same magnet can be rendered magnetic by the magneto elec machine.

Note The small cylendrical battery would not act this morning; examined it found that the reduced metal had been deposited along the sticks which seperate the zinc and copper and thus prevented the action

---

[5] According to "Contributions III," Goddard provided Henry with 1500 *yards* of wire (paragraphs 9 and 35).

[6] Faintly and vertically in the left margin: "With about 1/6 the length of wire **shocks** prod."

[7] Francis Watkins.

"RECORD OF EXPERIMENTS"
Henry Papers, Smithsonian Archives

May 26th 1838

Exp 1 Made a Metallic Thermometer with wire from the end of the spiral dippin[g] into pool of mercury after the manner of De La Rives arrangement—a current of galvanism se[n]t through but the effect was not very striking. Thermo electricity produced no action or in other words with this instrument gave no indication of a current of heat.[1]

---

[1] Henry continues his experiments with the thermopile employed the previous day. He now tests for heating effects produced by the current from the thermopile. The metallic thermometer, used to measure "calorific effects" of a current, was due to Breguet. It consisted of a metallic helix composed of thin strips of different metals. The helix was con-

Exp 2 Repeated the experiment with the electrical machine—1st wires 4 inches apart, Large Jar alone—needle magnetized slightly contrary direction. 2nd smaller charge, needle more strongly magnetized—3rd Large Jar + battery, needle magnetized in the same direction—with the wires 2 inches apart magnetism stronger, same direction

These exp. in keeping with those made in Phil[d] where with the large battery the secondary current was always found in the same direction with the primary

Exp 4 Decomposition produced with the secondary current for the long helix with the apparatus of Clarke's machine[2]—with Faradays voltametre[3] no decomposition could be obtained. The other article has very fine points resembling almost the guarded ones of Wallaston.[4]

(This exp. was made yesterday)

Exp 5[th] Repeated the exp. for determ[in]ing the direction of the needle with galvanic currents. Found as before that the secondary current is always in the same direction as the battery current, no change of direction observed. It would appear from the circumstance of the permanency of the direction of the 2[nd] current by galvanism, that it resembles in its action a heavy charge of common electricity since with Dr Hare's battery no <action> change is perceptible.[5]

---

nected to one pole of the pile at its top end. Its lower end was dipped into a pool of mercury connected to the other pole. Due to the unequal expansion of the superposed metals, the helix twisted and untwisted with very slight changes in temperature and registered the results on a dial.

A.-A. De La Rive used such a thermometer in research reported at the 1837 Liverpool meeting of the British Association, which Henry attended. *BAAS Report, 1837* (1838), part 2, pp. 27–28. The instrument is explained in De La Rive's *Treatise on Electricity*, 3 vols. (London, 1853–1858), *1*:33–34. Bernard S. Finn of the Smithsonian Institution assisted us in interpreting this experiment.

[2] The magnetoelectric generator.

[3] Described in Series Seven, paragraphs 704–712, *Experimental Researches in Electricity*, Faraday's voltameter was based on his law that the decomposing action of a current is constant for a constant quantity of electricity.

[4] Wollaston devised the "guarded points" for an experiment on electrolysis by the current from an electrostatic generator in an attempt to show the identity of common and voltaic electricity. Wollaston covered fine wires with an insulating material and then removed a tiny section of insulation from each wire. The exposed points were then immersed in water and when electricity was passed through the wires, the water was decomposed without sparks. "Experiments on the Chemical Production and Agency of Electricity," *Phil. Trans.*, 1801, pp. 427–434.

[5] A page which Henry skipped between the first and last part of this entry contains two related notations, one dated and the other not: "Send charge of battery through thick wire around file. The exp doubtfull before on account of the alternations of the currents—"; and, "For an extraordinary effect of the secondary current, see Jour of Com[merce] or Newark daily for Saturday may 26th 1838". Henry had a clipping of the article which reported "Singular Effects of Lightning" in New York. A house at 10th and Broadway was struck by lightning. At the same time, two men in a house on 9th Street felt "an extraordinary sensation of heat" and witnessed the sudden melting of a candle that sat on a table in front of them.

May 28, 1838

TO CHARLES COQUEREL
Miscellaneous Manuscripts Collection, Library,
American Philosophical Society[1]

Princeton, College of New Jersey
May 28th 1838

My Dear Sir

I have received a letter from my agent Mr O Rich No 12 Red Lion Square London informing me that your package of the numbers of the library of useful knowledge was sent in August last to M. Baillier[2] Rue de l'Ecole de Medicine. It was addressed to M Galibert[3]—was this the name you gave me on your memorandum?

I hope you will be able to find the articles, Mr Rich thinks the mistake is on your side of the water. They were sent at the time mentioned and according to the directions you gave me on a piece of paper. There is certainly a great remissness in reference to the transaction of all commercial affairs in your *Belle France*. I have some cause to complain on this score since the articles I purchased of M Pixii and all the books I left in his charge to be forwarded to New-York have not even yet been received—I have however just received a letter[4] stating that they were shipped on the 23[d] of April at Haver and consequently may now be shortly expected to arrive. They were to have been shipped on the 1st of Oct 1837. So much for the punctuality of the Inhabitants of the *"Focus of civilization."*

You have probably long before this time received the Package I sent to you by My Friend Dr Hun. I regret that the articles it contained were not more valuable or interesting. If you should happen to meet with Dr Hun you will find him a very amiable and intelligent Person. He has resided several years in Paris and intends to remain in that city until next autum

---

[1] A draft in the Henry Papers, Smithsonian Archives, contains the following paragraph deleted from the outgoing letter:

I have seen a notice in one of the English Journals of a most interesting experiment by M Provost of Geneva namely the product of electricity from the nerves of animals. The current of electricity is rendered manifest by a soft iron needle which becomes magnetic when the spinal marrow of the animal is irritated. I intend to attempt to repete this experiment as soon as an oppertunity presents itself.

J.-L. Prevost's experiment with a frog was originally described in "Note sur le développement d'un courant électrique qui accompagne la contraction de la fibre musculaire," *Bibliothèque universelle*, 1837, *12*:202–204. Henry tried the experiment unsuccessfully in August. See his "Record of Experiments" entry of August 3, 1838, below.

[2] Jean-Baptiste-Marie Baillière (1797–1885), a prominent bookseller and publisher in Paris whose firm specialized in medical and scientific works. M. Prévost and Roman D'Amat, eds., *Dictionnaire de Biographie Française* (Paris, 1948), *4*:1305–1307.

[3] Probably Léon Galibert, editor of the *Revue britannique*.

[4] Not found.

when he will return to this country for a permanent settlement in the line of his Profession. I hope you will form an acquaintance with him since I am confident you will be pleased with each other.

I saw our Friend Dr Sprague a few weeks since. He was well pleased with the autographs you sent him and bid me send his respects to you.

I received a short time since a letter from Professor Olmsted of New Haven thanking me for transmitting to him the copy of your memoir on the shooting stars.[5] He appears pleased with the compliment you paid him in noticing his memoir and will probably in future send you copies of his publications.

I have been attending a little to the subject of light but am as yet quite a novice in the study.[6] I hope h[o]wever to make some progress when my long expected books and apparatus arrive from France. I am much indebted to Babenet for the kind schooling he gave me and hope to prove myself not an unapt Pupil.

I have lately been much occupied on a subject I am more at home in than that of light, namely, Electricity, & have succeeded in developing some new and interesting Phenomina.

I hope soon to be able to send you a copy of my memoir on the subject.

You have probably heard of the result of the great experiment of navigating the Atlantic by steam. The two ships which arrived in this country made quite a sensation and returned crowded with Passengers. The experiment must have an important influence on the future destinies of the old as well as the new world—a voyage in a short time across the Atlantic will <now> be scarcely more tedious than one across the channel formerly.

We may now hope to see you in America do not forget where I live

With much Respect
Yours sincerely
Joseph Henry

[5] We have not found Olmsted's letter. Henry is probably referring to "Lettre de M. Charles Coquerel au directeur de la Revue britannique, sur l'apparition des étoiles filantes, observées à Paris le 13 Novembre 1836," *Revue britannique*, October 1836, 4th ser. 5:375–382. A reprint of the article is in the Henry Library. In the letter, Coquerel relied heavily on Olmsted's observations of the November 1833 meteor shower. Coquerel was a collaborator of the *Revue britannique*, which was devoted to translations of British periodical literature. He may have been the translator of an earlier article on Olmsted's observations, "Des Étoiles filantes, de leur apparition périodique et de leur origine, d'après Olmsted," *Revue britannique*, July 1836, 4th ser. 4: 31–46.

[6] There is little evidence of Henry's work on light at this time. In his letter to Lewis R. Gibbes of April 28, 1838, above, he indicates his intention of making his class demonstrations on light more sophisticated. In the "Record of Experiments" entry for April 20, 1838 (above), Henry mentions working with Joseph Saxton on light. Other than this, there are only a few apparently random observations. See, for example, the notebook entries for [January 1838] and February 12, 1838.

"RECORD OF EXPERIMENTS"
Henry Papers, Smithsonian Archives

May 29th [1838]

Exp 1 Put the large battery to the large magnet—sustained 3587[1] lbs with the compound lever attached

Without the acid on one occasion for about a 1/4 of a minute 1500 lbs were supported without the action of the acid or in other words when the connection with the battery was broken.

Exp. Applied iron filings to a platin[um] wire rendered red hot by the galvanic current—adhesion took place and continued until the filings were melted to the wire

Try if the attraction will take place between melted iron and the wire.
Also the attraction of ampere[2] between two wires both white hot.

Exp Placed two coiles paralel to each other. Each coil was about 2 feet in 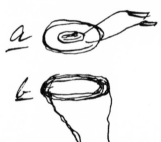 diameter. The one formed of coil (ribbon) No 1 and No 2. The other of coil No 3 [and] No 4. The coils were gradually seperated and needles made magnetic at each distance until at the distance of about two feet all signes of magnetism disappeared.[3] The magnetism was constantly in the same direction as that of the current from the battery. No change of direction could be observed. The magnetism disappeared at that distance on account principally of the oblique action of the two sides of the coil.

Exp 3rd The shocking spiral was put within the upper coil the two ends of which were not in contact. The shock at the distance of 16 inches was very disagreable. The ends of the coil *a* were not[4] placed in contact. No effect or a very slight one was now perceptable (good exp)

Exp Put the compound lever on the large magnet, magnetized it by the large battery arranged as 8 plats. Suffered the whole to remain until next morning (May 30). Found that it required 621 lbs to detach the armature. The exp was made by means of a sliding weight

---

[1] About the maximum lifting power of Henry's largest electromagnet. *Henry Papers*, 2:123n.

[2] The attraction between two parallel wires when their currents run in the same direction.

[3] We presume Henry attached a magnetizing spiral to the secondary coil.

[4] Did Henry mean to write "now" rather than "not"? With circuit *a* closed, the shocking spiral would be screened.

"RECORD OF EXPERIMENTS"
Henry Papers, Smithsonian Archives

June 4th 1838

Aranged the coils and one helix (the 2nd) for producing the secondary shock.[1] Attempted to get the direction of the current but did not succeed either by decomposition or making magnets.

Seperated the helix from which the shocks were produced, by means of blocks from the coil to the distance of 7 or 8 inches. Still the effect was produced so that the 2nd current acting at a distance produces shocks similar to the battery current.

When the two handles were rubbed together sparks were produced from the tertiary current

I am anxious to produce some decisive evidence of the direction of the tertiary current since I now suspect that its direction is opposed to that of the secondary current and that the screening effect is produced in the same manner as in the case of common electricity. May not the first discharge act like the large battery (Dr Hares) and produce currents always in the same direction and may not the current thus produced act on account of its smallness like a small battery or jar and give rise to a secondary or rather to a tertiary current in an opposite direction at all small distances or at the distances at which the coiles are placed in the experiments?[2]

To test this make secondary and tertiary currents interfere.

[1] Apparently two coils and the helix are in use for testing tertiary currents (see below). The purpose of these experiments is again to determine the directions of higher order induced currents.

[2] In parentheses after this query: "This supposition found to be correct".

"RECORD OF EXPERIMENTS"
Henry Papers, Smithsonian Archives

July 11th 1838

Lectures to the class have prevented any experiments until to day

Tried the following Exp. Put a quantity of lamp oil into a glass vessel, connected one end of a wire with the large machine of the college, the other placed above the surface of the oil. Also held in the hand another wire at the same distance above the surface

When the machine was turned a depression was formed under each wire as if the oil were repelled.

When the ends were plunged into the oil a violent motion was observed from each point producing currents apparently in the oil at the same time a film of oil was seen to be repelled up the side of the wire and then thrown off in a spray in some cases on all sides but most generally in straight lines to the sides of the glass thus—

These phenomena indicate a great <*attraction*> repulsion between the particle of the oil when electrified and also between the wire and the oil and this takes place even when these bodies act as the plus and minus pole and illustrate the fact that a <*body*> the particles of a body are mutually repellant even when conducting a stream of electricity.

The vase containing the oil was nex[t] partially filled with water so that a stratum of oil about ¾ of an inch deep covered the water. The + pole was then plunged through the oil (and insulated from it by a glass tube) into the water. When a wire was held over the oil a violent oscillation took place; both the upper and lower surface of the oil became concave until in some cases the watter appeared through. This appearance was probably produced by the same action as that mentioned above. The oil is a worse conductor than the water. The repulsions of it are therefore more apparent. The water in the vessel in this arrangement acts as the one pole while the wire held over it is the other and for the same reason a depression was formed under each wire, a depression from each pole is here produced. The whole effect is pre[cise]ly analogous to what takes place in the air.

I was induced to try this exp from reading an article in the annals de chem &c. for Aug 1836.[1]

The dimples or depressions produced when both the wires were out of the liquid was probably produced by the repulsion of the air which became electrical and was thus affected.

---

[1] Georges Aimé, "De la masse du fluide électrique," *Annales de chimie et de physique*, 1836, 2d ser. 62:419–422. Aimé's experiment on the electrically-induced motions in water and oil was part of an investigation of electrical mass. Aimé, too, related the motions to the difference in conductibility of oil and water. He believed the effect analogous to the "motions of mercury," where a combination of acid and mercury subjected to an electrical discharge underwent similar violent perturbations (see *Henry Papers*, 3:27–28, 35).

FROM THURLOW WEED[1]
Joseph Henry Papers, Duke University Library

Albany, July 18, 1838

Dear Henry,

Mr Rowan,[2] who contemplats a short professional visit to Princeton, hits off "Likenesses" admirably. He was here some years ago and drew many of our citizens "to the life." He is withal a gentleman who duly appreciates civilities. I have told him that you are "a good natured man" and hope you will not make me a false one by refusing to become his first "wictim."

All well, and prospering Agriculturally and Politically.

Very Truly Yours
Thurlow Weed

[1] Weed, the Whig political leader, was a close friend from Henry's Albany days.
[2] We have been unable to identify any portraitist by the name of Rowan who was active in this period. No portrait of Henry by Rowan is known to exist.

"RECORD OF EXPERIMENTS"
Henry Papers, Smithsonian Archives

July 18th [1838]

Made some exps on the long small wire helix with the Shaker battery[1]— shock produced with smallest coil with three pairs of plates; with about 10 pairs sparkes. The shock quite intense but the spark very feeble.

Induction with the small battery from the larger of the three helices to the second perceptible but not intense as tested by the shock—from the 1st to the 3rd coil no apparent action—from the 2nd to the 3rd with the rasp action some what intense.

[1] See Henry's related experiment number 5 of April 10, 1838, above.

"RECORD OF EXPERIMENTS"
Henry Papers, Smithsonian Archives

July 19 [1838]

Arranged the coils, No 2 as a primary current from one division of the battery, coil no 1 was arranged as 2 coils one half in No 1 other half out so as to form an 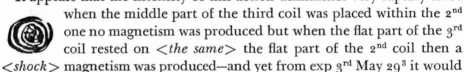 arrangement for currents of the third order. The third current was induced on the thin ribbon coil N 3 and its direction determined by the magnetizing spiral and needle. The needle was strongly magnetized but its *direction was contrary* to that of the battery current. The experiment was repeated several times with the same result and from the degree of magnetism exhibited by the needle no doubt could be entertained relative to the direction

I had before concluded from the analogy of common electricity and the imperfect indication of the 1st exp May 7th that the direction of the 3rd current is the same as that of the 1st and 2nd but from this it plainly appears that my first opinion was not correct[1]

This correction is very important since it gives a clue to the interference or screaning effect. It would appear from this that the wave of electricity in the secondary currents produces [an] effect similar to that of common electricity—at a very small distance probably the current changes its <*distance*> direction and thus acts in opposition to the current from the battery[2]

It appears that the intensity of this action diminishes very rapidly since when the middle part of the third coil was placed within the 2nd one no magnetism was produced but when the flat part of the 3rd coil rested on <*the same*> the flat part of the 2nd coil then a <*shock*> magnetism was produced—and yet from exp 3rd May 29[3] it would appear that the action extends to some considerable distance, this however may only be of sufficient intensity to produce shock by means of the long helix

1 Try the third current with the apparatus of tin foil in spirals within and without
2 Try Interferance of currents of different orders
3 Try Interferance of magnetism
Iron in one coil[4]

---

[1] This is an incorrect reference. Henry seems to refer rather to experiment 8 of May 5, 1838, just above the one cited in his "Record of Experiments."

[2] i.e., Henry believed that the instantaneous secondary pulse acted like an ordinary static discharge. Although the evidence was still inconclusive, Henry thought the direction of currents induced from static charges depended on the distance between the inductive circuits. See the follow-up experiments of July 20 and 21, below, as well as paragraphs 127–128 of "Contributions III."

[3] See above, "Record of Experiments," May 29, 1838.

[4] See the next day's "Record," below.

"RECORD OF EXPERIMENTS"
Henry Papers, Smithsonian Archives

July 20th 1838

Exp on the interferance of currents of different orders

1 Arranged coil no 1 for the 1st or battery current, put on this coil no 3, under it coil No 4; attempted to pass these through long helix No 2 but the electricity was not sufficiently intense[1]

2 Joined the two currents to coil no 2.[2] When the currents passed in same

direction the shock was quite intense, when the ends of the ribbons were crossed then there was no action, complete interferance of two currents from the same source[3]

Exp 2nd Sent the secondary current from the large Helix which was enclosed in coil No 2 through the glass apparatus with a spiral of tin foil on the out side and in,[4] magnetized needle, not very intensely but markedly found the direction of the tertiary current the same as that of the primary. Hence the action of the secondary curent is precisely the same as that of a discharge of common electricity, and with the experiment of yesterday shows that there is a neutral point & that the current changes its direction[5]

Exp 3rd The interferance with magnetism. Placed coil No 2 in connection with the battery, helix no 1 within this and helix no 2 within this again. Shocks of course could be obtained from the 2nd helix when the ends of Helix No 1 were not joined; when several pieces of iron were placed in the shock was more intense. When the ends of helix No 2[6] were joined the screaning influence was produced but not to such a degree as to neuetralize all action, a slight shock could be felt, but when the iron was in this shock was much greater. The screening effect did take place when the iron was placed within the helix but the action was not as intense as when the screaning arrangement was made

[1] Apparently the secondary currents in coils 3 and 4 are passed through helix 2.

[2] A coil is substituted for the helix.

[3] At the bottom of the page is this notation: "The [?mere] wave sent through a wire by induction also produces a current by induction in an other wire and hence it must also be under the same influence."

[4] i.e., a glass jar with tin foil circuits on the outside and inside.

[5] See the previous day's "Record of Experiments," where Henry speculates that distance is a factor in the direction of higher order currents. Below this experiment, Henry notes "Repeated this exp on the 21st July with the same result needle feebly magnetized"—apparently a reference to experiment 5 of July 21, 1838, below.

[6] Presumably, he meant helix no. 1. The magnetization of the iron core, Henry conjectured, inhibited the circuit's screening action.

Exp 4 on screening. Performed one of the original exp cut plate into the form in the figure, drew out current—found its direction the same as that of the original current.[7] This exp was devised in the first stage of the inquiry.

Exp 5 Attached lon[g] helix to the ends of the spindle of the magneto elec machin with the armature on for sparkes.[8] The 2nd helix was placed within the first and arranged for shocks, no perceptible effect but when the ribbon coil No 1 was substituted for the long helix then 2nd currents were produced. Hence the same inductive action takes place between a neutral wire and a current of magneto electricity as between the currents of the same kind from the galvanic battery. The current under these circumstances may be called the tertiary current since the current from the magneto electrical machine is itself a current of induction.

Exp 6 Made a needle magnetic by the induced current from magneto electricity but the direction of the induced current was not determined by it on account of the precaution not being taken of guarding against the effect of alternations[9]

Try the following exp. Put large iron into large ribbon coil and above this placed several plates of lead to screen the action of the lower coil. By this means we can seperate the magnetic effects from the galvanic and thus study the two seperately.[10]

---

[7] This experiment figures prominently in "Contributions III," paragraphs 62–63, where Henry tests the hypothesis that the screening effect of plates depended on the induction of currents in the plates. The plate cut in this fashion no longer screened. To deal with the possibility that induction took place through the opening in the plate, Henry cut another plate in the same way, put a glass plate between them, and "so arranged [them] that the opening in the one might be covered by the continuous part of the other." Still there was no screening as would occur with a continuous plate. A gloss beside experiment 4 describes it as "Catching the current from the plate."

As Henry informs us in his publication, paragraph 61, the idea that currents might be induced in the plate was inspired by Arago's wheel and the "ingenious variation of this principle by Messrs. Babbage and Herschel . . . ." Arago made the discovery that the rotation of a copper disc made the disc magnetic. Attempting to explain the magnetism in terms of Ampère's electrodynamics, Babbage and Herschel tested the effect of continuity on the induction of the magnetism. They cut radial slits in the disc and found the magnetism destroyed. The British investigators were not willing to go so far as to attribute the magnetism to circulating electric currents. Faraday, too, picked up the idea of Arago's wheel to perform basic experiments that left him dubious of Ampère's electrical theory of magnetic action. See L. Pearce Williams, *Michael Faraday* (New York, 1965), pp. 170–173.

[8] A comparison of inductive effects from other sources of electricity. In the left margin, Henry labeled this experiment: "Secondary currents from magneto elect."

[9] i.e., the alternating current from the primitive dynamo.

[10] This is an attempt to deal with the results of experiment 3, above. See the follow-up on July 21, 1838, below.

"RECORD OF EXPERIMENTS"
Henry Papers, Smithsonian Archives

July 21st [1838]

Tried the above exp without success—no shock could be obtained from the <*wire*> iron with the above arrangement. It is however probable that the intensity of action of the iron was not sufficient to give a shock

Exp 2nd Arranged third helix with rod of iron inside put magnets in connection with each end so as to form a magneto electrical current. A scroll of copper ribbon was then interposed between the spiral and the iron but the same action was exhibited at the galvanometer as before. No screening could be observed perhaps the action was due to the ends of the iron and these were [?un]covered by the copper.[1]

Exp 3 Placed plate of zinc between coil Nos [1, 2][2] needle made slightly magnetic; withdrew zinc needle strongly magnetic; screening only partial—as usual action in the same direction with the battery current. Repeated exp of screening between 2nd & 3rd current by means of the shock not perfect but quite perceptible by means of the zinc plate[3]

Exp 4 Arranged the coiles and helices so as to produce a shock at a distance with the tertiary current—distance constantly increased, shock continually decreases in intensity—at the distance of about a foot the effect appeared to suddenly cease—no effect was observed beyond—In another [?arrangement] shock [?12] inches[4]

Ex 5 Repeated the exp of day before yesterday on the direction of the tertiary found it in an adverse direction to that of the 2nd and primary current[5]

The magnetism was at first very strong when the two spirals were near

---

[1] The external magnets magnetized the iron core, whose normal inductive effects on the helix Henry expected to screen with the copper sleeve. When the screening fails, Henry tentatively identifies the exposed external magnets as the cause of the inductive action.

Henry later came back to this experiment and added the following: "May 12th 1839 See exp of this date," and, probably at the same time, the following philosophical observation: "This exp illustrates the importance of Regersting all the facts observed within, in accordance or not with previous results since I now find that there is a remarkable difference in the action of this arrangement and the other cases of screening."

The cited entry appears below under the new dating May 13, 1839, experiment 2. On repeating the experiment at that time, Henry still failed to get screening.

[2] An ink smear has obscured the designation of the interacting coils.

[3] It is unclear to us whether Henry did or did not get screening with the zinc plate.

[4] Apparently a later notation. The "12" inch reading is uncertain.

[5] See above, July 19, 1838.

each other, it gradually decreased and at the distance of about 6 inches interely disappeared.

Exp 6 Placed compound helix (that is first and second) around the end of the large hollow electro magnet. The same screening effect was produced but not quite as intense as in the case of the coils

Exp 7 Stretched two wires each 130 feet long parallel to each other and almost in contact through[out]. Sent seccondary current through one, induced current in the contrary direction. The distance of the wires in this exp may be considered as the diameter of one of them needle strongly magnetic

"RECORD OF EXPERIMENTS"
Henry Papers, Smithsonian Archives

July 25th [1838]

My attention to day was directed to a singular case of capillary attraction. A lead tube was soldered at one end to the plate of a galvanic battery and the other which was several inches higher was plunged into a cup of mercury. The metal was seen on the plate of the battery having passed apparently through the tube like water through a syphon (made arrangements to investigate this)[1]

[1] It was apparently an accidental observation in the laboratory that triggered Henry's curiosity about metallic capillarity, the subject of two brief publications by him. Although Henry's March 1839 publication "Capillary Transmission Through Solids," *APS Proceedings*, 1838–1840, *1*:82–83, refers to investigations in progress, the laboratory entry of this day is the only one on capillarity prior to that publication. Henry's article gives one version of what happened, excluding any mention of the galvanic plate. A lead tube, 8 inches long and a half inch in diameter, was left for a few days with one end immersed in a cup of mercury. He observed the mercury had disappeared from the cup and was found on the floor at the end of the tube. Henry did some preliminary experiments which satisfied him that the mercury crept through the lead itself and not through the hollow axis, or merely along the tube's outer surface.

Henry's recorded experiments on the phenomenon commence on September 5, 1839, below, and appear sporadically until 1845, the date of his second publication, "On the Capillarity of Metals," *APS Proceedings*, 1843–1847, *4*:176–178, where the investigation extends to other metals and leads to certain conclusions about the molecular state of matter.

"RECORD OF EXPERIMENTS"
Henry Papers, Smithsonian Archives

July 26$\underline{^{th}}$ 1838

Exp 1 Arranged 4 posts, and on these placed a thick wire about 2 feet or 2½ high in the form of a parallelogram. Then sent a shock from the battery of 12 jars through the thick wire—a long wire, which was wound several times (5 times) around the posts and a magnetizing [spiral] formed of one part of it <*the shock*> [?received] the lateral action.[1] The needle was constantly magnetized in an adverse direction to that of the current while the rope of wires (which was covered) was constantly elevated. The action still continued until the rope was at the distance of about 2½ feet from the lower wire; this was the limit of altitude yet tried.

Exp 2 Instead of the rope of many strands a single wire was next placed in its stead.[2] The small magnetizing helix was used. With the same discharge as to quantity the needle was magnetized so as to indicate an inverse current to the former, or a current in the same direction as the battery current. NB The rope was not removed during the experiments with the single wire and probably its presence had some influence on the result.

This a very puzzling result
The magnetizing helices were nearly of the same diameter but not of the same size of wire. It was at first thought that the result might be due to the difference in action of these helices[3]

The one however was substituted alternately for the other with still the same result

Exp 3 Several spires of the rope seperated to the distance of about an inch from each other
1   needle in marked end which is nex the battery needl slightly magn direction *N*. current *reverse*
2   slightly mag. N " reverse
3   strand slightly more seperated   no magnetism
4   magnetism very slight if any

---

[1] Henry tests induction from static electric discharges on a grand scale, concentrating on current direction. "Lateral action" refers in this case not to the lateral discharge but to parallel inductive effects.

[2] As the secondary circuit.

[3] Henry's marginal gloss alongside this experiment, "See page 146 2$\underline{^{nd}}$ Book," takes us below to September 23, 1840, further experimentation on induction from ordinary electricity, where the form of the magnetizing spiral indeed affects his results. There Henry also refers us backward to the present experiments.

Exp 4 Put helix on single wire which is in the midst of the strands of the other

1   needle mag N slightly current adverse
2   small shock *strongly* N current adverse
3   small shock 10° strong N—adverse
4   Removed the rope strand with its end to the distance of 2 feet upwards magnetism strong S current in the direction of battery current

Exp 5

5   Rope of wires brought down to the same place needle *slight* mag N current *adverse*
6   Same as above discharge strong no magnetism perceptible—
7   Same as above Charge feeble mag N current *adverse*—
8   Arrangt same as above except ends of the rope open no magnetism NB The rope was stil above

Arrangement the same as the last mag N—current *adverse*—discharge feeble mag *decided*

Exp 5[4] Rope shoved up charge *small*

1	needle mag strong *South* current *direct*	
2	Rope down mag not quite as strong S. current direct discharge feeble.	
3	Charge still less mag N—	reverse
3	Charge still smaller (30 turns) N	reverse
4	Charge still less (20 turns) N	reverse
5	Charge smaller (10 turns) N stronger	reverse
6	Same as before (10 turns) rope circuit shut	no magnetism
7	same except rope open mag N—	reverse

Ex 6 Rope put up Small charge

1	mag feeble S—current	direct
2	Same large charge mag strong South—	direct

   It is evident from the above exps that the mere proximity of the rope coil changes the direction of the current in the single wire, and that the intensity of the magnetism is stronger with the same small charge when thus reversed than when direct

Exp 7 The single wire removed, the rope used alone at the distance of 9 inches

[4] Sic.

1	with strong charge, no magnetism or very feebly N.—	*reverse*
2	with very feeble charge mag stronger—N	*reverse*

Exp 8. Same arrangement, except rope brought down in contact with conducting wire

1	*no magnetism* strong charge	[?o]
2	Small charge 10 turns strong N. current—	reverse

It would appear from all these experiments that the several spires of the compound wire act on each other so as in some way to reverse the current— a feeble current is more easily reversed than an intense one
The following conclusions are deducible[5]

1 With a single wire and the battery the current is in the same direction as the battery current
2 With the <*strand*> rope of wire the current is in the opposite direction; more feeble with large current
3 The proximity of the rope to the single wire inverts the curent when the rope has its strands together
4 The single wire indicates a current in the same direction, and the intensity constantly increases with the intensity of the charge
5 no so the inverse current
6 When the rope has its end joined no magnetism or very feeble one

Exp 9 Sent charge from battery through coil, current in 2nd coil with glass interposed in the <*same*> adverse direction. This agrees with the experiments on the long wires.

Put plate between with cut in, current still adverse—

[5] Apparently dissatisfied with these initial conclusions about the change in direction, Henry noted in "Contributions III" (paragraph 118) that experiments on the form of the circuit, etc., gave "anomalous [results] and are not sufficiently definite to be placed in detail before the Society." Following this, Henry gave only a brief statement of general facts.

"RECORD OF EXPERIMENTS"
Henry Papers, Smithsonian Archives

July 27 1838

Exp 1st
1 Coil as in the last exp., except second coil interposed with the ends open, charge feeble, current still in the *adverse* direction
2 Placed a single turn of wire around the coil, magnetism *adverse*

3 Stretched out the two coils used in Exp 1 into two parallel ribbons
NB magnetism in the same *direction*

Exp 2ⁿᵈ

Put the rope wire with the strands seperate around the great reel,[1] sent through this the battery current. Caught the induced current first on the lower wire— found it—*direct*

1 Again put small single wire above, caught the current on this, found it as before *direct*

2 The current (battery) was sent through the thick bottom wire & the discharge caught on the compound wire and at two different parts of the circuit, the current was *adverse* in bothe case[s]

Passed current through the small wire—received induction as before on the compound wire (midle strand) magnetism pretty strong N—Current *adverse* NB As the small wire is a worse conductor than the large wire, a larger charge was required to produce the same degree of magnetism when the small wire was the conductor

From these exp. it appears that

1ˢᵗ The compound rope wire acts like a single wire in inducing a current on an other wire

2 a thin wire produces the same kind of induction as a thick wire

3 When the compound wire is the receiver then a small charge produces the greater magnetic effect

Ex[p] 3ʳᵈ Arranged the strands of the compound wire on each side of the single wire. Sent the discharge through the latter—

1 current at first slightly   *adverse*
2 No magnetism *stronger* charge   o
3 Charge feeble magn. well marked   *adverse*

---

[1] See the set-up for the previous day's experiments. Henry is again testing the effect of different configurations of conductors on the direction of induced currents. In the first two experiments, the galvanic battery is the source of the primary current.

FROM ADOLPHE QUETELET
Henry Papers, Smithsonian Archives

Bruxelles le 29 juillet 1838

Monsieur,

Je profite de l'obligeance de Monsieur Bache[1] pour vous exprimer mes regrets de ne pas m'être trouvé à l'observatoire lorsque vous m'avez fait l'honneur d'y venir,[2] et d'avoir manqué par là l'occasion de faire votre connaissance.

Tout ce que m'a dit M. Bache avec qui j'ai eu le plaisir de passer quelques jours ne fait qu'augmenter encore les regrets que j'éprouve.

Je désire vivement que vous consentiez à me dédommager de cette contrariété, en me donnant quelquefois de vos nouvelles et en me tenant au courant de vos utiles travaux. Si vous pouviez me communiquer de temps en temps vos recherches, je serais heureux d'en enrichir ma *correspondance mathématique*.[3]

Je saisis avec empressement cette nouvelle occasion pour vous prier d'agréer l'hommage de mes sentimens les plus distingués.

Votre très obeissant serviteur
Quetelet

[1] This letter was enclosed with his letter to Bache of July 30, 1838, Rhees Collection (RH 2102), Huntington Library.

[2] Henry visited Brussels and the Brussels Royal Observatory in July 1837 but missed meeting the vacationing Quetelet. See *Henry Papers*, 3:417, 420–421.

[3] Quetelet was founder and co-editor of the periodical *Correspondance mathématique et physique*.

TO C. B. GOODRICH
Henry Papers,[1] Smithsonian Archives

Princeton July 31st 1838

Dear Sir

Your letter of the [. . .] inst[2] was received a few days since. I was much pleased to learn that you are still in the way of well doing and constantly making some advances towards the temple of science.

[1] This is either a retained copy or a letter which Henry never sent. The letter is folded for sending and addressed to Goodrich in Fowler, St. Lawrence County, New York.

[2] Not found; Henry left the exact date blank.

Labour conquers all difficulties and nothing worth possessing can be obtained without it or in other words the Gods have place[d] a price on that which is valuable and he who would possess must labour for the prize.

I was much at a loss for want of an assistant after your departure and at length was obliged to go to Philadelphia to repeat some of my results on a larger scale with Dr Hare's apparatus. I did not find time to finish the investigation before the beginning of the summer collegiate course of lectures and since then my time has been too much occupied to make much progress.

I have however much extended the experiments since you left and have suceeded in developing many new and interesting results. These I have communicated to the American Philosophical Society of Philadelphia and expect soon to have the paper published. Since you appeared somewhat interested in the investigation I have been thus particular in mentioning the state of the affair and will forward you a copy as soon as the article appears.

The long expected articles of apparatus from Paris have at length arrived. Most of the articles came safely and now form a very important addition to the apparatus of the College.

The electrical machine proves to be an excellent one[3]—during the present warm and unfavourable weather it gives sparks of nearly a foot in length. The large jar of three or four gallons capacity which you may reccollect was used in our experiments can be charged with the new machine in about three seconds.

I have not seen Dr Torrey but once since you left Princeton. I however intend visiting the city in the course of a few days and then will probably have the pleasure of a long interview.

Our new house is nearly finished and we expect soon again to be inhabitants of the college Campus. Living so far from my Lecture room has been to me a great inconvenience.

In haste Yours Sincerely
Joseph Henry

[3] Henry had bought a large electrical machine from Pixii (*Henry Papers*, 3:542).

REVIEW OF "REPORT OF THE COMMITTEE ON NAVAL AFFAIRS, TO WHOM WAS REFERRED THE MEMORIAL OF HENRY HALL SHERWOOD . . ."[1]

Biblical Repertory and Princeton Review, *July 1838*, 10:506–509[2]

July 1838

We notice this report in order to express our disapprobation of the high encomiums pronounced by the committee of Naval Affairs on the labours of Dr. Sherwood, and to protest in behalf of the scientific character of our country, against the plan of discussing such subjects in Congress before proper means have been taken to determine their true character. The committee state that they have availed themselves of the opinions of scientific

---

[1] The remainder of the title reads: ". . . Claiming to Have Made New and Important Discoveries in Magnetism Generally, and More Particularly in the Magnetism of the Earth: and Representing that He is the Inventor of an Instrument Called the Geometer, Whereby, Etc. Washington, pp. 23."

As later documents will show, Sherwood's petition to Congress and the official response caused a furor in the scientific community. The report of the Senate Committee on Naval Affairs (*Senate Documents*, 25th Congress, 2d Session, July 3, 1838, No. 499 [in Henry's pamphlet collection]) sheds some light on Sherwood's life. He was reared in New York State and earned a medical degree. Although supporting himself by a medical practice, he was preoccupied with problems in the field of magnetism, which he considered fraught with ignorance and error. His proposal to Congress was apparently his first attempt to revise magnetic theory and to derive useful applications from his new understanding. One of Sherwood's later publications was entitled *The Astro-Magnetic Almanac, for 1843. In Which All the Motions of the Earth are Demonstrated in Accordance With the Theory of the Ancient Eastern Nations.* Other pamphlets dealt with esoteric medical applications of electricity and magnetism. Animal magnetism was a prominent topic in his medical journal, the *New York Dissector,* which he edited between 1844 and 1847.

Sherwood petitioned Congress for financial support to publish a new theory of terrestrial magnetism and to perfect his "geometer," a navigational device based on these principles. The crux of his theory was that the earth had a single magnetic north pole rotating around

the terrestrial pole and that the magnetic axis made an angle of 23° 28' with the terrestrial axis. Proofs and other details are discussed in Henry's review.

The Senate Naval Committee was impressed with the novelty of Sherwood's discoveries and especially with the promised benefits to navigation. In his letter of August 9, 1838, to Bache, Henry detailed the congressional actions. Henry's review of the Naval Committee report focussed on alleged fallacies in Sherwood's scientific theories (even though some of the scientific principles involved were still in a state of flux). But also at issue were matters of ideology and form. Henry attacked the qualifications of those who refereed Sherwood's memorial, not for their lack of eminence but the want of specialized expertise—a critical aspect of Henry's professional ethos. The public, Henry implied, should defer to scientists on matters within their intellectual domain. Henry also took offense at tell-tale signs of quackery in Sherwood's approach to scientific problems. His review, for example, took a sarcastic swipe at one of Sherwood's odd locutions: the reference to angles "instinctively" assumed by magnetic axes. The reviewer preferred the less animate sounding "spontaneously." Furthermore, Sherwood's easy leaps from data to broad theoretical concepts violated Henry's sense of the dignity and rigor of scientific discovery.

[2] Henry's review for the journal published by friends at the Princeton Theological Seminary was, as was customary with that journal, anonymous. Henry also preferred it that way, for reasons which are given in his letter to James Henry of September 11–13, 1838 (below).

gentlemen, and that these opinions are annexed, and form a part of the report. Now, the name of but *one* person known to science is attached to this article,[3] and he acknowledges that he has not examined the subject with proper attention. Yet "from these opinions, as well as from their own examination, the committee are fully persuaded that the discoveries and invention of Dr. Sherwood are entitled to the most serious consideration of the public, and to the encouragement and patronage of congress. The committee regard them as highly interesting and important to the navigation and commerce of the United States, and as bidding fair to open a new era in the history of the science of magnetism.

"They deem the subject of so much importance that they do not hesitate to express the opinion that an enlightened policy on the part of the Government should induce congress to grant the requisite aid. The committee will, as soon as they are able, present, for the consideration of the senate, such a bill as shall be best calculated, in their judgment, to carry out the recommendations of this report."

Now, notwithstanding this very favourable opinion of the committee, derived in part from their '*own examination*,' we do not believe that there is a person of any scientific reputation in our country, who has paid attention to this subject, who will not immediately say that the whole affair is perfectly puerile and entirely unworthy, for a moment, of the serious attention of congress.

An account of the labours of Dr. Sherwood is given by Dr. Dwight:[4] they relate, 1. To "important discoveries" in the magnetization of plates of iron. 2. To the deductions from these of the laws of terrestrial magnetism, and 3. To the invention of an instrument, called a Geometer, for determining, by magnetism, the latitude and longitude of places with practical accuracy. We are first informed that "Dr. Sherwood has succeeded in magnetising a continuous ring and circular plate of iron, which has heretofore been considered impracticable." To prove this, an extract from Dr. Roget's treatise in the Library of Useful Knowledge[5] is quoted, and misapplied. The true meaning of the extract is simply this; not that a ring cannot be magnetized, but that it may be so magnetized that it will exhibit no polarity until broken into pieces, the several poles in contact mutually neutralizing each other.

---

[3] Thomas P. Jones, Patent Office Examiner and editor of the Franklin Institute's *Journal*, is also the "Dr. J." criticized in the last paragraph.

[4] Sereno Edwards Dwight (1786–1850), son of Yale President Timothy Dwight. An 1803 Yale graduate, he assisted Benjamin Silliman and tutored in mathematics, rhetoric, and classics. He went on to a career in law and the church and, from 1833 to 1835, served as President of Hamilton College. *DAB*. Dwight strongly endorsed Sherwood's proposals to the Senate Naval Committee.

[5] P. M. Roget, *Treatises on Electricity, Galvanism, Magnetism, and Electro-Magnetism* (London, 1832).

But who ever doubted that a circular plate could be magnetized? Perhaps the committee, certainly not Dr. Roget, since at page 7, Art. Magnetism, of the same work, he has given a wood cut to illustrate the magnetism of the very article in question.

A detailed account in a very unscientific form is next given of experiments made with circular and oblong plates. These were magnetized, if we understand the account aright, regularly and irregularly. In regard to the irregular magnetism, it is perhaps not known to the committee that from the experiments of Haldat,[6] plates of any form may with a strong magnet be magnetized with any number of poles from one to a thousand or more; nay, that Dr. Sherwood's name may be traced on a plate in magnetic but not imperishable characters, and that these will become visible only when iron filings are strewed over the surface. There is no end to the variety of polarity which can be thus given to a plate, but there is nothing important in all this, since the whole may be referred to a few well known principles.

In reference to the regular magnetism, Dr. Sherwood's discoveries, as far as they are susceptible of generalization, may be thus stated,

1. When an oblong plate of sufficient width is magnetized in the usual manner, he finds that the poles are not at the end of the plate, but a little within or towards the middle.

2. That the axis of magnetism does not coincide with the axis of the plate; that is, with a line drawn through the middle of its length.

3. "That when the magnetic fluid is allowed by the portions of the plate to act freely, the angle instinctively taken by the two axis, seems to be in all cases 23 deg. 28 min. The same phenomena are exhibited in the magnetism of circular plates.

4. "The discoveries of these laws led necessarily to their application to terrestrial magnetism," and he "at once concluded that the laws of magnetic influence in the magnet and in the earth are one and the same."

With regard to the first mentioned discovery, that the pole is not at the end of the plate, this is certainly true, but unfortunately for Dr. Sherwood's claims to scientific honours, it is by no means new, and is mentioned in almost all the elementary works on the subject, even in the one quoted by Dr. Dwight himself—Art. Electro Mag. p. 86, ¶ 282.

The second important discovery, that the two axes do not coincide, is also

---

[6] Charles de Haldat du Lys (1770–1852), French physicist. Allen G. Debus, ed., *World Who's Who in Science* (Chicago, 1968).

equally true and equally original, as may be seen by again referring to the same elementary work, Art. Mag. p. 58. ¶ 253.

The third discovery, that of the instinctive angle of 23 deg. 28 min., we must confess is entirely new, for we can find no statement so perfectly absurd in all the records of science. The angle which the two axes spontaneously assume is purely accidental, and is scarcely ever the same in two similar plates, for the truth of this we refer to the experience of all those who have ever measured the angle in question. The quantity 23 deg. 28 min. is well known in Astronomy as the approximate value of the inclination of the plane of the earth's equator to the ecliptic, and we can easily see how, with some, vague ideas of the connection of phenomena, Dr. Sherwood has himself "instinctively taken" this mysterious angle, not from experiment, but from some crude hypothesis.

Next, as to the laws of terrestrial magnetism, deduced from the foregoing experiments; namely, that the earth has one magnetic pole in the north; that this pole is at the distance of 23 deg. 28 min. from the true pole; that the line of no variation is a true circle, &c.

By these deductions Dr. S. is fairly brought to the *reductio ad absurdum*, for they are entirely at variance with some of the best established facts in terrestrial magnetism. The earth, from the labours of Hansteen and others, is now proved to have four magnetic poles, two in the northern[7] and two in the southern hemisphere. The position of one of the former was determined from actual observation, in the northern part of our continent by Capt. Ross;[8] that of the other in Siberia by a scientific corps, under the direction of Hansteen, and at the expense of the Russian government. Again, the line of no variation, instead of being a circle, as is asserted by Dr. Sherwood, is a line in the eastern hemisphere extremely tortuous, which may be represented, with some degree of accuracy, by SS thus placed, $\begin{smallmatrix}S\\S\end{smallmatrix}$

But how does Dr. S. explain these discrepencies? very easily; he "perceives, from the general laws of magnetic forces as established in the iron plate, that this account is wholly erroneous;" that is, all the actual observations made in the east of Europe, by men of science and respectability, to establish the position of the points, and consequently the line of no variation, are erroneous. This forms, certainly, a "new era," not in the history of magnetism, but in that of absurdity and presumption, and we shall scarcely be surprized to learn hereafter, through the medium of a congressional document, that all our maps, constructed from actual survey, have

---

[7] Although Henry was expressing the scientific consensus of 1838, in 1839 Gauss published a persuasive argument for a single north magnetic pole. See *Henry Papers*, 2:190n–191n, and Sydney Chapman and Julius Bartels, *Geomagnetism*, 2 vols. (Oxford, 1940), 2:925–927.

[8] James Clark Ross.

been proved erroneous by some new experiments on the laws of projectiles.

The space allowed for this notice will not permit us to make any comments on the invention called the Geometer. We may, however, say that an invention, founded on false principles, can never give uniformly true results.

We presume that Dr. Sherwood himself entertains a sincere belief of the importance of his discoveries, but interested as we are in the welfare of American science, we cannot, in silence, suffer its character to be injured abroad, and the public name to be abused at home, without endeavouring to expose the error. In conclusion, we must state our regret at seeing the name of a gentleman attached to this report, who has been long and favourably known to science, and who, we know, possesses much valuable and practical scientific knowledge. Magnetism, however, is not in his line, and since even Homer himself sometimes nods, Dr. J. may be allowed to be a little oblivious on this subject.

"RECORD OF EXPERIMENTS"
Henry Papers, Smithsonian Archives

Aug 1st 1838

Enlarged the fram[e] of the real so as to make the whole circuit about 120 feet. 1st put compound wire above where the circuit was broken in one place, the needle put in an other, became powerfully *directly* magnetic. This effect must have been produced by the elect cutting across for when the strands were seperated no effect was produced.

2nd Strand united and in one continued circuit—very litle magnetism but in *contrary* direction—

3 Seperated the wires again ie removed the spires about a foot from each other. The needle magnetic, but in *direct* manner

4 Again not quite so much seperated current *direct*

5 The wires were placed together so as to form again the rope, very litle or no magnetism. Ang 60°—very strong charge

6 Again the same as above but the charge weak magnetism decided, current adverse—

The ends of the rope were grasped, shock [?received]—spark very brilliant and of a peculiar appearance—

N.B. Current was attempted to be found in direction by the decomposition of the iodide of pottash but without effect.

Removed the rope wire substituted for it long singl[e] <*wire*> ribbon—charge about 35°, distance one foot,[1] current   *direct*[2]

Repeated the same, elect 33°—
Same result—   *direct*

Repeated the same except distance increased to 2 feet elect 30°—
(magnetism feeble)   direct

Repeated the same excep[t] elect 60°. Magnetism very feeble current
                                                                            direct

Elevated the ribbon about a foot higher magnet[iz]ing in the
same direction but feeble, elect 30°   direct

Again the same as above elect 60—no current or very feeble
opposite direction   o

Again the same arrangement elect 70 magnetism decided   *direct*

raised the ribbon to the height of 5 feet, elect 30°—
magnetism decided current   *direct*

The same arrangement elect 60° magnetism stronger, current
                                                                            direct

Again the same, different sized needle,
elect 30 mag stronger cur   Direct

Small wire substituted for the ribbon magnetism descided
elect 30°   current *direct*

Flat <*coil*> ribbon brought down ends open elect 30°—   current *direct*
magn decided.

Same arrangement ends of flat ribbon open magnetism feeble
                                                                  Current *direct*

Attached spiral ribbon No 1 to the end of the ribbon current, still in the
same direction
(two exper[imen]ts same result magnetism strong)   *direct*

NB Discovered that most of the experiments had been made this afternoon
with out a supply wire to the machine; consequ[ent]ly the charges were not

---

[1] The distance between the inductive circuits. The angle is a reading of the electrometer showing strength of the primary discharge.

[2] Vertically, to the left of this and the following data, Henry noted, "In all these experiments the single wire gave a current direct".

as great as was indicated by the electrometer since the battery was placed on a stool with glass legs.[3]

1   Repeated the above exp with small charge current *adverse*
2   Again needle direct charge *same*
3   Again charge 10°—*adverse*
4   Again charge 10°—*adverse*

Strength of magnetism depends apparently on the kind of needles used

5   Again charge about 8° direct

[3] The source of static charge was a Leyden jar battery supplied by an electrical machine. Henry found that the battery was not properly grounded, perhaps invalidating the afternoon's results.

TO THE EDITOR OF THE NEWARK DAILY ADVERTISER
Draft, Henry Papers, Smithsonian Archives

[August 1, 1838][1]

Mr Editor[2]

You published a few days since a certificate signed by a number of highly respectable gentlemen in favour of an improved modification of the lightning rod,[3] invented by Dr King[4] of Boston. The certificate states, that the

[1] This letter, in slightly emended form, appeared in the August 1, 1838, issue of the *Newark Daily Advertiser* under the heading "Lightning Rods." Henry must have actually written it sometime during the previous week as it is in response to an item in the issue of July 24.

[2] William Burnet Kinney (1799–1880), born in Speedwell, New Jersey, entered journalism after a brief career at West Point and instruction in law from his brother. In 1830, after ten years as a literary advisor to Harper and Brothers, Kinney became editor of the *Newark Daily Advertiser*. Having received an honorary degree from Princeton in 1836, Kinney was a Trustee from 1840 until 1850. Appointed by President Taylor to represent the United States at the Court of Sardinia in 1850, Kinney served until 1853, after which he resided in Florence. He returned to Newark in 1865 but did not reenter journalism. *DAB*; *Princeton Catalogue*, p. 21.

[3] The certificate to which Henry refers appeared in the Tuesday, July 24, edition and was signed by Josiah Quincy, President of Harvard; John Snelling Popkin, Professor of Greek at Harvard; Charles Wells, former Mayor of Boston; Elisha Bartlett, Mayor of Lowell, Massachusetts; Samuel A. Eliot, Mayor of Boston; John Pierpont, Pastor of Hollis Street Unitarian Church; Levi Lincoln, former Governor of Massachusetts; and John Downes, Captain Commandant, Navy Yard, Boston. According to the certificate, which was reprinted from the Dedham, Massachusetts, *Advertiser*, Benjamin Silliman, Sr. also endorsed the article.

[4] William King (d. 1839?), self-styled "Medical Electrician and Lecturer on Electricity and Galvanism," first appears in 1810 as an itinerant lecturer in North Carolina. Billing his lectures on electricity as "Rational Amusements," King made extensive use of the properties of what he termed "Electrical Fluid," illuminating portraits of Washington, shocking animals, lighting candles, and ringing bells. An additional benefit of this fluid was, according to King, medical. Among the ailments

principal feature in the new rod consists in its presenting points to the atmosphere, in all directions &c.

We have no personal knowledge of Dr King and would be sorry unjustly to disparage his invention yet a sense of duty to the Public compels us to state, that the new modification of the rod, appears to us not founded on sound philosophical principles.

In the first place, it is a well established fact, that, a single point becomes much more highly electrified and consequently acts at a much greater distance than a ball under the same circumstances; or than a point in the vicinity and under the influence, of other points. These considerations appear to have induced the French Philosophers to reccommend but one point at the upper end of the rod.[5]

Again, a number of points, along the course of the rod, would as it appears to us tend to give off the electricity; and thus produce dangerous consequences from the lateral action of the discharge.

With these views, until some new principle be discovered in Electricity, we shall adhere to the well known form of the conductor reccommended in a report to the French Academy of Sciences in 1824 by Poisson, Fresnel, Gay Lussac and others.

One word in reference to the highly respectable names attached to the certificate. We would say that in all ordinary matters we would pay them sincerely due defference but in the present instance, endorsing an improvement in science, they loose with us a little of their wonted influence.[6]

F.[7]

King treated by administering electricity were bruises, burns, hysterics, madness, and headaches.

King's 1825 publication, *A Manual of Electricity*, indicates that he possessed a good knowledge of electrical theory and was aware of recent developments in the field. A considerable portion of the book concerns lightning and the means to avoid it; also included is an extensive discussion of the medical uses of electricity.

From 1831 until 1838, King appears in Boston City Directories. A notice in the Boston *Atlas* of April 16, 1839, advertises King's estate sale. Two electromagnets, two electromagnetic machines, illuminations (fireworks), and chemical apparatus are included in the estate of the "distinguished electrician." William King, *A Manual of Electricity* (Newbern, North Carolina, 1825); King, *Rational Amusements* (broadside, n.p., ca. 1800).

[5] In a report, "Instruction sur les Paratonnerres," presented to the Académie des sciences of Paris on April 23, 1823, a commission composed of Poisson, Lefèvre-Gineau, Girard, Dulong, Fresnel, and Gay-Lussac concluded that "the most advantageous form that can be given to a lightning-rod appears evidently to be that of a very sharp cone." John Farrar, *Elements of Electricity, Magnetism and Electro-Magnetism* (Cambridge, Massachusetts, 1826), pp. 367–372.

The full report originally appeared in *Annales de chimie et de physique*, 1824, 2d ser. 26:258–298.

[6] Henry's reworded version of the final paragraph, see below, appeared in the newspaper. This rather pointed comment is another example of Henry's impatience with non-scientists who ventured into scientific waters.

[7] Because of the subject of the letter, it is probable that Henry was using the pseudonym "F" to suggest Franklin.

In an effort to lend authority to Henry's letter, the editor followed it with the following note: "When we say this communication

(Private note)

I have long intended to commence furnishing you from time to time with some small contributions in the way of science.[8] I have however constantly thought myself too much engaged in other matters. If you can decipher the scrawl please give the article on the other leaf a place in your paper. It is intended as much for the gentlemen who have signed the certificate as for Dr King.[9]

> With Respect & Esteem
> In haste yours
> J.H.

One word in reference to the <*highly respectable*> opinions of the highly respectable Gentlemen who have signed the certificate. These in all ordinary matters would be received by us with due respect and attention but in the present instance endorsing a scientific invention we do think they lose a little of their wonted influence.

---

comes from one whose opinions are received in the world of science, if not as demonstration, at least as true *prima facie*, we secure for its suggestions the attention of our readers. ED."

[8] We are uncertain whether Henry ever provided any more scientific contributions. In 1843, however, he wrote Kinney once to ask that he not reprint a certain article and once to request that the announcement of Bache's appointment as Superintendent of the Coast Survey be in the proper style.

[9] Henry's dispute with King over the correct configuration of lightning rods did not end with this letter. In the August 18, 1839, *New-ark Daily Advertiser*, King replied, asking for evidence in support of Henry's statements and suggesting an experiment which would prove his point. A further rejoinder signed "F." appeared on August 24. Although an original has not been found, we presume Henry is the author of this letter. He restated his case, citing the work of Franz Achard, and claimed that King's modifications did not represent improvements. The letter ends with a proposal to submit King's apparatus for inspection by an impartial scientific society, such as the Franklin Institute.

FROM JOHN TORREY
Historic Letter File, Gray Herbarium Library, Harvard University

New York. Aug[t] 2nd. 1838.

My dear friend.

It is a long time since I have heard from you. The accompanying printed notice[1] will show that I have not been idle. Please tear off that part of the sheet & give it to Jaeger, & tell him that if he will send to Chilton's he will find a parcel for him, containing botanical specimens.

---

[1] Although the notice is no longer with the letter, we suspect Torrey is referring to an advertisement for the *Flora of North America*; see below, footnote 12.

I have done but little this season in the way of Chemistry, except while instructing my private pupil & I *finished him off* several weeks ago. While experimenting on potassium to see the strange motions that are produced when it is placed on mercury, I was induced to try how *Sodium* would act. The moment the two metals came into contact, there was a strong explosion. At first I supposed this was owing to some moisture on the quicksilver, but the explosion took place even when both metals were perfectly dry. No author has noticed this curious fact except Berzelius, & he mentions it very briefly.[2] I suppose this is only an example of the general fact that light & heat are extricated whenever two substances enter into rapid chemical combination, but it is not usual for two substances of the same class—& especially two metals to act thus.[3] Something like it, however, is seen in the explosive combination of platinum with tin & one or two other metals when moderately heated together.

The Scientific Corps of the Exp[g]. Exped. have received orders to be at Norfolk by the 6th inst, as the vessels are to sail (so they *say*) on the 10th. Johnson[4] Hoyle,[5] Eights,[6] young McMurtrie[7] and some others are left off. D[r]. Gray has resigned, & has been appointed Prof. Bot[y]. in the Univ. of Michigan. He will proceed to Detroit next week, & in the autumn probably go to Europe.[8] I have not rec[d] the mirrors, but I suppose they will come in

[2] Berzelius writes: "A volume égal, le mercure s'unit au *potassium* avec dégagement de lumière. . . . Le *sodium* et le mercure se combinent avec une telle violence, que la masse devient rouge. . . ." *Traité de chimie*, trans. Esslinger, 8 vols. (Paris, 1831), 3:118, in the Henry Library.

[3] The fact may not have seemed so exceptional to Henry who in 1837 had heard Faraday lecture that "the combination of all metals produce heat like any other chemical union," with the combination of potassium and mercury given as an example. *Henry Papers*, 3:248.

[4] For Walter R. Johnson's separation from the Wilkes Expedition, see *Henry Papers*, 3: 132. The expedition sailed on the eighteenth.

[5] Raphael Hoyle (1804–1838), a British born landscape painter who came to America in 1823, was to be a draftsman for the Wilkes Expedition. Hoyle had fallen ill and died on August 12. G. C. Groce and D. H. Wallace, *The New-York Historical Society's Dictionary of Artists in America, 1564–1860* (New Haven, 1957), p. 331.

[6] James Eights. See *Henry Papers*, 3:122, 125n–126n, 517n.

[7] William Birch McMurtrie (1816–1872), Philadelphia artist, had been appointed as one of the natural history draftsmen of the expedi-

tion but was dropped at the last minute. McMurtrie later served as draftsman for a U.S. Coast Survey expedition on the Pacific coast. J. Russell Harper, *Early Painters and Engravers in Canada* (Toronto, 1970), p. 210. McMurtrie to J. K. Paulding, August 27, 1838, Letters Received by the Secretary of the Navy Relative to the U.S. Exploring Expedition, 1836–1842, RG 45, National Archives (McMurtrie's letter of complaint asking for compensation).

[8] For Asa Gray's dealings with the Wilkes Expedition, see *Henry Papers*, 3:106n, 517n. After vacillating between the still chancy position on the delayed exploring expedition and an uncertain offer from the newly founded University of Michigan, Gray opted to wait for a definite offer from Michigan, which came on July 17, 1838. Torrey was instrumental in getting him the job, which, in contrast to the exploring expedition, allowed Gray the opportunity to continue his collaboration with Torrey on the *Flora of North America*. According to Gray's biographer, he "received an appointment to the first chair devoted exclusively to botany in any American educational institution." A. Hunter Dupree, *Asa Gray, 1810–1888* (New York, 1968), pp. 66–67, 68 (for the quotation). Although Gray resigned from the University of Michigan in 1842 with the Univer-

good time. Have you written to Pixii? If he dont do better, I shall make interest with the Univ^ty of Michigan to employ some other manufacturers. I sent you a few days ago the report of the Senate respecting the pretended discovery of a man in Magnetism.[9] Why will you not use your influence in putting down this miserable spirit of quackery in our country. Mr. Talmedge[10] & Dr Dwight[11] ought to be severely handled.

You must get the college to subscribe to our Flora. We cannot give away copies. Our bills on Part I. alone amount to more than $350. We pay as we go, & if any thing is to be made we will have it ourselves—At any rate no one shall suffer loss by us. If our botanists & literary institutions don't patronize the work, we cannot go on.[12] My very kind regards to Mrs. Henry, & all your family. Yours,

John Torrey

---

sity still not in operation, Dupree argues that the choice of Michigan over the exploring expedition had a decisive effect on Gray's botanical career (pp. 68–69).

Gray's European trip began in November. His goals, aside from the official one of buying books for the University, were to establish channels of communication with European botanists and especially to examine North American plants in European herbaria. Dupree, op. cit., p. 74.

[9] Henry had already published an attack on the Senate Naval Committee's report on Henry Hall Sherwood's memorial. See above, July 1838.

[10] Senator Nathaniel P. Tallmadge (1795–1864) from New York. He submitted the favorable report of the Naval Committee. *Biographical Directory of the American Congress.*

[11] Sereno Edwards Dwight.

[12] The *Flora of North America*, the great collaborative work of Torrey and Gray, appeared in several fascicles beginning in August 1838. Publication stopped short of completion in 1843, however, because of Gray's duties at Harvard and the flood of botanical specimens from the western explorations. The *Flora* completed the shift in America from the Linnaean classification to the natural system. *DSB*, s.v. "Gray" and "Torrey."

"RECORD OF EXPERIMENTS"
Henry Papers, Smithsonian Archives

Augt 2nd 1838

Charge the battery[1] very long 6 7 8 10 &c, all gave the current

magnetism strong	direct
Again[2] charge 40° mag feeble current—	*adverse*

[1] Although not specified, the experimental set-up probably remains as on August 1, when Henry's results were unfortunately marred by an improper connecting of the Leyden jars. Despite the furious data-taking below, Henry is frankly confused by the bewildering shifts in the direction of the induced currents. He hazards a guess as to the cause at the end of the day's experimentation but, as footnote 4 (below) reveals, later explained the results in a different fashion.

[2] A marginal note along this series of readings states: "Ribbon at the distance of a foot in all the exp, coil attached".

Same with a short needle, charge the same (40°)	
mag strong current	*direct*
Again with short needle	
Charge 40° (strong)	direct
Wire closed which was around in the same plane with the ribbon	
mag slight elec 10°	*adverse*
Again elect—5°	
mag slight	*adverse*
Again elect 40°	
mag tolerably strong	*adverse*
Wire opened mag slight,	
elect 5°—current	*adverse*
Again elect 10 mag feeble	
current	*adverse*
Again elect 10—slight—	
	adverse

Apparently every condition the same as when the circuit was open before

Again seperated the wire in one spot, where it touched the ribbon
still mag slight but decidedly repuls
or cur   *adverse*

Removed the iron [. . .][3] which united the wires to the mag helix.
    Same effect elect 10°
current   *adverse*

Put ribbon under coil with same charge still *adverse*

Brought the coil near the large wire, which transmitts the shock still
adverse

Spark from long wire *very* intense

Same series continued[4] with the coil, needle put not so far in to the \<coil\>
helix, all else the same still—
current   —*adverse*
mag still slight.

---

[3] An illegible word.

[4] Henry later glossed these experiments with a revealing admission: "September 24th 1840, all the experiments given in the four or five pages along here, were at the time of making them, exceedingly perplexing, but I think they can now all be explained by the action of the spiral and the coil causing the initial or terminal current, to predominate"—a hypothesis that Henry will entertain in subsequent experiments below and put forward in "Contributions IV."

 Charge still 10°—wires crossed, a spark was seen to pass from one of the ribbons to the other; needle now strongly mag current still   —*adverse*

Seperated the wires mag same but very slight —adverse

Removed the strand more from each other[5]
Still adverse   still   adverse

Series with the coil
Opened the circuit so as to remove the coil out of the influence of the wires
charge 10° <*current*> mag feeble, doubtful,
current still   —*adverse*

Elect 40° mag strong
current   +*direct*

Elect 20° mag feeble
current   +direct

Elect 10° current tolerably strong—   +direct

Elect 20°, mag feeble
current—   +direct

Series with the coil continued
1 Apparatus arranged as before
Elect again at 40° mag feeble
current   —*adverse*

2 Elect at 60° Strong mag
current   —*adverse*

New Series.[6] Same arrangement
Elect 3°—mag strong
current   +*direct*

Elect 5° mag strong
current   +*direct*

Elect 8 mag still strong
current   +*direct*

---

[5] Since evidently two readings are given, this may possibly refer to *two* trials, reading as if: "Removed the strand—still adverse, more from each other—still adverse".
[6] Using a gradually increased charge.

Elect 10° mag little stronger
              current   +*direct*

Elect 15° mag not quite as strong
                     +*direct*

Elect 18° mag about same
              current   +direct

Elect 25° about same
              current   +direct

Elect 30 little weaker
              current   +direct

Elect 35 mag about same
              current   +direct

Elect 40 mag weaker
              current   +direct

Elect 45° mag about same, or little strong[er]
              current   +direct

Elect 50° mag <*feeble*> weaker
              current   +direct

Elect 60° mag stronger
                     +direct

Again
Elect 5°—mag weak
              current   +direct

Elect 20—mag stronger
              current   +direct

Elect 40° mag strong
              current   +direct

Coil[7] removed wire remaining the same elect 15°—no magnetism
              current   *0*

Again same
           current the same   *0*

---

[7] In the margin, referring to this and the next test: "Probably caused by ribbon near circuit".

Again elect 5°—magnetism feeble, but decided

current—   *—adverse*

Same, elect 20°
mag decided but feeble,

current   +*direct*

Same elect 5°, mag feeble,

current direct   +direct

Same elect 20, very feeble

current   +direct

Same arrangement, shock through the [?hand] from the ribbon very severe. But no spark at 5°—

Is it not possible that the direct induction may have some effect in producing the direct discharge.[8] Thus both ends give a current, but the one next 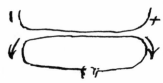 the + end, or near the jar, will be the stronger and thus produce a current in the same direction, but this will not account for the current in the adverse direction, although it will serve to explain some of the results obtained before. Thus when the <wir> ribbon was seperated from the wire at the first side, the effect was very small.

Made a new arrangement Thus. as before, small wire arranged as whole battery, the magnetism was 1½ feet

Large circuit of large wire c d, needle at f. With the feebly + at the distance of

With 2 jars it was — and when the distance of 2½ feet the needle adverse, but one of the jars broke in Repeat this exp, put spiral at d

the wires were seperated to c became strongly — ad- the discharge. c and also at f.

---

[8] By "direct," Henry means currents in the positive direction. He is giving a tentative hypothesis for correlating directions of the primary and secondary currents from static electric induction.

"RECORD OF EXPERIMENTS"
Henry Papers, Smithsonian Archives

Aug 3rd [1838]

Exp 1 To test the idea of yesterday relative to the [...][1] which the extra particle might have in determining the <*charge*>[2] current—commenced exper[iment]ing with the apparatus described before
The jar was placed on glass stand. Charge sometimes + and sometimes minus on inside. The following was the result

Jar — inside, extra particle outside

current—direct

Inside charged + extra particle inside

current—direct

Inside + extra quantity outside

current—direct

Inside — extra part on outside

current—direct

Inside + extra particle outside

current—*direct*

Exp 2 Repeated this many times always with the same result. So that with this arrangement the lateral action has no effect

Mr Blaney[3] has made a number of experiments with the rope wire and the frames as arranged last afternoon. The result is that the current with the compound wire is constantly in the *adverse* direction at all distances and with all charges also with two jars and with [...][4] With 3 jars the needle became highly charge[d] on two occasion[s] when the jars brok[e]—

Exp 3 I opened the rope wire at one spot. The distance of wires about one inch, needle strongly magnetic in the *direct current*. This looks like the

---

[1] One illegible word.

[2] Or possibly <*change*>, referring to change in current direction.

The purpose of these experiments is to test the extent to which apparent inductive effects from static electricity were actually due to ordinary lateral discharge. "Extra particle" or, equivalently, "free electricity" were contemporary theoretical terms referring to the excess of positive or negative electricity on the inside or outside coatings of the Leyden jar that was the cause of lateral discharge from the jar. See *Henry Papers*, 3:53n–54n. In these experiments the adjacent inductive circuits are considered theoretically equivalent to the coatings of the Leyden jar. Experiment one shows that the direction of the induced current was not affected by changes in the location of the "extra particle." From this Henry generally concluded that he had produced genuine inductive effects with static electricity equivalent to those from galvanism. See "Contributions III," paragraphs 104–107.

[3] James Van Zandt Blaney (1820–1874), a Princeton senior, assisted Henry in the laboratory. He later practiced medicine in Chicago and was Professor of Chemistry there at Rush Medical College. W. E. Schenck, *Biography of the Class of 1838 of the College of New Jersey* (Philadelphia, 1889), pp. 42–45.

[4] Possibly "9."

action of Ampere[5] at right angles to the wire which acting on the wires thus would produce a current in 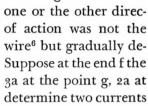 one or the other direction. Thus suppose the intensity of action was not the same through[ou]t the whole wire[6] but gradually decreased toward the negative pole. Suppose at the end f the intensity of action (repulsion) is 3a at the point g, 2a at h it will be nothing and this will determine two currents one each way towards h, but one of these, that from f, will be the stronger and thus a current will be produced in the direction of f, h or in the adverse direction to the primary current. The currents of galvanism may possibly be produced by a similar action

Attempted[7] this afternoon the exp of Provost with a Frog. An iron needle was first heated red hot then thrust into the thy of the Frog, iron filings were next heated red hot to deprive them of magnetism. The result was watched with an eye glass, but no magnetic effect could be observed. I was assisted by Dr Allison[8] of Philadelphia. Dr Allison showed me the heart of a Fish (cat Fish) which pulsated several hours after being removed from the body.

[5] Referring to Ampère's theories of the interaction of two current-carrying wires.

[6] Beside the illustration in the margin Henry wrote "Repeat this exp". This attempted theoretical explanation of the observed direction of induced currents is like that given at the end of the entry of August 2, 1838, above.

[7] The remaining remarks were inserted above one section of experiment 3. The notion of performing this experiment had come to Henry earlier. See above, Henry to Coquerel, May 28, 1838, footnote 1.

[8] Joseph J. Allison was an 1837 graduate of the University of Pennsylvania Medical School and was interested in venous pulsation. *Catalogue of Alumni of the Medical Department of the University of Pennsylvania* (Philadelphia, 1877).

FROM STACY G. POTTS[1]

Henry Papers, Smithsonian Archives

Trenton Aug 3, 1838

Dear Sir,

At a meeting of citizens of this place a few evenings since, it was resolved to form an Institute[2] for the diffusion of Scientific knowledge; and a com-

[1] A lawyer by profession, Stacy Gardiner Potts (1799–1865) held a number of political and civic posts, climaxed by a term (1852–1859) as a member of the New Jersey Supreme Court. He also was a leading lay figure in the Presbyterian Church. Princeton granted him an honorary degree in 1844. *Biographical Encyclopaedia of New Jersey of the Nineteenth Century* (Philadelphia, 1877), pp. 62–63.

[2] In the wake of a "Philosophical Lecture, by Mr. Brown" in July 1838, some of the leading younger citizens in Trenton founded the Trenton Institute. Modeled after the lyceums, the Institute's primary objective was to promote public understanding of science through public lectures. Officially established in Sep-

mittee consisting of Rev Mr Starr[3] Drs Ewing[4] & Coleman[5] Mr Sherman[6] and myself were appoint^d to procure an Introductory Lecture, at as early a period as possible.

This Committee have requested me to Solicit your acceptance of this duty[7]—and to ask you to be kind enough to afford us an opportunity of conversing with you on the subject, on Monday afternoon next, at 4 oclock, or if that time will not be convenient, to inform us *when* you will be at leisure.

With great respect
I am yo. ob. servt.
Stacy G. Potts

---

tember 1838, the Institute survived until March 1844.

Of the five men mentioned in this letter, at least four served as officers of the Institute. Potts was a vice-president; Ewing and Starr were members of the executive committee; Coleman was one of the curators.

John O. Raum, *History of the City of Trenton* (Trenton, 1871), pp. 228–229; *Emporium and True American*, August 3, 1838; August 24, 1838; August 31, 1838.

[3] Samuel Starr (1807–1862) was educated at Trinity College (Connecticut), graduating in 1829. He became rector of St. Michael's Church (Episcopal) in Trenton in 1836. In 1855 he left St. Michael's for Grace Church, Cedar Rapids, Iowa. Hamilton Schuyler, *History of St. Michael's Church* (Princeton, 1926), pp. 198–199.

[4] Francis Armstrong Ewing (d. 1857) graduated Princeton in 1824. He received his medical degree from the University of Pennsylvania in 1828. *Princeton Catalogue*, p. 137.

[5] A graduate of the Yale Medical School (1829), James Beakes Coleman (1806–1869) established his practice in Trenton in 1837. He contributed a steady stream of papers to the Mercer County Medical Society on surgical subjects. Another of his interests was forced-air ventilation of public buildings. In 1841, while physician to the New Jersey Penitentiary, he designed a ventilating system for the prison which Henry was asked to evaluate. Henry questioned the practicability of the system; his skepticism proved to be well founded, since the system required more power than the prison could offer. In the long run, however, Coleman's design was vindicated, as it became a widely accepted form of ventilation. *Biographical Encyclopaedia of New Jersey*, pp. 458–460.

[6] Probably one of two brothers: James T. Sherman or William P. Sherman. James T. (1814?–1862), a Yale graduate, was editor of the *New Jersey State Gazette* from 1835 until 1853. His elder brother had become editor of the *New Jersey State Gazette* in 1829, but remained with the newspaper for only a few years. Francis Bazley Lee, *History of Trenton, New Jersey* (Trenton, 1895), pp. 243–245; Trenton City Directories, 1854–1855; Raum, *History of the City of Trenton*, p. 229.

[7] Although Henry's response has not been found, he accepted the invitation to give the introductory lecture to the Trenton Institute on August 28, 1838. *Emporium and True American*, August 24, 1838; Francis A. Ewing to Henry, August 23, 1838, Henry Papers, Smithsonian Archives. Unfortunately, no account of the lecture has been located.

"RECORD OF EXPERIMENTS"
Henry Papers, Smithsonian Archives

Aug 4th 1838

Repeated the experiment on screening with the coils and common electricity with the same resul[t]s as at first[1]

[1] See July 21, 1838, experiment 3 and July 20, 1838, experiment 4, both above.

Exp 1st 1st Put zinc plate between then took out plate, needle magnetized in the 2nd case not in the first

Several times repeated the expermts.

 Exp 2nd Put lead plate between, caught current, current *contrary*, tolerably strong with one jar no mistake about this

Exp 3 Experimented again with the rope wire

1 3 jars distance one foot
open current strong
    direct
2 3 jars d 3 feet
open strong
    direct
3, 3 jars dist 3 feet
shut   slight
    direct   adverse[2]

charge 60°

9 jars dist 3 feet
open no current *0*
9 jars charge litle higher
shut   *direct*

40°

3 jars 3 feet
open strong   direct

60°

3 jars 3 feet
shut slight   adverse

60°

3 jars 3 feet
open strong   *direct*

60

Changed the position of the coils so that the opening and the cylender would be on the opposite side of the parallelogram

3 jars mag strong dist one foot
   open, current   *direct*
3 jars, current shut, dist same
   mag feeble   *adverse*

---

[2] There is an illegible word beneath this observation in the original.

TO RICHARD TAYLOR[1]
Draft, Henry Papers, Smithsonian Archives

College of New Jersey
Princeton Aug 9th 1838

My Dear Sir

I fear you will think me very remiss in not before writing to you relative to the scientific memoirs.[2] I have defered from time to time my communication with the hope of being able to give you some more definite encouragement than I now can even now offer to your <*project*> proposition of continuing the work.

Almost immediately after my return to this country I consulted with my acquaints in New York and Philadelphia relative to an agent for the work in the United States but was advised to take another cou[r]se namely to send out the circulars which you gave me to the principal Scientific Persons in the country and to state at the bottom in writing that the work could be ordered through the principal importe[r]s of English Books in New York and Philadelphia.[3]

I was advised to adopt this course inorder that you might not have any difficulty in settelling your accounts with an agent in this country. The Book sellers above alluded to will order thru agents in London as many copies as will be nec[e]ssary to supply the demand. The sail will thus be affected without trouble or risk on your part.

A number of the persons to whom I addressed the circular have signified their desire to subscribe for the work <*but still the whole number is yet small*>. In this way I have the promis of about 20 names. This is a small number but there is a <*very*> rapidly increasing attention to scientific subjects in this country and were the work continued I doubt not but the number might be increased in a year or two many fold.

I hope you will pardon my long silence. Since my return to America my college duties have been very arduous. I have been obliged in part to mak[e] up for my absence and besids have been engaged in a series of exper[iments]

---

[1] Henry had met the English publisher on his 1837 trip (see *Henry Papers*, 3:214, 357).

[2] Taylor's *Scientific Memoirs* contained translations of non-English language scientific writings and was very important in its day. Henry's spiral conductor article appeared in its first volume (pp. 540–547), apparently the only work in English reprinted by Taylor. In the preface to this volume, Taylor expresses appreciation for the encouragement received from Hare, Henry, and Bache, as well as a number of Britons. Taylor reported a sale of less than 250 copies and appealed for additional subscribers. The second volume came out with the aid of funds from the British Association.

[3] Taylor did not take this advice. The subsequent volumes followed the practice of the first, listing Dobson of Philadelphia and Goodhugh of New York as agents.

of which I hope in a few weeks to send you an account from the transactions of the American Phil society.[4]

I hope you will find it to your own interest as I am sure it will be to that of science to continue publication of the memoirs and be assured that I will do all in my power to make the work known <*and cause it to be subscribed for in this country.*> and properly encouraged in this country.

I shall always retain a lively reccollection of my visit to England and of particularly

It will be much to be regretted if you cannot find it to your interest to continue the publication of the scientific memoirs. There is no work more wanted and none which can have a more important influence on the cause of science in every part of the world where the English lang[uage] is spoken.

I do not receive the numbers of the Philosophical magazine quite as promptly as I could wish. My last number is one for March. I get it through O. Riche Red Lion Square.

---

[4] Henry's "Contributions III: Electro-Dynamic Induction" was reprinted in the *Phil.* *Mag.*, 1840, 3d ser. *16*:200–210, 254–265, 551–562.

TO ALEXANDER DALLAS BACHE[1]
Bache Papers, Smithsonian Archives

Princeton Aug 9th 1838

My Dear Bache

I start tomorrow morning at ½ past 3 o'clok to put on board the ship Toronto, the magnetic needles which I have vibrated in this country and which I hope will reach London in proper time to meet you there, just before you leave for America. I do not know when you have concluded to sail but suppose you will start just after the meeting of the British Association next month. I send the Package directed to the care of Mr Vaughan and will request the Capt of the Toronto[2] to deliver it with his own hands.

I have not made out the observations but send you an exact copy of the

---

[1] Although Henry wrote at least one other letter to Bache between the time he left Europe and the time Bache returned home, this is the only such letter extant. In this August 9 letter, closed hastily on August 10, Henry reflects on his experiences in Europe and informs Bache of developments at home. Two partial copies by Mary Henry are in the Henry Papers. The August 9 portion is printed in Nathan Reingold, ed., *Science in Nineteenth-Century America: A Documentary History* (New York, 1964), pp. 81–90.

[2] Robert H. Griswold (*Henry Papers, 3*:514).

records. The observations are made according to the old method. Since I was most accustomed to this I concluded there would [be] less danger of mistake. In the series of observations made in London I was assisted by Mr Robinson the Instrument maker of Devonshire street. We found no difficulty in identifying the place [of] observation as described in your letter.[3] The observations in this country were made at Princeton with the assistance of Mr Alexander. The results with Rusty and Bright from your observations in London and from mine and Robi[n]son at the same place you will find do not well agree. One cause of the difference is the long exposure the needles were subject to in the interval. Another and probably the principal cause is that when we came to examine the needles one of which as you may reccollect was fastened into the lining of my hat and the other into the tail of my coat the stirrups which were formed of tin foil were rubbed into pieces. We collected the fragments weghed them with accuracy and substituted an equal weght of fine platina wire. The compensation was not however complete since it was impossible to give the mass precisely the same distribution as in the case of the tin foil stirrup. You will find in the square box two additional needles made by Robinson. He neglected to mark these and the letters put on are by myself. There is a possibility that I have not given them the proper mark, that is the one called A perhaps should on the reccord be called *B*. You will however easily determine this by a comparison of the times. I did intend sending the needles by the last London packet but was not able to get to the ship in time. I however prefered to send them by the Capt of the Torronto since I came home with him and can put more confidence in his care of the articles. They will in all probability reach London at a proper time before your departure and with the least delay. So much for the needles and now for other matters. I have twice visited Philadelphia since I wrote to you[4] concerning my visit to your Mother's. One was a short visit of a day or less the other was with Mrs H and consisted of 4 or 5 days. My time however was continually occupied with some experiments in Dr Hares laboratory on electricity with his large electrical machine and battery. This was at the First of May and since then I have heard nothing from the city. My time since my return to America has been constantly occupied and since the commencement of the last College year I have had scarcely a moments leisure. Not only my ordinary duties were to be attended to but also much was expected in the way of working up the lea way of my long absence. Besides this I commenced during the spring vacation a series of experiments on electricity which have engaged my attention at every moment not devoted to professional duties. I hope you will pardon me for

[3] Of July 16, 1837 (*Henry Papers*, 3:410–412).   [4] Letter not found.

not having written to you frequently as I promised and as I really intended. I have commenced since my last several letters but did not finish them at the time—did not like to send a short letter, procrastinated from day to day, suffered much from stings of conscience on account of the same, consoled myself a little with the reflection that I had heard nothing from you &c &c.

I have now again got into my old track and things go on with me something after their usual fashion. When I first returned from England however I was much dissatisfied with many things both in reference to my own affairs and those of the public generally. An absence from a place for a single year makes many changes and you will probably find My Dear Bache that the two years you have been absent has made as great a change in the disposition of things which you once controlled as if you had been consigned to the grave during that period. Persons with whom you have associated and perhaps controlled have learned to do without you and measures and plans which you have laboured to advance are set aside for others not as good but carried into operation because the production of others and those on the spot. Besides this the charlatanism of our country struck me much more disagreably when I first returned than before or even now. I often thought of the remark you were in the habit of making that we must put down quackery or quackery will put down science. You have probably heard of the wonderful sensation produced in the country by magnetic machines. A company was formed in New York which succeeded in raising $12,500 dollars for experiments on the machine and after much puffing and the expenditure of the above mentioned sum the whole of course fell through.[5]

[5] Henry is referring to a joint stock association set up to provide money for the development of Thomas Davenport's electric motor. Davenport patented his invention on February 25, 1837. A week later, he and his partner Ransom Cook, also a rural mechanic, entered into a financing arrangement at the suggestion of Edwin Williams (1797–1854, *DAB*). Retaining most of the stock themselves, they authorized Williams to sell the remaining 1,000 shares to raise $50,000 to be applied toward experimental work and living expenses. Williams agreed to pay Davenport and Cook $12,000 within thirty days of the agreement. The proprietors eventually received only half this amount and in March 1838 filed a bill of complaint in the New York Court of Chancery against Williams, alleging evasiveness and fraud in his agency. Williams subsequently went bankrupt.

Davenport's attempts at further development of his motor drew a variety of responses from the scientific community. In 1835 Henry had praised Davenport's ingenuity but advised him to abandon his motor except as a curiosity for exhibit. Henry, and others, felt that the cost of producing power from a motor was far too high, in comparison with steam, to make it a viable alternative (*Henry Papers*, 2:416n–417n, 445–448, 452n). Charles G. Page, also working on motors at this time, regretted that the invention was "a subject of mercenary speculation, when in reality it has no value except as an experiment . . ." (*Silliman's Journal*, 1839, *35*:107). Benjamin Silliman strongly endorsed further development and encouraged the public to support it regardless of potential financial reward (ibid., 1838, *33*:194). Thomas P. Jones, editor of the Franklin Institute *Journal*, was also an enthusiastic supporter and felt electric motor power would prove to be cheaper than steam power (Franklin Institute *Journal*, 1837, 20:342–343).

From 1837 until 1843, Davenport remained in New York City trying to improve his motors. He finally returned to Vermont, having failed

Again a great sensation was produced by the magnetic Telegraph of Professor Morse who first claimed or his Friends for him the entire origin of the project.[6] But the most disgusting piece of charlatanism which has been got up in this country since your departure is that of Dr Sherwood in connection with the committee of naval affairs in the senate of the United States. Dr S. brought before congress last session a great discovery in magnetism no less than that of the solution of the whole problem of terrestrial magnetism, a ridiculous and puerile affair. It was however refered to the committee of naval affairs who reported on it in the most flattering terms, stated that from the opinion of several scientific gentlemen as well as their own examination the discoveries and inventions of Dr Sherwood were of the highest importance, worthy the confidence of the public and the patronage of congress. They proposed to bring in a bill for the reward of Dr S. but fortunately for the honor of the country congress adjourned previous to this disgrace being inflicted on the country. I will attach to the package a copy of the report for your inspection. 5000 copies extra of the report were ordered printed for the edification of the people of the United States and of the world, for I have no doubt but many of these will find their way across the atlantic.

This article you will say is a disgrace to the country. I have given a notice of it and made a protest, in behalf of the scientific character of the United

---

in his attempts, including a request to Congress for a federal appropriation, to get adequate financial backing.

DAB, s.v. "Davenport." Walter R. Davenport, *Biography of Thomas Davenport* (Montpelier, 1929), esp. pp. 114–117. *King*, pp. 265, 269. A copy of the bill of complaint is in the Henry Library.

[6] Although S. F. B. Morse had conceived of his telegraph in 1832 and been working on it since 1835, he did not begin demonstrating it until September 1837. In the next few months he greatly increased its effectiveness and gained widespread publicity and praise. Responding to a request from the Secretary of the Treasury, who had been asked by the House of Representatives to report on a telegraph system for the United States, Morse demonstrated his invention in February 1838 at the Capitol in Washington. Enthusiasm for Morse's electromagnetic telegraph eclipsed the rival semaphoric telegraph proposals. On behalf of the House Committee on Commerce, Chairman F. O. J. Smith strongly endorsed Morse's system in his report of April 6, 1838. He also claimed its originality:

This invention consists in the application, by mechanism, of galvanic electricity to tele-

graphic purposes, and is claimed by Professor Morse and his associates as original with them; being so, in fact, as the committee believe, letters-patent have been secured, under the authority of the United States, for the invention.

House Reports, 25th Congress, 2d Session, 1837–1838, No. 753, p. 1 (the report is reprinted in Thomas C. Cochran, ed., *The New American State Papers: Science and Technology* [Wilmington, Delaware, 1973], 8:52–61). Carleton Mabee, *The American Leonardo: A Life of Samuel F. B. Morse* (1943; reprint ed., New York, 1969), chapter 17.

In a climate of popular excitement, there was little inclination for an analysis of Morse's debt to basic research, the similarity between his system and those of foreign rivals, or the specific technical contributions of his associates. These questions were to arise later and plague Morse for the rest of his life. His famous dispute with Henry did not begin until the late 1840s. Prior to this, he and Henry were on friendly terms. Henry publicly endorsed Morse's telegraph system and willingly advised him on technical problems. See their correspondence in April and May 1839 (printed below).

States, against the custom of publishing scientific articles among the documents of congress before their true character is ascertained.[7] Bad as this is it is not quite equal to a memorial published amoung the documents early last winter on the subject of the explosion of steam boilers. The author set forth the wonderful fact that the explosions were generally produced by the generation of *negative* and *positive electricity* in the boiler!![8] I think you will be somewhat displeased with several of the selections for the Franklin Journal since your departure. Sillimans Journal in the last numbers is tolerably decent but contains little that is new or interesting but for the year before this it was filled with a mass of trash relative to electricity and electro magnetism which would disgrace the annals of electricity. One Fellow actually stated in a paper on electro-magnetism that he had succeeded in making the magnets by substituting copper instead of iron within the coil.[9] I had an interview with Professor Silliman and complained to him of the injury done to the character of american science by such publications. He said that if I could see what he rejected I would scarcely complain of what he inserted.[10] I also hinted the importance of having collaborators in

---

[7] Henry's protest is printed above, July 1838. A second Naval Committee report, essentially an expansion of Sherwood's memorial and not an evaluation, appeared on February 22, 1839. Referring to criticisms of the first report, the committee defended its actions:

They, however, deem the subject of sufficient importance to have the views of the memorialist extensively spread before the country, that they may thereby attract the attention of scientific men, and lead to investigation which will tend to establish the correctness of his theory.

Senate Documents, 25th Congress, 3d Session, 1838–1839, No. 253.

[8] The January 1838 memorial was by Jonathan Morgan of Portland, Maine. Morgan argued that the causes of steam boiler explosions could not be determined through observation and experiment but only through analogy. Claiming that steam boiler explosions had the same effect, except in magnitude, as "electrical explosions in the heavens," he concluded that they shared a cause: "the sudden mutual and violent attraction of positive and negative electricity." Although citing the Franklin Institute experiments in support of his theory, he chided its committee for "going upon the mechanical instead of the philosophical principles of the case." One of Morgan's proposals was to equip steam boilers with modified lightning rods. *House Documents*,

25th Congress, 2d Session, 1837–1838, No. 100 (reprinted in Thomas C. Cochran, ed., *The New American State Papers: Science and Technology* [Wilmington, Delaware, 1973], 6:358–372).

[9] In claiming a unique form of motor, Benjamin Rush McConnell mentioned that he got nearly equal results from electromagnets made of either copper or iron wrapped in iron wire (*Silliman's Journal*, 1838, 33:188–190).

The most sensational article on electricity appeared in the next number (pp. 394–398) under the title "Extraordinary Case of Electrical Excitement, with Preliminary Remarks by the Editor," communicated by Dr. Willard Hosford of New Hampshire at Silliman's request. Hosford described how a "lady of great respectability . . . became suddenly and unconsciously charged with electricity" during an aurora in January 1837. The lady's electrified state, manifested by her ability to give off sparks, lasted until mid-May. Hosford studied the effects of variation in her clothing and mood, atmospheric pressure, humidity, temperature, etc., finding that her greatest "electrical power" was at 80° F. Far from suggesting skepticism, Silliman found "the belief in the facts to be universal, particularly on the part of persons of judgment and science. . . ."

[10] Henry recalled this conversation in a letter to G. P. Fisher after Silliman's death:

In reply to some remarks on an article of less scientific merit than the general stan-

the different departments of science for a journal of the kind. The hint was not however taken & shortely after the name of the Professors son was attached to the Journal.[11] I have the highest personal regard for Professor Silliman and feel much attached to him for his kindness to me and his readiness to give me often much more than my proper share of credit. Still I am now more than ever of your opinion that the real working men in the way of science in this country should make common cause and endeavour by every proper means unitedly to raise our scientific character, to make science more respected at home, to increase the facilities of scientific investigations and the inducements to scientific labours. There is a disposition on the part of our government to advance the cause if this were properly directed. At present however Charlatanism is much more likely to meet with attention and reward than true unpretending merit.

But I fear I will tire you with this long story of ills and proposed remedy and I will now change the subject to that of the British association which you are about to attend. You have seen the report of the last meeting in the Atheneum and found honorable mention of your own name there.[12] My reccollections of the meeting on the whole are plesant. There were however some circumstances which were at the time not very agreable and which I mentioned briefly in my last letter.[13] The principal of these was a slight altercation I had with Dr Lardner relative to the speed of American steam boats. I had resolved to keep myself perfectly cool and not to put myself too much in advance. I concluded, on account of my character at home more than from a desire to show myself at the meeting, to give to the mechanical section a few words on the subject of the internal improvements in the

---

dard of the Journal, Professor Silliman once said to me,—"Could you see what I reject, and the amount of correspondence which such rejection involves, you would not be surprised that I should occasionally suffer an article to appear not strictly in accordance with my own views."

George P. Fisher, *Life of Benjamin Silliman*, 2 vols. (New York, 1866), 2:333.

[11] On the title page of volume 34, July 1838. Benjamin Silliman, Jr. (1816–1885) had only recently graduated from Yale and was assisting his father in his laboratory and lectures. His later career as a chemist and geologist closely paralleled that of his father: as Professor of Chemistry at Yale, as the author of popular scientific textbooks, as a mining consultant, and as editor of *Silliman's Journal*. *DSB. DAB.*

In 1840 Asa Gray began collaborating with the Sillimans on botanical material; see below, Torrey to Henry, January 15, 1840, especially footnote 5.

[12] Bache did not attend the 1837 British Association meeting at Liverpool. As the result of an earlier conversation, however (*Henry Papers*, 3:238), Baden Powell began a communication on heat radiation by referring to Bache's work:

The object of this communication is to call the attention of the Section to the researches of Prof. Bache of Pennsylvania, which seem not to have been so fully appreciated in this country as they deserve.

Athenaeum, 1837, p. 745.

[13] Henry's letter of October 1, 1837 (*Henry Papers*, 3:506–510).

United States and to the Physical section an account of my researches on the lateral discharge. I had been requested by Mr Tanner of Philadelphia to present a map to the society containing all the lines of railways and canals in this country up to 1836. In presenting this map I occupied the time of the section about 6 or 7 minutes on some general remarks relative to the topography of the country, the extent of navigable rivers, canals and railways constructed &c. My remarks were listened to with much attention and received with great applause; but just as I was stepping from the platform a person amoung the audience arose and requested to ask me one question in reference to the speed of American steam boats. He said he wished authentic information. The chair man said the question was not strictly proper and I might answer it or not as I chose. It did not belong to the subject of my communication. I stated that I had no objection to give what Information I possessed on the subject—that I was not a practical engineer, although I had paid some little attention to steam navigation in the United States, that I had lived on the banks of the Hudson and had been in the habit of going up that river in the swift boats, and that I had gone the distance of 150 miles from N York to Albany up the river in the space of 9 hours but that there was a tide in the river of from perhaps 2 to 3 miles an hour at the time which assisted the passage. Dr Lardener then arose and stated that the section did not want popular information of the kind I had given and that he did not believe that a vessel ever passed through the water with the velocity I had stated. The chairman Dr Robinson the astronomer then interfered and made some very severe remarks on the turn the affair had taken and the impropriety of treating a Foreignor who had favoured the Association with a communication in such a manner &c &c. Fortunately I did not get in the least degree excited although the whole room was in a state of commotion. I next made some explanatory remarks and stated that in reference to science I did not consider myself a Foreignor, that truth and science was of no country and that I wished no more courtesey shown my communications than those made by the other members of the association. I next made some statements relative to the length breadth &c of our boats, quantity of fuel burned &c. I then left the room when Mr Russel of Edinburgh the wave man took up the cause and informed the section what I had done for science &c &c. The affair though very unplesant at the time and entirely unprovoked or unlooked for by me ended rather pleasantly than otherwise since during my stay in Liverpool I met constantly with marked attention and many persons introduced themselves to me and expressed their regret that I should have any cause to think that America and Americans were not highly esteemed in England and particularly in Liverpool.

When my paper on electricity was presented at the Physical section the room was much crowded and the communication was receved apparently with much interest.

My opinion however is that it is not in very good taste for a stranger to occupy much of the time of the section and had I not been urged to the affair and supported in it by the example of De La Rive and Leibig the chemist I would have hesitated to offer any thing.[14] I however took good care to make my communication as short as possible, my drawings on the black board previously prepaired and my lesson well covered. I was much pleased at the association to make the acquaintance of Professor Moll of Utrecht. He promised to write me and send a copy of an engraved portrait of himself but I have not yet receved the letter or the article.[15]

Daniel and Faraday were there and on every occasion treated me with marked attention. Faraday was of great importance to me since he made it a point to come to me even through a crowd and introduce me generally to all arround. These introductions I found had more weight than even Mr F. appeared to attach to them. I found it necessary to walk with much circumspection and can easily see how our Friend Dr H. of Philadelphia erred in his intercourse with the science of Great Britain.[16] There is a great prejudice and perhaps in some respect a just one, (from the persons who have visited England) against Americans. They treat us with great kindness and I have no doubt but many of the persons with whom you and myself associated had a real respect for us and were prompted by proper feelings to show us the attention we received but still there was in my case the appearance of a little hesitation in allowing the same merit in public as in private. You may probably remark something of the same kind. It may arise from the in-

---

[14] De La Rive presented two communications to the mathematical and physical science section of the British Association in 1837; Liebig presented one to the chemistry and mineralogy section. Both were, unlike Henry, corresponding members of the Association. *BAAS Report, 1837* (1838), part 2, pp. 10, 27, 38.

Liebig's communication, read by Faraday, was more than politely received. In his concluding remarks, he chided the host country for giving too little attention to organic chemistry. The section responded by asking Liebig to prepare a report on organic chemistry. *Athenaeum,* 1837, p. 748. For the relationship between this assignment and Liebig's *Organic Chemistry in Its Application to Agriculture and Physiology* (1840), see Margaret W. Rossiter, *The Emergence of Agricultural Science: Justus Liebig and the Americans* (New Haven,

1975), p. 27.

[15] Henry was apparently unaware that Moll had died in January. A later notation in his address book (p. [14], Box 17, Henry Papers, Smithsonian Archives) reads:

Promised to send me his picture but he died before the end of the year.

[16] Assuming that the friend is Robert Hare, the exact nature of his errors is unclear. After a long conversation with him in February 1837, Henry reported that Hare "was highly pleased with his reception by Scientific men in England and France but remarked that he had attempted rather too much and thus were he to do the thing again particularly at the association he would bring forward only a few articles and have these well prepaired." *Henry Papers, 3:153.*

fluence of the aristocratical and political Institutions of the country and the general low opinion which is [?enter]tained relative to American science and literature.

I think you will not be much impressed with the scientific character of the British association. There is such a mixture of desplay of ignorance and wisdom—of management in the compliments given and the honors received that the whole makes rather an unfavourable impression on a person admitted a little behind the scenes. I was at first a litle at a loss to know what good was promoted by the meeting. A little reflection however showed me that the principal advantage of the Institution is the ammount of money it gives to real working men for the prosecution of their respective branches.[17] This money is in the hands of the committees and they are wisely composed only of those who have some reputation for science. The great body of the members have no voice in the management of the Institution and in this respect the society is quite as aristocratical as the government of the nation.

This arrangement however I am far from considering improper. On the contrary were it otherwise the *third* and *fourth* rate men would soon controll the affair and render the whole abortive and ridiculous. Much has been said since my return of the propriety of a meeting of the kind among us,[18] but I am convinced a promiscuous assembly of those who call themselves men of science in this country would only end in our disgrace. At the close of the meeting votes of thanks were given in some form or other to almost all the principal men connected with the association. The names of four Foreignors were mentioned namely Moll, De La Rive, Leibig & my own. Also a vote of thanks was given to our Minister Mr Stevenson[19] who rendered himself very popular by a speeach which he made at one of the dinners. I was pleased at this since when he first arrived I feared he would have made himself ridiculous with some remarks he was about to make at the Physical section on the subject of Light. I told him rather plainly that the subject did not belong to his line and that he knew nothing about it. At this he appeared somewhat offended. His speach however made proper amends; he left the association well pleased with himself and with the good opinion of all who heard him.

I informed you that I had visited Sir David Brewster, staid two days with him and was highly delighted with my visit.[20] He gave me a letter to Dr Sprague of Albany which contains some remarks relative to American

---

[17] Henry made similar comments in an October 1837 letter to Charles Coquerel (*Henry Papers*, 3:511–512).

[18] For one such proposal, see John Collins Warren to Henry, September 29, 1838, and Henry's reply of October 16, both printed below.

[19] Andrew Stevenson (*Henry Papers*, 3:212).

[20] See *Henry Papers*, 3:473–483, 490–492.

Science and makes honorable mention of our names. Dr Sprague proposed to me to publish the letter[21] but as I did not know how you would be pleased with the notice I thought it not worth while without some special reason to take this step. I found your Friend Professor Stevely[22] a very fine fellow and I am much indebted to him for his kind attention to me while at the association. We will however be able to form a more proper estimate of the different persons when we come to compare notes.

But to turn to another subject. Do you reccollect the project we had of procuring for this country a set of the Elgin marbles.[23] On my return to England I again spoke to Mr Children on the subject and he gave me the directions how to proceed in the affair, to get some of the most influential persons of Philadelphia to join in an application and if possible to have this backed by the government. On my First visit to Philad[a] after my return I called with Mr Rogers on Mr Biddle, informed him that while we were together in London we had been informed that the marbles could be obtained without much difficulty by a proper application &c. He appeared pleased with the affair and said he would give the matter proper attention. He however appeared to misunderstand the proposition for since it came from you he concluded that the copies were to be obtained for the Gerard College and said that he would place the matter before the board of trustees at the next meeting. I again called on him relative to the same affair but he was then much engaged and said that the gentleman sent to this country by the Bank of England[24] had promised to attend to the subject on his return to England and that he had seen a short time before an account that any person could procure copies by merely paying for the expense of the work.

[21] Not found.

[22] John Stevelly (ca. 1795–ca. 1867) was Professor of Natural Philosophy at the Belfast Royal Academical Institution from 1823 to 1849. A native of Cork, he received a B.A. from Trinity College, Dublin, in 1817. From 1849 until his resignation in 1867, he was Professor of Natural Philosophy at Queen's College, Belfast. Queen's College historians describe him as a "veteran popularizer of science" and a "man of wide learning." The *Royal Society Catalogue* lists nine articles by Stevelly on mathematics and meteorology. Theodore William Moody and J. C. Beckett, *Queen's, Belfast, 1845–1949*, 2 vols. (London, 1959), *1*:117. *Queen's College Calendar, 1882–1883* (Belfast, 1882), p. cxci. John Jamieson, *The History of the Royal Academical Institution, 1810–1960* (Belfast, 1959), pp. 52, 64. George Dames Burtchaell and Thomas Ulick Sadleir, eds., *Alumni Dublinenses: A Register of the Students, Graduates, Professors and Provosts of Trinity College in the University of Dublin (1593–1860)* (Dublin, 1935), p. 780.

At the 1837 British Association meeting, Stevelly was a secretary of the mathematical and physical science section. The *Athenaeum* reports of the meeting record many comments by him, including some on Henry's lateral discharge presentation (*Athenaeum*, 1837, p. 717).

[23] See *Henry Papers, 3*: 530–532.

[24] Two agents of the Bank of England were in Philadelphia to protect the Bank's loan of £6,000,000 to American banks in England by collecting debts owed to the American firms. W. Marston Acres, *The Bank of England from Within, 1694–1900*, 2 vols. (London, 1931), 2:465–466.

Here the affair ended and I have heard nothing more in reference to it. Will it not be well for you to make some further inquiries relative to the expense of procuring, the mode, &c inorder that something may yet be done to procure a set for this country.

While I was in London my Friend Henry James wished to procure something as a present to the Albany Institute. I advised him to get a copy of the Rossetta Stone from the Museum and gave him a letter to Mr Gray[25] with the request that he would assist my Friend to procure the article. The stone was copied, the whole cost was only 5 dollars and the Institute was delighted with the present[26] & the papers from Georgia to Maine proclaimed the generous deed.

Our new house is just finished and we are about to enter it or at least hope to move in a few days. The college is still in a flourishing state. The University of Pennsylvania is also in tolerably good condition. Dr Ludlow[27] I think is increasing in popularity and gradually extending his influence. Your successor[28] appears to be a very kind and worthy man but exceedingly queer in his manner. He is said not to be very successful as an experimenter in the way of Chemistry and Natural Philos before his class. Professor Vethake has lately published a work on political economy. He comes out against the Banking System of the country and is in favour of protecting literary as well as other property.[29] I have heard nothing from Dr Lock since my return except a communication of his in Silliman and another to the American Phil Society on the dip variation &c.[30] Saxton has a good situation in the mint. He spent a few days with me in the Spring at Princeton. We had a very plesant time in experimenting. Professor Daubeny started for Europe on

[25] John Edward Gray (*Henry Papers*, 3:229). We have not found Henry's letter.

[26] The copy of the Rosetta stone from the original in the British Museum is no longer in the Albany Institute.

[27] John R. Ludlow, Provost of the University of Pennsylvania (*Henry Papers*, 1:106n).

[28] Roswell Park (*Henry Papers*, 3:87).

[29] For earlier comments on Vethake's book, see Henry's letter to Thomas Hun of March 5, 1838, above. Vethake considered his attempt to analyze "immaterial or intellectual products" in addition to material property a "*bold innovation*" (p. vii). He did not specifically address the question of international copyright, something which Henry endorsed and which American authors were beginning to advocate. Henry's Library contains a copy of *A Plea for Authors, and the Rights of Literary Property. By an American* (New York, 1838).

The author illustrated how the U.S. copyright laws, which extended protection only to American authors, encouraged the pirating of foreign works; American authors were driven out of the market by the necessarily higher cost of publishing their works.

[30] John Locke's letters to Silliman of January 28 and February 10, 1838, appeared as "Prof. Locke on Magneto-Electricity, and Electro-magnetical Machines," and "Additional Remarks, by Prof. Locke, on Electricity Produced by Motion, and on Motion produced by Magnetic Electricity," *Silliman's Journal*, 1838, 34:125–130, 130–132. "On the Magnetic Dip at Several Places in the State of Ohio, and on the Relative Horizontal Intensities of Cincinnati and London," read to the American Philosophical Society on June 15, 1838, appeared in APS *Transactions*, 1839, n.s. 6:267–273.

the 8th of July. I did not have the pleasure of meeting with him while he was in the country.[31] Dr Torrey is much engaged in preparing a general Flora of the United States. One volume of the work is now in the Press.

The scientific expedition it is said will sail in the course of a few weeks. It is now under the command of Lieut. Wilks. Johnson, Coats[32] and several others have been dismissed in the process of cutting down the number of scientific corps.

You have probably learned by the papers that this summer has been one of the warmest for many years. The thermometer at Princeton has stood at 100° in shade several times. Pixii has treated me in a very shameful manner. I purchased of him a large collection of articles which I paid for in advance. These he promised to send to New York so that they would reach the Custom house about the time I might be expected to arrive. I waited very impatiently for them all winter and have only receved them within about 6 weeks of the present time. When I came to examine the invoice I find that he has still not finished a part of the order & I know not when he will send the remainder. Also when the chemicals bought of Robiquet[33] &c were unpacked there was a deficiency of articles to nearly the amount of 200 Francs. So much for the honesty of the French.

New York Aug 10th 1838

Dear Bache

In order to be sure not to miss the stage I did not go to bed last night. I left home at ½ Past 3 and have just arrived in this city. The ship sails in about an hour. I scribbled nearly all night but have not had time to read what I have written. My best respects to Mrs Bache and your sister.

All your Friends will be rejoiced to see you home again and none more than

Yours as ever
Joseph Henry

P.S. I will direct this letter to the care of Mr Vaughan.[34] I have also written one to him.[35]

My other letter was to Huttenger[36] and Co Bankers Paris.

---

[31] For Daubeny's visit to the United States, see *Henry Papers*, 3:517–518.

[32] Reynell Coates, a Philadelphia physician, was one of the less qualified members of the scientific corps. By his own admission, his appointment as one of the zoologists was due to political influence and not ability. William Stanton, *The Great United States Exploring Expedition of 1838–1842* (Berkeley, 1975), p. 47. W. J. Snape, "Reynell Coates (1802–1886): Politician, Poet, Editor, Naturalist, Lecturer and Physician," *Transactions of the College of Physicians of Philadelphia*, 1968, 35:112–118.

[33] Pierre-Jean Robiquet (1780–1840, *DSB*), a manufacturer and retailer of chemicals as well as a research chemist. Henry had bought supplies for J. R. Chilton.

[34] The letter is addressed to Bache in care of Petty Vaughan.

[35] Not found.

[36] i.e., Hottinguer.

FROM JOHN TORREY

Historic Letter File, Gray Herbarium Library, Harvard University

New York. Aug^t [29][1] 1838.

My dear friend.

Last week in passing up the river in a steamboat I was introduced to President S. E. Dwight,[2] & although I avoided him, yet Col. Stone,[3] who was also in the boat, seemed anxious that I should *argufy* with him about the pretended magnetic discoveries of Dr Sherwood. I, of course, took a stand against Dr S., & on enquiring of the learned President whether he had read a piece in the Princeton Review,[4] he seemed to be much annoyed, & made some severe remarks respecting its author, which I resented warmly. He acknowledged that he had merely glanced over the article, as he was unwell when Dr Sherwood showed it to him. I reproved him for condemning what he had never read—but he said, that he did not possess the work, or something to that effect. I did not enter into any discussion with him, as to Dr. S's claims, partly because I did not understand the subject well enough, & partly because I knew *him* to be *quite* ignorant of it. He made several assertions, (& seemed fully to believe them) as to those discoveries, & I should like to know from you what they really are. If you have an extra copy of your article I should be very glad to see it, for I am unacquainted with any person who takes the Review. Perhaps, if the article is not long, you will get one of the students to copy it for me. By the way President D. seems to have been soured by disappointment, & I think he is an unhappy man.

Dr. Gray has not returned from Michigan. We received a letter from him to-day, & he speaks in the strongest language of the beauty of the country & the enterprise of the Managers of the University. I regret to learn, however, that they have employed Davis[5] as their architect, for I don't entertain a very high opinion of his science. Dr Gray thinks as I do about him. The D^r says, that the plans which they expected from Mr D. had not all arrived, & that the architect thought it best to go on to Michigan & see the grounds himself. Dr G. will probably wait there for him,[6] & then return to New York. He says

---

[1] The postmarked date.

[2] See above, Henry's review of July 1838, footnote 4.

[3] William Leete Stone (1792–1844), journalist and historian (*DAB*). Stone's voluminous writings included at least one on animal magnetism (1837), which may account for his interest in H. H. Sherwood mentioned by Torrey below.

[4] i.e., Henry's attack on the Naval Committee report on the Sherwood memorial, printed above, July 1838.

[5] The architect Alexander Jackson Davis (1803–1892). *DAB*. He designed four state capitols and the Patent Office in Washington.

[6] Gray wanted to keep a close eye on the plans to make sure the faculty received good accommodations. He especially wanted the professors' houses to be comfortable and away from the students. Such accommodations, he felt, would help attract good professors, such as Henry and Torrey. Once he got the campus

that the Council are determined to make one or two prospective appointments in the autumn, & that *you* will be one of them[7]—Keep this close. I will give you more particulars when the D^r returns. Mr. Whipple,[8] an old friend & pupil of mine, who was at West Point when I was stationed there, is one of the chief men in the University & can carry any reasonable plan. He will be in New-York in a week or two, & stop at my house, both on his way to Philadelphia & on his return. It may be well for you to *happen* this way when I give you a hint.

I hope that the account of Sherwood's discovery did not reach the British Association, & thus expose us to ridicule before that noble body. We must do all in our power to put an end to quackery in our land, & every man must feel so jealous of his own particular science as to refute all pretended discoveries.

Did you get the plants for Jaeger? They were not exactly what he asked for, but I sent him some rare species in lieu of those which I have not on hand at present.

I am working at the Flora every day, but have not much [he]art for the labor, when I have to pay all the costs & get scarcely any returns.

My very kind regards to Mrs. Henry & all our good friends at Princeton.

Yours sincerely
John Torrey

Tuesday morning. Dr Gray has just returned from Detroit. He says that a meeting of the Council will be held on the 10th prox. when it is probable that some appropriations will be made for apparatus. They will probably begin with $5000, part of which will be expended for chem^l articles. This money will be for foreign app^s only. Now Dr G. wishes you to sit down & make out a list of articles in your branches, with an estimate of the probable cost of each, to the amount, say, of $3000. I will furnish a catalogue of the

---

plans from Davis, Gray hoped to submit them to Torrey, Henry, and other prospective faculty for suggestions. Jane Loring Gray, ed., *Letters of Asa Gray*, 2 vols. (London, 1893), *1*:77, 82.

[7] Gray used his influence with the administration to secure the best possible faculty appointments especially in scientific fields (see also Gray's letter to Henry below of November 6, 1838). Although Gray was convinced Henry would be approached in the fall and although the Regents of the University considered Henry a top choice for the Natural Philosophy chair, Henry never received an offer. *Proceed-*

ings of the Board of Regents of the University of Michigan, 1837–1864 (Ann Arbor, 1915), pp. 37–38. Jane Loring Gray, op. cit., p. 78.

[8] Charles W. Whipple (1806–1855), a prominent Michigan politician, served in the state legislature and on Michigan's Supreme Court. Charles Lanman, *The Red Book of Michigan, a Civil, Military and Biographical History* (Detroit, 1871), p. 497. *Detroit Daily Free Press*, October 26, 1855. Secretary of the University's Board of Regents, Whipple was described by Gray as "the moving spirit of the whole." Jane Loring Gray, op. cit., p. 76.

chemicals. He wishes to send the statements immediately to the Board. Get all ready by Friday, when the Doctor will make you a visit.

Yours J.T.

Make out also a list of books in Natural Philosophy![9]

[9] We are unaware of the existence of any lists by Henry.

FROM E. R. TREMAIN[1]
Henry Papers, Smithsonian Archives

Clinton Hall
New York Sept 1st 1838

Sir

I am directed by the Board of Directors of the Mercantile Library Association[2] of this city to extend to you an invitation to deliver a course of Two or Four Lectures on Electro Magnetism,[3] at any period during the approaching winter, when it may suit your convenience.

You are, without doubt, well aware of the existence and object of the Ass[n] in behalf of which this request is made, and I will only add, that by acceding to the request you will confer a benefit upon the Institution, which would be duly appreciated by its numerous members.

With sentiments of the highest respect I am sir,

Very respectfully
Your obt sert
E R. Tremain Chairman
Lec. Com[e] of M. L. A.

[1] Edwin R. Tremain was a hide and leather dealer at the time of his correspondence with Henry. During the next decade his success in business enabled him to expand his operation, move to more fashionable addresses, and eventually establish himself as a broker on Wall Street. New York City Directories, 1839–1851.
[2] Discussed in some detail in *Henry Papers*, 2:471.
[3] Henry accepted the invitation. He delivered four lectures on electricity and magnetism, plus an additional two on sound, during January and February of 1839. Henry's motivations for accepting, the negotiations with the Mercantile Library Association, and Henry's perception of the audiences' response are documented below in his correspondence between October 1838 and the end of February 1839.

TO [PETER BULLIONS][1]
Retained Copy, Henry Papers, Smithsonian Archives

Princeton Sept 4th 1838

My Dear Sir

I have just received a letter[2] from James Furguson.[3] He states that you showed him my article on the Sherwood descovery[4] and requests that if the article be again published that a note be added to inform the public that James Furguson of the Coast Survey is not the author of the communication appended to the Report on the magnetic discoveries of Dr Sherwood.[5]

If you should think fit to have the paper republished in Albany please append a note of the above import.[6]

Margaret[7] started on Saturday morning at about 8 o'clock in company with the Ladies who had offered to take charge of her.

She would be taken to their house and there kept until a proper opportunity ocurred for sending her to Washington. This was the promis of Miss McCullow[8] and I have no doubt but it would be kept. Nothing new since you left. I have or rather Nancy has receved a letter from Albany in answer to those you carried.[9] Dr Gray came on to Princeton on Saturday and was very urgent relative to the Michigan affair. They have made an appropriation for apparatus and the Dr is about to proceed to England to make the purchase.

[1] Although the copy does not indicate the recipient, internal evidence, especially in light of Henry's letter to James Henry of September 11–13, 1838 (printed below), points to Bullions (*Henry Papers, 1*:129), an old friend of Henry's.

[2] Not found.

[3] James Ferguson (1797–1867), at this time the second ranking member of the Coast Survey. *Henry Papers, 2*:16–17.

[4] For Henry Hall Sherwood's theory of magnetism and Henry's response to it, see above, Henry's review of July 1838, and Henry to Bache, August 9, 1838.

[5] Appended to the Committee Report on Sherwood's theory was a letter to Senator Nathaniel P. Tallmadge, dated June 21, 1838, written in Washington, D.C. The writer, one "James Ferguson," summed up Sherwood's theory and advised further investigation, but did not actually endorse the theory. We have no idea whether Ferguson was a pseudonym or simply a coincidence that Sherwood was exploiting. He doesn't appear in contemporary Washington, D.C., city directories.

[6] When Henry's review of Sherwood's theory was reprinted in the September 6, 1838, issue of the *Albany Evening Journal*, a footnote was added as requested by Ferguson.

[7] Bullions.

[8] Perhaps Mary L. McCulloch (b. 1821), who resided near Baltimore. She was the sister of Richard Sears McCulloh, a former student of Henry's. Alice N. Parran, *Series II of "Register of Maryland's Heraldic Families": Tercentenary of the Founding of Maryland* (Baltimore, 1938), pp. 238–239.

[9] Not found.

TO JAMES HENRY

Family Correspondence, Henry Papers, Smithsonian Archives

Princeton Sept [11–13][1] 1838

Dear James

Your two letters,[2] since our communications by Mr Bullions, have been received. We are much rejoiced to hear that Caroline has got safely through the difficulties of that situation so common and yet so much to be dreded. We must congratulate you on the arrival of the Little Lady.[3] Long may she live to be a pleasure to your manhood—a stay and comfort to your declining days.

John Platt will, after a time, have a powerful rival in your affections. Girls do not make quite so great an impression at first but they steal on by degrees until they get full possession.

I have some idea of making a short visit to albany soon after our commencement and will endeavour to prevail on Harriet to go with me. I know not however whether I will succeed. We are just about to move and hope to get into the new house in the course of the present week. James Meads[4] leaves for Albany on Friday. I may therfore defer sending this letter until he goes.

I was not much pleased with the well intended compliment of Friend Weed—first because I did not wish my name mentioned in connection with the Sherwood article and secondly because I do not like in any way to be counted with the Political slang of the day. I am however convinced, that although the article was not in good taste, yet it was well ment.[5]

Nancy will go to Albany with me. She was much grieved after the de-

---

[1] Henry dated this letter September 11 but finished it on Thursday, September 13.

[2] Not found.

[3] Harriet Henry, the first daughter born to Caroline and James Henry. Caroline Morrow Henry had two daughters from a previous marriage.

[4] James Meads (1820–1850), son of John and Louisa Crane Meads of Albany, attended the Albany Academy from 1829 to April 1838. He was later a clerk with the Albany Waterworks Company. Hun, "Albany Academy." *Howell and Tenney*, p. 640.

[5] Thurlow Weed, the Whig editor of the *Albany Evening Journal*, reprinted Henry's anonymous review of the Naval Committee's report on H. H. Sherwood's memorial from the *Biblical Repertory and Princeton Review* in the issue of September 6, 1838. On the same page he identified Henry as the author:

The article which we publish to-day, exploding Dr. Sherwood's Magnetic theory, is from the pen of Professor HENRY, of Princeton College, whose name is reputably associated with much that brightens the Literary and Scientific character of our Country. Professor HENRY is an Albanian, and though originally belonging to that class of citizens whom the Globe stigmatizes as "*Coblers and tinkers*"—having served a regular apprenticeship as a Silver-smith—he has attained an elevation which enables him to look down upon the highest Demagogue in the Palaces of Loco Focoism.

When the *Newark Daily Advertiser* reprinted Henry's review on August 15, 1838 (p. 2), it identified the author only as a "high authority on this subject."

parture of Mr Bullions that she had not gone with him. She thinks you are offended with her on account of her staying so long in Princeton particularly at this time and she feels very unplesant about the affair. I hope the illness of Caroline is in no way serious and that she will soon be about again. Stephen is making great preparations to observe with due precision the elipse of the sun which takes place next week.[6] He has been several days engaged in erecting a small observatory in his yard. The eclipse is to be annular at Princeton and will on this account present an interesting appearance.

Thursday Evening We had a tremendous rain last night and yesterday. It commenced raining and blowing yesterday morning very early, continued all day and night until this morning.

Thursday Evening. James Meads starts tomorrow. I send by him several books some of which I wish to be half bound others full bound. I will probably bring with me some others but wish those I now send to be finished as soon as convenient. Let great care be taken with the plates so that they may readily fold into place and not readily get out of order. The sample I send was bound in the shop of Hoffman & White.

We commenced to move to day and expect to get through by tomorrow night. Since Caroline may stand much in need of the assistance of Nancy she thought of starting with James Meads but he goes tomorrow while she was under the impression that he intended to stop until Monday. I[t] will be impossible to get her articles in order to go in the morning as we are all in confusion. Write immediately as we will be anxious to hear how Caroline is getting on.

[6] See Henry to Vaughan of October 13, 1838, printed below.

TO THOMAS THOMSON

Mary Henry Copy, Henry Papers, Smithsonian Archives

Princeton College September 28th. [1838]
My dear Sir. I embrace the opportunity of sending a small parcel.[1] The articles may not be of much interest to you yet I hope it will serve in some respects to express my remembrance of the kindness and attention I received from you in Glasgow.[2] I was highly gratified with my visit to Europe and

[1] The parcel may have contained publications.

[2] See *Henry Papers*, 3:493, 507, for Henry's meeting with the chemist Thomson.

particularly so with my intercourse with the men of science in England and Scotland. I have returned to America with views more expanded and opinions somewhat modified as well in reference to Government as in science and literature.

The successful experiment of Atlantic steam navigation will I hope have a favorable effect on the intelligence of our country and we will not now be so remote a province of Great Britain in reference to literature and science as we have been. . . I have just received a letter from my friend Professor Bache,[3] who visited you about two years since, announcing his safe arrival in the Great Western.[4] . . . Permit me to assure you that with respect and esteem I am Yours Sincerely

Joseph Henry.[5]

[3] Not found.
[4] Bache left Bristol on September 8 and arrived in New York on September 24. *The New York American*, September 25, 1838.
[5] Mary Henry's transcription includes the following additional material after the signature which may or may not have been in the original letter:

What a change in one year, we have been brought within one half the distance from Europe. The average passage this way has been thirty-three days by the liners, we may now consider the average at fifteen days. The news of the coronation of George the Third reached New York in eighty-three days, an ordinary voyage in that time. The account of the coronation of your present sovereign in fourteen days.

FROM B. SMITH[1]
Henry Papers, Smithsonian Archives

Albany 28. Sept 1838

Sir

You will excuse me—a stranger personally—for troubling you with an inquiry upon the subject of *magnetism* as I understand it is interesting to you.

I want to know if there exists a substance or combination of substances in nature that will intercept or obstruct the attraction of the magnet, so that by placing it between the magnet and the metal to be attracted the magnet will have no force upon the metal through it.[2]

Sir I know you only by reputation as a student and a scholar and one who

[1] Probably Bartholomew Smith, owner of a flour and seed store in Albany. Albany City Directories.
[2] Smith held two patents for agricultural devices, both issued before 1838. *Burke's Index*, pp. 24, 312. However, we do not know the reason for his interest in magnetic screening, nor has Henry's reply been found.

has given much attention to the subject of magnetism. And being recommended to you particularly by Mᵣ M. McPherson[3] of this city I solicit your reply to this inquiry as a favour that will be most gratefully received.

I am
Sir
Yours assuredly
B Smith 449. S. M. St

[3] Murdow McPherson, an Albany printer. *Henry Papers, 1:*103.

FROM JOHN C. WARREN[1]
Henry Papers, Smithsonian Archives

Boston. Sept. 29. 1838.

My dear Sir,

Professor Faraday charged me with the eleventh, twelfth, and thirteenth series of his Experimental Researches for you. Not having found a way of sending them safely, I write to ask that you would inform me what mode of conveyance will be agreable to you.[2]

Since my return I have conferred with gentlemen here on the subject of establishing an Association for the promotion of Science.[3] The plan has

[1] John Collins Warren (1778–1856) graduated from Harvard in 1797, then went on to study medicine in London, Edinburgh, and Paris. He became Adjunct Professor of Anatomy and Surgery at Harvard in 1809. Promoted to Professor in 1815, he remained in that position until 1847. Contemporaries thought him an outstanding surgeon; he was also famous for his demonstration of ether anesthesia. His scientific interests included geology and paleontology.

In June 1837 Warren went to Europe on what was primarily a pleasure trip, although he did meet with members of the European medical and scientific communities and attended scientific meetings, including the 1837 meeting of the British Association, where he gave a paper and met his fellow American, Joseph Henry. Warren returned to America in July 1838, highly impressed by the role of scientific associations in European science.

Edward Warren, *Life of John Collins Warren, M.D., Compiled Chiefly from His Autobiography and Journals,* 2 vols. (Boston, 1860); *DAB.*

[2] Henry's reply of October 16, 1838, is printed below.

[3] On September 15, 1838, Warren met with Joseph Story (1779–1845, *DAB*), an Associate Justice of the Supreme Court and Professor of Law at Harvard, and Edward Everett (1794–1865, *DAB*), Governor of Massachusetts, both fellow members of the American Academy of Arts and Sciences, to discuss the idea of founding an American equivalent of the British Association for the Advancement of Science. This meeting was followed by a more general meeting attended by some of the leading intellectual figures of Boston, Salem, and Cambridge. One of the decisions reached was to ask the American Philosophical Society to organize the association. Although the initial, informal response from the APS was positive, the final formal decision rejected the idea. Combined with the attitudes of such men as Henry and Torrey, who felt that such an organization would be taken over by charlatans because of the few competent scientists available in the United States, and was therefore premature, the rejection by the APS ended

been most favorably received and will probably be accomplished. We thought the most judicious and *safe* way of proceeding was to invite the gentlemen of the American Philosophical Society to undertake the organization. My son[4] is now in Philadelphia to try their feeling. If they decline we shall adopt other measures.

Your co-operation by every means in your power will be of the greatest importance;[5] and I wish you could send us any suggestions that may occur to you.

Accept the salutation of yours, with much esteem,

J. C. Warren

Warren's hopes of establishing the American Institution for the Cultivation of Science.

Warren, *Life of John Collins Warren, 1*: 340; Sally G. Kohlstedt, *The Formation of the American Scientific Community: The American Association for the Advancement of Science, 1848–1860* (Urbana, 1976), pp. 48–54; John Collins Warren, printed circular letter, November 1, 1838, Henry Papers, Smithsonian Archives; Henry to Torrey, November 7, 1838; Torrey to Henry, November 9, 1838 (both printed below).

[4] Jonathan Mason Warren (1811–1867) studied medicine at Harvard, then spent three years of further study in Europe. Upon his return in 1835 he embarked on a career as a surgeon. Although respected for his skills, he did not have the reputation of his father. *Proceedings of the American Academy of Arts and Sciences*, 1868–1873, *8*:15–18.

[5] This letter was not part of a mass mailing, but one of a very select number of letters written to generate support for an American scientific association. Warren's journal (Massachusetts Historical Society) mentions only three personal letters written for this purpose: this one to Henry; one to William E. Horner, a medical man very active in the American Philosophical Society, written on September 21; and one to Benjamin Silliman, Sr., dated September 29. With minor variations, the Silliman letter (now in the Silliman Family Papers, Sterling Library, Yale University) is the same as the letter to Henry of the same date.

TO MICHAEL FARADAY

Faraday Papers, Institution of Electrical Engineers, London[1]

Princeton, College of New-Jersey
Oct 9th 1838

My Dear Sir

This letter will be delivered, to you, by my Friend and former Pupil, Mr Henry James of Albany. Under ordinary circumstances, I would hesitate to give almost any person an introduction to you, knowing how much you are occupied, and how arduous your duties are, but Mr James has some peculiar motives for wishing your acquaintance.[2] Of these however I am but

[1] Previously published in L. Pearce Williams, ed., *The Selected Correspondence of Michael Faraday*, 2 vols. (Cambridge, England, 1971), *1*:319–320. A retained copy is in the Henry Papers, Smithsonian Archives.

[2] Probably to discuss Sandemanianism. Biographers of Henry James, Sr., contend that James became acquainted with the ideas of the

partially informed and must therefore refer you to himself for an exposition of them.

You will find him an intillgent and interesting young gentleman. He is highly esteemed in this country, and belongs to one of our most wealthy and respectable Families. I am deeply interested in his welfare and am principally indebted to his kind attention, to my affairs, for the pleasure and the profit of my late visit to your hospitable shore. Permit me to request as an additional favour to myself that you will give him your candid and free advise and direction relative to the objects for which he seeks your acquaintance. Mr James has devoted himself more to moral and literary subjects than to science and will therefore want one community of feeling with you; you will however find in him qualities of head and heart sufficient to make ample amends for this.

He is aware how much your time is occupied and will not therefore tresspass too much on your engagements.

Give my kind regards to your estimable wife and permit me to assure her and you that I shall always retain a lively reccollection of the pleasures of my visits to the Royal Institution.

I left your country with warm feelings highly gratified with the kindness I had received, and with the unreserve and liberality with which I was instructed in various branches of science.

I had a pleasant and what was then called a quick passage of 26 days across the atlantic.[3] Nothing very unusual occured although we had one death in the cabin and was on one night in considerable danger from a violent thunder storm. Every spar and mast for a time was tipped with an electrical brush.[4] The ship was not furnished with a conductor—fortunately however we escaped unscathed.

Since my return my time has been much occupied in making up the leaway of a long absence. I have however devoted some time to some new elec-

---

Scottish theologian Robert Sandeman through Michael Faraday. Evidence suggests, however, that James was already a Sandemanian when he met Faraday. *Newark Daily Advertiser*, September 1, 1845, p. 2, columns 5–6. John Hall, ed., *Forty Years' Familiar Letters of James W. Alexander*, 2 vols. (New York, 1860), *1*:273. Giles Gunn, ed., *Henry James, Senior: A Selection of His Writings* (Chicago, 1974), p. 18. Frederic Harold Young, *The Philosophy of Henry James, Sr.* (New York, 1951), pp. 4, 27, 309. Austin Warren, *The Elder Henry James* (New York, 1970), pp. 32–33. Faraday's involvement with Sandemanianism is discussed in L. Pearce Williams, *Michael Faraday* (New York, 1965), pp. 2–6, 102–106.

[3] The inauguration of regular transatlantic steamship service in April 1838 had dramatically reduced the time necessary to travel between Europe and the United States. See above, Henry to Robinson, April 28, 1838, footnote 3. Henry's pre-steam era crossing, in October 1837, is described in *Henry Papers, 3*.

[4] Henry is describing the phenomenon known as St. Elmo's Fire, which was often observed during storms at sea. *Henry Papers*, 3:515, footnote 8.

trical investigations and hope soon to be able to send you a copy of a paper on the subject.[5]

I am very anxious to receve a copy of your late papers and hope soon according to your promis that they will be forth coming. Your investigations are of a very extraordinary character. They tend to unsettle what was considered some of the best established laws of statical electricity and were the investigations not from yourself I would be inclined to be some what sceptical in reference to their accuracy.[6] Our theories however well they may agree with present knowledge are only expressions for approximate truth and it is only those new facts not immediately referable to them that promise a rich harvest of new developement.

My Friend Professor Bache arrived safely in the Great Western about a week since. I hastened to New York to meet him but we unfortunately missed each other. I hope to see him within a few days and to hear a long account of all his adventures since we parted in Paris. Give my respects to Prof. Daniel. I intend to write to him in a short time.[7] I regret that I did not meet with him immediately before my departure from London. Now that steam has become triumphant we may perhaps hope to see him or some of his Family on this side of the Atlantic. It would give me much pleasure to have an opportunity of reciprocrating some of the kindness I received from him.

The account of the meeting of the British association has just been received but I have not yet given it an attentive perusal. I have not met with your name on the list and suppose that you were not present.[8]

With Respect and Esteem
I am most sincerely yours &c
Joseph Henry

[5] A reprint of Henry's "Contributions III: Electro-Dynamic Induction," bearing the inscription "To Dr. Faraday with the Respects of his Friend the Author," is in the Faraday Papers, Institution of Electrical Engineers, London.

[6] Unknown to Henry, Faraday had already entrusted John C. Warren with copies of the Eleventh, Twelfth and Thirteenth Series of *Experimental Researches in Electricity* for forwarding to Henry. Henry would receive them within the month. The Eleventh Series, read to the Royal Society in December 1837, was Faraday's great paper on electrostatic action, in which he applied the theory of the electrotonic state to electrostatics and ruled out electrical action at a distance. See L. P. Williams, *Michael Faraday* (New York, 1965), pp. 283–299. Faraday was undoubtedly developing these concepts when Henry visited him in the spring and summer of 1837. Apparently the theory was generally discussed, but Henry's diary of his meetings with Faraday (in *Henry Papers, 3*) is silent on the issue. In fact, Henry's brief comment on electrostatics in this letter is one of his few explicit references to Faraday's revolutionary theory. One suspects that Henry's skepticism was greater than he admitted to Faraday.

[7] We have been unable to find any such letter.

[8] The eighth annual meeting of the British Association for the Advancement of Science was held at Newcastle in August 1838. Faraday was only an occasional participant at these meetings, and in general did not take a leading role in the affairs of the Association. L. P. Williams, *Michael Faraday*, pp. 355–356.

October 13, 1838

TO JAMES HENRY

Family Correspondence, Henry Papers, Smithsonian Archives

{ Princeton Oct 13th 1838
{ Saturday evening

Dear James

We arrived safely at home on friday at about ½ past one o'clock after a somewhat pleasant passage.

Harriet stole in upon me on Friday morning while I was in the act of puting on my jacket. She gave me the first intelligence of the illness of little Helen. We came home with considerable anxiety but found the little one much better than we expected; she is not however entirely recovered, but is now in no danger. The ship Wellington did not sail until friday morning. She took with her no less than 6 Albanians namely Henry James, John James, Edward James and Robert do.[1] Also Joel Rathbone and his wife.[2] The gentleman last named goes out for his health. Harriet has got well. She was however very much fatigued before we reached home. On the steam boat she found a number of acquaintances namely Mrs. Governor Yates and her daughter & Mrs. Van Antwerp (Jane Yates that was).[3]

She found me at Mr Irelands[4] No 3 Jay Street. We called at McMullen's. Lucinda[5] has promised to come to see us at New Year. The Pears are locked up, as something very precious, and not to be touched until ripe and not then but on especial occasions. We have been making a great outlay in the way of Olmsted's stoves.[6] We have been obliged to purchase no less than 3, one for the Hall, one for the Parlor and a third for the study. The pictures came safely, and make quite an addition to the ornaments of the front parlor. Helle asked where Aunty was when her mother returned. She now looks very pale and requires constant attendance. Aunt has visited Stephen's house, to day, inorder to see that no person had removed it and also to feed

[1] Henry James, Sr., his younger brothers John Barber James (1816–1856) and Edward James (1817 or 1818–1856), and his nephew Robert W. James (1821 or 1822–1875), who were students at the Albany Academy during Henry's tenure there. Hun, "Albany Academy."

[2] Joel Rathbone (1806–1863) ran a successful wholesale stove business in Albany. His wife was Emeline Weld Munn (1810–1874). Albert Rathbone, *Samuel Rathbone and Lydia Sparhawk, His Wife, A Record of their Descendants and Notes Regarding Their Ancestors* (privately printed, 1937), pp. 61–62.

[3] Ann Elisabeth DeLancey Yates (d. 1864), third wife and widow of New York Governor Joseph C. Yates; her daughters Ann Alida Yates (b. 1806) and Jane Josepha Van Antwerp (b. 1811, married to Tunis Van Antwerp). *Contributions for the Genealogies of the Descendants of the First Settlers of the Patent and City of Schenectady from 1662–1880* (Baltimore, 1976), p. 301; *New York Genealogical and Biographical Record*, July 1948, 79:162.

[4] *Henry Papers*, 2:250.

[5] For John and Lucinda McMullen, see *Henry Papers*, 2:6n–7n.

[6] Probably the anthracite coal stove patented by Denison Olmsted in 1834. Olmsted claimed a new method for distributing the heat by means of a "radiator." *Franklin Institute Journal*, 1835, 15:407–409.

the cat. It is a pity to send a blank space in a sheet of paper when the postage is so high and therefore I must put something in my letter if it be not of very great importance. John McMullen received a letter from James Henry Selkirk of Texas[7] the day I called. The gentleman was well, and doing well. He had built a house for which he had been offered 17 hundred dollars. It is doubtful if he will recover his Fathers property.

Frank sailed on Friday, a week ago yesterday; he had made his wife believe that we had used him very badly.[8] It has been quite cold to day and should the wind fall to night we will probably have a frost that will stop the further growth of potatoes. There is a prospect of a large addition to the numbers of students at the commencement of the next term. The blow-up at the New York University will give us a few. There is a talk in New York that Columbia College will purchase the University building and sell its own great establishment.[9] Of the result of the election I can give you as yet but little news. It is supposed that the state has gone for the Whigs by a small Majority.

Harriet sends love to all your family individually and collectively. You must kiss Johnny Platt and Litle Puss for her.

I will write Stephen in a few days relative to Butter Potatoes &c &c. You need not inform his wife that her husband was seen gallanting a Lady in the streets of New York. It is possible that the gentleman had some very urgent reasons for coming down the river. Of this I do not wish to say too much.

[7] Henry's cousin, probably one of the sons of his Aunt Elizabeth Henry Selkirk and James Selkirk. At least part of that family moved to Texas.

[8] Dr. Francis N. Selkirk, *Henry Papers*, 2:8.

The problem may again concern the doctor's medical fees (see *Henry Papers*, 2:432).

[9] See *Henry Papers*, 2:115, 155. The rumor about the Columbia campus never came to pass.

TO JOHN VAUGHAN

Archives, American Philosophical Society

Princeton Oct 13th 1838

My Dear Sir

Your letter of the 2nd has been just received.[1] I have been absent on a visit to the North for two weeks and have just returned. I purpose visiting you in a few days and will take with me a list of the volumes of the transactions

[1] Not found.

wanting to complete our list. I have spoken to day with the vice President[2] on the importance of completing our set of the work and he has agreed to make the purchase.

My Brotherinlaw Mr Alexander and myself observed the eclipse. He attended to the astronomical part and I watched the Physical Phenomena. An account of the whole will be given to the Society as soon as possible after the return of Mr A from Albany where he has now gone on a visit to his Friends.[3]

I am glad you have commenced the journal you mention it will be of great importance in the way of securing priority.[4] I am now just commencing to review all my experiments on Electricity previous to the preparation of a paper for the Society. I devoted all of last vacation to the subject but did not get quite finished before the beginning of the college term—during the whole of the college course I have been so much occupied that I found it impossible to attend to anything but the making up the lee-way of my long absenc.

The rail road to Philadelphia through this place[5] is expected to be completed this Autum and if so I will then be able to take a more active part in the duties of the Society and will make it a point to attend almost every meeting of business.

I was yesterday in New York and embraced the opportunity of a Friend's[6] going to London to send your Brother a small package.

Yours with the highest
Respect &c.
Joseph Henry

---

[2] John Maclean.

[3] An APS committee consisting of R. M. Patterson, S. C. Walker, R. T. Paine, and Andrew Talcott was collecting observations on the annular solar eclipse of September 18, 1838. The Princeton observations were presented at the meeting of November 2, 1838 (*Proceedings*, 1838–1840, *1*:50–51).

Henry observed with a Dollond telescope fitted with a dark red screen glass while Alexander used an optically-superior Fraunhofer equipped with a yellow-green screen. Their most interesting observation was of an arch and then brush of light between the cusps. The Dollond telescope picked this up before and with far greater articulation than the Fraunhofer. Alexander speculated that this must be due to the nature of the rays of the arch and brush, which were better transmitted by the red screen. Alexander later added that this "seems to furnish evidence of the existence of a lunar atmosphere, through which, as through our own, the red rays have the greatest penetrative power." (Ibid., *1*:65).

[4] Sometime after June 15, 1838, the Society began publishing its *Proceedings* at three-month intervals, starting with January–March 1838 as number 1.

[5] A branch of the Camden and Amboy Railroad from Trenton to New Brunswick. Wheaton J. Lane, *From Indian Trail to Iron Horse: Travel and Transportation in New Jersey, 1620–1860* (Princeton, 1939), p. 291.

[6] Henry James, Sr.

TO JOHN C. WARREN
Retained Copy, Henry Papers, Smithsonian Archives

Princeton Oct 16th 1838

My Dear Sir

I have been absent from Princeton for two weeks past on a visit to my Friends in Albany and have therefore but just received your favour of the 29th ult.[1] I intend devoting the remainder of the present college vacation to the review and extension of a series of experiments on electrical Induction which I commenced last spring vacation and I am very anxious to see Mr Faradays late papers on the same subject previous to the publication of my memoir. You will therefore much oblige me by sending the articles by mail as soon as convenient.

I am deeply interested in the cause of American science and will most cheerfully co-operate in any plan which may serve to advance it.

After your suggestion to me at Liverpool[2] of the importance of the formation of a similar association in this country I gave the subject considerable thought and came to the conclusion that a meeting of the real cultivators of science in the United States would be of great importance but that the plan of the British association would require some modification in order to suit it to the wants and the character of our country. I will write to you in detail on this subject when I have more leisure.[3] In the mean time accept my thanks for your kind communication and permit me to assure you that I am with much respect & esteem

Yours &c
Joseph Henry

[1] Printed above.
[2] At the British Association meeting of 1837.
[3] We have not located such a letter.

"RECORD OF EXPERIMENTS"

Henry Papers, Smithsonian Archives

Oct 16th 1838

Arranged two coiles one from the thick wire 50 feet long. Other cotton covered long wire each coil about 4 feet diameter the one of the small wire a little [? larger] perhaps 4½ feet.[1]

Passed shock through the large wire coil several times in succession with the coils at different distances from 2 or 3 inches to 15 inches in all cases current   *adverse*[2]

When the circuit of the screening coil was closed by the hands the discharge through the other by induction gave no shock.

2nd Passed the charge through the small long wire now the magnetism of the needle was more intense and still

adverse

3rd Sent charge through the long thin coil received from the thick wire spiral at *a* current

adverse

4th Next added another long piece of wire so as to make a break for the spiral at *b* current still tolerably strong

adverse

Ex 5th (Same figure as the last). Opened the long wires at *a* spiral at *b* no magnetism. In this exp care *was taken to put the needle* in the *spiral after the battery was charged* as I descovered that in charging the battery sparkes were given off by induction from the outer coating which passing through the air to the receiving coil might magnetize the needle and in some of the previous experiments have vitiated the results. Repeated the same with the same effect[3]

Repeated the same with a small charge same effect no magnetism

Exp 6 Shut the circuit at *a* now needle magnetic as at first magnetism

adverse

---

[1] A continuation of the experiments of August 4, 1838.

[2] According to Henry's marginal annotation, four Leyden jars were used in these experiments.

[3] A marginal annotation states that four jars were used, the needle was "strongly magnetized," and the charge was "sent through the thin wire."

NB In these experiments the conductor from the machine did not come in contact with the knob of the jars.

Exp 7th opened the coil at *b*; same figure helix as before. No magnetism.

It appears therefore from these experiments with two coils that the results are always definite and the current adverse.

NB (The long wire made 13 turns the thick wire 4 turns) It must be recollected that in these experiments care was taken to guard against the effect of free electricity by putting the end of the conductor which led from the machine at the distance of an inch from the knob of the battery. It would be charged by sparkes and thus there be but a small excess of electricity on the one side or that there might be but little free electricity in the discharge which might interfere with the result. Besides in these experiments the spirals were insulated which might *also* tend to give more constant results

I should have before mentioned that the magnetism was generally the stronger when the battery charge was sent through the long wires and the resulting action received by the shorter one.

Exp 8th Took down the large thick wire spiral and suspended in the centre of the long cotton wire spiral the helix of ribbon No. 2. Sent charge through long wire received the action on ribbon coil in centre. Magnetism feeble but

adverse

4 jars as before
    Repeated the same magnetism feeble

but adverse

Exp 9 Placed the flat helix near the side of the coil magnetism stronger

still adverse

With smaller shock magnetism about the same and

adverse

Reversed the coil; mag reversed

Ex 10th The same arrangement as before except that the smaller coil was now placed with its plane at right angles to the plane of the larger one now no magnetism appeared.

Exp 11th Substituted again for the ribbon the large circle of thick wire which was used in the 1st &c exp of to day magnetism strong   current still *adverse*

    The magnetizing spiral was placed in the above experiment in the middle. To eliminate every cause of action on account of the ends of the wire the coil was turned around the vertical axis. The effect was still the same namely the current

adverse

Exp 12th Placed inside of the long coil used before a single circle of wire open at [a] for the insertion of the helix. The magnetism in this case was tolerably strong.   current *adverse*

    Reversed the inner ring, so that the side which in the last exp was turned to the east is now turned to the west

very strong adverse

When the discharge was made a spark was seen to pass between the knob of the battery and the near end of the conductor. Thinking that possibly the free electricity thus communicated might have some effect the battery was removed beyond the striking distance but the result was still the same.

magnetism strong

current adverse[4]

Next arranged two single rings of covered wire, each about or nearly 4 feet in diameter.

With a small charge the magnetism was tolerably strong and in the direct direction

direct

With a large charge the current was in the same direction but very feeble

Again with a strong charge magnetism the same but very feeble

direct

Again with a small discharge the magnetism was strong and

adverse

Possibly the elect did not make the whole circuit and went back small distance as ther was a [? tail piec] to the wire

---

[4] In an annotation dated September 24, 1840, Henry wrote: "This experiment is a little at variance with my supposition that a single wire gives a direct current. The descrepancy however may be due to the kind of magnetiz–[ing] spiral used." On that date Henry had discovered that the parameters of the spiral could influence the readings of the direction of the induced current (see the "Record of Experiments" entry of that date, printed below).

Again with small charge

adverse

Again with small charge

direct

With large charge

direct

NB appeared to touch
Small charge

direct

It would appear from the exp of today that in all cases with a double circuit the current is *adverse* but with a single wire as the conductor of the discharge the induced current at the same distance is direct

It is possible that the cutting across may have some influence on the last results since the wires were seperated by corks. To test this properly it will be necessary to pass the wire carrying the discharge through glass tubes[5]
{ Try the effect of a single wire for the discharge and a compound one for the induction

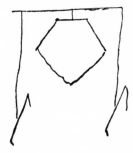

[5] Which Henry did in the experiments of the following day.

"RECORD OF EXPERIMENTS"
Henry Papers, Smithsonian Archives

Oct 17th 1838

Made a pentagon of glass tubes enclosing a copper wire also another set of tubes enclosing a wire for receiving the induction.

Exp 1st Passed charge from 4 jars through the conductor the spiral placed at a, needle strongly magnetic

current *direct*

In this experiment there could be nothing like cutting across of the electricity

In charge the battery with the long conductor the end of the same happened to be coated with lime accidentally put on in the white-washing of the room. When the spark passed through the white-wash the light was of a beautiful crimson [. . . gh][1] about ¼ of the length of the spark. Make experiments on this with the large conductor and different substances put on[2]

Exp 2ⁿᵈ Sent very feeble charge through conductor. With the 4 jars[3]
      Magnetism feeble

                          current still *direct*

Exp 3ʳᵈ Small charge with 9 jars
      needle strongly magnetic

                          current *direct*

Exp 4th Strong charge
      current strong

                          mag[4] *adverse*

9 jars Small charge

                          direct

9 Jars Large charge elect 60°

                          direct

9 Jars Large charge elect 64°
      Magnet feeble, tolerably

                          adverse

9 Jars Charge elect 50°
      mag strong, current

                          direct

4 Jars elect 64°
      mag strong

                          current *direct*

      Same continued

---

[1] One word partially obliterated.

[2] We are unable to uncover evidence of any systematic follow-up of this accidental observation by Henry.

[3] In a marginal notation dated September 24, 1840, Henry wrote: "I regret that in these experiments I have not mentioned the kind of magnetizing spiral which was used since probably some of the changes were induced by this." This is a reference to Henry's discovery of September 24, 1840, that the direction of an induced current as indicated by a magnetizing spiral would vary according to the distance between the spirals. Without knowing the specific spiral in use, Henry was unable in retrospect to know whether changes in direction of the induced current were real. See Henry's "Record of Experiments" entry of September 24, 1840, printed below.

[4] In taking down the results of this experiment, Henry switched the data; for current, read magnetism, and vice versa.

9 jars elect 62°
> mag strong —

> > current *adverse*

9 Jars, elect 60°
> mag strong +

> > current *direct*

9 Jars elect 64°
> mag +

> > current *direct*

9 Jars elect 62°
> mag strong

> > current *direct*

9 Jars elect 60
> break made in the farther end of the circuit still
> mag strong +

> > current *direct*

9 Jars elect 64°
> magnet feeble —

> > current—Adverse

9 Jars charge 20°[5]
> magnetism feeble +

> > current—*direct*

9 Jars charge 40°
> magnet + much stronger

> > current *direct*

9 Jar charge 62°
> magnetism feeble

> > current direct

10 small + one large jars 60°[6]
> Magnetism strong

> > current *direct*

---

[5] In another marginal notation Henry wrote: "In all these exp the wires were about the mean distance of 1/2 an inch apart."

[6] Henry circled this and the following experiment. Diagonally across the two experiments is written: "doubtful charge may have passed rong." For reasons unclear to us, Henry suspected a short circuit.

10 same charge 42°		
mag strong		
		current direct
10 Jars charge 64°		
strong mag		
		current *direct*
10 Jars charge 60°	not strong	*direct*
10 „ 58	stronger	direct
8 Jars 64° strong		*direct*

FROM E. R. TREMAIN

Henry Papers, Smithsonian Archives

Clinton Hall New York
Oct° 17, 1838

Sir

On the 1st Sept last[1] I had the pleasure of addressing you an invitation in behalf of the Board of Directors of the Mercantile Library Association, to deliver a course of two or four lectures on Electro Magnetism.

Mr Coffin,[2] our President, has informed the Come that at an interview with him, you expressed a willingness to lecture before our Assn, and that he expected you to call again on him, on your return from Albany, and arrange more definitely in regard to a short course, on such subjects as you named to him.

The Come, being disappointed in not conferring with you again, beg you to inform them, at your earliest convenience, of the subjects you would select, the number of lectures you would prefer delivering; and the time when it would be most convenient to you.[3]

[1] Letter printed above.

[2] Edmund Coffin (1812–1884) headed an auction and commission firm in New York City until the crash of 1857 and then conducted a real estate business in Irvington, New York. Obituary in the *New York Times*, December 23, 1884, p. 5.

[3] Henry drafted his reply on the second page of Tremain's letter:

Answered Oct 19th
Why did not call sickness of child. I had stated my willingness to lecture but subject of elect-magn. not alone but in connection with mag. generally.

I had also stated that the subject of sound would be interesting connected with musical instruments. The course should be as short as a clear exposition of the science would permit. If a course on Mag 4 lectures on sound 2 or 3. Not accustomed to lecture. Would on some accounts prefer sound. Hazard less in my first essay before the public.

Hoping that nothing may prevent us from having the satisfaction of adding your name to the list of Lecturers for our next course, I have the honor to remain, Sir,

> Very respectfully
> Your obt. ser^t
> E R Tremain
> Chairman Lec. Com^e M.L.A.

In a cours on mag. experiments interesting even if man[y] unfortunate.
Course embrace terrestrial mag.
Time some time in Jany. Leave to the comittee the time of beginning and days of lectures.

We have not found his outgoing letter.

"RECORD OF EXPERIMENTS"
Henry Papers, Smithsonian Archives

Oct 18th 1838

Arranged apparatus to determine the effect of the extra quantity.[1] For this purpose made use of the arrangement in the figure. The Large conductor was placed in connection with the out side of the jar so as to make the extra quantity on that side. The needle was still

magnetized *direct*

Repeated many times in succession changed the arrangement so that the extra quantity was on the inside but the + charge was on the out side still

magnetism strong

current *direct*

It would appear conclusive from these experiments as well as from those I have made before that the extra particle is not the cause of the magnetization of the needle.

The following experiment would lead to the supposition that the extra quantity had some influence.[2] Connected the large conductor with the inside of the jar so as to increase the quantity of electricity and now the current was adverse twice in succession

Adverse

---

[1] Previously investigated on August 3; see that entry (printed above), especially footnote 2.

[2] Henry bracketed the next three paragraphs and added "Error" in the margin.

Seperated the large conductor and the current was

direct

This result was probably caused by the touching of the wires a small current only passed through which gave a change in the direction. See subsequent experiments same day.

Again with 20 turns of the machine[3] and the large conductor not on, the current was

+direct

With twenty turns of the machin conductor on

current *direct*

Again 25 turns without conductor
      magnetism not strong

direct

same number of turns with the conductor on

direct

Next gave about 40 turns with the conductor on now the current was still

direct

Repeated this experiment with various not very small charges always with the same result and could not again get a adverse current. At length concluded that in the cases of the adverse current that the main body of the charge has cut across in the discharge. To test this supposition, in which I was the more strengthened by the sound of the report which in the case of the adverse current was loud and almost like the breaking of the jar, the wires were placed across so that the main part of the discharge would not pass through the circuit and in this case twice in succession an adverse current was obtained. To know whether this current (adverse) was produced by the small charge which passed around the wire, or by some other cause a very [. . .] charge[4] was passed round and in this case an *adverse* current was produced twice in succession. The magnetism was however feeble.

With about [. . .] turn[5] magnetism feeble but decidedly

        — current

adverse

With 5 turns
      mag—feeble

current *adverse*

---

[3] Marginal annotations indicate that from this point on, unless otherwise stated, Henry used three Leyden jars in this day's experiments.

[4] Henry left out the adjective.

[5] The number of turns of the machine is not given.

NB in the above exp the long conductor was on.
   With 5 turns conductor off

magnetism little stronger	*adverse*

   With 6 turns also   *adverse*
   With 7 turns scarcely no magnetism

current	nothing

   With nine very little magnetism

If any	*direct*

   With 12 turns magnetism still increasing and now decidedly

	direct

   Again with 15 turns
        magnetism still feeble

but	*direct*

   With 20 turns still stronger

	direct

   Again with 4 turns
        magnetism +   *adverse*
   With 6 turns slight   +   direct
   Again with 8 turns   adverse
   With the large conductor on, 4 turns decidedly
              repulsive   *adverse*
   Again with conductor 15 turns magnet feeble

but	*direct*

   20 turns magnetism much stronger decidedly

	direct

From all the experiments made to day it would appear that the lateral action has little or nothing to do with the phenomina and that at the distance at which the wires have been placed about ¾ of an inch there is a turn in the direction of the current with a small charge with 3 jars from adverse to direct. The change in the direction depends on the intensity of the charge.[6]
   With *one Jar* magnetism was

with 4 turns	adverse

   With one jar 6 turnes

	adverse

---

[6] In "Contributions III," Henry was much less confident about the conclusiveness of his experiments. Intensity of discharge was just one of the variables he tested in ascertaining the conditions which determined the change in direction of the induced current. He concluded that the results were too anomalous to be presented to the American Philosophical Society (paragraph 118).

With 10 turns feeble but

                            still   adverse

With about 20 turns the current

                                 was   direct

Arranged the apparatus at a greater distance inorder to note the effect of a change of distance on the direction of the current.[7] With 8 jars, distance 10 inches (Exp Preliminary)   current pretty strong

                                  adverse

With 8 jars Elect 60
    distance 2 inches
        current   *adverse*
    dist 4 inches 60°   *adverse*
    dist same   10   adverse

[7] Henry found this a much more fruitful line of inquiry than the intensity of discharge. He quickly became certain of the role of the distance between conductors in determining the direction of the induced current. "Contributions III," paragraphs 115–116, 119–120.

"RECORD OF EXPERIMENTS"
Henry Papers, Smithsonian Archives

Oct 19th [1838]

Experiments relative to the distance continued.[1]

10 Jars distance 5 inches elect 4°
    current   *direct*

In this experiment the discharge appared to be but partial perhaps the discharge cut across
    see next exp.

10 jars dist 5 *inches* elect 40°
    magnetism—pretty strong

		current		adverse
same	same	elect	6°	—*adverse*
same	elect		10°	+*direct*
same	same	elec	15°	+*direct*
————	————	———	20	+*direct*

[1] From the day before.

⎯⎯	⎯⎯	feeble	30	+*direct*
			35	*direct*
			40	+*direct*
			50	+*direct*
		very feeble	60	*direct*
		feeble	62°	*adverse*

distance same 4 jars elect   50

                  current—   direct

same   same

                  current   70°   direct
                  strong

In these two altered the position of the battery[2]
distance 2 inches 4 Jars elect 60   *direct*

Repeted removed the orig conductor
from the machine still   direct

turned round still   direct

Changed the distance a little further of[f]
—3 inches still 4 jars
        and still direct   *direct*

The only difference in the arrangement and that of yesterday is that the
4 jars stood on a stool with glass legs

with 8 jars   *direct*

Put on the stool still the same   *direct*

Removed the distance to 10 inches
                  4 Jars   direct

dis 9 inches	⎧ With 8 jars distance 10 inches	
	strong charge elect 60°	*adverse*
	⎨ With 4 jars elect 60	
	current	*direct*
	⎪ With 8 jars elect 25	*direct*
	⎩ 8 With Charge of 50°	*direct*

4 inches apart	⎧ 8 jars 4 inches apart	
	elect 45°	*direct*
	⎨ 8 jars elect 60° feeble	*direct*
	⎩ Do Do Do	*direct*

[2] Henry means his group of Leyden jars.

6 inches apart	8 jars mag feeble[3]		
	elect *60°*	curr.	*direct*
	8 jars elect 25°	feeble	*direct*
	8 jars elect 10°		*direct*
	4 jars elec 60°	feeble	*direct*

10 inches

10 inches apart	4 jars elect 55°	feeble	direct
	8 jars elect 55°		
		mag *strong*	*adverse*

8 jars elect 40°	mag feeble	direct

10 inches	10 inches elect 60°	
	mag not strong	
	distance same as last	adverse

[3] Henry wrote "all feeble" vertically and to the right of this and the next four specifications.

"RECORD OF EXPERIMENTS"
Henry Papers, Smithsonian Archives

Oct 20[th] 1838

Tired with attemp[t]s to get some more definite information relative to the action of parallel wires I commenced this morning with the first spiral apparatus.

Exp 1[st] Exp sent shock through it from battery of 4 jars. Current as always before $\qquad$ *direct*
Again from battery of 8 jars highly charged and again

direct

Magnetism in both cases very strong.
Attempted to get a shock

NB Noticed a singular phenominon in the discharge of the 8 jars through the spiral apparatus. I noticed that after one discharge the ends of the tin foil were turned up. Repeated the shock from the 8 jars and now the ends of each piece of tin foil were turned back and even curled backwards <*as if acted on by a force emanating from the discharge at right angles.*> where the slips overlaped holes were perced in the tin foil in the lap

The turning up took place on the tinfoil through which the discharge passed and the action is therefore as if the parts of the tin foil were strongly repulsive.[1]

Exp 2nd Pasted slip of tin foil on glass plate. Sent charge through foil thrown up along the whole course. The parts should lap over each other

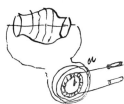

Exp 3^d Arranged the apparatus to get a shock from the secondary curent or rather the tertiary current. Large flat coil no 2 connected with glass cylinders and long coil no 1 put into this. With small charge of battery with 8 jars small shock; with large charge no shock

Substituted for receiving coil *a* No 1 flat coil and for the long helix *b* flat coil No 2. No shock with this arrangement nor with the long helix on coil No *one*

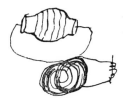

4th Exp on tertiary currents. Placed flat coil No 1 in connection with spiral apparatus and No 2 on this. Current from 2nd; 3rd current

adverse

> With piec of Zinc between, current   nothing
> With piec of glass between magnetism 40, elect
>
> *adverse*
>
> Again with a thin piec of tin foil between, current
>
> *direct*[2]

Without tin foil current   direct
Small charge gives needle more magnetism but still   *direct*

Attempted to get a 4th order of currents with common elect but did not suceede

---

[1] This "good class experiment," as Henry described it in a marginal annotation, appeared in paragraph 126 of "Contributions III: Electro-Dynamic Induction." There Henry ascribed the action to the mutual repulsion of the several parts of the discharge of the Leyden jar, claiming that this was another instance where static and galvanic electricity operated analogously. In the case of galvanic electricity, Ampère had discovered that consecutive parts of a galvanic current repulsed each other.

[2] Henry annotated the bracketed set of results: "Same irregularity betw[ee]n these as the others." In the confusing world of the determination of the direction of induced currents, even regularity in the irregularity was welcome.

5th Produced a strong inductive current from the large conductor direction
magnetism strong   direct

Exp 6th

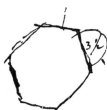

Sent current from large conductor[3] through large coil in glass rods, 3 strands, inductive current *adverse* wires about 1½ inches apart

2nd Seperated the wires to about 4 inches
still *adverse*

Seperated the wires to a distance of a foot. Made the discharge as before on end of the wire being attached to the rubber of the machine

current *adverse*

Removed to the distance of about 18 inches still slightly magnetic

current *adverse*

7th Changed the position of the magnetizing helix but the effect was still the same
adverse

Also put the helix on the compound strand and the discharge through the other still the direction continued
adverse

8th Put up the single coil so as to have to single wires

still current *adverse*

From these experiments it would appear that the same changes are produced by the current from a large conductor as with a jar but perhaps the effect is somewhat more simple.[4]

These explain some of the anomalies which were obtained with the large reel. Lateral currents were in some cases produced which interfered with the results

In these experiments no cutting across could take place since the coils were formed with wire in glass tubes three times plied. The whole length of wire thus covered with glass tube in the compound circuit was 6 x 3½ x 3 = 63. The ends or joints of the hexigon were secured by pieces of mica interposed so that no escape of elect could take place there. The whole effect was therefore due to induction.

---

[3] A marginal annotation for this set of experiments reads "currents from large conductor."

[4] Henry never attempted to work out in detail the differences, if any, that he thought might exist between currents induced by the discharge from a Leyden jar and from a large conductor.

NB In these exp with the long conductor the farther end of the wire was attached to another which led to the cushion of the *machine*

Tried the same with two flat coils   *adverse*   *adverse*

1 With plate of zinc between   *no current*

2 With glass between   adverse

3 With piec of tin foil between current stopped.

FROM E. R. TREMAIN

Henry Papers, Smithsonian Archives

Clinton Hall New York
Oct 22nd 1838

Dear Sir

Your valuable favor of 19th inst[1] was rec[d] Saturday, and was laid before the Lecture Com[e], by whom I am instructed to say, that it is their wish, that you should deliver the *two courses*, mentioned by you—viz: four lectures on Magnetism, in general, including, as you say, Electro-magnetism and terrestrial-magnetism; and two lectures on Sound, "Considered in its analogies with light, and in its connection with the philosophy of musical instruments." Commencing about the 15th Jan[y] and giving one lecture each Tuesday and Friday evening until finished. The *particular* day of commencing might be left to the Com[e], who will give you timely notice.

The Committee would like, if agreeable to you, and within your power, to have you specify the particular subject of each lecture, that they may be placed seperately, on our "prospectus" in the order in which they will be delivered.[2]

In reference to that clause of your letter, when you say that "you know not how you may succeed before a large and popular audience," I would merely say, that although you may expect to meet a *large* and *popular audience*, you would find them very *indulgent*, in case you should be so unfortunate, as to test it; but this we do not expect, since many gentlemen, whose names stand far below yours on the Scroll of Fame, have lectured to them, with unqualified success.

With sincere respect, I am Sir,

Your most obt sert
E. R. Tremain Chairman
Lec Com[e] M. L. A.

[1] Not found. However, Henry's draft of the letter has survived. See above, Tremain to Henry, October 17, 1838, footnote 3.

[2] For Henry's response, see below, Tremain to Henry, November 14, 1838, footnote 2.

"RECORD OF EXPERIMENTS"
Henry Papers, Smithsonian Archives

Oct Monday 22nd 1838
Arranged the compound circuit with glass rods so that the spark would be drawn from the farther end and thus a smaller dispersion take place on account of the lateral discharge.

Seperated the two (ie compound and single) circuit from distance of 3 or 4 inches to about 20 inches current constantly

adverse

At the distance of about 4 feet no magnetism

Put up in place of the single circuit of wire covered with glass the compound one of cotton 13 turns. At distance of about 4 feet very feeble

Singular magnetism *adverse*

result Compound circuit in the middle of the other

No magnetism[1]

Reversed this exp slight magnetic[2]

adverse

Two flat coils seperated by glass one on. In contact with large conductor spark drawn from farther end.

current *adverse*

NB Made a number of experiments with the small magnetizing helix to determine if it were possible to procure a reversion of polarity but always the current was direct with a spark from the large conductor also different charges from a battery of 4 jars

Exp 2nd Arranged the battery (large) to repeat some of the old experiments—used box of the battery No 5

---

[1] Obviously, the result of this experiment was unanticipated by Henry. But it isn't clear from the description or illustration whether it was a case of unexpected screening, or a short circuit, or the result of the poorly designed experiment. In any case, Henry did not dwell on the result.

[2] This sentence was originally squeezed in the right hand margin, as if it were a later addition.

"RECORD OF EXPERIMENTS"
Henry Papers, Smithsonian Archives

Oct 23rd 1838

 Made a very long coil of fine copper wire and attached it to helix No 1 (long) and placed this within ribbon coil no 2 needle magnetic very strong, current *direct*[1]

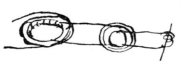 Current adverse *ie* the induced current from the primary to the secondary is direct but from the secondary to the tertiary it is *adverse*

Arranged the apparatus so as to produce 2^n 3rd, & 4th order of currents found a change in the direction of the 1st & 3rd, 3rd & 4th

 *Exp on screening.*[2] Sent battery charge through coil No 1 placed long helix in flat coil No 2 held the one over the other. When the ends of flat coil open, shocks very severe but when closed shock scarcely nothing. The two namely the helix and the coil in this exp are both at the same distances from the exciting coil and nothing is interposed to action of the lower *flat* spiral. The effect was purely the one of interferance and explains the experiment of Mr Faraday inwhich two wires are bound together &c.[3]

---

[1] In the margin Henry wrote: "never before suceeded in this exp." Unfortunately, we have been unable to figure out the uniqueness of this experiment; the description and illustration are too ambiguous.

[2] Henry's marginal annotation reads "Important Exp." Published as paragraph 69 of "Contributions III," this experiment represented what Henry concluded was an incontestable contradiction of his initial hypothesis regarding screening. He had thought that screening was analogous to an interference phenomenon in which the electrical pulses were out of synchronization. Such an effect would vary according to the length of the path and/or intensity of the current in the screening material. Such variation did not appear in the experiments reported in paragraphs 68–72, however, and in paragraph 73 Henry rejected the interference explanation.

[3] This appears to be a reference to *Experimental Researches in Electricity*, Ninth Series, paragraph 1096, where Faraday discussed doubling an insulated wire and tying the two halves together. Under such circumstances little or no spark was observed at the breaking of the circuit. However, when the two halves were untied and extended, "a very good" spark could be seen. Faraday assigned the cause of the phenomenon to the contrary

Decomposition of acidulated water by the induced current. Nitric acid and water put into the apparatus of the magneto-electric machine copious disengagement of gas, some when the coils were at the distance of 6 inches. The coils used were No 1 flat coil and helix No 1.

When the wires were drawn from the mercury sparkes were produced

Again instead of helix no 1 coil No 2 was used. With this decomposition was also produced but not so copiously as with the other

The decomposing apparatus was next placed in connection with the arrangement for the third current decomposition was again produced. Next tried the heating effects. Put small wire of platina in the circuit of the flat coil No 2 wire heated to redness.

Intensity converted into quantity!!⁴ Small Shaker battery put in connection with long helix No 1. Shocks produced. Next flat coil No 2 put on this. Needle [in.] Helix connecting the extremities: the short helix which produces no magnetism with the long helix. The inclosed needle tolerably strongly magnetic

direction of the current

direct

Repeated this important exp with the same result. Tried with the same arrangement to decompose; very feeble effect no shock but magnetism strong also *spark*

Intensity converted into quantity the reverse of the experiments ever made before

---

and therefore neutralizing inductive currents produced in the halves of the wire when bound.

⁴ Henry's discovery of the principle behind the electrical transformer was announced in "Contributions III," paragraphs 40–41.

"RECORD OF EXPERIMENTS"
Henry Papers, Smithsonian Archives

Oct 24ᵗʰ 1838

Exp 1 Made another experiment relative to the conversion of intensity into quantity or rather to the production of a quantity current by means of an intensity one. Attached to the ends of the flat ribbon coil no 2 which surrounded the long helix no 1 the wires of a small soft iron electro magnet of which the wire was of the thickness of common bell wire, and about 6 or

8 feet long.[1] The magnet became excited by the induced current from the ribbon coil. When the same horseshoe was placed in connection with battery wires or formed part of the circuit of the battery current no magnetism could be perceived. This experiment appears conclusive in reference to the fact of the quantity quality of the current or that the action is directly the inverse of that which takes place when a current of low intensity. The battery used was the litle shaker one.

It is probable the same effect might be produced by common electricity were it possible to perfectly insulate the several spires of a long helix through which the primative current should be passed.

Attached the same magnet to the ends of the flat coil for the production of the tertiary currents. Attraction took place of the same jaring kind as in the case of the magneto-electric machine. But when the long helix was employed to receive the induction for the tertiary current no magnetism was produced although violent shocks could be given. Also made magnet by the 2nd current.

Exp 3[d] Arranged the two ribbons No 3 & 4 in one strand and then wound them into a flat spiral. When the ends of one of these was placed in contact with the battery and the ends of the other seperated from each other the spark was loud and brilliant but when the two ends of the second were placed in contact the spark was feeble; the sparks did not intirely cease. This arrangement which is the same as one of Mr Faraday,[2] indicates the reciprocation of the two currents on each other

 The following arrangement was next made: the two ends of the second coil were attached to the ends of coil no 2 and helix no *one* put into the mid[d]le of the latter. In this way the current which was before disguised and which produced no perceptible effect was rendered manifest by producing intense tertiary currents.

The secondary current in this arrangement was quite intense and it would appear from this experiment that to form the most powerful compound coil for shocks &c the plan would be to mingle large wires with small

---

[1] This experiment differs from the one Henry described in "Contributions III," paragraph 40, only in the coil used. In the published experiment Henry utilized coil no. 3; here he utilized coil no. 2.

[2] Both the arrangement and the results were identical with those described by Faraday in paragraph 1090 of his Ninth Series of *Experimental Researches in Electricity*. Faraday related the phenomenon to the mutual and reciprocal inductive action of two currents in paragraph 1097 of the same publication. Henry's published version of the experiment appeared in paragraph 95 of "Contributions III."

in the same helix the former to convey the battery current and the latter for the shocks or with the same apparatus quantity could be produced from the induction of intensity. With the arrangement of the last, sparkes were produced between the ends of the tertiary wires.

Exp 4th Tried the effect of distance of the *tertiary* coil from its secondary with the arrangement of the last experiment shocks were felt when the coils were 20 inches apart

Plate of copper interposed no effect. When thin sheet of tin foil was substituted then the action was quite as intense as without the presence of metal.[3]

---

[3] Tipped into the "Record of Experiments" at this point is what appears to be a rough draft of this entry, differing from the final version in the order of the experiments and the details supplied. For example, the first experiment of the "Record of Experiments" entry appears in somewhat less detail as almost the last experiment in the draft.

"RECORD OF EXPERIMENTS"
Henry Papers, Smithsonian Archives

Oct 27[th] 1838

Exp on screening. Put zinc plate on top of the long helix. No shock. Withdraw plate intense shock. Plate larger than the coil or helix.

 Another variation of the same exper offers a striking exhibition of the neutralizing action. Suspend the in[d]uctive coil from a string then introduce between the two coiles a circle of metal[1] the action is almost intirely neutralized

---

[1] Probably the circular lead plate used in the experiment described in paragraph 62 of "Contributions III: Electro-Dynamic Induction."

FROM ASA GRAY

Henry Papers, Smithsonian Archives

Monday, Oct. 29th, 1838

Dear Sir

Will your business bring you to New York any time this week, or by Monday of next week? I wish you to see the plan for the Michigan University building,[1] now in the hands of the Architect here. He is going to work upon the details very soon. If you come, will you do me the fav to call on the Goldsmith, watch-repairer, or whatever he may be called, at Princeton and bring Mrs. Torrey's watch, which has been in his hands a long time. If we are not to see you please send it by some good opportunity. If none is like to occur let me know and I will come for it. The time fixed for my departure is Wednesday of next week. I shall of course be very busy till that time.

Yours truly
Asa Gray

---

[1] See above, Torrey to Henry, August 29, 1838.

"RECORD OF EXPERIMENTS"

Henry Papers, Smithsonian Archives

Oct 29th [1838]

Surrounded the large coil of wire which I have borrowed of Dr Gale[1] and which contains 5 miles of copper bell wire with coil no 1 received the shock through one finger, exceedingly intense so as to affect my arm up to my body and to give me a slight turn in the head.[2]

The magnetizing effect of this arrangement was exceedingly feeble. The

---

[1] Leonard Dunnell Gale (1800–1883) was Samuel F. B. Morse's scientific advisor on the telegraph. *Henry Papers*, 2:94. The wire, described in "Contributions III: Electro-Dynamic Induction," paragraph 10, was loaned to Henry while Morse was in Europe promoting his telegraph.

[2] Published as paragraph 34 of "Contributions III," this experiment was a follow-up to the second experiment in the "Record of Experiments" entry of May 25, 1838 (printed

above). Henry had discovered that the length of a wire which could be formed into a shock-inducing helix was limited by the diameter of the wire. Long thin wires produced barely perceptible shocks. This experiment, using relatively thick wire, confirmed his assumption of May 25 that increasing the diameter of the wire would allow an increase in length of the wire without decreasing the intensity of the shock.

magnet with small horseshoe. This large coil is one half of the wire which has been prepared for the experiments on the electrical telegraph

NB One box of the large magnet[3] was used for these exp

---

[3] A slip of the pen. Henry meant to write "battery."

"RECORD OF EXPERIMENTS"
Henry Papers, Smithsonian Archives

Oct 30th [1838]

1 Made to day a small galvanometer of about 150 turns. Put this in the arrangement of Mr Faraday 10th series[1] to determine the direction of the cross current at *a* but the result was not very satisfactory. Must repete this with some variation[2]

2 Put in the galvanometer in the circuit of the secondary current needle deflected to the side indicating a current +. The effect was much increased by introducing into the same circuit a decomposing apparatus to retard the current

3 Again put the same apparatus into the circuit of the tertiary current and here the motion of the needle indicated a — current or one in an opposite direction to that of the battery

---

[1] A slip by Henry. The arrangement of the apparatus was clearly copied from paragraph 1079 of the Ninth Series of Faraday's *Experimental Researches in Electricity*. Like Faraday, Henry used the apparatus to measure the direction of the self-induced current. Henry had found ("Contributions III: Electro-Dynamic Induction," paragraph 92) that the direction of the higher orders of induced current alternated in direction, with one exception: the primary and secondary currents were both in the same direction. But if he could show that the direction of the self-induced current was opposite that of the primary and secondary, he could argue that the self-induced current had in fact induced the secondary, preserving the concept of alternating directions for induced currents. Unfortunately for his theory, his results were identical with Faraday's. The direction of the self-induced current was the same as the primary ("Contributions III," paragraph 93).

[2] In "Contributions III," paragraph 93, Henry made it clear that he had attempted this experiment a number of times without any variation in the results and had accepted the negative result as conclusive. There are no later indications that Henry again challenged Faraday's conclusions on this topic.

October 30, 1838

TO JAMES HENRY

Mary Henry Copy, Family Correspondence, Henry Papers,
Smithsonian Archives

Princeton Oct. 30th. 1838

We are all well and now pretty well settled in our new house. I have been much engaged in my experiments and intend going to Phil. on Friday next to submit my researches to the American Philosophical Society.

We do not much admire the name of your little girl.[1] I do not hold to the custom of transmitting unpleasant names because they have belonged to a relative. We need no names to keep in remembrance those we honor.

I would never have named a child Joseph and would regret that anyone whom I loved should inflict such a name on his offspring.

---

[1] The James Henrys had named their daughter Harriet.

TO JOHN TORREY

Torrey Papers, Library, New York Botanical Garden

Princeton Oct 30th 1838

My Dear Dr

The recept of your letter[1] on Friday last gave us much pleasure. Mrs H. had requested me the day before to write to you relative to the health of Mrs T. Your kind letter anticipated our intentions and we have now the gratification of congratulating you and yours on the safe arrival of the Little Gentleman.[2] Long may he live to be a joy to his parents and a blessing to his country and the world—If he be not a Philosopher in the widest sense of the term then will he want much of that inheritance which should be his birthright both from Father and Mother.

We are all well and pleasantly settled in our new house and shall be happy to provide you and yours with comfortable quarters when you come to Princeton. The mirrors shall be forth coming the latter part of this week. If I can get Joseph to make a box for them they will be sent to the canal

---

[1] Not found.

[2] Herbert Gray Torrey (1838–1915), Torrey's only son and Asa Gray's godson, was born on October 12. After graduating from the College of the City of New York in 1860, he became Assistant Assayer of the New York Assay Office. In 1873, with Henry's backing, he succeeded his father as Assayer-in-Chief. As a private mining consultant, Torrey traveled extensively to examine gold and silver mines. William M. Brown, ed., *Biographical, Genealogical and Descriptive History of the State of New Jersey* (New Jersey, 1900), pp. 208–209. C. C. Robbins, "John Torrey (1796–1873): His Life and Times," *Bulletin of the Torrey Botanical Club*, 1968, 95:563, 626–627.

tomorrow. As to the pay we will settle that at some time when it is perfectly convenient to yourself. I will certainly inspect the new rod but shall take good care to keep at a respectable distance during a thunder storm. I have no idea of being Popes "favoured man by touch etherial slain."[3]

I have been laboriously engaged at my series of experiments since my return to Princeton and intend to go to Philadelphia to present them to the Society on Friday next. I will try to get my paper published immediately since I have not been very secret in refer[ence] to the affair and may perhaps be anticipated. I was somewhat uneasy about the late investigations of Mr Faraday but I have lately received his papers through Dr Warren of Boston and find that he is on entirely a different track.[4] I have worked harder on these experiments than on any I ever before engaged in and have overcome more difficulties and developed more new facts than were dreamed of when I commenced the series. I regret that I cannot send by Dr Gray a lot of my papers. I will however send him a package for distribution. His letters will be prepared this week before I leave for Philadelphia. I am to lecture in Jany at the Clinton Hall, two lectures on sound and four on magnetism &c. I intend to give them a touch in reference to the patronage of science in this country, and shall indeavour to do justice to my Friends in the city.

> In Haste as ever
> Yours
> Joseph Henry

[3] From *An Essay on Man in Four Epistles*, epistle 3, line 68.

[4] Henry may have heard that Faraday's Eleventh, Twelfth, and Thirteenth Series of Experimental Researches were on induction and feared that he was being anticipated again. Faraday, however, was conducting a highly theoretical investigation of the laws of static electricity. See L. Pearce Williams, *Michael Faraday* (New York, 1965), pp. 283–315. Faraday only approached Henry's area of investigation at the end of the Thirteenth Series (from paragraph 1653) where he returned to electromagnetic induction and the action of currents on currents. It was not until Faraday's Fourteenth Series that Henry found their work intersecting once again.

TO CHARLES G. PAGE

Retained Copy,[1] Henry Papers, Smithsonian Archives

Princton Oct 31 1838

Dear Sir

The last number of the american journal of Science contains an Interesting paper from your pen on the subject of the annlisation[2] of Electro-

[1] This copy is not in Henry's hand. Despite the many misspellings, Henry made few corrections. The only clear ones are "Fe^by" for the copyist's "Fifty" and "render" in the last sentence which the copyist had given as "made."

[2] Henry might have intended "analyzation."

magnet as a moving power in the arts. In this you state that Mr Sturgeon was the first to produce a mechanical motion.[3] In reference to this point premit me to state that I think you must have fallen into an error by confounding some other invention of Mr Sturgeon with the motion in question. I have all ways supposed myself to be the first in this invention. Mr Sturgeon makes no claim of the kind in any of his publications with which I am acquainted[4] and in the Fe[by] number of 1838 of the Philosophical magazine there is an artical by Mr Watkins which gives an account of my invention and state that it was the first attempt of the kind.[5]

The affare is not one of much concequence and is scarcely worth the correcting sence time settles with perfect impartiality all matters of this nature. You may however have some infermation on the subject with which I am unacquainted and you will therefore confer a favour by giving me a refferance to the same.[6]

The circumstance which has called forth this letter will probably be considered as an apology for my addressing you with out an introduction and the fact that we are fellow labourers in the cause of american Science would, as I have persumed render any formality of the kind unnessary.

> With much respect
> Yours &c
> Joseph Henry

[3] In an article in the July–October 1838 number of *Silliman's Journal*, Page had written:

> The first successful step towards the attainment of this object, of which we have any record, was made by Mr. William Sturgeon, a distinguished philosopher of England. The next original invention by which an independent motion was obtained from electromagnets, was the oscillating apparatus of Prof. Henry, described in a previous No. of this Journal.

"On Electro-Magnetism as a Motive Power," *Silliman's Journal*, 1839, 35:106.

This was only another instance of Henry's priority problems with his electric motor, first described in his article "On a Reciprocating Motion Produced by Magnetic Attraction and Repulsion," *Silliman's Journal*, 1831, 20:340–343. See *Henry Papers*, 2:162n–163n, 446n.

[4] Sturgeon in fact credited Henry with "the first form of a working model of an engine upon the principle of reciprocating polarity of soft iron by electro-dynamical agency" and reprinted Henry's 1831 article in "Historical Sketch of the Rise and Progress of Electromagnetic Engines for Propelling Machinery," *Annals of Electricity, Magnetism, and Chemistry*, March 1839, 3:430–432.

[5] See above, Hare to Henry, April 21, 1838, especially footnote 2.

[6] Page's reply of November 8, 1838, is printed below. Robert Post discusses this exchange in *Physics, Patents, and Politics: A Biography of Charles Grafton Page* (New York, 1976), pp. 21–22.

"RECORD OF EXPERIMENTS"
Henry Papers, Smithsonian Archives

Oct 31st 1838

Made to day a new galvanometer[1] of 600 turns of very fine wire of copper  covered with silk. This gave indication of a current from a continued stream of ordinary electricity. With sparkes the effect very little

When one end of the coil was put into a plate of acid dilute and the mere point of a zinc wire attached to the other extremity touched the same and the needle whirled around.

Three plates in a row with dilute acid the needle made nearly a revolution when the same zinc point touched the further plate

The electricity of the thermo pile would not pass through.

With the above apparatus I tested anew the direction of the tertiary current and found it as before — minus[2]

[1] Henry describes this apparatus in more detail in "Contributions IV: Electro-Dynamic Induction," paragraph 4. It was used with currents of high intensity but small quantity.

[2] The sketch below is of the apparatus to indicate an electric current through the decomposition of water which was used during the previous day's experiments. This may have been just a convenient blank space.

TO JOHN HERAPATH[1]
Mary Henry Copy, Henry Papers, Smithsonian Archives

Princeton, College of New Jersey
Nov. 1st. 1838.

Dear Sir.

I fear you will think me very ungrateful in not before answering your letter[2] and acknowledging the receipt of your kind present of books. The

[1] John Herapath (1790–1868), the British physicist and journal editor, is remembered today for his early suggestion of a kinetic theory of gases, a theory which met with much resis-

truth is the package, by some unaccountable delay, did not reach here until eight months after the letter. It was also received at a time when I was occupied in college duties and had besides nothing interesting to send you. Indeed I have nothing at present worthy of your acceptance but have however made up a package of a few articles. These I send in charge of my friend Dr. Gray of New York. . . Should you meet with Dr. Gray you will find him an intelligent and interesting young man much esteemed in the line of Natural History.

The affair of the Canadian rebellion has I believe entirely blown over. It was never countenanced in the United States, but by the low and desperate, who are to be found in every country, ready to embark in any project, which will afford a prospect of being thrown up from the dregs of society. The measures of our government, although somewhat tardy in reference to Canada, were such I presume as to give general satisfaction in Great Britain.[3]

I had a pleasant passage home of twenty days; found my wife and little ones disposed to give me a warm welcome from the dangers of the deep. I have been so much occupied in making up in college duties for my long absence that I have found no time for general scientific intelligence, and have therefore little of importance to communicate in the line of engineering. The great commercial revulsion, and the total disarrangement of our currency, has paralyzed for a time all operations in reference to most of the projected works on internal improvement in our country. . . . I have heard that a work has lately appeared in England on the subject of American engineering from the pen of Mr. Stevenson. . I am informed that it contains a number of mistakes; among others one in reference to the pressure of steam used on the Hudson river which is said—in the work—to be at fifty pounds to the square inch; the maximum pressure of the celebrated rapid

---

tance in his time (but, as will be seen below, was appreciated by Henry). Considered a scientific eccentric and apparently unable to earn a living at science, Herapath turned to railway engineering, benefitting from the English railway boom of the 1830s and 1840s. In 1836 he became editor of the *Railway Magazine and Annals of Science*, which later appeared as *Herapath's Railway and Commercial Journal. DNB. DSB.*

Although Herapath's name is absent from his European diary, Henry met him in England in 1837. Herapath sent Henry issues of the *Railway Magazine*, volumes 2 and 3 of which survive in the Henry Library. At the front of volume 2 is this undated Henry annotation recalling a cordial meeting:

Mr Herapath the editor of this magazine was very polite and attentive to me while I was in England in 1837. He gave me the numbers of this work which I have in my Library. He was a man of genius and the author of one of the first investigations of the dynamic theory of heat.

[2] Not found.

[3] Although President Van Buren had issued a neutrality proclamation in January 1838 the border regions of the United States were staging areas for more than a dozen raids against Canada during the Canadian rebellion of 1837–1838. For another reference by Henry to the rebellion, see his letter to James Henry of March 22, 1838.

boats on this river is not more than from twenty to twenty-five pounds.[4]

I suppose you are much pleased with triumph of steam in successfully buffeting the waves of the Atlantic. On this subject you will find some remarks in a paper in the last number of Silliman's Journal of Science,[5] the one for 1838. Projects are on foot, in New York and Philadelphia, for establishing lines of American steam packets.[6] I hope the business will not be overdone, that the whole will settle down as a regular mode of communication between the two countries. Great complaints were made by the passengers of the Great Western, on account of the bad accommodation and want of proper attendance on board.[7] This should be remedied, since the packet ships abound in comforts and luxuries. The public however will suffer considerable inconvenience to be assured of a quick and safe passage.

[4] David Stevenson (1815–1886; *DNB*), of the Scots family of civil engineers, took a professional tour of Canada and America in 1837, reporting his observations in *Sketch of the Civil Engineering of North America* (London, 1838). Impressed with the speed of Hudson River steamboats, Stevenson stated that the steamboat *Rochester*, at racing speed, carried pressures as high as forty-five, not fifty, pounds to the square inch (p. 125). Noting that many of his countrymen doubted the reported velocities of the American boats (for Henry's personal encounter with a British skeptic, see *Henry Papers*, 3:508–510), Stevenson maintained that a few plying the Hudson River and Long Island Sound deserved their reputation, performing "their voyages safely and regularly, at a speed which far surpasses that of any European steamer hitherto built. . . ." (p. 140).

[5] Junius Smith, "Letters on Atlantic Steam Navigation," *Silliman's Journal*, 1839, 35:160–167 (the 1839 date is the last date for the entire volume), argues that the "navigation of a ship by steam power is more philosophical than by sails. . . ." For steam crossing of the Atlantic see Henry to [Thomas Romney Robinson], April 28, 1838, footnote 3.

[6] The immense success of America's sailing packets slowed the introduction of a domestic fleet of steam vessels. Philadelphia's early plans for transatlantic steamboats (*Report of the Philadelphia Committee on the Subject of Transatlantic Steam Navigation*, February 7, 1839, N. Biddle, Chairman, Philadelphia, 1839) were unsuccessful and the first American transatlantic steamer from Philadelphia was the "Lafayette" in 1851. America's first steamship company, the Ocean Steamer Navigation Company, was founded in New York in 1845. Their first ship sailed for Liverpool in 1847. N. R. P. Bonsor, *North Atlantic Seaway* (Prescot, Lancashire, England, 1955), pp. 49, 50–52, 71.

[7] Probably from Bache's reports. In his letter to Henry of April 20, 1839, below, Henry James complained of overcrowding on board.

TO WILLIAM STURGEON

Retained Copy,[1] Henry Papers, Smithsonian Archives

Princeton College new Jersey
Nov 1ˢᵗ 1838

Dear Sirs

This letter will be given you by my friend Dr Asa Gray late of New York but now professor of natural History in the new university of michigan.

[1] Not in Henry's hand. The copy has been subject to several sets of alterations, including those of Mary Henry. Misspellings by the original copyist have been retained.

He is not directly in your line but is well known and highly appreciated by those in his own. He is now engaged with Dr Torrey of New York in preparing a general Flora of north armerica. You will find him worthy of your kind attention and you will confer a favour on me by introducing him to the meetings of the Electrical Society. I owe you many thanks for your kind attentions to me while in London and for your rememberances since in sending the copy of the address to the Electrical society.[2] My time has been so much occupied in making up the lee way of my long absence that I have defered to acknowledge the recipts of the paper till now. I have however devoted one of my college vacations to the investigation of one of the branches of our favourite science and will be able short[l]y I hope to send you a copy of my paper on the subject which I have just submitted to the armerican Phil. Society. I send you a small package containing a copy of a report of a comittees of congress on a ridiculous discovery in magnetism and my answer to the same.[3] The article may have [co]me [to] you through some other channel but you must not suppose that it is a fair sample of the general inteligance of our country. Men of any standing in science generaly have treated it with contempt.

I ordered the numbers of your Journal to be sent by mail as soon as published by Mr O Rich No 12 Red Lion Square. He has however been far from punctual. The last number received is one for april of the present year. If I can be of any servece to you in this country command my serveces. With the best wishes for your continued success in the prosecution of sciences.

> I remain with much
> Respect yours &c
> Joseph Henry

[2] A copy of an address by Sturgeon to the London Electrical Society delivered on October 7, 1837, survives in the Henry Library with a notation by Sturgeon, "To Professor Henry From the London Electrical Society."

In this address (reprinted in *Annals of Electricity, Magnetism, and Chemistry*, 1838, 2:64–72) Sturgeon outlined the goals of the London Electrical Society, formed in May 1837 as an outgrowth of a series of lectures he delivered. For Sturgeon, the Society represented an effort to place electrical investigations "on the same footing as the most acknowledged exact science." The organization was to encourage electrical research by providing a forum for discussion and dissemination of information open to amateurs as well as established scientists.

[3] Henry is referring to the Sherwood Memorial.

TO ASA GRAY

Historic Letter File, Gray Herbarium Library, Harvard University

Princeton Nov 1ˢᵗ 1838

My Dear Dr

I have been of late overwhelmed with letters and extraneous business—business as well as trouble seldom comes alone. I have been working very hard at my paper and have broken off by force today to fulfil my duty to you in the way of preparing letters for Europe. I regret that you had not so arranged your affairs as to spend a day or two with me at Princeton previous to your departure since in conversation a thousand things would be suggested which the pen cannot call up. I have given you a letter to Mr Sturgeon[1] who you will find a very honest and hardworking man who has raised himself to considerable standing from the lowest situation. He and Mr Faraday are not on good terms. Mr Sturgeon is at the head of the second rate philosophers of London.[2] I esteem him and think he may be of some advantage to you. Do not fail to give him my letter since it contains other matters than the introduction. You can put the letter into the Post should you not see him and leave the packages at the office of the Electrical Journal. I owe E M Clark Optician Lowther Arcade 12£ 17s. 6d for some app[aratus][3] purchased for the college[4] and enclose money to about that amount which you can dispose off when you purchase the gold coin for your pocket money. Please to pay him as soon as convenient after your arrival in London. Clark is a very good workman and will be very attentive to you. Be cautious with him and while you treat him with apparent unreserve be some what guarded. He treated me very kindly indeed but still I did not put myself in his possession. If I have time I will write to Watkins.[5] Dr Torrey will probably give you a letter to him. You will find him a good fellow and I think very friendly to Dr Torrey and myself. You must patronize him if you can in the way of his business. I will write to him in a few days in answer to a kind letter I received from him.

I also send by you a letter and package to Mr Heripath[6] a cousin of the

---

[1] Printed immediately above.

[2] Sturgeon's passion for formulating theoretical explanations for electromagnetic phenomena in obscure language damaged his reputation. Henry's feelings were mixed: he appreciated Sturgeon's skills as an experimenter, but not as a lecturer or theorist. *Henry Papers*, 3:202, 250, 307–308. For a less charitable view of Sturgeon, see below, Bache to Henry, November 16, 1839.

[3] A tear in the letter.

[4] While in Europe Henry had ordered a galvanometer, a magnetoelectric machine, and a micrometer eyepiece from Clarke. Folder of Accounts with Various Instrument- and Apparatus-Dealers, Joseph Henry for the College of New Jersey, 1837, Princeton University Archives.

[5] Henry didn't write Francis Watkins until June 19, 1839 (printed below).

[6] John Herapath. This letter is printed above.

chemist.[7] This person is an engineer he has sent me several volums of the Rail way Journal. I do not know that he will be of any service to you I have however mentioned you in my letter. This letter you can drop into the office and leave the package at the rooms of the Royal Society in the care of the Assistant Secretary Mr Roberton.[8]

I also give you a letter to Nicol[9] of Edinburgh who was very kind to me. My letter is therefore one of acknowledgment as well as of introduction of you. Please send it by the post if you should not see him. I hope you take according to the promise of Dr Torrey some specimens of fossil wood for Nicol—do not forget [?them. I][10] also give you a letter to Kemp[11] whom you will find a very ingeneous man and very willing to communicate to any person.

I also give you a letter to Dr Holland[12] of London a gentleman to whom I believe I never was regularly introduced but who was always attentive to me when we met. He appears to be a person of leisure is much about the Royal Society and the Royal Institution and I believe is a manager of the latter. He is a great admirer of Mr Faraday and will probably be of service to you. The clock this moment strikes 11 and I start early tomorrow for Philadelphia. I have not given as many letters as I intended you will however find no difficulty on that score too many letters would rather be a burden to you. Should you meet with Dr Torrey's young Quaker friend Mr Christie[13] give him my best respects. I was obliged much against my inclination to name a day on which I would dine with him the time however was well spent and the company at his Fathers[14] house highly respectable and very agreeable. I have little to say in the way of advice. You will probably find it difficult to preserve your equinimity and not find yourself falling into an unnatural state of feelings and actions or in otherwords assuming a character not intirely your own. You will of course be a little watchful of yourself on this point and endeavour to carry yourself as modestly and un-

---

[7] William Herapath (1796–1868) was one of the founders of the Chemical Society of London and the first Professor of Chemistry and Toxicology at the Bristol Medical School. He was frequently called upon as an expert witness in criminal trials. *DNB.*

[8] John David Roberton. *Henry Papers, 3:* 188–189.

[9] Henry had visited William Nicol (1768–1851) twice while in Edinburgh in August 1837. *Henry Papers, 3:*460. The letter of introduction for Gray has not been found.

[10] Rip in the letter.

[11] Kenneth T. Kemp (1806–1843) taught practical chemistry at the University of Edinburgh. *Poggendorff.* We have not discovered the letter to Kemp.

[12] Charles Holland (1802–1876) received his M.D. from the University of Edinburgh in 1824. He was a Fellow of the Royal Society, a Manager and Vice-President of the Royal Institution, and the President of the Royal Medical Society of Edinburgh. Frederic Boase, *Modern English Biography,* 6 vols. (1892–1921; reprint ed., London, 1965), *1:*1507. We have been unable to locate the letter of introduction for Gray.

[13] William Christy, Jr. (1805–1839), the British botanist. For an account of Henry's evening at the Christy residence, see *Henry Papers, 3:*270.

[14] William Miller Christy (1778–1858).

assumingly as is consistant with true dignity of character. England is to us a Fairy Land & when we find ourselves actually there and in the presence of those whom we have long considered almost more than human and find them but men inferior perhaps in some respects to ourselves and treated by them with that attention which forms a part of their hospitality we find ourselves at first a little unsettled when placed in this unnatural condition. Give old Pixii a blowing up about Chiltons apparatus[15] which I purchased and paid for. I am laying out of the use of my money all this while and cannot settle my accounts until the arrival of the articles. Tell him I will advise all americans from dealing with him unless he fulfills his engagement. I regret that I have not a lot of my papers to send with you. I hope however that I will get the article published before you leave England. The investigations are the most important I have ever made. I have an agent in London Mr O Rich no 12 Red Lion Square. I will write to him by the next Packet and thus introduce you. He will be of much service in the way of purchasing books.

Did time and paper permit I would say much more. Send me your address in London. With my warmest wishes for the success of your mission and your safe return to relatives and Friends I bid you a sincere and affectionate adieu.

Joseph Henry

I send the money for Clark to Chilton for him to purchase the bill or the sovereigns.

The package will be sent to Chiltons by Mr Van Doren[16] of Princeton who starts on monday morning.

Dr Holland is vice President of the Royal Institution.

[15] Henry's activity as a go-between for Chilton and Pixii while in Europe is discussed in *Henry Papers*, 3:344. Although Henry was unaware of it, the order for Chilton was finally in transit. The bill which accompanied it was dated October 10, 1838. "Accounts 1837–1838," Box 31, Henry Papers, Smithsonian Archives.
[16] The Princeton College Treasurer John Van Doren (1804–1892). *Henry Papers*, 2:378.

FROM ASA GRAY

Historic Letter File, Gray Herbarium Library, Harvard University

New York, Nov. <7>[1] 6, 1838.

My Dear Sir

Yours of 1st Nov.[2] was duly received, and I thank you very much for your attention, as well as the hints and kind advice you offer. But I am sorry to

[1] Here, and at the end of the letter, Gray wrote the wrong date then corrected himself.
[2] Printed immediately above.

say that the parcels, as well as the letter & enclosure to Chilton have not yet arrived, or had not at 2. P.M. and I had supposed I should have been obliged to sail without the letters of introduction &c. But I am this evening informed that the sailing of the vessel is postponed until Thursday, so that I still have a chance. I need not say that I shall promptly and carefully attend to your several commissions. I wish you would write to Pixii, Dᵣ Torrey will forward your letter with others to meet me at Paris, and then your blowing up will come with more point than through a third person. I would have much pleased to spend a day or two with you, but it has been out of the question wholly. Even now I should not have been ready had not the day been postponed.

When you commence your lectures here, if you should not be here sooner, I wish you would call, with Dᵣ Torrey upon Mr. Davis the Architect, and give him proper views as to the arrangement of rooms for Natural philosophy, Chemistry &c of Our University. He wants data very much, and the assistance you might render would be very important.

Mr. Christie was according to the last accounts very sick, and not expected to survive long.[3] A tumor or some other disease of the spine is said to be the malady.

You may continue to address me in London to the care of your own agent O. Rich of Red Lion Square. It is probable that I shall have business relations with him. Dᵣ Torrey will from time to time be advised of my movements on the continent. Best regards to Mrs. H.

With many thanks for the expression of your kind wishes, I remain

Cordially and very truly

Yours, A. Gray.

P.S. When a definite proposition from Our Board of Regents reaches you, as I hope it may some time next month, I hope you will give the subject a careful consideration—I also hope your views of duty may lead you to embrace the offer.[4] I wrote some time ago to a member of the Board, recommending them to try also for Prof. Alexander, and in case of their being obliged to look among the clergy for a Chancellor, advising them to attempt Dᵣ Ludlow. Silliman it is more than probable will not and could not, leave New Haven, where he is part and parcel of the College.[5] Adieu

A. G.

P.S. 2ⁿᵈᵒ· (Nov. <8> 7ᵗʰ) Parcels arrived at Chilton's. All right.   A.G.

---

[3] William Christy, Jr. (*Henry Papers*, 3:270) died on July 24, 1839.
[4] No offer was made to Henry. See above, Torrey to Henry, August 29, 1838, footnote 7.
[5] There is no evidence in *Proceedings of the* *Board of Regents of the University of Michigan, 1837–1864* (Ann Arbor, 1915) that either Stephen Alexander, John R. Ludlow, or Benjamin Silliman was considered for an appointment.

TO JOHN TORREY

Torrey Papers, Library, New York Botanical Garden

Princeton Wednesday
night ½ past 10 o'clock
PM [November 7, 1838][1]

My Dear Dr

I regret that you have been obliged to send for the mirrors. I have just got back from Phil^d. Started at 10 AM and arrived here at about 7 PM. I went to the city to attend a meeting of the Society and to present my budget of experiments.[2]

Saw Bache who is about to open his new establishment—the Girard College on a small scale.[3] Also our friend Dr Green[4] and his young Daughter of whom he is excessively fond. Dined with Dr Hare and exhibited to him some of my experiments. The Phil^d gentlemen are not disposed to join the Bostonians in the formation of an association for the promotion of science. They think that charlatanism would choak the science.[5] When I returned I found that Little Mary had been quite sick. She is now however somewhat

[1] Supplied from the context and the date of Torrey's reply (November 9).

[2] Henry presented "Contributions III: Electro-Dynamic Induction" to the American Philosophical Society on November 2. A summary appeared in APS *Proceedings*, 1838–1840, *1*:54–56. The paper was referred to Bache, Patterson, and Hare who reported in favor of publication at the meeting of December 21 (ibid., p. 65).

[3] Although Bache and the Board of Trustees hoped to open Girard College in the fall of 1838, at least on a small scale, the College did not open then or at any time during Bache's Presidency.

The counsel to the City of Philadelphia, which was entrusted with carrying out Stephen Girard's will, insisted that according to the will, the College could not open until the buildings were completed. Construction of the first five buildings, designed by T. U. Walter, had begun in 1833. Due to restrictions in the will, Nicholas Biddle's insistence on a monumental Greek Revival style for the main building, depreciation of the currency, and friction between the Board of Trustees and the City Councils of Philadelphia, the buildings were not finished until 1847.

Bache spent much of 1839 preparing his *Report on Education in Europe to the Trus-* *tees of the Girard College for Orphans* (Philadelphia, 1839). In mid-1840 the City Councils recommended that the Girard Board of Trustees discharge the President as his services would not be needed for several years. Bache responded in September by requesting that his salary be discontinued and that he be allowed to devote his time to Central High School (of which he had already been serving as President, without salary, for almost a year). At the close of 1841 the Councils formally abolished both the office of President and the Board of Trustees. Girard College finally opened in 1848.

Following his separation, Bache was allowed to retain temporarily the books and apparatus he had purchased for the College in Europe. He was also allowed to continue operating the magnetic observatory at Girard College; the results of five years of observations (May 1840– June 1845) were published in three volumes in 1847.

Cheesman A. Herrick, *History of Girard College* (Philadelphia, 1927), especially chapters 1 and 5. Merle M. Odgers, *Alexander Dallas Bache* (Philadelphia, 1947), especially chapter 8.

[4] Jacob Green.

[5] See above, J. C. Warren to Henry, September 29, 1838.

better. Prospect of a large class in college.[6] I have determined that the lower room shall be put in some kind of order immediately—the new articles are quite exposed. I hope to have my paper out in a few weeks. It has cost me much labour but was considered in Phil[d] as a very important one.

Mrs Henry sent a letter by mail to Chilton containing 62 dollars intended for Dr Gray to pay a debt of mine in London. The package and the letter were to be sent by Mr Van Doren who notwithstanding his promis to her went off without the articles. The affair gave my wife much trouble and has caused some risk in the conveyance of the articles.

We are pleased to hear that Mrs T is getting on well. I write this while your man is getting something to eat.

In great haste
Yours as ever
Joseph Henry

[6] There were 250 students in 1838–1839 compared with 225 the preceding year and 216 the following year. *Princeton Annual Catalogues*, 1838–1840.

FROM CHARLES G. PAGE

Henry Papers, Smithsonian Archives

Washington Nov 8th 1838

Dear Sir

I recd. yesterday yours of the 31st ult.[1] I am obliged to you for this favour, and should I have committed an error in reference to the claims of individuals to discoveries or inventions in the application of Electro-Magnetism will most readily make reparation in a future communication. I am residing on My Fathers plantation some distance from the city[2] and have therefore no means of immediate access to the journals to refer to dates. I got the impression that Mr Sturgeon was first in the field from a description given in one of the early Nos. of his Annals of a machine which he exhibited in London at an early period of Electro Magnetic science. I had also the impression from Silliman's journal that your invention was later.[3] As soon as oppor-

[1] See above.

[2] Page's father, Jere Lee Page, a retired Salem sea captain, had moved from Massachusetts to Virginia earlier that year. His plantation, which he christened "Pageville," was located five miles west of Washington on the road to Leesburg. Robert C. Post, *Physics, Pat-ents, and Politics: A Biography of Charles Grafton Page* (New York, 1976), p. 7.

[3] In his "Description of an Electro-Magnetic Engine for Turning Machinery," *Annals of Electricity*, 1836, *1*:75–78, Sturgeon stated that his machine was constructed in the autumn of 1832 and first exhibited on March 21, 1833,

tunity offers I will examine the subject particularly, and if I have done you any injustice be assured that I shall be prompt to acknowledge it.[4] I am always desirous, that credit shall be given where it is due, and if I should fail in so doing, that it should be imputed to ignorance on my part rather than to any interested motive. It will give me pleasure to consider this accidental correspondence as an introduction to a good understanding between us, and better feeling than exists generally among the labourers in the cause of science.

Very respectfully yours
Chas. G. Page

---

during a lecture series at the Western Literary and Scientific Institution in London. Henry's machine, reported by him in "On a Reciprocating Motion Produced by Magnetic Attraction and Repulsion," *Silliman's Journal*, 1831, *20*:340–343, anticipated Sturgeon's by over a year.

[4] Page acknowledged Henry's priority in a letter to Silliman which appeared early the following year. *Silliman's Journal*, 1839, *36*:143.

FROM JOHN TORREY[1]
Historic Letter File, Gray Herbarium Library, Harvard University

New York, Nov[r] 9th 1838.

My dear friend.

My assistant Mr. Bourne,[2] (who is an excellent fellow & will do well) brought the mirrors safely—but the *cage* is missing—nor is there any ring for holding a ball. He lost nothing so that if there was any other article belonging to the apparatus it must have been left in Princeton. Please send it if there as soon as you can. There are chances occuring almost every day, & if left at Chilton's I shall get it soon. By some blunder I lost my honest chap Goodrich. He misunderstood my last letter, & supposed I did not wish him, whereas I was greatly disappointed when he told me that he had gone off in rather a sad state of mind to the west to seek his fortune. This new one I know, & he is of excellent family, & hungry for knowledge. I am pleased to hear of your new discoveries in Magnetism & Galvanism. You will doubtless let me know all about them in due time.

I rather think with the Philadelphians, that we can hardly get up yet an

---

[1] Previously published, with minor variations in the text, in Nathan Reingold, ed., *Science in Nineteenth-Century America* (New York, 1964), pp. 90–92. This is in response to Henry's letter of November 7, 1838, printed above.

[2] Probably the R. H. Bourne who attended the College of Physicians and Surgeons during 1835 and 1836. *Columbia Alumni*, p. 253.

Assoc^n for the promotion of Science. There is indeed too much Charlatanism in the Country—enough to overpower *us modest men.*

Dr Gray did not get off till this morning. He was detained yesterday by adverse winds. He got your money & will doubtless faithfully attend to your commissions. He will make a good impression wherever he meets with men who are capable of appreciating him.

If you expect me to come on in the spring, do try & have the lower room fitted up for the class. It is a disgrace to the College that this matter is left unattended to so long, & not only shows me plainly what estimate is put on my branch, but exposes to the public the little interest taken in science by the College.

The University Professors are out with their pamphlet[3] but I don't know whether it will do much good. All but a very small clique understand the whole business very well. It may be of some importance however to put the history in a permanent form.

I went to see some of Davis's plans of the Michigan University a few evenings since. It will be rather an imposing gothic building, but I fear that Davis will not be able to make *working plans,* & that some grievous blunders as to the disposition of the rooms &c. will be made. I gave my views respecting the accommodations for the Chemist & I hope you will give yours when you come here to lecture. It is time that you commenced preparing those lectures. Let me urge you to *write out the lectures in full,* & have them at your fingers ends, & then make an abstract of them. Let all your experiments be numbered & *don't show too much.* You will do well *if you don't try too hard!*

I wish you would lend me for a few days a few articles of electro magnetic app^s—after you have completed the notes that you commenced for me. My class has never seen the El.-Mag. spark. I have not procured these things because they don't properly belong to my course & also because I cannot yet afford to buy them.

When you come to the city I shall of course expect you to use my house as if it were your own. With very kind regards to Mrs. Henry I remain faithfully yours

John Torrey

[3] Professors of the Faculty of Science and Letters, *History of the Controversy in the University of the City of New York* (New York, 1838). For more on the difficulties at New York University which resulted in the firing of almost the entire faculty in September 1838, see *Henry Papers,* 2:155.

FROM E. R. TREMAIN
Henry Papers, Smithsonian Archives

Clinton Hall New York Nov 14th 1838

Dear Sir

On the 22nd ult. I had the pleasure of answering your favor of 19th Oct. requesting you to give the Ass[n] four lectures on magnetism and two on sound, commencing *about* the middle of Jan[y], and asking you to give us the particular subject of *each lecture*, that it might be announced on the programme—since which I have not heard from you.[1]

As it is absolutely necessary that the Lecture Com[e] make a final report of the whole arrangements entered into, in a *few days*, I am obliged to request your attention to the above by *return of mail*.[2]

Sincerely hoping that nothing has occurred to prevent your compliance with the wishes of the Com[e]. I remain Sir

Sincerely and respectfully
Your obt sevt.
E R Tremain Ch[n]
Lec Com[e] M. L. A.

---

[1] For Tremain's letter, see above, Tremain to Henry, October 22, 1838.

[2] A draft, written on the back of this letter, is all that survives of Henry's response. Henry wrote:

answered this the same day it was received. Gave the following program

Lectures on sound
1st Lect. On the origin and propagation
2nd Lect On the Sensation and Instruments of Sound
Lectures on Magnetism &c
1st Lect On Ordinary magnetism
2nd Lect On Terrestrial magnetism
3 Lect On Electro-magnetism
4th Lect On Magneto-Electricity
The first course includes some of the analogies of light and sound and also the general Theory of musical instruments.

The two first lectures on magnetism give an exposition of the principles of the variation of the needle and the application of Terrestrial magnetism to the navigation. The last two give the latest discoveries in electricity and magnetism.

Cause of my long delay in ansring letter been engaged in a series of researches which occupied all time and thoughts.

Program now sent produced upon the spur of the moment &c.

The printed lecture schedule of the Mercantile Library Association for the 1839 season lists Henry's lectures according to the outline given here. Henry's copy of the schedule, postmarked November 27, 1838, is in the Smithsonian Archives.

FROM LEONARD D. GALE

Henry Papers, Smithsonian Archives

New York 32 Waverly Place Nov 23[d] 1838

My Dear Sir,

I am candidate for the Professorship of Chemistry Mineralogy and Geology in Jefferson College[1] at Washington Missisippi which is to go into operation in the month of March next. The Professors however are to be elected as early as practicable and as I am to put in for a chance no time is to be lost. Will you do the favor to address a line directly to the Chairman of the Board of Trustees of Jefferson College Washington Mi. in reference to me as candidate for the above professorship[2] and very much oblige

Your Ob[t] Serv[t] L. D. Gale

P.S. If you have finished your experiments with the wire[3] it would be well to send it so that it may reach here before the closing of navigation for the season but if it be desirable you can keep it till the opening of Spring. If I do not hear from you very soon that the box will be here I will understand that it will remain with you till spring or until further orders. It is probable that nothing will be done with the wire the current season as it is the aim of the company to sell the right directly to the government.[4] The prospect of doing the same with the French Government is quite flattering and Professor Morse is in Paris for the Purpose of completing the negotiation now pending.[5]

[1] Jefferson College was established by the Legislature of the Mississippi Territory in 1803. Lack of an endowment and disputes over the location of the school delayed its opening as an academy until 1811. Various problems continued to plague the school throughout its existence. In March 1838, the President and entire faculty resigned. The Board of Trustees reorganized the college, and sought a new faculty. B. L. C. Wailes, "A Historical Sketch of Jefferson College," in *The Charter and Statutes of Jefferson College, Washington, Mississippi* (Natchez, 1840).

[2] A file note indicates that Henry sent a recommendation to Jefferson College and answered Gale. Neither letter has been located.

[3] For Henry's experiments with Morse's wire, see the "Record of Experiments," October 29, 1838, above.

[4] Morse outlined his ideas for a telegraphic system in a letter to Levi Woodbury in September 1837, offering to demonstrate his invention the following January. Claiming priority in the invention, Morse was willing to sell his rights to enable the government to establish a system administered by the Post Office Department. "Letter from the Secretary of the Treasury, Transmitting a Report Upon . . . Telegraphs," *House Documents*, 25th Congress, 2d Session, 1837–1838, No. 15, pp. 28–31.

[5] Morse obtained a French patent for his telegraph late in 1838. To continue the patent for more than two years, however, the invention had to be put into operation in France. After a successful exhibition of the telegraph before the Académie des sciences, Morse attempted to interest the French government in constructing a line. Morse was still waiting for an audience with the Minister of the Interior in February 1839 and returned to the United States without official French cooperation or endorsement. Carleton Mabee, *The American Leonardo: A Life of Samuel F. B. Morse* (1943; reprint ed., New York, 1969), pp. 218–225.

TO JAMES HENRY

Family Correspondence, Henry Papers, Smithsonian Archives

Princeton Dec [8–17][1] 1838

My Dear James

We are all well. I was much better, but not immediately so, after the working of the pills. Mary Ann[2] arrived the day after your departure and appears quite well pleased with her residence in Princeton. We have also David Kelly[3] with us. He does not sleep however in our house but at his room in the Seminary. Nothing new I have scarcely been out of the campus since your visit. Mary has entirely recovered. The Tavern keeper whom you mention in your letter has gone, it is said, to that common sewer of all rogues, Texas.[4] His furniture was sold to day by the sherif. What a situation the Government of Pennsylvania has got into. We will require a standing Army to keep down mobs &c.[5] I fear our children will not be able to spend there lives under the goodly tree of liberty planted by the heroes of the Revolution. The spirit of 76 appears to be fast evaporating and after it has entirely disappeared we may look for general anarchy and after that peace purchased by the surender of liberty to a Despot.

I am still much engaged in College affairs and am obliged to do double duty on account of my premeditated absence to New York. I am toled that Noah Webster has made an attack on our friend Mr. Bullions through the papers in reference to the appropriation of the labours of the latter gentleman by the former.[6]

[1] Henry dated this letter December 8 but finished it on Monday, December 17.

[2] Mary Ann La Grange (*Henry Papers*, 2:43).

[3] David Kelly (*Henry Papers*, 2:97n) was a second cousin of Henry's.

[4] We have not identified the tavern keeper. The new Texas Republic was viewed as a haven for criminals, derelicts, and adventurers. Although the heavy immigration into Texas in the ten years of the Republic included many less than ideal citizens, the reputation was an exaggeration. See William Ransom Hogan, *The Texas Republic: A Social and Economic History* (Norman, Oklahoma, 1946), especially pp. 266, 297.

[5] Henry is referring to the "Buckshot War," the aftermath of the Pennsylvania gubernatorial and legislative elections of 1838. Although the Democratic candidate for Governor, David R. Porter, received more votes than the incumbent, Joseph Ritner, the Anti-Mason candidate, alleged fraud in Philadelphia left eight House seats contested, enough to deter-

mine the legislative majority and thus affect the certification of the gubernatorial election.

When two rival Philadelphia delegations arrived in Harrisburg, partisan riots began. After President Van Buren refused to send Federal troops, Ritner called in the state militia (who were supplied with buckshot). Meanwhile armed Democrats headed for Harrisburg to prevent a seizure of the governorship by Ritner. The crisis was resolved when disgusted Whig and Anti-Mason senators sided with the Democrats to recognize the Democratic majority in the House. Philip S. Klein and Ari Hoogenboom, *A History of Pennsylvania* (New York, 1973), pp. 133–135. L. S. Shimmel, *A History of Pennsylvania* (Harrisburg, 1900), pp. 205–206.

[6] Henry evidently meant to say that Webster had accused Peter Bullions of piracy. Webster frequently charged other authors with using material from his dictionaries, grammars, and spelling books. By his own account, Bullions had indeed engaged in what was common prac-

The lace sent by Harriet was intended for a collars for Nancy and Mary Ann. The weather has been quite coald since saturday night.

The tavern keeper before mentioned is the person whom you must have seen at the house where you stoped. He was a youngish looking man with blue cloathes. I have forgotten what you told me about the person to whom you loaned the 10 dollars & who lives at Trenton. Write me all the particulars and I will attempt to collect the money. I have the due bill in my pocket book.

I see by the papers that Daniel D Barnard has been lecturing before the Mechanics Institute of Newark.[7] He also is to lecture or has done so before the Mercantile Library association of New York.[8]

Monday Evening Dec 16th[9]

Your letter to Mary Ann was received this afternoon and reminds me that I commenced a letter to you some days since which was at the time interrupted and has not since been resumed. We are sory to hear that Nancy has been unwell but hope she will soon be better. We are all still in good health. A regular snow has commenced this evening which bids fair to give us a foot or more of snow. Little Helen fell against the stove last week and burned her arm somewhat badly. She is however getting along with it pretty well. We are pleased to hear of the mental and Physical developement of the little Henrys in albany. The rising generation of the name form quite a phalanx of genius and precosity. Our children are certainly wonderful specimens that is if their mothers opinion on the subject be taken. Love from all to all. Harriet and the rest of the Family are now in the Parlor attending to a small company consisting of Mr Clow's family and Stephen and Louisa.

As Ever Your
Brother

Mary[10] Ann & I intend to write a joint letter to you soon. One piece of

---

tice, particularly for textbook authors. In the preface to a revised edition of his *Principles of English Grammar* (New York, 1842) he wrote:

> Utility, not novelty, has been aimed at. In collecting materials I have freely availed myself of the labours of others. . . . The works of Murray, Angus, Connel, Grant, Crombie, Hiley, Webster, and others . . . have been consulted; and from all of them has been carefully selected, condensed, and arranged, whatever seemed to be suitable to my purpose.

[7] Probably the Newark Mechanics' Association, organized in 1826 or 1827. By 1834 it had a library and collection of philosophical apparatus. *A History of the City of Newark, New Jersey . . . 1666–1913*, 3 vols. (New York, 1913), 2:770.

[8] Barnard's address, "Commerce as Connected with the Progress of Civilization," was published in *Hunt's Merchants' Magazine*, July 1839, *1*:3–20.

[9] Monday was actually the 17th.

[10] The following, which appears in the margin of the first page of the original, is by Harriet Henry. We are omitting several sentences scribbled by James Henry on the last page of the original near the address. The content (New Year's greetings) indicates that James Henry returned the letter to Joseph shortly after receiving it. If this was common practice

intelligence Jos has not given you. Our poor old Cow lost one of her horns last week—but is recovering. M A & I are going to an Auction.

Love to All

H

---

for both brothers, it may explain why so many of Joseph Henry's letters to his brother survive in the Henry Papers, Smithsonian Archives, and why so few of James Henry's letters to Joseph are found there.

TO WILLIAM C. REDFIELD

Redfield Papers, Beinecke Library, Yale University

Princeton Dec <*8*> 17[th 1] 1838

My Dear Sir

I intend to visit Philadelphia <*next*> this week and will <*then*> attend to your commission[2] with much pleasure. At a meeting of the American Philosophical society a few weeks since at the request of Dr Hare I communicated the facts you had mentioned to me relative to the production of storms by artificial means.[3] Dr Hare was much interested in the matter and took your address for the purpose of writing to you on the subject.[4] I wish at your earliest leisure you would draw up a paper of all the facts since they are very interesting and you should have the credit of collecting them and of first directing attention to them.[5] If you wish, I would be pleased to present your paper to the american Philosophical society. You may however have some hesitation in giving your communication to that body on ac-

[1] Henry apparently began the letter on the 8th and resumed it later, changing the date and some words in the text.

[2] No letter from Redfield dealing with the "commisson" has been found.

[3] Henry's communication was recorded as follows in the minutes of the American Philosophical Society, November 2, 1838:

> Prof^r Henry, at the request of Dr Hare, made a verbal communication to the effect that (on the authority of Mr Redfield) a fire made on a conical hill had been followed by a flowing of the wind towards the fire, a formation of a cloud, violent electrical snaps & a shower: He further referred to a second similar case, the details of which were in the possession of Mr Redfield.

> Dr Hare stated that he considered these facts together with the account of the recent Tornado, given by Mr Allen of Providence, as strongly confirmatory of his theory of Tornadoes.

[4] Hare was interested in the electrical phenomena as evidence for his theory that electricity caused tornadoes (Hare to Redfield, November 6, 1838, Redfield Papers, Beinecke Library). Redfield responded that the account Hare got from Henry was not quite correct, i.e. that the "thunder shower" Hare asked about was more of a nature of "dry columnar whirlwinds." (Redfield to Hare, November 8, 1838, Redfield Papers, Beinecke Library).

[5] Redfield quickly turned out an article, dated December 31, 1838, for *Silliman's Journal*, 1839, *36*:50–59, entitled "Some Account of Violent Columnar Whirlwinds, which Appear to Have Resulted from the Action of Large Circular Fires."

count of the tardiness of publication. They have however of late much improved in this respect.

I regret on my own account and not on your's that you will probably not be in the city at the time of my lectures.[6]

I have been so much employed in college duties and also in the review and preparation of my experiments on electricity for publication that I have as yet not given a thought to my course in New-York. I intend however to begin to make preparations this week.

My paper will contain a greater number of new generic facts than any I have ever published. It has cost me much labour and opens a wide field for farther investigation. Could we in this country devote our whole time to science as is done in Europe and with the same advantages in other respects something more might be achieved to raise the character of our country. Your whirlwinds however have done good service and I hope my papers will not be entirely useless in the same way—but enough of egotism—

With much Respect
Yours sincerely
Joseph Henry

P.S. I have not seen the article to which you allude in the Saturday Courier. Mr Espy is I believe a very honest man and ardently attached to science—in some of his publications however I think he exhibits a want of prudence.[7]

J.H.

---

[6] To the Mercantile Library Association.

[7] Espy's meteorological article, entitled "The Storm of March 17, 1838, Rationale of the Meteorological Discovery," appeared in the *Philadelphia Saturday Courier* of December 1, 1838. The same article appears in the *Franklin Institute Journal*, 1838, 22:224–230. Meteorologist of the joint meteorological committee of the American Philosophical Society and the Franklin Institute, Espy regularly used the Institute's journal to propound his centripetal, or convective, theory of storms (see *Henry Papers*, 2:196n).

Henry's comments reflect the ongoing controversy between Redfield and Espy over the motion and theory of storms. Simply stated, Espy's theory, based on a mechanism of heat and moisture, held that storm winds blew toward the center (the area of low pressure) while Redfield maintained the winds circulated around the area of low pressure. For an analysis of the conflict between the pioneering meteorologists, see Gisela Kutzbach, *The Thermal Theory of Cyclones: A History of Meteorological Thought in the Nineteenth Century* (Lancaster, Pennsylvania, 1979), chapter 2. References to the debate will appear in later documents in this volume.

Redfield, Bache, and evidently Henry, felt that Espy tended to leap too quickly from data to theoretical conclusions, Redfield of course differing on the validity of those conclusions. Although generally sympathetic to Espy, Bache wrote to Humphrey Lloyd of "the strange course recently taken by my friend Mr Espy" (May 4, 1839, Bache Papers, Smithsonian Archives). Later letters in this volume contain cryptic allusions to disparaging comments by Henry on Espy's theories, for example, in Henry to Bache, July 9, 1840.

TO [TRUSTEES, COLLEGE OF NEW JERSEY][1]
Draft, Henry Papers, Smithsonian Archives

[1838][2]

Gentlemen permit me to <*draw your*> ask your atten[tion] to a few statements in reference to my situation in the Philosophi[cal] Hall. <*When I accepted*> Before I was called to the chair of Natural Philosophy in this Institution <*the apparatus*> no lectures had been given on the subject nor experiments show[n] to the class for many years. The apparatus was not only very <*imperfect but also what existed was in a very imperfect state*> defic[ie]nt in quantity but also the articles in a very bad state of preservation. I was only enabled to give my first course of lectures (an imperfect one) by employing a young mechanic to whom I gave board and Instruction for his services at this time how[ever]. Some attendance was given occasionally in the Hall by the college servants but their duties becoming more arduous on account of the increase of students in the college a perminent carpenter was hired one of whoes duty was to attend in the Hall the morn[in]g of my lectures. He however soon became so much occupied in other matters as to be scarce ever in attendance and the next year I was obliged inorder to get along with my course to employ a young [. . .]. This person I retained three years, gave him board and tuition the 1st year and 75 dollars per year in addition the two last years.

<*Since my return from*> During the last year I have had no regular attendance and no assistance but such as has been voluntarily given me by the students of the college and some resident graduats. This kind of assistance I have found by repeated experience to be of little or no value. The young gentlm[en] are unwilling to wash bottles to sweep and carry water and

In conclusion I can truly say that 1/3 of all my time since my connection with this institution has been <*therein employed*> waisted in making extemperary articles <*of apparatus*> to supply deficences of the apparatus and in doing the d[r]ugery of a mere servant. The duty I owe a you[ng] and rising family will no longer permit me to incur the expense of employing an assistant and a consideration of the value of my time at this period of my life <*will not permit*> forbi[d]s me long to wast[e] my time in duties incompatible with the dignity of a professor or the prosecution of Science.

---

[1] We assume the Princeton Trustees were the intended recipients of Henry's plea for laboratory help. We cannot say if this draft was actually formally presented. Henry did receive a laboratory assistant in spring 1840 (see below, Henry to James Henry, December 23, 1840).

This messy draft has been subjected to considerable silent editing for the sake of clarity.
[2] We infer the date from Henry's possible allusions to his return from Europe at the start of paragraph two.

TO THE EDITOR[1]

Retained Copy, Henry Papers, Smithsonian Archives

[ca. 1838][2]

MR EDITOR I perceive that you have copied into the last no of your interesting and amusing publication an article which has been going the rounds of the papers under the title of *Powers of Electricity* in which it is stated that a salad of mustard or water cresses may be produced in a few moments by the assistance of electricity and that rain water apparently free from any noxious animalcule in an hour may be rendered full of insects.[3] Permit me to assure you that both these statements are without foundation. The first has been periodically called from temporary oblivion by the papers in this country for the last 30 years. It was first published in the Travels of a young American (E Watson) in Europe,[4] who saw a Parisian jugler perform the 'trick' of producing a crop of salad in a few minutes and gravely published the "sleight of hand" as the important discovery of a new electri[cal] action. The second is from the wonderful accounts of the experiments made by Mr Cross of England a few years since which however have been proved to be incorrect by several members of the British association. The water used by Mr Cross was previously impregnated with the eggs of the insects and after the exposure of *nine* or *ten* days to the constant action of a galvanic battery the animals were developed. Where pure water was employed no effect of the kind was produced and it has not yet been proved that the result was not due to the ordinary vivifying influence of the air and warmth or that electricity had anything to do with the process.

F.[5]

[1] This retained copy contains neither the name of the publication nor of the individual to whom a final copy may have been sent. Henry's characterization of the publication as "interesting and amusing" suggests a magazine, rather than a newspaper.

We have been unable to locate a published version of this letter.

[2] The letter is undated. Henry's reference to a British Association meeting "a few years back" indicates a post 1837 date.

[3] On September 17, 1836, the *Genessee Farmer* printed an article entitled "New Application of Electricity." This was reprinted with only minor variations in the *Newark Daily Advertiser* on October 25, 1836, as "Electricity," in *The Cultivator* (Albany) in November

1836, under the original title, and in the *Pennsylvanian* on January 24, 1837. A note concerning the apparent generation of insects by electricity reported by Andrew Crosse (see *Henry Papers*, 3:320–322) appeared in the *Norfolk Advertiser* (Dedham, Massachusetts) as "Wonders of Galvanism" on September 30, 1837. Apparently both stories were still in circulation several years later.

[4] Neither Elkanah Watson's *Men and Times of the Revolution* nor *A Tour in Holland* contains this story. A search of various travel accounts of Americans in Europe prior to 1820 has not revealed the source of the tale.

[5] Henry's letter to the Editor of the *Newark Daily Advertiser* (see above, August 1, 1838) was also signed "F."

⊰{ 1839 }⊱

TO ALEXANDER DALLAS BACHE
Bache Papers, Smithsonian Archives

[January 3, 1839][1]

My Dear Bache

My lectures on sound commence next week in New York and on account of an \<*review*\> article which has just appeared in the New York revew, I am now somewhat anxious to exhibit some of Savarts late apparatus.[2] If you think it compatible with your duty can you furnish me with some pieces which are new and would answer for exhibition. Send them by the bearer or give me information when they will be ready and I will send a special messenger for them. The Bearer[3] is a son of Dr Alexander and will be careful of the articles.

In great haste
Yours as ever
Jos Henry

[1] The date is from a file note.
[2] The article (*New York Review*, January 1839, *4*:164–178) was a review of Benjamin Peirce, comp., *An Elementary Treatise on Sound* (Boston, 1836), a book which Henry acquired in August 1838. The reviewer was familiar with Savart's work. He mentioned in particular Savart's study of Chladni figures and his method of copying them by using litmus and adhesive paper, as well as Savart's demonstration of streams and sheets of water dancing to music.

The *New York Review* was a quarterly which appeared from 1837 to 1842. The editorship was held at various times by the Reverend Francis L. Hawks, the Reverend Caleb S. Henry, and Joseph G. Cogswell (all *DAB*). The *Review* covered science, economics, education and political science in addition to religion and literature. Frank Luther Mott, *A History of American Magazines, 1741–1850* (New York, 1930), pp. 367, 669–671.
[3] Samuel Davies Alexander.

FROM ALEXANDER DALLAS BACHE
Henry Papers, Smithsonian Archives

Philad. Jany 12. 1839

Dear Henry,

Your notice has been rather short, tho' I have laid by every thing to attend to it. I have not been able to get hold of the art. in the N.Y. review in time. I have only a metallic bell (timber) of Savarts & am sure that the sand would not show on it at night and that for a large audience it would be a failure.[1] The articles of Cagniard de Latour[2] I send as follows. They are

[1] A very thin membrane was stretched over the opening of a bell, circular bowl, or simi-

larly shaped instrument. If sand was scattered on the membrane, the instrument served as a

novelties. As they are not my own I impose a condition viz: that they be not used with the mouth but with a bellows. Do not I pray you neglect this. If this go hard have a chimney made, the prismatic square ones ought to have such a thing but I do not find it. ab is the art. & slides into the prism, it contracts the puffing aperture. If the translation of Cagniards last observations on the voice[3] is not done in time for Mr Alexander I shall send it to you by mail forth with, it is in hand.

Now for the articles.

N° 1. Bears on action of glottis. If the same sound proceeds from both plates their vibration is not perceptible. A bit of wax on one or the other, its size being regulated, will regulate the sound & bring them to the same tone, if not now right. It will illustrate the [?reed] action if not to a larger class [?what] it is intended for. This has a chimney.

N° 2. Sounds produced by mere interruption of vibrating columns periodically.

Manner of interrupting column determines quality (timber) & intensity of sound. Thus—

A. Prismatic tube with a partition. Var 1 four leaves closing twice per rev^n Var. 2. Two leaves on one plane.

With partition the closure is sudden without it is gradual.

B. Prism without partit^n Var 1. four leaves to compare with n° 2. A. Var. 1. Var 2. 3 leaves. When in motion this one keeps moving in same direction if current be reversed, or *drawn in* after being *puffed out*.

C. Round tube with partit^n for comparison with B Var. 1.

D. Ditto with partition lengthened so as to make closure gradual & confirm the idea above stated as to cause of change of quality & intens^y Gradual should *soften* sound.

E. Round like B. Var I. With a cross tube to represent ventricules their effect in reinforcing the sound of the voice. Var I. Var 2. With variable size of pipe to show that when size is of certain extent doubling it will not change materially the tone. When an india rubber bag is added so as very greatly to extend size then a change is produced. This piece is broken (a) is to be soldered to (b). The piston requires leathering.

---

delicate detector of sound waves. This would be a fine demonstration apparatus for a small class. Benjamin Peirce, *An Elementary Treatise on Sound* (Boston, 1836), p. 151.

[2] Charles Cagniard de la Tour (1777–1859). *DSB.*

[3] This is probably a reference to Cagniard's "Recherches sur la voix humane," *Extraits des procès-verbaux des séances de la Société Philomatique*, 1838, pp. 21–24, 105–108. The translation has not survived in the Henry Papers.

No 3. Trumpet Syren[4] by enlarging opening of Syren & dim^g number of holes quality changes.

You have the old Syren

Yours ever

A D Bache

N°s 1 & 2 are in the box.

N°3. Mr Alexander took charge of to put in his trunk. Be careful in packing it as the points are frail.[5]

---

[4] An instrument to produce sound by controlling the flow of a fluid through a pipe by means of a rotating, perforated disk. Described by Cagniard in 1819, the siren produced the same sound whether the fluid was air or water, demonstrating that pitch was independent of the medium through which the sound waves were sent. Peirce, *Treatise on Sound*, p. 67. Henry had purchased one while in France. *Henry Papers*, 3:543.

[5] Originally written under the address on the outer side of the sheet.

FROM JAMES KAY, JR.[1]
Henry Papers, Smithsonian Archives

Philad. 18 Jan. 1839.

Dear Sir,

Along with this sheet you will receive the first proof of your paper in the Transactions, which is sent to you by Mr Lea's[2] request for your approval. He requests, if agreeable to you, that the proofs may be read in this city, as the transmission of proofs, as I have learnt from experience in the case of Princeton, is attended with great delay. Owing to my ill health, we are doing no composition except that of the Phil. Transact., and if the proofs are sent out of the city, the single workman we have would not have employment nearly all his time, and might leave us. After presenting these considerations, I will leave to your discretion to decide as may be in your opinion most expedient. Mr Lea has sent your figures to a wood engraver to be executed in wood, none of which we have as yet received. The proof now sent has references to one or two of them; but whether they should be inserted at the places which refer to them, I am at a loss. I am afraid that the paper has been written in the idea that the figures were to be placed collectively on one or more copperplates. If my surmise should be correct, I do not know how we shall determine where the cuts are to come in. I have

---

[1] James Kay, Jr. (ca. 1804–1856), a prominent Philadelphia publisher, was the American Philosophical Society's printer. *Hough*, p. 233.

[2] Isaac Lea, a member of the Committee of Publication.

glanced through the paper, and do not see anything which will remove this difficulty. We send this proof, however, without the cuts; & if any should be inserted, please mark them at the proper places.[3] I may remark, by the way, that the paper does not appear to be finished. It makes sense at the conclusion; but has not a full point at the end of it. Paragraph 133 is the last.[4]

On the other leaf of this sheet we transmit a bill which we believe has not been settled. The last time we applied for it was in May 1837, and probably you were in Europe at the time. We have added the interest for the delay after the ordinary period, which we hope you will think right and fair.

I have a recollection that you called at our store & requested some extra copies; but I have forgotten what the number of copies was, if you said anything on the subject. Also say, if you should need any, whether you wish the paging altered from that of the Transactions, and if you will need a title page. I believe you had 120 copies last time.[5]

This sheet and the proof are sent to New York by direction of M[r] Lea, and if you should be able, we hope you will send them back by return of mail.

very respectf.
James Kay, Jr

M[r] Lea proposes that Professor Bache should read your proofs.

Philad. August 15, 1835.

Professor Henry
   To Kay & Brother, D[r]
To printing 120 Extra copies of his paper in the Transactions
   of the Amer. Phil. Society ———————————————— 23.97 ½
     Cr.
1835.   Oct. 6.   By Cash ———————————————— 9.00
                                                  $14.97 ½
Interest for 3½ years at 6 percent per annum   3.00
                                                  $17.97 ½

[3] The sixteen woodcuts in "Contributions III" are scattered throughout the text.
[4] Henry added a concluding paragraph (#134) to satisfy Kay's objection.
[5] Henry did order reprints of "Contributions III." A copy in the Henry Library has a title page and a table of contents. The pagination, which differs from that of the *Transactions*, is a continuation of the pagination of the reprint of "Contributions I and II."

TO HARRIET HENRY
Family Correspondence, Henry Papers, Smithsonian Archives

New York Wednesday Jany [23, 1839]

My dear H

I made my debut last night[1] and although the weather was quite stormy I had an audience of more than a thousand persons.

I was much pleased to learn that the lectures were not public but only to the members of the association. There has been a great call for tickets but none are to be procured. The whole affair is exclusive and consequently excites the more interest. I called on Mr Irlans[2] family and left my card for Anna[3] which is a passport for my friends. I allso gave John McMullen a ticket for himself and Lucinda.[4] I saw them among the audience. After the lecture the most inquisitive of the Institution keept me until ½ past 10 o'clock answering questions & giving additional explanations so that the subject excited much interest. I got along I think tolerably well—not a single experiment failed. I have commenced to day to prepare for my next lecture so as to take time by the fore lock. I am making arangements for the interesting experiment playing the enchanted Lyer by sympathy *ie* to transmit the sound of one instrument to another at a distance.[5]

I was somewhat unwell yesterday did not sleep well for some nights but I am much better to day. Mr Blany[6] was quite anxious to have Miss Rice[7] at the lecture and procured a ticket for the purpose but the stormy weather prevented her attendance (The younger Miss Rice).

I have no news. I see nothing of the city but confine my self to the library the lecture room and my study.

I hope you are all getting along smoothly at home. I intend to be with you on saturday night if I should not happen to be left by the cars. Dr Torrey called yesterday and was sorry he could not attend my lecture. It was lecture night with him.

Thomas Shankland[8] called on me and requested that I would come and stay with him but I have not found time to call as yet.

I have received from the printer at Philadel[phia] the first proof of my paper. He says that it will be impossible for him to go on with the printing

---

[1] His Mercantile Library Association lectures.
[2] i.e., Mr. Ireland.
[3] Maybe John R. Ludlow's wife.
[4] Lucinda McMullen.
[5] See the next document.
[6] J. V. Z. Blaney, for whom see above, "Record of Experiments," August 3, 1838.

[7] Probably one of the four daughters of Benjamin Holt Rice, pastor of the Presbyterian Church in Princeton, 1833–1847. *Hageman*, 2: 133–143.
[8] Probably a relative of P. V. Shankland of Albany.

if the proof is not read in the city. I have therefore been obliged to call again on Bache to take charge of the article and see that it is well done.
Wednesday evening

This is a very cold night. Dr Torrey has just left me. He came all the way f[rom. . .][9] to see me. He is about mak[ing] efforts to establish a galery of science in New York.[10] Intends to apply for an act of incorporation. There is to be a meeting at his house some time next week on the subject.

I intend to go to bed immediatly, it is now about half past ten. This letter will be taken by the servant to the office early in the morning so good night my Dear little W. I wish you and ours were with me but I hope to see you in the course of a few days.

Your own as ever
J H

---

[9] The letter is torn at the seal. About one missing word.

[10] See above, Henry to Torrey, April 16, 1838, footnote 5.

TO ALEXANDER DALLAS BACHE
Bache Papers, Smithsonian Archives

New York Jany [25][1] Friday
1839

My Dear Bache

I have this evening finished my short course on sound.[2] The whole has passed off with considerable eclat. I had a very select audience on each night

---

[1] The date is that of Henry's second lecture on sound.

[2] Henry divided his two lectures on sound into "The Origin and Propagation of Sound," delivered on January 22, and "On Sensation and Instruments of Sound," delivered on January 25. *New York Daily Express*, January 22 and 25, 1839.

Henry prepared carefully for these lectures and illustrated them heavily with drawings and demonstrations. Many of the items in the folder "Lectures on Sound," Box 18, Henry Papers, Smithsonian Archives, were probably part of his preparation for the two Mercantile Library Association lectures. The material includes drafts of remarks, lists of experiments, sketches, and reading notes. The first item,

almost certainly a partial draft of remarks for this occasion, includes the following:

I accepted the invitation with considerable hesitation since the art of lecturing is one to which I have paid little or no attention and I now present my self almost for the first time before a large and popular audience <and> not knowing not how I may succeed. I have however been assured by your committee that I <will> shall find here an indulgent and liberal audience who will be more disposed to regard the matter of my communication<s> than the manner in which it is presented. . . My object will be to communicate useful <know> interesting and useful knowledge <to attempt

of from 1000 to 1200 persons. I exhibited nearly a hundred experiments and among others the one by Wheatston on the conduction of musical sound. The effect of this was really magical. The audience appeared mute with astonishment. The arrangement was as follows. An upright piano was placed in an adjoining room, the door between was opened and the orifice filled with a double temporary door through which the rod from the soundingboard passed. Two rubber bottles prevented the touching of the rods with the sides of the hole in the doors. The rods were carried upwards to the middle of the large lecture room a distance of about 40 feet and there terminated in one of the bottom holes of a guitar into which the strings were fastened. The instrument had the appearance of being suspended in mid air and at a signal gave forth enchanting sounds. I was surprised and delighted with the effect and had no idea of the loudness and distinctness of the music which could be produced in this way.[3]

I made but little use of the articles in the small box but exhibited with good effect the plates. They perform admirably. The round one with a hole in the centre gave 6 or 8 concentric circles of the most perfect regularity. The large ones also are very perfect. These plates and the other experiments have excited so much interest that I have been requested to repeat some of them to the Ladies on Wednesday.[4]

---

merely to amuse would be beneath the dignity of science and unworthy this audience> in as simple and plain a manner as possible. And I <*shall*> must therefore consider my audience all interely ignorant of the subjects on which I speak. This I know is far from being the case but what is known to one may be new to another.

Henry then gave a definition of sound and the principles of its production and propagation. In the lecture on the perception of sound, he discussed musical sounds and instruments, described the structure and functioning of the human ear, and made further comments on the vibration of plates. Throughout the lectures, he illustrated his remarks by speaking through tubes, ringing gongs and bells, vibrating plates and rods, making tuning forks dance and plates speak.

[3] This experiment was based on Charles Wheatstone's enchanted lyre. See Brian Bowers, *Sir Charles Wheatstone* (London, 1975), pp. 7–8.

[4] The production of Chladni figures was a perfect demonstration for Henry's course. The geometric patterns formed by the sand when the plates were vibrated not only illustrated the principles of the vibration of surfaces but were very beautiful and intrigued the audience.

TO ROBERT HARE

Retained Copy, Henry Papers, Smithsonian Archives

New York Jany 29th 1839

Dear Sir

I left Philadelphia so early on monday morning after my interview with you that I could not call for the long wire coil which you were so good as to consent to sell me at the price of cost. Will you send it to me by the bearer Mr Turnbull[1] of New York. Below I have drawn a check on the Princeton Bank for 25 dollars which will be honored as soon as presented. I will pay you the ballance should there be any when I next visit your city.

If it be convenient will you do me the favour to lend me your ribond coil to use with the long wire one. I will re[turn][2] it before you will have occasion to use [it].

I have finished tonight my third lecture before a select audience of about 1200 persons. The lectures are not public but are to the Members of the Clinton Hall Library association.

I wish to show as many interesting experiments as possible and am therefore desirous of having your coil.

Will you direct your man to put up the articles in a box directed to me care of the Mercantile Library association New York.

N.B. Please send in the same box my Thermo Electrical apparatus.

With Much Respect
Sincerely yours &c
Joseph Henry

[1] John Turnbull frequently acted as a go-between for Henry and other scientists, as well as a scientific informant. *Henry Papers, 1:*355.
[2] This letter is torn at the bottom.

TO HARRIET HENRY

Mary Henry Copy, Memoir, Henry Papers, Smithsonian Archives

New York [Tuesday][1] ½ past 10 [February 5–6][2] 1839

My dear H   I have just come from the Hall. I have been holding forth to a large and attentive audience. I was much afraid when I commenced that I would not have sufficient matter to occupy the hour and a half, but although a part of my experiments had to be abandoned I found I had prepared more than sufficient to fill the time. I lectured on electro-magnetism. I produced something of a sensation by my remarks on the subject of the quackery in the city of New York. The audience however took the whole in good part and appeared impressed with the truth of my statements.[3]

[1] The copyist incorrectly wrote "Friday."
[2] Henry's lecture on electromagnetism, the fifth in the series, took place on February 5, 1839. *New York Commercial Advertiser*, February 5, 1839.
[3] See also Henry to Bache, October 28, 1839, below.

Wednesday evening—I have been out all day arranging matters for my next lecture. Will be home on Saturday. I have received some of the first sheets of my paper now publishing in Philadelphia and I am much pleased with its appearance.

TO JAMES HENRY

Mary Henry Copy,[1] *Henry Papers, Smithsonian Archives*

Princeton, Feb. 12th, 1839

Dear James. We plead guilty in having been very remiss in reference to the answer of your many letters. We have, however, some excuse to offer but know not if it will be considered valid. This session of college has been one of the most laborious seasons of my life. I was at first engaged in preparing for the press a series of experiments until about six weeks since, when I commenced to make drawings and preparations for a course of lectures before the Mercantile Library Association of New York, and in order to get away from college in the midst of the session, I was obliged to do double duty. My course in New York is just finished. I returned on Saturday after a residence of three weeks in New York. My lectures, six in number, were on sound and magnetism. They were not public and only attended by the members of the Association and the female relatives of the members. The whole went off as well as I could expect. Although the subjects were not such as to be generally popular, most of the members became highly interested. The audience, every night, was large—from eight to ten hundred—and attentive. I did not accept the invitation on account of fame. To be considered a lecturer is not in the line of my ambition.

I went with the prospect of being well paid and I was not disappointed. I received six hundred dollars for six lectures with the expense of the apparatus and the arrangements of the lectures. I have now commenced with my class and intend to take the world a little easier until the end of the session. In the New York Times there is a notice of my lectures in which the writer says, I stated that the electro magnetic power can be obtained on a large scale for machinery.[2] I made no such statement but said, that in the

---

[1] The text of this letter is actually a composite of two different Mary Henry Copies. The opening two sentences come from a version in the Mary Henry Memoir, Henry Papers, Smithsonian Archives; the remainder is from the text cited.

[2] We have been unable to locate such a notice in the *Times and Commercial Intelligencer*, or in any other New York newspaper.

present state of Science it could not be obtained sufficiently cheap to compete with steam, that it would cost at least one hundred times more to do the same amount of work with galvanism than with steam. . .[3]

[3] Henry is simply repeating a position he had taken as early as 1835. *Henry Papers,* 2: 448. For a fuller discussion of Henry's evaluation of electricity as a source of power, see Arthur P. Molella, "The Electric Motor, the Telegraph, and Joseph Henry's Theory of Technological Progress," *Proceedings of the Institute of Electrical and Electronics Engineers,* 1976, *64*:1274–1276.

FROM ROBERT M. PATTERSON

Henry Papers, Smithsonian Archives

(*Strictly Confidential.*)

Philadelphia, Feb. 12/39.

Dear Sir,

A change is contemplated in the Mint which will leave vacant the office of Melter and Refiner.[1] Let me ask if you would be willing to accept this situation. The salary is $2000, only, but the occupation (crede experto) is far more pleasant than that of a teacher. You would have time for your favorite pursuits, and means at command. Then you could give popular lectures, &c. &c.

Think of this. If you speak of it, it must be only to your wife, and with strict injunctions of secrecy. Either answer me by letter, or, what will be better, come to see me.[2]

Very truly your friend,
R. M. Patterson.

[1] Franklin Peale (1795–1870), who had held the office since 1836, was vacating it to become Chief Coiner. While Evans calls him a "model officer," Taxay notes that President Pierce's dismissal of Peale in 1854 "closed a chapter in the history of scandals which distinguish the second Philadelphia Mint." George G. Evans, ed., *Illustrated History of the United States Mint,* rev. ed. (Philadelphia, 1887), pp. 110–111, 112. Don Taxay, *The U.S. Mint and Coinage* (New York, 1966), pp. 178–183, 185–191; quotation from p. 191.

[2] Henry's reply of February 18 is printed below.

TO JOHN TORREY

Torrey Papers, Library, New York Botanical Garden

Princeton Friday Evening
Feby [16–19] 1839[1]

My Dear Dr

I embrace the first leave after my return to make out a few notes for you on the subject of electro magnetism.[2] I can not find those I formerly prepared for you. My library and papers have been twice removed since they were penned. I hope you will be able to make out something from my scrawl but fear you will find some difficulty.

I am now much engaged in making up for lost time with my class and have lectured 5 times this week besides heard recitations. I am also superintending the repairs of the upper room of the Philosophical hall which (the hall) is now in a state of great confusion.[3] I am obliged to prepare my exper[imen]ts in the little room and then carry the apparatus over to the Library in the room adjoining which I now lecture. The room upstairs in the Phil Hall will be finished before you arrive and it is with a view to this that I am hurring on with the work.

I found my Family all well when I reached home—was much rejoiced to have finished my not very agreeable job. I however was pretty well reconciled to the affair by the pay which I receved. The sum was the same as that which you had stated 100 dollars per lecture. The money comes in good time since my expences in getting into our new house has been quite heavy.

I hope you and Mrs T will forgive me for not calling at your House. I receved a scolding from my wife for not doing so but I was sick all the time during my lectures and on saturday was only just able to get my articles packed and to get off for Princeton in the evening line. I will make up for all remissness when I next visit the city and will probably stay so long that you will become tired of me.

When you come on in march bring Mrs T and the litle ones with you particularly the little chemist. Mrs H is anxious to see the little gentleman.[4]

Mr Blaney informes me that James Chilton was quite unwell when he

---

[1] February 16, 1839, was a Saturday, not a Friday.

[2] See above, Torrey to Henry, November 9, 1838.

[3] Extensive renovations were undertaken in Philosophical Hall during 1839. The remodelling, which involved both Henry's natural philosophy quarters on the upper floor and Torrey's chemical laboratory below, put heavy demands on Henry's time and hampered his experimental output. Despite his not infrequent complaints on that score (which appear throughout this volume), Henry seemed well pleased with the improvements made under his superintendence (see especially his letter to Torrey of May 31, 1839, below). *Princeton Annual Catalogue*, 1839.

[4] Herbert Gray Torrey, who had been born the previous October. See above, Henry to Torrey, October 30, 1838.

left the city on Tuesday. I hope his illness is not of a serious nature. I have anounced to the class that you will exhibit to them the interesting experiment of the solidification of carbonic acid.[5] Mr Blaney informes me that your apparatus suceeds most admirably.

I learn by the papers that Dr Mathews has resigned his office in the University and that Thedor Freelinghuysen of Newark has been appointed to succed him.[6] What does this portend? I have been receving wood from Mr Jager[7] in order to settle the amount of his debt to you, good hickory at the rate of 6 dollars per cord. What a melancholy affair the loss of the American Packets is.[8] Have you as yet heard from Gray. It is time almost that a letter should arrive.[9]

I do not intend to visit Philadelphia until you come on to Princeton. Perhaps you will find time to accompany me.

Feby 19th 1839

I have been interrupted every night for some time past and have not found time to complete my notes for you until this evening. I lecture to the class every morning and have recitation in the afternoon and besides this am engaged in attending to the work men who are engaged in the Hall. Your kind letter[10] came to hand to day and much to my joy did not give me a scolding for my remissness. The class are nearly all provided with books and I gave notice this afternoon that no one should be without one by the first of march. I hope you will be able to make out something from the notes I send you but I have written them so hastily that I fear it will be a difficult matter. The college will take your apparatus and be much obliged by the opportunity. The appropriation will be made at the next meeting of the Board in april. I will have my litle room put in order for you and strive to make your stay in the Borrough agreeable. I will speak to Mr

---

[5] For this experiment, which Henry had seen performed in Paris in May 1837, see *Henry Papers*, 3:371–374.

[6] James M. Mathews's controversial tenure as chancellor of the University of the City of New York (now New York University) is discussed in *Henry Papers*, 2:115, 155.

Theodore Frelinghuysen (1787–1862), New Jersey attorney and Princeton graduate, was unanimously elected chancellor of the University on March 18, 1839, following Mathews's resignation on February 11. Frelinghuysen, who had achieved national prominence in the U.S. Senate (1829–1835), was the unsuccessful Whig vice-presidential candidate in 1844. *DAB*; Theodore Francis Jones, ed., *New York University, 1832–1932* (New York, 1933), p. 54.

[7] Benedict Jaeger.

[8] The "Liverpool Hurricane" of early January 1839, off the west coast of England, was the greatest single disaster to befall the New York packet fleet. Two ships, the *Pennsylvania* and the *St. Andrew*, were destroyed, while two others, the *Oxford* and the *Cambridge*, escaped with only minor damage. Fifteen lives were lost, all from the *Pennsylvania*, the heaviest death toll in the New York packet service between 1824 and 1847. The total marine losses resulting from the storm were estimated by Lloyd's at £500,000. The disaster led to the establishment of England's first life-saving service. Robert G. Albion, *Square-Riggers on Schedule* (Princeton, 1938), pp. 209–210.

[9] Asa Gray had sailed for Europe on November 9, 1838.

[10] Not found.

Maclean about a boy—you will find no difficulty in getting assistants. There are several who will be glad to come under your direction in that line.

I have set Mr Blaney at the job of making out a catalogue of the artcles on hand with the quantities of each so that you will know what we want by what we have. The office is closing and therefore I must also close in Haste Yours as Ever

TO ROBERT M. PATTERSON
Mary Henry Copy, Henry Papers, Smithsonian Archives

Princeton Feb. 18th 1839

Dear Sir   Your kind communication[1] came to hand just as I returned from my course of lectures in New York and extra college duties have prevented my reflecting seriously on your proposition until Saturday. I have conferred with my wife on the subject and have come to the conclusion that while the salary is no less than that we receive in Princeton the advantages for the prosecution of science, with the exception of being in the city, are no greater than those I now enjoy. The Trustees of the college have lately erected for us a very pleasant commodious house and a series of improvements are in progress for my better accommodation in the philosophical line. I have now to thank you for three propositions of the kind and although I have not accepted the offers they will always be remembered by me as an evidence of your esteem and friendship.[2]

[1] Of February 12, above.

[2] In 1835 Patterson recommended Henry to be his successor at the University of Virginia when he resigned to become Director of the Mint (*Henry Papers*, 2:421). A year later Patterson nominated Henry for Bache's Chair of Natural Philosophy and Chemistry in the University of Pennsylvania (*Henry Papers*, 3:82–83).

In a letter to President Van Buren of March 11, 1839, Patterson outlined the steps he had taken so far to fill the office of Melter and Refiner. After recommending James C. Booth, who had no political affiliation, Patterson explained:

It was my wish that this office should be filled,—not by <*an active politician*> a busy partisan,—but by a known Democrat, and, with this view, I have applied confidentially to three unexceptionable individuals, and I regret to say that, <*they*> in consequence of the low salary of but $2000, they all declined being named to you for the place.

They are Professor Henry of Princeton, and Professor Vethake and Franklin Bache of this <*place*> city.

(General Correspondence, Records of the U.S. Mint at Philadelphia, Records of the Bureau of the Mint, RG 104, National Archives). Henry's refusal was not however based on salary; Princeton paid him $1,500 a year plus the use of a house. Furthermore, Henry always preferred to keep his political affiliations to himself. See his comment to John Stevens Henslow in his letter of December 2, 1839, printed below.

Despite Patterson's recommendation of Booth, the appointment went to Franklin Peale's friend Jonas R. McClintock. Using political pull himself, Booth became Melter and Refiner in 1849 and held the post for the rest of his life. George G. Evans, ed., *Illustrated History of the United States Mint*, rev. ed. (Philadelphia, 1887), pp. 112–113. Don Taxay, *The U.S. Mint and Coinage* (New York, 1966), p. 182. *DAB*, s.v. "Booth, James Curtis."

I have received the first sheet of my paper and am much pleased with the execution of the wood cuts &c. With respect and esteem

Yours &c &c Joseph Henry

FROM LEONARD D. GALE
Henry Papers, Smithsonian Archives

Friday morn
[February 1839][1]

My Dear Sir,

Mr Smith[2] to whom Prof Morse communicated the latest information that has reached here from Paris where Prof M. now is, is now in the city and has permitted me [to] read it. The date is Decr 7 '38.[3] I will [copy] an extract or two in his own words relative to the present condition of the telegraph.

"The Government have received the report of the Admistrator of Telegraphs and have given opinion in favor of mine and the matter is daily expected to come before the chamber of Deputies.[4] I have since my last made great improvements in the portrule and have so simplified the whole apparatus that it may be put into a box 9 inches long 6 wide & 4 deep—I do away with all but a single alphabet of type and therefore have no use for boxes of type or composing sticks. Each type is used as wanted by a single touch of the finger and falls into its place when it has struck the letter.[5]

---

[1] From Henry's file note; Gale did not date the letter.

[2] Francis O. J. Smith (1806–1877) was one of Morse's partners. A Democratic Congressman from Maine from 1833 to March 1839, Smith was chairman of the House Committee on Commerce in 1838 when Morse presented his telegraph for consideration. Shortly after signing a partnership agreement, Smith recommended an appropriation of $30,000 for Morse. He then took a leave of absence from Congress to accompany Morse to Europe to arrange foreign patents. Leaving Morse in Europe, Smith returned in October 1838 to serve out his term. Although the Morse-Smith relationship soon soured, Smith clung tenaciously to the partnership and repeatedly asserted his rights to profits from the telegraph. Morse's son claimed that "his animosity and unscrupulous self-seeking constituted the greatest cross which Morse was called upon to bear" (Edward Lind Morse, ed., *Samuel F. B. Morse: His Letters and Journals*, 2 vols. [Boston and New York, 1914], 2:313). See Carleton Mabee, *The American Leonardo: A Life of Samuel F. B. Morse* (1943; reprint ed., New York, 1969), especially chapter 17.

[3] Not found either in Smith's papers at the Maine Historical Society and New York Public Library or in Morse's papers at the Library of Congress.

[4] See Gale to Henry, November 23, 1838, above.

[5] Morse gave a more detailed description of the new transmitter in a letter to Smith of January 28, 1839:

The invention of the correspondent, I think you will say, is a more essential improvement. It has been my winter's labor, and, to avoid expense, I have been compelled to make it entirely with my own hands. I can now give you its exact dimensions—twelve and a half inches long, six and a half wide, and six and a half deep. It dispenses entirely with boxes of type (one set alone being

Besides this new method which is exceedingly simple [. . .][6] great amount of time and labor are saved, there was an apparent if not a real advantage in Wheatstones that when he wished to communicate any thing he commenced at once upon his instrument which showed the first letter instantly while I had first to take the type of that letter set it up & pass it through the machine and afterwards to distribute my type all of which consumed time and gave him an apparent advantage. I now have the same, with the always paramount advantage of writing the intelligence permanently. The whole telegraphic apparatus is now so simplified and so reduced in size that it may be included within the space occupied by an ordinary mantel clock and communicates intelligence nearly as fast as an expeditious clerk could copy it."[7]

Excuse the haste with which I am obliged to write as I have got hold of the letter on the eve of leaving town for a day or two.

Yours
L. D. Gale

---

necessary), and dispenses, also, with the rules, and with all machinery for moving the rules. There is no winding up, and it is ready at all times. You touch the letter, and the letter is written immediately at the other extremity.

Printed in S.I. Prime, *The Life of Samuel F. B. Morse* (New York, 1875), p. 377, and E. L. Morse, op. cit., p. 117. This later letter makes it clear that Morse had not improved the portrule (the device for moving rules of sawtooth type past a lever which made and broke the circuit), but had instead abandoned it.

[6] One or two illegible words.

[7] Morse tried at least six forms of transmitter, or correspondent, before opting for a single key operated manually. The method described here employed a keyboard, with one key for each letter and numeral. Under the keyboard was a metal cylinder with a distinctive raised metal pattern under each key. When the cylinder revolved and a key was pressed, a roller under the key passed over the raised metal pattern, making and breaking the circuit and producing dots and dashes on the register tape.

Three earlier portrule versions used sawtooth type, the jagged edges of which represented either numbers or letters. Type for a message was composed and placed in a trough, or rule, and then fed under a lever which made and broke the circuit.

Although all of Morse's variations produced a permanent record of the transmission, unlike the needle telegraph of Wheatstone, the disadvantage of the portrule versions was that type had to be composed before transmission and then sorted after transmission. With the keyboard transmitter, and with the later key, an operator could begin transmission immediately.

Alfred Vail gives a detailed description of the various forms of correspondent in *The American Electro Magnetic Telegraph* (Philadelphia, 1845), pp. 32–41.

PLEDGE TO PRINCETON COLONIZATION SOCIETY[1]
Maclean Papers, Princeton University Archives

Princeton, Feby 1839

We agree to pay, to the Princeton Colonization Society, the sums annexed to our respective names, in aid of the Plan to establish a regular line of Packets between Liberia & the United States,

Sam[l] Miller[2]—$5:   paid.
John Maclean—   3.   "
James Carnahan— 5   paid
Joseph Henry[3]   3
A Alexander[4] $3.   paid.
James W. Alexander[5] $3.   p[d]
Jos. Addison Alexander[6] $5.   pd.
Charles Hodge $3.
Jas S Green[7] $3:   paid.
C M Campbell[8]   2 paid

---

[1] Organized in 1817 in an attempt to solve America's racial problem by transporting Free Blacks to Africa, the American Colonization Society (ACS) had limited success. It initially received broad support and was able to establish colonies in what eventually became the nation of Liberia (which declared its independence in 1847). By the late 1830s, however, the ACS was facing a number of problems. Radical abolitionists had attacked it as too conservative, while Southerners increasingly opposed even the gradual emancipation represented by colonization schemes. Local chapters of the ACS began exerting their independence from the national organization, sometimes coming into open conflict. As a result the financial situation became critical. Although the ACS survived the immediate crisis—and indeed it continued in existence into the twentieth century—it had lost much of its early vitality by 1840. Thereafter the ACS would periodically revive in response to increased racial strife and Black unhappiness, only to decline again during stretches of relative calm and good times. During this period the restricted resources of the ACS were a major factor in limiting its efforts at colonization. Early Lee Fox, *The American Colonization Society, 1817–1840* (Baltimore, 1919); Philip J. Staudenraus, *The African Colonization Movement, 1816–1865* (New York, 1961); Edwin S. Redkey, *Black Exodus: Black Nationalist and Back-to-Africa Movements, 1890–1910* (New Haven and London, 1969), pp. 17–23, 73–149.

The Princeton Chapter of the ACS was founded in 1824. Most of its leaders were either faculty or Trustees of Princeton or the Princeton Theological Seminary. In turn, the Princeton Colonization Society served as the nucleus for the New Jersey Colonization Society, founded in 1838. *Hageman, 1:236–237; Newark Daily Advertiser*, July 12, 1838.

[2] Samuel Miller (1769–1850), a Princeton Trustee and a member of the faculty of the Princeton Theological Seminary.

[3] For Henry's attitudes on Blacks, slavery, and racial differences, see *Henry Papers, 3:431.* Henry continued to be an advocate of colonization when faced with the problem of Free Blacks. Henry to Asa Gray, May 22, 1862, Historic Letter File, Gray Herbarium Library.

[4] Probably Archibald Alexander, whose *History of African Colonization* appeared in 1841.

[5] James Waddel Alexander (1804–1859), the son of Archibald Alexander. *Henry Papers, 2:177.*

[6] Joseph Addison Alexander (1809–1860) was on the faculty of the Princeton Theological Seminary. *Henry Papers, 3:148.*

[7] James Sproat Green (1792–1862), a Trustee of Princeton, had been one of the original Vice Presidents of the Princeton Colonization Society. *Henry Papers, 1:440; Hageman, 1:236.*

[8] A neighbor and friend of Charles Hodge,

Charles Muir Campbell was a coachmaker, harness repairman, and prosperous landowner. At the time of this pledge he was still an important figure in Princeton, but financial reverses were soon to force him to begin selling his holdings.

Our thanks to Wanda S. Gunning, Vice President of the Historical Society of Princeton, for this information.

FROM ALEXANDER DALLAS BACHE
Henry Papers, Smithsonian Archives

Mar 16 [1839][1]

Dear Henry,

Send me *at once* your verbal com^n for I must get out a No. of the Proceedings if possible by next meeting.[2]

Why did you take no notice of Ettingshausen's[3] cutting the keeper to stop the induced current from injuring his results. You had some reason but I forget it. Would it not be well for me to make some general statement thereon which can go in our proceedings & not look as if I had been by & skulked from [. . .]ing[4] what I had seen done. Tell me what you think.

In the name of all that is rational what did you mean by hinting that if we were nearer we might be further off in friendship: if you imagine *jealousy* to be one of my traits you mistake—except in one respect that I am jealous of the regard of friends & hence would be perhaps *exacting* more than you might like, in the way of wishing to see you & all that. Do you not feel more

[1] The year is given in a file note.

[2] Henry's response is given below in his letter to Bache of March 20, 1839.

[3] Baron Andreas von Ettingshausen (1796–1878) was educated at the University of Vienna. After two years as Professor of Physics in Innsbruck, he returned to Vienna in 1821 as Professor of Mathematics. He remained at Vienna until his retirement, exchanging the professorship of mathematics for that of physics in 1834. His early research was in mathematics, but in the 1830s he became interested in electromagnetic induction, especially in response to the work of Faraday. The magnetoelectric machine which bears his name, described in 1837, was his major contribution in this area. *Nature,* June 20, 1878, *18*:197.

The source of Bache's unease was a report he had presented to the American Philosophical Society the same evening that Henry read his "Contributions III." Based on observations of Ettingshausen's experiments made while Bache was in Vienna, the report contained information which had not yet arrived in the United States in published form. The improvements made by Ettingshausen on the magnetoelectric machine, as reported by Bache, were similar to those suggested by Henry in section 76 of "Contributions III," although Henry's suggestion was based on deductions from his earlier experiments on electromagnetic induction rather than specific experiments with a magnetoelectric machine. Henry's solution was to add a note at the end of "Contributions III" to explain the situation and acknowledge Ettingshausen's independent discovery. See below, Henry to Bache, March 20, 1839.

[4] A tear in the letter.

pleasure at seeing things go ahead than if they went slower, & all by your own effort. Say.

Regards to yr. spouse & my pretty porcelain baby

Ever Yrs, A.D. Bache

Sat^r Ev^n Kay[5] has just sent in another proof.

I have taken up ½ sheet, but never mind.

I have found a letter from Mr Vaughan saying that he had paid for the Magnetic app^s out of my money as requested by you. So you need give yourself no concern until it is perfectly convenient to make payment. The cost was 5 £ according to Mr Vaughan's letter but mine cost 5 £ 5 so it is better to wait until I have his account.[6] Yrs

---

[5] James Kay, Jr.

[6] According to a receipt dated September 28, 1839, Henry paid Bache $25 (£5) for the vacuum magnetic intensity apparatus paid for by Petty Vaughan. Folder of Accounts with Various Instrument- and Apparatus-Dealers, Joseph Henry for the College of New Jersey, 1837, Princeton University Archives.

FROM ALEXANDER DALLAS BACHE[1]
Henry Papers, Smithsonian Archives

Philadelphia March 16th [18]39

Dear Sir

At the last meeting of the British Association for the advancement of science I was requested to prepare a report on the progress of meteorological science and on the meteorology of the United States.[2] As you have been a valuable contributor in this field and I should be most unwilling to pass over any point of your contributions which may happen if I trust to my own research I must beg of you to be so good as to send to me at as early a date as practicable a list of your papers giving the titles and the works in which they may be found, or if you find this too inconvenient refering me to the works where the papers may be found with the volume or volumes containing them.

I should feel further obliged to you for any hints as to points of inquiry which you may consider interesting to be particularly noticed in the progress of our meteorological knowledge or in the meteorology of our country.

---

[1] A form letter soliciting scientific information, this document does not appear to be in Bache's hand.

[2] See *BAAS Report, 1838* (1839), p. xx, and Bache to Sabine, April 16, 1839, footnote 7. The British Association resolution did not include any funding for Bache's report.

By as early an answer as may consist with your convenience you will much oblige me. My object is, if possible, to prepare this report for the next meeting of the British Association, as requested.[3]

> Very respectfully Yours.
> A. D. Bache

[3] Henry's lengthy reply follows. Despite several reminders from the BAAS, Bache apparently never completed the meteorological report.

TO ALEXANDER DALLAS BACHE
Bache Papers, Smithsonian Archives

Princeton March [19–27][1] 1839

Dear Sir

In answer to your favour of the 16ᵗʰ I commence to day a long letter in which I intend to give you all the ideas which may occur to me from reflection and otherwise and also the facts which I may happen to meet with in the course of reading and conversation. I will present them to you just as they occur to me informally and undigested. Perhaps from the abundance of worthless chaff you may select a few grains of some value.[2]

1 In order that none of my valuable labours in meterology may be overlooked I will refer you to the meterological Reports of the Regents of the University of the State of New York. On the title page of the first numbers I am mentioned as one of the colaborators of the work. You will probably duly appreciate the important service which I then rendered to science when I inform you that my labours principally consisted in reading the proof sheets of the work.[3]

2 Having thus in the first place done justice to myself I will now proceed to give you other information of a less important nature.* The proposition of a series of meterological observations under the direction of the Regents of the university of the state of New York originated with my old Friend the late Simeon DeWitt Esq. This fact is mentioned by Dr T R Beck of Albany in an oration pronounced on the occasion of the death of Mr De-Witt.[5] I have a copy of the printed article which is at your service. The rain

* See note at the bottom of page 7.[4]

[1] Henry dated this long letter March 19 but did not complete it until March 27.

[2] In the 1850s, Henry surveyed the subject in "Meteorology in its Connection with Agriculture," which appeared in the Agricultural Reports of the Commissioner of Patents from 1855 to 1859, and is reprinted in the *Scientific Writings of Joseph Henry*, 2 vols. (Washington, 1886), 2:6–402.

[3] See *Henry Papers*, *1*:107n.

[4] i.e., the note at the end of the March 19 portion of the letter.

gages and thermometers were constructed under my direction. Mr Espy has a bound copy of the 1st 10 numbers perhaps the only ones to be procured which I loaned to him some years since, this I will request him to deliver to you. The original copies of observations are deposited in the library of the albany Institute. They contain the daily observations and for some investigations would be found very valuable.

3 Could not some observations be made without occupying much time and immediate results be obtained of some value by taking the temperature of all the wells of a city say of Philadelphia and comparing the mean of the whole with the mean temperature of the place. The temperature however thus obtained would probably be influenced by the geological formation of the place yet the experiment would not be without interest and some results of importance might possibly be obtained. I forgot that your city of hydrants has no wells but the experiment could be made in New York and perhaps would afford an approximation to the mean temperature of places where a series of observations have not been made.[6]

4 Will the temperature of artezian well form a part of your report? You know that there is a very deep one in New York bored for the use of Holts hotel[7] which has never been examined. Also there is one in Albany more than 500 feet deep which should be studied in reference to its temperature. This belongs to an Uncle of mine (by marriage)[8] and any facilities for observation would be given.

5 In a report of the geological survey of the State of Michigan, I find some remarks on the rise of the waters of the great lakes which is a meteorological phenominon and is produced by an unusual rainy season.[9] I have also a paper on the same subject by Mr Geddings[10] of Lockport New York. These documents I will put into your hands.

---

[5] T. Romeyn Beck, *Eulogium on the Life and Services of Simeon DeWitt* . . . (Albany, 1835).

[6] The idea that the temperature of water at the bottom of a well was an approximation of the mean temperature of a place was not a new one. It is mentioned, for instance, in a book by Samuel Williams cited by Henry later in this letter: *The Natural and Civil History of Vermont*, 2d ed., 2 vols. (Burlington, 1809), *1*:54.

[7] A hotel at the corner of Fulton and Pearl. New York City Directory, 1837.

[8] We have not been able to identify the hotel or its owner.

[9] In Douglass Houghton's second report, dated February 4, 1839, the water level in the Great Lakes is discussed at several places. Be-cause of economic consequences, Houghton thought it important to understand the causes of fluctuation and to determine the maximum and minimum level. Houghton attributed the recent rise to unusually cold and wet seasons. An assistant, S. W. Higgins, mentioned the increased rain and melting snow in the watershed. George N. Fuller, ed., *Geological Reports of Douglass Houghton* (Lansing, 1928), pp. 187–195, 263–266, 294–296, 312.

[10] In *An Inquiry into the Causes of the Rise and Fall of the Great Lakes . . . to Which is Annexed a Letter to Dr. H. H. Sherwood on his Theory of Magnetism* (Lockport, New York, 1838), Edward Giddins pinpointed snow as the major cause of fluctuation. A copy is in the Henry Library.

6 The same Michigan report contains a long extract from one of my earliest papers (without an acknowledgement however) on the topography of the state of New-York[11] and this has brought to my reccollection the fact that the paper in question was written principally in reference to the meterology of the state. I collected all the elevations of the principal places in the s[t]ate inorder to make a topographical map to accompany the Regents report and to determine if possible the influence which altitude and configuration of surface had on the Meterological character of a place. The paper however is confined to the topography of the country. I did intend to extend my study of topography to the whole of the United States but some other hobby was mounted for a time and my removal to Princeton completely threw me out of its track. The subject however is an interesting one and there is no part of the world where the materials for its prosecution are more abundant than in the United States. Every part of the country has been traversed by exploration lines for railways and canals. If the minutes of these were collected and properly arranged they would form the elements of an important topographical map of the country, as correct as could be desired in reference to the elevations and depressions of the surface.

7 You will of course notice what has been written on what is called the Indian summer. Several articles on this I think are to be found in Sillimans Journal.[12]

8 I recollect that there are some remarks on the meterology of this country in general and on that of Vermont in particular in Williams history of that state.[13] Also there are in the Travels of Dr. Dwite[14] (once President of Yale College) some statements relative to the same subject which might be found interesting.

9 An inquiry into the change of the volumn of water which is transmitted to the ocean by a river after the land which gives rise to it has been cleared of woods might be interesting and this inquiry can be made with

---

[11] The passage, which discusses the height above sea level of Chautauqua Lake and neighboring features, occurs in the report of S. W. Higgins, topographer (Fuller, op. cit., p. 255). It is enclosed in quotation marks but without citation. Higgins prefaced his report by stating that much of his information came from the records of public works in neighboring states. Henry's 1829 "Topographical Sketch of the State of New-York, Designed Chiefly to Show the General Elevations and Depressions of its Surface" was printed in the *Transactions* of the Albany Institute and in the introduction to David H. Burr's *Atlas of the State of New York* (Albany, 1829), pp. 21–29. *Henry Papers,* 1:250n.

[12] i.e., "On the Cause of the Peculiar Aspect of the Air, in the Indian Summer" (1830, *18*:66–67); "Essay on the Indian Summer" (1835, 27:140–147); and Lyman Foot, "Remarks on Indian Summers" (1836, *30*:8–15).

[13] In the second edition of Samuel Williams, *The Natural and Civil History of Vermont*, 2 vols. (Burlington, 1809), Williams discussed meteorology and gave tables of magnetic variation, temperature, rainfall, and wind direction in chapters four and five of the first volume.

[14] Timothy Dwight, *Travels; in New-England and New York*, 4 vols. (New Haven, 1821–1822); a copy is in Henry's Library.

a prospect of success in this country because her large forests are in the process of being cleared off.[15]

10 Perhaps you could manage to mention the economical uses of showers which fall on the regions of the sources of our atlantic rivers particularly those on the heads of the Hudson the Delaware and the Susquehanna. Along the small streams which form these, immense rafts of boards and timber are constructed during dry weather and when a shower comes the water rises and the raft is wafted on the swell to the deep part of the river and thence they easily find their way to the ocean.

An interesting anecdote is related of General Sulivan while on his Indian expidition. Wishing to transport his troops and baggage through the wilderness he produced an artificial flood by throwing a temporary dam across the outlet of Cooperstown Lake the head of the susquehanna. When all was ready his men and baggage on rafts the dam was cut away the waters poured forth in an immense wave and the whole flotilla was borne on its crest for miles down the river.[16] If you adopt the plan of modern compilers of chemical text books you can certainly manage to introduce facts more foreign to your subject than the above since they are at no loss to form an encyclopedia of science under the title of elements of chemestry.[17]

11 It is asserted by Jefferson in his notes on Virginia that there is a marked difference in the temperature of places under the same parallel on different sides of the Aleghanies.[18] Dr L. C. Beck has published an article on this point in the transactions of the Albany Institute.[19]

[15] There was a great deal of debate over the effects of timber clearing on climate, particularly on temperature, winds, and runoff. In his "Meteorology in its Connection with Agriculture," Henry noted that "the whole subject of the removal of forests is one which deserves more attention. . . ." Citing floods over cleared land and the benefits of trees as windbreaks, he warned against the "indiscriminate destruction" of forests (*Scientific Writings*, 2:19).

[16] The event took place during General John Sullivan's 1779 campaign against the Iroquois. It was General James Clinton, however, who dammed Otsego Lake at Cooperstown and then broke the dam to float over 200 heavily loaded bateaux down the Susquehanna to join Sullivan's forces. William W. Campbell, *Lecture on the Life and Military Services of General James Clinton* (New York, 1839).

[17] Another facet of Henry's dissatisfaction with contemporary science textbooks. The imponderables (light, heat, electricity) were often taught as part of chemistry and were therefore included in chemistry textbooks. Benjamin Silliman's popular *Elements of Chemistry*, 2 vols. (New Haven, 1831) begins and ends with these subjects.

[18] Based on traveler's accounts, Jefferson wrote that at the same latitude, the climate of the Mississippi Valley was warmer than that of the Atlantic coast. As confirmation, he cited the existence of certain plants and animals in the west which were unknown in the east. Thomas Jefferson, *Notes on the State of Virginia*, 2d London edition (London, 1787), pp. 125–126.

[19] Lewis C. Beck, "An Examination of the Question, Whether the Climate of the Valley of the Mississippi under Similar Parallels of Latitude is Warmer than that of the Atlantic Coast," *Transactions of the Albany Institute*, 1830, *1*:34–54. Because Jefferson's theory had been uncritically adopted and widely circulated in the writings of C. F. Volney and Hugh Williamson, Beck devoted much of his article to the weakness of Jefferson's evidence. He then presented data on mean temperature and flowering plants and concluded that Jefferson was wrong.

12 There is a paper in the american Philosophical transaction on the temperature of the gulf stream.[20] I know not however if it will, in any way, be connected with your report. I may mention in passing that there is a review of the first volums of *our* Transactions in one of the early numbers of the Quarterly review. The paper above mentioned is the only one which finds favour and this appears to be on account of the author's being an Englishman.[21]

13 You will find in Darby's views of the United States published by Tanner in 1828 several chapters on the climate of this country.[22] I think he mentions one fact which I have often noticed namely whole orchards of apple trees leaning in the same direction indicating the course of the prevaling wind at the place.[23] You know that an article has been published by Volney on the Climate of the United States.[24]

14 One of the subtheories of Espy rests on the assumption that air is impervious to the vapour of water and that no diffusion of the latter takes place unless motion be produced in the air. I believe that I have mentioned to you that I have made some experiments on this point[25] and have also collected some references to the experiments of others on the same subject.

15 Some person has proposed to form a table of the weather or rather of the state of the seasons relative to vegetation by cutting sections of large trees perpendicular to the length and noting the width of the rings.[26] Some

[20] William Strickland, "On the Use of the Thermometer in Navigation," APS *Transactions,* 1802, 5:90ff.

[21] The acerbic review of the fifth volume of the APS *Transactions* was by Henry, Lord Brougham. Referring to the articles written by Americans, Brougham wrote, "of all the academic trifles, which have ever been given to the world, these 89 pages are the most trivial and dull." Brougham found Americans to be "proportionally deficient in scientific attainments," and lacking in all but "mercantile and agricultural talents." *The Edinburgh Review, or Critical Journal: for April 1803 . . . July 1803,* 7th ed. (Edinburgh, 1814), 2:348–355.

[22] William Darby's *View of the United States, Historical, Geographical, and Statistical* (Philadelphia, 1828), published by H. S. Tanner, is in the Henry Library. Chapter 10 is on climate.

[23] On page 424, Darby noted that the prevailing winds over North America were from the west with the result that "orchards and forests generally, particularly along the Atlantic slope, invariably incline to the eastward or southeastward."

[24] C. F. Volney, *A View of the Soil and Climate of the United States of America,* trans. C. B. Brown (Philadelphia, 1804), also in the Henry Library.

[25] Espy had advised Henry on how to conduct the experiments; see *Henry Papers, 3:* 533–534.

[26] Henry was probably thinking of Alexander C. Twining. In a letter to Benjamin Silliman (*Silliman's Journal,* 1833, 24:391–393), Twining noted the correlation between variation in annual growth rings and variation in climatic conditions. He suggested that a comparison of cross sections with each other and with meteorological records "would elicit a mass of facts, both with respect to the progress of the seasons, and their relation to the growth of timber, and might prove, hereafter, the means of carrying back our knowledge of the seasons, through a period coeval with the age of the oldest forest trees, and in regions of country where scientific observation has never yet penetrated, nor a civilized population dwelt."

As with eighteenth-century suggestions of dendrochronology by Duhamel and Buffon, Linnaeus, and Burgsdorf, Twining's suggestion was soon forgotten. Dendrochronology was not

years since two large trees were blown down in the college campus. I examined their cross sections and found that they each indicated plainly the years in which the growth had been most luxurient. By counting back from the outer ring these years were readily determined.

16 You will find a number of notices in the transactions of the American Academy[27] of the appearance of brilliant auroras particularly in the oldest volumes. It might perhaps be interesting to settle if possible the question of the periodical activity of the aurora. This you know has been raised and it has been asserted that we are now living in one of the paroxisms of the meteor. Perhaps there may be something in the opinion.[28]

17 Appended to Nuttal's travels into the Arkansa Territory there is a table of observations in that country made during the year 1819.[29] Also Parkers travels beyond the Rocky mountains printed at Ithaca NY 1838, contains a similar table.[30]

18 In the transactions of the Society of arts of the State of New York you will find a Meterological Journal by Dr Eights for 1813 & 14.[31] Dr T R Beck has incorporated this table into a paper on the mean temperature of Albany in the Transactions of the Albany Institute Vol 2 No 1.[32]

19 Would it not be possible for you to collect the data for a map of

---

developed into a science until the work of A. E. Douglass in the early twentieth century. R. A. Studhalter, "Tree Growth: I. Some Historical Chapters," *The Botanical Review*, 1955, 21:1–72. See also H. C. Fritts, *Tree Rings and Climate* (London, 1976).

[27] i.e., the *Memoirs of the American Academy of Arts and Sciences.*

[28] At this time it was vaguely recognized that there were periods of frequent auroras and periods when they seemed to disappear. In connection with his 1832 article on the aurora, Henry mentioned to Benjamin Silliman that he thought the aurora was in a period of maximum intensity. (*Henry Papers*, 1:409–410). Henry remained interested in the problem of the determination of the secular periodicity of the aurora. He later published Denison Olmsted's "On the Recent Secular Period of the Aurora Borealis," *Smithsonian Contributions to Knowledge*, 1856, 8:article 3, and Elias Loomis, "Aurora Borealis, or Polar Light; Its Phenomena and Laws," *Smithsonian Annual Report for 1865* (Washington, 1866), pp. 208–248. Loomis hypothesized a maximum of auroral intensity every 59–60 years and a subordinate maximum every 10 years. He noted the similarity to the periodicity of sunspot activity and magnetic storms. Carl Störm-

er, *The Polar Aurora* (Oxford, 1955), p. 25, gives these maxima as about 55 years and about 11 years, respectively.

[29] Thomas Nuttall, *A Journal of Travels into the Arkansa Territory, During the Year 1819* (1821; reprint, Ann Arbor, 1966); the fourth section of the appendix gives a daily record of morning and afternoon temperature.

[30] Samuel Parker, *Journal of an Exploring Tour Beyond the Rocky Mountains . . . Performed in the Years 1835, '36, and '37 . . .* (Ithaca, 1838), a copy of which is in the Henry Library. Parker recorded the temperature three times a day and noted whether it was clear, cloudy, or rainy.

[31] Jonathan Eights noted temperature, barometric pressure, and wind direction, and computed mean temperature and barometric pressure. He also recorded sicknesses and auroras. *Transactions of the Society for the Promotion of Useful Arts, in the State of New-York*, 1816, 4, part 1, pp. 86–108.

[32] "Abstracts of Meteorological Observations Made at the City of Albany, and Calculations Tending to Establish its Mean Temperature," *Transactions of the Albany Institute*, 1833–1852, 2:1–29. Beck also used observations by Simeon DeWitt in 1795 and 1796 and his own observations from 1820 to 1832.

isothermal lines of this country to accompany your report. An approximation only to accuracy would be valuable.[33] Observations on the temperature of wells might assist you in this.

---

* *This should have been inserted at the bottom of the first page* and is intended to explain the modest language of the beginning of this letter.

Note A Painter wishing to commemorate a great public event and inorder to do honor to all engaged in it requested from each a portrait for the purpose grouping the whole into one picture. The piece was finished but instead of giving satisfaction to those whom it honored each thought himself wronged, those in the rear by not occupying a more prominent position and those in the foreground because every part of their person was not fully exhibited without a shadow. The picture however was a good one conceived in the spirit of truth and executed with the skill of a master. It was well received by all unbiased critics, the cause of truth was advanced by it and the painter in due time found his reward in true fame. You take?

Princeton March 27th 1839[34]

My Dear Bache

I was prevented by some college duties from answering yours of the 23[d]. I received the proof of the last form of my paper on monday morning and sent it back corrected by the return mail. I was well pleased with the note and only made an alteration in one word inorder to make the whole read a litle more like my mode of expression. I have given in this letter a quantity of matter which I fear will scarcely repay the trouble of reading; some part of it however may by association of ideas suggest what may be of use. I will give you in detail and in a state for publication the facts relative to the aurora which I mentioned to you if you still think it worth publishing.[35]

[33] Alexander von Humboldt is usually credited as the originator of isothermal charts based on an 1817 publication. H. E. Landsberg notes, however, that Simeon DeWitt first suggested the idea in 1792. H. E. Landsberg, Early Stages of Climatology in the United States," *Bulletin of the American Meteorological Society*, May 1964, 45:269.

At the Smithsonian, Henry was concerned with improving the accuracy of isothermal charts. He criticized those produced by the Medical Department of the Army and termed those prepared by C. A. Schott under his direction "the first trustworthy approximation to an exhibition of the temperature of the various portions of the United States which has ever been published." *Smithsonian Annual Report for 1874* (Washington, 1875), p. 13.

[34] The remainder of this letter is in response to Bache's first letter of March 16 (above) and his letter of March 23 (below).

[35] Later in the year, Bache reported to the APS on observations by Henry and Stephen Alexander of the September 3, 1839, aurora (*Proceedings*, 1838–1840, *1*:132–134), but we do not know what Henry is referring to here.

The first Thursday in april will happen during our examination week and therefore it will be impossible for me to leave Princeton to attend the meeting of the Franklin Institute.

I regret that Mr Vaughan has been so long out of his money and I now wish to settle with him as soon as possible. I would like to get an achromatic object glass to an Adams microscope[36] through Mr Vaughan. Perhaps the article can be purchased by means of your account. This articles must be paid for by the college and Mr Vaughan should be allowed interest on his money. Respets to Mrs B Yours as ever

J H

Mrs H bids me say that she hopes you will soon finish your report[37] and that Mrs B and your self will not forget the promised visit to Princeton.

If I can be of any service in the way of experiment or otherwise in reference to your report command me.

---

[36] The firm founded by George Adams (1704–1773), and continued by his sons George (1750–1795) and Dudley, ceased operation about 1830. The microscope may have been part of the apparatus purchased for Princeton by John Maclean, Sr. at the turn of the century. *Wer-* *tenbaker*, pp. 124–125. For the Adams firm, see the *DNB* and Maurice Daumas, *Scientific Instruments of the Seventeenth and Eighteenth Centuries* (New York, 1972), pp. 237–238.

[37] i.e., Bache's report for Girard College.

TO ALEXANDER DALLAS BACHE
Bache Papers, Smithsonian Archives

Princeto[n Wednesd]ay[1]
Morning M[arch 2]oth[2] 1839

My Dear Bache

Your letter[3] yesterday came to hand at so late an hour that I could not get all my comments to the office before the closing of the mail. I send you to day on the opposite page the concluding paragraph of my paper[4] which since it is only a verbal addition intended principally to give a some what less abrupt closing to the article I have thought it may be added without a formal consent of the society.

---

[1] A tear in the upper right corner of the original has obliterated several words here and later in the body of the letter. Several letters along the margin of the original are also missing.

[2] The date was obtained from a file note on the second page of the original.

[3] This letter provides a point by point reply to the questions raised by Bache in his first letter of March 16, 1839, above.

[4] No longer with the letter. The ragged edge and missing letters along the margin of the original indicate that Bache detached the paragraph to send it to the printer.

In reference to the improvements of the electro magnetic machine—what I have given in my paper is entirely independant of any communication relative to the experiments of Ettingshausen communicated by you. I at first thought of appending a note to my paper at the place where the subject is mentioned but at length concluded to add an appendix at the end giving your statement of the experiments but in some way I gathered from your remarks that you did not think this n[e]cessary unless in reference to my own feelings. I need not assure you that I wish to do full justice to every person engaged in the cause of science and that I will be pleased if you will give a statement to the society and also append to the appendix which I have written an account of the experiments. I think in justice to Ettingshausen the account should be added to my paper since then the experiments of the German will be circulated with mine.

Would it be improper to let the printer set up this appendix before you have brought the subject before the society? If leave should not be granted for the appendix to be added that part of the paper could be suppressed. I am only anxious th[. . .]ld not be longer delayed in publicati[on. . . .] alterations in the sentiments or wording of [the ap]pendix which you may think proper inorder to do full justice to the German (I forget his name).

If I err in an affair of this kind it will be becaus[e] I have not in all cases a proper idea of the method of proceeding inorder to be strictly just.

Let there be no breezes between us as the brush maker said to the bellows mender. The only feeling which influenced me while making the sentimenta[l] speech to which you allude was that my intercour[se] at present with you and with Philadelphia is of so pleasant a nature that no change except in the way of more frequent intercourse could make it more agreeable. I thought you alluded to my being at some time connected with Girard College and I wish it to be distinctly understood between us that my present arrangements and labours are in no way connected with an anticipated change of this kind. When you are called on to select officers for that Institution you will do it without reference to friendship or any other considera[tion] but the good of the college.[5] I wish to continue to cultivate with you the strictest habits of friendship and to continue to be as much interested in all your affairs and labours as if they were my own. I am almos[t] selfish in this, since I know that I shall be a gainer in every respect by the continuance of our present delightful communications. I feel however that I am much your debtor although not an ungrateful one. You must find much in me to condemn but I am sure you will attribute my errors to the

[5] Henry was never formally connected with Girard College.

head and not the heart. The mail is again on the point of closing so in haste again Yours as ever

Joseph Henry

P.S. Your meteorological letter[6] was received this morning and will receive an answer in a few days.

---

[6] Bache's second letter of March 16. Henry's reply is dated March 19–27, 1839.

FROM ALEXANDER DALLAS BACHE
Henry Papers, Smithsonian Archives

March 23rd. 1839.

Dear Henry,

I have requested M[r] Kay to send you a proof of the last form of your paper finding the responsibility more than I can take. Cut No. 16. does not appear to me to be right. The note is better than an appendix, but I am not sure that it is not awkward. Make a better one. Your Sam Wellerism[1] was *"wery conwincin"*, and I never expected breezes nor suspected that you had the Girard College in view. Come down to the next Conversation meeting of the Franklin Institute & show your experiments is a request which I make you on the part of the Committee on the said meetings. The next one will be too soon being next Thursday but the one for April will be in good time; the fourth Thursday in April.

M[r] Blaney called here to day. I have not Ehrenberg's book[2] but will send

---

[1] Henry's "Sam Wellerism" is the first sentence of the fifth paragraph of his letter of March 20, immediately above. The term "Wellerism" is derived from Sam Weller, Mr. Pickwick's servant in Charles Dickens's *Pickwick Papers*, and is defined as "an expression of comparison comprising a usu. well-known quotation followed by a facetious sequel (as 'every one to his own taste,' said the old woman as she kissed the cow)." *Webster's Third New International Dictionary*.

[2] Bache had met Christian Gottfried Ehrenberg (1795–1876, *DSB*) during the summer of 1838 in Berlin (Bache to Torrey, March 28, 1839, Bache Papers, Smithsonian Archives). A professor at the University of Berlin and a member of the Berlin Academy of Sciences, Ehrenberg's chief work was the description and classification of microorganisms. By showing that simple animals had all of the organs of higher animals, Ehrenberg argued against spontaneous generation and the "chain of being." His discovery that certain rocks and even complete strata were composed entirely of fossil microorganisms astonished geologists and had great influence in paleontology.

In 1838 Ehrenberg published *Die Infusionsthierschen als Vollkommene Organismen* (Leipzig) based on study of collections from his Middle East expedition, with comparative material from his northern travels. Ehrenberg's work on the Infusoria was widely noticed in the United States and stimulated microscopical work in general and study of the Infusoria in particular. In 1839 American researchers, especially Torrey and Jacob Whitman Bailey, began supplying Ehrenberg with American specimens which he studied and described in several publications.

Dr Torrey what I have of his, & he can return it by you or on occasion. Also some of his bugs of recent origin & some fossil Italians. Regards to your "lady."

Yours
A D Bache

FROM LEONARD D. GALE
Henry Papers, Smithsonian Archives

New York March 30, 1839

My Dear Sir,

Permit me to offer my thanks for your kind letter to the Trustees of Jefferson College and to inform you that my application was successful.[1] I leave for New Orleans probably the latter part of the coming week. Will you have the goodness to see the wire belonging to the Telegraphic Company delivered to the Room (Geological Lecture Room) whence it was taken should it not arrive before I leave. Professor Morse who is now on his return from Europe in the Great Western will probably be here in a fortnight or sooner and may require it.

I shall be happy to hear from you at Washington Mi whence I am destined [to] hail hereafter. I would like to know of you whether you think the machine Electro-magnetic put up by Stimpson and now at 58 Gold St is the most economical arrangement of power or for producing motion; I was informed that you gave your opinion and supposed they had misunderstood you. For it occurred to me that it would have been better had the magnets been so arranged that the ends of the rotating magnets should move in the same circle as the fixed magnets so that when each movable magnet passes a fixed magnet the axis of each will correspond or be in the same line with that of the other. But the arrangement which you will doubtless recollect in the machine constructed by Stimpson is bar cylindrical magnets arranged on the periphery of a cylindrical wheel parallel with its axis and made to rotate while the fixed magnets are arranged on a cylindrical frame parallel with the first but without them and within the twentieth of an inch of contact.

---

[1] See above, Gale to Henry, November 23, 1838. On February 2, 1839, the Jefferson College Board of Trustees, having received letters of recommendation from Torrey, Silliman, and Ellet, as well as Henry, unanimously ap- pointed Leonard Gale Professor of Natural and Experimental Philosophy, Chemistry, and Mineralogy. Journal, Jefferson College Board of Trustees, pp. 128–129, Jefferson College Papers, State of Mississippi Archives.

If I have made myself understood is the arrangement in the machine in question more economical in your opinion than that which I have supposed?[2]

I remain with great respect your obedient

Servant
L. D. Gale

[2] According to the *Journal of the Franklin Institute*, the inventor of the machine was Solomon Stimpson, of New York City. He is not listed in any New York city directories for this period, and we have been unable to locate any additional information.

Stimpson's machine, patented September 12, 1838, although relatively sophisticated in construction details, was nevertheless apparently as impractical as similar devices for producing power by electromagnetism. The Franklin Institute dismissed the invention with the remark that "the attainment of an available motive power by electro magnetic influence, is a thing not to be hoped for in the present state of our knowledge." *Journal of the Franklin Institute*, July 1839, 24:157.

TO [LEONARD D. GALE][1]
Mary Henry Copy, Henry Papers, Smithsonian Archives

Princeton April 2. 1839

My time has been so engaged in college duties, that I have not had an opportunity of making the experiments with the long wire which I intended. I have however obtained some results with it and these are incorporated into my paper which has just been published, after several months delay in the transactions of the American Philosophical Society of Philadelphia. Our term closes this week and if it be possible I would like to retain the coil of wire for about ten days longer. . . . I should think if Mr. Morse should not want the use of the coil for a few days after his arrival he could have no objection to my retaining it for that time.

Some time last summer I was shown a small model of Stimpson's machine which appeared to perform as well as any I had before seen. I gave a certificate stating that it might be well in order to set the public mind at rest in reference to the application of electromagnetic power to machinery that a large machine should be made and that when finished it should be submitted to the experiments of a committee of distinguished men of science. . I stated publicly and explicitly in my lectures in New York—that *in the present state of knowledge* the application of the[2]

[1] Mary Henry erroneously gave Page as the recipient.
[2] The copy breaks off. We assume Henry was giving his standard criticism of electromagnetic engines as being uncompetitive with coal and steam power.

FROM LEONARD D. GALE

Henry Papers, Smithsonian Archives

New York April 8th 1839

My Dear Sir,

I thank you for your communication by Dr Torrey.[1] The Wire may remain with you as you desire. The only request I have to make with regard to it is that you see it safely deposited in Prof Morses Rooms in the University when returned to the city. I will make the matter right with him. A copy of your paper would be thankfully received by him and might be left at the office of the New York Observer—care of S. E. Morse.[2]

I will thank you for a copy of your paper when you may find convenient you know my address both in Missisippi & in New York if it be sent to me at New York (after May 1st) it should be addressed to me at 119 Cedar st where Mrs Gale will remain during my absence (till July 15th) otherwise at Jefferson College. I leave this week on Saturday 13th inst by sea to Natchez. I thank you for your remarks on Stimpson's machine.[3] The only point of my query related to a remark made by Williams[4] the agent that you recommended the arrangement adopted in the large machine as the best that could be devised; knowing Mr W. to speak often at random in regard to other subjects presumed he might have done so here. But on reflection I am undecided wether there would be any gain in the arrangement I proposed or not—that is whether the increase of power gained in the one pole (on the proposed arrangement) would not be counterbalanced by the loss sustained in the opposite pole. A gentleman of my acquaintance had one constructed on the proposed plan that went remarkably well as a toy but I have no means of comparing its power with that of one of the Stimpson machines of like size & proportions. With regard to the competition of Magnetism with Steam I believe I have never had but one opinion and that is in the negative.

I thank you for your kind wishes & congratulations for me & mine. Mrs G. joins me in kind remembrances to your Lady and would be happy to have

---

[1] Printed immediately above.

[2] Sidney Edwards Morse (1794–1871), brother of Samuel F. B. Morse, was a graduate of Yale (1811) and a student at the Andover Theological Seminary (1817–1820). In 1816, he helped establish the Boston *Recorder*, the first religious newspaper in the United States. With his brother Richard Cary Morse, he founded a similar newspaper, the *New York Observer*, in 1823, turning it into a major influence within evangelical Protestant circles. Like his elder brother, Sidney Edwards Morse was interested in mechanical improvements. His earliest patent, granted in 1817 and held jointly with Samuel F. B. Morse, was for a flexible piston pump. *DAB*.

[3] Discussed above, Gale to Henry, March 30, 1839.

[4] Possibly Edwin Williams, who acted as an agent for Thomas Davenport's electric motor. See above, Henry to Bache, August 9, 1838, footnote 5.

a call from her & you should you be in town at her (Mrs G's) fathers residence 119 Cedar St 2 doors below Greenwich.

Very respectfully your Friend & Servent
L. D. Gale

TO JOHN TORREY
Torrey Papers, Library, New York Botanical Garden

Princeton April [13–15][1] 1839

My Dear Dr.

Your favour of the 8th[2] was receved on the 10th. I immediately gave your intelligence to Professor Dod but he had concluded to start for the south as soon as the college business should be adjusted. We are very sorry to learn that Mrs T. has not much improved by her visit to Princeton, she appeared better the 2nd day but probably took too much exercise for her very feeble state. I hope the excursion to the north will produce more descided effects in the way of improvement.

Mrs Henry heard that Steadman[3] had an offer for the house from a Person from Trenton. I know not however how true this is. I tried to see Steadman to day but learned that he had been for several days in Trenton. Dr George Maclean[4] intends spending the next winter either in the Island of Madeira or in the South of France on account of the delicacy of his wifes health. She has had several attacks of spitting of blood. His house will be for sale or to Let and is one which perhaps would be very pleasant to you. It is large and very convenient. Should you come to Princeton this summer nothing in a formal manner can be done relative to the enlargement of the chemical course except to put it on the old footing since that change can be made without the consent of the board of Trustees.

The affair will come before the Trustees at the next meeting in a proper manner and I will use what influence I possess to have the matter arranged to your satisfaction.[5]

Monday April 15th

I have seen Steadman to day. He says that he has not definitely let the

---

[1] Although Henry began this letter on Saturday, April 13th, he did not finish it until Monday, the 15th. According to a file note, Torrey replied on April 20th. His letter has not been located.

[2] Not found.

[3] Princeton architect Charles Steadman,

Henry Papers, 2:422n.

[4] George Maclean (*Henry Papers*, 2:100).

[5] The minutes of the next meeting of the Princeton Trustees, on September 24, 1839, contain no mention of Torrey's chemistry course.

house but that he will wait a few days until he can hear something definitely from you. A box arrived this afternoon from Hightstown which I have not yet opened but which probably contains my coils &c. I will probably commence with them tomorrow. The workmen are engaged in the Philosophical Hall but get along slowely. The Trustees agreed to the proposition of a servent but they neglected to make any special appropriation for the repair, and increase of apparatus.[6] Dr Carnahan thinks however that money can be appropriated for this object without an act of the Board since it was only an oversight which prevented it on their part. Dr Green[7] is now in Princeton relative to his house. He has purchased a lot of ground and intends bringing on a house complete with the exception of putting together by way of the canal. Great improvements are about to be made in the college grounds. Matthew Newkirk[8] of Philadelphia has taken the matter in hands and the work is to proceed immediately under the superintendance of an English gardener. The front and rear campus are to be graded and planted with an abundance of trees. I sent you through Chilton a number of copies of my paper which you will oblige me by sending to Ireland.[9] I will send you by mail a copy from Dr Robinson[10] of Armagh which I forgot to put into the package. You will please to do it up for me and send it with the others if it be in good time. I also enclose a copy of my paper for Goodrich which I wish you would find some means of transmitting to him.[11] The infusoria is a subject which is at present attracting much attention. Dr Green was much interested in it. Have you seen Mr Mersch the german who wrote the article in the New York review on the subject?[12] You will find him a very intelli-

---

[6] At the Trustees' meeting of April 9, 1839, a resolution was passed stating "that the Faculty be empowered to employ a person to aid the *Professor* of *Chemistry* in his department." Trustees' Minutes, *3*:356, Princeton University Archives.

[7] Jacob Green.

[8] Matthew Newkirk (1794–1868), retired Philadelphia merchant, was involved in the construction of the Philadelphia, Wilmington and Baltimore Railroad, had extensive holdings in Philadelphia real estate, and was an active member of the Presbyterian Church and the Pennsylvania State Temperance Society. A member of the Princeton Board of Trustees for thirty years, Newkirk, as chairman of the committee on improving the college grounds, oversaw the substantial landscaping program for the front campus begun in 1839. This project included planting trees and shrubbery, constructing gravel paths, laying a brick pavement in front of the campus and the installation of a stone wall and iron fence enclosing the whole front of the college grounds. *The Biographical Encyclopaedia of Pennsylvania of the Nineteenth Century* (Philadelphia, 1874), pp. 35–36. Trustees' Minutes, September 25, 1839, *3*:364, Princeton University Archives. *Wertenbaker*, p. 252.

[9] Henry sent copies of "Contributions III" to several Irish scientists, including James Apjohn of the Royal College of Surgeons, Thomas Andrews and John Stevelly of the Royal Belfast Institution, Humphrey Lloyd, and Robert Kane. Address Book, Box 17, Henry Papers, Smithsonian Archives.

[10] Thomas Romney Robinson, director of Armagh Observatory. *Henry Papers*, *3*:505.

[11] This sentence, preceded by an X, was originally a marginal notation.

[12] Karl Friedrich Mersch (1810–1888), born in Luxemburg and Professor of Chemistry at the Atheneum, came to the United States in the late 1830s. In 1843, he joined the western expedition of Sir William Drummond Stewart. Mersch was involved in engineering in San

gent person. You can find him through Sam.! Ward Jun Esq Wall Street Lately elected the President of one of the New Banks.[13] I sent your umbrella and some articles forgotten by Jane[14] by Mr Topping[15] former tutor in college, he promised to leave the whole with our general agent Dr C. I have not yet got your money although I have been promised it tomorrow. The funds are now in the Bank but the trasurer is not in the village to day. He will be here tomorrow. I have paid Clows account also got the bill of the carriage hire which is pretty well charged at one dollar per time. The following is your account and for the ballance I enclose my check which you will probably find the readiest method of getting the money.

Cr by amount of salary	3.50[16]
Dr to cash advance by me	25
„ to cash paid clow	12
Due on mirrors &c	3.50
Ballance $310. due	$40.50

The whole amount paid me by Prof Jager[17] was $31.50 the French articles are $35.[18] I will preserve for you the French bill and also Jagers account. I have been quite unwell to day with a distressing shortness of breath and have take a quantity of lobelia.[19] This has releived the paroxism but left me in rather a disagreeable state of depression.

Mrs H joines me in respects to Mrs T. With

Yours Truly
Joseph Henry

Francisco and an import business before returning to Luxemburg to serve as Railroad Commissioner, Councilor, and Curator of the Atheneum. Susan Delano McKelvey, *Botanical Explorations of the Trans-Mississippi West, 1790–1850* (Jamaica Plain, Massachusetts, 1955), pp. 785–787.

Mersch's review of Ehrenberg's book, *Die Infusionsthierschen als Vollkommene Organismen*, to which Henry refers, appeared in the *New York Review*, January 1839, 4:224–228. For Ehrenberg, see above, Bache to Henry, March 23, 1839.

[13] Samuel Ward (1786–1839), a Manhattan financier, participated in the founding of the Bank of Commerce of New York and became its first president. His son, also Samuel Ward, studied under Mersch in Europe and subsequently invited him to the United States. *DAB*.

[14] Jane Torrey, Torrey's eldest child.

[15] Evert Marsh Topping (d. 1865) received his A.B. from Princeton in 1830 and was employed as a Tutor at Princeton from 1835 to 1839. From 1839 until 1846, Topping served as Adjunct Professor of Ancient Languages. *Princeton Catalogue*, p. 143.

[16] $350.00.

[17] Benedict Jaeger.

[18] Henry had purchased two pieces of apparatus for Torrey from the firm of Pixii, Père et Fils in Paris. One was a set of two large parabolic mirrors to show the radiation of heat. The other was a lighter made of a crystal container for compressed air to demonstrate the release of caloric.

Henry retained the bill for this purchase. Folder "Accounts, 1837–38," Box 31, Henry Papers, Smithsonian Archives.

[19] Lobelia inflata, or Indian tobacco, a native North American plant, was used in the treatment of asthma and other respiratory diseases. An acronarcotic poison, lobelia was also employed as a sedative and an emetic. Robley Dunglison, *A Dictionary of Medical Science* (Philadelphia, 1846), p. 453.

April 15, 1839

TO WILLIAM C. REDFIELD[1]

Redfield Papers, Beinecke Library, Yale University

Princeton april 15ᵗʰ 1839

My Dear Sir

I have just finished reading the article in the Edinburgh Review on the labours of yourself and Col. Read[2] and although the *"hour has reached in nights black arch the key stone"* I cannot refrain from stealing a few moments more from sleep to congratulate you on the highly complimentary tone of the review and the clear and interesting manner in which your labours are thus placed before the world.

You have long since felt the consciousness of having arrived at an important truth but this was not a sufficient reward for your labours; this truth required to be appreciated and acknowledged, by what is considered, high authority abroad, inorder that it might be received with confidence by the public generally and thus be placed in the way of practical application. That you may long be enabled thus to add to the honor of our country and to advance the cause of science and humanity is the sincere wish of

Yours &c

Joseph Henry

[1] Also in Nathan Reingold, ed., *Science in Nineteenth-Century America* (New York, 1964), pp. 101–102.

[2] *Edinburgh Review*, January 1839, *68*:406–432. The review was of William Reid's *An Attempt to Develop the Law of Storms by Means of Facts, Arranged According to Place and Time; and Hence, to Point out a Cause for the Variable Winds, with the View to Practical Use in Navigation* (London, 1838) and of four important meteorological articles by Redfield: "Remarks on the Prevailing Storms of the Atlantic Coast of the North American States;" "Hurricane of August, 1831;" "Observations on the Hurricanes and Storms of the West Indies, and the Coast of the United States;" "On the Gales and Hurricanes of the Western Atlantic." As Redfield reveals to Henry in his reply of June 3, 1839, below, the reviewer was David Brewster. Sir William Reid (1791–1858, *DNB*), who became a Major-General in the Royal Engineers and a Colonial Governor, based his *Law of Storms* chiefly on personal observations of the results of the disastrous hurricane that struck Barbados on August 10, 1831. Reid corresponded extensively with Redfield on the storm and attempted to confirm Redfield's theory that American storms were whirlwinds moving in curved tracks. For this, Reid collated data from logbooks of British warships and merchant vessels. He also attempted to confirm the theory that storms south of the equator move in the opposite direction.

American investigators, notably Redfield and Espy, pioneers in the rising field of meteorology, were particularly hopeful for signs of European recognition, which was soon forthcoming. The favorable opinion of Brewster (and the other European notables enumerated by Redfield in his reply to Henry, below) not only signaled Redfield's scientific success but gave his whirlwind theories an important boost over the centripetal hypothesis of Espy. Espy's reaction to Reid's corroboration of Redfield is discussed below in Redfield's reply to Henry.

ALEXANDER DALLAS BACHE TO EDWARD SABINE

Sabine Papers,[1] Records of Kew Observatory,
Public Record Office, London

Philadelphia April 16th, 1839.

My dear Major.

Your kind letter has been heartily welcome though somewhat disappointing in not saying a word about your intended visit to these climes. The spring *was* to have been the time. Is your intention changed? Or being a man under authority, as well as in authority, has it been changed for you?[2] My friend Prof. Henry would be scandalized at the idea of your having looked into the printed document[3] which you return to me without the explanation which accompanied it in his letter to me. He sent [it] as a specimen of the attempt at scientific humbug in high political places. It has done some good in bringing out refutation upon refutation of the folly & thus showing that even Senatorial dignity was no shield behind which nonsense could take refuge. The same individual has followed up this report by a second, [?by] which he has well laid strong cords to fasten himself without, as he will find should he attempt to *move* at the next session of the Senate. I avail myself of the opportunity of two medical gentlemen Professors[4] going to purchase app[s] on your side of the great salt lake to send you the proceedings of our Philos. Society for the last year, by which you will see that we are not entirely idle. For my single self my report upon the educational institutions visited while away from home has occupied me almost entirely. Finding too matters in regard to the Girard College less advanced than [I][5] had expected, and our City Councils not so active in [making] up for the lea way as I desired, worried me, and [?combined] with changes of life (by resuming sedentary occupations) to [injure] my health very materially & thus to retard the completion of my literary labour, and to allow me to pass to something more congenial. This report done I shall go to work upon that for the Association on the progress of Meteorology in the U.S.[6] I hope unless

---

[1] BJ3/25. Transcripts of Crown-copyright records in the Public Record Office appear by permission of the Controller of H. M. Stationery Office.

[2] Sabine was to have come as a member of a joint commission to survey the disputed northeast boundary of the United States. In his reply of July 3, 1839 (RH 2207, Rhees Collection, Huntington Library), he wrote that the plan had fallen through.

[3] The report on H. H. Sherwood's memorial to Congress on terrestrial magnetism, which

Henry had sent to Bache with his letter of August 9, 1838, above. Sabine replied that he couldn't remember even looking at it.

[4] Not identified.

[5] A corner of the first sheet of the original has been torn off. We have supplied, in brackets, the missing material here and below from a letterpress copy in the Bache Papers, Smithsonian Archives.

[6] Bache had already sent out letters soliciting information for this report. See his second letter to Henry of March 16, 1839, above.

the task proves more difficult than I had expected to complete it in time for the next meeting. Should I be disappointed in this you must *explain* for me. By the bye let me beg you to get from Phillips the resolution requesting this report & to send it to me. I made no memorandum of it & have not the wording in my mind. My impression is that it referred to the progress of meteorology and not to any elaborate discussion of climate & the like. Do not fail me I beg you on this point, but be so kind as to send me the resolution as soon as you can.[7] The magnetic news which you give is highly cheering,[8] & I long for more. Lloyd had apprised me of your probable success but nothing so definite had occurred when he wrote. *Our* expedition has been heard from after touching at Rio Janiero. They had been shoal hunting under the equator.[9] They have instruments & mean to use them, of the results we shall see. I do not know Capt. Wilkes but Renwick endorses him, & he certainly watched the oscillations of your Hansteens a great while ago[10] & has since been engaged in similar operations and even extended his inquiries to the mode of pendulum observations. The needles sent out by Prof. Henry have not returned. Should they not have been sent I pray you expedite them as they may be losing, to our loss. I opened my Gauss the other day to see that all was right & found every[th]ing apparently in beautiful order. I am not able yet to [get] the instrument mounted tho' I shall not wait for an observatory to place the variation instrument.[11] Gauss' resultate are very well if one must read a foreign tongue, but the study is so much lightened by the translation ready made that I hope soon to see Taylor's Memoirs.[12]

Let me hear soon again from you & gain hopes of seeing you. Mrs Bache

---

[7] In his reply of July 3, Sabine quoted the resolution as given by John Phillips, Assistant General Secretary of the British Association: "That Professor Bache of Philadelphia be requested to furnish a report on the state of Meteorology in the United States for the next meeting of the Association."

[8] Presumably news of the government's approval of the network of magnetic observatories and the Ross expedition to the Antarctic.

[9] The U. S. Exploring Expedition reached Rio de Janeiro in early November 1838 after stopping at Madeira and the Cape Verde Islands. Wilkes penned a long report to James K. Paulding, Secretary of the Navy, on November 27, 1838 (on roll 5 of NARS microcopy 75). Despite patient searching, the squadron found none of the shoals indicated on various charts; Wilkes recommended that they be stricken from future charts.

[10] See *Henry Papers*, 2:87.

[11] Bache eventually set up the two Gauss instruments in the Girard College Observatory. Both the declination magnetometer and the newer bifilar magnetometer were made by Meyerstein of Göttingen. *Observations at the Magnetic and Meteorological Observatory, at the Girard College, Philadelphia . . . 1840 to 1845*, 3 vols. (Washington, 1847), *1*:vi.

[12] Bache is referring to C. F. Gauss and W. Weber, eds., *Resultate aus den Beobachtungen des magnetischen Vereins*, which reported the work of the German magnetic association for the years 1836 to 1841 and appeared in six volumes from 1837 to 1843. The second volume of Taylor's *Scientific Memoirs*, 1841, published translations of much of the material from the early reports.

unites with me in remembrance & hopes to make Mrs Sabine's acquaintance. Present me kindly to Mrs Sabine & believe me

Very truly Yours
A. D. Bache

P.S. I received a very *old* letter, August, from Duperrey last December, in great excitement which I trust is allayed by your frankness.[13] Have you heard from him?

---

[13] Louis-Isidore Duperrey (1786–1865, *DSB*) was a French naval officer who made valuable contributions to terrestrial magnetism, particularly observations made on his 1822–1825 expedition on the *Coquille*.

Duperrey's letter of August 10, 1838, is a long complaint about Sabine's 1837 report to the British Association on terrestrial magnetism. Two slightly different copies of the letter, addressed to both Quetelet and Bache, are in the Rhees Collection, Huntington Library (RH 1119 and RH 1120), as is a related letter from Quetelet to Bache of August 19, 1838 (RH 2105).

At Sabine's request, Duperrey had sent him data for the report, including his own observations from the *Coquille* voyage. Duperrey was furious when Sabine failed to mention him and proceeded to attack the report in general, particularly Sabine's claim (page 2) that most of his material was new and original. Duperrey wrote, "je cherche et ne trouve rien de neuf ni même d'original dans ce rapport."

Sabine had also neglected to mention Bache's work in terrestrial magnetism. Quetelet's letter indicates some friction between Bache and Sabine over this: "M. Sabine m'assure . . . qu'il n'a eu nullement l'intention d'omettre ce que vous avez fait pour la science. . . ."

In 1838 Sabine made up for his previous omission by publishing an appendix to his 1837 report. Praising the work of Duperrey and Bache, he explained that he had never received the data sent by Duperrey and that Bache's observations in the United States had not yet been connected with those of Europe. The appendix is in *British Association Report, 1838* (1839), pp. 318–320. The 1837 report is on pages 1–85 of the previous volume.

RECOMMENDATION FOR SAMUEL DAVIES ALEXANDER[1]

Retained Copy, Henry Papers, Smithsonian Archives

Princeton College of New Jersey
April 16th 1839

Samuel Alexander during the present year has been acting as an assistant in the Philosophical and chemical laboratory of this Institution and has been very industriously engaged in the acquisition of knowledge. He is a

---

[1] The son of Archibald Alexander, Samuel Davies Alexander (1819–1894) graduated from Princeton in 1838. He remained as Henry's assistant with the title of Resident Graduate until 1840. After three years (1840–1843) as a civil engineer on the New York and Erie Railroad and another as a student of law, Alexander entered the Princeton Theological Seminary in 1844. Ordained in 1847, he held pastorships in Philadelphia, Freehold, New Jersey, and New York City. William Edward Schenck, *Biography of the Class of 1838* (Philadelphia, 1889), pp. 29–32; *Roberts*, p. 136; *Princeton Annual Catalogue*, 1839, 1840.

graduate of the College and it gives me pleasure to recommend him as a young gentleman of good mind and irreproachable character.

Joseph Henry
Profes. Nat. Phil.
College of N.J.

TO WILLIAM H. ELLET[1]
Mary Henry Copy, Henry Papers, Smithsonian Archives

Princeton April 17th 1839

To Prof Ellet.

The honor[2] was entirely unexpected and had I been aware of any proposition of the kind I would have requested that it might be deferred until I could establish a more unexceptionable title to it. My friends with whom I have advised on the subject consider that as the degree was conferred in consideration of my scientific labors that it is due to the proper appreciation of this department of knowledge in our country that I should accept it, but I assure you that far from feeling elated by it I am only impressed with a sense of obligation to make more vigorous efforts in the same line. Please to communicate these sentiments to the Board at the next meeting and present my thanks for the high honor conferred upon me and my assurance of a due appreciation of it coming as it does from so celebrated and responsible an institution.

[1] Ellet (*Henry Papers*, *1*:337) was professor of chemistry, mineralogy, and geology at South Carolina College.
[2] The Board of Trustees of South Carolina College had awarded Henry an honorary LL.D. on December 7, 1838. *Columbia Telescope*, December 12, 1838. For the background of the award, see *Henry Papers*, *3*:523.

FROM ALEXANDER DALLAS BACHE
Henry Papers, Smithsonian Archives

Philadelphia. April. 19. 1839.

My dear Henry.

Excuse me for saying that circumstances alter cases. Nothing would give me more pleasure than to fulfil my promise of reading the report at Princeton, but it is *un* possible I fear. Imprimis they are at work on my preparatory school[1] & I dare not leave town for fear of a call for information, or to act or counteract. This question will not be settled until Thursday next. Should it fail which Heaven forefend! I might come but for family circumstances—viz; a pretty niece came on to stay with us who cannot be left—and a sister coming—neither of which events were known or suspected when the promise was made. Should the school pass muster, the Trustees will meet at once to settle their part of the business. You as a philosopher & *madame* as a philosopher's wife will see the force of the argument. If I can come I will, and *therefore* if I cannot you "must"—is not this logical & has it not the force of several horses. Ferguson's illustration of Sherwood's calculations by the attitude of a youth at 10 & 16 yrs. of age is very capital—tho' not strictly scientific.[2] Such nonsense would be well handled by some penny a liner.

I am now writing at my last school. Your needles per north Star have just come back[3] & I want you to help oscillate. I do not send you the accompanying letter *for fear* the precious results may be lost between this & Nassau Hall. It is from Ross.[4] Let me keep it 'till you come. The needles were entered as such in the manifest & by tariff are duty free! Perhaps you will say this is a new reason why I should come to *you*. I admit its force but none is needed to incline me to come if possible—as I said before if un—Your memento to "Miss Bache" was honestly returned by the Naval Hero! I confess that in a like case I should have appropriated the foreign coin.

I have received two fine maps of India one the triangulation, the other the geographical map from Major Jervis.[5] Come & see them.

Draper is fussily anxious about your paper—we have had a long talk. He went to N.Y. yesterday[6] & will probably pay you a visit on Monday next or

---

[1] Girard College.

[2] Perhaps "A Critique on the Pretended Discovery of Dr Sherwood," which James Ferguson read to the Albany Institute on April 11, 1839. Minutes, Albany Institute Archives. We have not located a published version.

[3] The needles which Henry sent to Bache in England with his letter of August 9, 1838, printed above.

[4] Letter not found.

[5] Thomas Best Jervis (1796–1857) was an engineer and surveyor with the East India Company from 1813 to 1841. On leave in England from 1837 to 1839, Jervis worked with data from the partially completed topographical and triangulation surveys of India. Henry and Bache may have met him at James South's observatory where Jervis worked while in Lon-

don. In 1837 Jervis published "Memoir on the Origin, Progress and Present State of the Surveys of India," *Journal of the Royal Geographical Society of London*, 1837, *7*:127–143.

After retiring from the East India Company, Jervis returned to England and set up a private press where he printed maps and papers relating to India. After providing maps for the British Army during the Crimean War, and emphasizing the importance of accurate maps for the Army, Jervis became head of the new Topographical and Statistical Depot of the War Department. *The Quarterly Journal of the Geological Society of London*, 1858, *14*:liv–lx. W. P. Jervis, *Thomas Best Jervis* (London, 1898).

[6] John William Draper (1811–1882, *DSB*) had just been invited to become Professor of Chem-

thereabouts. I fear he has been working up some ploughed soil, but perhaps has harrowed it. His kink of sending his paper abroad has prevented me from knowing exactly. What he tells me savours strongly of Pouillet. Great men you know &c.[7]

This is already twice as long as I expected. How nice it would be to meet once a week *regularly* to uncork.

Yours ever truly
A.D. Bache

istry at New York University. Born in England, he studied chemistry with Edward Turner at University College, London, received an M.D. in 1836 from the University of Pennsylvania, and taught chemistry and natural philosophy at Hampden-Sydney College.

Draper's arrival in New York City in the Fall coincided with the arrival from Paris of the details of the daguerreotype process. Draper took one of the first photographic portraits and then initiated astronomical photography with a daguerreotype of the moon. Draper also applied photography to his studies of the chemical effects of radiant energy, taking the first photograph of the diffraction spectrum of the sun. As first President of the American Photographical Society from 1859 to 1866, Draper encouraged more extensive use of photography by American scientists. See Deborah Jean Warner, "The American Photographical Society and the Early History of Astronomical Photography in America," *Photographic Science and Engineering*, 1967, *11*: 342–347.

In the mid-1850s, Draper began studying history and the relationship between science and religion. His role as a defender of science against religion is explored in Donald Fleming, *John William Draper and the Religion of Science* (Philadelphia, 1950).

[7] Draper had consulted Bache about his paper "On the Use of a Secondary Wire as a Measure of the Relative Tension of Electric Currents," which was about to be published in the *Phil. Mag.*, 1839, 3d ser. *3*:266–279, 339–349. From a letter of Bache to Draper, February 13, 1839 (Bache Papers, Smithsonian Archives), it is clear that Draper had not given Bache the details of his "secret" discovery. Bache chided him for publishing abroad and offered to get him a copy of Henry's "Contributions II: Spiral Conductor" and of "Contributions III: Electro-Dynamic Induction" as soon as it was printed. Evidently Draper was uneasy about publishing his paper without seeing Henry's work.

FROM HENRY JAMES
Henry Papers, Smithsonian Archives

New York April 20, 1839
Astor House

My dear Friend:

I found your letter addressed to me at Albany, lying at the office yesterday morning, on getting in from home, and received this afternoon your note attached to Mr Bache's letter.[1] I sent Mr B's eggs yesterday by the Cars to Philadelphia—but have very little hope that they continued in the shape of

[1] Neither letter has been found.

eggs during the long voyage in the Gt Western. The vessel was so warm in every part, that it was impossible to find a suitable spot for them, unless they were suspended from one of the masts, or over the stern; either of which positions however w[oul]d have been rendered insecure by the violence of the gales we encountered. If they are hatched, I hope he will attribute the circumstance to the proper cause—the warmth of the ship, and not my carelessness.[2]

I am very much obliged to you for your kindness and for your invitation, which I shall be glad to avail myself of at some future day, being just now too much occupied with some matters that claim my attention here and in A. to allow of my going away. I brought you a letter from Prof Faraday[3]— which I was so excessively stupid as to leave in Albany in my desk—but which I will send you on Tuesday next from there, as I intend going up the river on Monday Eveng. I was much indebted to you for your letter of introduction to him.[4] He came to see me immediately on my sending it to him, and offered me in the kindest manner every furtherance to my pursuits that lay in his power—invited me to attend his lectures—visit his house—use his library &c &c. All these latter things I was afraid to do, as I might be in his way, or might divert his attention from his regular avocations, but I saw him two or three times and had very pleasant intercourse with him. He spoke in the highest terms of you in every way—and reverted so frequently when I saw him to the subject, and always in a manner so cordial and evidently affectionate, as to shew that he remembered your visit with very great pleasure. I thought I should remember many of his kind expressions and messages, for they gratified me as much as I supposed they would you—but the details of them have slipped my memory. However his letter will supply my lack.

I had a gratifying visit to England—very much so. I was in Paris two months nearly—but it was a comfortless residence compared with London, from my unskilfulness in the language, and my disrelish for the peculiar ways, of the French people. I was glad to get back again to England, where I could never go out into the streets without meeting some one or some thing to remind me of "Hail Columbia, happy land." Our trip in the Great Western was the most important one I presume yet achieved in respect to the question of the feasibility of steam navigation. We had the roughest

---

[2] Our only clue to this matter is a letter from Bache to Petty Vaughan (Bache Papers, Smithsonian Archives, February 22, 1839) in which Bache stated the eggs were for his German friend and assistant Trewendt. Bache warned "77° of Fahrenheit will turn the eggs into worms! Cold does not injure them." How Henry James ended up with this sensitive assignment is unknown to us.

[3] Not found.

[4] Printed above, October 9, 1838.

weather one could desire for such an experiment for upwards of two weeks
—as the published log will shew you—and were never forced to stop a moment I believe for the repair of the machinery. I should prefer a passage in
her I think—were I crossing again—to any of the packets. She takes 50 too
many passengers—though probably the comparative novelty of the enterprise just now requires a large number to ensure the stockholders a profit
upon their investment. But I have no doubt that as the boats become more
numerous, and ways of lessening the consumption of fuel and other expenses are devised—they will limit their passengers and be in *all* respects—
what they are now only in *some*—preferable to the packets.

I saw Hunn in Paris frequently. He was preparing to pull up his stakes
and return to America for good. He is a very worthy fellow, and I have no
doubt will maintain a very dignified stand in his profession here. He was
looking at Homeopathy before I left—and I hope will fall in love with it.[5]
I presume I shal[l] see you shortly either here or in Albany—as your vacation
approaches. Should you have occasion to favour me with a letter shortly
direct to me in Albany. Remember me affectionately to Mrs Henry—Mr
Alexander & all my friends. And believe me

Ever truly & affectionatly
Yours
H. James

P.S. I beg of you dont honour my poor name with the prefix of Revd Aside
from any more serious considerations, it would perplex me much to tell
what I should be held in reverence for; and as to the custom of distinguishing certain officers in a church from their fellows, by that title, the laws of
the churches of christ delivered to us in the New Testament leave us in no
darkness as to its origin—in the silly pride of the human heart. If you will
therefore substitute the word "Unrev^d" it will not only be more consonant
to the truth of things, but will provoke no remonstrances on my part.

---

[5] If he did, he had clearly fallen out of love with it by 1863 when he characterized it as a "remarkable system of folly and imposture." See note B of Thomas Hun, *Address Before the Medical Society of the State of New York* (Albany, 1863), a pamphlet in the Henry Library.

FROM SAMUEL F. B. MORSE[1]

Henry Papers, Smithsonian Archives[2]

New York April 24th 1839

My Dear Sir,

On my return a few days since from Europe I found, directed to me, through your politeness, a copy of your valuable "Contributions" for which I beg you to accept my warmest thanks. The various cares which press upon me after so long an absence from home, have prevented me from more than a cursory perusal of its interesting contents. Yet I perceive many things of great interest to me in my Telegraphic enterprize. I was glad to learn by a letter received in Paris from D[r] Gale that a spool of 5 miles of my wire was loaned to you, and I perceive that you have already made some important experiments with it.[3] In the absence of my Associate D[r] Gale who has gone to the South, I feel a great desire to consult some scientific gentleman on points of importance bearing upon my Telegraph, which I am about to establish in Russia, being under an engagement with the Russian Government Agent in Paris to return to Europe for that purpose in a few weeks.[4] I should be exceedingly happy to see you, and am tempted to break away from my absorbing engagements here, to find you at Princeton. In case I should be able to visit Princeton for a few days, a week or two hence, how should I find you engaged? I should come as a learner, and could bring no "contributions" to your stock of experiments of any value, nor any means of furthering your experiments except, it may be the loan of an additional *5 miles of wire*, which you may think desirable to have.

I have many questions to ask, but should be happy, in your reply to this letter, if you could answer this general one.

---

[1] Like subsequent Henry-Morse correspondence, this letter has been printed previously in Morse biographies and the partisan literature which developed from the later dispute between the two men. Examples include *A Memorial of Samuel F. B. Morse, from the City of Boston* (Boston, 1872), pp. 59–60, Edward Lind Morse, ed., *Samuel F. B. Morse: His Letters and Journals*, 2 vols. (Boston and New York, 1914), 2:138–140, and *Shaffner's Telegraph Companion*, 1855, 2:12–13. It is the first correspondence between Morse and Henry. Morse later claimed that it represented the first contact between the two men. Henry, however, in a court deposition presented in 1849, claimed to have met Morse in the autumn of 1837. There is no surviving documentation to support Henry's claim. *Shaffner's Telegraph Companion*, 1855, 2:12–

16, 107–108.

[2] Morse's draft is in the Morse Papers, Library of Congress.

[3] For Henry's use of Morse's wire, see above, "Record of Experiments," October 29, 1838.

[4] Although Baron Meyendorf, the Czar's agent in France, was greatly impressed by Morse's telegraph, Czar Nicholas I refused to sign the agreement for a twenty-mile telegraph line. The reason usually given for Nicholas's refusal was his fear that a device which rapidly transmitted information would ultimately undermine the government. Morse did not hear of the Czar's refusal until August 1839. Carleton Mabee, *The American Leonardo: A Life of Samuel F. B. Morse* (1943; reprint ed., New York, 1969), pp. 222–225; Morse, ed., *Morse*, 2:147.

Have you met with any facts in your experiments thus far that would lead you to think my mode of Telegraphic communication will prove impracticable?

So far as I have consulted the savans of Paris, they have suggested no insurmountable difficulties, *none* of a scientific nature. I have however, quite as much confidence in your judgment from your valuable experience, as in that of any one I met abroad. I think that you have pursued an original course of experiments, and have discovered facts more immediately bearing upon my invention than any published abroad.

I will not trouble you at this time with my questions, nor until I know your engagements.[5]

Accompanying this is a copy of a report made by the Academy of Industry of Paris on my Telegraph[6] which I beg you to accept.

> Believe me Dear Sir
> With the highest respect
> Y^r Mo. ob. serv^t
> Sam! F: B: Morse

[5] For Henry's response, see below, Henry to Morse, May 6, 1839.

[6] This has not survived in the Henry Library.

TO JOHN TORREY

Torrey Papers, Library, New York Botanical Garden

Princeton April 25th 1839

Dear Dr

The chek has been receved and accepted at the Princeton Bank so that the business is settled with the exception of my getting your order cashed by Mr Van Doren—he was out of Town when I called. I am much obliged to you for the hints relative to the putting-up of the papers and will endeavour to profit by your directions.[1] I will send you some articles for scotland by the first opportunity. Henry James has returned from England brings me a communication from Faraday which however has not yet been forwarded to me. Henry was highly gratified with his reception by Faraday and appears from his letter to be much pleased with him as a man.[2]

[1] Torrey probably offered Henry suggestions on how to prepare his copies of "Contributions III" for mailing and distribution.

[2] See above, James to Henry, April 20, 1839.

As soon as I can get Joseph to pack up the articles I will send them to New York to your man Prosh[3] although I spoke to Pike about them and perhaps ougt to give him the job—no bargan however was made and I presume it is an affair of litle consequence since the cost of the repairs should not amount to much. I will endeavour to procure the money for your carbonic apparatus at the begining of the college term.

I have spoken to the Dr[4] about his house. He says that he would be glad to accomodate you but the house is much out of repair has not been inhabited for some time does not think it would suit. I have also spoken to Steadman informed him that you had concluded not to hire his house. He says you can have it for three or four months if you choose. Perhaps it would answer as well as the Dr's.

I start for Philadelphia tomorrow morning to attend a meeting of the Franklin Institute.[5] The hall is in such confusion with workemen and apparatus that I can do nothing in the way of experiment and intend therefore to take a litle recreation.

The improvements have commenced in the campus. We have now quite a number of men engaged on the fence and also several putting down trees and grading the grounds.

If it should come in your way I wish you would make inquiry relative to the expense of moving Clows house.[6] Unless this be put in an other position and the whole enclosed within a high fence the grounds can never be kept in good order.

Mrs. H. joins me in respects to Mrs Torry. The scarfs were greatfully received. Mrs H bids me ask if Mrs T wishes crackers baked for her.

Yours as ever
Joseph Henry

---

[3] George W. Prosch, an instrument maker in New York City, constructed Samuel Morse's first camera, following directions in an instruction manual brought from France. Among the earliest suppliers of daguerreotype equipment in the city, Prosch opened his own daguerreotype gallery by mid–1840. He was later associated with Benjamin Pike, the optician. William Welling, *Photography in America: The Formative Years, 1839–1900* (New York, 1978), pp. 8–9; *Humphrey's Journal*, 1854, 6: 327.

[4] George Maclean.

[5] Henry attended this meeting after visiting Jacob Green and Alexander Dallas Bache. Exhibited at the meeting were objects of curiosity brought from Germany by Bache, and Stephen Alexander's models, in mica, of crystals. Henry to Harriet Henry, April 1839, Family Correspondence, Henry Papers, Smithsonian Archives.

[6] See *Henry Papers*, 3:91, especially footnote 7. Henry Clow's house blocked the view of Whig Hall from Nassau Street.

TO SAMUEL F. B. MORSE[1]
Morse Papers, Library of Congress

Princeton May 6th 1839

Dear Sir

Your favour of the 24th ult[2] came to Princeton during my absence which will account for the long delay of my answer. I am pleased to learn that you fully sanction the loan which I obtained from Dr Gale of your wire and I shall be happy if any of the results are found to have a practical bearing on the electrical telegraph.

It would give me much pleasure to see you in Princeton after this week my engagements will not then interfere with our communications on the subject of electricity. During this week I shall be almost constantly engaged with a Friend[3] in some scientific labours which we are prosecuting together.

I am acquainted with no fact which would lead me to suppose that the project of the electro magnetic telegraph is impractical,[4] on the contrary I believe that science is now ripe for the application and that there are no difficulties in the way but such as ingenuity and enterprise may obviate. But what form of the apparatus or what application of the power will prove best can I believe be only determined by careful experiment. I can say however that so far as I am acquainted with the minutia of your plan I see no practical difficulty in the way of its application for comparatively short distances but if the length of the wire between the stations be great I think that some other modification will be found necessary in order to develope a sufficient power at the farther end of the line.[5]

[1] This letter has been published a number of times (with minor variations in spelling and punctuation) by partisans of Morse as evidence that Henry neither invented the relay, nor even conceived of it until long after Morse had invented it. Particular emphasis was placed on the last sentence of the third paragraph, which Morse supporters contended was Henry's admission that he was ignorant of the principle of the relay.

Henry's retained copy of the letter is in his papers, Smithsonian Archives.

[2] Printed above.

[3] A. D. Bache. See below, Henry to Bache, May 20, 1839.

[4] For an exposition of Henry's support for the telegraph, in sharp contrast to his belief that the electric motor was impractical, see Arthur P. Molella, "The Electric Motor, the Telegraph, and Joseph Henry's Theory of Technological Progress," *Proceedings of the Institute of Electrical and Electronic Engineers*, 1976, *64*:1273–1278.

[5] Henry annotated his copy of *A Memorial of Samuel F. B. Morse from the City of Boston* (Boston, 1872)—which survives in the Henry Library—at this point of its reprint of this letter (p. 61):

When I wrote this I had in my mind the plan devised by Mr Wheatstone to renew the current by closing a circuit shown to Mr Bache and myself in 1837 [*Henry Papers*, 3:219], I am morrally shure that Morse had no k[n]owledge of a local magnet until he went to England in 1838.

On the same page, responding to a claim that Morse had developed the relay *"before*

I shall however be happy to converse freely with you on these points when we meet. In the mean time I remain with much

Respect yours &c
Joseph Henry

---

he had read Professor Henry's paper," Henry wrote: "This may be true though as stated it is intended to convey a false impression. Dr Gale made Morses machine work by knowledge derived from me and my works."

TO WILLIAM BUELL SPRAGUE

Gratz Collection, Historical Society of Pennsylvania

Princeton May 6th 1839

Dear Sir

I send by Dr Campbell the enclosed autograph[1] which has become less valuable to me since I have lately received a long letter from the same hand.[2]

Perhaps the following statement in reference to the writer may be considered of some interest. *"Michael Faraday Esq, D C L, F. R. S, Fullerian Prof. Chem. Royal Institution, Corr. Memb. Royal and Imp Accdd of Science Paris, Petersburgh,* Florence, Copenhagen, Berlin &c. &c."—was originally an apprentice to a book binder—accidentally acquired a taste for reading—was presented by a customer, who found him reading the book he was to bind, with a ticket to the lectures of Sir H Davy—after this he resolved to devote himself to science and at his own earnest solicitation was admitted as an assistant to the laboratory of the Royal Institution. Here he became the secretary, the pupil and finally the successor of Davy. He is now 48 years old still laboriously devoted to science and is undoubtedly the first living Experimental Philosopher. He has particularly distinguished himself by his important discoveries in Electricity.

In haste with much
Respect & Esteem
Yours &c
Joseph Henry

---

[1] The Faraday autograph does not survive with this letter or in the Sprague Papers at Yale. It may have been only Faraday's signature. It is unlikely that Henry would give away a substantive Faraday letter.

[2] The letter that Henry James brought back from England. See his letter to Henry of April 20, 1839, printed above.

"RECORD OF EXPERIMENTS"
Henry Papers, Smithsonian Archives

May 13th 1839

Another long interregnum in my experiments.[1] In the mean time I have published my paper 3rd series electro dynamic Induction, given a course of Lectures in New York but have been chiefly prevented from experimenting by a series of changes going on in the arrangement of the Philosophical hall and the room below and these I have been superintending.

I have lately received Dr Faradays 14th series and find that he has crossed the track of my last paper but in reference to the screening influence draws an intirely oposite conclusion.[2] There is however no doubt but that he is

---

[1] The last "Record of Experiments" entry is dated October 31, 1838.

[2] Faraday had searched for materials which would affect the transmission of magnetic forces analogous to the manner in which dielectrics affected electrical lines of force. Much to his surprise he found no evidence of screening. The inductive effect was equally powerful whether conductors or insulators were interposed between the coils. *Experimental Researches in Electricity*, Fourteenth Series, paragraphs 1723 and 1735. These results directly contradicted Henry's conclusions published in paragraph 59 of "Contributions III." Henry discussed his differences with Faraday in his letter to Bache of May 20, 1839, printed below. He conducted additional experiments to confirm the correctness of his conclusions on May 14, 1839, October 14, 1839, and October 15, 1839 (see the "Record of Experiments" entries of these dates, printed below), and announced his findings to the American Philosophical Society via his letter to Bache of October 16, 1839, also printed below.

Throughout the following year, Henry continued to explore the inductive force created when a galvanic current was begun or broken. On June 19, 1840, he presented part of "Contributions IV" to the American Philosophical Society. In that paper, expanding upon and clarifying the results announced in his letter of October 16, 1839, he concluded (paragraph 52) that the inductive force consisted of two parts with differing properties. The low intensity part could be interrupted by a drop of water, did not magnetize steel needles, and was not screened by metal plates, with the exception of iron. The induced current produced by the motion of a conductor in relation to the current or of the battery itself was primarily of this form. The high intensity part

was not interrupted by water, gave shocks, and magnetized needles, but was screened by all metal plates or closed coils. Currents of the third and higher orders were primarily of this type.

Henry presented a general framework for his empirical observations in the remainder of "Contributions IV," read before the American Philosophical Society on November 20, 1840. He reported that the phenomena he had been investigating over the previous four years could now be reduced to three laws:

1. During the time a galvanic current is increasing in quantity in a conductor, it induces, or tends to induce, a current in an adjoining parallel conductor in an opposite direction to itself.

2. During the continuance of the primary current in full quantity, no inductive action is exerted.

3. But when the same current begins to decline in quantity, and during the whole time of its diminishing, an induced current is produced in an opposite direction to the induced current at the beginning of the primary current.

(Paragraph 56.) Through these laws Henry was able to enumerate every inductive current which occurred in a particular experiment. Using graphs to clarify his discussion, and relying heavily on the assumption that the deflection of the galvanometer is independent of the intensity of the current, Henry demonstrated how particular inductive phenomena could be explained in terms of the additive or neutralizing effects of the intensities and quantities of the currents involved. For example, he showed (paragraphs 81–82) that the screening effect occurred because of the reduction of the intensity of the induced current in the

in error in the enunciation of the proposition since my results are on such a scale as to leave no doubt as to their nature. Commenced to day some experiments to determine the cause of Dr F's not getting the same results.

Exp 1 Arranged the electrometer by Clark. Sent charge of galvanism through coil No 2 helix no one connected with the galvanometer. Lowered helix on coil current in one direction; raised helix current in the other. Put plate of thick lead between, no diffifference. Plate at rest still no difference. Plate in motion with the helix no difference.

Exp 2ⁿᵈ Put a circu[i]t of long thin wire around the armature of the compound magnet and over this wire put another then connected the ends of the 2ⁿᵈ wire with the galvanometer. The slightest motion of the keeper caused motion in the needle. Next joined the ends of the inner wire. Not the least difference [in] the action was perceived. The needle still obeyed the slightest motion of the

keeper. I before in an experiment made last summer, put a band of copper around the armature of two straight magnets and found no effect as it regards interference (See July 21ˢᵗ 1839).[3] In the above exp with the compound magnet clarks galvanometer was used.

Exp 3ʳᵈ Attempted with the arrangement of the coil and helix as described in exp 1 to detect the electro tonic state.[4] A continued current was passed through the coil while the helix was placed on it and the ends suddenly joined but no action was perceived at the galvanometer.

---

helix by the action of the current induced in the screen; hence no shock. In contrast, the currents induced in the helix at the beginning and ending of the induction in the screen were equal in quantity (although different in direction) and thus the galvanometer deflected as if no screen were interposed. This explanation supplanted Henry's earlier artifice of a two-part inductive current with differing properties, which, as later marginal annotations indicate, quickly appeared inadequate to Henry.

[3] Henry meant July 21, 1838. By connecting the ends of the coil, Henry was trying to get a screening effect from the closed coil. This was equivalent to the copper screening experiment of that date. In both cases Henry obtained negative results.

[4] In paragraph 1729 of his *Experimental Researches in Electricity*, Fourteenth Series, Fara-

day expressed his belief that electromagnetic induction was transmitted over distances in the same manner as static electric induction; namely, by the action of the intervening particles of matter which had been placed in what he called the "electrotonic state." Having failed to find experimental confirmation of his hypothesis, however, he admitted that the evidence was not conclusive.

We surmise that Henry believed that by sending a constant current through the coil he was establishing an electrotonic state or state of strain in the neighboring helix. When the ends of the helix were suddenly closed, the particles of matter would attempt to relieve the strain by inducing a current in the helix.

In the "Record of Experiments" entry of October 14, 1839, printed below, Henry would again attempt to develop experimental confirmation of Faraday's hypothesis.

"RECORD OF EXPERIMENTS"
Henry Papers, Smithsonian Archives

May 14th [1839]

Repeated the 1st exp of yesterday with small galvanometer plate between. Action the same as when air intervened also the motion of the plate with the coil made no difference.[1] Attempted same exp with the interrupted current with a file but the current was so strong as to change the polarity of the needle of the galvanometer. Try the same exp with needles rendered magnetic. From these exp it appears that that there is a difference in action of induction [of] the continued current and the interrupted one

Exp 2nd When the same arrangement was made as before the induction took place through a plate when the battery was lowered or raised, show that a gradual increase or diminution of the quantity of the current causes an induction which passes through a plate.[2] In this respect the induction resembles the attraction and repulsion of the currents

[1] Henry discussed this experiment in "Contributions IV," paragraphs 34 and 35.

[2] This experiment appeared in paragraph 37 of "Contributions IV."

TO ALEXANDER DALLAS BACHE
Bache Papers, Smithsonian Archives

Princeton, Monday May [20][1]
1839

My Dear Bache

I hope you will pardon my tardiness although I have nothing to plead in excuse for suffering your letter[2] to remain unanswered a week except the bustle of commencing a new college term, Faculty meetings and preparations in the Phil. Hall for beginning my course of lectures. I sympathize with you in the result of your labours relative to the preparatory school. You have however the consolation of knowing that every thing has been done on your part proper and necssary to bring the affair about and I have but little doubt that the whole affair will be finally arranged to your satisfaction. Fitful opposition cannot always withstand steady and well directed perseverance. Perhaps it will not be well to press the affair too much just now and I would advise that you make yourself easy for the present and

[1] From the postmark.

[2] Not found.

devote the whole power of your mind to the report. Do not spare the polishing process but make the article in every respect equal to one of your best efforts. That which should be well done can only be done with labour.

The world never asks about the time expended in the production of a literary work nor ever allows an apology for a hasty performance. I am some what earnest on this point because I think that this your first essay before the Public in connection with Girard college is of much importance to yourself and to the cause of education generally in the United States. There[3] are persons in this country I believe who would be pleased to find even an error of orthography in your report. There is no little ill feeling in reference to the college amoung some of the clergy. I mentioned to you I think the fact that the Rev Dr Hawks[4] denounced it in his introductory lecture before the Mercantile Library association as a school of infidelity and which would prove a curse to this country.[5] I mention this not for the purpose of disquieting you unnessarily since I am sure that if your life be spared the Institution will become all that its friends wish it to be and not what its enemies desire but I would have you make your first appearance before the public generally in your very best style. You are no longer Professor Bache of the University of Penn[a] but the first President of Girard College and will therefore be more anxious about the perfection of your publications than about the number of them. I am glad that you concluded to defer

[3] There is a penciled strike through the passage beginning with this sentence and ending in the middle of the fourth sentence with the words "not what its enemies desire but." Penciled notations by Mary Henry, "omit" and "commence here," indicate that the strike is hers. She also struck out the name "Hawks."

[4] Francis Lister Hawks (1798–1866, *DAB*), an Episcopalian minister, was rector of St. Thomas' Church in New York City and an editor of the *New York Review*.

[5] A provision in Stephen Girard's will made clerical opposition inevitable:

> . . . that no ecclesiastic, missionary, or minister of any sect whatsoever, shall ever hold or exercise any station or duty whatever in the said college; nor shall any such person ever be admitted for any purpose, or as a visitor, within the premises appropriated to the purposes of the said college.

Although Girard's purpose was to protect the orphans from sectarian controversies and proselytizing, the provision was misinterpreted by both clerics and freethinkers as hostility to religion. Clerics denounced Girard College as a school of infidelity while freethinkers applauded it for the same reason. Both overlooked the fact that the provision did not ban religious instruction at the school. Bache's report helped allay the clergy's fears. See the reviewer's comments in the *New York Review*, April 1840, *6*:369–417, and in *The Biblical Repertory and Princeton Review*, April 1840, *12*:244–268.

Daniel Webster focused on this provision in *Vidal* v. *Philadelphia* (1844), a suit brought by Girard's relatives to break the will. Although the Supreme Court upheld the will, deciding that only denominationalism and ecclesiasticism were excluded, not religion itself, Webster's arguments characterizing Girard as an atheistic institution opposed to the Christian religion perpetuated misconceptions of the role of religion at Girard College.

Cheesman A. Herrick, *History of Girard College* (Philadelphia, 1927), chapter 6. Carl B. Swisher, *History of the Supreme Court*, volume 5, *The Taney Period, 1836–64* (New York and London, 1974), pp. 215–217 (quotation from page 216).

your report on meteorology[6] until next year. It would have been impossible to do justice to the subject and give the proper attention to your school report at the same time.

On the same account I cannot say that I regret the non passage of your primary school proposition just at this time since your mind may now be exclusively devoted to the report. I know that I am hypercritical in this matter yet I am certain that a general sketch of an article was never made so good but that it might be improved by repeated touching. I wish you would go over the whole article before we again read together since time will be spared and the article will then have all the advantage of a third reading.

Mary has got much better but is not yet well. We are some what apprehensive that she has taken the hooping cough. Young Abert[7] gave me your letter[8] this morning and on the recept of it I immediatly commenced this answer. I will have an eye on the gentleman and introduce him to my family. I had a visit from Morse and on the whole was much pleased with him. I gave him my opinion freely in reference to his telegraph. The evening after you left us I took up Mr Faradays 15th Series[9] which I had not before seen (I had copies before of only the 12th, 13th & 14th) and was much surprised to find that he has again directly crossed the track of my experiments particularly in reference to the screening influence of a plate of metal between two coils but my surprise was still greater when I found that he had arrived at conclusions directly opposite to those which I have published. He found no screening influence with the most delicate arrangement and from this draws a conclusion in favour of his molecular theory. See article 1735 also compare the statement of art 1723 of Mr Faraday with article 59 of my contributions. The next evening after reading the article I commenced a series of experiments to determine the cause of the discrepancy between Dr F and myself and soon found that there is in reality a difference in the action of a metal plate placed between two instantaneous secondary currents such as are produced by the rupture of a current as in my experiments and between two currents formed by the motion of a magnet or a galvanic current.

I have thus opened to me a new field of research and for once have found

[6] The report which Bache had promised to do for the British Association.

[7] Charles Abert (d. 1897) entered the freshman class at Princeton on May 17. A son of John James Abert (*DAB*), he graduated from Princeton in 1842 and became Bache's brother-in-law in 1845 when he married Henrietta Constantia Bache. Faculty Minutes, May 17, 1839, Princeton University Archives. *Princeton Catalogue*, p. 162. Alexander James Dallas, *Dallas . . . of Philadelphia . . .* (n.p., 1877), p. 17.

[8] Not found.

[9] An error; Henry goes on to discuss the Fourteenth Series, not the Fifteenth.

Mr Faraday tripping. He has drawn a general conclusion from a particular fact. The results given in my paper are so striking and on such a scale that there is no doubt of their truth. Resp to Mrs. B.

Yours as ever
Joseph Henry

FROM SAMUEL F. B. MORSE
Henry Papers, Smithsonian Archives

New York May 20th 1839.

My Dear Sir,

I send you what I promised when I left you last week.[1] I know not if the discovery of the existence of two distinct orders of colors in the various prismatic circles seen in nature,[2] will result in any thing important, but as was observed, nothing in nature is unimportant, and every new fact however trivial it may in itself appear, adds to the treasures which true philosophy uses in building the fabric of truth.

I have prepared a parcel for Paris enclosing the numbers of your "Contributions" to the persons for whom you directed them. I have sent a copy to M. Arago[3] and one also to M. Amyot.[4] Hoping your family is restored to health and with respects to M[rs] Henry

I remain D[r] Sir with many thanks for your politeness,
Y[r] Mo. ob. serv[t]
Sam[l] F: B: Morse.

The only specimen of metallic rings by the blow pipe wh[ic]h I have, is on *lead* which I send you.

[1] Morse had visited Henry at Princeton on May 15, 1839, to discuss problems he was having with the telegraph. Morse to A. Vail, May 14, 1839, Morse Papers, Library of Congress.

[2] The "Twilight Bow" which Morse described in *Silliman's Journal*, 1840, *38*:389–390. It was a double prismatic arch observed at morning and evening twilight. In an editorial note the Sillimans expressed their belief that the phenomenon had been observed frequently in the past, but never before described in print (ibid., p. 390).

[3] D. F. J. Arago, the eminent French scientist.

[4] The Frenchman who assisted Morse in his efforts to persuade the Russian government to establish a telegraph system. Possibly Charles-Jean-Baptiste Amyot (1799–1866), better known as a lawyer and entomologist. Edward L. Morse, ed., *Samuel F. B. Morse: His Letters and Journals*, 2 vols. (Boston and New York, 1914), 2:122, 147; *Dictionnaire de Biographie Française*.

TO JAMES HENRY

Family Correspondence, Henry Papers, Smithsonian Archives

Princeton May 22nd 1839
Wednesday

My Dear James

Stephen has not yet arrived. We have heared that he is detained by sickness at albany and therefore the Family are quite uneasy in reference to him. The last letter which came from him was received on Monday. Perhapse he may be here to night. We have not had a letter from you in a long time. Harriet says that the house is just cleaned and in good condition to receive a visit from you and yours. Cary, the girls, Nancy, John Platt, Aunty and all the rest. Nothing new. We are much engaged in making improvements in and about the college buildings. The term has commenced with a good accession to our numbers which will now be some what over 250. I sent by Stephen a lot of my papers for distribution among some of my friends in albany.[1] We had had several letters on business from Stephen but none which gave us any news relative to our friends. I suppose he will give us a budget when he arrives. I mentioned in one of my letters that I had receved a visit from Jessy Young.[2] I have now to inform you that we have lately been honored by a call from another albanian a hard looking subject who said he knew you and that he was a son of Dr Woodruff[3] deceased. He beged for some articles of old clothes—was sober but appeared to be a man of bad habits. How many examples of this kind have been furnished by the sons of the better classes in albany. We are to have a great encampment of United States troops at Trenton which has been ordered by the war departement and will consist of several thousand individuals.[4] This will probably have the effect to increase the price of provision in Princeton and be of some inconvenience to the college since the students will soon get a taste of the company of the Officers. Harriet has concluded to get an oil cloth for the hall and therefore wishes you to get the article according to your promis. We will want 8 yards of the width of 2 yds and 7 inches—and 6 yards of *one* yard and 8 inches wide. American oil cloth of good quality will answer we cannot go the english. Also we want 7 yards of wide stair carpeting nearly

---

[1] Henry's distribution list for reprints of "Contributions III" is found in his Address Book. The Albany names were, in addition to James Henry, Matthew Henry Webster, Joel Wing, James McNaughton, T. R. Beck, Philip Ten Eyck, William Bullions, Gideon Hawley, William Campbell, Ebenezer Emmons.

[2] Unidentified.

[3] The Albany physician Hunloke Woodruff (d. 1811)? *Howell and Tenney*, pp. 206, 209.

[4] The troops assembled at the race ground near Trenton for a "Camp of Instruction." They began to arrive during the first week of June and were to remain for the summer season. *Trenton Emporium and True American*, May 17, 24, 31, June 7, 14, 1839.

Asa Gray (1810–1888), 1838, crayon portrait by Sir David McNee.
Crown Copyright; reproduced with the permission of the
Controller of Her Majesty's Stationery Office and of
the Director, Royal Botanic Gardens, Kew.

Robert Hare (1781–1858), ca. 1820–1825, painting from life by Rembrandt Peale. Courtesy of Independence National Historical Park Collection.

Letter from Joseph Henry to Alexander Dallas Bache, January 3, 1839.
Courtesy of the Smithsonian Archives.

William C. Redfield (1789–1857), n.d.
Courtesy of the Smithsonian Archives.

James P. Espy (1785–1860), n.d.
Courtesy of the Smithsonian Archives.

The Princeton Campus. Lithograph by J. H. Bufford, 1837,
in the Princeton University Library.
Courtesy of Margaret Smith-Burke and Cary S. Hart.

Philosophical Hall, Princeton University, 1870.
Courtesy of the Princeton University Archives.

John William Draper (1811–1882), ca. 1851–
1853, salt print by J. DeWitt Brinckerhoff.
From the collection of George R. Rinhart.

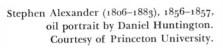

Stephen Alexander (1806–1883), 1856–1857,
oil portrait by Daniel Huntington.
Courtesy of Princeton University.

Antoine-César Becquerel (1788–1878), n.d.
Courtesy of the Smithsonian Archives.

Charles Grafton Page (1812–1868), n.d.
Courtesy of Mrs. J. W. Hazell.

a yard wide—say 7/8 of a yard wide. Also 12 stair rods to match the carpet. Send the articles by the first opportunity with a bill of them and I will send you a check for the same. William is well and bids me tell you and John Platt that he has got a rabbit to show you & wishes you would come to Princeton and stay 100 years also that Aunt Nancy and all the rest will come with you. Mary and Helen are gone to bed. Mary is better in reference to her attack of feaver but she has we fear taken the hooping cough. Helen is quite well. Mary Ann Lagrange is well she talks of going up in June. Aunt is out of all patience to hear from Stephen. She has several times gone over to the other house and set the table expecting the arrival but has again and again been disappointed. They do wrong in Albany not to write.

The cars have arrived but no word of Stephen. Great disappointment to the old folks.

TO CHARLES N. BANCKER[1]
Retained Copy, Henry Papers, Smithsonian Archives

Princeton May 27th 1839

My Dear Sir

It will give me much pleasure to have an eye on the son[2] of your Friend Mr Dennis.[3] He has concluded to join the Freshman class and will not therefore come under my instruction for some years. I will however make frequent inquiries relative to his standing and be more particularly interested in him since you have reccommended him to my attention.

The intelligence that the missing book on colours[4] had been found gave me much relief. I am very sorry that I did not suceed in replacing the papers of colours. I send you by Mr Dennis a copy of my paper from the transactions of the society which I hope you will find time to look at. It has cost

[1] Charles Nicoll Bancker (1778?–1869) was a member of the American Philosophical Society who assisted Henry in his research by procuring apparatus and by lending him instruments from his own extensive collection. *Henry Papers*, 2:160n.

[2] An 1842 graduate of Princeton, James Upshur Dennis (1823–1900) was admitted to the Maryland bar in 1845. He served in both houses of the State Legislature and as a delegate to the State Constitutional Conventions of 1850 and 1864. *The Biographical Cyclopedia of Representative Men of Maryland and District of Columbia* (Baltimore, 1879), p. 342; *Princeton Catalogue*, p. 162.

[3] John Upshur Dennis (1793–1851) was educated at the University of Pennsylvania. A planter in Worcester County, Maryland, Dennis married three times and fathered twenty-one children. James Upshur was his son by his second wife. Lynn Perry, *Dennis & Co.* (Coral Gables, 1963), pp. 77–78.

[4] We presume that this and the following sentence refer to material which Bancker had lent Henry. However, we have no idea of the specifics or the circumstances.

me considerable labour and I think developes some new and important phenomina.

I have just received a copy of Mr Faradays 14th series and am somewhat surprised to find that he has been almost on my tracks in one particular and that his results are diametrically opposite to mine. I have hastily examined the cause of our difference and find it in a peculiarity of action not before noticed and which will probably lead to some new results. The books were duly received.

(In haste)

> With much Respect
> Yours &c
> Joseph Henry

FROM ALEXANDER DALLAS BACHE
Henry Papers, Smithsonian Archives

Philad. May 28th [1839]

Dear Henry

Our correspondence goes by jerks & for fear I should get too far in your debt I in dite to thank you for your letter of advice[1] imprimis & secundo for that on lightning rods & the N.Y. Review.[2] In the sentiments expressed in the first letter I agree with you in the main. Only I doubt the desire to pick flaws in quarters where the picking will be of serious disservice. That the N.Y. Rev. will not give me a favourable notice unless by chance Reed be invited to review me[3] I make no doubt, but that this can harm me I do doubt: as to orthography that is the printer's affair & is not one of my weakest points— such criticism I should laugh at. There are other graver points upon which my Report will be attacked & I have made up my mind to bide the brunt— magna est veritas et prevalebit.[4] I am not of the material fit for controversy but where truth is at stake will not flinch for the fear of the lash. Now the deductions of my report are to me like the deductions from any complex set of phenomena observed, arranged, & studied with a desire to come at

[1] Of May 20, above.
[2] Letter not found.
[3] Probably either William Bradford Reed (1806–1876, *DAB*), a Philadelphia lawyer, or his younger brother Henry Hope Reed (1808–1854, *DAB*), Professor of Rhetoric and English Literature at the University of Pennsylvania. William B. Reed is listed in *Poole's Index to Periodical Literature* (3d ed., 1882) as the author of the favorable review of Bache's report in the *North American Review*, July 1840, *51*:23–46. No author is given for the review in the *New York Review*, April 1840, *6*:369–417, which was also favorable.
[4] i.e., truth is great and will prevail.

truth, with a knowledge of the uncertainties of the questions too: having arrived at these conclusions I will not blink them though party spirit in Church & State should assail me, for it would be flinching from duty in the station in which the disposer of all has placed me. Do not think that I do not see the difficulties of my position & the danger of ship wreck, for some time I have seen it to be this, & have collected no example of success under it to cheer me onward. I trust in the purity of my motives & on success from the fountain of all help or for strength to bear up against defeat. My position is this. My views in regard to education lead me to a natural connexion with the clerical party, my position in the Girard College renders that party my natural enemies. The natural supporters of the institution are those with thorough worldly views & principles, with them I have no affinity. The predicament is pleasant to human view but I have firm trust in an over-ruling providence and do not believe that an effort to train up the Orphan in Christian nurture & admonition will be allowed to fail. This is the first time I have ever given these views out of myself, but they have been for a *long* time, comparatively part and parcel of myself. There is one point on which I do not exactly agree with you. You speak of my being no longer *Professor* Bache etc. Now by science the little reputation which I have has been made, & by science it must be sustained in a great degree. I do not mean to descend from that vantage ground to cope on the pedagogical field with scholars. As an observer I have made my tour & communicate the results, and hope to practice by the lights of the experience thus acquired which is larger than many life times in one situation could have given. But I have no idea of relinquishing a scientific career, to do which would place me in the most false of all imaginable positions, for it should be the pride of the Girard College that its first President was a man of science, and one occupied in endeavouring to extend, not merely to diffuse, the science of the day.[5]

As to the lightning rod it shall be dissected as you require & in regard to the N.Y. Rev. which I have not seen your letter gives me room to fear what the last number led me to suppose that the Scientific articles are in the hands of quacks or very careless fellows. There was a very handsome notice of the Institute Report on Explosions, apropos to a whipping which they gave the editor of the new edition of Tredgold, a certain Mr. Woolhouse.[6]

---

[5] In modern terms, Bache wanted to be known for contributions at the research front of science. Maintaining a clear distinction between the "increase" and "diffusion" of knowledge was important to some research-minded scientists of the period. Confronted with a mandate to increase and diffuse knowledge at the Smithsonian Institution, Henry, like Bache, argued for the priority of research, regarding the diffusion of knowledge as a subsidiary function of the newly-founded institution.

[6] W. S. B. Woolhouse published a revised edition of Thomas Tredgold, *The Steam Engine,* in 1838. We were unable to locate any notice of this work in the *New York Review.*

I am preparing my magnetic observations for the Philo[sophical] Soc. & have taken a rest from my report which will be of service to me. It is probable tho' not certain that I shall go up to Harrisburgh on Friday about the Observatory, it depends upon the Report of Mr Kane who is there now as to whether we can do any thing or not.[7] The report of the Commissioners on the State Survey, of wh. I am one, I shall send up to-morrow.[8] Thank you for your promised assistance. I have determined to have nothing to do with publishing my report to the Trustees of G.C. as a Commercial matter.[9]

I have a great deal more to say but must close just now. Do vibrate & send me the needle as a vessel goes from here to London in a few days.

Yours ever truly
A D Bache

Kind regards from me & mine to you & yours.

The London *Athenaeum* published three extremely critical notices in the issues of February 9, March 2, and April 6, 1839. All three complained of Woolhouse's ignorance of the investigation by Bache and the Franklin Institute:

This series of experiments, for accuracy, extent, and usefulness, is only to be compared with those of the French Institute, and yet there is not a syllable about them in the whole book.

(February 9.) The second characterized Woolhouse's work as a "dense mass of error."

[7] Bache and J. K. Kane were members of the American Philosophical Society's Committee on Astronomical Observatory. Joining with the Philadelphia School Board and City Councils, the APS petitioned the state legislature for permission to jointly equip and operate the observatory at the Philadelphia Central High School and to appoint a director. The bill was introduced in the Senate on May 31 and in the House on June 18. Although it was printed as a law of June 25, 1839, it had not actually passed in the Senate, where it appeared as an amendment to another bill. A similar effort later in the year also failed.

Whitfield J. Bell, Jr., "Astronomical Observatories of the American Philosophical Society, 1769–1843," APS *Proceedings*, 1964, *108*:7–14.

[8] Bache and William P. Alrich had been appointed commissioners to determine whether the present state map was accurate enough for the representation of the geological and mineralogical survey results or whether a new map based on further topographical and geodetic surveys was necessary. In their "Report of Commissioners Relative to a Topographical Survey of the State of Pennsylvania," read in the House and Senate on June 13, 1839, they concluded that the present map was inadequate and a new map desirable, but that pecuniary and scientific considerations argued against further surveys at this time. *Pennsylvania House Journal*, 1838–1839, volume 2, part 1, pp. 1068–1071. *Pennsylvania Senate Journal*, 1838–1839, 2:751–755.

[9] After the *Report* appeared, Bache was urged to prepare a shorter, more popular version, designed for a wider circulation. The *New York Review* notice (cited in footnote 3) assured him of "the thanks of his countrymen, and a ready sale" (p. 374). See also Merle M. Odgers, *Alexander Dallas Bache* (Philadelphia, 1947), p. 88.

May 31, 1839

TO JOHN TORREY
Torrey Papers, Library, New York Botanical Garden

Princeton May 31st 1839

My Dear Dr.

Your kind and very acceptable present of the lamp and the accompany-[ing] tube came to hand safely. I would have answered your letter[1] before this time but the commencement of a new college term and the beginning of my summer course of lectures amid all the confusion of apparatus in the Hall has occupied me more than usual. I have sent off a reccomendation for Ficher[2] and hope he may succeed since you think him worthy and needy. The matter of the brass tube is certainly a very curious substance. If a sufficient quantity can be procured you should by all means stick to the examination of it and little by little you will get at the truth. I have not as yet tried its detonating property; the specimen is carefully preserved for the present as an article of curiosity.[3] I regret that in hastily opening your letter the little scale of mica was lost in the street. The society[4] you mention was spoken of when I was in London. Bailey[5] will do honor to himself and to the country by his attention to the microscope. He has zeal and is well grounded in a thorough scientific education. I fully agree with you in the remark relative to the importance of good instruments and just before the receipt of your letter I had exclaimed in mock heroic: *This is the dipping needle of the College of New Jersey*!!

[1] Not found. However, in a jotting at the top of Henry's letter to him of April 25, 1839 (above), Torrey noted, "Ansd. May 5th by Miss Ellet—sent Lamp & gas pipe."

[2] Possibly James Cogswell Fisher (d. 1880), a graduate of Yale who studied medicine at the College of Physicians and Surgeons in New York City and served as Professor of Chemistry and Mineralogy at New York University, 1839–1840. Fisher assisted S. F. B. Morse in his efforts to obtain government funding for a test of the telegraph and later supervised preparation of the telegraph wire laid between Baltimore and Washington. Disputes over the thoroughness of Fisher's testing methods led to his dismissal by Morse in 1842. *Columbia Alumni*, p. 205. Carleton Mabee, *The American Leonardo: A Life of Samuel F. B. Morse* (New York, 1969), pp. 251–252, 254, 262–263, 268–270.

[3] We have been unable to identify this substance.

[4] We do not know to what specific society Henry is referring. However, the Microscopical Society of London was founded on September 3, 1839, and may well have been in the planning stages during Henry's European visit. The formation of this society, later the Royal Microscopical Society, is an indication of the increasing use of microscopy in science, due in part to the development of the achromatic lens and subsequent technical advances in microscope design. American scientists, returning from travel and study in Europe, pioneered the use of microscopes in universities and medical schools in the United States in this period. Savile Bradbury, *The Evolution of the Microscope* (Oxford, 1967), pp. 200, 204, 206–207.

[5] Jacob Whitman Bailey (1811–1857), Professor of Chemistry, Mineralogy and Geology at West Point and a close friend of Torrey. Bailey was particularly distinguished for his botanical research and for his work with the microscope, which earned him the title "the father of microscopic research in America." *DAB*. See alo Andrew Denny Rodgers III, *John Torrey: A Story of North American Botany* (New York, 1965) for documentation of the friendship between Torrey and Bailey.

The carpenter work of the upper room of the Hall is finished and the whole painted you can scarcely imagine how well the old affair now appears. The superintendance has cost me considerable trouble and confined me to Princeton during the vacation. The workmen are now engaged in putting up the shelves in the cases below, they have not yet commenced to put up the seating. I will write you again on the subject soon.

Professor Dod is much engaged in fitting up a mathematical room in the old clio. hall.[6] It is nearly finished and makes quite a smart appearance.

The college has opened with a good addition to the numbers. We have now on the ground upwards of 240 students and will have nearly if not quite 270 on the catalogue. The improvements now making in the lecture rooms are of a nature to increase the facilities of instruction and therefore will probably have a good effect in adding to the reputation of the college.

I have lately had several communications from Europe a very kind letter from Capt Ross relative to magnetism and a still better one from Faraday.[7] He wishes my opinion and private criticism on his new theory of electricity and in order that I may do him justice I have been studying the subject with considerable attention.

Mr F. sends me a copy of his 14th series of researches and I am much surprised on reading it to find that although it appears to be on a totally different track yet it actually crosses the path of my last paper and what is still more surprising Mr F. comes to diametrically opposite conclusions to those given in my paper. Had I received the article in the early part of the vacation I would have gone immediately to work on the subject and made out the cause of our discrepancies. As it is I have only been able to make a few hasty experiments and from these it appears that there is a difference in the action of induced currents generated by different means which has not been before suspected and that Mr Faraday has been led into an error by supposing an identity where none existed. My results are correct since they are obtained on too large a scale to admit of doubt. Mrs H sends love to Mrs T and the children. Mrs H bids me say that if you have given up the idea of coming to live in Princeton this summer you can at least give us a visit. We will be happy to see you and all yours. The country air did Mrs T. so much good the last visit that she had better try it again. We have the same accomodations as before and will be as pleased to see you. We are all well

---

[6] Prior to the construction of a new building in 1838, the Cliosophic Society had occupied quarters on the top floor of the Library, which it shared with its rival, the American Whig Society. See *Henry Papers*, 3:89.

[7] Neither letter has been found. The Ross letter is mentioned in Bache to Henry, April 19, 1839, above. Faraday's is referred to by Henry James in his letter of April 20, 1839, printed above.

except little Mary. She has had an attack of the billious feaver[8] but has partially recovered from this only to take the hooping cough.

James Alexander[9] lost his oldest child last saturday. You may reccollect that it was a deformed child blind and helpless. The family however was much attached to him and are deeply afflicted with his death.

---

[8] A term applied in the early nineteenth century to a variety of related ailments generally characterized by feverishness, chills, vomiting, and general debility, thought to originate as a liver disorder. Elisha Bartlett, *The History, Diagnosis, and Treatment of the Fevers* of the United States (Philadelphia, 1847), pp. 303–405.

[9] James Waddel Alexander (*Henry Papers,* 2:177), Professor of Rhetoric, Latin, and Literature at Princeton. Alexander had lost another son in 1834. See *Henry Papers,* 2:304.

FROM WILLIAM C. REDFIELD[1]

Henry Papers, Smithsonian Archives

New York June 3ᵈ 1839

Dear Sir

Your esteemed favor of the 15ᵗʰ ult.[2] was duly received and I owe you my acknowledgements for the kind and flattering manner in which you speak of my investigations in the matter of the storms.

Although the subject has attracted but little notice from abroad till within the last two years, yet the manner in which it is now received and treated by some of the most distinguished votaries of Science in Europe, cannot but be gratifying to my feelings. The Article in the Edinburgh Review, to which you allude, was written, according to my private advices, by Sir David Brewster. An Article on the same subject from Sir John Herschel was also expected in the last (London) Quarterly Review for April, which owing to some cause does not appear. I received however a few days since a polite letter from Capt Basil Hall, accompanied with a copy of an article on the same subject from the Foreign Quarterly.[3] In this Article the Capt. does much to show the practical application and importance of our newly acquired knowledge of the law of storms. I have also just seen a portion of

---

[1] A slightly different, retained copy of this letter can be found in Redfield's letterbooks, Beinecke Library, Yale University, and was published in Reingold, *Science in Nineteenth-Century America* (New York, 1964), pp. 102–103.

[2] Actually April 15, 1839, printed above.

[3] In the April 1839 number of the *Foreign Quarterly Review,* Hall reviewed two of Redfield's articles: "Meteorological Sketches" and "Mr Redfield, in Reply to Mr Espy, on the Whirlwind Character of Storms," from, respectively, *Silliman's Journal* and the *Franklin Institute Journal.* No review of Redfield's work has been found in the *Quarterly Review.*

another review, in the May No. of the United Service Journal, from an unknown hand.[4]

It is a matter of sincere regret with me that our friend Espy is not content with his own position, but thinks it necessary to renew his attacks upon my statements and conclusions relating to the storm of 1821, as you have seen in the March No of the Journal of the Franklin Institute.[5] To this I have felt it necessary to reply and to speak with some freedom as well as candor of his general course of proceedings in this matter, all which I was desirous to avoid.[6]

I am indebted to you for a copy of your late paper on electricity which I have read with much interest, and trust that you are pursuing your inquiries in this interesting branch of physics. I am interested to know if any thing yet discovered will show any minute relations of the electric phenomena with the involute rotations of a small whirlwind. In the magnificent electrical developments which are often made in storms, I cannot yet persuade myself that electric action stands in the relation of *cause* to the attending phenomena, but rather in that of an *effect*;[7] notwithstanding the opinions of the reviewer in the U. Service Journal. But if a spiral coil or helix produces such strong inductive effects in electric experiments, why may not the rapid and extensive interwinding of heterogenous* layers of atmosphere in the rapid involutions of a powerful whirlwind, produce analogous effects and on a grand scale? This is a matter of which you can best form a correct estimate.

> I am with much respect
> Yours very truly
> Wm C. Redfield

---

* Heterogeneous as regards temperature and hygrometric & electric conditions.

[4] In his letterbook copy, Redfield attributed the review to "Capt. Smyth R.N. Astronomer &c." The reviewer, presumably William Henry Smyth, heartily endorsed the work of Redfield and Reid on hurricanes, although he differed with the former on the relationship of electricity to storm phenomena, a topic which Redfield addresses below, again citing this review.

[5] "Col. Reid's Law of Storms Examined," March 1839, 23:149–148, in which Espy attempted to refute Redfield's opinion that the "Great Storm" was a gigantic whirlwind. Espy maintained that the wind blew inward at the borders of the storm.

[6] Redfield's reply, "Remarks on Mr. Espy's Theory of Centripetal Storms, including a Refutation of his Position Relative to the Storm of September 3rd, 1821: with some Notice of the Fallacies which Appear in his Examinations of other Storms," appeared in the May and June issues of the *Franklin Institute Journal*, 23:323–336, 363–378. Redfield accused Espy of not sticking to the facts and of being blinded by his fixed idea that aqueous condensation was the cause of nearly all atmospheric effects. Henry's synopsis of the Espy-Redfield debate appears in the *Biblical Repertory and Princeton Review*, January 1841, pp. 144–148, as part of his "Report of the Tenth Meeting of the British Association for the Advancement of Science."

[7] Possibly Robert Hare provoked these questions about the causative role of electricity. See above, Henry to Redfield, December 17, 1838, especially footnote 4.

TO ANTOINE-CÉSAR BECQUEREL[1]

Retained Copy,[2] Henry Papers, Smithsonian Archives

Princeton June 19 1839

My dear Sir

I sent you a few weeks since a copy of my last paper from the transactions of the American Philosophical Society on Electro Dynamic induction.[3] I hope the article has reached you and that my labours will again find a favourable notice in your admirable work on Electricity and Magnetism.[4] Some of my results are in direct opposition to those of Dr Faraday. See N° 59 of my paper and N° 1723 of 14th Series of Dr Faraday. I have experimented on so Large a scale and have repeated the results so often that I cannot be mistaken. I receive through my Friend Mr Warden[5] of the Institute the numbers of the *Comptes* Rendus and have lately been much pleased with your admirable experiments on the Phosphoresence of substances by an Electrical discharge.[6] This subject appears to open a new field of investigation which promises a rich harvest under your culture. There will be a great demand for your book in America as soon as its merits become known. I will mention it to all my friends particularly now that I am myself interested in its circulation since my labours are mentioned in it.

I have received tome V premier partie. I promised to give you a particular description of my large magnet which readily supports 3600 lbs with the battery connected and 1200 lbs for a short time without the battery. I do not think however that the subject is of sufficient importance to deserve any farther notice. All the big stories which you heard from America relative to the Application of Magnetism to the movement of machines have proved to be false. Nothing has been done which merits the least attention. You will find in Sillimans Journal some ingenious modifications of instruments described by Dr Page.[7] Should you think fit to send me any copies of your

[1] Henry met Becquerel, a leading French mineralogist and physicist, during his trip to Europe. *Henry Papers*, *3*:355. Although this is the only known correspondence between the two, it is an indication of Henry's efforts to maintain contact with European scientists.

[2] This copy is not in Henry's hand.

[3] "Contributions III," sent to Paris by Morse.

[4] Becquerel cited Henry's paper "On the Production of Currents and Sparks of Electricity from Magnetism," recognizing Henry as the first to discover self-induction, in *Traité Expérimental de L'Électricité et du Magnétisme*, 1837, *5*:paragraph 1261.

[5] David Bailie Warden.

[6] "De quelques propriétés nouvelles relatives au pouvoir phosphorescent de la lumière électrique," *Comptes Rendus*, 1839, *8*:216–223. Henry's own experiments with phosphorescence, prompted by those of Becquerel, will be treated in a future volume of the *Henry Papers*.

[7] Charles Page published frequently in *Silliman's Journal*; Henry is probably referring to "Magneto-Electric and Electro-Magnetic Apparatus and Experiments," *Silliman's Journal*, 1839, *35*:252–268.

Memoirs please give them in charge to Mr Warden and he will transmit them to me.

> I have the honor to
> be with respect Yours &c
> J Henry

TO CHARLES COQUEREL

Miscellaneous Manuscripts Collection, Library,
American Philosophical Society

> Princeton College of New Jersey
> June 19th 1839

My Dear Sir

I embrace the opportunity of sending by My Friend Mr Litton[1] a package containing a copy of my last paper and some other articles which I hope may be found interesting to you.

Mr Litton will deliver to you a letter of introduction from our Friend Bache and therefore I need not add that we will be much obliged if you will give the young Gentleman your advice relative to his course while in your city of wondors, fashion and science.

I hope you have found long since the missing numbers, of the library of useful knowledge, which I was commissioned to purchase. If the articles have not yet come to light send me a list of them and I will endeavour to procure them in this country. I have now on hand after completing my own set a number of duplicates and it is very probable that among those will be found some of your missing ones.

My Friend, Dr Hunn has lately returned to this country, after a residence during the winter, in Paris and now intends to remain permanently in the practice of his profession in Albany (State of New York). I have not as yet seen him since his return. He resides about 200 miles from me but this

---

[1] Abram Litton (1814–1901) was born in Ireland but was brought to America in 1817. Educated at the University of Nashville, he held an interim appointment to the chair of mathematics and natural philosophy there during the absence of James Hamilton in Princeton. Litton spent a year in Paris and nearly two years in Germany, including six months with Liebig at Giessen and one year with Wöhler in Göttingen. Shortly after his return he became Professor of Chemistry in the St. Louis Medical College, a position he held until his retirement in 1891. He concurrently held the chair of chemistry at Washington University, St. Louis, from its founding until his retirement. *St. Louis Daily Globe-Democrat*, September 23, 1901.

distance is now considered a trifle in these days of steamboats and rail ways.

Bache and myself are about 45 miles apart yet we meet frequently. I visited him yesterday by the rail way and found him engaged with a large German magnetic needle preparing for a series of observations which he is to make next week contemporaneously with Professor Lloyd of Dublin, Ireland.[2] These observations will probably lead to some interesting results. I have litle news to communicate. All things are quiet in america although we have had some indications of a quarrel with canada, relative to the boundary line.[3] We heard by the last Steam ship that you have had an outbreaking and something like an other rebellion.[4] We are now quite anxious to hear further news from your city.

Joseph Bonaparte lives about mid way between Princeton and Philadelphia.[5] We pass near his house when we go to that city. He lives like a plain American citizen and is often seen in the rail way cars, between his house and the city. He appears quite healthy and much younger than he really is.

The paper I send you is one which has cost me much labour but it developes some new and, my friends are pleased to say, important phenomena. Babenet has not written to me yet. He proposed to send me a letter at the solstice and I was to write to him at the equinox. The equinox is passed but the solstice has not yet come!! He is a very good fellow however, was kind to me while I was in Paris and I shall always remember with pleasure my

[2] Bache and Lloyd wanted to test a technique for determining differences in longitude by taking simultaneous readings of changes in magnetic declination at Philadelphia and Dublin. Lloyd failed to make the June observations. From simultaneous observations in November 1839 they concluded that there was "*no correspondence whatever between the smaller changes of the declination at Dublin and at Philadelphia*" and that the difference in longitude over so great a distance could not be determined in this way. *Proceedings of the Royal Irish Academy*, 1840, *1*:459–465.

[3] A reference to the northeast boundary dispute between the United States and Canada, whose formal settlement did not occur until the signing of the Webster-Ashburton Treaty of 1842.

[4] Disagreement among a coalition of French political leaders had left the country without a cabinet since the collapse of the Molé government on March 9, 1839. Public opinion blamed the king, Louis Philippe, for prolonging the crisis by causing further dissension among the politicians, and on May 12 an insurrection took place in Paris. Two or three hundred insurgents, drawn from a variety of secret societies, seized three buildings and successfully opposed government troops for several hours. The uprising served to force the various political factions into organizing a new ministry. Louis Blanc, *The History of Ten Years* (1845; reprint ed., New York, 1969), pp. 597–610.

[5] After fleeing France in 1815, the former king of the Two Sicilies and Spain settled on an estate, Point Breeze, near Bordentown, New Jersey. Joseph Bonaparte remained in the United States, taking an active interest in the estate, personal investments, and fellow emigrés and family, until late 1839. Michael Ross, *The Reluctant King* (New York, 1977), pp. 246–273.

intercourse with him. Write to me occassionally. There is something pleasant in the fact of receiving a letter from across the "vasty deep" but this pleasure is heightened when the letter comes from one in whom we are interested.

> With much Respect I have the honor
> to be Yours Sincerely
> Joseph Henry

TO CLAUDE-S.-M. POUILLET[1]

Retained Copy,[2] Henry Papers, Smithsonian Archives

> Princeton College of New Jersey
> [June][3] 19th 1839

My dear Sir

Permit me to introduce to your attention My young Friend Mr Litton who goes to Paris for the purpose of improvement in science. He has heard of the vivacity and force with which you present the truths of science in your admirable course of Lectures and will constantly be found among your numerous auditors.

He is also acquainted with some of your many contributions to science and is well prepared by study to appreciate your Labours. Permit me to thank you for a copy of your memoir on *La Chaleur Solaire*[4] &c &c. The article has given me much pleasure and instruction. I sent to you through the Institute a copy of my last paper on Electro dynamic induction which I hope you have received. It will give me much pleasure thus to continue to exchange papers with you. Any article you may wish to send will reach me in safety if sent by the French Institute to the care of Mr Robertson[5] Assistant Secratary of the Royal society of London. My address[6]

Your work on Physique[7] is in the hands of all the teachers of this branch

---

[1] Henry had met Pouillet (1790–1868), then Assistant Professor of Physics at the Faculty of Sciences in Paris, during his European trip. *Henry Papers*, 3:365.

[2] But not in Henry's hand.

[3] The copy is dated July 19, although it is obvious that this is one of a number of letters Henry wrote on June 19.

[4] "Mémoire sur la chaleur solaire, sur les pouvoirs rayonnants et absorbants de l'air atmosphérique, et sur la température de l'espace," *Comptes Rendus*, 1838, 7:24–65.

[5] J. D. Roberton.

[6] Henry's retained copy omits the address.

[7] *Éléments de physique expérimentale et de météorologie*, 2 vols. (Paris, 1827). The Henry Library contains the fourth edition of the work, published in 1844.

of science in the United States and the part on Meteorology was translated a few years since and published in a periodical.[8]

> I am with much esteem,
> Yours &c &c
> Joseph Henry

[8] We have not located this article.

TO J. D. ROBERTON[1]

Mary Henry Copy, Henry Papers, Smithsonian Archives

Princeton June 19th 1839

My dear Sir. I have been much gratified by the kind attention I have received from the friends I made in England and in France since my return. Mr. Faraday, Mr. Daniell have forwarded me each several articles. Mr. Daniell has sent me his work on chemistry.[2] The proceedings of the Royal Society &c &c. Prof. Lloyd of Dublin has sent me a number of pamphlets. Mr. Babbage a copy of his Ninth Bridgewater treatise. Mr. Herapath the address of the Electrical Society.[3] The articles are not only of much value to me they also give me much pleasure as testimonials that I am still remembered. Babinet has not written to me yet. He promised to send me a letter at the solstice and I was to write to him at the equinox. He is a very good fellow, was very kind to me when I was in Paris. I shall always remember with pleasure my intercourse with him. I sent through Mr. Vaughan a large package made up principally of copies of my paper. Will you favour me by distributing these to the various persons to whom they are addressed.[4] The article has cost me considerable labour and I hope will be found not unworthy the attention of those engaged in scientific pursuits. Write to me occasionally. There is pleasure in the fact of receiving a letter from across the "vasty deep" and the pleasure is heightened when the letter comes from one in whom we are interested.

[1] Mary Henry incorrectly gives the name as J. D. Robinson.

[2] Perhaps the first edition of *An Introduction to the Study of Chemical Philosophy*, which appeared in 1839. Only the second edition (1843) survives in the Henry Library.

[3] The only London Electrical Society address in the Henry Library is one sent by Sturgeon which Henry mentions in his letter to Sturgeon of November 1, 1838, above. Mary Henry may have misread Sturgeon's name in the original of this letter.

[4] Page [22] of Henry's Address Book (Box 17, Henry Papers, Smithsonian Archives) may be a list of the recipients of the "Contributions III" copies sent to Vaughan. Of the thirty-five people listed, most are English or Scots scientists although De La Rive, Plateau, and Vrolik also appear.

TO JAMES CLARK ROSS
Sabine Papers, Library, Royal Society of London[1]

Princeton College of
New Jersey June 19th 1839

My Dear Sir

Your kind letter[2] and the accompanying needles were received some time since. Our Friend Bache has acknowledged the receipt of the needles and I would have answered your interesting letter before this but defered until I could find an opportunity of sending a package containing a copy of my last paper and some other articles which I hope may be found of some interest although they are not as valuable as I could wish. The reports of the Regents of the University of the State of New York contain the results of a series of meteorological observations continued since 1825. You will find in the two nos. I send[3] a list of the Auroras which have been seen in this country during the two last years and if this could be compared with a similar list of Auroras seen in England some agreements might be detected. The back numbers of the Report cannot now be obtained in full but there are a number of full sets in this country and from these a complete list of all the auroras since 1825 might be compiled and a comparison of this with a similar European list would without doubt lead to some interesting deductions.

You will see by my paper that I am particularly interested in the experimental part of our favourite science and that I am more nearly in the line of Dr Faraday than in that of Sabine and yourself. I feel however deeply interested in every departement of this interesting subject and am anxious to do what I can directly or indirectly towards its advancement. Any observations which I may make on terrestrial magnetism will be thrown into the hands of my Friend Bache, who has taken up this branch in our country with much zeal and every requisite necssary to its successful prosecution.

It has been announced in the American papers from Georgia to Maine that the British Government has directed the preparation of an expidition to the south for magnetic observations under your command.[4] I hope that

[1] A retained copy, lacking only the last three sentences, closing, and postscript, is in the Henry Papers, Smithsonian Archives.

[2] Not found.

[3] According to a note in Henry's address book, page [22], he sent the reports of 1838 and 1839.

[4] In September 1839, the Ross expedition left England for four years of exploration in the Antarctic. Although preceded by the expeditions of France and the United States, Ross had the greatest success both in terms of geographical discovery and scientific results. See James Clark Ross, *A Voyage of Discovery and Research in the Southern and Antarctic Regions During the Years 1839 to 1843*, 2 vols. (London, 1847), and L. P. Kirwan, *A History of Polar Exploration* (New York, 1960), chapter 12.

The Ross expedition was part of Edward Sabine's "magnetic crusade" (*Henry Papers*,

nothing will interfere to prevent so desirable an object and that the results will be a harvest of as much value as your important labours in the north have already secured.

Bache and myself are about 40 miles a part but thanks to the introduction of the rail way system we meet quite often. He spent some days with me a few weeks since and I yesterday gave him a short visit. I found him busily engaged in fitting up one of Gauss large magnetic needles inorder to be in readiness to commence next week with a series of contemporaneous observations with Professor Lloyd of Dublin. Observations simultaneously made in places so distant cannot but afford interesting results. Accept my thanks for your kind offer of attention to my affairs on your side of the atlantic and let me assure you that it will give me much pleasure to be of service to you in any way in this country. Should you have any communications with Dr Robinson[5] of armagh please give him my respects. You may reccollect that I made his acquaintance with you at Liverpool. I had however the pleasure of meeting with him afterwards in London. With much Respect

and esteem I [am] most sincerely
Yours &c &c
Joseph Henry

P.S. Excuse my use of a wafer.[6] I close this letter at New [York] in a book shop.

3:303–304). Initially proposed to the government by the British Association, it was co-sponsored by the Royal Society which drew up instructions and invited international co-operation. See the Royal Society's circular of July 1, 1839, and the American Philosophical Society's memorial of December 20, 1839, both printed below.

[5] Thomas Romney Robinson (*Henry Papers*, 3:505).

[6] An adhesive disk used to seal letters.

TO WILLIAM VAUGHAN
The Pierpont Morgan Library[1]

Princeton College of New Jersey
June 19ᵗʰ 1839[2]

My Dear Sir

I have the pleasure to acknowledge the recipt through your kindness of a parcel from Mr Roberton of the Royal Society containing a copy of Pro-

---

[1] Henry's retained copy of this letter is in the Henry Papers, Smithsonian Archives.

[2] According to a notation on the outside of the letter, it was carried to Europe by Abram Litton.

fessor Daniell's new work on chemistry, a memoir from M Plateau[3] of Brussels, the proceedings of the Royal Society and a pamphlet from Mr. Lubbock.[4] I have also received a copy of Mr Babbage's ninth Bridge water treatise and several papers from Professor Lloyd, Daniell, Faraday &c. The receipt of these articles gives me much pleasure not only on account of their intrinsic value but because I am thus assured that I still live in the remembrance of those whom I esteem.

I visited Philadelphia yesterday and took a ride with your Brother[5] to visit our friend Bache who has removed to a cottage near by the buildings of Girard College. We found the Professor engaged preparing for a series of observations which he is to make next week contemporaneously with Professor Lloyd of Dublin. They wish to determine if there be any motions of the needle which take place simultaneously at Philadelphia and Dublin. The observations will probably lead to some interesting results. Your Brother appeared quite smart but says that he does not enjoy very good health this summer. He has not altered much since my return from Europe but appears somewhat more feeble. I have endeavoured to prevail on him to spend a few days at our house in the country but he says it is impossible for him to leave the city for a single night.

The paper I send you has cost me much labour and my friends in Philadelphia are pleased to say that it developes some new and important phenomina. I hope it may meet with as favourable an opinion on your side of the great waters. The acquaintances I have formed in England are not only a source of great pleasure to me but of much importance in the way of giving me early intelligence of any important discovery in the line of science and also in directing the attention of the English Philosophers to my own labours however humble and in thus bringing them more immediately before the world.

It would give me much pleasure to have an opportunity of reciprocating the favours I have received from you and your Nephew[6] but should an occasion of the kind not occur I must endeavour to discharge the debt in part

---

[3] Joseph Antoine Ferdinand Plateau (1801–1883) was Professor of Physics at the Institut Gaggia in Brussels from 1830 through 1835. He then accepted a professorship at the State University of Ghent, where he remained until his retirement in 1872. Most of his early research was in physiological optics, including the invention of a form of stroboscope and investigations into accidental colors. In the 1840s he turned his attention to molecular forces. *DSB*. The memoir was probably "Sur l'Irradiation," *Mémoires de l'Académie royale des Sciences et Belles-lettres de Bruxelles*, 1838, *11*.

[4] Educated at Trinity College, Cambridge, John William Lubbock (1803–1865) published extensively on tidal theory and other mathematical and astronomical topics while pursuing a career in the family bank. *DSB*. The pamphlet Henry received was *An Elementary Treatise on the Tides* (London, 1839). The presentation copy still survives in the Henry Library.

[5] John Vaughan.

[6] Petty Vaughan.

by the method recommended by the early friend of your family Dr Franklin namely by doing a similar kindness to some other person.

Give my respects to Mr Solly[7] and to your Nephew and be assured that I remain with the highest respect

and esteem yours sincerely
Joseph Henry

PS. I send you a drawing of the college of N.J.[8]

---

[7] Henry and Bache had spent a considerable amount of time with the chemist Edward Solly (1819–1886) while in London. *Henry Papers*, 3:249–250, 287, 425.

[8] According to a notation on the outside of the letter, Vaughan sent a duplicate of the plan to Faraday on July 16, 1839. There is no record of the exact drawing or plan sent Vaughan by Henry.

TO DAVID BAILIE WARDEN[1]

Warden Papers, Library of Congress

Princeton College of New
Jersey June 19th 1839

My Dear Sir

Permit me to introduce to your acquaintance my friend Professor Litton who intends to stop some time in Paris inorder to improve himself in the way of science. He will be much profited by your advice and direction in the city and you will find him an intellegent and interesting young Gentleman who will gladly reciprocate all your kind offices.

I send you by Mr Litton a copy of my paper from the transactions of the American Phil. Society. I have sent copies of it to Becquerel, Pouillet and others. The numbers of the Comptes Rendus come with considerable regularity and afford me much interesting instruc[tion] relative to what is going on in the Focus of Science, the French Institute.

I send you by Mr Litton [. . .] dollars[2] as the amount of the subscription for three years.

I hope you are now enjoying better health than when I left Paris. Dr Hun has returned but I have not seen him since his arrival or I would have received all the news relative to my Friends in Paris.

The life which was published in the Biographie Contemporains I have

---

[1] David Bailie Warden (1772–1845), the former American consul in Paris, frequently acted as a liaison between the American and French scientific communities. See *Henry Papers*, 3: 387.

[2] There is a blank in the manuscript preceding this word.

caused to be translated with the intention of having it published in some of the Periodicals of the country.[3] It will be interesting to many of your friends on this side of the Atlantic and I hope not unplesant to you.

> With much Respect
> I remain sincerely yours &c
> Joseph Henry

[3] *Biographie Universelle et Portative des Contemporains*, 5 vols. (Paris, 1836), 5:886–888. We have discovered no evidence of Henry having published a translation of the biographical sketch of Warden.

TO FRANCIS WATKINS

Retained Copy,[1] Henry Papers, Smithsonian Archives

Princeton College of New Jersey June 19 1839

My Dear Sir

I hope you will pardon my long long delay in acknowledging the receipt of your interesting letter of the 22[d] of May 1838.[2] I defered the answer at first for a time with the hope of being able to send you a copy of my paper[3] but the printing of the article has been so long delayed and my movements so tardy that I fear you will think me very negligent and ungrateful. I believe that my heart is in the right place and that I am not disposed to forget past favours but I am unfortunately the slave of the sin of procrastination particularly in the way of letter writing and frequently nay habitually put off from time to time that which in the doing really gives me pleasure. With this confession I hope you will wipe off old scores and trust me on a new account. When I left Paris Babinet of whom I had received considerable attention proposed that we should correspond during the remainder of life. He settled the periods of writing with scientific precision. I was to address him at the *Solstice* and he to answer me at the Equinox. My first Solsticial epistle was sent in 1837 but the Equinoxtial answer has not yet arrived.[4] I hope our correspondence although less scientific in its arrangements and occasionally interrupted will be more satisfactory to both parties.

[1] This copy is not in Henry's hand. On the verso of the third page is a copy or draft by Henry of the opening of his letter to Ross of the same date, printed above.

[2] Not found.

[3] "Contributions III: Electro-Dynamic Induction."

[4] In a letter to J. D. Roberton written the same day (printed above), Henry indicated that he had been assigned the equinoctial communications and that Babinet was to take the solstice. The first correspondence between the two men appears to have been Henry's letter of March 1838, printed above; no letters from Babinet to Henry have survived.

Your letter gave me much pleasure. The intelligence that it contained relative to the favourable impression I had made on those whom I respect and esteem could not be otherwise than highly gratifying.

Our friend Mr Saxton is still in Philadelphia connected with the United States Mint but I am sorry to say that he has not as yet received that encouragement which his merits deserve and which he had reason to expect on his arrival in his native land.[5] He has all the modesty and perhaps some of the pride of true worth which will prevent his pushing the claims necessary to a proper competition with others of less merit but more pretentions, particularly in this land of bustle and of noise. It is probable he does not like writing and that he is on this account a bad correspondent. He has however I am sure a warm heart and will not readily forget his Friends in England. He spent several days with me last summer and we had quite a feast in the way of experiment &c. I have not met with Dr Lock since my return from Europe and have seen a copy of but one of his letters. They were published in a western Newspaper and did not have an extensive circulation.[6]

I am much indebted to you for the very flattering notice you gave in the Phil Magazine of my little vibrating machine[7] and hope to have frequent opportunities of returning the compliment relative to your various labours in the way of science. The paper I send you has cost me considerable labour and my Friends in Philadelphia are pleased to say that it contains some new and important developements. I hope it will be received with as good a character in your land of critics. You will find some facts mentioned in it relative to the improvement of the magneto Electrical machine which may not be unimportant in the construction of the instrument and perhaps be worthy of your attention in a practical point of view.

There are several points in the series of investigations which require further developement and to which I have given some attention with the design of placing the results before our society in another paper. I have lately received some kind communications from Dr Faraday and have been engaged in studying his series of experiments with attention in order to form a proper opinion of his new views in Electricity. I consider the whole series as doing honor to himself the nation and the age and although future experiments will indicate many corrections yet the general laws and Phenomina which he has developed must be as enduring as science and truth.

---

[5] Watkins had been one of the participants at the farewell dinner for Saxton which Henry had attended in London in April 1837. *Henry Papers*, 3:323.

[6] John Locke had accompanied Henry on one of his visits to Watkins's London work-shop in 1837. See *Henry Papers*, 3:424. A search of Cincinnati newspapers of the period revealed no evidence of letters Locke may have written.

[7] See above, Hare to Henry, April 21, 1838, especially footnote 2.

Professor Bache has given the bearer of the letter an introduction to you. I have lately made the acquaintance of Professor Litton he comes warmly recommended to us and I have been much prepossessed in his favour by our short acquaintance. He stops but a short time in London at present and leaves for the Continent with the intention of visiting it again before his return to America. Should you meet Dr Snow Harris[8] give him my respects. I have intended to write to him for more than a year past but my beseting sin has prevented. I remain with respect and Esteem yours sincerely

Joseph Henry

NB Let me hear from you as often as convenient by mail or otherwise. Postage is almost nothing a letter from London costs less than 6 pence.

[8] *Henry Papers*, 3:173.

FROM W.H. SMYTH[1]
Henry Papers, Smithsonian Archives

ROYAL SOCIETY,
1ˢᵗ July, 1839.

SIR,

In pursuance of the directions of the President and Council of the Royal Society of London I have the honour to forward you the annexed papers, being copies of a Report made by the Joint Committee of Physics and Meteorology of the Society to the Council on the subject of an extended system of Magnetic Observation, and of the Resolution of the Council taken thereon;[2] and to acquaint you that, in consequence of the representations made, Her Majesty's Government has ordered the equipment (now in progress) of a naval expedition of discovery, consisting of two ships under the command of Captain James C. Ross, to proceed to the Antarctic Seas for purposes of magnetic research, and also the establishment of fixed magnetic observatories at St. Helena, Montreal, the Cape of Good Hope, and Van Diemen's Land, having for their object the execution of a series of corre-

[1] This is a printed form letter with the day of the month, Henry's name, and the closing and signature filled in by hand.

[2] No longer filed with this letter. Henry's Library contains *Report of the Committee of Physics and Meteorology of the Royal Society Relative to the Observations to be Made in* the Antarctic Expedition and in the Magnetic Observatories (London, 1840) and the slightly different *Report of the Committee of Physics, Including Meteorology, on the Objects of Scientific Inquiry in those Sciences* (London, 1840), as well as later supplemental instructions.

sponding magnetic observations during a period of three years, in consonance with the views expressed in that Report. The Court of Directors of the Honourable East India Company have also, in compliance with the suggestions of the Royal Society, resolved to establish similar observatories at Madras, Bombay, and at a station in the Himalaya Mountains.

As it is manifestly of high importance to the advancement of the science of Terrestrial Magnetism that every advantage should be taken of so distinguished an opportunity for executing a concerted system of magnetic observations on the most extended scale, the Royal Society,—on whom the arrangement of the proceedings of the fixed observatories has devolved, and to whom the scientific objects of the naval expedition have been referred by the Lords Commissioners of the Admiralty, and under whose direction the construction of the instruments to be used in these operations is actually proceeding,—is earnestly solicitous that observations corresponding to those intended to be prosecuted in the observatories should be made at every practicable station; and in forwarding to you the papers alluded to, I am directed at the same time to express their hope that the cooperation of Professor Henry will be afforded in executing, or procuring to be executed, such observations, and communicating their results and details to the Royal Society, through the medium of their Foreign Secretary.[3]

The general tenor of these observations is sufficiently indicated in the Report annexed, but a more particular programme of them will be forwarded to you as soon as the details are sufficiently matured to admit of its printing and circulation: but it may here be noticed that one essential feature of them will consist in observations to be made at each station, in conformity with the system (in so far as applicable) and at the times already agreed on by the German Magnetic Association, either as they now stand or as (on communication) they shall, by mutual consent, be modified.

A series of meteorological observations subordinate to, and in connexion

---

[3] In 1837, Henry had discussed the projected system of observations with S. H. Christie in England. See *Henry Papers*, 3:303–304. In addition to the sources listed there, see Walter F. Cannon, "History in Depth: The Early Victorian Period," *History of Science*, 1964, 3:20–38, for comments on unexplored aspects of the magnetic crusade and suggestions for further research. John Cawood's article, "The Magnetic Crusade: Science and Politics in Early Victorian Britain," *Isis*, 1979, 70:493–518, focuses on the dynamics of the "geomagnetic lobby," stressing Edward Sabine's dominant role. See also Kurt-R. Biermann, "Alexander von Humboldt als Initiator und Organisator Internationaler Zusammenarbeit auf Geophysikalischem Gebiet," and J. A. Cawood's comments on that paper, in E. G. Forbes, ed., *Human Implications of Scientific Advance* (Edinburgh, 1978), pp. 126–138, 139–149.

We have not found a letter by Henry in response to Smyth. Henry was, however, a member of an American Philosophical Society Committee set up to achieve American cooperation with the British network. See the committee's memorial of December 20, 1839, printed below.

and co-extensive with, the magnetic observations, will be made at each station.

The following is a list of the instruments intended to form the essential equipment of each observatory:

LIST (with estimated Prices).

Instrumental equipment for one fixed magnetic observatory:

		£	
1 Declination Magnetometer } Grubb,[4] Dublin		73	10
1 Horizontal Force Magnetometer }			
1 Vertical Force Magnetometer — Robinson		21	0
1 Dipping Needle — Robinson		24	0
1 Azimuthal Transit — Simms		50	0
2 Reading Telescopes — Simms		6	6
2 Chronometers		100	0

The above are all the instruments required for magnetical purposes.

The declination and horizontal force magnetometers are similar, with slight modifications, to those devised by M. Gauss, and already in extensive use; so that the observations made with the latter instruments and with those specified above will be strictly comparable.

The observatories will be also *each* furnished with the following meteorological instruments:

1 Barometer ⎫
1 Mountain ditto ⎬ Newman.
1 Standard Thermometer ⎭

1 Osler's[5] Anemometer

Wet and Dry Bulb Thermometers ⎫
Maximum and Minimum Thermometers ⎬ Adie, Liverpool.

Daniell's Hygrometer. ⎭

An apparatus for atmospherical electricity.

> I have the honour to be,
> Sir,
> Your obedient Servant,
> W:H: Smyth:—For[n] Sec[y]

---

[4] Thomas Grubb (1800–1878, *DSB*).
[5] Follett Osler (1808–1903). W. E. K. Middle- ton, *Invention of the Meteorological Instruments* (Baltimore, 1969), pp. 189–190.

"RECORD OF EXPERIMENTS"
Henry Papers, Smithsonian Archives

July 8th 1839

After experimenting with the large battery with the class I arranged it with the parts so as to form 4 alternations of zinc and copper. Then united three flat ribbons so as to make a coil of about 180 feet long an[d] about 4 feet in diameter. The long helix contains just one mile of wire and is 4 feet in diameter. The two were seperated gradually until the distance was 6 feet 3 inches still the shock was quite perceptible through the tongue[1]

---

[1] Henry's marginal notation to this entry, "great distances," captured the essence of these experiments. In his published description of similar experiments, which appeared in paragraph 31 of "Contributions IV: Electro-Dynamic Induction," Henry reported perceptible shocks when the helix and the coil were separated by a distance of "nearly seven feet."

TO ALEXANDER DALLAS BACHE
Bache Papers, Smithsonian Archives

Princeton July 9th 1839

My Dear Bache

Your favour of the 6[th][1] was received yesterday but I am sorry to inform you that college duties will prevent my leaving Princeton for two weeks to come. I begin my course of lectures on Light tomorrow and they will occupy the time above mentioned. I thought to have had an easy time this season but thus far I have been constantly engaged and have the prospect of but little time until the end of the session.

You must manage to set the Printer at work on that part which has passed the filing process and keep back the other until the affairs of old Nassau will admit of the absence of so important a person as myself.

I came to Princeton on my return the last time from Phil[d] with Mr Biddle. I had a talk with him about the Elgin marbles.[2] He said he would attend to the affair and was glad that I had mentioned the subject again to him.

He asked me if I had seen you and what matter of science you were engaged in. He said that you had done your part in reference to the starting of

---

[1] Not found.

[2] See above, Henry to Bache, August 9, 1838, and *Henry Papers*, 3:530–532.

the College and that you must now make your mind perfectly easy on this matter and devote your self to your scientific investigations.

The needle shall be forth coming or going this week. I have nothing new in the way of science. My time has been so much occupied in teaching and in putting the Phil Hall in order without assistance that I have made but a single experiment and that was yesterday.[3] After exhibiting my large battery I tried to what extent the induction of the secondary current at a distance could be carried. For this purpose 3 of my flat ribbon coils were united into one length and thus formed about 180 feet of conductor which was coiled into a ring of 4 feet in diameter. A ring formed of copper wire 1/16 of an inch in diameter and one mile in length and of the same diameter as the ring of ribbon was prepared for reciving the induction. With this apparatus the shocks were perceptible when the two rings were seperated to the distance of 6¼ feet with the boards of two tables intervening.

Our children are getting better. They have had a very bad time however. The Boy in particular has been and is still very feeble. The journey to Phil[d] was too much for him. He is however I think on the mending hand. My respects to Mrs B and your sisters.

Yours as ever
Joseph Henry

[3] See above.

TO HARRIET HENRY

Family Correspondence, Henry Papers, Smithsonian Archives

Turner Green near
the Girard College
Thursday morning
[July 25, 1839][1]

My Dear H

I have been at this place almost continually since I came to Philadelphia. I arrived in the city about 2 o'clock called on Mr Vaughan found him surrounded with books and papers busily employed in the affairs of the society and although some what feaverish much better.

[1] Dated from the postmark and internal evidence, especially the discussion of the presidency of Rutgers.

I then went out to the Girard college found Bache at home commenced operations immidiatly.[2] Sent next morning your letter to James with the intention of following it but as yet have not found time.

I saw by the papers yesterday that Dr Ludlow had been elected pres. of Rutgers College.[3] The notice was connected with some very complimentary remarks and a warm expression of desire that the Dr should not be permitted to leave Philad.ª Bache says he is rapidly increasing in popularity and is exerting a good influence in the city.

Baches little sister[4] who has been at school in washington says that it is understood in that city that Margaret Bullions is engaged to be married to a naval officer.

I have nothing new to communicate although I am some what anxious to return home and feel somewhat uneasy about you and our dear little ones particularly at night. This however is nothing strange. I am not sure that I will get off tomorrow but will be with you on saturday. I will attend to all the commissions tomorrow.

In haste as ever your own

dear   H

P.S. Kiss all the children for me.

---

[2] Presumably terrestrial magnetic observations.

[3] John R. Ludlow's election was announced in the July 24, 1839, issue of the *National Gazette*, a Philadelphia newspaper. Ludlow, however, declined the office, remaining Provost of the University of Pennsylvania. William J. R. Taylor, *Sermon of the Life, Character, Services and Death of the Rev. John Ludlow* (New York, 1857), pp. 18–19.

[4] Henry's usual terminology for Maria Fowler, Bache's sister-in-law.

TO BENJAMIN SILLIMAN, SR.

Daniel C. Gilman Collection, Library, Johns Hopkins University

Princeton Aug 17th 1839

My Dear Sir

I hope you will pardon my long delay in answering your kind letter[1] relative to the nos. of the journal you recived through Dr Chilton. I penned an answer immediatly on the recipt of the letter with the intention of sending it and the money due on the journal by a friend but was disappointed and since then I have defered writing from time to time with the hope of meeting an other opportunity.

---

[1] Not found.

The numbers of the journal were not sent with the most distant idea of receiving pay for them but only with the hope of their being useful in making up sets of the work which might be called for by new subscribers. Indeed they were forwarded to New York before I had seen your advertisement.[2] They are the duplicates of numbers which I have picked up from time to time in this country and in England and France for the purpose of completing my copy of the journal previous to 1832. The only return I intended to ask was that you would furnish me with nos. 27 and 45 which are still wanting to complete my set but these I perceive are also among your missing numbers.

I cannot accept of your liberal proposal for the settlement of our account. I expected to get for the numbers I sent but two in return and I will therefore deduct the price of these from my account and instead of the 10 dollars which you proposed I send 21 which I consider a much more equitable adjustment.

I sent you some months since a copy of my last paper on Electro-dynamic induction. The article cost me much labour and is considered by some of my friends as being the most important contribution to science I have yet been enabled to make.

I have lately received a letter from D[r] Faraday and a copy of his 14th series in which he gives results directly in opposition to the most important principle of my paper. I have repeated my experiments with a view to discover the cause of our descrepancy and have succeeded in detecting some new distinctions in the action not before noticed which misled Mr Faraday and caused him to infer a general law from what was only a particular case. The results given in my paper were obtained on so large a scale that there can be no doubt of their truth. I intended writing to you in reference to the insertion of an account of my paper in the journal but my time during the last year or since my return from Europe has been so much occupied with college duties that everything else has been neglected. Why do you not publish the proceedings of the American Phil Society? They are reported in a small sheet every two months and contain some interesting matter which does not see the [?general] light.[3]

With much Respect and Esteem yours
Joseph Henry

[2] A notice at the beginning of volume 36 (July 1839) offered payment, credit, or an exchange for certain back numbers of the *Journal*.
[3] Silliman began reprinting the APS *Proceedings* in the October-December 1839 number of the *Journal* (*38*:153–193) with the explanation: "We were ignorant until recently, that the American Philosophical Society published reports of their doings. Had these reports been earlier transmitted, they would have been sooner noticed."

One exp of my paper affors an amusing class exp namely the induction through a wall (See par. No 51) with a coil of wire 4 miles long loaned me by Mr Morse. I got shocks at the distance of 6 feet perceptable through the toung.[4]

I have done scarcely anything in the way of experiment since last Nov. vacation. We have been making great changes in the Philosophical rooms and the superintendance of these and increasing college duties have occupied all my time.

---

[4] The paragraph reads:

I may perhaps be excused for mentioning in this communication that the induction at a distance affords the means of exhibiting some of the most astonishing experiments, in the line of *physique amusante*, to be found perhaps in the whole course of science. I will mention one which is somewhat connected with the experiments to be described in the next section, and which exhibits the action in a striking manner. This consists in causing the induction to take place through the partition wall of two rooms. For this purpose coil No. 1 is suspended against the wall in one room, while a person in the adjoining one receives the shock, by grasping the handles of the helix, and approaching it to the spot opposite to which the coil is suspended. The effect is as if by magic, without a visible cause. It is best produced through a door, or thin wooden partition.

TO JAMES HENRY

Family Correspondence, Henry Papers, Smithsonian Archives

Princeton Augt. [18–19] 1839
(Sunday Evening)

Dear James

Nancy arived here safely with Stephen and his wife about 8 o'clock last night and came just in the nic of time since our *third* daughter[1] came into this breathing world at seven minutes past 12 o'clock at noon to day.

The young lady made her appearance rather unexpectedly. She is however quite smart and well made. The other children were sent to Uncle Stephen's at the time. They made quite a wonderment of the affair at least the two little girls. William was disappointed. He had been as it appears suspecting the event and wished to have a little brother.

Monday Evening I did not get off my letter last night in time for the mail and of course it was obliged to stop until this evening. Harriet and the child

---

[1] Caroline Henry (d. 1920).

are doing well. The litle one has slept almost continually since it was born.

Nothing new. Mr Bullions has not yet arrived and we do not expect him to night since we have ha[d] quite a damp and rainy afternoon with the prospect of a long south east storm. I have just learned that the Steamer Liverpool has arrived but have heard but little of the news. Our fellow townsman Capt. Stockton who has been figuring for some time past in London came home in her.[2] Jessy Buel[3] delivered an address at Princeton on Saturday a week ago on the subject of agriculture. He was invited by a committee of a new agricultural society lately got up in this place.[4] Mr B. was accompanied with his daughter.[5] They called at our house but would not stop over night but went on after the address to Trenton. The judge was listen to with much attention by a large and respectable audience. He gave good satisfaction although his pronunciation was somewhat tinctured by Yankey and Dutchisms.

Our Senior class has been examined and has left until commencement. I am now lecturing to the Juniors and will continue with them for about two weeks. I have a Polish Refugee for a servant in the Hall just landed. He says he was a major in the Russian Army but is now quite willing to wash

[2] After a ten-year furlough, Robert Field Stockton (*DAB*) returned to active duty in 1838 and sailed for the Mediterranean. Before returning home, he studied naval armaments and facilities in Great Britain and relayed messages from the Administration to the U.S. Minister in London. Samuel J. Bayard, *A Sketch of the Life of Commodore Robert F. Stockton* (New York, 1856), p. 76.

[3] Jesse Buel (1778–1839, *DAB*), the prolific and influential agricultural reformer and educator, died less than two months after his visit to Princeton. Buel was a printer and newspaper publisher in Albany until 1820 and served in the New York Assembly from 1823 to 1835. His dominant interest following his retirement from newspaper publishing was the practice and promotion of scientific agriculture. To educate the farmer, Buel conducted the *Cultivator* (from 1834), under the auspices of the New York State Agricultural Society, and lectured frequently.

See Henry J. Carman, *Jesse Buel, Agricultural Reformer: Selections from his Writings* . . . (New York, 1947), and Margaret W. Rossiter, *The Emergence of Agricultural Science: Justus Liebig and the Americans, 1840–1880* (New Haven and London, 1975), pp. 8–9.

[4] At the meeting of August 10, 1839, the Princeton Agricultural Society (founded in 1835) reorganized as the New Jersey State Agricultural Society. Its stated purpose was to increase production by using science to aid the farmer. The Society was incorporated in February 1840 but failed to get an appropriation from the legislature to support its activities. Woodward finds no record of it past 1842, although Hageman's sketch of 1879 (*Hageman*, 1:259–260) describes it as continuing its "thrifty and useful existence." (Hageman is probably confusing it with the later New Jersey State Agricultural Society, founded in 1855). Printed proceedings are extant only for the 1839 organizational meeting.

Buel's address was published in the *Cultivator*, November 20, 1839. He encouraged the society to hold competitions, educate the farmer through journals, support agricultural education in schools, and seek support from the legislature.

Carl Raymond Woodward, *The Development of Agriculture in New Jersey, 1640–1880* (New Brunswick, 1927), pp. 178, 190, 202–205, 209.

[5] Julia Catherine Buel (b. 1816). Albert Welles, comp., *History of the Buell Family in England and in America* (New York, 1881), p. 18.

bottles and sweep the laboratory—he has however the appearance of an intelligent and accomplished man.[6]

Nothing more at present
from your Brother

[6] Not identified. In his book on Polish immigrants to America following the Polish revolution of 1830–1831, J. J. Lerski notes that noblemen and officers found it particularly difficult to find jobs. Jerzy Jan Lerski, *A Polish Chapter in Jacksonian America: The United States and the Polish Exiles of 1831* (Madison, Wisconsin, 1958), p. 120.

FROM BENJAMIN SILLIMAN, SR.
Mary Henry Copy, Henry Papers, Smithsonian Archives

Aug. 24, 1839

Would you like to publish in the Journal any revision of your and Faraday's differences? Perhaps that would require a previous publication of your entire memoir or an abstract of it.[1] The former if you desire it I will do as soon as I can find room but an abstract certainly at once, and no one can make that as well as yourself. Let me hear from you on these points and your wishes on the subject.[2]

[1] Silliman later repeated his offer to publish "Contributions III." See below, Silliman to Henry, November 2, 1839.

[2] This is all that survives of the text of the letter.

FROM A. LITTON
Henry Papers, Smithsonian Archives

Paris August 25th 1839

Dear Sir

With the hope, that during my stay in this city of learning & science, I may have it in my power to repay in some measure your kindness & friendly civilities,[1] I seize the first opportunity to send you my address. I have been here but a few days, but sufficiently long to see how many are the advantages of a residence here, for a young votary of science. My ignorance of the language however has as yet been a great impediment & prevented me from

[1] On June 19 (above), Henry wrote several letters of introduction for Litton.

profiting by many of the scientific meetings that have been held since my arrival. This deficiency however I hope to make up, before the season of scientific festivity again comes round, & shall then be better qualified to make known what is doing among the Savants.

All your letters & packages for persons in England were delivered, as also those for your friends in Paris. Your late Contributions to the Philosophical Transactions had reached P_____ before my arrival,[2] & I am happy to inform you that its reception has been highly creditable to your own reputation & to that of our young country. I have heard it highly spoken of, & it has been read & eulogize by those who are fully capable of appreciating the labor, research & originality of its author.[3] It is to be hoped that you can steal sufficient time from the delightful (said by one who certainly knew nothing of it by experience,) task of teaching the young idea, how to shoot,[4] to complete the investigations which you have so successfully commenced.

Your friend Warden I have found all that a stranger in a strange land could desire. He has a true Irish heart, & I cannot defray the obligations to you & Prof Bache, for his invaluable acquaintance. You mentioned in your letter to him that you had sent by me a copy of your Contributions & some money. This you may have intended to do, & I recollect your leaving me in New York for the purpose of either getting or changing money for this purpose, but you gave me none, having forgotten it by the confusion caused by the trunk.

I shall send you the explanation of Daguerre's process; (as the latest scientific news,) & which has been reported upon by Arago. The discovery has been bought by government, & for which the sum of 10,000 francs is to be paid annually during the life of the discoverer.[5]

[2] The Académie des Sciences noted receipt of Henry's paper on June 24. Morse had sent a package of Henry's papers to Paris in May. See his letter of May 20, above.

[3] David Bailie Warden reported the same reaction in a letter of August 20 to John Vaughan: "His Memoir has excited much interest among the *savants* who are occupied with the same subject." American Philosophical Society Archives.

[4] Litton is paraphrasing James Thomson (1700–1748) in *The Seasons, Spring*:

Delightful task! to rear the tender thought,
To teach the young idea how to shoot.

[5] On August 19, 1839, Arago explained Daguerre's hitherto secret process to a joint meeting of the Académie des Sciences and the Académie des Beaux Arts. Paris had been eagerly awaiting this explanation since Arago's preliminary announcement of Daguerre's invention in January 1839.

Daguerre had initially intended to promote his invention commercially. To overcome public skepticism, he approached Arago and other scientists for an endorsement. Enormously impressed with Daguerre's product, Arago encouraged him to forego commercial development and offer the invention to the government in return for an annual pension. The exact process was to be kept secret until the government agreed to this course.

In arguing for this unique arrangement with the government, Arago claimed that a patent could not protect Daguerre because the process was simple enough to be applied by anyone. Gay-Lussac, reporting to the Chamber of Peers, argued that rapid improvement would result if the process were public property, a prediction which soon proved accurate.

Remember me to your kind friend Bache & tell him that his valuable package of letters was received only a few hours before I sailed, otherwise the due acknowledgments should have been made. With Sentiments of esteem & respect

I remain Yours
A. Litton.

My address is to the care of D. Cutter

102 Rue Richelieu

I shall probably remain here during a year.

Pixii requested me to inform you that your plate should be sent in about fifteen days. As he had none on hand of the first quality, a delay has been necessary in order to have one made.

Mr Coquerel requests me to remember him to you & also to give his thanks for the pamphlets.

Following a complex series of agreements, scientific evaluations, and legislative hearings, the government passed a law in early August giving an annual pension of 6,000 francs to Daguerre and one of 4,000 francs to Isidor Niépce, the son of Daguerre's late partner and co-inventor Nicéphore Niépce.

Substituting for a nervous Daguerre on August 19, Arago addressed a packed hall. The Gernsheims (p. 102) describe the "daguerreotypomania" which swept Paris following Arago's explanation: "Within a few days all the physicists, chemists, and savants of the capital were pointing their cameras at the principal monuments." As soon as a manual describing the process reached America in September, the frenzy was repeated there. See below, Henry to Bache, October 28, 1839.

Helmut and Alison Gernsheim, *L. J. M. Daguerre: The History of the Diorama and the Daguerreotype*, 2d rev. ed. (New York, 1968), chapters 3, 4, and 5.

"RECORD OF EXPERIMENTS"
Henry Papers, Smithsonian Archives

Aug 30th [1839]

Mixed alcohol and water and while the two were mingling observed with two tourmalines the light through the mixture to determine if there were any depolarization[1] of light could observe nothing. A piece of wax pressed between the fingers instantly showed the light. It would appear that liquids do not possess the property of acting on light except perhaps in the case of a solution of some salt in water as in the experiments of M Biot[2] or perhaps

---

[1] Henry had received an account of the discovery of the depolarization of light while visiting David Brewster in Scotland. *Henry Papers*, 3:477–478.

[2] We have been unable to locate a reference to the depolarization of light by saltwater in the writings of Jean-Baptiste Biot (1774–1862, *DSB*). However, Biot did discuss depolarization by turpentine in his *Traité de physique expérimentale et mathématique*, 4 vols. (Paris, 1816), 4:450.

the thickness of the strata might have had some effect on the exp. This exp has some bearing apparently on the exp of Mr Faraday with tourmalines and a galvanic current.[3]

When the tail of one of Prince Ruperts drops[4] was placed between the tourmalines depolarization was at once manifest. I also thought that when nitric acid was made to act on murcury in a tube on the sides of which tourmalines were placed that the bubbles of nitric gas depolarized the light when however all the light was excluded by closing the tube on all sides by tin foil no effect of the kind was perceptible

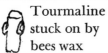 Tourmaline
stuck on by
bees wax

[3] Twice Michael Faraday tested for evidence of the electrotonic state by sending polarized light through liquids which were subjected to electric currents, hoping that the electrotonic state of the fluids would affect the light in some manner. Both the series of experiments of September 10, 1822, and May 2 through May 6, 1833 (Thomas Martin, ed., *Faraday's Diary*, 7 vols. [London, 1932–1936], *1*:71, *2*: 69–73; the latter work was published in the Eighth Series of Faraday's *Experimental Researches in Electricity*, paragraphs 951–954) proved negative. The electrotonic state did not manifest itself. Fluids which ordinarily did not interact with polarized light continued to show no effect. Turpentine, which depolarized light, continued to do so.

All Henry had done was to confirm the well-known fact that certain liquids did not affect polarized light. His suggestion about the possible influence of the thickness of the strata on the results was invalid.

[4] This form of glass is described in *Henry Papers*, 2:21. Its ability to depolarize light had been discovered by Brewster a quarter-century earlier. David Brewster, "Experiments on the Depolarisation of Light as Exhibited by Various Mineral, Animal, and Vegetable Bodies, with a Reference of the Phenomena to the General Principles of Polarisation," *Phil. Trans.*, 1815, p. 43.

"RECORD OF EXPERIMENTS"
Henry Papers, Smithsonian Archives

Sept 3$\underline{rd}$ [1839]

A brilliant aurora appeared to night. First saw it about ½ pas 8 o'clock well formed corona steady and perfect for ½ an hour. Light crimson and greenish. Mr Alexander[1] determined the position of the *corona*. I made a series of experiments relative to the fact of polarization with two tourmalines, also with a Nicols prism and a piece of mica but although the light of

[1] Henry and Alexander's observations were sent to Alexander Dallas Bache, who presented them at a meeting of the American Philosophical Society. *Proceedings of the American Philosophical Society*, 1838–1840, *1*: 132–134.

the aurora was sufficiently intense to be seen through these no polarization could be observed.[2] Also the polarscope of Savart[3] was used which is a very delicate instrument but with the same result. I am therefore inclined to think that the auroral light is not from a reflected surface.

[2] Such was the conclusion of Jean-Baptiste Biot in 1817. Subsequent observers came to the same conclusion as Biot and Henry. Scientists who argued that the aurora was analogous to the discharge of electric light in vacuo seized upon this information, since the electric light also showed no evidence of polarization. A. A. De La Rive, *A Treatise on Electricity, in Theory and Practice*, 3 vols. (London, 1853–1858), *3*:295.

[3] Henry had been shown this instrument while in Paris. See *Henry Papers, 3*:388.

TO JOHN TORREY
Torrey Papers, Library, New York Botanical Garden

Princeton Sept 4th
1839

My Dear Dr

Your favour of the 22nd ult.[1] came to hand last week and I have since been on the look out asfar as my time would permit for such a situation as you mention. I have however not been out in the direction towards Lawrence-ville but there is a very pleasant spot which can be procured about a mile and a half from the village on the New Brunswick road near the House lately purchased by Dr Rogers[2] of New York. It is on the same farm and would be disposed of at a moderate price but you must come and see for yourself. I hope you will not forget your promise to be with us at commencement. You will find some improvements have been made during the summer and that many more are required. In reference to your modest Friend's L.L.D[3] I have only to say that he cares but lit[t]le for the honor and does not intend to use the title until he conceves himself somewhat better intitled to it. He is however not unwilling to derive as much advantage as may be from it in Europe where titles &c are not quite as cheap and more esteemed than here. Your proposition in reference to sympathetic ink[4] is worthy the invention of the friend of the modest gentleman you mention.

[1] Not found.

[2] James H. Rogers "of the City of New York" purchased a 112-acre farm from Elias Theodore Schenck on February 25, 1839. Mercer County Deeds, Book A, p. 450.

[3] On December 7, 1838, the Board of Trustees of South Carolina College had awarded Henry an honorary LL.D.

[4] Invisible ink.

I will do what I can for you in the way of suggestions in reference to lectures[5] but I think in that line you will want but little assistance.

I would have written to you long since but learned that you were spending the summer in the western part of the state, and engaged in your botanical survey.[6] Dr Carnahan has just returned from a tour in Virginia[7] and will send you a draft for the amount of the cost of the carbonic acid machine. I have been during the whole year almost continually since my return from New York last winter ingaged in college affairs and have not found time nor convenience for continuing the subject of my last paper although some new and interesting points have opened to my view in reference to it since the publication.

Mr Faraday has sent me his last paper and in this most strange to say he crosses the path of my investigation but what is still more strange he brings out results diametrically opposite to the most important results of my paper. These resul[t]s have been incorporated in the new work of Daniell on chemistry and have led Mr Faraday to modify his theory of electricity.[8]

I have since examined the cause of our discrepancy and in so doing have discovered some new distinctions in induced currents not before noticed. Mr Faraday for once is entirely in the wrong & has drawn a general conclusion from what is only a particular case. I have just received a lot of Journals &c from England, which came by the Great Western more than a month ago. They were forwarded to New Brunswick by a Mr P I Nevius,[9] and there carefully put into a store house to be kept until called for!!! Fortunately I received a letter from London[10] stating that they had been sent and therefore put our friend Chilton on the search. I have lately receved several interesting communications from England and France. *These* I will show you when you come on. Did you see the splendid exhibition of the aurora last night? I have never seen so good or rather so perfect a corona as appeared at this place from ½ past 8 to 9 o'clock. I made a series of observations in

[5] Torrey was scheduled to deliver a series of ten lectures on the "Chemistry of Nature" at Clinton Hall in New York City in early 1840.

[6] This trip was one of the few Torrey took in connection with his work for the New York Natural History Survey. With the resources of a state-wide network of botanical exchange at his disposal, Torrey found extensive field work unnecessary. Michele L. Aldrich, "New York Natural History Survey, 1836–1845" (Ph.D. dissertation, University of Texas, 1974), p. 202.

[7] The Princeton Board of Trustees had given Carnahan permission to spend the summer traveling for his health. *Maclean*, 2:306–308.

[8] Henry apparently forgot that he had already written to Torrey on this point (see above, Henry to Torrey, May 31, 1839).

Faraday's failure to find any evidence of electromagnetic screening was summarized in paragraph 836 of J. Frederic Daniell, *Introduction to the Study of Chemical Philosophy* (London, 1839), p. 493.

[9] Peter I. Nevius (1779–1869), descended from a distinguished Dutch family, established a successful grocery business in Manhattan based on a monopoly of the trade in flour and other merchandise with the Maritime Provinces. A. Van Doren Honeyman, *Joannes Nevius and His Descendants* (Plainfield, New Jersey, 1900), pp. 554–557.

[10] Not found.

reference to polarization but could not detect with the most delicate arrangement the least trace of polarized light.[11] I am much obliged to you for the interesting specimens of the Instruments of the Nocturnal musicians. They are very curious and made with a perfect knowledge of the science of sound. Insect music is a very interesting subject and I would gladly attempt to make some advance in it but we have no glasses fit for such persuits. I can see the organs you mention and am much interested in the view.[12] You are always very kind in sending me items of interesting information and I am much in your debt for the same.

Our kind regards to Mrs. Torrey. Please inform her that we have an addition to our family in the person of a third daughter. The little stranger made her appearance in this breathing world two weeks ago on Sunday. Mrs Henry is quite smart and were it not that to day is wet and unplesant she would come down to dinner. We will make arrangements relative to the division of apparatus and the purchase of additional articles when you come on. As ever yours &c

Joseph Henry

[11] The Princeton *Whig* provides a more descriptive, if less scientific, account of the aurora borealis:

When our attention was called to it at about 9 o'clock, the centre of the phenomenon appeared to be immediately in the zenith. From this point, which seemed a radient cloud, a deep red, bright rays streamed in every direction quite to the horizon, changing their hues continually.

Princeton *Whig*, September 9, 1839, p. 1.
[12] Early nineteenth-century entomologists were very careful to refer to insects as musicians, not singers. In his study of insects of Massachusetts, Thaddeus Harris noted that, "with crickets, as with grasshoppers, locusts, and harvest flies; the males only are musical; for the females are not provided with the instruments from which the sounds emitted by these different insects are produced." Harris attributed the noises of crickets to a shuffling of wing covers. Thaddeus W. Harris, *Report on the Insects of Massachusetts Injurious to Vegetation* (Cambridge, Massachusetts, 1841), pp. 121–122.

"RECORD OF EXPERIMENTS"
Henry Papers, Smithsonian Archives

Sept 4 [1839]

Fitted up today the long wire of Spool of Mr Morse with 4 miles of wire (the other mile is on the large wheel) for the purpose of producing shocks from the magnetism of the earth[1] but no effect could be observed. The wire perhaps were not properly arranged

[1] Henry had tried to get shocks from terrestrial magnetism on April 21, 1838. See his "Record of Experiments" entry of that date, above.

"RECORD OF EXPERIMENTS"
Henry Papers, Smithsonian Archives

Sept 5 [1839]

Put in action [one] of the boxes of the large battery. Found it leaked. Poured in cement first burned some paper in the box to dry it and heat the pitch. The pitch caught fire and in the melted state ran into the cracks and stoped the leaks. Jacoby states in a paper in the Philosophic magazine[1] that there is no magnetic development on the out side of a circuit, and that in all cases the iron must be on the same side as the axis of the coil to become magnetic. To try this one of the coils was attached to the battery and a piece of hollow iron placed within say at *a*.  It of course became strongly magnetic. The same piece was then removed to the position *b* without the circuit. The magnetism in the last case was not quit[e] as strong as before but still very decided. This exp. conclusively shows that the statement of Mr Jacoby is not correct. He experimented probably with so small a battery that the effect was not perceptible.

Exp 2 Placed a smal[l] ring of iron or rather a short cylinder 2 inches diameter one inch in he[i]ght within the coil. No magnetism appeared on the inside but strong on the outside.

Exp Made a small cylindrical coil about one inch internal diameter 1½ inch long. Lined this inside with tin foil. Put in iron filings, sent charge through from one division of large battery (same as used last exps). The filings formed into strings reaching from one end of the cylinder parallel to the axis. Very little attraction but at the ends. Appeared loose at the middle because the whole formed one magnetic bar attraction at the end. Probably in a long cylinder attraction acts the same as in the hollow piece of iron.

Made the following arrangement in reference to the penetration of mercury through lead.[2] *a b* are two syphons of lead *c d* two cups of mercury the large battery very weakly charged. The circuit of the galvanic current is indicated by the arrows. The apparatus was put away at about 5 oclock.

[1] M. H. von Jacobi, "On the Galvanic Spark," *Phil. Mag.*, 1838, 3d ser. *13*:401–405.

[2] For the first time, Henry explored the problem of the penetration of lead by mercury with a galvanic current. Earlier and most later experiments treat the phenomenon as capillary movement or the mechanical diffusion of one metal through another. See, for example, Henry's "Capillary Transmission Through Solids," *Proceedings of the American Philosophical Society*, 1838–1840, *1*:82–83, and "On the Capillarity of Metals," *Proceedings of the American Philosophical Society*, 1843–1847, *4*:176–178.

"RECORD OF EXPERIMENTS"
Henry Papers, Smithsonian Archives

Sept 7ᵗʰ [1839]

Examined the above arrangement[1] found in the cup at the bottom of the siphon *a* globule of mercury about the size of a pea but mercury in the cup at the bottom of *b*. The battery apparently had ceased to act except very feeble. Put some fresh acid to the battery and let the arrangement act for some days longer.[2]

[1] Described in the preceding entry.

[2] We are uncertain how long Henry left the experimental set-up undisturbed. His next "Record of Experiments" entry is dated October 8 and is concerned with an entirely different subject. No other record of the results of this particular experiment has been located.

FROM JOHN TORREY
Henry Papers, Smithsonian Archives

New York. Sept. 18th 1839

My dear friend

Your letter of the 4th.[1] has been nearly a fortnight on hand. I have been looking out for the advertisement of Commencement in the college. My catalogue has been mislaid, or destroyed, & I know not when the show takes place. Please send me a catalogue by mail as I am *off and on*, & wish to arrange my affairs so that I can be with you, if possible when Commencement occurs.[2]

If I can manage so as to purchase four or five acres of land in a pleasant situation, I would have the foundation of a house dug & the walls carried up part of the way this autumn. I am going up the river this afternoon to see a house that my friend Downing[3] has just finished in his Bot. Garden

[1] Printed above.

[2] Commencement was held on September 25.

[3] Andrew Jackson Downing (1815–1852), architect and landscape gardener from Newburgh, New York, known especially for his treatises on rural residences. Downing's architectural ideal called for a harmonious blending of structure and landscape and he displayed a marked preference for the gothic style. For his Newburgh home, see Arthur C. Downs, Jr., "Downing's Newburgh Villa," *Bul-* *letin of the Association for Preservation Technology*, 1972, 4:1–114. Downing's classic work, *A Treatise on the Theory and Practice of Landscape Gardening, Adapted to North America* (1841) went through many editions and established him as the country's first important landscape gardener. He is also considered one of the leading figures in American horticulture. *DAB*; Wayne Andrews, *Architecture, Ambition and Americans* (New York, 1964), pp. 106–109.

at NewBurgh. When I saw it last Summer it suited my *notions* entirely, & now that it is done, I think I shall not change my opinion. I should like to copy the plan very nearly, & shall borrow Mr. D's drawings. I wish to diminish my expenses of living, & in this way, to reserve more time for study —for I am now obliged to labor like a dog to keep the pot boiling! In New Jersey I feel pretty sure that I can live handsomely on $2000, a year—whereas now I spend full $3000.

It is indeed a little remarkable that Mr. Faraday should have arrived at conclusions diametrically opposite to yours! One or the other of you must have got upon the wrong track, & you must go back till you reach the "turn out," for philosophical examinations are something like travelling on a rail road—if you start wrong you are very likely to keep wrong, till you are brought up *all standing* against some obstacle. Only philosophers don't often get their heads broken! Whether you or Mr. F. is out the way, I know that the mistaken one will be very frank to *own* his mistake.

I hope that Mrs. Henry is doing well, & that the little daughter No III.! will live & be a comfort to her parents. It is a great responsibility that is added to you in this accession to your family & I trust that you view the matter in this light. Our little boy[4] grows finely. We are just about weaning him & discharging his nurse.

If I go to Commencement we must find time to divide the apparatus & make an estimate of the articles that will be indispensable for the new laboratory & lecture room. There is I suppose much to be done in fitting up the rooms, & I fear that the work will be left again until it is too late for me. I urged Dr Carnahan to tell me what I might expect, but he has not replied to my letter. You must in case I am to lecture next spring (which is not certain) tell the Doctor that I cannot think of using the room unless it is put in order.

My brother[5] expects to sail in the Victoria, when she leaves here on her next trip, so that if you wish to send parcels to London, they will be taken care of. I have a good chance to send some small articles to Scotland, if they are placed in my hand within 4 days. Have you nothing for Forbes? I frequently have such opportunities, & if you would leave your parcels with me, I would forward them for you with pleasure.

I am preparing for my labors in the medical college. We intend, this year,

---

In 1838, Torrey, Downing and Jesse Buel founded the Horticultural Society of the Valley of the Hudson. Although a meeting was held in May 1838, the Society never took root and soon disappeared. George Bishop Tatum, "Andrew Jackson Downing, Arbiter of American Taste, 1815–1852" (Ph.D. dissertation, Princeton University, 1949), p. 60. Henry later had contact with the landscape architect in connection with Downing's design of the Mall and the Smithsonian grounds.

[4] Herbert Gray Torrey.

[5] We have not ascertained which of Torrey's four brothers sailed for Europe at this time.

to give a *few lectures* in *October* merely to keep the students here. This plan has been adopted by the colleges in Philadelphia with good effect.

Hare of Philadelphia made me a visit lately, & I have also had a call from Dᴿ Gibbes of Charleston S.C. He has given up Medicine & has accepted an appointment in the College of Charleston, where he teaches Mathematics, Physics & Chemistry! He is a good fellow & will do all he can in science, but they have given him too many branches. He has gone to Boston & will call on you in a few days.[6] My very kind regards to Mrs. Henry & to the other members of your family.

As ever, yours
John Torrey

[6] We have found no further mention of the expected visit by Lewis R. Gibbes (*Henry Papers*, 3:536).

FROM WILLIAM STURGEON
Henry Papers, Smithsonian Archives

Westmoreland Cottage
Pomeroy Sᵗ Old Kent Road
London
Septᵣ 23ᵈ 1839[1]

My Dear Sir,

I have received your very interesting paper on successions or series of electric currents, with which I am quite delighted. You will percieve by looking at page 112, vol. 1, of the *Annals*, that I have proceeded as far as tertiary currents, by means of the *Magnetic Electrical Machine*:[2] but you have gone much farther, and the results of your experiments are really beautiful. I shall place them before our English experimenters in the January number of the Annals.[3]

You will see that I have published the principal part of this letter in the 21ˢᵗ Nº of the Annals. My object for doing so is that of giving philosophers

[1] This letter is postmarked Philadelphia, January 23, and was evidently not received by Henry until after that date.

[2] The correct reference is 2:112. Using a magnetoelectric machine and two coils, Sturgeon produced a current in the second coil.

[3] When Sturgeon reprinted "Contributions III" (*Annals*, 4:281–310) he added two footnotes of his own. In paragraph 93, Henry failed to explain the apparent anomaly in the direction of the secondary current on breaking the circuit. Sturgeon noted, "Our theory, as given in Vol. I. of these Annals, fully explains the whole phenomena. Edit." In paragraph 126, Henry used strips of tin foil to illustrate the "divellent" effects of a discharge. Sturgeon referred to his prior illustration in *Annals*, 2:86.

an opportunity of testing my theory of *Magnetic Electricity*, as given in vol. 1. of the "Annals of Electricity &c" with your extensive series of successive currents.[4] You have given a series of symbols expressive of the directions of the currents to the fifth degree, by *opening the circuit*. Now, if my theory be correct, I can easily predict the direction of the currents which would be brought into play by *closing the circuit*, which series would be very different to that given by *opening the circuit*. The two will stand as follows.

	On opening the circuit		On closing the circuit
Primary Current	+		+
Secondary Do	+		−
Current of the 3^d order	−		+
Do 4th	+		−
Do 5	−		+
	&c.		&c.

I have not tried the experiments, but I have no doubt of your finding them as I have predicted.[5]

You will see by the 21st N^o of the Annals, that I have ventured to propose a system of *fixed* Lightning Conductors for Shipping: which I hope you will scrutinize very closely, as I shall hold your opinion, on the plan, in very

---

[4] Sturgeon published the first two paragraphs of this letter, ending with the sentence following the table, in the October number of the *Annals* (4:240). In addition to correcting the *Annals* reference in the first paragraph, he made several minor changes.

According to Sturgeon's theory (*Annals, 1*: 198–200, 251–265, 266–277), a conductor through which a current was passing was surrounded (like a magnet) by magnetic "effluvia" arranged in "polar magnetic lines." These lines were the direct agent in producing a secondary current in another conductor. Sturgeon believed that his "polar magnetic lines" reduced electromagnetic phenomena to "the principles of magnetics" (p. 265).

[5] Because of the delay in the receipt of this letter, Henry first learned of Sturgeon's prediction in November when he saw a copy of Sturgeon's letter to Silliman of August 6, 1839. His angry reaction to Sturgeon's claims is in his letter to Bache of November 12 and in his letter to Silliman of November 18 (both printed below).

Henry responded in print to Sturgeon's letter in "Contributions IV" (paragraph 27), read on June 19, 1840. He could now experimentally produce currents of higher orders on making a circuit and thus gave a table of directions which matched Sturgeon's:

In connection with the results given in the last two paragraphs, it is due to Mr. Sturgeon that I should state, that in a letter addressed to me and published in the *Annals of Electricity*, he has predicted from his theory, that I would find on examination the series of alternation of currents for the beginning induction which I have here given. I may however here add, it appears to me that this result might have been predicted without reference to any theory. There was no reason to suppose the induction at the beginning would be different in its nature from that at the ending, and therefore the series which would be produced from the former might be immediately inferred from that belonging to the latter, by recollecting that the direction of the induction at the beginning should be opposite to that at the ending. I do not wish it to be supposed however from this remark, that I had myself drawn any inference from my experiments as to the alternations of currents which might be produced by the beginning induction; the truth is, that this action was so feeble with the arrangement of apparatus I employed, that I supposed it could not produce a series of currents of the different orders.

great respect. I have investigated Mr Harris's plan of conductors, and have given my opinion of it pretty freely, but I hope I have done no more than justice, in so important a case, absolutely requires.[6] You will see that I have submitted my paper to the consideration of all the principal philosophical Societies in Europe and America, I am aware of this being a novel mode of proceeding; but our British Societies give reasons for *appeals* else where; and I have no hesitation in saying that any Society which will not give ear to, or not notice, any scientific discovery, or project, but such as emanates from its own members, can have but little claim to the character of being a promoter, or even a well-wisher, of the general interests of Science. I shall send a printed copy of my memoir to each Society mentioned in the heading.[7]

In the 36 N^o of the *Bibliotheque Universelle* of Genève, I find an article, by De la Rive,[8] stating that he and some other philosophers, had tried to repeat my experiment in which the *positive pole* wire of a voltaic battery becomes red hot, but the *negative pole* wire never comes to that temperature, but had failed. De la Rive says that he would have doubted a circumstance so extraordinary and unexpected, had <Mr Gassiot> it not been seen by Faraday, Daniell and others. The fact is, De la Rive did not employ a sufficiently extensive series, nor do I think that he operated properly, his information being merely from a note of Mr Gassiot's which appeared in the last december N^o of the Phil. Mag.[9] I have given something like an out-

---

[6] Sturgeon's paper, "On Marine Lightning Conductors," *Annals of Electricity, Magnetism, and Chemistry*, October 1839, *4*:161–191, triggered an acrimonious year-long dispute with William Snow Harris. Sturgeon was trying to prevent the Admiralty's adoption of Harris's plan, which had already been endorsed by a naval committee, by alleging defects and advancing a system of his own. He reprinted from the *Phil. Mag.* Harris's responses to his charges and also printed his correspondence with Harris. The debate was colorful and full of italics; Sturgeon accused Harris of "unelectro-invective" and "*Electrophobia*" (*4*:420, 500).

One of Sturgeon's criticisms involved the nature of lateral explosions. Harris, backed by Faraday and Wheatstone, felt that these were caused by poor conductors and could therefore be easily avoided. Sturgeon, citing Henry's work on lateral discharge, claimed they were due to induction in the conductor and therefore unavoidable. His solution was to keep the conductors away from vulnerable parts of the ship. Henry later (1859) referred to Harris's failure to deal with this problem

as the one drawback of an "otherwise admirable arrangement." *Scientific Writings of Joseph Henry*, 2 vols. (Washington, D.C., 1886), *2*:341.

[7] Sturgeon listed twenty-five societies on the title page of his paper. He explained to Harris that he did this because of the subject's "paramount importance to every maritime country" (*Annals*, *4*:191). His comments to Henry expose a different motivation: doubt of the objectivity of the British scientific societies.

Sturgeon's paper was specifically addressed to the British Association meeting at Birmingham. When the paper was not presented, Sturgeon implied suppression by Harris, who was one of the secretaries of the mathematics and physical science section. Harris claimed he had not seen or even heard of the paper while at the meeting (*Annals*, *4*:236, 325).

[8] *Bibliotheque Universelle de Genève*, 1839, n.s. *18*:369–371.

[9] "On a Remarkable Difference in the Heat Attained by the Electrodes of a Powerful Constant Battery. By J. P. Gassiot, Esq.: in a Letter to Mr. Brayley," *Phil. Mag.*, 1838, 3d ser. *13*:

line of the process in page 421 vol. 3 of the Annals,[10] but I suppose De la Rive had not seen it. Should you have occasion to show it to your Class, let me advise you to have an extensive series, certainly above 100 pairs, and the larger the plates are, the better. Wrap cloth or paper round the wires where you hold them, otherwise they will burn your fingers. Bring the wires into contact either at the extreme points or by crossing them, at an inch or two distant from the points. Now separate the wires slowly until you get a good flame playing between them. In a short time the wire in connexion with the positive pole will become red hot.[11] It was about 8 oClock in the evening when I discovered this beautiful fact, after being experimenting without intermission from 3 in the afternoon. The rest of the party were resting at the time. As soon as I became certain that I was not deceived, I called M[r] Mason[12] to look at it, and when he had become satisfied, we called M[r] Gassiot and M[r] Walker[13] to look at it. After that we varied the experiment in several ways. The battery consisted of a series of 160 pairs, in jars holding nearly a pint each. The copper cylinder of each jar was immersed in a solution of Sulphate of Copper, and the zinc cylinder (inside the copper one) in a solution of common salt, the liquids being separated by brown paper.[14]

I am my Dear Sir
yours very truly
W. Sturgeon

436–437. Gassiot's letter did not describe the experiment in detail and referred to a more lengthy description to appear in the *Transactions of the London Electrical Society*. A note by Brayley mentioned that Faraday and Daniell were present at a repetition of the experiment.

John Peter Gassiot (1797–1877, *DSB, DNB*), a wealthy wine merchant, was Honorary Treasurer of the London Electrical Society. As often happened, the experiments Sturgeon is describing were conducted at his house and with one of his huge batteries. A generous benefactor of science, Gassiot also conducted important researches in electricity which helped provide confirmation of the identity of static and voltaic electricity and supported the chemical theory against the contact theory. In 1863 he received the Royal Medal of the Royal Society for his investigation of discharges through gases at low pressure.

[10] The account, from the "Proceedings of the London Electrical Society," was actually by C. V. Walker with editorial comments by Sturgeon. *Annals*, January 1839, 3:419–423. Walker published a more complete version in

Transactions of the London Electrical Society, 1837–1840, *1*:57–72, 97–102.

[11] Henry later tried the experiment himself. See the "Record of Experiments" entries of March 27 and July 17, 1840, below.

[12] Probably T. Mason, Jr. (*Annals*, 3:13–14).

[13] Charles Vincent Walker (1812–1882, *DNB*), electrical engineer and later editor of the short-lived *Electrical Magazine*. From 1845 until his death he was an electrician with the South-Eastern Railway Company where he introduced several improvements in communications. He was also involved in submarine telegraphy and time-signalling for astronomical observations.

Walker was the editor and translator of several major works in electricity, including A. A. De La Rive's three-volume *Treatise on Electricity* (London, 1853–1858). In 1855 he became a Fellow of the Royal Society and in 1876 President of the Society of Telegraph Engineers and Electricians.

[14] Sturgeon seems to have had a knack for alienating his colleagues. Walker later protested Sturgeon's description of these experiments as given in his letter to Silliman of

P.S. I am sorry to say that in consequence of my Bookseller, Mr Dobson neglecting to send me the proper returns, I shall be obliged to decline sending the Annals to America without having an agency in London. Wiley and Putman of New York have a house in London at which the Annals are delivered.

August 6, 1839, which was published in *Silliman's Journal*, April-June 1840, *39*:29–32. Walker accused Sturgeon of claiming too much credit for joint experiments and alleged that the observation on the heating of the plus pole was accidental and not the result of an experiment designed by Sturgeon to test certain of his theoretical ideas as Sturgeon claimed (ibid., January-March 1842, *42*:383–386).

ALEXANDER DALLAS BACHE TO JAMES RENWICK, SR.

Letterpress Copy, Bache Papers, Smithsonian Archives

Philadelphia, Sept. 30. 1839

My dear Sir,

In a recent letter from our mutual friend Major Sabine he urged strongly the undertaking of a magnetic survey of our country.[1] The advantage of a visit from Professor Henry has enabled me to mature ideas on this subject & we have concluded to submit to you the propriety of forming an association for [?conducting][2] this Survey & for concentrating the efforts now making in a desultory way in our country, of uniting the conductors, & of stimulating others to aid in the matter. This idea would no doubt require for its successful prosecution the formation of a nucleus about which those who have the requisite instruments for research in relation to dip & intensity, who would procure them, or to whom it might be deemed advantageous to

---

[1] In Sabine's letter to Bache of August 30, 1839, he introduced C. J. B. Riddell who was on his way to Canada to set up a magnetic and meteorological observatory at Montreal and also to make a magnetic survey of British North America. Sabine wrote: "May we not hope that under your auspices, a similar magnetic survey may be obtained of your great country."

Sabine intended traveling magnetic surveys to complement observations made at the network of fixed magnetic observatories and by the Ross expedition (described above in the July 1, 1839, circular of the Royal Society of London). The desiderata for the surveys are given in the *British Association Report, 1841* (1842), part 1, pp. 40–41. In a letter of November 12, 1839, Sabine urged Bache to complete a magnetic survey of the United States in four years, at which time, after the Ross expedition returned, Sabine intended to do maps of dip, variation, total and horizontal intensity, and Gauss was to revise his theory of terrestrial magnetism:

> Would it not be possible to complete within that time a Magnetic Survey of the United States? and would not you and Mr Henry superintend such a work?

Sabine's letters to Bache are in the Rhees Collection (RH 2208 and RH 2209), Henry E. Huntington Library and Art Gallery.

[2] Bache's handwriting is illegible; we assume this is the sense of the word.

supply them, might rally, & who would [?enter the labouring war][3] in collecting as well as observing. Will you give your advice, influence, & cooperation in aid of this undertaking? & join a Committee which might consist of Professors Bartlett & W. B. Rogers, Henry, yourself & me, or be otherwise increased to meet your wishes in taking the necessary preliminary steps in the matter.[4] Would it suit you to meet us in Philadelphia? Professor Henry desires his best regards.

Very respectfully & truly Yours
A. D. Bache

[3] A tentative reading.

[4] Letters inviting the participation of W. H. C. Bartlett (September 30, 1839) and John Locke (December 10, 1839) are in the same letterpress volume; one to Elias Loomis (October 23, 1839) is in the Loomis Papers, Beinecke Library, Yale University.

In a letter to Sabine of March 18, 1840 (Sabine Papers, Records of Kew Observatory, Public Record Office, London), Bache reported that the previous August and September the committee had written to others and gotten promises of aid from Loomis and Locke in the west. James Renwick was to be responsible for New York State. Henry and Bache were to cover Pennsylvania, New Jersey, Delaware, and perhaps more. Rogers was to do Virginia, and Bartlett parts of New York and the northeast. No one had been found to make observations in the south and southwest.

It is difficult to assess the accomplishments of the magnetic association or even whether it continued as a cohesive group. Although early references to American efforts are to the association (e.g., Herschel's comment in "Terrestrial Magnetism," *Essays from the Edinburgh and Quarterly Reviews* . . . [London, 1857], p.

126, reprinted from the *Quarterly Review*, June 1840), later references in correspondence and in the *BAAS* Reports are simply to individuals. Of the seven original members of the magnetic association, only Bache, Loomis, Locke, and Renwick made magnetic surveys in the next few years. Bache surveyed Pennsylvania in the summers of 1840 and 1841 and parts of New York and Canada in the summer of 1843. Loomis surveyed Ohio, Indiana, Illinois and Missouri. Locke covered a large area from the central mid-west to the Atlantic on the east and the Canadian border on the north. Renwick made observations in New York and in 1844, under Coast Survey auspices, surveyed from Rhode Island to Annapolis while Bache observed from Annapolis to the Gulf of Mexico.

Even with the backing of an association, the surveys would have been demanding for individuals. Those few observers who had the expertise required instruments and the time and money for traveling. Recognizing the limits of individual effort, Bache urged that the surveys be undertaken by the states and eventually made magnetic surveys part of the work of the Coast Survey.

"RECORD OF EXPERIMENTS"

Henry Papers, Smithsonian Archives

Oct 8th 1839

Exp Repeated the exp of Davy[1] according to the variation of Nobile[2] *ie* by passing down over a surface of clean mercury two wires at an ob-

[1] Described in Humphry Davy, "On a New Phenomenon of Electro-magnetism," *Phil. Trans.*, 1823, part 2, pp. 153–159.

[2] Leopoldo Nobili, *Memorie ed Osservazioni*, 2 vols. (Firenze, 1834), *1*:306–307.

tuse angle thus——  When the current from one of the
divisions of the large battery was passed through a
whirling was ob- served between the points of the
wire and a slight depression at each point. Nobile says in this arrangement
[the] phenomenon is produced with less galvanic power than in the arrangement of Davy where the wires are passed through the bottom of the
vessel containing the mercury and terminate below the surface. The action
however I did not find very energetic.

Exp Repeated the exp according to the method of Davy. Made a small box
by cutting out the surface of a square block to the depth of about 1/4 of an
inch passed through the bottom of this two wires so that the points (amalgamated) just came through the same trough used in the last exp, now gave a
much more rapid motion of whirling and threw up over the points a small
cone of mercury. The *cone was projected from each wire*. The whirling appeared to be with the sun[3] around the pole from the *Zinc* negative and in
the opposite direction around that from the copper (positive).

N.B. The cones in the last arrangement and the depression in the first appear to be due to the repulsive action discovered by Ampere[4] which exists
between the consecutive parts of the same current

Repeated the experiment of <*Nobilie*> Davy with common electricity
(See Nobile's memorie page [. . .][5]). The box used in the last exp served for
this. In the first attempt with two (gallon) jars, no effect. The stratum of
mercury was too thick but could not be made thinner without thrusting up
higher the points through the bottom of the box and in this case they required to be guarded by a coating of cement. With these precautions and
two jars no effect was produced but when three jars were employed the
mercury was thrown with so much force from the + point as to strike me in
the face. The result was therefore in accordance with the observation of
Nobile, and affords another example of the similarity of action of common and galvanic electricity.

Tried to magnetize needles by sticking them into the bottom of the box
through the stratum of mercury, but without success.

Attempted to repeat an experiment of Peltier[6] on the production of

---

[3] i.e., in the same direction as the sun's apparent motion.

[4] Described by Ampère in his *Mémoire sur
la théorie mathématique des phénomènes
électrodynamiques, uniquement déduite de
l'expérience* (Paris, 1827), p. 39. Henry probably knew of it through secondary sources,
such as P. M. Roget, *Treatises on Electricity, Galvanism, Magnetism, and Electro-Mag-*

netism (London, 1832), "Electro-Magnetism,"
pp. 62–63.

[5] Henry left a blank in his notebook. Nobili's
variation of the Davy experiment with common electricity appeared in *Memorie, 1*:305–
306.

[6] Jean C. A. Peltier, "Expériences Électro-
Magnétiques," *Annales de chimie et de physique,* 1835, n.s. *60*:261–271.

electricity by agitation of the particles of a metal. For this purpose attached one end of a thick piece of copper plate to the one wire of a galvanometer and the other to a rasp then drew the end of the copper plate over the rasp. Needle appeared somewhat aggitated but not sufficient to indicate certainly a current; perhapse with a galvanometer with short wires an effect might be produced

FROM WILLIAM LEITHEAD[1]
Henry Papers, Smithsonian Archives

"Gallery of Natural Magic"
Electrical Department,
Colosseum,
Regent's Park,
8 October, 1839.[2]

My Dear Sir!

Although our personal acquaintance is slight, I take the liberty of requesting a favour of you, a liberty, which I hope will be forgiven in a fellow-labourer in the same field with yourself. This letter will be delivered to you by my friend, M.ʳ Wilkin,[3] who has made up his mind to seek his fortune in your Country. If you can in any way forward his views, I shall feel deeply obliged by your exerting your influence on his behalf.

I can only say, that I shall be at any time most happy to execute any commission for you in England, or to pay every attention in my power to any friend of yours who may happen to visit London.

There is absolutely nothing doing in the scientific way here worthy of notice. You will probably hear wonderful accounts from Russia; but you must allow a considerable percentage for exaggeration. Jacobi *has* a ten-oared boat; but, by means of electro-magnetism, it moveth not. The professor *has* also a very powerful Voltaic apparatus; but he cannot decompose water with it so rapidly as to enable him to supply his oxy-hydrogen microscope with the mixed gases, as has been reported.[4]

[1] Leithead was Secretary of the London Electrical Society. *Henry Papers*, 3:182–183.

[2] A notation in Henry's hand indicates that this letter was not received until 1842. The reason for the delay is suggested by the address on the letter: "D.ʳ Henry, Professor of Natural Philosophy, Yale College, Philadelphia, United States." Leithead's confusion may have derived in part from an article which

had appeared earlier in Sturgeon's *Annals* identifying Henry as a professor at Yale. See *Henry Papers*, 3:181n.

Another notation by Henry reveals that he answered this letter on November 19, 1842. This response has not been located.

[3] We have been unable to identify Mr. Leithead's friend.

[4] Although the electromagnetic boat ulti-

I have heard nothing of, or from Crosse[5] lately; but the magician is still busy with his electrical incantations.

I am engaged at the Colosseum to manage the stupendous electrical machine at that place.[6] Our plate is 7 feet in diameter, the prime conductor, 5, and the negative conductor 3 feet in diameter; but the room in which the apparatus is at present placed is too small to enable us to test the powers of the instrument. We have as yet only obtained a spark 23 inches long. But the proprietor intends to remove the machine into a more commodious apartment, and to employ steam-power to turn the plate.

One word more respecting my friend. You will find him a most intelligent gentleman, and by forwarding his views, you will greatly oblige, (My Dear Sir)

Yours respectfully,
& faithfully,
Wm Leithead

---

mately proved to be a failure because of the high cost of the fuel and the inability of the inventor to solve the problem of the production of toxic fumes, Jacobi was making day trips on the Neva with ten to twelve people on board as early as the fall of 1838. *DSB.* During the winter of 1838–1839 he claimed his voltaic apparatus was decomposing three to four cubic feet of gas an hour, sufficient to illuminate an entire room. M. H. von Jacobi to Michael Faraday, June 21, 1839, in L. Pearce Williams, ed., *The Selected Correspondence of Michael Faraday*, 2 vols. (Cam-

bridge, England, 1971), *1*:343–346. Faraday had a translation of the letter printed in the *Phil. Mag.*, 1839, 3d ser. *15*:161–165.

[5] Andrew Crosse, an amateur electrical experimenter Henry had met in England. Crosse achieved notoriety as a result of a report in which he noted that electrical currents through water had apparently generated insects. *Henry Papers, 3*:320–321.

[6] The Colosseum is described in the *Henry Papers, 3*:423–424. According to *The Times* (London) the giant electrical machine was placed on public exhibition on June 17, 1839.

"RECORD OF EXPERIMENTS"
Henry Papers, Smithsonian Archives

Oct 9th 1839

Made a course galvanometer with about 40 turns of bell wire,[1] used for the first time the connectors which I had made by Chilton, me[re]ly small cylinders of copper of this form Found they operated very well.

---

[1] Described in "Contributions IV: Electro-Dynamic Induction," paragraph 4, this gal-vanometer was used when Henry was using currents of large quantity but low intensity.

"RECORD OF EXPERIMENTS"
Henry Papers, Smithsonian Archives

Oct 10th 1839

Arranged Pages little apparatus[1] to produce a secondary current used with it the part of the large battery used in the exp of the 8th inst.[2]  The motion of the electrepeter was exceedingly rapid and the secondary shock too powerful to be taken. The tertiary shock from Helix no 2 on no 1 was also very intense. When a plate of sheet lead was interposed the neutralization was not complete but when the large plate of zinc was placed between nothing could be felt

I afterwards arranged the apparatus so as to get shocks from the current of the 4th order by placing coil no 2 on helix no 1 and connecting with the former coil no 3 on which was placed helix no 2. Thus

By this arrangement quantity is converted into intensity and intensity into quantity. When a plate of metal was placed between any of the coils adjacent the screening influence was exhibited. From this it appears that the 2nd current from the magnet electrical machine acts precisely the same as that from the battery.

The best way to exhibit the screening influence to a class would be to suspend the coil after the method used by Dr Hare[3] and then to introduce different substances between the two while they are kept *continually* at the same distance.

The shock from the tertiary current with the foregoing arrangement was from the rupture of the current and not from the induction at the begining for while the tertiary current was so powerful as scarcely to be indured from the induction at rupture the same current at forming contact could scarcely be perceived through the tongue

Sent the current from the little machine through the long wire spool (4 miles). Put helix no 1 on top, but found no result. Sent the current from the little machine through two garded points in the bottom of a box to see

---

[1] Described in Page's "Magneto-Electric and Electro-Magnetic Apparatus and Experiments," *Silliman's Journal*, 1839, 35:258–259, the "Compound Magnet and Electrotome" had been completed in April 1838. This prototype of the induction coil had separate primary and secondary windings and a self-acting circuit breaker. Robert C. Post, *Physics, Patents, and Politics: A Biography of Charles Grafton Page* (New York, 1976), pp. 24–25.

[2] See the "Record of Experiments," October 8, 1839, printed above.

[3] Hare suspended the helix and coil in the vertical plane on opposite sides of a pulley. *Proceedings of the American Philosophical Society*, 1838–1840, 1:199.

if the cones of mercury would be produced as in the experiments of Davy[4] but no effect was perceived.

Arranged two lead syphons in mercury at the upper end so that a current of galvanism might pass up one and down the other. Put the whole away with the shaker battery attached to note the effect on the morrow.[5]

Made some experiments on the light from the little machine.[6] First whirled before the spark a disk with such velocity that figures on it could not be observed by ordinary light, these however were distinctly visible by the spark showing that its duration was excedingly small.

2nd The spark was viewed in the mirror of a whirling appartus made for me by Mr Saxton[7] and which revolves more than 30 thousand times in a second. In this it appeared elongated which shows that although the duration was very short still it was not instantaneous.

The appearance of objects by the spark was singular. All appeared in a kind of vibratory motion which affected the senses very unpleasantly

3rd The spectrum from the spark was viewed through a prism and presented a very singular appearance. The red part was small also the blue part but the *yellow* and *violet* quite abundant

This should be studied again under better circumstances from a surface of mercury not surrounded with glass as in this case.

As an illustration of the power of the little machine when in full action and excited by a large battery I may mention that a labouring man one of Mr Clows servants being requested to take hold of the handles immediatly fell to the floor his hands spasmodically grasping the handles

[4] Henry had performed this experiment using a battery and then Leyden jars on October 8, 1839. See the "Record of Experiments" entry of that date, printed above.

[5] Henry was out of town on October 11 and was unable to get back to this continuation of experiments begun on September 5 and 7, 1839 (see the "Record of Experiments" entries of those dates, printed above) until the 12th. In a note of that date, but placed in the "Record of Experiments" entry for October 10, immediately following this paragraph, Henry wrote:

Inspected the above. Found that but little mercury had come over but that the greater quantity was on the negative side. The same result was obtained with the arrangement with the large battery.

The "Record of Experiments" entry of October 12, 1839 (printed below) includes an experiment on the penetration of lead by mercury without using current.

[6] For other discussions of the electric light, see *Henry Papers*, 2:125n–126n, 491–493; 3:217.

[7] Henry had first used this apparatus in his experiments of April 20, 1838. See the "Record of Experiments" entry of that date, printed above.

TO JAMES HENRY

Family Correspondence, Henry Papers, Smithsonian Archives

Princ[eton October 10–11, 1839][1]

My Dear James

The misterious box [. . .] in good condition the day bef[ore yester]day (Tuesday) and was opened w[ith] much avidity. The articles were [. . .] in excellent condition and were receiv[ed] with much rejoicing. The only drawback was the idea that you had robed yourself to gratify us. The contents of the box was guessed at before it arrived. We are all well although I have been almost laid up with a pair of sprained wrists. In attempting to assist Willey in raising his kite I fell over a pile of stones. Both of my arms were considerably hurt but one of them has given me much more trouble than the other. I have so far recovered as to be able to use my hands for light [. . .] Mary was very busily engaged [. . .]ngs since in writing to John Platt [. . .] Aunt Nancy that she could not [. . .] but Jony Platt could. William [. . .] to day of writing to Uncle James [. . .] young lady No 4 is making some noise [. . .] the world we have given her the name of the trumpeter. She makes almost as much noise as the Princeton Band. Helen was dressed a few days since in a suit of Wills. cloathes and then was called John Platt. Nancy is much better and appears to enjoy herself very well. I believe that I have not written since our commencement. The whole went off quite finely and was one of the best and most pleasant we have had since we have been in Princeton.

I have been on a visit to Philadelphia since the begining of the vacation, stoped most of the time with Bache at the Girard College. The building is going on very slowly and will not be finished in less than five years. I almost always see Clark More[2] when I go to the city. He keeps a fancy store in the arcade under the old cite of the Philadelphia Museum. You may reccollect he was once an auctioneer in Albany. He informed me that Judge Van Rensselaer[3] had borrowed 75 dollars of him and that he put him in jail and kept him there for two months until his father paid the debt. He also informed me that he had frequently seen Winn Halenbake,[4] that the last time he saw him he was quite deacent but before that he had been in a bad way,

[1] A corner of the first page is missing. Henry finished this letter on Friday, October 11. We assume he began it on October 10. The brackets in the first paragraph indicate the missing material; where possible we have inserted the probable text.

[2] Clark Moore (*Henry Papers*, 2:197n).

[3] Not identified.

[4] Giles Winn Halenbake (1801–1865), a native of Albany, taught school in Philadelphia before settling in central Pennsylvania, where he operated a coal mining company and later a farm. *Commemorative Biographical Record of Central Pennsylvania* (Chicago, 1898), pp. 597–598.

was very intemperate, kept school somewhere in the country near the city. Friday Evening Oct 11th—Stephen, William and myself have been to day to visit the establishment of Mr Hasler[5] at Montrose about 6 or 7 miles to the north of Princeton. It is on a hill and is one of the points of one of the large triangles. We had a very plesant visit and were very kindly entertained by Mr H. and his assistants.[6] They have had good weather while in this vicinity and will be ready to leave in a few days for a point in Pennsylvania. You know I presume that Mr H is the principal of the coast surveyors and that Mr Furguson[7] of Albany is his first assistant. The whole company consists of 13 men and they have about 10 or 11 tents. Mr Furguson is with an other party some where in Pennsylvania.[8] The principal news is that of the suspension of specie payment by the banks of Philadelphia.[9] The election news you will have received before this letter reaches you.[10]

Give me the form of the note which you wished endorsed and I will add my name as directed. Nancy wishes all the children kissed for her and is anxious to hear farther about Jane Johnson.[11] We had a letter from Scotland a few weeks since which gave the intelligence that Aunty Clark died a few weeks after I left Girvan.[12] The rest of our friends are well. I will however give you more of the contents of the letter in my next as I cannot just now put my hand on it. We requested David Kelly to speak to the Galway people about butter but I know not if he will attend to it. He promised to write on the subject but we have not as yet heard from him. I perfectly agree with you relative to his fitness for the calling you mention rather than the one he has chosen.[13] I most sincerely hope he will not return to Princeton particularly if he expects me to assist him farther in the way of support. His father[14]

---

[5] Ferdinand Rudolph Hassler, head of the Coast Survey.

[6] See the "Record of Experiments" entry immediately below.

[7] James Ferguson (*Henry Papers*, 2:15n–16n).

[8] The preceding two sentences are in the margin of the third page of the original.

[9] Following the boom of 1838 and early 1839, the suspension of specie payments by the Bank of the United States in October signalled the beginning of the Crisis of 1839. Although banks south and west of Philadelphia followed its lead, northern banks did not and bank failures were not as widespread as in the Panic of 1837. The Crisis and subsequent depression, which lasted through the early 1840s, were marked by a severe deflation. Production was relatively unaffected, however, and unemployment was not widespread. See Peter Temin, *The Jacksonian Economy* (New York, 1969), chapter 5.

[10] Although the New Jersey returns showed a majority for all six Whig candidates for the United States House of Representatives, five of the six races were so close that the seats were contested. The dispute eventually threatened the organization of the House. See Henry to James Henry, December 16–18, 1839, printed below.

[11] Perhaps Jane Alexander Johnston (1797–1840), a cousin. *Henry Papers*, 2:150.

[12] We have not found the letter. Henry visited Girvan, Ayrshire, his mother's birthplace, in September 1837. Aunty Clark may be one of his mother's sisters who remained in Scotland when most of the family emigrated to America.

[13] David Kelly, a second cousin of Henry's, was attending the Princeton Theological Seminary (*Henry Papers*, 2:97n).

[14] David Kelly's parents were James Kelly (ca. 1784–1842) and Abigail Alexander Kelly

is richer than I am and if the young Gentleman cannot get along himself he had better teach a school for a year or two until he can help himself.

(1790–?), the daughter of Joseph and Harriet's uncle John Alexander (1760–1841). In 1841 the Kellys left Galway, New York, and moved to Illinois. *Reminiscences of Mary*

Lydia Kelly (Rock Island, Illinois, 1914). Henry R. Kelly, *Imprints on the Sands of Time Left by Certain Kelly's . . .*, 3d ed. (Towson, Maryland, 1972), p. 255.

"RECORD OF EXPERIMENTS"
Henry Papers, Smithsonian Archives

Oct 11th 1839

Visited to day with Mr S Alexander Mont Rose where Mr Hasler has one of stations for the trigonometrical survey of the coast of the united states. We were much pleased with the operation of the heliotrope,[1] the instrument for throwing a beam of light to answer as a signal. It consists of a piece of looking glass about 2 inches long by one wide attached to the end of a telescope in such a position that when the telescope is directed to the distant object a beam of light is thrown on the same object.

To understand the most simple arrangement of this heliotrope let *a* be a mirror, *c* a telescope with two screenes, *d e* with a hole in each so that the centers of these will be in the same line parallel with the axis of the telescope. Now let the telescope be directed to the distant object and at the same time the mirror so turned that a ray of light from the sun shall pass through each hole in the screen on the telescope then it is evident that the beam will pass parallel to the axis of the glass and be thrown on the object to which the instrument is pointed.

From the station at Mount Rose 8 stations are visible and from 6 or 7 of these light was streaming from as many heliotropes like so many stars of the first magnitude. They were mostly distinctly visible by the naked eye although at the distance of 17 miles the *nearest*

---

[1] Designed by Gauss around 1821, the heliotrope became part of the standard equipment in large-scale triangulation. Modified post–1840, the instrument remained an important piece of apparatus until the advent of aerial surveying. *DSB*, s.v. "Gauss;" *Quarterly Journal of Science, Literature, and the Arts*, 1822, *13*:421–422.

October 12, 1839

"RECORD OF EXPERIMENTS"
Henry Papers, Smithsonian Archives

Oct 12th [1839]

 Arranged a Leyden jar within a coil sent current from little machine through coil or rather helix (no 1). Placed tongue near the knob of jar but could discover no effect

Arranged the small decomposing apparatus belonging to the magneto-electrical machine so as to produce decomposition in two small tubes containing acidulated water. Found the current in the first arrangement +. In the 2nd arrangement which gave a tertiary current the current was —

 Sent secondary shocks from the small machine (Pages) through a glass tube containing nitrate of zinc. Tourmalines placed on the side so as to observe if any polarization of light was produced at the instant the discharge took

place. *No effect was observed.*[1] The tube was covered interely with tin foil and two holes made in this to transmit the light*

 Made a short syphon of lead. Put the long leg into a cup of mercury. Put it away to determine if the mercury will be delivered at the shorter leg[2]

* made same exp with oil of anis seed no result

[1] This appears to be another attempt by Henry to obtain experimental confirmation of Faraday's electrotonic state by observing light sent through liquids subjected to electricity. For an earlier experiment see the "Record of Experiments" entry of August 30, 1839, printed above.

[2] Henry returned to this entry to record the progress of the mercury over the next two weeks. A concluding post-factum paragraph reads:

Inspected the above arrangement on monday the 14th but found no indications of mercury at the shorter end. Inspected the same on the 15th, found that the mercury had reached the surface of the section of the shorter leg, but there was no apparent tendancy to pass out it stood like a dew on the lead. Inspected this again on the 28th inst remaining the same, lead saturated nearly throughout ex[ce]pt perhaps a small cylinder around the axis.

"RECORD OF EXPERIMENTS"
Henry Papers, Smithsonian Archives

Oct 14th 1839

Exp 1

Arranged coil no 1 and 2 so as to form a compound coil of two strands. Attached the ends of no 1 with the battery and the ends of no 2 with the ends of no 3. Then connected helix no 1 with a galvanometer. This being arranged the battery was plunged into the acid and afterwards the helix moved up and down over the third coil, the needle was deflected and by timing the motion of the helix the needle was made to discribe more than 90 degrees.

If there be no falacy in this experiment it is a very important one and determines the existance of a state of induction called by Mr Faraday electrotonic which has never been shown to exist.[1]

Found a falacy in the above experiment the electricity cut across from one coil to the other, the insulation of the several spires was not perfect.[2]

It however establishes the fact of the imperfect insulation between the spires of the coil covered only with cotton cloth and also that the secondary currents by motion can be produced with a small current. I shall therefore be in possession of a simple method of studing them.

Attempted to get a current of the 3rd order by means of motion but did not succeed with the two large coiles and the large helix (no 1)

With the large coil (no 1) attached to the battery and helix no 1 brought down on it a secondary current was produced and no difference appeared to be produced whether the plate of zinc was interposed or not or whether the zinc was in motion with the helix or at rest.[3]

Attempted with an arrangement of coiles 1 & 2 at the battery, 3 connected with no 2 and 4 connected with the galvanometer with many turns. No effect

Made a secondary current with the little machine by drawing the end of a file magnet over the end of the bundle of wires which forms the core. The presence of the current was indicated by the motion of the galvanometer needle

The circuit was then completed between the ends of the large wire which surrounds the bundle of iron wire but the same result was produced indicating that no screening influence in this case was produced. This exp is the repetition of one described in the latter entries of the old book.[4]

---

[1] Henry believed that the steady field established by the primary coil set up a state of strain which the moving helix disturbed. The disturbance was demonstrated by the electric current detected by the galvanometer. It was quite similar to his earlier attempt to detect the electrotonic state recorded in the "Record of Experiments" entry for May 13, 1839, experiment 3, printed above.

[2] In a marginal notation Henry later referred to the "Record of Experiments" entry of April 17, 1840 (printed below), where he further explored this type of short circuiting.

[3] In "Contributions IV," paragraphs 34–36, Henry indicated that the results of this type of experiment were quite unexpected and were important in his coming to the conclusion that two different types of electrodynamic induction existed. He had assumed that when the metal plate was also in motion, currents would be induced in it, resulting in screening. Yet no screening was evident. He had conducted similar experiments in this vein on May 13 and May 14, 1839.

[4] Probably a reference to the second experiment of May 13, 1839.

Thought of a new way of exhibiting the screening influence. Placed coil no 1 in connection with the battery and between this and helix no 1 placed coil no 2 & 3 joined together first so that the induced current from the lower coil would go in the same direction with that in the upper one. Now the shock from the helix was very severe. Next turned the lower coil of the two middle ones over so that the current by induction would be sent in an opposite direction through the other from the first. With this arrangement the effect was nothing scarcely. The shocks were only just perceptible.

I have several times thought that the zinc plate used in the experiments performed better than the lead plates and this I have proved by exp. At first I was disposed to attribute the effect to the difference of action in the metals but I have just thought that the difference might be due to the greater surface of the zinc plate it being of about twice the area of the lead plates. To settle this the helix (no 1) was placed over coil no 1 attached to the battery and the zinc plate placed between them. When the middle of the plate coincided with the axes of the two coiles, the shock could not be felt or very slightly but when the plate was placed so that its edge was projected scarcely at all beyond the edge of the helix the shock was very considerable. This exp is important it appears to me in reference to the production of secondary currents from ordinary magnetism

"RECORD OF EXPERIMENTS"
Henry Papers, Smithsonian Archives

Oct 15 1839

Exp 1 Inspected a piece of lead through which mercury has passed, found the amalgamation principally on the outer part. A core of pure lead was left in the axis of about the 20 of an inch in diameter.[1]

Inspected a piece of copper which was placed in a solution of nitric acid with sulphuric and mercury. The mercury after three days has penetrated the copper so as to render it soft and very brittle. Its tenacity is almost entirely destroyed and the plate (the copper is of this form) appears some what increased in thickness. The copper remained in the acid one night and when taken out it was only coated with mercury but not penetrated by and retained its original toughness but by laying on the table since then it has assumed its present state of brittleness. In the same solution and at the same time I placed another piece of the same plate of copper but connected at

---

[1] A continuation of the experimentation of October 12, 1839.

its upper end with a piece of zince. When examined next morning the [mercury] was found to have coated the lower end of this in apparently the same manner as the other piece but the two now appear very different the one being almost in a disintegrated state and the other retaining its original toughness. The piece of zince was al[l] disolved off even with the surface of the solution when I took the metals from the acid. It appears to me that this difference is in some way due to a galvanic action between the copper and mercury. Perhaps the copper takes on a polar state similar to that of steel which prevents the action of the acid and mercury. This idea is in conformity with the experiments described under the head of Oct 10[th2]—the greatest quantity of mercury was found at the wire connected with the negative pole. The copper is negative pole under the acid and from the above the mercury should be repelled from it.

Arranged two piecs of wire in the same way as the pieces of copper plate before mentioned.

Put away a syphon of tinned iron to determin whether the mercury passes along the surface.[3]

Exp 2 Connected the large coil (no 4) with the battery. Placed over this the long helix (no 1) and connected the ends of this with the galvanometer of 500 turns. First passed current through coil by means of rasp with metal between conductors. Needle deflected. Next placed zince plate between. Deflection about the same, although shock 100 times less. Next placed piece of lead between in addition to the zinc, still needle deflected with this arrangement however a slight sensation could be perceived on the tongue. After this placed in addition between the two conductors coil no 2 with its ends joined. With this not the least sensation could be felt through the tongue. Still the action on the galvanometer was the same

Exp 3 In the above exp. the contact was made and broken by the file or rather rasp and the needle was observed to be strangely affected as if sometimes suddenly stopped in its vibration, and moving first in one direction and then in the other. It was concluded that perhaps these anomalies were produced by the interruption of the current by means of the rasp and therefore the circuit was made and interrupted by means of a cup of mercury. When with this arrangement the current was commenced the needle was observed to move in one direction and when in the opposite when the circuit was broken. The impulses were apparently equally strong. This is a remarkable result first because all the articles to produce the most perfect

[2] Printed above.
[3] Henry later added: "Mercury did pass along the surface."

screening are made to intervene and not the slightest action is perceptible through the tongue. 2^n because in the case of the shock this induction at the commencement of the current is scarcely perceptible while that at the end is very intense but in this case as indicated by the needle they are equally powerful. The directions of these motions were found as determined by Mr Faraday the one at making contact in the opposite direction and the other in the same direction as the primary current

Exp 4 Removed all the metal from between the two conductors made the contact. North end of needle swings to right. Broke contact, north end swings to the left about the same distance and what appears to be very important the swing was about the same, full as great but not greater than when the screening apparatus was between. The shock however on making contact could only be felt through the tongue while that on breaking contact was felt through the arms. These experiments establish the fact of the existance of two kinds of currents in the same induction, one which produces the shock and the other which affects the needle.[4]

Exp 5 Repeated the same with the difference of putting helix no 1 directly on coil no 1 without intervening space as in the last exp. In this case the shock at making contact was much stronger through the tongue and could be felt in the hands but the shock at breaking contact was extremely sever[e]. When these were observed by the galvanometer they appeared equally intense. The needle under the influence of each described nearly a quadrant.

Exp 6 When the plate of zinc was interposed the needle was deflected to the same degree, the screening influence appeared to have no effect. The screening effect was howev[er] manifest as before with the shocks both at making and breaking contact. The former could not be felt with the hands while the plate intervened while the latter was very perceptible the screening not being perfect

Put needle in magnetizing spiral the long one[5] see old book[6] while the zinc plate was between the conductors. No magnetism at making or breaking contact but when the plate was removed the magnetism at breaking contact was considerable while at making contact scarcely perceptible

NB Exp 2 3 4 5 & 6 all made with the galvanometer of 500 turns

[4] Henry later wrote in the margin next to this entry: "I have since found a different explanation; See my paper no 4." The reference was to "Contributions IV," paragraphs 81–83.

[5] Described in paragraph 5 of "Contributions IV," this magnetizing spiral consisted of one hundred turns of long, fine wire about a hollow piece of straw approximately two and a half inches long. It was used in experiments when Henry anticipated currents of high intensity but small quantity.

[6] We have been unable to locate this reference in the "Record of Experiments."

Made arrangements with coils no 1, 2 & 3 and helix no 1 & no 2 to get the tertiary current but although the shock was very intense at breaking contact and nearly perceptible at making contact yet but little indications could be got from the galvanometer of 500 turns and none from those of a smaller number of turns. From this it appears that although the shocks from the tertiary current is great yet the [?magnetizable][7] current is small.

Substituted for Helix no 1, to receive the tertiary current, coil no 4 which was placed on coil no 3. No effect or next to none with the long galvanometer. Also got none with the next galvanometer in length. Try with the others (Tried this with Clark's galvanometer succeeded coil no 2)

[7] One word has been erased or has faded.

TO ALEXANDER DALLAS BACHE
Bache Papers, Smithsonian Archives[1]

Princeton Oct 16th 1839

My Dear Bache

We were much disappointed in not seeing you here on Monday according to agreement and much regret the cause of your detention. The pleasure however of a visit from you and yours is yet to come but I hope you will not let it be so long delayed that the cold weather will interfere with our plans. Do not forget that we are to have a Whirlwind hunt and a magnetic intensity feast in the open air. Drop me a line before you start since I intend to visit New York sometime during the present vacation and should not be well pleased to have you come when I am among the missing.

Mr Alexander sends you to day an account of the aurora of last month as copied from his notes taken at the time and you will see by the paper which he sends you that an unusual appearance of the same kind was observed at London on the same night and at about the same moment of absolute time. I feel somewhat interested in this matter since it furnishes another instance in illustration of my old position that brilliant auroras are generally active at the same time in Europe and America. While Mr Alexander was engaged in determining the position of the corona and noting the phases of the

[1] An earlier draft of the portion of this letter intended for Bache personally (up to the sentence beginning, "Since the publication of my last paper . . .") survives in the Bache Papers, Smithsonian Archives. The last paragraph of the draft shows signs of reworking, and Henry apparently decided to recopy what he had already written (with slight emendations) before proceeding to the section of the letter intended for formal communication. Mary Henry used both in preparing her memoir, marking this copy, "to be preserved."

meteor I was busy in attempting to detect polarized light in the beams of the aurora. For this purpose I first used Savarts apparatus and afterwards the arrangement of Arago, but although the light appeared of sufficient intensity to exhibit the phenomena of polarization yet none could be observed.[2]

I have been engaged most of the time since my last visit to Philadelphia in my old business of experimenting and have succeeded in developing some facts which appear of so much importance that I must request you to place them before the society inorder to secure an early date. Since[3] the publication of my last paper I have recived through the kindness of Dr Faraday a copy of his <*14ᵗʰ*> Fourteenth series of experimental researches and in this I was surprised to find a <*result*> statement directly in opposition to one of the principal results given in my paper. It is stated in substance in the 59 paragraph of my communication that when a plate of metal is interposed between a galvanic current and a conductor the secondary shock is neutralized. Dr Faraday finds on the contrary under apparently the same circumstances that no effect is produced by the interposition of the metal.[4] As the fact mentioned forms a very important part of my paper and is connected with nearly all the phenomena described subsequent to it, I was anxious to investigate the cause of the discrepancy between the results obtained by Dr Faraday and those found by myself. My experiments were on such a scale and the results so decided that there could be no room for doubt as to their <*correct*> character. A secondary current of such intensity as to paralize the arms was so neutralized by the interposition of the plate and riband of metal as not to be perceptible through the tounge. On the other hand I was led by a little reflection to conclude that there might exist a case of induction similar to that of magnetism in which no neutralization would take place and I thought it possible that Dr Faraday's results might have been derived from this. I have now however found a solution to the difficulty in the fact that there are <*in some cases (and probably in all)*> in an electrical current from a galvanic battery *two* distinct kinds of dynamic

[2] Stephen Alexander's letter to Bache, dated October 15, 1839, survives in the Rhees Collection, Huntington Library and Art Gallery (RH 780). The description of the aurora borealis contained in the letter was read by Bache to the October 18 meeting of the American Philosophical Society, and was printed in the *Proceedings of the American Philosophical Society*, 1838–1840, *1*:132–134. For Henry's record of the observations, see above, "Record of Experiments," September 3, 1839.

[3] The remainder of this letter (up to Henry's signature) was intended for formal communication to the October 18 meeting of the American Philosophical Society. Bache complied with Henry's request later in the letter, noting on the top of the first page "A.P.S. Oct: 18. 1839—(Read)." Bache made at least one change on the original ("Fourteenth" for "14ᵗʰ"); further emendations appear in the printed version, *Proceedings of the American Philosophical Society*, 1838–1840, *1*:135–136.

[4] This reprint survives in the Henry Library. Henry circled the relevant words in paragraph 1723.

induction: one of these produces, by means of a long wire, intense secondary shocks at the moment of breaking the contact, and feeble shocks at the moment of making contact; also this kind of induction is capable of being neutralized by the interposition of a plate of metal between the two conductors. The other kind of induction is produced at the same time from the same arrangement and does not give shocks but affects the needle of the galvanometer. It is of equal energy at the moment of making contact and of breaking contact and is not affected by the introduction of a plate of copper or zinc between the conductors.*[5] The phenomina produced by the first kind of induction form the subject of my last paper as well as that of the one before, while it would appear from the arrangement of Dr Faradays experiments that the results detailed in the first no of his series and those in the 14th were produced by the 2nd kind of induction.

A[l]though I may be too sanguine in reference to the results of this discovery yet I cannot refrain from adding that it appears to lead to a separation of the electrical induction of a galvanic current from the magnetic (see paragraph no 1731. &ct. 14 Series of Mr Faraday) and that it is a step of some importance towards a more precise knowledge of the phenomena of magneto electricity.

Yours as Ever
Joseph Henry

Will you do me the favour to make this communication to the society on Friday night. From some experiments made immediatly after your visit to Princeton in May last I was led to infer the existance of two kinds of induction and this fact I stated to you in a letter[6] I believe but it was not until this week that I succeeded in seperating them or that I found them simultaneously existing in the same galvanic current.[7] Respects[8] to Mrs B and Capt E[9] both are to accompany you to Princeton. I wish to show you my results in the electrical line therefore come!

---

* Since writing the account of the two kinds of induction I have found that the second kind although not screened by a plate of copper or zinc is affected by the introduction of a plate of iron. In the case of the first kind of induction iron acts as ordinary metal.

[5] Here, Henry refers Bache to a note in the margin of the first page. We have treated it as an author's footnote, as in the APS *Proceedings*.

[6] See Henry to Bache, May 20, 1839, above.

[7] Henry later modified his conclusions. After further experiments, he attributed Faraday's results to the hypothesis that an induced current consisted of two parts. Still further experimentation led him to the conclusion that the observed inductive phenomena were the result of the somewhat complex interaction of currents of differing intensity and quantity. See above, "Record of Experiments," May 13, 1839, footnote 2, and "Contributions IV," paragraphs 52, 81–83. A large "GRRRR" scrawled in the margin next to the letter in the Henry Library copy of the APS *Proceedings* is perhaps an indication of Henry's regret at having the letter printed.

[8] This final personal note to Bache was written on the outside of the letter, below the address.

[9] Unidentified.

TO WILLIAM VAUGHAN
The Pierpont Morgan Library

Princeton New Jersey
Oct 18th 1839

My Dear Sir

Your favours of the 20th of July the 5th of August and the 7th of September[1] have all been received. The last came to hand to day and as I intend to visit New York tomorrow I will call on Mr Vaughan and get the observations of the Edinburgh observatory[2] which you have been so kind as to forward to me. The papers from Mr Faraday and Wheatstone[3] have been receved.

I owe you many thanks for the copy of your book,[4] the perusal of which has given me both pleasure and instruction. I do not wonder that you are proud of old England and that you regard with pleasure the rapid improvements she has made during your own day in all the comforts of life and the developements of mind. It must be a very gratifying reflection that you have not only endeavoured to be useful to your fellow men but that your labours in this respect have been crowned with success. That individual is certainly fortunate who with the desire to do good possesses the talents and industry necessary to effect his object.

I visited your Brother a few days since and found him almost entirely recovered from the effects of his accident. All his wounds have healed except a small spot on the top of the head. He appears as cheerful and active as before and I agree with you in the wish that he could be made half a century younger, not to increase his usefulness, but to prolong it.

I have lately recived a letter from Mr Litton in Paris; he appears much pleased with his visit to Europe, and will doubtless make the best use of his time in the way of acquiring knowledge, useful to himself and our country. He mentions that my paper has been reported on and translated by the Philomathe. Society of Paris.[5] I am now busily engaged on another series and hope soon to be able to send you a copy. I receved a letter sometime since from Capt Ross[6] informing me of his intended voyage to the South.

[1] Not found.

[2] Probably the first volume of *Astronomical Observations Made at the Royal Observatory, Edinburgh*, published in 1838.

[3] Wheatstone's paper on binocular vision. See Henry to Wheatstone, [December 1839], printed below.

[4] William Vaughan, *Tracts on Docks and Commerce, Printed Between the Years 1793 & 1800, and Now First Collected; With an Introduction, Memoir, and Miscellaneous Pieces* (London, 1839); a presentation copy is in the Henry Library.

[5] Litton did not mention this in his letter of August 25, 1839 (printed above), his only letter from Paris which we have found. Proceedings of the Société Philomathique as reported in its *Extraits des procès-verbaux des séances* and in *L'Institut, Journal Général des Sociétés et Travaux Scientifiques de la France et de L'Étranger* do not mention Henry's paper. The Society recessed after the meeting of August 31 until November 9.

[6] Not found.

I rejoice that nothing has prevented his sailing and that the expedition has been fitted out in a style commensurate with the importance of the object and worthy the enlightened views of your government.

I expected a visit from Our Friend Bache and his wife this week but have recived a letter[7] from him stating that he was prevented from fulfilling his engagement by sickness. He has not enjoyed as good hea[lt]h since his return from Europe as before but I hope that after his report has been printed and he gets settled he will be better in health and spirits. His report will be through the press in a few weeks and will make a volume of more than 600 pages.

I have written to day to your Nephew[8] and sent to his care the model of an improvement in the Organ invented by a friend of mine,[9] to be presented to the London Society of arts. Please give my respects to Mr Solly and to his son Edward and accept for yourself the assurance that I remain with the highest Respect

And Esteem Yours &c
Joseph Henry

[7] Not found.
[8] Letter not found.

[9] John Meads. See Henry's letter to Stephen Alexander of April 16, 1838, printed above.

"RECORD OF EXPERIMENTS"

Henry Papers, Smithsonian Archives

Oct 24th 1839

Since the last experiment I have visited new New York to view the apparatus at the Fair of the American Institute[1] but on the whole I was disappointed in the exhibition.

Received a letter[2] from My Friend Bache this morning stating that my letter[3] anouncing the results of my last experiments those of Oct 15th to the Society had been listened to with much interest and that a new number of the proceedings was to be printed in order to announce me.

[1] The twelfth annual fair of the American Institute of the City of New York opened on Monday, October 7, 1839. It consisted primarily of agricultural exhibits, but also included other examples of mechanical ingenuity and invention. *Journal of the American Institute*, 1839, 4:561–562. For more on Henry's impressions of this fair, see below, Henry to Bache, October 28, 1839.

[2] Not located.

[3] See Henry to Bache, October 16, 1839, printed above.

Arranged coil no 1 in connection with the battery. No 2 on this to act as a screen. No 3 on this again to receive the induction. Put a needle in magnetizing spiral. Needle strongly magnetized at breaking contact with the battery. When the two ends of the intervening coil were joined no magnetism was perceptable. No magnetism at making but strong at breaking. This is inconformity [with] my old experiments as described in my paper[4]

The same arrangement as before with the exception that for the magnetizing spiral the short galvanometer was substituted. The needle in this case was affected equally apparently at the begining and ending of contact and also when the ends of the screening coil were connected

---

[4] Although this appears to be a reference to "Contributions III," none of the experiments described in that publication corresponds precisely to the experiment in this entry. The ex-periment described in paragraph 68 is similar in structure, but there Henry attempted to screen shocks, not magnetism.

"RECORD OF EXPERIMENTS"
Henry Papers, Smithsonian Archives

Oct 25th 1839

Made a coil of hoop iron, connected it with the battery. Broke contact with file. Shock from long helix placed on top of iron very strong. Interposed Coil no 2 ends joined no shock. Ends seperate shocks tolerably severe. Hence the screening with an iron coil the same as with the copper. The coil of iron was not more than 15 feet long perhaps a greater length might have acted differently.[1]

Arranged the coils so that no 2 was in contact with the battery. The iron coil on this and helix no 1 on this. The ends of the helix were connected with the long wire galvanometer. The ends of the iron coil were then joined; the contact made. The galvanometer was deflected in the same manner as if a plate of copper or a ribbon of the same metal were interposed. The ends of the iron were next seperated. The same result [pro]duced. It appeared

---

[1] Henry is trying to isolate and test all the possible variables which might affect the screening of induction. Here he has tested whether the composition of the conductor of the primary current would have any influence. A marginal notation to this paragraph shows Henry alert to other possible variables: "Compare this with copper, same length at making." We have been unable to discover whether Henry ever actually carried out the experiment suggested in the margin.

that if any difference existed it was that the action was a little stronger when the ends were opened but I am not certain of this[2]

It would appear from these experiments that when the current is passing through a coil of iron no peculiar transverse action is produced more than in the case of a coil of copper wire under the same circumstances.[3]

Made to day a differential galvanometer of about 30 turns each strand. Also differential magnetizing spiral.

There is a difference in most cases between the two inductions (Oct 15th):[4] one is produced in a definite time and the other is instantaneous. Perhaps this difference may exist even in the induction where both shocks and motion of the galvanometer is observed. The one only affects the galvanometer because it is of some duration the other has such intensity that no effect is produced.

[2] This paragraph was also annotated in the margin, as Henry reminded himself of the limitation of this experiment: "In this experiment the effect on the shock was not noted by interposing the iron coil with the ends open and shut and in comparison with the copper coil."

[3] In the margin Henry included a reference to the "Record of Experiments" entry of April 22, 1840 (printed below). There Henry recorded the results of experiments using iron plates as screens.

[4] A reference to the "Record of Experiments" entry of October 15, 1839 (printed above), especially the conclusion of experiment 4.

"RECORD OF EXPERIMENTS"
Henry Papers, Smithsonian Archives

Oct 26th 1839

Coil no. one was arranged perpendicularly [to] the horizon between coil no 3 & 4 which were attached to the differential galvanometer. Between coil no one and coil no four coil no 2 was interposed so that by uniting the ends of the latter the screening influence would be exerted.

* The battery used in all the experiments thus far in these researches (Oct. 1839) was one of the divisions of the large battery. Observing to day that the action was very feeble I ordered the old acid to be thrown out when it was discovered that one of the hand vices used to make the connection had fallen into the acid and had been acted on by the acid in a singular manner. The iron was so desolved as to exhibit the stria of the metal. The sketch in the margin showes the appearance of the nut which before the action of the acid was perfectly smooth. This resembles Mr Daniels dissection of alum[1]

[1] J. F. Daniell found that when alum was partially dissolved in water, its internal structure manifested itelf in embossed geometrical figures on the surface. Acid exposed the crys-

The two coils were then so adjusted in reference to distance that the two induced currents passing in different directions could not move the needle. The ends of coil no 2 were then joined so as to produce the screening influence the needle still remained stationary shows that the screening influence amounted to nothing.

To exhibit the effect of the other kind of induction the galvanometer was removed and its place supplied with a differential magnetizing spiral. A needle placed in this became strongly magnetic at the moment of breaking contact but exhibited little or no magnetism at the beginning of the battery current when only one of the coils was attached. When both coiles were attached so that the currents passed in opposite directions around the needle then no magnetism was developed. While the distances were preserved at which this effect was produced the coil no 2 acting as the screen was closed when the needle was strongly magnetized by a current from no 3 as determined by the direction of the polarity of the needle. The coil was used in the two previous experiments in preference to a plate of metal because I have always found that the screening influence of it is greater than that of a plate

The action was varied by substituting for coil no 4 helix no 1 and removing coil no 3—also in substituting for the differential the long galvanometer. The current was formed not by breaking or making contact but by immersing the battery into the acid.[2] No screening could be observed. The needle moved in one direction when the battery was plunged in and in the other when drawn out. This appears to be a modification of the induction produced by the motion of a helix near a coil through which a current is passing. I forgot to mention that the interposed coil was closed and afterwards opened the same effect however was observed in both cases.

While the arrangement of the last exp remained the same with the exception of a change for the galvanometer of a magnetizing spiral no magnetic effects could be produced either with a short or long spiral.[3] Arranged coil no 1 coil no 2 on it and the latter connected with coil no 3. On this was placed Helix no 1 which was attached to the galvanometer. With this arrangement a very feeble action was observed on the needle at making

talline structure of metals. Daniell, "On Some Phenomena Attending the Process of Solution, and Their Application to the Laws of Crystallization," *The Journal of Science and the Arts*, 1816, *1*:25, 30–33.

[2] In the margin Henry summed up the experiment, writing "seacond current by gradually immersing battery." He added a cross-reference to the "Record of Experiments" entry of July 8, 1839. This cross-reference is inaccurate. Henry's earlier experiments on inducing currents by plunging the plates into the battery acid occurred on May 14, 1839 (see the "Record of Experiments" entry of that date, above), which is the entry just preceding that of July 8 in the notebook.

[3] Another summary marginal notation by Henry accompanies this experiment: "no magnet by immersing battery."

and breaking contact. That at breaking indicated a current in the direction adverse to that of the battery current, in accordance with the exp. detailed in my paper No 3.[4] No action could be observed on the needle at the moment the battery was plunged into the acid. The tertiary current produced in this way is too feeble to be rendered appreciable by this means.

Arrangement as before, except the tertiary current was induced in coil no 4 and was therefore a quantity current. The galvanometer of a medium number of turns was used, the action was slight but decided, and the same at making as at breaking without any diminution when coil no 5 was interposed with its ends joined.[5] The effect however was very different when the small magnetizing spiral was used, the contained needle in this case came out strongly magnetized indicating a current in the adverse direction to the battery current, but this effect was interely neutralized when the coil (no 5) was interposed.

The effect on the galvanometer appears to decline very rapidly with the currents of different orders.[6]

Next attached the small horse shoe magnet—see my paper no 3[7]—to the ends of coil no 2 which was placed on coil no 1 connected with the battery. The hor[s]e shoe became magnetic for the time, although in a fitful manner. The ends of the interposed coil no 5 were then joined, the screening influence was very perceptible, but was not perfect since the magnet showed some signes of magnetism, notwithstanding the screen. This is as might have been expected, since the same current which will deflect the needle is generally sufficient to develope magnetism in soft iron.

 Connected the hollow iron cylinder, which is surrounded with copper wire, with the battery. Put on this helix no 2 and outside of this helix no 1 and on either side of these coil no 3 & 4 so as to screen as perfectly as possible. The ends of helix no one was connected with the long wire galvanometer. The needle was thrown 180 degrees around at the making of contact and the same at breaking although the ends of all the wires and coils were joined showing that little or no screening took place.[8] The needle in this exp was very powerfully affected and the screening was not perfect with two coils

[4] "Contributions III," paragraph 92.

[5] Henry's marginal summation of this experiment was "galvanic current in the 3rd conductor, no screening."

[6] Henry published this conclusion as paragraph 24 of "Contributions IV."

[7] The horseshoe, used as an indicator of currents of considerable quantity, is described in "Contributions III," paragraph 12.

[8] Henry wrote in the margin that there "should be no screen with galvanometer," which we interpret to mean that Henry had concluded, at that point, that the effect of inductive currents on galvanometers could not be screened.

and the helix. The needle in the last trial whirled several times around at making and also at breaking.

Attempted by putting on another coil to render the screening more perfect but did not succeed

Observed that at each breaking of the battery current which surrounds the soft iron hollow cylinder a spark of electricity passed between the wire and the iron of the tube. Probably due to imperfect insulation and when this is remedied the action will most probably be still more energetic. The defective screening in this case is probably due to the long wire of the inner helix offering some considerable resistance to the passage of the induced current.

TO ALEXANDER DALLAS BACHE
Retained Copy, Henry Papers, Smithsonian Archives

Princeton Oct 28[th1] 1839

My Dear Bache

Your favour of the [. . .][2] was receved a few days since but as I had just returned from a trip to New York and wished to make some further experiments I delayed the answer until to day. I have again gone over the experiments on which the results given in my last letter[3] were founded and although I have got some new light on the subject yet I have found nothing to alter the views I gave in my letter.

I agree with you in reference to the magnetic observatory and would prefer something of the astronomical kind which would be of equal or greater importance to the college and be particularly interesting to Mr Alexander.[4] I visited New York partly on business and partly to see the exhibition of american ingenuity at the Fair of the American institute.[5] I was however rather disappointed. There were to be sure many prety articles but in the way of substantial work and ingenious mechanical inventions the exhibition was far inferior to the one I attended at the Masonic Hall in Philadelphia.[6]

---

[1] The date is unclear and could possibly be the 25th. However the 28th agrees more closely with internal evidence.

[2] Left blank in the original. Bache's letter has not been found, but a portion of it is mentioned in "Record of Experiments," October 24, 1839, above.

[3] October 16, 1839.

[4] Presumably a reference to facilities for Princeton.

[5] See "Record of Experiments," above, October 24, 1839.

[6] One of the Franklin Institute Exhibitions, the most recent of which was held in 1838.

I almost always return from New York dispirited in the way of science. I am there thrown as it appears to me amoung all the Quacks and Jimcrackers of the land—I am disgusted with their pretentions and anoyed by their communications. How different is my feelings on a return from the [city] of Brotherly love! ! ! There is there jealousy and rivalry but also science and intelligence, and speculation and money not the only things which occupy the mind.

I stopped with our friend Dr Torry. He intends <*re*>moving to Princeton next summer if a suitable house can be procured. There is a great stir about the Photograph and perhaps not less than 20 persons are engaged in attempting to bring it to perfection. I saw several tolerable specimens but none whic[h] could be called good. A book has lately been published on the process and translated from the french into English.[7] I saw Bailey[8] of West Point. He has just returned from a long tour to the west and has brought with him a collection of fossil infusoria from beyond the Mississippi. Should you have an opportunity of sending a package to Erenbergh[9] Prof B would be pleased to forward to him some specimens.

Dr Torrey informed me that there is a Brother of Dr Reed of Edinburgh in New York in very indigent circumstances.[10] He came to this country a year or two ago, took rooms for the purpose of giving lessons in practical chemestry but has met with little or no encouragement—and is now almost in a starving condition. He has with him a little son 5 or 6 years old and unless he can get into some employment for the winter he will be in a very bad condition. Should you know of any situation in the way of practical chemestry, an assistant to a lecturer or in the brewing line[11]

See Bruce Sinclair, *Philadelphia's Philosopher Mechanics: A History of the Franklin Institute, 1824–1865* (Baltimore and London, 1974), chapter 4.

[7] Daguerre's pamphlet revealing the secret of his photographic process, entitled *Historique et description des procédés du Daguerréotype et du Diorama*, was published in Paris on August 21, 1839, and almost immediately translated into English, German, Italian, Spanish, and Swedish.

Evidently unknown to Henry, Bache provided an abstract of the Daguerre pamphlet, sent to him from a scientific friend in Paris (Litton?), for Philadelphia's *United States Gazette* of September 25, 1839. Bache's abstract, reprinted in the *Franklin Institute Journal*, 1839, 24:209–210, is characterized by one source as the first American account of the Daguerreotype process. Julius Sachse, *Photographic News*, 1893, 37:295.

The arrival of Daguerre's publication aroused an immediate flurry of photographic activity in the United States, the details of which are presented in Beaumont Newhall, *The Daguerreotype in America*, 3d rev. ed. (New York, 1976), pp. 15–27.

[8] See above, Henry to Torrey, May 31, 1839, footnote 5.

[9] See Henry to Bache, March 23, 1839, footnote 2.

[10] Lawrence Reid, brother of the ventilation pioneer David Boswell Reid, whom Henry met in London in 1837. Lawrence (1811–1874), a graduate of the University of Edinburgh, eventually landed a position as Professor of Chemistry at the College of Pharmacy of the City of New York. Curt P. Wimmer, *The College of Pharmacy of the City of New York* (Baltimore, 1929), pp. 45, 47, 130, 194.

[11] The copy ends here in mid-sentence.

"RECORD OF EXPERIMENTS"
Henry Papers, Smithsonian Archives

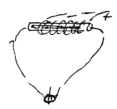

Oct 28th [1839] monday
Put a helix of small wire into the axis of the hollow cylinder of iron, attached the ends of the helix to the long wire galvanometer. Current from battery through wire around the hollow iron. Needle of galvanometer moved the same when the wire was disconnected hence infered that the movement was produced by the magnetism of the hollow iron although at the distances of 7 feet.

Placed the galvanometer at the distance of 14 feet, so that the needle was unaffected by the magnetism of the hollow iron. The needle then remained stationary when the battery current around the iron was made and broken. The helix of long wire was then withdrawn from the axis of the hollow iron and placed parallel with it along the outside. The needle was then slightly affected. This exp shows the screening influence of iron.[1] No shocks could be felt

---

[1] Summarized by the marginal notation "Iron does screen," this experiment provided information missing in Henry's earlier account of the two apparent types of induction. In his letter to Bache of October 16, 1839 (printed above), Henry only discussed the failure of copper or zinc to screen the induction from the galvanometer. In order to update his report, Henry added a footnote to the published version of his letter (*Proceedings of the American Philosophical Society*, 1838–1840, *1*:135–136), pointing out the screening ability of iron.

"RECORD OF EXPERIMENTS"
Henry Papers, Smithsonian Archives

Oct 29th 1839 Tuesday
Prepared to day and yesterday a bundle of iron wires about 17 inches long. The wire is [. . .][1] of an inch and the bundle consists of 137 seperate wires. They are not insulated for the 1st experiments. Around this bundle a wire 1/10 of an inch thick of copper was wound passing in two layers. The whole forms a powerful electromagnetic magnet.

Exp 1 When Helix no 2 was held near the end of the magnet so that the axis of the magnet was in the <*same*> direction of the axis of the helix the

---

[1] Henry left out the diameter of the wire.

shock could be felt when the helix was at the distance of 6 inches from the end. Same effect with helix no 1, also with helix no. 3 but less in intensity.

Exp 2 A cylinder of cast brass—the old pump chamber—was put over the magnet. Shocks were received through this from helix no. 1. The shocks  with this arrangement could not be felt when the helix was at *a* but as it approached the middle of the bar, the shocks became more intense and appeared to be most energetic at *b* the middle. The screening was far from perfect in this case.

Exp 3 Compared the hollow magnet with the one of many wires found the latter much more powerful the action was felt at a greater distance showing the advantages of a number of strands of wire.

Exp 4  Arranged the magnet of iron wires so that coil no. 3 might surround it. When the ends of this were closed, the shocks from helix no. 1 were much less intense than when the ends were seperate. The same effect however was not produced when the coil was put on the farther end; then the shock were quite intense.

Exp 5 When several coils were put on one end and helix no. 1 on the other, the shock was not quite as severe when the ends of the coils on the far end of the magnet were joined as when the same were seperated. The difference however was not as striking as I had anticipated.

A fact analogous to this is mentioned by Dr Page. He says that when the wire around one leg of a revolving armature on the magnetic electrical machine [is joined] the other ceases to give any shocks.[2]

Exp 6 Arranged the apparatus with pieces of wire so as get the effect on the needle. For this purpose put around it helix no. 2 and around this helix no. 1. The ends of the first were joined. The effect on the needle was powerful but not more so than in the arrangement with the hollow magnet or at least this was the appearance without very certain results.[3]

---

[2] As part of a series of experiments to illustrate the action of closed secondary circuits, Page joined the ends of the wire coiled on one leg of the curved armature of a magnetoelectric machine, while leaving the coil on the other leg connected to the break piece. He found that the resulting shocks were greatly reduced. However, when the ends of the first coil were open, the intensity of the shocks was restored. In the context of his experiments, Page interpreted these results as pointing to the advantage of short, straight armatures for magnetoelectric machines. Charles G. Page, "Magneto-Electric and Electro-Magnetic Apparatus and Experiments," *Silliman's Journal,* 1839, 35:257.

[3] Henry's marginal annotation for this experiment was "in accordance with other exp." Screening experiments with the hollow electromagnet occurred, for example, on July 21, 1838 (see the "Record of Experiments" entry of that date, printed above).

Made a very powerful tirtiary current by putting coil no. 2, 3 & 4 on the wire magnet and connecting all the ends of these with coil no. 1. On the latter was placed helix no. 1 which was again connected with the long galvanometer. The needle was only slightly agitated as if affected by two forces one tending to urge it in one way the other in the other. It appears to me at this stage of the inquiry that the induction which acts on the needle partakes of the nature of a continued current and as such like the original current from the battery it produces an induction which does not change its direction as the other induction does. The secondary current being a mere wave, its induction will therefore have little of the nature of that of a continued current and hence little effect will be perceived on the needle.[4]

Next used for detecting the peculiar action of the tertiary current, a short wire galvanometer, but not the least effect could be observed, although the shocks were very intense the action was less than with the long wire and hence if a still longer wire were used probably an action might be detected.

Replaced the galvanometer [with] the long wire made a break in the tertiary current and put the two ends in acid. The action on the galvanometer appeared greater in this way than when the ends were joined in metallic contact not very descided however

The screening influence in this case appeared to be operating but very feebly. The direction of the current at breaking contact was the same as that determined by my former experiments namely—minus[5]

---

[4] Henry is by now certain that the tertiary current affects the galvanometer quite differently than the secondary. Not until October 30, 1840 (see below), however, does he fully work out a satisfactory explanation of the tertiary current and its effect upon the galvanometer.

[5] In a later annotation, Henry reported that he "repeated the exp with distilled water with different result. This was a tertiary current— the other exp alluded to was a secondary one." This annotation possibly refers to Henry's discovery that distilled water disrupted low intensity inductions, a discovery more fully developed in "Contributions IV," paragraph 50.

"RECORD OF EXPERIMENTS"
Henry Papers, Smithsonian Archives

Oct 30th 1839

Attached coil no. 1 to the battery, and placed a piece of iron in it split open. Connected this with the magnetizing spiral by two wires one from each edge of the opening in the iron. Made and broke contact several times with the battery but no magnetism could be perceived in the needle. Next attached the

Mr. Vaughan[1] seems to be in a fair way for recovery; but his attack has been a very rough one for a man of 85, and I fear he will hardly again be *qualis erat.*

[1] John Vaughan, Librarian of the American Philosophical Society.

TO ROBERT M. PATTERSON

General Correspondence, Records of the United States Mint at Philadelphia, Records of the Bureau of the Mint, RG 104, National Archives

Princeton Jany 29th 1841

Sir,

Your letter of the 27th inst. with the enclosed communication from the secretary of the Treasury was received yesterday. I accept with much pleasure the appointment of one of the commissioners to attend your next assay and will not fail to be in attendance at the mint on monday the 8th proximo at half past nine in the morning.[1]

With much respect
Your Obt. Servt.
Joseph Henry

[1] The minutes of the 1841 annual assay, signed by Henry and the other commissioners, are also in RG 104.

WILLIAM BURNET[1] TO THOMAS T. KINNEY[2]

Kinney Family Papers, New Jersey Historical Society

Princeton. Feb 3ᵈ 41.

Dear Friend and Class-mate.

According to your request, I will now let you know, what we are doing here.

[1] William Burnet (1820–1911), resident of Newark and member of the Princeton Class of 1841, was a friend and neighbor of Thomas T. Kinney, the recipient. Though Kinney was a member of the influential Burnet family of New Jersey (the great-grandson of Dr. William Burnet, member of the Continental Congress and Medical Director of the Continental Army), he had no direct relation to the author of the letter, as far as we know. Isabella Neff Burnet, *Dr. William Burnet and His Sons Jacob, Isaac, and David* (Charlottesville, 1938); William Burnet, *The Burnet Family History* (Asbury Park, New Jersey, 1894); *Princeton Annual Catalogue*, 1841; "William Burnet," Alumni Files, Princeton University Archives.

[2] Thomas Talmadge Kinney (1821–1900)

We have rec[d] two very interesting lectures from Prof Henry this week on Steam, with numerous experiments &c.[3] Prof. Henry leaves Princeton to-morrow for Phila—from which place; he will not return before Tuesday night.[4] Therefore we will not have another lecture from him, before Wednesday, he will have us on that day, and the remaining days of next week.

Dr Carnahan will have us, the remainder of this week and until next week Wednesday, on Moral Philosophy, giving us a lecture on it, in the morning, and a recitation in the afternoon. So if you wish to remain in Newark a week longer, you can do it without losing anything. The lessons in Moral Philosophy, you can get, when we review it.

Nothing new here. When you see Henry Roger[s],[5] I wish you would ask him, if he has any letters to send to me. We have had one lesson in Télémaque.[6] As we get along very slow in that book, you will lose very little, by not being here.

Yours
William Burnet.

---

was a member of the Princeton Class of 1841, and the son of William Burnet Kinney, editor of the *Newark Daily Advertiser*, Trustee of the College of New Jersey, and Henry's friend. *Henry Papers*, *4*:81n. Henry's personal interest (Kinney was Henry's assistant during his senior year) may have influenced the younger Kinney in his adoption of steam power in the presses of the *Advertiser* after his father left the paper to become Chargé d'affaires at the Kingdom of Sardinia in 1850. William H. Shaw, *History of Essex and Hudson Counties, New Jersey*, 2 vols. (Philadelphia, 1884), *1*:225; *DAB*.

[3] The student notebooks of A. Alexander Hodge and Frederick S. Giger at Princeton University Archives provide the content of the lectures. The notebooks are undated, but Hodge and Giger were both members of the Class of 1841, as were Kinney and Burnet.

Henry devoted seven lectures to steam this year, immediately after his lectures on heat. The steam lectures were experimental and technological in orientation. For example, steam tables were given, not as theoretical conclusions, but as the experimental results of a particular apparatus, which was described in detail. Large sections of the lectures dealt with steam engines, steam locomotives, steamships, and steam boilers, and their detailed description, operation, and history. Though Burnet refers to experiments, one cannot tell

from the notebooks which, if any, were actually demonstrated, and which only discussed. The lectures betrayed a certain amount of American chauvinism, with Henry proud of Fulton's achievement, certain that American locomotives and steamships were superior to European products, and eager to ascribe that superiority to the necessity for power and locomotion in a large and not yet developed country.

Both the Princeton University Archives and the Smithsonian Institution Archives contain student notebooks for a range of years. Weiner, "Joseph Henry's Lectures," has a typescript of a syllabus, and a description of content based on an 1846 student notebook.

[4] The American Philosophical Society minutes show Henry in attendance at the February 5, 1841, meeting. Minutes, American Philosophical Society Archives.

[5] This person is tentatively identified as Henry Rogers, a Newark attorney. Newark City Directory, 1840–1841.

[6] Fénelon (François de Salignac de la Mothe, 1651–1715), *Les aventures de Télémaque, fils d'Ulysse* (Philadelphia, 1840) or one of the eight similar editions published in Philadelphia from 1827 to 1839. The text, a didactic prose poem written in 1699, was in common use in the nineteenth century in teaching French, an elective subject at Princeton at least since 1829.

FROM BENJAMIN SILLIMAN, SR., AND
BENJAMIN SILLIMAN, JR.[1]
Henry Papers, Smithsonian Archives

Yale Coll N Haven Feby 8th 1841

Dear Sir

Yours of the 28th came duly to hand[2] for which accept our thanks. Before this you will have recd the Jany N° of the Journal & by this mail No 81 is sent to Dr Maclean as you request, & the future Nos will follow. On the 18th we leave this for Boston to be absent until April, visiting Phil[a] befor returning to attend the meeting of Geologists to be held there.[3]

Dr Hare has communicated another long letter to Prof Faraday (Sir M.)[4] It will not appear before July. We recd it only today & have not yet read it.

It will be as well to give the constant battery the go by perhaps now. It is pretty late in the day to do any thing about it.[5]

We are pained to hear the death of Dr Green announced in the papers. How & of what Disease did he die. Will you not have the goodness to furnish a brief notice of his life or at least of his death* for the obituary of our April N°. He has been the contributor of many articles on Trilobites to its pages.[6]

We are much obliged by your attention to our prospectus.

Very truly & respectfully
Yours ever
B. + B. Silliman

N.B. We will reengrave the cuts of your new article[7] & thus save the trouble wh occurred before.

* & labors in science

[1] This letter is not in the handwriting of Benjamin Silliman, Sr. The hand may be that of his son.

[2] Letter not found.

[3] The second meeting of the Association of American Geologists was held in Philadelphia in early April 1841. Benjamin Silliman, Sr., chaired the meeting.

[4] Robert Hare, "Second Letter to Prof. Faraday," *Silliman's Journal*, 1841, *41*:1–14. L. Pearce Williams discusses Hare's importance to Faraday as a stimulus to revision and clarification of his theoretical views in *Michael Faraday* (New York, 1965), pp. 306–307, 309–311, 365, 373–375, 379. See also Hare to Henry, October 14, 1843, printed below.

[5] Silliman had offered to reprint Henry's 1835 article on his convertible (not constant) battery.

[6] Jacob Green, a friend and colleague of Henry's since his Albany years, died on February 1, 1841. For the obituary, see below, Henry's reply of April 26, 1841, and Silliman's letter of May 17, 1841.

[7] "Contributions IV: Electro-Dynamic Induction."

FROM LUKE F. NEWLAND[1]
Henry Papers, Smithsonian Archives

Albany 12th Feby 1841

My Dear Sir

Knowing as I do the value of your time and the super-abundance of your occupations, I would not needlessly intrude upon you even the trouble of reading a letter, were it not concerning an affair in which I feel most deeply interested and in which I hope to awaken your sympathy before I have done.

The matter concerns my wifes brother David[2] and as you may not be aware, precisely, of his present situation in health and circumstances it will be proper to state them briefly.

After an entire suspension of the use of his voice for more than a year, he gradually began to recover it so as to converse first in a low and at last in a full audible tone. He then began to use his voice in public, first in small places such as schoolhouses and for a few minutes, and afterwards in larger places of assembly and for longer periods of time. Last year he preached an ordination Sermon in Philadelphia, which effort was too much for him, and at a later period he took upon him the whole duties of a days services in a church at Newburgh and was materially injured by it. A medical *friend* whom he had the opportunity of consulting, on understanding that he had been in early life afflicted with asthma, and was still somewhat troubled with it, candidly told him that he must give up all idea of ever returning to the stated work of the ministry, and assigned as the reasons the following, viz. That after recovery from the throat complaint, when such recovery does take place, the muscles of the throat remain stiff and difficult of action, and require an extraordinary supply of air to force them into motion, that the disease of asthma is a thickening of the membrane that forms and divides the air cells in the lungs and this from its nature forbids, the necessary supply of air from being obtained.[3] The result of all this is that he must find

---

[1] An Albany jeweler and shopkeeper. *Henry Papers*, 2:72.

[2] Newland's brother-in-law, David Law Proudfit (1810–1847), Professor of Biblical Literature at the Theological Seminary of the Associate Reformed Church of New York from 1840–1842, subsequently edited *The Christian Instructor* and sold books. Kenneth Hasbrouck, *Hasbrouck Family Genealogy* (New Paltz, New York, 1961), p. 634.

Proudfit is revealed as a friend of Henry's in a later letter (December 19, 1846, Henry Papers, Smithsonian Archives), in which he asks for a recommendation for the position of chaplain at West Point.

[3] Although not specifically linked to asthma, a common occupational disease among ministers of mid-nineteenth-century America was follicular inflammation of the throat and air passages, or "Clergyman's Sore Throat," which could ultimately result in total loss of the voice. Various causes were blamed for the disease, including overwork, constrictive clothing, consumption of excessive amounts of tea

some other occupation of a literary kind than preaching or all the benefit of his education, his great natural powers and constitutional habits of studious industry must be lost.

It is true he has been appointed a professor of Theology in the Seminary of Newburgh, that he has performed its duties with distinguished success and great acceptability, but these are empty honors indeed, when they cannot pay the little salary which is attached to the appointment.

I state what I know to be the opinion of competant judges when I say that David Proudfit might without presumption aspire to a Professorship in Moral & Mental Philosophy, or in the antient Languages (Hebrew included) in any College in the Union.

I have recently seen that there is a Professorship of Moral Philosophy and some others vacant in the University of Virginia.[4] I have reason to believe that a word from *you* in that quarter would be of essential service. Can you and will you make an effort to serve an excellent and most worthy man?

No one knows of this letter and that and your answer shall be alike secret (if you desire it) should you oblige me with a reply.[5]

> With great respect
> I am
> My Dear Sir
> Yours very truly,
> Luke F. Newland.

---

or coffee, and chronic indigestion. Incidences of the disease declined as ministers simply began taking better care of their voices. James H. Cassedy, "An American Clerical Crisis: Minister's Sore Throat, 1830–1860," *Bulletin of the History of Medicine*, 1979, 53:23–38.

[4] There was no vacancy. George Tucker served as Professor of Moral Philosophy from 1825 until 1845, when he was succeeded by William H. McGuffey. Thomas Perkins Abernethy, *Historical Sketch of the University of Virginia* (Richmond, 1948), p. 14.

[5] Neither Henry's reply nor a letter of recommendation has been found.

HENRY NOTEBOOK ENTRY
Commonplace Book [10615], page 199, Henry Papers,
Smithsonian Archives

February 17, 1841

Beot and Becquerel have made experiments of a very interesting nature on the phosphorescence produced by discharges of electricity. Will the same effect be produced by the magneto electrical machine of Page (Try the exp. Feby 17ᵗʰ 1841). See Becquerel vol 6 p 265 &c.[1]

It does take place. Try the phosphorogenic properties of different deflagrations, such as mercury, copper leaf, gold do &c.

[1] Henry is citing the section on phosphorescence in A.-C. Becquerel's *Traité expérimental de l'électricité et du magnétisme* (1840, 6:259–319). In 1839 he had read an account of Becquerel's experiments on phosphorescence produced by electrical discharge as reported in the *Comptes rendus (Henry Papers, 4:231).* Becquerel and Biot interposed various substances between the discharge and the substance to be made phosphorescent and concluded that the cause of the phosphorescence was not the light from the discharge but rather a new type of radiation which Becquerel termed "phosphorogenic emanation."

Henry demonstrated phosphorescence to his students on February 25 (below), and made preliminary announcements of his experiments to the American Philosophical Society on April 16 (*Proceedings*, 1841–1843, 2:46) and to Benjamin Silliman on April 26 (below). It was not until the spring of 1843, however, that he recorded a series of experiments on phosphorescence which culminated in a paper to the APS (*Proceedings*, 1843, *3*:38–44).

In most of his experiments Henry used a Leyden jar to produce the discharge and sulfuret of lime (calcium sulfide) as the phosphorescent substance. He interposed various solids and liquids to test their permeability to the emanation and confirmed Becquerel's finding that electrical light and the phosphorogenic emanation differed in their ability to pass through the same substances. After examining the reflection, refraction, and polarization of the emanation, Henry concluded that although the emanation often acted like ordinary light, it was not identical but rather a distinct radiation.

"RECORD OF EXPERIMENTS"
Henry Papers, Smithsonian Archives

<March 14> Feby 25ᵗʰ 1841[1]

I gave this evening a lecture on electrical light[2] and showed for the first time the interesting experiment of Becquerel in reference to Phosphorescence by the electrical discharge[3]

A quantity of Homburg's phosphorous was prepaired by calcining a quantity of clam shells with an equal quantity of sulphur.[4] A small quantity of this article was placed in two paper trays—each of about 2 inches square. The one of these was covered with a thin and very transparent piece of

[1] Henry changed the date from March 14, that of the next entry in this notebook.

[2] Probably to the students of his natural philosophy course.

[3] See above, Henry Notebook Entry, February 17, 1841.

[4] Henry misnamed his substance. Homberg's phosphorus (after Wilhelm Homberg, German chemist [1652–1715], *DSB*) was calcium chlorate, though at the time it was known as calcium chloride (*chlorure calci-* que). Henry's chemical procedures yielded Canton's phosphorus, calcium sulfide (after John Canton, English natural philosopher [1718–1772], *DSB*), which was widely discussed in contemporary literature. J. J. Berzelius, *Traité de chimie*, 8 vols. (Paris, 1829–1833), 2:361, 4:62; William Thomas Brande, *A Manual of Chemistry* (New York, 1821), p. 63; *Encyclopaedia Britannica*, 8th ed., s.v. "Light," by T. S. Traill, especially pp. 456–457.

glass, the other with a piece of rock crystal of several times the thickness of the glass but of about the same transparency. The two were placed side by side on the table of the universal discharger and immediatly under the balls of the discharger so that the light from the discharge between the balls would equally illuminate each. When the discharge was made from a single galon jar the room being darkened the phosphorou[s] under the rockcrystal was seen to glow with such a brilliancy as to render it visible in the most distant part of the lecture room—while that under the equally transparent glass was dark and indicated no phosphorescence.

This experiment may be varied in reference to different kinds of light also in regard to the fact of the polarization or not of the emination which produces the phosphorescence[5]

[5] For Henry's concern with polarization, see Experiments in Optics, May 1841, and his letter to John Vaughan, June 18, 1841, both below.

Immediately below this "Record of Experiments" entry, Henry wrote in parentheses, "See my paper on this subject." This note clearly referred to "On Phosphorogenic Emanation," a paper delivered at the centennial celebration of the American Philosophical Society and abstracted in the *Proceedings* (1843, *3*:38–44). For the chronology of Henry's work on phosphorescence, see Henry Notebook Entry, February 17, 1841, above.

TO JAMES HENRY

Mary Henry Copy, Family Correspondence, Henry Papers,
Smithsonian Archives

Feb. 25. 1841.

I see by the papers there is quite a strife between you Albanians and the Trojans relative to a bridge across the Hudson. In the report of the Corporation of 1814 (I think it is) the arguments appear quite conclusive that a bridge should not be built but time changes all things and perhaps the laws of damming ice and forming bars in rivers are no longer the same.[1]

[1] In 1814 began the first serious agitation for the construction of a bridge across the Hudson River at Albany. The citizens of Troy staunchly opposed the proposal, maintaining that the bridge would create ice-dams and bars in the channel that would hinder navigation from their city. After furious debate, a bill authorizing the construction of such a bridge was defeated in the legislature. The matter was brought up again in 1831 and repeatedly thereafter, again without a positive response from the legislature. The 1841 agitation was likewise fruitless, even though proponents of the project now maintained that modern techniques of bridge pier construction obviated the problem of ice-dams. Finally, in 1856, a bill was passed authorizing the incorporation of the Hudson River Bridge Company to erect a bridge for railroad travel and transportation. The first Hudson River bridge at Albany was completed in 1866. The debates over this issue and their history were thoroughly reported in the *Albany Evening Journal*, which was pro-bridge, from February through May 1841. Arthur James Weise, *The History of the City of Albany* (Albany, 1884), p. 490. *Howell and Tenney*, p. 493.

TO ISAAC LEA[1]

Henry Papers, Smithsonian Archives

Princeton Feby 26th 1841

My Dear Sir

I am begining to be somewhat anxious about the publication of my paper,[2] and particularly since I have learned by a late no of the *Comptes Rendus* that M. Mattiucci[3] has announced to the French Institute that he is engaged in investigating the subject which forms the principal part of my paper.[4]

I was much pleased to find that Becquerel in his sixth vol. of Electricity and magnetism has translated the whole of my last paper and incorporated it in his work.[5]

With much Respect
Yours &c
Joseph Henry

[1] An eminent malacologist and Philadelphia publisher, Lea (1792–1886) was on the Committee on Publications of the American Philosophical Society. *Henry Papers*, 2:185.

[2] "Contributions IV: Electro-Dynamic Induction."

[3] Carlo Matteucci (1811–1868) was educated at the University of Bologna and the Sorbonne. Appointed Professor of Physics at the University of Pisa in 1840, he developed the first large Italian research institute for physics. His primary research interest was physiological electricity. *DSB*.

[4] Henry is referring to "Expériences sur les courants secondaires," *Comptes rendus*, 1840, *11*:240–243. Matteucci was in the midst of a series of experiments in which he paralleled Henry's work on induction from ordinary electricity. Similar conclusions were drawn regarding the direction of the induced current and the possibility of screening. Like Henry, Matteucci measured the variation caused by changing the intensity of the discharge or the distance between the spirals. There is no doubt, however, that Henry had secured priority this time.

[5] Becquerel's chapter on self-induction and secondary induction by a current appeared in the second part of volume 5 of *Traité expérimental de l'électricité et du magnétisme* (Paris, 1840), pp. 87–106. While not literally translating "Contributions III," Becquerel did present all the salient features of Henry's work. He introduced his presentation with the comment that "les résultats auxquels il [Henry] est parvenu sont d'une telle importance, particulièrement en raison de l'intensité des effets obtenus, que je crois devoir les exposer ici avec quelques détails" (p. 87).

"RECORD OF EXPERIMENTS"

Henry Papers, Smithsonian Archives

March 14th 1841

The idea has occurred to me that the phenomenon of the change in the directions of the currents with a change in the distance can be explained by the fact discovered by Mr Wheatstone in connection with the action of the spiral which contains the needle. 1st the ending induction in the case of ordinary elect should be as powerful as the beginning. Since the wave <*meets*> arrives last at the middle the two halfs of the wire must be in different states hence if the + be the most powerful the — minus will be nuteralized and a + current produced when the two are very near but a — minus current will appear when the two conductors are far apart on account of the tendency of the spires of the helix to produce an opposite kind of magnetism.

Perhaps the two ends of a long wire may indicate different kinds of induction[1] ⎯⎯⎯⎯⎯⎯⎯⎯⎯⎯⎯ Try this experiment

[1] The reference was to Charles Wheatstone's "An Account of Some Experiments to Measure the Velocity of Electricity and the Direction of Electrical Light," *Phil. Trans.*, 1834, pp. 583-591, on which Henry made reading notes (*Henry Papers*, 2:491-493). He explicitly copied the last page of the article, where Wheatstone said: "The disturbance of electrical equilibrium in a wire communicating at its extremities with the two coatings of a charged jar, travels with equal velocity from the two ends of the wire, and occurs latest in the middle of the circuit." Now, six years later, Henry tried to use this observation to explain the different directions of induced currents at different distances from the primary current. The question had devilled him in "Contributions III" and "Contributions IV: Electro-Dynamic Induction," and resulted in the theory of oscillatory discharge of "Contributions V: Induction from Ordinary Electricity; Oscillatory Discharge."

In this entry, Henry's musings amplified on Wheatstone's conclusions by considering the two arms of the circuit as being in two different electrical states. But after that point his explanation became confused: the account of the positive induced current had nothing to do with that of the negative, and neither was linked to Wheatstone's idea. In his final comment, Henry merely reiterated his original thought: that the fact of different electrical states in the same wire at the same time *might* be used to derive different inductive states at different distances from the primary conductor.

WILLIAM B. KINNEY[1] TO THOMAS T. KINNEY
Kinney Family Papers, New Jersey Historical Society

NewArk, Monday night, March 15th. [1841]

I was prevented from devoting the accustomed time to you last night, my very dear son, by my friend Mr Miller,[2] the new Senator, who came in from Washington on Saturday evening, and remained with me till this morning. And I have but a moment now to write. If you find, as it would seem

[1] See *Henry Papers*, 4:81n.
[2] Jacob Welsh Miller (1800-1862), U.S. Senator (Whig) from New Jersey, 1841-1853, was a lawyer in Morristown and a member of the New Jersey Assembly and New Jersey Council prior to entering the Senate. *Biographical Directory of the American Congress.*

by your letter, that your extra attendance upon Prof. Henry seriously in-terferes with more important duties, suggest it to him *courteously*.[3] He undoubtedly intended to compliment you in inviting you to wait on him, & doubtless supposes it a benefit, whatever you may think of it. And it is in fact a privilege to be with an accomplished philosopher, whose name is in high repute among men, familiarly. You should, therefore, in consulting your own influence be scrupulously respectful towards him. That is at once your duty & interest. To gain his confidence & respect is an important point. You can say therefore that having a speech to write, which requires all the time that you can possibly spare from the indispensable studies of your class, you are constrained to ask to be allowed to forego the pleasure of serv-ing him, if another can as well supply your place, until some future time. This would be respectful, conciliate his regard, and secure your object. We must learn to stoop to conquer. To conciliate without compromising princi-ple is a great art: an art by which much may be accomplished.

I am thinking of a trip to Washington. Uncle & Aunt B. are there at the White House,[4] & I may go on for a few days unless they conclude to come to NewArk. When does your vacation commence?[5] I long to see you, and if I go to Washington will let you know in time to meet me at the depot. It is uncertain however.

I have much to do yet before retiring, and it [is] now near midnight, so once more good night dear Tom.

Very tenderly
Wm B. K.

Tuesday Morn^g
P.S. It snowed so severely this morning that I did not get out to mail this, and therefore send it by the paper package. It is the severest snow storm of the season.

[3] The younger Kinney was Henry's assistant during his senior year. William W. Shaw, *History of Essex and Hudson Counties, New Jersey*, 2 vols. (Philadelphia, 1884), *1*:225.

[4] Probably Senator Jacob and Rebecca Bur-net, the uncle and aunt of William Burnet Kinney through his mother Hannah Burnet. Jacob Burnet (1770–1853) was born in Newark and was Senator (Whig) from Ohio, 1828–1831. Afterwards, he practiced law in Cincin-nati, and was President of the Cincinnati Col-lege and Medical College of Ohio, and of the Cincinnati branch of the Bank of the United States. Burnet was at the White House to visit President William Henry Harrison, also an Ohio Whig, whose administration was inaugu-rated March 4, 1841, and whom Burnet had succeeded as Senator from Ohio in 1828. *Biographical Directory of the American Con-gress.*

[5] The winter term of 1840–1841 ended April 15, 1841.

FROM HENRY JAMES[1]
Henry Papers, Smithsonian Archives

5 Washington Place, N York
March 15. 1841

My dear friend:

Chilton,[2] I have no doubt, begins to hate the sight of me by this time, so now I will address headquarters at once, and inquire whether "Professor Henry ever designs showing his face in this city again?" I have done nothing but open Chilton's door with this enquiry all winter, letting in a tremendous draught of cold air every time, and interrupting a hundred abstruse calculations and preparations, till at length I fear they will feel it advisable to hand me over to a magistrate, as a nuisance. What think you of the enquiry? Will he come again or not? And if yes, when will he come? What has kept him all this time in Princeton? Why has he not come over before? Why has he not attempted our enlightening this winter by a lecture or two on some of the more knowable points of his electrical discoveries? We are capable of holding knowledge, when it is poured out into us, if we are not of acquiring it, and you are much mistaken if you suppose we would not be as boastful of the former faculty as of the latter. However this may be, I want to see you very much in my own house, at my own tea table, or dinner table, with my own wife, and all my own things around me, and have been much disappointed that I have not had the pleasure of so doing all winter. Come along then soon—and confess that next to your own house, and your own wife, and your own things, you would certainly be best satisfied with mine.

I write at this particular moment, at the suggestion of *Menaeas*, the Greek,[3] whose course of lectures has ended at the College, and who is an

---

[1] *Henry Papers, 1*:19.

[2] James R. Chilton, *Henry Papers, 2*:20n.

[3] Constantine G. Menaeos, enrolled at the College of Physicians and Surgeons in New York City during the academic year 1841–1842. He and a fellow countryman, Luke Oeconomos, graduated from Princeton in 1840. *Princeton Catalogue*, pp. 158–159; *Annual Catalogue, College of Physicians and Surgeons, 1841–1842* (New York, 1842), p. 7.

They were among the last of dozens of Greek students sent by missionaries in the late 1820s and early 1830s to receive an education in the United States. The students traveled at the expense of the American Board of Commission-

ers for Foreign Missions, and their education was underwritten by various groups sympathetic to the Greek cause. Most attended Amherst or Yale. Clifton J. Phillips, *Protestant America and the Pagan World* (Cambridge, Massachusetts, 1969), pp. 139–144.

At Princeton, the Nassau Hall Education Society, organized by students in 1821 to aid indigent youths deserving of a liberal education, appealed to the Trustees to supplement their efforts to support the two Greeks. The usual fees for tuition, board, rent and other expenses were waived by the Trustees, a course often followed for needy students. Report of the Board of Managers, Nassau Hall

utter loss what to do with himself for the future. He says you may have heard of some occupation for him in Philadelphia, which he may pursue in the interval of the Medical Lectures, and so find a maintenance. I would be glad to sustain him myself—but it is more than I can justly do, together with my other claims. I told him I would make the enquiry of you, whether you could advise any definite course for him, and of Prof. James Alexander[4] also. Will you not be good enough before you write me, and provided you are ignorant of any resource for him, to let Mr Alexander know of his situation; perhaps he may counsel some plan by which he may get along comfortably through the summer. Remember me very kindly to all of your family—& believe me Ever my dear

> friend,
> Yours most affectiona[te]ly
> H. James

Be sure to direct me to Washington *Place*, not Square. Recollect, when you come to town yourself, Washington Place comprises the *South* side of the two blocks between the University & Broadway.

Education Society, July 30, 1836, Princeton University Archives; Trustees' Minutes, 3:327, Princeton University Archives.

Oeconomos died of consumption May 9, 1843, in Alexandria, Virginia; Menaeos also died within several years of graduation. John Hall, ed., *Forty Years' Familiar Letters of J. W. Alexander*, 2 vols. (New York, 1860), 1:373; *Maclean*, 2:304.

[4] James Waddel Alexander, Professor of Belles Lettres and Latin at Princeton. *Henry Papers*, 2:177.

TO RICHARD TAYLOR[1]

Mary Henry Copy, Henry Papers, Smithsonian Archives

Princeton College of New Jersey April 9th 1841

My dear Sir. I am much gratified by the republication of my paper on electrodynamics in your valuable Journal and I probably owe to this circumstance that [of] the translation of it into German and French.[2] I now

[1] Henry had met Taylor, editor of the *Scientific Memoirs* and co-editor of the *Philosophical Magazine*, in England in 1837 (*Henry Papers*, 3:214, 257; 4:94-95).
[2] "Contributions III: Electro-Dynamic Induction" was published in the *Phil. Mag.*, 1840, 3d ser. *16*:200-210, 254-265, 551-562. Later French and German translations, whether based on the complimentary copies Henry sent abroad or on the *Phil. Mag.* version, appeared in Poggendorff's *Annalen der Physik und Chemie*, 1842, Ergänzungsband *1*:282-312, Becquerel's textbook (see above, Henry to Lea, February 26, 1841), and in the *Annales de chimie et de physique*, 1841, 3d ser. *3*:394-407.

send by the British Queen, a proof copy of the 4th no. of my Contributions and should you think fit to publish it you will oblige me by giving it an early insertion in the Philosophical Magazine. I send at present to Europe but the one number since I am desirous that the article should first appear in your Journal and thus be given to the world abroad through the most respectable medium. I wish however in the course of a few weeks to send a few copies to my friends in England in the way of compliment and therefore ask for the early insertion.[3]

I received yesterday through Dr. Bache the February no. of the Phil. Magazine and also the last no. of the Scientific Memoirs. I always look with much interest for the arrival of these works and generally get them either four or five weeks after their publication. I have been delighted with Ohm's paper on the galvanic current. We need no other evidence of the value of the Scientific Memoirs than the fact that so valuable a contribution should have so long been unknown to the English reader.[4]

My friend Dr. Hare has been ordered to England by his physician on account of his health. He started a few days since from Philadelphia for Liverpool. You will probably see him in a short time in London.[5]

I am sorry that there exists some cause of irritation between this country and England, in reference to the Boundary Question and the affair of McLeod but I feel assured that no serious difficulty will result. The intelligent and influential in this country are all in favor of a friendly intercourse with England.[6]

> With much respect,
> Yours &c,
> Joseph Henry.

[3] Henry didn't send a copy to *Silliman's Journal* for over two weeks (see his letter of April 26, below). He began sending complimentary copies in late April and early May. Because the part of the APS *Transactions* volume which contained his paper was not published until the end of the year, the "official" publication was preceded into circulation by the complimentary copies, and the versions in *Silliman's Journal*, April–June 1841, *41*:117–152, and the *Phil. Mag.*, June 1841, 3d ser. *18*:482–514.

[4] The last two parts of volume 2 of Taylor's *Scientific Memoirs* (1841, 2:401–436, 437–506) contained "The Galvanic Circuit Investigated Mathematically," a translation from the German of Ohm's *Die Galvanische Kette, mathematisch bearbeitet* (Berlin, 1827). Previously, scientists who could not read German had to rely on Moritz Hermann von Jacobi's 1835 exposition in French of Ohm's theory or an English translation of Jacobi, which Taylor had also published (*Scientific Memoirs*, 1837, *1*:503–531). Henry had first expressed interest in Ohm's Law in 1834. In 1837 Charles Wheatstone loaned him Jacobi's pamphlet so that he could make an English translation for his own use. See *Henry Papers*, 2:299 and 3:220.

[5] A letter written by Hare during his trip is printed below, August 11, 1841.

[6] In addition to the longstanding dispute with Great Britain over the northeast boundary of the United States, incidents such as the McLeod case further inflamed anti-British sentiment in the United States. Alexander McLeod was arrested in New York in November 1840 and charged with murdering an American during the Canadian destruction of the *Caroline* in American waters in 1837. Although

P.S. I reside forty miles from Philadelphia and therefore could not attend to the printing of my paper as well as I could wish. I have made a few verbal corrections and will be much obliged if you will give attention to these in the reprint.[7] I have another number under way and will send you a copy as soon as possible.[8]   J.H.

McLeod was eventually acquitted in October 1841, the case touched off violent Anglophobia in Congress and among the public. Parties on both sides of the Atlantic called for war at various points. The Webster-Ashburton Treaty of 1842 finally put an end to an era of hostility. Albert B. Corey, *The Crisis of 1830–1842 in Canadian–American Relations* (New Haven, 1941), especially chapter 9, and Howard Jones, *To the Webster-Ashburton Treaty: A Study in Anglo-American Relations, 1783–1843* (Chapel Hill, 1977), especially chapter 4.

[7] A proof copy of "Contributions IV: Electro-Dynamic Induction" in the Henry Library shows four minor corrections written in by Henry. The *Phil. Mag.* version includes three of them.

[8] We have not located any further correspondence between Henry and Taylor. The next communication by Henry to appear in the *Phil. Mag.* was his 1844 presentation to the American Philosophical Society on cohesion (*Phil. Mag.*, 1845, 3d ser. 26:541–543).

TO HARRIET HENRY

Family Correspondence, Henry Papers, Smithsonian Archives

Philadelphia April [19][1]
Monday morning 1841
At Mr Vaughans Room

My Dear Wife

Stephen wrote on saturday and I now occupy a few moments of leisure to assure you that those at home are not forgotten. Stephen and myself have been very much occupied. The meeting at the society passed off very well and Stephen made so good an impression that Dr Ludlow[2] gave him quite a warm congratulation on his success.[3] *Do you not think he is in some danger of becoming quite conceited?*

---

[1] Henry erroneously dated this letter April 20; the postmark reads the nineteenth, a Monday in 1841.

[2] Ludlow was Provost of the University of Pennsylvania and an old family friend from Albany (*Henry Papers*, 1:106).

[3] Although Stephen Alexander had been elected a member of the American Philosoph-

ical Society in October 1839, he was formally introduced and signed the laws at the meeting of April 16, 1841. He made a communication on a meteor he observed at Princeton on March 15. Henry briefly mentioned repeating experiments of Becquerel and Biot on phosphorescence. APS *Proceedings*, 1841–1843, 2:43–46.

We have thus far been almost continually at Dr Ludlows. We went to Dr Cuylers Church and after service spent the evening at the Drs.[4] His daughter who was sick is much better and has walked out several times. You probably heard from Stephens letter that Jane Cuyler had lost her child. She is much more recconciled to the loss than her husband is.[5] He was much attached to the child and thinks it took cold by being placed on the floor on some occasion. Stephen and myself took breakfast this morning with old Mr Vaughan. This morning was the first that Mr Vaughan had met any of his Friends at Breakfast.[6] While I am writing this letter he is giving Stephen a long account of olden times. We are to dine at Bache's and then to go with him to the Girard College in the afternoon. In the evening we have an engagement for a meeting at the observatory to test the new tellescope.[7] Stephen appears to enjoy his visit very much. I have called on Dr Hodge[8] and he has directed to take some simple medicine and to remain in the city for a few days. I hope however to return to Princeton on Wednesday. I feel better now than I have done in several weeks.

Dr Ludlow as usual has been very kind and Mrs L[9] was almost inclined to be offended that you had not come along.

I have spoken for a bible for Mary and made some inqueries relative to the health of the children. I hope that with the fine weather they will improve and that you will all be in much better health and sperits when I return than when we left. There is to be a greate parade tomorrow in the way of funeral solemnities. All business will be stopped and the stores closed.[10] My coat will cost 26 dollars and is to be finished on Wednesday afternoon.

Kiss the little ones for me and I will repay you with interest in the same currency when I return.

> In haste my Dear Little
> Wife I am as ever
> Yours only

[4] Cornelius C. Cuyler, pastor of the Second Presbyterian Church of Philadelphia and also a family friend from Albany days (*Henry Papers*, 2:267n).

[5] Jane Cuyler was married to Joseph Patterson, a Philadelphia merchant and banker (*Henry Papers*, 2:422n).

[6] i.e., the first since being ill.

[7] An eight-foot equatorial, with movement regulated by clockwork, which had been made for the Central High School Observatory by Merz & Mahler of Munich. The superior quality of this refractor and of an Ertel meridian circle, which also arrived in the fall of 1840 but was left unmounted for several years, led to further importation of German telescopes by American observatories. Franklin Spencer Edmonds, *History of the Central High School of Philadelphia* (Philadelphia, 1902), pp. 86–91. Elias Loomis, *The Recent Progress of Astronomy* (New York, 1850), pp. 165–168.

[8] Hugh L. Hodge, Philadelphia physician and brother of Charles Hodge of Princeton (*Henry Papers*, 2:241n).

[9] Anna Ryley Ludlow, an old friend.

[10] The ceremonies were for the late President William Henry Harrison, who had died on April 4 after only a month in office.

FROM ENOCH HALE[1]
Henry Papers, Smithsonian Archives

Boston April 19, 1841

My Dear Sir

You whose engagements keep you familiar with the knowledge of general science & the progress of discoveries, must be content to be *pumped* sometimes, by those of us who can only occasionally turn aside from our professional labors to investigate some particular topic or to make some partial observations. This is my apology for asking your assistance on two or three points. I remember, you mentioned in conversation, some one, who had extended D͞r Wells' observations on the subject of Radiant caloric in the production of Dew.[2] Will you do me the favor to tell me who has done this (for I have forgotten) & where the paper is to be found, or if in a separate work, its title. I think you also told me that some observations have been made in or near Paris on the quantity of Rain at different elevations.[3] I have the same request to make in regard to these, that you will inform me where the account of them is found. I would not thus trouble you, but in the presumption that your familiarity with the facts will enable you to answer my inquiries with very little inconvenience. I am about to communicate to our Academy a paper on meteorological observations, & another on the quantities of Rain at different heights, & although I have no design of going very extensively into the observations of others, I do not wish to write in entire ignorance of them.[4]

[1] Enoch Hale (1790–1848), nephew of the Revolutionary patriot Nathan Hale, was a prominent Boston physician whose scientific interests extended beyond medical research. Before receiving an M.D. from Harvard in 1813, Hale attended Silliman's chemistry lectures in New Haven. Following graduation, Hale practiced medicine in Maine, where he was encouraged by Benjamin Vaughan to study meteorology, particularly in connection with epidemics. In 1818 Hale moved to Boston where he remained for the rest of his life as a leader of the medical community. *DAB.*

[2] William Charles Wells, *Essay on Dew*, first published in 1814, was regarded by Henry's contemporaries as a model of a scientific investigation using the inductive method. J. F. W. Herschel, for example, recommended it as "one of the most beautiful specimens we can call to mind of inductive experimental enquiry lying within a moderate compass" (*A Preliminary Discourse on the Study of Natural Philosophy* [London, 1830], paragraph 168). Two editions (London 1818

and 1866) are in the Henry Library. Wells concluded that dew was condensation of water vapor on a body when it became colder than the surrounding air by heat radiation. Although many investigators studied heat radiation in connection with dew, Henry later singled out Macedonio Melloni for verifying and extending the work of Wells. "Meteorology in Its Connection with Agriculture," Part IV, *Report of the Commissioner of Patents for 1858: Agriculture* (Washington, 1859), p. 456.

[3] Probably Arago's observations at the Paris Observatory which were published in the mid-1820s and later discussed by James D. Forbes in his "Report upon the Recent Progress and Present State of Meteorology," *BAAS Report, 1831 and 1832* (1833), p. 250.

[4] Neither paper was published in the *Memoirs* of the American Academy of Arts and Sciences. Related manuscript material survives in the Academy manuscripts on deposit at the Houghton Library, Harvard University.

My wife[5] & I often find occasion to recal your visit here with much pleasure. I beg you will remember us kindly to professor Alexander; & she desires to be remembered particularly to Mrs Henry, & to her mother & Aunt.

I hope you have rec[d] notice of election into our Academy, a long time ago. I should not allude to the election, but that our corresponding Sec[y] has sometimes been oblivious of his duty in giving notifications. The election took place nearly a year ago.[6]

very respectfully & truly yours
Enoch Hale

[5] Hale's third wife, Jane Murdock.

[6] Henry was elected an Associate Fellow of the American Academy of Arts and Sciences on May 26, 1840. His acceptance letter, however, is dated August 29, 1843 (printed below).

FROM ALEXANDER DALLAS BACHE

Bache Papers, Smithsonian Archives

Philad. April 21. 1841.

Dear Henry.

In reference to the Albany observations, will you take charge of inquiring of Dr. Hawley[1] whether Prof. Forbes' wishes can be met?[2] Prof. F. says:—
"I know not whether you can assist me in procuring the regular series of the "American Meteorological Observations (in the State of New York I mean) "which I have received *down to 1837* thro' the kindness of Dr. Romeyn "Beck & Prof. Henry,—but not since.[3] The importance of these you may "conclude from the circumstance that I received lately from Prof. Dove of "Berlin a very anxious request to complete for him four years of the Ameri-"can Temperatures which he could not procure in Germany, in England, "or in America (being out of print).[4] Fortunately I was able to supply him

[1] Gideon Hawley, Secretary of the Board of Regents of the University of the State of New York. See *Henry Papers, 1*:50. No record of Henry's request was found, but see Beck to Henry, October 4, 1841, below.

[2] James D. Forbes, Professor of Natural Philosophy at Edinburgh University (*Henry Papers, 1*:437–438). Forbes made his request to Bache in a letter of December 8, 1840 (RH 1208, Rhees Collection, Huntington Library).

[3] Henry had sent Forbes the reports for 1835 and 1836, as indicated in a letter of June 7, 1836 (*Henry Papers, 3*:74), and four earlier numbers on June 30, 1834 (*Henry Papers, 2*:204).

Henry met Forbes in London, while on his European trip, but they apparently did not

communicate again until Forbes directed his meteorological requests to Henry. On January 3, 1842, Forbes wrote to say that the packet of observations that Henry had sent was destroyed at the London Post Office, and to request a replacement (Forbes Papers, St. Andrews University Library). Henry replied on July 2, 1842, printed below, saying he would send the material by a courier, Mr. Theodore L. Cuyler, then embarking on a trip to Scotland.

[4] Heinrich Wilhelm Dove (1803–1879) was a long-time professor at the University of Berlin, with a special interest in meteorology. A prime example of a Humboldtean scientist, Dove prepared maps of mean temperature and wind patterns for Europe and the New World.

"with the years he wanted & I am now having them copied to send to Ger-
"many. This shows the advantage of a complete set, & I hope you will assist
"me in carrying on mine."

Would not Dr. Hawley use his influence to procure a reprint of the earlier
volumes of the part of the Regents Reports relating to meteorol! obsn's?[5]
If Forbes can be supplied I will forward the numbers to him with pleasure.

A few other points have suggested themselves in reference to <*the compilation of*> these observations:—

first, would it not be interesting to discuss particular storms as far as the
observations permit, & thus develope at once certain deficiencies as to the
time of recording the beginning & ending of rains &c. which would at once
appear.

Second,—would the character of the clouds & the estimate of the sky covered
in 8ths. be too much to ask to have added to the other observations.

Third, might not the force of the wind be estimated & recorded without
adding too much to the labour of the observers.

Fourth, is it impossible to have observations of the barometer at these
points. The legislature of Penn[a] has appropriated to supply each county
with a standard barometer.[6] Why will not the New York legislature do
likewise?

Fifth,—remarks once for all, in order to explain the anomalous directions
of winds at the several places would be of high interest. The currents are
obviously in many cases determined by local circumstances the influences
of which are readily estimated. For example at West Point the Wind must
of necessity almost, be from a northern, or a southern quarter.

Sixth,—would it not be desirable to enter on every register the *non-*
occurrence or occurrence of an aurora, to show that an observation has
been made in reference to the Aurora.[7]

His primary contribution was the 1827 Law of Rotation, which characterized the weather of any particular spot by the cyclic change of winds and storms, corresponding to the clockwise rotation of a weather system. Dove thought that wind was the independent variable in weather, and thus ran afoul of later theoreticians, who ascribed the causes of weather changes to temperature and pressure gradients. Dove was also the promoter of international exchanges of meteorological data, and international cooperation among meteorologists. He was Director of the Prussian Institute of Meteorology from its formation in 1849. *DSB.*

[5] From 1829 to 1850, meteorological data gathered at various academies in the state were appended to the *Annual Report of the Regents of the University of the State of New York.* See *Henry Papers, 1*:106–107. These took the form of temperature, rainfall, and wind direction observations from around the state, along with various digests of the data to give means and comparisons with past years. Also included were observations mentioning first frosts, auroras, spectacular storms, earthquakes, and the like.

[6] In 1837. *Henry Papers, 3*:370n.

[7] Bache was not the first to object to the means of data collection for New York State, whose reports gave only what could be ascertained from a rain gauge, wind vane, and thermometer. On both the national and state levels, there were numerous calls throughout

Enough you will say for once. Excuse haste & *a bad pen.*

Yours ever truly
A D Bache

---

the 1840s for a selective upgrading of observations. The American Agricultural Association suggested improvements in the system in a report of 1845 (Franklin B. Hough, *Results of a Series of Meteorological Observations, 1850–1863* [Albany, 1872], p. v). The Regents addressed the same issue numerous times in their annual reports to the legislature. In 1842, they "respectfully suggested that different instruments of observation should be placed in the hands of at least a portion of the academies now observing." *Fifty-Fifth Annual Report of the Regents of the University of the State of New York* (Albany, 1842), p. 10. (See also Beck to Henry, October 4, 1841, below.) The call was repeated in 1843, 1847, and 1848. In 1849, the Regents published, as an appendix to their *Report*, the "Official Instructions for Observers at the Meteorological Stations in the Kingdom of Prussia, by William Mahlman [1812–1848], Berlin, Sept. 1847." Mahlman's suggestions, not Bache's, formed the basis of the New York State observations throughout the 1850s and early 1860s, for in 1849 the state legislature appropriated funds for improving the observations.

Arnold Guyot (1807–1884), a colleague of Agassiz and resident of Cambridge, Massachusetts, was entrusted with the change, i.e., standardizing the instruments, selecting the locations of the improved stations, and training the observers, who became salaried. He thus acquired the skills which enabled him to perform a similar service for the Smithsonian in its meteorological program. Some of the New York stations were operating by 1850, most by 1851.

In reference to Bache's suggestions individually, the reformed New York State observations consisted of the following. 1) Particular storms were reported as before, that is, haphazardly, not regularly. 2) The relative cover of the sky was recorded, but decimally, as Mahlman suggested, not in eighths. 3) The force of the wind remained unrecorded. 4) Barometric observations were widely made. The different barometers were corrected to the same temperature, 32°F, but not for differences in elevation. The call for more barometric readings had been constant throughout the 1840s, and each year in that decade the records of four or five stations were published in the *Annual Report.* Far more barometers were

in use after the 1850 reform, for the major block in getting wider reporting was the cost of the instrument. 5) The anomalous direction of winds was not discussed, except to say that "the greatest deviation from a due west point is observed in valleys open to the north and south." (Hough, *Results,* pp. vii–viii.) 6) As before, "the important negative fact of the non-appearance [of an aurora] when the sky was clear was not noted." (Ibid., p. xxviii.) Thus some of the finer points of Bache's comments were lost, while the universal demand for barometric readings was met. In distinction to Bache's comments here, but in accordance with an 1839 proposal of the American Philosophical Society (*Henry Papers,* 4:318), the stations recorded the humidity of the air by means of a psychrometer, or wet and dry bulb thermometer.

The New York State system ironically gave better results and functioned worse after the reform than before. Though higher quality data were collected, their annual compilation and publication in the Regents' reports ceased. After 1863, the annual salary of the observers ceased as well and so did the observations. With great difficulty, Franklin B. Hough (1822–1885, *DAB*), a doctor, census-taker, and forester, obtained a grant from the legislature and published the fourteen years of records (1850–1863) in comparative and reduced form in 1872. Hough had similarly collected and published the returns for 1826–1850, in 1855.

The New York State observations declined, according to Hough, because the Smithsonian Institution was engaged in similar and co-operative activities. (Hough, *Results,* p. vi.) The New York observations were made on forms supplied by the Smithsonian, and were sent in duplicate to the Regents in Albany and to Washington. Similarly, four stations in New York—Albany, Buffalo, New York City, and Syracuse—had instruments supplied by the Smithsonian and reported directly to it by telegraph. Thus, we surmise, when the exigencies of war strained the finances of the state, the legislature saw no need to duplicate measures undertaken at the national level, and in 1863 the observations ended.

Guyot's role in the meteorological work of the Smithsonian will be discussed in future volumes of the *Henry Papers.*

TO BENJAMIN SILLIMAN, SR., OR
BENJAMIN SILLIMAN, JR.[1]
Daniel C. Gilman Collection, Eisenhower Library, Johns Hopkins University

Princeton April 26th 1841

My Dear Sir

I send you by this evenings mail a copy of my paper which I hope may reach you before you have finally arranged the matter of the next no. of the Journal.[2] On account of the closing of the vol. of the transactions my article, which forms the beginning of the next vol, has been delayed in printing much longer than I anticipated.

I have made several verbal alterations and corrections which you will oblige me in having attended to in the reprint. Also please to give the title which is at the head of the article and not the one on the title page.

My last paper on the subject of electro-dynamics[3] has met with more [suc]cess abroad than any other of my labours. Becquerel in his complete work on Electricity has inserted it entire instead of giving as he has done in other cases an account of the results. It has also been translated into German and an account of it given in the Italian[4] and Russian Languages. I have two other numbers of my contributions under way but I have been so occupied with college duties that I have found little time for research since last summer. By performing double duty last winter I have now however nearly finished my course of instruction for the present college year and hope to be able during the coming summer to resume my experiments.

You requested me to furnish a Biographical sketch of Dr Jacob Green for the next no. of the Journal. I have written to his Father, the Rev Dr Ashbel Green of Philad[a], on the subject and expect in the course of two or three weeks to be able to send you an article prepared by Dr Green which will answer your purpose. I have received from Dr G. Maclean the amount of one years subscription for the Journal which I will transmit to you with the dues from me by the first opportunity.

I have lately been much interested in repeating, with perfect success, the recent experiments of Becquerel and Biot on the properties of the emination, which produces the phenomena of phosphorescence, as in the case of calcined oyster shells exposed to solar action or an electric spark.[5] This emination passes with undiminish[ed] intensity through thick plates of

---

[1] This is how Henry addressed the letter.

[2] "Contributions IV: Electro-Dynamic Induction," appeared in the April–June 1841 number (*41*:117–152).

[3] "Contributions III: Electro-Dynamic Induction."

[4] e.g., in Majocchi's *Annali di fisica, chimica, e matematiche*, 1842, 7:165–177.

[5] See Henry's notebook entry of February 17, 1841, and his "Record of Experiments" entry of February 25, 1841, both printed above.

quartz or of crystalized gypsum, but is almost entirely interrupted by thin plates of the most transparent glass. It differs in its properties from both light and heat and appears to be a distinct principle. The further exploration of this subject will probably lead to some new and interesting results.

With Much Respect
Yours Sincerely
Joseph Henry

TO HANS CHRISTIAN OERSTED[1]
Oersted Papers, Royal Library, Copenhagen[2]

Princeton College of New Jersey
April 27th 1841

Respected Sir,

My Friend Mr Steen Bille[3] the Chargé de affaires from Denmark has kindly offered to transmit to you a small package containing some scientific pamphlets[4] which you will please to accept not on account of their value but as a token of my high respect for your scientific character. Science is of no country and the discoveries you have made do not belong alone to Denmark but to the whole human family. Your name is as well known in the United States of America as in any part of Europe. You possess in every part of the civilized world the enviable reputation of being the founder of a new science and all that has been done by others in the same line is but the exploration of the riches of the new region which you discovered. I hope you will pardon the freedom of these remarks since they are the spontaneous expression of the feelings of one who has been, and still is, much devoted to the study of your science.

I regret that I am unable to send you a full set of my papers. I have copies

[1] Danish physicist and natural philosopher. *DSB*. See *Henry Papers, 1*:158.

[2] A retained copy of this letter, containing an additional paragraph in which Henry expresses his skepticism regarding the use of electromagnetism as a power source, is in the Henry Papers, Smithsonian Archives. Oersted's copy, printed here, appears with slight deviations from this text in *Coulson*, pp. 147–148, and in M. C. Harding, *Correspondance de H. C. Ørsted avec divers savants*, 2 vols. (Copenhagen, 1920), 2:383–384.

[3] Steen Andersen Bille (1781–1860), Danish

career diplomat, was appointed Consul General to the United States from Denmark in 1830. He obtained permission from Congress to reside in Philadelphia, where he joined the American Philosophical Society (1832). Bille left the United States in 1857. *Dansk Biografisk Leksikon* (Copenhagen, 1979).

[4] According to a notation in his address book, Henry sent Oersted a variety of pamphlets, including "Contributions III" and "Contributions IV: Electro-Dynamic Induction." Henry's address book (Box 17, Henry Papers, Smithsonian Archives), p. [31].

only of the two last. My first experiments on Electro-magnetism were made in Albany state of New-York in 1829–30. Of these you have probably seen an account: they were on the developement of great magnetic power in soft iron; and were made before Dr Moll's experiments on the same subject were published.[5] I was assisted in them by Dr Ten Eyck.[6] I next invented a machine which moved by magnetic attraction and repulsion (See Silliman's Journal vol 20 for 1831 page 340).[7] This was the first movement of the kind ever made but I have received no credit for it in Europe. Professor Jacobi in his publications has never mentioned that I was before him in the invention.[8] I next discovered in 1832 the induction of a current on itself, or the means of getting shocks from a battery of a single element by means of a long conductor. I mention these results of my earlier labours inorder that you may identify the person who addresses you and because I think I have not received for them the credit in Europe which is my due.

You will find in the package a copy of the meteorological report made by the Acad[emies] of the state of New-York. These observations were established in 1825 by order of the directors of the academies under the superintendance of Dr Beck[9] of Albany and myself; they have been continued ever since. If you are interested in them, I will have your name put on the list of Persons to whom they are to be presented, and you will then receive them annually through Mr Bille. I have read with much interest and instruction your article on Electro-magnetism in the Edinburgh Encyclopedia[10] and I have lately imported from Paris one of your articles of apparatus for exhibiting to my class in "Physique" your discoveries in the compression of liquids.[11] I have also read with much interest your paper on whirl winds published in the Edinburgh Journal and also republished in America.[12]

[5] Gerrit Moll, the Dutch physicist whose 1830 article "Electro-magnetic Experiments" prompted Henry to publish the results of his research in electromagnetism. See *Henry Papers*, *1*:301–302.

[6] Philip Ten Eyck, Henry's successor at the Albany Academy. *Henry Papers*, *1*:214.

[7] "On a Reciprocating Motion Produced by Magnetic Attraction and Repulsion."

[8] For Jacobi, and Henry's problems with priority, see *Henry Papers*, 2:447.

[9] Theodric Romeyn Beck, *Henry Papers*, *1*:4–5.

[10] Oersted's article on electromagnetism is contained in the section on thermoelectricity in the *Edinburgh Encyclopaedia* (1830, third edition). Oersted concentrated primarily on the contributions of Europeans to the field.

[11] Henry purchased one of Oersted's apparatus from Pixii in 1837. See *Henry Papers*, *3*:541. Henry was to use this instrument not only for classroom demonstrations, but also in his own laboratory work; see below, "Record of Experiments," May 13, 1842.

According to the *DSB*, Oersted's work on the compressibility of gases and fluids was his second major research interest. Henry might have known of his work from the description "On the Compressibility of Water," *British Association for the Advancement of Science Report, 1833* (1834), pp. 353–360.

[12] "Ueber die Wettersäule" appeared as "On Water-Spouts" in *Silliman's Journal*, 1839, *37*:250–267. The article was also published in the *Philadelphia National Gazette and Literary Register*, August 28, 1839.

It would give me much pleasure to receive a letter from you. Any communication addressed to me and sent through Mr Bille will reach me safely.[13]

With much Respect I
am yours &c
Joseph Henry

[13] No reply, if any, is known to us. Harding (see above) cites some slight evidences of later interactions.

TO J. J. BERZELIUS[1]
Library, Royal Swedish Academy of Sciences[2]

Princeton College of
New-Jersey April 29, 1841

Respected Sir

I send to you through the Swedish *charge d'affaires*[3] in New York a small package containing a few scientific pamphlets. Amoung these you will find the two last nos. of my contributions to Electricity and Magnetism.[4] You have done me the honor to mention some of my earlier experiments in your valuable Annual Report on the progress of science and I hope you will find the articles I now send of sufficient importance to deserve a notice in the same interesting publication.[5]

I regret that I am unable to send you a complete set of my papers. My first experiments were made in Albany (NY) in 1829–30 on the development of magnetism of great power in soft iron. I afterwards invented the

[1] This is the only correspondence we have found between Henry and Jöns Jacob Berzelius (1779–1848, *DSB*), the eminent Swedish chemist.

[2] A Mary Henry Copy dated May 1, 1841, is in the Henry Papers, Smithsonian Archives.

[3] Gustavus de Nordin (or Gustaf af Nordin, 1799–1867). *American Almanac and Repository of Useful Knowledge for the Year 1841* (Boston, 1840), p. 107. Gustaf Elgenstierna, ed., *Den Introducerade Svenska Adelns Attartavlor* . . . , s.v. "Nordin."

[4] According to Henry's address book, p. [31] (Henry Papers, Smithsonian Archives), he also sent a Princeton catalogue, New York Regents' reports, reports on Oregon and the Northwest Territory, and a report on the preservation of timber by "Kyanizing" it, i.e.,

saturating it with corrosive sublimate (*Senate Documents*, 26th Congress, 1st Session, 1840, No. 428).

[5] Berzelius' annual reports (*Arsberättelser över Vetenskapernas Framsteg*, 1821–1848) were best known in German translations, most of which were done by his former student Friedrich Wöhler (1800–1882, *DSB*). The 1834 volume of the German edition is in the Henry Library. Berzelius mentioned Henry's two 1831 articles in *Silliman's Journal* on powerful electromagnets (citing specifically *19*:408 and *20*:201) in the 1833 volume (*Jahres-Bericht über die Fortschritte der physischen Wissenschaften*, *12*:45), and referred to Henry's ribbon coils in the 1839 volume (*18*:72). On the question of further references see Henry's letter to Torrey of December 20, 1841, below.

first magnetic machine which was moved by attraction and repulsion. I next discovered the induction of a current of electricity on itself or the method of giving shocks with a battery of a single element by means of a long conductor. This was in 1832.

I mention these results of my earlier labours inorder that you may identify the Person who addresses you and also because I think I have not had sufficient credit for them in Europe.

We are so far removed in America from the great centres of science that we have found it very difficult to make our labours known in Europe. Within the last two or three years however we have received more attention and since a visit which I made in 1837 to England and France I have found no cause to complain of a want of attention to my papers.

The German language is beginning to be studied very generally in our colleges[6] and the translation into that language of your interesting *annual report on the progress of science* is becoming extensively known amoung us. The French translation of your great work on Chemistry is on the shelves of the libraries of all our chemists.[7]

You will find in the package a number of the Reports of the academies in the State of New York on Meterology. These Reports were begun in 1825 under the direction of Dr Beck and myself of Albany and they have been continued ever since. If the articles will be considered of interest by you I will send a copy every year.

> With the highest Respect I
> have the honor to be
> your humble servt.
> Joseph Henry

To Professor Berzelius
Member of the Institu[te] of France &c
&c

[6] Following a period of relative ignorance of German language and literature in the United States, Harvard and the University of Virginia offered German as a subject in 1825. In 1835 Bache described it as "the unknown tongue" (*Henry Papers*, 2:325–326). In many colleges, as at Princeton, German was probably first offered as an elective if there was someone on the faculty who could teach it. Benedict Jaeger was apparently the first to teach German at Princeton in 1832 (*Princeton Annual Catalogues*, 1831–1847).

An article by C. H. Brigham, "On the Study of German in America," *The Christian Examiner*, July 1869, 87:1–20, reviews forty years' growth of German studies in America, from a time when "German studies were eccentric, the sign almost of a disordered mind; were discouraged by wise professors, and dreaded even by curious students" (p. 2), to a time when German had become "a necessity to a scholar in any department" (p. 18).

See A. B. Faust, *The German Element in the United States*, 2 vols. (1927; reprint ed., New York, 1969), especially 2:209–217, and Henry A. Pochman, *German Culture in America* (Madison, 1957), especially pp. 114–124.

[7] Berzelius' *Traité de chimie*, 8 vols. (Paris, 1829–1833), is in the Henry Library. Henry had long been familiar with the work. See *Henry Papers*, 2:189, 293–294.

TO DAVID BAILIE WARDEN[1]
Warden Papers, Library of Congress

Princeton May 1st 1841

My Dear Sir

Permit me to introduce to your attention and kind direction my young Friend and Pupil Mr R L Smith.[2] He goes to France for the purpose of instruction in Science and I hope he will make the best use of the many advantages which Paris offers in this line. He is a Gentleman of talents and generous feelings and I commend him to your regards.

I send by Mr Smith two copies of the fourth no. of my contributions to electricity and magnetism and I also send a copy of the same to your care for M Peltier[3] the electrician.

I receve the numbers of the Comptes Rendus pretty regularly through Mr Vaughan and I forwarded through him last year the amount of my debt to you for the work up to the time.

> With Much Respect
> Most Sincerely your Friend
> Joseph Henry

[1] The unofficial American cultural ambassador to France and liaison for American scientists. *Henry Papers, 3*:387.

[2] R. Lawler Smith, of Retirement Seat, Mississippi, was a member of the Class of 1841 at Princeton, but did not graduate. *Princeton Annual Catalogue*, 1841.

[3] Jean Charles Athanase Peltier (1785–1845) was a French experimental physicist. *DSB*.

FROM BENJAMIN SILLIMAN, SR.
Henry Papers, Smithsonian Archives

New Haven May 17, 1841

My dear sir

Your memoir was duly received & is in the printer's hands—we will attend to your wishes as regards corrections title page &c. The figures being few in number & not expensive we have directed to be recut. In future however there need be no difficulty in transmitting wood cuts from Phil[a] as Harnden's Express[1] (office corner of 3[d] & Chestnut Street Phil[a] & No 2 Wall Street New York) will transmit them to & from the New Haven Steam

[1] A service begun by William Frederick Harnden in 1839 to provide regular and reliable transportation of small packages. *DAB*.

Boat with perfect safety & our people here are very prompt and careful in delivering parcels. I am gratified but not surprised that your memoir was so well received abroad as it appeared to me to contain many extraordinary results and I trust you will go on like Faraday in a successful career of Discovery to which your summer of exemption from college duty will no doubt contribute. I thank you for the measures taken for obtaining from the venerable Dr Green a notice of his son. As it has not yet come to hand, it will be too late for July as that No is more than full but will I trust be in season for October. If in season it might perhaps be the leading article.[2]

I am anxious to know more of the emanation to which you allude and which causes phosphorescence. I have seen nothing of it and should be glad to receive a notice of the matter for the miscellany of the Journal. If different from light & heat what is it? Is it electricity or some new principle & if so what?

Dr Hare as you will see in the forthcoming N$^{\underline{o}}$ of the Journal has given an answer to Faraday. I was in Phil$^{\underline{a}}$ April 5 and just missed my old friend who sailed for Europe two days before—I regret to say in bad health. My son & his lady unite with me in kind remembrance to M$^{\underline{rs}}$ Henry & our friends the Macleans.

I remain my dear sir as ever

yours very truly
B Silliman

The money which you mention can be remitted by mail whenever it is conveni[ent]—the PM can frank it if he will—if not we will pay the postage.

---

[2] For some reason, no sketch of Jacob Green appeared in *Silliman's Journal*.

EXPERIMENTS IN OPTICS[1]
*Notebook [7170], pages [51-57], Henry Papers,
Smithsonian Archives*

[May 1841][2]

My exp with Babenet aparatus[3]

1 Interferance of light

Knife edge on end of ruler—prism of Pouillet[4] on middle—Lense longer

---

[1] The following are four consecutive entries from an undated Henry notebook. Pagination in this notebook has been supplied and refers to the double pages of our working copy. Thus the thirteen original pages of the notebook entries take up the six-and-a-half

focus on at about 30—screen behind beautiful fringes can be seen by the whole class.

2 Diffraction by small hole—Lense No 20 with focus of about ¾ inch placed on the end of the support—hole plate no 8 placed at about a foot from lense screen at distance of 8 feet concentric circles very distinctly seen. Lens does not appear to improve this much

---

sheets, numbered 51 through 57, of our working copy.

The material in these experiments, or, rather, perfected demonstrations, was in optics, a field outside Henry's primary research, but fully within his physics repertoire. Henry made these experiments in order to better understand the phenomena, especially in relation to the wave theory, and to be able to demonstrate them to his classes in natural philosophy.

These runs of experiments also indicate the extent to which Henry went back to his previous work and restudied, revised, and extended it. The undated notebook was probably started in the early 1830s. For the most part it contains reading notes on various papers. In early 1841 he began to restudy this work in various contexts. For example, the Wheatstone *Philosophical Transactions* paper on the velocity of electricity is abstracted in the notebook (pp. [5–7]), and formed the basis for Henry's speculations of March 14, 1841 (above). The early parts of the notebook also contain material on the magnetization of needles and on electroacoustics (pp. [8–10]), which were the major topics of Henry's 1841 summer researches. Most importantly, the notebook contains a great amount on optics. Much of this is background material, entered after he returned from his European trip in 1837, for it relates to optical instruments he had seen there. For example, Henry had an amanuensis prepare a copy of an article, "Polarizing Light," by J. F. Goddard (*Transactions of the Society for the Encouragement of Arts, Manufactures, and Commerce*, 1837–1839, 52:40–68, pp. [18–35, 57–60] of the notebook), which he had requested from John Vaughan on June 18, 1841 (see below). He queried the Philadelphia instrument collector, Charles N. Bancker, and prepared descriptions and operating procedures of Fresnel's prism, Nörremberg's polarizing apparatus, Soleil's monochromatic (sodium) lamp, Pritchard's polarizer, and (written in another hand) Babinet's diffraction apparatus (pp. [39–50]). Henry also added reading notes on Airy's ex-

planation of double refraction in quartz from the *Phil. Trans.* for 1833. These instruments and associated experimental techniques, coupled with his own knowledge and past observations, formed the basis for the demonstrations and researches given in these four entries.

While most of the information was apparently gathered in the late 1830s, Henry inexplicably waited until 1841 to do the experiments. Certainly he needed the apparatus which he had ordered in Paris. But this had arrived by 1839, when he mentioned a Savart polariscope, part of the order, in a "Record of Experiments" entry. (*Henry Papers*, 4:254–255.) Henry's intent was to perfect his technique in order to show the optical phenomena to his class in natural philosophy; most likely he waited until he had sufficient time to do an extended series of observations.

Henry's researches appeared in public only in his September 17, 1841, demonstration of optical apparatus, resulting in the publication, "On a Simple Form of the Heliostat," *Proceedings of the American Philosophical Society*, 1841–1843, 2:97–98.

[2] These experiments were conducted between May 20, when Henry returned from his trip north, and June 24, when he mentioned them in his laboratory notebook. "Record of Experiments," June 19 and 24, below. They inaugurated two months of sustained laboratory work; Henry did not teach in the summer term until his August geology lectures. Henry to Silliman, April 26, 1841, above; Henry to an unidentified recipient, July 1, 1841, Mary Henry Copy, Henry Papers, Smithsonian Archives.

[3] The first entry (pp. [51–53]) deals with the diffraction apparatus which Henry saw, described, and sketched when he visited Babinet. Henry ordered this instrument while in Paris. *Henry Papers*, 3:387–392, 543.

[4] Although we have not determined the form of the prism, the reference is to Claude-Servais-Mathias Pouillet (1790–1868) of the Sorbonne. *Henry Papers*, 3:365n; *DSB*.

3 With the hole in plate 7 same result

4 The plates with [?discs] on the 1 2 3 &c when placed behind the lense with short focus gave on a screen circular shadows surrounded with a ring of Light and a broad band of faint light within the geometrical shaddow

5 To show the exp of Grimaldie and Young[5] with two holes in a piece of lead the direct light of the sun must be used or a metalic mirror to reflect in the suns rays. The images cannot be made to overlap unless the image of the disc of the sun through a small hole be use this subtending the same diameter as the sun itself dilates so that the image from each hole overlaps the other

6 To show the fringes from one edge of a screen place cylindrical lense near the hole in the window—*screen* at the distance of 18 inches catch shadow on screen or wall at the distance of 8 feet.

7 To form the fringes with the horse hair no 11 put on the end of the scale either the cylindrical lense or the knife edge apparatus. Also place the eye glass behind and throw the image on a screen. If a plate of metal with a sharp and well defined edge be brought up near the hair on[6] one side the interior fringe disappears

8 To show the phenomenon of grating look at the bright image of the point of light from the solar microscope[7] with a telescope through a gause of wire. Through a cloath produces the same effect less distinctly

9 To exhibit the experiment with <*Fresnels*> Pouillet's prism put the knife apparatus on the end of the stand prism near middle eye glass on end screen at small distance—image very fine with sun—put screen on one side stripes disappear—put glass in the beam stripes throw on one side

10 To exhibit the experiment with the screen with two openings formed by two parallel wires and with sun light. Put the solar microscope into the window withe the lens of short focus so as to get a cone of light from almost a point—place the <*knife*> wire apparatus at a short distance before the object glass of a telescope which must be drawn out to distinct vision then two sets of bands will be seen the external broad and coloured which are

[5] Francesco Maria Grimaldi (1618–1663), Italian astronomer and optician, and Thomas Young (1773–1829), English natural philosopher, both *DSB*. The experiment alluded to is the interference of two cones of light emerging from circular holes in a screen.

[6] Henry wrote "one," which we changed to "on."

[7] The construction and operation of the solar microscope is explained with the aid of a clear diagram in W. H. C. Bartlett's *Elements of Natural Philosophy*, 3 vols. (New York, 1852), *3*:265–266.

those of diffraction and an other set narrow and dark and white within the luminated space these are the bands of interferance. When the glass is passed before the two openings no change is perceived—but when the glass is a cross one opening while the other is open then the fringes of interferance disappear. When one of the openings is closed with the <*wire*> frame which carries the glass then the fringes of interference disappear

I was much perplexed with the experiment. When I attempted it on the scale of Babenets apparatus the lense did not magnify sufficiently to exhibit the fringes of interference but only those of diffraction these are not affected by the interposition of the glass[8]

11 To show the grating spectrum throw in the beam of light by means of the microscope mirror. Let the beam fall on the prism (cylindrical)—place the graduated glass before the object glass of the telescope and the telescope at several feet distance behind the cylindrical lense or prism. The spectrum or rather spectra thus formed are most beautiful

Aragos Exp[9]

To show the experiment of the fringes thrown aside place the first stand near the end of the long tube on the long support place the stand containing the wires and the mica at the distance of 44 inches or their about and

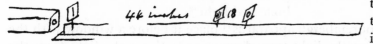

the stand with the eye glass 18 inches behind[10]

The fine fringes are those which are thrown aside

The fringes of interference are those which are from the two openings on the two sides of the middle wire. These are fine fringes—a small distance will produce sufficient deviation of the ray to give stripes

Colour of Depolarization[11]

The reason why the interposed plate shows no colour at certain possitions is that in these the plane <*of one*> of the wave<*s*> <*into*> which passes

---

[8] Immediately below entry 10, Henry added: "The reason why I did not see the interior fringes was that the eye glass was not sufficiently far behind. June 1843."

[9] This second entry (p. [53]) referred to experiments which are described in the *Encyclopaedia Britannica* article, "Optics," by David Brewster. See the eighth edition, volume 16, page 609. This was probably derived from the article "Light," by J. F. W. Herschel, in the *Encyclopaedia Metropolitana*, paragraphs 737–739.

[10] At this point Henry inserted, "If the eye glass is not sufficiently far behind the fringes will not be distinctly seen. See page but one before," a reference to his added notation, dated June 1843, of the previous entry (see note 8).

[11] For an explanation of this term, see *Encyclopaedia Britannica*, 8th ed., s.v. "Optics," by David Brewster, Part VII, Section VII—"On the Depolarization of Light." This third entry comprises pages [54–55] of the notebook.

through the polarizer allso passes through one of the planes of polarization of the interposed plate. All the light thus passes. When the plate is turned 90 degrees the same plane passes through the other plane of polarization of the plate and again the light all passes but when the interposed plate is turned 45° then the plane wave which passes the polarizer is divided into two one passing along the axis of great compression or least velocity the other along the axis of least compression and greatest velocity. These waves are at right angles to each other and consequently without the aid of the analyser cannot interfere. If however these waves are received on the analyser they will be resolved into 4, two vibrating in say a horizontal plane and two in a vertical.

<In one position of the analyser the horizontal> The wave which pases with the greater velocity and also the one which passes with the less is thus resolved so that the two horizontal waves will consit of one rapid and one slower wave. These two will then be in a condition to interfere. If the difference of the two paths be such as to produce an interferance of the red then we will have the complementary colour to red namely green. The rays will also be half a wave behin[d] because the first part of one wave and the second part of the same will be divided and again this will be divided again and the[12]

Polarized light[13]

1 To use the Nourembergh apparatus[14] place it before a window with the glass for polarizing the light turned up so as to throw the light from the clouds *down on the silvered glass*

It will then pass up through the eye pice or analyzer to the eye in a strongly polarized beam. To exhibit the beautiful colours of the irregularly anealed glass place the article on the mirror at the bottom look down on it through the tourmaline eye pice. The most beautiful desplay is shown when the analyzer or eye piece is turn so as to make the field of view dark

---

[12] The explanation breaks in mid-sentence. This is one of the few times that Henry expressed himself so clearly in the language of the undulatory theory of light. See *Henry Papers*, 4:xx.

[13] This fourth entry takes up pages [55-57] of the notebook.

[14] A Nörremberg polarization apparatus was ordered from Soleil Fils, Paris, when Henry was on his European trip. *Henry Papers*, 3:543.

Johann Gottlieb Christian Nörremberg (also spelled Noremberg, 1787-1862) was a land sur-

veyor, Professor of Mathematics, Physics, and Cartography at the military school of Darmstadt from 1823 to 1833, and Ordinary Professor of Physics at the University of Tübingen from 1833 to 1851 (*Poggendorff*). A description of his polariscope is found in Claude-Servais-Mathias Pouillet, *Éléments de physique expérimentale*, 4th ed., 2 vols. (Paris, 1844), 2:393. Henry's experiments and demonstrations dealt with the polarization produced from crystals, from anisotropic glass, and from the optical axes formed by heat and pressure.

2 To show to the best advantage the plate of *amathist* place this on the upper glass in the focus of a lense of short focus. The structure of the mineral will be shewn with great distinctness

3 To exhibit the colors of quarts place on the lower glass, the mirror, a circle of white paper 3/4 of an inch in diameter. On the glass of the stage a thick plate of quarts perpendicular to the axis. And on this place the prism of calcareous spar (or the one of quartz this is a borrowed article) look dow[n] on the disc of paper it will be seen double each image coloured with a shade the complement of the other. Turn the prism around and the colours will constantly change the image over lap when properly manage and at the contact show white colour

4 With this apparatus and the tourmaline analyzer the compression of glass exhibits a beautiful appearance. The slightest pressure with the screw is sufficient to develope the effect of the change of arrangement.

5 Also the effect of heat is shown on the square pieces of glass by dropping them into the square frame which has been heated with a sperit lamp
  So sensible is this apparatus that if the square pice of glass be placed on the lower glass (mirror) and then pressed with the finger and thumb of each ha[n]d so as to heat the angles the polarizing structure will be developed very perceptib[ly]

6 To show the colours of gypsum the prism must be cut into excedingly thin plates—this is perhaps best effected by means of a lancet

7 The bending of glass under the oblique glass of this apparatus with the force of the fingers exhibits the polarizing structure

8 To show circular polaration of quartze <*place the different sections of quartze*> put the tourmaline analyzer at the eye place the point at the zero of the graduated circle then turn the tourmaline until the field appears dark now introduce on the stage a plate of quartz the field will become light again and when the analyzer is turned to the right or left of its first position the image will [?again] become dark. The number of degrees through which the analyzer is twisted gives the amount of the circular polarization. If another pice of quarts cut in the same manner perpendicular to the axis be substituted for the last the degree of turning will be greater or less before the image again disappears according as the plate of crystal is thicker or thinner

June 18, 1841

TO JOHN VAUGHAN
Archives, American Philosophical Society

Princeton June 18th 1841

My Dear Sir

Will you do me the favour to send me for a few days the 52 vol. of the Transactions of the London Society of arts. I wish to consult a paper in it on the construction of an article for the Polarization of Light. It is in the volume for 1838 if I am not mistaken.[1]

I have been on a tour to the north since my last visit to Philadelphia. I hope to be able to visit you in a few weeks with a budget of matter for the society.[2] If you have any papers for me or numbers of the *Comptes Rendus* please send them by the Bearer Mr Cooley one of the Instructors in our College.[3]

In haste with
much Respect
Yours sincerely
Joseph Henry

[1] A communication by J. F. Goddard in the *Transactions of the Society for the Encouragement of Arts, Manufactures, and Commerce,* 1837–1839, 52:40–68, described a polariscope constructed by the author to be used with an oxyhydrogen microscope. Henry had the entire article, including diagrams, copied into the notebook he was using for his notes on light (notebook [7170], pp. [18–35, 57–60]). Other entries from that notebook are printed immediately above.

[2] Henry didn't attend an American Philosophical Society meeting until September 17, 1841, when he exhibited a heliostat. APS *Proceedings,* 1841–1843, 2:97–98.

[3] William Scudder Cooley (d. 1882) was a graduate of Princeton and at this time a tutor there. He later taught in Philadelphia. *Princeton Catalogue,* p. 141. Philadelphia City Directories, 1857–1878.

"RECORD OF EXPERIMENTS"
Henry Papers, Smithsonian Archives

June 19th 1841

Made a series of experiments with the Daguerre apparatus to determ if an impression could be made on a prepaired plate by means of the spark from the electrical machine. The apparatus employed was that belonging to a Person who was taking portraits in the village. It was well arranged and the plates prepared by the him[1] were very sensitive to solar radiation but no

[1] Henry intended to write either "by the person" or "by him," and combined the two forms.

effect could be observed although the operation was kept from one minute to five or six[2]

N B I made no experiments last vacation my duties had been so arduous during the winter that I was obliged to take a trip to the north in the way of recruiting[3]

---

[2] At this point, Henry wrote: "Afterwards suceeded with this exp. See vol 3nd p. 44." In this reference to experiments of May 11, 1843, printed below, Henry originally wrote "2nd" and then covered over the two with a three. The "phosphorogenic emanation" provided the context for these experiments as well as those of May 11.

[3] Henry used the word "recruiting" not in the sense of enrolling new students, but rather as a synonym for "recovering strength and health." *Webster's Third New International Dictionary.* He used the spring vacation of April 15 to May 20 to travel with his wife to Albany to visit his brother, James, and to New York City, where he stayed with John Torrey. Henry to James Henry, April [May] 20, 1841, Family Correspondence, Henry Papers, Smithsonian Archives. (Misdated April, the letter is postmarked May.)

"RECORD OF EXPERIMENTS"
Henry Papers, Smithsonian Archives

June 2<5>4[th] 1841

I commence to day the investigation of the subject of electrical induction. Since last Oct. I have been much engaged in College duties. My time has been almost constantly occupied until within the last four weeks since Dr Torrey commen[ce]d his summer course on chemestry. This time I have devoted to the study of light and to the repetition of the ordinary expermts on interference polarization &c.

I have succeeded in nearly all that I have attempted and have registered the processes employed in another book.[1]

Preparatory to the experiments on induct &c I arranged 7 cups of the constant battery—substituting for the bladder a cylinder of paper with a wooden bottom—the paper was cemented at the edges with sealing wax and the bottom which was formed of a piece of round stick was tied with wire at the lower end of the cylinder and made so tight as to hold water. The whole were charged with a saturated solution of sulphate of soda on the side next the zinc and a saturated solution of sulphate of copper on the side next the copper. This arrangement was made at the suggestion of Dr. Torrey but the effect appeared to be very feeble. A slight spark was produced with the large coil in the curcuit. When a small quan-

---

[1] For the notebook entries on light, see Experiments in Optics, May 1841, above.

tity of sulphuric acid, diluted with 12 times its bulk of water, was poured into the paper cells the action was instantly increased. The action appeared to be increased after the apparatus had stood some 20 minutes—the effect was however much less than with strong acid on each side of the diaphragm. The arrangement of the apparatus may answer pretty well for large batteres where the action is to be continued for some time

Placed rod of round iron ¾ inch in diamtr 3 feet long in thick wire spiral put microphone on the end—sound very distinct.[2] When the ends of outside coil were joined the sound decicededly less but not entirely neutralized.

When the large iron bar was put in no sound could be heard. The arrangement with the *microphone* is much superior to that with the plate of glass, a less sound is perceptible

Next with Dr Torrey made some comparative experiments on the action of 6 cups charged with paper, sulphate of soda, and sulph of copper, and six other cups with bladders, sul acid, and sul acid and sulphate of copper. The six first gave 5 cubic inches of gas in 3 minutes the 6 last gave the same quantity in one *minute*. The paper diaphragms appear to act tolerably well

With the six jars charged with acid and sul. of copper attached to the large coil no. 6. the <s> noise or sound from the rod of iron was like the stroke of a smal hammer—and when the rod was held in the hand at the moment at making and breaking contact something like a blow or concusion was felt in the hand. Dr T. compaired it to the sensation produced by a small shock. This effect might possibly be produced by the action of the wire on the iron in the way of attraction

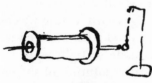

Suspended against the end of the rod which projected from the end of the large spool an ivory ball but could see no motion produced by the striking of the rod agans the ivory.

Large glass tube put into the large coil with this the sound could be heard at putting in as well as out.

---

[2] This was the beginning of a new round of experiments on electroacoustics, last investi- gated, as far as we know, on June 16, 1840. *Henry Papers*, 4:414–415.

When the discharge of the battery was sent through the out side wire of coil No 6 no sound was produced at begining the action but only at ending. Hence the length of the wire may be to <*long*> great for the [. . .][3] production of the magnetism on which the sound depends

N B This spool or reel consits of 9 wires each 60 feet long rolled around a cylinder of wood and each wire so soldered to the others, that the whole transmits a current as if <*of*> but one wire were used

When the glass tube wheld against the out side on the end of the iron rod the same noise was heard.

The sound was the loudest when the iron rod was suspended in the centre of the coil with the <*ele*> buttons of the microphone in the ears.

Whith the large iron bar the sound with 12 cups was very distinct. I should have mentioned that the last experiments were made with 12 cups

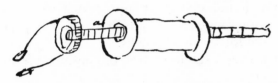

Large iron bar put into the middle of coil No 6. Helix no 1[4] was put on the end of this but no shocks could be felt. The helix was then moved up towas the end of the reel—when the shock became perceptible

The same effect was produced when the bundle of insulated wires were put in. When these projected about a foot beyond the reel then no shock when the helix was placed over their ends but when the whole was pushed in so that the helix was near the end of the reel a powerful shock was obtained

The bar in the above experiment was magnetic more powerful at the ends but it was also so along the whole length

With twelve cups the iron wires in the reel no 6 so that the end were in the plane of the endboard of the reel and the Helix no 1 placed on this— the shock at the making was feeble but at breaking quite severe. The wires were then taken out the intensity of the shock was now reversed. The more intense one was felt at the moment of making the contact although both were feeble. The shock is therefore not as much increased at the beg[inn]-ing by the induction of soft iron as at the ending. This is in accordance with results previously obtained.

Globule of mercury placed be[t]ween the two wires a palpitating motion took place on the principle of the little vibrating machine which I have described in this

---

[3] One illegible word.
[4] Henry appears first to have written "3" and then written over with "1".

book page [. . .]).[5] The spark and motion were produced at the positive pole of the battery. There was a small quantity of water around the drop as the power of the battery declined the effect could not be produced.

 Observed to day in using the <*g*> vol[t]ameter of Mr Faraday that the apparatus became boiling hot and this was the case 2 or 3 hours after the arrangement was put in operation. It is a well known fact that the action of the acid on the zinc in the generating cells generates heat but I have not before heard it stated that the same effect is produced in the decomposing cell as a liquid is converted into two gases. At first sight we might suppose that cold would be produced[6]

After the battery with acid as described on page [. . .][7] had been in action more than 3 hours, its decomposing power was again tested. The six jars then gave 4 cubic inches in a minute of the mixed gases. This battery was fitted up with bladders. It was found that the papers which were substituted for the bladders in the other set of jars stood very well. The paper was of the stout brown kind, used for wrapping books.

I will now set about constructing a single battery of considerable size with paper

[5] Left blank with a single parenthesis. Perhaps this was a reference to the entry for April 9, 1840. *Henry Papers*, 4:342–343.

[6] On the principle that heat is required to produce a gas from a liquid.

[7] Left blank—a reference to the beginning of this long entry, which took up five-and-a-half pages in Henry's notebook.

"RECORD OF EXPERIMENTS"

Henry Papers, Smithsonian Archives

June 25th [1841]

Made no experiments to day was engaged in directing the making of a larger single battery also made a model of a crystal of carbonate of lime to explain double refraction[1]

In the evening, returning from Dr Hodges[2] with Dr Torrey, we were much surprised to perceve something like a heavy shower when we were under the trees along the road but not in the open space. At the time the air was almost opaque with a dense fog but no rain was falling

[1] A reference to Henry's ongoing optical experiments (see Experiments in Optics, May 1841, above), and a further indication that one important purpose for doing them was to prepare for classroom demonstrations.

[2] Charles Hodge.

We attempted to make some observations which would tend to explain the phenomenon of the shower under the trees but not with much success. The cause of the fog was however readily made out. We placed a thermometer on the grass and found that it stood after a few minutes at the tempeatur of 72° Fah. The same thermometer swung in the air for a short time sunk down to 69 showing a difference of 3° between the temperature of the air and that of the ground. The vapour <*thus*> given off from the moist earth would thus be condensed and the fog formed in the same way that the fogs are generated over rivers the waters of which are warmer than the air immediately above. The temperature of the ground would be kept up by the non radiation on account of the fog. Perhaps the dripping from the trees may be explained on the principle of surface action the capillary attraction, or rather the attraction of cohesion would infilm the leaves with the water from the fog. This would attract other until the weight would form a drop which would fall and the dripping be thus produced.

The battery which was made on this day (June 24)[3] was formed of a cylinder of zinc of about 5½ inches in diameter one foot high; it was surrounded by copper with a diaphragm of paper between the two metals and then plunged into a stone-ware pot filled on one side of the paper with strong acid and on the other with the same adde[d]to Sul coper

[3] An obvious misstatement.

FROM THE SENIOR CLASS OF THE COLLEGE OF NEW JERSEY[1]
Henry Papers, Smithsonian Archives

June 25. 1841.[2]

The subscribers, members of the Senior Class, having heard of Prof. Henry's willingness to deliver a short course of Lectures on Geology, at the 9 o'clock bell, and being anxious to avail themselves of so excellent an opportunity of increasing their Knowledge of this branch of Natural Science,

[1] Fifty-three members of the senior class signed, out of the seventy-three members given in the 1840–1841 *Princeton Annual Catalogue.*
[2] The date, though clearly given on the document, is curious because at the faculty meeting of May 21, 1841, Henry was assigned the geology lectures. Faculty Minutes, Princeton University Archives.

present the assurances of their highest esteem to Prof. H., and request that the course may be dilivered at such time as his leisure will permit.[3]

A. J. M. Cumming La
Joseph M. Atkinson V<u>a</u>
Daniel A. Ulrich Penn<u>a</u>
J. Warren Royer Pa.
John T. Duffield Penn
C. C. Baldwin jr. N J
W<u>m</u> S Ward. N. J.
L D Potter N. J
N. M. Owen N. Y.
Fred<u>k</u> S Giger
Z. S. Claggett
John Linn
William B. Olds.
Robert R. Crawford.
Jno. O. Halsted
S. S. Hartwell
Chas. H. Parkin.
Saml Mott Leggett
James P. Miller.
John Rodgers
William Halsted jr
William Burnet.
Jno. T Nixon
W<u>m</u> W Scudder
Jona. T. Brown
W. C. Sturgeon
R. C. De Armond
Geo M Giger
Jn° N Houston
Edw<u>d</u> W. Scudder
James K. McCurdy.
Amzi Dodd.
Jn. M Ross

Wm M. Giles Miss.
James B. Dayton
J G Witherspoon
Francis Minor V^a
B. C Snowden
J. B. Gibson
E H. Bowen
Nathaniel Evans
Theo. Ledyard Cuyler
Thomas T. Kinney
Eli Whitney
John H Voorhees
J Craig Biddle
R. W. Walker
F. P. Blair
Felix Gorman
A. A. Hodge
John Sergeant jr.
William R. Phillips
J. J. Norcott

---

[3] These were the first lectures in geology presented at Princeton. While the Princeton faculty minutes indicate that Henry was requested to deliver six lectures, Henry's own notes indicate five, with the sixth possibly being "Geology and Revelation" (Arthur P. Molella et al., eds., *A Scientist in American Life: Essays and Lectures of Joseph Henry* [Washington, 1980], pp. 23–29). These lecture notes survive, but are undated and in many

variant and often fragmentary copies, which makes it difficult to know what the form was in 1841. Access to the 1841 lectures comes most easily through the notes of a student, George M. Giger (Presbyterian Historical Society, Philadelphia), even though the notes are incomplete. They consist of a last page and summary of lecture one, complete notes on lectures two and three, and an outline of lecture four. The contents of lectures five and six, on paleontology and on revelation, are known from Henry's notes in the Smithsonian Archives.

Henry's background disposed him to discuss physical geology to a greater extent than was usual in such courses. He presented Laplace's nebular hypothesis, backed up by William Herschel's observations, and discussed the temperature gradient in the earth's interior. In discussing strata, he followed Werner's system of primary (usually called by Henry "primitive"), transitional, secondary, tertiary, and diluvial and alluvial layers. He also followed Werner in ascribing stratification to the agency of water. Henry's discussion of unstratified primitive rocks placed their origin in the cooling earth, on the basis of Edward Hitchcock's *Elementary Geology* (Amherst, 1840; pages 201–224 were excised from Henry's copy and inserted in the lecture notes). Fossil-containing rocks were presented through the field of paleontology; Henry mentioned Cuvier's work and his classification of animals as vertebrata, radiata, mollusca, and articulata. In the sixth lecture, geology and revelation, he maintained that "geology rightly understood will be found to agree with the Bible rightly interpreted." ("Geology and Revelation," p. 28.) The lecture basically adopted a "two aspects" view of the problem of reconciliation, science dealing with phenomena and natural laws, religion with moral life.

From Henry's comments in letters (of August 10, 1841, printed below) and in his lecture notes, and from Giger's notebook, we know that he relied on Hitchcock's *Elementary Geology*, William Buckland's Bridgewater Treatise *Geology and Mineralogy Considered with Reference to Natural Theology* (Philadelphia, 1837), and the findings of the geological surveys of Maryland, New York, Virginia, New Jersey, and Pennsylvania. He also had printed in Princeton a sixteen-page glossary of geological terms, followed by two pages giving an arrangement of the plant and animal kingdoms according to Cuvier, and the stratigraphy of the earth, correlated with fossils.

In all, Henry's lectures were a concise, complete, and well-organized introduction to a rapidly growing and contentious subject. Henry was conversant with the most recent literature, and presented a view which adhered to established authorities fairly closely, that is, Werner, Laplace, and Cuvier. However, he also conveyed a feeling for the richness of the sources, and the excitement in piecing together and arranging the material which lay literally beneath his students' feet.

"RECORD OF EXPERIMENTS"

Henry Papers, Smithsonian Archives

June 26th (Saturday) 1841

Put 12 cups of the battery in operation—put into the spool No 6, 5 wires of soft iron—the ends of the secondary wire being connected with the Galvanometer. The deflections at putting in and taking out the end of the wire from a cup of mercury forming one of the poles of the apparatus were nearly equal particularly when the poles had been previously joined with a short slip of <*cop*> lead to discharge the accumulation

The merely putting in and drawing out of the bundle of wires (the whole bundle) produced a greater deflection of the needle than the making or breaking of the battery contact

When the wires were not in the spool the shock at making the contact, with the arrangement of 12 cups was the more intense. When the iron wires were put in, the shock at breaking was the most intense—the intensity however of boath was increased by the reaction of the iron <*to*> & that of the ending the most +

In these experiments a very singular phenominon was observed. When the bundle of wires was inserted into the axis of the spool and the two handles brought into contact with the tongue a series of pulsations were felt as if the battery gradually accumulated <*in*> electricity and when the quantity increased to a certain degree a discharge took place. The effect was quite novel and will require further investigation

Placed hollow gun barrel in the spool noted the deflection of old ribbon galvanometer—it was 60°. Next placed in a bundle of wire of little less diameter the deflection was now 52°. The handles were substituted and the shock to be softened was passed through a cup of water the shock with the wires was much the more intense

 Long bar in large spool and thick wire coil over this with its ends attached to the galvanometer (Clarks). When the coil was placed at the end of the bar farthest from the spool—7° deflection— one foot from do—18°, 2 feet 30°, 3 feet 60°—4 feet over 90°

Made an arrangement to get the current of the third order by attaching the ends of the outer wires of the long spool to the ends of helix no 1. Helix no 2 being placed in this and the handles attached to its ends the tertiary shock was very severe[1] and it was observed that the right hand and arm were affected when the battery current was begun and the left hand when the same current was stopped. This effe[c]t took place with two assistants and it would seem to furnish a new method of determing the direction of the shock the motion involuntarily given to either hand may serve as an indication of the direction of the current

With the primary current the effect was also the same but on account of the severity of the shock the difference became imperceptible

---

[1] The long spool was doubly wound: the inner wires carried the primary current, the outer the induced secondary. This secondary current was also routed through helix no. 1. When helix no. 2 was placed on top of this, a tertiary current was produced in it.

"RECORD OF EXPERIMENTS"
Henry Papers, Smithsonian Archives

June 28th 1841
Monday

To repeat the experimnt of the effect of putting a steel magnet into a coil, so as to react on the secondary current see page [. . .][1]

For this purpose put two small coils on a magnetized file and connected these with 2 cups of the Daniell battery also placed a third coil of wire between the other two on the same file and connected it with <*the*> Clark<*e's*> Galvanometer

Magnet put in with currents Non conformable and conformable and contact made with the battery[2]

1	Non conformable *contact* made		15°	+
	2nd Do	Do	8°	+
2	Conformable	Do	15°	+
	2nd Do	Do	10°	+
3	Non conformable	Do	14°	+
	2nd Do Do	Do	10	+
4	Conformable contact made		15	+
	2nd Do	Do	10°	+
5	Non conformable Do		15°	+
	2nd Do	Do	10°	+
6	Conformable	Do	14¾	+
	2nd Do	Do	10°	+
7	Non conformable		14¾°	+

From these results it appears evident that the effect depends on the change in the state of the magnetism and it is indifferent in which direction this is. The second contact in each case gives less induction than the first and this appears to be due in one case—the conform<*ed*>able—to the increase of the strength of the magnet which arrives near to the point of maximum magnetism for the force of the coil and therefore when the next induction is made the change in the magnet will not be as great as before. There is not magnetic force left for so great a developement. Also in the noncon-

---

[1] Left blank. A reference to the experiments of June 4, 5, and 6, 1840. *Henry Papers*, 4:403–409.

[2] Conformable in this case meant that the magnetic field generated by the coil was of the same polarity as that of the magnetized file within the coil. Non-conformable meant it was of opposite polarity. The two contacts were two sequential connections of both small coils to the battery.

formable case—the fall of the magnetism is the greater at the first and the curve of descent will be less the next time

The file was magnetized more strongly and the contact made—file conformable

Deflection   8°

This in accordance with the above view.

If a magnet could be perfectly saturated before being placed in the coil no increased effect would be produced and if a pi[e]ce of iron not susceptible of magnetism were put in the same result would follow

A piece of soft iron was put in at the contact of the battery and the conductor. The needle was deflected—   20°

When the iron was suddenly pulled out of the coil the deflection was also

20°

But with magnetized file when the contact was made the deflect was

8°

When the same file was drawn out the deflect <*was*>

15°

The change of magnetism in the drawing out was total, in the putting in the bar received magnetic force but only a small addition to what it had before and as the effect was due to the change the result was not as great as before

FROM DAVID BAILIE WARDEN[1]

Gratz Collection, Historical Society of Pennsylvania

Paris, 28 June .41.

Dear Sir,

I have presented the copies of your interesting Memoir to Gay-Lussac,[2] Pouillet,[3] Savary,[4] Peltier, Pixii,[5] Arago,[6] Babinet,[7] and to the academie

[1] A response to Henry's letter of May 1, 1841, printed above.

[2] Henry had met the French chemist Joseph Louis Gay-Lussac (1778–1850) during his European trip of 1837. *Henry Papers*, 3:365.

[3] Claude-Servais-Mathias Pouillet (1790–1868) was a member of the French physics community with whom Henry had had contact while in Europe. *Henry Papers*, 3:365.

[4] The astronomer and geophysicist Félix Savary (1797–1841). *Henry Papers*, 2:320.

[5] Henry had purchased a considerable amount of scientific instrumentation from the firm of Pixii, Père et Fils. This reference is to the father, Nicolas Constant Pixii-Dumotiez (1776–1861). *Henry Papers*, 3:180n, 540–543.

[6] D. F. J. Arago (1786–1853) was another member of the French physics community whom Henry had met while in Paris. *Henry Papers*, 3:365.

[7] Warden had introduced Henry to Jacques Babinet (1794–1872) during Henry's stay in Paris. *Henry Papers*, 3:387–392.

des Sciences. Peltier will make it known to the Societe Philomatique.

In my note by Dr Lang[8] I fear that I wrote Savary instead of Savart. The latter is no more.[9]

It has afforded me much pleasure to be acquainted with Mr. Smith.[10]

Yours with great esteem,
D B Warden

[8] Perhaps Edmund Lang (d. 1856), who graduated Princeton in 1837 and received his M.D. from the University of Pennsylvania in 1840. *Princeton Catalogue*, p. 152. The note has not been found.

[9] Félix Savart died on March 16, 1841. *DSB.* (Savary died on July 15, 1841. *Poggendorff.*)

[10] R. Lawler Smith.

"RECORD OF EXPERIMENTS"
Henry Papers, Smithsonian Archives

June 29th 1841

For the continuation and extension of the experiments made yesterday I prepaired this morning a double coil <*of wire*> the inner part consisting of a coil of bell wire 60 feet long the outer one of finer wire from helix no 3 of about the same length. The inner one was connected with the battery and the outer with Clark's galvanometer.

1 Coil with out magnet or iron and 2 cups of the battery—

		Circuit	formed		5°
		Circuit	Broken		5°
2	Do Do	circuit	formed		4°
		— —	broken		4°
3	Magnet thurst in without battery				11°
	Do Drawn out "				12°
4	Do Thurst in "				13°
	Do Drawn out "				13°
5	Magnet conformable with battery				
	Do Do	circuit	made	R	13½—
	Do Do	circuit	broken	L	13½+
6	Do Do	circuit	made	R	12°—
	Do Do	"	broken	L	12°+
7	Magnet non conformable	circuit	made	R	12—
		"	broken	L	12+
8	Do Do	circuit	made	R	12—
	Do		broken		10+

9 Mag non conformable

	circuit	made	12°—	R
	circt	broken	10+	L

10 Mag conformable

	circt	made	13°—	R
	circ^t	broken	12+	L

11 Mag conformable

	cirt	made	10°	

12 Mag drawn out battery in action

			14°+	L
Do pushed in Do			13—	R

13 Piece of soft iron thurst in battery in action   16°

Do   Drawn out   „   15°

14 Soft iron in and <contact>

	circuit	made	20°—	R
	circuit	broken	20+	L

In all these experiments the magnet appears to have changed but little its intensity and this was to be expected because but one coil was used—where as in the other exp 2 coils were placed on the length of the magnet[1]

To determine the effect of putting the coil on different parts of the magnet

1 Magnet conformable coil on the middle of the length

	circuit	made	10	R
	circit	broken	10	L

2 Coil on the south end of magnet

	circuit	made	7°	R
	„	broken	6°	L

3 Coil on <North end> middle of magnet

	circu^t	made	10	R
		broken	10	L

4 Coil on North end of magnet

	circuit	made	6°	R
	Circuit	broken	5½	L

5 Same exp. with bundle of wire 18 inches long—coil on middle of Length

	circt.	made	35°	R
		broken	30°	L

[1] This paragraph, which compared the on-going experimental results with those of the previous day, was originally a marginal notation.

6   Coil at the end of the bundle

		made	14°	R
circt.		broken	13	L

7—Bundle drawn from the middle

30°

NB Observed to day that a piece of wire which had been used for coil no 3 was extremely brittle and this fact would agree with what I was once informed of by Chilton[2] that a piece of wire appeared to grow rapidly harder by being used for the conduction of an induced current. I have tried this with a piece of wire but without any definite result

Experiments with needles instead of the galvanometer, with the same arrangement of coil and battery as described at top of page 172.[3] Three coils were used, one of two strata of wire, one with the strands widely seperated the other with the same close together.

They all gave the same indication in every case except one and probably this was from a mistake in putting in the needle wrong

1 Coil alone
       at making circuit 1 & 3 sperals magnetized slightly   —
       at breakin circu^t all strongly   +
2 Coil with bundle of wires
       at making circuit 1 spere slightly   —
       at breaking circuit very strong all   +
3 Coil with magnet conformable
       at making circuit all slightly   —
       at breaking Do. all strong   +
4 Coil mag. nonconformable
       at making circu^t all slightly   —
       at breaking Do all strongly   +

With one cup of the battery the magnetism of the needles at the completing of the circuit was scarcely perceptible but at the breaking of the same it was quite strong

Sky beautifully clear on the evening of this day copious dew under the open sky but under the trees in the campus none[4]

---

[2] James R. Chilton, *Henry Papers*, 2:20n, or his father, George, ibid., *1*:295.

[3] The first page of this entry.
[4] Originally a marginal comment.

"RECORD OF EXPERIMENTS"
Henry Papers, Smithsonian Archives

June 30th 1841
Thermometer
at 86 in study in the Hall
In the Lecture Room thermometer at 93°[1]
From the experiments of yesterday and the day before, I am inclined to think that some reaction should be produced on the secondary current by a second current which should represent the currents in the magnet which produces the reaction of soft iron. This idea has occured to me before as I find by refering to page 153[2]

To bring this to the test a triple coil was formed by <*rooling*> winding about 40 feet of bell wire over the out side of the compound coil, used in yesterdays experiments. The inner one of these, the same used in last experiments, was connected with a battery of one (cup) element—<*and*> the middle coil of small wire (from helix No 3) was connected with Clark's galvanometer and the out side coil was placed in the circuit with 6 cups of the battery. The contact was then made and broken with the battery of one cup—while the circuit of 6 cups was suffered to remain constant but no peculiar effect could be perceived. The induction with this apparatus was very feeble and did not deflect the needle more than 2 or 2½ degrees.

Arranged the batteries in two sets—one of 3 cups, the other of 4—the former was connected with the circuit to be ruptured. The effect appeared in this case to be greater with the compound circuit, of this however I am not certain.

Made new arrangement with three of the large coils. Coils No 1, 2 & 3  were arranged in the order mentioned. No 1 was connected with the battery of 3 elements, No 2 with that of 4 and No 3 with the galvanometer.

Contact broken with No 1 while no 2 was disconnected from its circuit deflection

at beg[inn]ing circuit	5°
Coil no 2 put in connection with its battery	
at beginning of circuit	5°
at ending of cir[t]	5°

---

[1] The comment is found at the top of the third page of this four-and-a-half page entry.

[2] The last paragraph of the October 24, 1840, entry, *Henry Papers*, 4:445–446.

Reversed the current in No 2
    at begining circᵗ of No 1   5°
    at ending   — — „   5°

The action was here very feeble and inorder to increase it a coil of bell wire much longer than coil no 3 was substituted for it with this the deflection was stronger

No 2 alone at begining gave	10°
No 1 „ „ „ „	10°
No 2 in alsone[3]	10
No 1 put in after	10°
No 1 alone in	10°
Reversed No	
At begining of no 1	10°
No 1 alone	10°

From these experiments which were very carefully made I am unable to infer any action of a current analagous to the reaction of soft iron. This would appear to establish a difference between the action of a soft iron magnet and a current.

Arranged the battery in two sets—13 cups in one and one cup in the other. Placed the coiles No 1 & 2 as before but on these helix no 1 with handles. Then closed the circuit of no 2 and the 13 cups, while the circuit of no 1 was ruptured—but no difference could be perceived except that the shock was less in all cases <*than with the*> with the compound circuit than with the simple one of no 1. This was the case also when the circuit was reversed. That the shock should be less with the circuit of No 2 closed is plain, since it then forms a shut circut, through which a closed current can circulate and this will tend to neutralize a part of the induction of No 1. It was in reference to this action that I arranged the 13 cups in connection with coil no 2 so that the seccondary current would find more difficulty in passing the increased number of alternations of the acid in the cups.[4] I am therefore thus far unable to get any indication of the reaction of a current on another current analogous to the action of soft iron on a current.

Next made experiment in reference to the action of soft iron betwen the

---

[3] Henry's intent was to write "alone."

[4] In this experiment, coil one and its battery were a simple circuit, coil two and its battery the analog to the soft iron magnet, and the helix was the means of testing the strength of the induced current. Henry observed that coil one would produce an opposing induced effect in coil two regardless of the direction of the current produced by coil two's battery. In increasing the number of cups of the battery, he hoped to diminish this by increasing the resistance in the circuit.

conductors. Used the two concentric thick wire coiles, connected the inner with the galvanometer outer with the battery placed between the two a number of soft iron wires. When the contact was made with the battery the needle was found to make a slight movement which was in one case noted to be 2° to the R and then to swing 5° to the L. This effect was produced several times in succession

The wires were next withdrawn and now I was surprised to find that the deflection was only 2°R

The results were obtained from 5 experiments with the wire in each gave
deflection 5°
and with two with iron wire out each
gave deflection 2°
In this experiment the action of the iron was greater than that of the coil the 2° of motion at first to the R was due to the sudden action of the coil and the 5° to L immediately to the adverse action of the iron— —Interesting exp.[5]

Exp farther on this point

See in connecction with this experiment see one top page 120 June 4[th] 1841[6]

Made experim[en]t on the rate of decomposition with the large spool in the circuit, first with iron wire in the hollow axis and again without wire the number of cups eleven

Iron wire in $\begin{cases} \text{1st 5 inches of gas in} & 55" \\ \text{2}^{\text{nd}} \text{ 5 inches of gas in} & 55" \end{cases}$

wire out $\begin{cases} \text{1}^{\text{st}} \text{ 5 inches of gas in} & 55" \\ \text{2} \quad \text{5 inches of gas in} & 55" \end{cases}$

In the battery of cups I have used for some time past paper cylinders these stand very well when made of thick brown paper. The cylinders require occasionally to be reamalgamated—otherwise they are rapidly acted on by the acid.

---

[5] Indeed an interesting experiment, as the reversal of current was (and is) unpredicted and irreproduceable. See Henry's experiments of the following day, below.

[6] Henry originally wrote 140, then wrote over 120. The date also shows a slip of the pen; it should read June 4, 1840. See *Henry Papers,* 4:405, experiment 9.

"RECORD OF EXPERIMENTS"
Henry Papers, Smithsonian Archives

July 1ˢᵗ 1841

Made arrangements to repeat the experiment of the last page.[1] For this purpose, tied around coil no 2[2] the wires so as to form a perfect cylinder and around the out side of this placed coil no 2 which was connected with the battery and <*coil*> helix no 2 with the galvanometer. The battery consisted of 13 cups. All the iron in deflection of the needle

1	at *making the circuit*	3°R
	At breaking circ^t	2 L
2	At making again	2½R

A slight agitation was noticed in this exp as if the needle first attempted to move in the other direction and then obeyed the greater force.[3]

3 The shock was next tried with all the wires in this was feeble scarcely perceptible when <*plunged in*> circuit was made but more sensible when the circuit was broken

4 Next about 30 degrees of the wire were removed. The deflection of the needle at making the circuit was about   3° R
<*5*> On breaking the circuit   3 L
Shock stronger but the one at breaking the circuit more intense

5 Next one ½ the wire removed
    action of the needle about the same as the last
    Shock increased in both

6 All the wire removed shock much increased as strong at beginning as at ending of the current
    Deflection of the galvanometer

at the beginning	4° L
at the ending	4° R

From the last result compaired with the others it appears that the direction of the current is reversed by withdrawing the wires. The deflection ob-

---

[1] That is, of the latter part of the entry of June 30, where Henry indicates the need for further experiments.

[2] Henry meant helix No. 2, as the figure and succeeding text show.

[3] As in the experiments of the previous day.

tained above 1, 2, 4 are due[4] to the action of the inner currents of the iron.

When therefore the coil is inclosed in a <*circular*> cylinder of rods of iron the compensation is not complete between the inside and the out and that the inner induction[5] of the cylinder is the stronger. The spaces without the  circle passing through the cylender of wires in the anexed figure are greater on the out side than those within and hence if the difference be sufficient a want of compensation will be the result. Suppose in the first place that the sum of the forces within and without this circle just balanced each other <*and then*> when the whole outer space was filled<*between the one*> and then equal quantities were subtracted from each space it is plain that the remainder would no longer be in equilibrium since the remainder the out side would be in excess. If a wedge contained between two radii of the larger circle were withdrawn then equilibrium would be still maintained and if the part without the inner circle were greater than that drawn from the inner circle then the currents of the inner would prevail. The problem may be solved mathematically at least approximately without much difficulty[6]

Put long coil of thick wire see figure p 179[7] into a stove-pipe attached the compound (extreme) ends to the galvanometer

1	When the circuit was formed with the battery deflection was	3°R
	circuit broken	2½L
2	circuit made	3 R
	circuit broken	3 L

The iron pipe was next removed and now the deflection at making the circuit

[4] The notebook page ends here, and two diagrams appear at the top of the next page. Drawn in pencil, the illustrations were probably added by Henry at a later date.

[5] "Inner" referring to the inner currents in the iron, as in the theory of Ampère, for the cylinder of iron wire is outside the helix. In addition, it may refer more specifically to the induction produced by those parts of the iron wire within the circle connecting the centers of the wires.

[6] A very unclear passage. Henry must explain why the absence of the wires reverses the direction of the induced current. His ex-planation seems tautological. Henry related the amounts of two opposing inductive forces to geometric areas. But he never fully explained how the relative areas—the relative amounts of force—corresponded to changes in the experimental set-up. At times he seems to be talking about relative amounts of wire inside and outside of the circle linking the centers. At other times, he appears to be considering a larger experimental set-up. What results is an explanation without a clear referent.

[7] The last illustration of the June 30 entry.

1	was still	3 R
	at breakin circuit	2 L
2	at making circuit	3 R
	at breaking do	2 L

From this result it appears that the direction of a current from the inside of a full cylinder of iron is the same as from the coil without the iron. This result is in conformity with what I obtained in June last see [. . .][8] in this arrangement it appears that the circles of the iron within and without perfectly neutralize each other, so that the same amount of induction is shown whether the iron is in or out. It would appear however from the exp page [. . .] that the same compensation is not quite perfect in reference to the shock[9]

Next made arrangements for studying the action of induction from within out through a continuous cylinder of iron. Coil no 2 was rooled up so as to fit into a short cylinder of thick sheet iron and a coil formed of a part of the wire from the large spool was put on the out side

1	Current through *inner* coil	
	circuit made	8 R
	circuit broken	5 L
2	Current through inner coil	
	circuit made	8 R
	do broken	5 L
3	Current through *outter* coil	
	circuit made	6°R
	circuit broken	5 L
4	Current through outer coil made	6 R
	circuit broken	5 L
5	Current through inner coil	
	circuit made	8 R
	circuit broken	5 L
6	Iron taken out circuit through inner coil	
	circuit made	14 R
	circuit broken	10 L

[8] Another reference, as in the last entry, to experiments of June 4, 1840. See *Henry Papers*, 4:403–405.

[9] Uncertain, but probably the same June 4 experiments of the previous note, as these used shocks to gauge the extent of screening.

7	Same arrangement	
	circuit made	13 R
	do broken	10 L
8	Through inner coil the current	13 R
	circuit broken	10 L
9	Current through outer coil	
	circuit made	12°R
	circuit broken	10 L

From these results it appears that a certain thickness of iron exerts a real screening influence. In the case of the thin stove pipe iron the effect appears to be the same with or without the iron. Here the effect is different.

The difference at the beginning and ending of the current is due to the accumulation of the battery. This is shown by using a single cup. The deflection with 2 cups as one was 13° at puting in and take out the wire

TO JAMES HENRY

Mary Henry Copy,[1] Family Correspondence, Henry Papers,
Smithsonian Archives

Princeton July 3. 1841

The students are making grand preparations this afternoon (Saturday) for the usual celebration of the Fourth. There is a prospect of a change in the order of vacations so that the Fourth of July will hereafter fall in the vacation[2] and consequently that this will be the last time of celebration, hence the illumination will be uncommonly brilliant and the fireworks very extensive. We expect a large company. Dr T[orrey?] is now at New Brunswick with a party of ten persons. He intends getting a large wagon and bringing the whole posse to see the fireworks in the evening. They will remain during the night; we have promised shake down beds if nothing better can be arranged.

I hear nothing new. All things move as usual in Princeton. I send two catalogues of the college. The number of students is nearly the same as

[1] There are two overlapping versions of this letter in the Family Correspondence. They have been combined to form the version we have printed. A third Mary Henry Copy, identical to the longer of the two versions in the Family Correspondence, is also located in the Henry Papers.

[2] Princeton did not move its commencement to June, with the resulting long summer vacation rather than a summer term, until 1843–1844. *Henry Papers,* 4:433.

last year although we have received a much larger accession this year. The diminution of the last two years on account of the money depression are more apparent in the present catalogue than in the last.[3] The students have petitioned me to give a course of lectures on Geology[4] and in order to do this I shall have to spend a week or two in Philadelphia in making preparations.

---

[3] The 1841–1842 decline in attendance was nineteen compared to the previous school year, *Princeton Annual Catalogues*, 1840–1842.

[4] See above, Senior Class to Henry, June 25, 1841.

"RECORD OF EXPERIMENTS"
Henry Papers, Smithsonian Archives

July 8th 1841

My experiments since the last date have been interrupted by the college duties consequent on the celebration of the 4th or rather on this year of the 5th of July.[1] The evening of the 5th was <cloudy> rainy the fire works

 Current from single battery the one from Boston[2] arranged with diaphragm and sulphate of copper strong magnetism on the outside none on the inside filings as per figure.[3] Used paper stretched over ring. The current in this experiment was passed around the outside of the hoop of iron about 12 inches in diameter 3 inches wide through coil no one. Snap was strong and loud when the contact with the cup of mercury was broken

 Coil No 2 was placed inside of the iron and the current from the same battery sent through this. The appearance of filings of iron when scattered or sifted on the paper was as in the figure—no magnetism appeared on the out side.

Tested the above with a magnetized needle suspended from a fine silk thread and either end was found to adhere to the inside of the iron. But the North end was attracted by the out side. The direction of the current was now changed the South end of the needle was attracted by the out side of the

This subject requires more investigation

---

[1] The fourth fell on a Sunday in 1841; the celebration would not take place on the Christian Sabbath.

[2] Most likely bought from Daniel Davis on the trip to Boston mentioned in the "Record of Experiments" entry for October 24, 1840,

Henry Papers, 4:444–445.

[3] A continuation of experiments on patterns of magnetization, last made in April and May 1840, *Henry Papers*, 4:360–362, 398–399. Henry was testing the ability of iron to screen magnetic action.

Passed large current or rather current from the large battery through the <*outside*> *inside* coil and current from two cups through the outside. With this arrangement the filings were arranged on the outside and inside when the currents passed in the same or in different directions

"RECORD OF EXPERIMENTS"
Henry Papers, Smithsonian Archives

July 9th 1841

Passed the current through coil no 2 on the inside of the iron ring. The filings arranged themselves as in the last figure on the last page.[1] The iron was then removed and the paper placed at the same distance from the coil as before the iron was removed. The filings now arranged themselves as in the figure in this margin radiating from the centre in every direction and not bounded by the coil as in the last arrangement. Hence something of the force which arranges the filings is due to the action of the coil.[2] In an other experiment the arrangement of the filings was as in Fig 2 in the middle where the coil did not reach the filings were arranged in lines perpendicular to the plan[e] of the paper

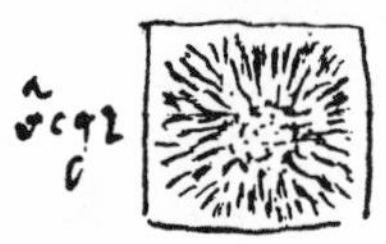

Tested magnetism with needle

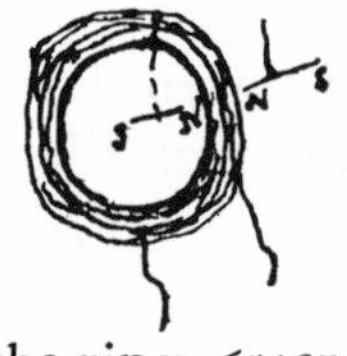

Put the iron hoop into coil no 1 magnetism strong on the out side apparently feeble on the inside but the polarity in the same direction on both. When the direction of the <*needle*> current was changed the magnetism also changed. The magnetism of the upper and lower edge of the ring <*were*> was opposite

This is in accordance with the theory of Ampere

Suppose the magnetism to consist of circles of electricity at right angles to the axis of the bar, then the needle should point to the centre of each circle with the same end in going interely around the circumference above the plane of the circle—and in passing around in the same way in a plane below the plain

---

[1] The second illustration of the last entry.
[2] Here (and perhaps also in the last appear-ance of the word) Henry used "coil" to refer to the iron ring.

of the ring the opposite point of the needle should be directed to the same centre. See figure in margin

Placed coil no 2 inside of the hoop of iron—tested the magnetism with a needle. The north end of the needle was constantly and powerfully attractd by the inside and the opposite end by the out side. This effect was farther proved by changing the direction of the current—the south end of the needle was now attracted by the inside and the north by the out side.

Sent same current through outside and inside coil but in opposite directions. The magnetism was now by the needle the same on the inside as on the outside—or in other words the north end of the needle was attracted by the edge of the iron on the out side and inside, or it was affected as if the coils alone acted on it

TO WILLIAM HAMILTON[1]
Archives, Franklin Institute

Princeton July 10th 1841

My Dear Sir

I thank you for the information relative to the Geological pictures and if it be not asking too much may I request that you will set the artist to work and have the articles copied as soon as possible provided that the cost be not greater than 8 or 10 dollars apiece.

I shall want them for my lectures in about two weeks and therefore have little time to spare. I hope to visit Philad. next week or the week after and I will then pay for the articles or should the money be required before I will send a check. The pictures are for the college and although we cannot afford to give much for them yet any trouble that you may be at in procuring them will be cheerfully recompensed.

Yours &c
Joseph Henry

[1] Actuary of the Franklin Institute. *Henry Papers*, 2:198n.

"RECORD OF EXPERIMENTS"
Henry Papers, Smithsonian Archives

July 12th Monday 1841

Sam my assistant provided a piece of the long gut of an ox. This was filled with acid and a current of electricity was passed through it from the battery of 12 cups. The current was feeble but gave a small spark when the circuit was broken. The connection of the gut with the battery was made by means of two wires of the bell wire size—the spark was less than when the circuit was completed without the introduction of the gut. The result of this experiment was that not the least effect could be felt in the tongue from <coil> Hilex no 1 when placed in the ring formed by the gut. This experiment however is not entirely satisfactory since the conduction of the acid was so small as to transmit to litle electricity to produce a shock

Coil no 2 was next substituted for helix no 1 in the last arrangement and the ends of the coil connected with the galvanometer but no effect could be observed when the circuit was broken. When helix no 1 was placed inside of the circuit of the battery without the gut forming a part a very slight sensation could be perceived on the tongue. The shock was not in the least increased by introducing coil no 2 into the circuit—this is in accordance with what I have published in my last paper[1]

Next compaired coil no 3 with an iron coil of a little less length but of greater sectional area. The snap from the two appeared about the same. If any difference existed to me it appeared that the iron coil gave the louder snap. The difference was very small

Next wound coil no 3 and the iron coil together so as to make a compound coil of two strands—the ends of the iron coil being seperated the copper ends were connected with the battery. The sparks appeared about as before or as in the last experiment. The iron ends were next connected with the battery, the snap appeared also as before so that the iron ribbon appeared to produce no peculiar effect.

The end of the copper ribbon was now joined, so as to make a shut circuit and the contact with the cups broken with the end of the iron ribbond the spark was feeble very little noise

The ends of the iron were now joined so as to form a shut circuit. The effect appeard the same as before. From all these results it appears that an iron ribbon produces no peculiar effect. The magnetism on the opposite sides of the ribbon must be nuteralized

The current was next passed through the copper coil and the magnetism

---

[1] "Contributions IV: Electro-Dynamic Induction," paragraph 11.

of the interposed iron coil or ribbon tested. It was very feeble—as was shown by bringing near it the end of a long wire of iron. This was scarcely attracted although a small bar magnet attracted it readily at the distance of ½ an inch. Compare this with an account of a magnet described in Elect Journ[2]

The last experiment may be varied by procuring a piece of sheet iron and coiling it into a cylinder with a coil of copper in its interior

[2] Not ascertained, but perhaps J. P. Joule, "On the Use of Electro-Magnets Made of Iron Wire for the Electro-Magnetic Engine," Sturgeon's *Annals of Electricity, Magnetism, and Chemistry*, 1839, *4*:58–62.

FROM CADWALLADER EVANS[1]

Mary Henry Copy,[2] Memoir, Henry Papers, Smithsonian Archives

Pittsburgh, July 12ᵗʰ 1841

Dear Sir:

Some time back, by my request, Prof. MᶜCullock,[3] of Cannonsburgh, left with you a working model of my Safety Guard—and I now take the liberty of sending you one of my cards describing the mode in which it is applied to boilers on our waters, which you will understand at sight.[4] This inven-

[1] Cadwallader Evans (d. ca. 1854) was the last surviving son of the late Oliver Evans (1755–1819), inventor of the high-pressure steam engine. Cadwallader and his two brothers, George and Oliver, Jr., engaged in many of the same activities as their father in Philadelphia and Pittsburgh, operating an iron foundry, a plow factory, and a steam engine works. Dorothy and Greville Bathe, *Oliver Evans: A Chronicle of Early American Engineering* (Philadelphia, 1935). Among several patents held by Cadwallader Evans were devices to prevent steam boiler explosions, the subject of this letter. *Burke's Index*.

[2] This copy is in the handwriting of W. L. Nicholson, as is the copy of the draft of Henry's reply of February 25, 1842, printed below.

[3] Richard Sears McCulloh, a former student of Henry's, was Professor of Natural Philosophy, Mathematics and Chemistry at Jefferson College in Canonsburg, Pennsylvania (*Henry Papers*, 3:83n–84n).

[4] Evans's safety guard was designed to prevent steam boiler explosions by automatically relieving either dangerously high pressure or excessive temperature in the boiler, thought to be two of the leading causes of explosions. Common safety valves were weighted to stay closed at normal working pressures but to open if pressure in the boiler got too high. Evans supplemented a common safety valve with a fusible metal plug so that his safety valve would also open if the water in the boiler got too low and the boiler began to overheat. At a certain temperature, depending on the composition of the alloy, the fusible plug would melt and open the valve. A detailed description of the safety guard appears in Cadwallader Evans, *A Treatise on the Causes of Explosions of Steam Boilers, with Practical Suggestions for Their Prevention: To Which Is Added a Description of Evans' Improved Safety Guard, or Engineers' Assistant* (Pittsburgh, 1850), a copy of which is in the Henry Library.

The French had been using fusible metal plates on boilers since the 1820s. Bache and

tion has been upwards of two years in use, giving entire satisfaction in every instance, and of its certainty in preventing explosions, having been tested under all circumstances in which boilers are liable to be placed—the alloy having melted in several instances under pressure, the valve being overladened, and in a number of instances owing to a deficiency of water, and in one instance by an accumulation of mud—the boilers having a considerable quantity of mud in them, it collected around the pipe containing the alloy—the water not coming in contact with the pipe, the alloy melted below the usual pressure, although a sufficiency of water. It has been the means of three incompetent engineers being discharged—heretofore the captains of boats had no mode of testing how far their engineer was competent or careful, and the only warning was an explosion, but now no carelessness can pass unnoticed. No increased pressure can be used, or depression of water take place, without every man on the boat being apprized of it. There are three things to be observed. First, the frequent melting of the alloy does not alter its fusible melting temperature. I have put a Safety Guard in operation 1530 times without changing the qualities of the metal in the least—the result always being the same—the alloy melting in every instance precisely at 128[lb] pressure. Secondly, in no case in practice will the fusible temperature of the alloy equal that temperature at which malleable iron begins to lose its strength, but on the other hand will be better prepared to retain a pressure than before the fire was applied. Thirdly, the first effect produced by opening the Safety Guard Value is to increase the ebullition, so as to cover the flues, which, however, can never exceed 10 or 12 degrees above that of the usual working pressure. Were I to occupy your valuable time by going into a full description of the arrangements of our engines, and the practice of engineering on the western rivers, for the purpose of showing you the necessity of the general introduction of my apparatus, you would not be surprized at the numerous explosions that have taken place, but would feel an equal astonishment with myself, that they are not more frequent.[5]

Evans, working independently, found that if the alloy were directly exposed to pressure, the more fusible parts would be forced out and leave the less fusible parts, which would thereafter require a higher temperature to fuse. To obviate this problem, they enclosed the alloy in a tube. To prove the safety guard reliable, Evans had to prove through repeated tests that the alloy would always fuse at approximately the same temperature. *Senate Executive Documents*, 30th Congress, 2d Session, 1848–1849, No. 18, pp. 21–23.

[5] Although steamboat accidents were also caused by fire and collision, boiler explosions caused the most accidents and the greatest number of casualties and were the most dramatic of the steamboat disasters. From 1836 to 1840, over six hundred people were killed by steamboat explosions. Louis C. Hunter, *Steamboats on the Western Rivers: An Economic and Technological History* (Cambridge, Massachusetts, 1949), chapter 6: "Steamboat Accidents."

I will now state the object of this letter, which I hope you will excuse, and will bear in mind however valuable a man's invention may be, if the general introduction of it depends solely on his own personal exertion, his patent term expires before he receives a reasonable compensation for his trouble, and in 99 cases out of 100 he is reduced to poverty—however successful I am, and may be in this place, where I can apply my personal attention, and with which I am perfectly satisfied, as all the new boats procure my apparatus, yet at a distance it requires other's opinions than my own to aid in its introduction—and as I wish to prepare by next Session of Congress to draw their attention to the subject, I have been at the expense of making a number of working models, and sending them to different Scientific Institutions to enable them to experiment with the same. I, therefore, most respectfully solicit your opinion on this invention when it suits your convenience.[6]

Your most obt Servant
C. Evans

[6] Congress had passed the first federal legislation to regulate steamboats in 1838. Obvious deficiencies in the new law and a peak in the number of accidents in the late 1830s led to numerous inventions of safety devices and appeals to Congress by their inventors for endorsement and testing.

Evans seems to have had little trouble getting endorsements from engineers and scientists. His 1850 *Treatise* (footnote 4) includes testimonials by John Locke and James Renwick, as well as McCulloh and Henry, and by groups of steamboat builders and engineers. Henry was of course familiar with the Franklin Institute investigation of steam boiler explosions and had even reviewed part of the report for two English periodicals in 1837 (*Henry Papers*, 3:67, 340–341, 376–377). His belated reply to Evans of February 25, 1842, is printed below.

Evans had already sent a memorial to Congress in 1839 asking for an appropriation to allow him to test his safety guard and for an evaluation by experts. Although we have not found a later memorial for this purpose (his widow did subsequently memorialize Congress for an extension of the patent), others urged that the government purchase the invention and require that it be used on all high-pressure steamboats. Evans's safety guard was one of the devices tested in 1843 at the Washington Navy Yard by a board consisting of Walter R. Johnson, Charles Reeder, and Thomas P. Jones. Several of the comments in their 1844 report (cited below) would have disappointed Evans:

Compared with a common safety valve, and with Easton's interior safety valve, the experiments show this apparatus to be much more sluggish in giving its indications of danger, and in returning to a condition for renewing its operation, than are those simple instruments which depend solely on mechanical principles. Besides this, its return to action and to the retention of steam is dependent on the engineer, who must wind up the weight, and thus close his valve.

In addition to the persistent charge that the fusibility of the alloy would change over time, Evans's safety guard was accused of being a "humbug" to attract passengers looking for the safest steamboats. It was also argued that a requirement that all steamboats use his safety guards would discourage other inventors from trying to design anything better. *House Documents*, 25th Congress, 3d Session, 1838–1839, No. 88. *Senate Documents*, 28th Congress, 1st Session, 1843–1844, No. 405 (quotation from page 44). *Senate Executive Documents*, 30th Congress, 2d Session, 1848–1849, No. 18, pp. 179–184. *Senate Reports*, 37th Congress, 2d Session, 1861–1862, No. 54.

Louis Hunter concluded that Evans's safety guard was too expensive to be popular and that it was never widely used on western steamboats even after Evans substantially lowered the price (Hunter, op. cit., p. 536).

The next major legislation in 1852 required the use of fusible metal safety guards without specifying any particular type. Shortly after this law passed, Evans published *A Statement of Experiments Upon the Temperature of Steam, the Operations of the Common Safety Valve, and Upon Government Alloys: with a Description of a Newly Invented Safety Valve, &c.* (Pittsburgh, 1854). He apparently died before he could promote his safety guard further. According to Bathe, op. cit., p. 271, only one of Oliver Evans's children, a daughter, lived beyond 1854. His wife, Jane B. Evans, appears as a widow in the 1856–1857 Pittsburgh City Directory.

For the history of attempts to prevent steamboat accidents, which involved not only technological solutions but also the education and professionalization of engineers, inspection, licensing, penalties, etc., see Louis C. Hunter, op. cit., chapter 13: "The Movement for Steamboat Regulation." See also John G. Burke, "Bursting Boilers and the Federal Power," *Technology and Culture*, 1966, 7:1–23.

"RECORD OF EXPERIMENTS"[1]
Henry Papers, Smithsonian Archives

July 15th 1841[2]
{ Effects of Lightning Mrs Hamiltons House struck

Last evening we were visited by a very severe thunder storm. Princeton of late years has been remarkably exempt from lightning near by—the storms generally come from the south west and seperate into two parts before reaching us. One part passes along Rocky hill the other along the canal. The one of last evening was the second severe storm of the kind we have had since I have resided in Princeton. It has been conjectured that the canal and rail road on one side and the hill on the other protect us and that a

---

[1] This entry was Henry's first extended account of observations on thunderstorms, but certainly not his last. Though his primary work was in the laboratory, Henry always maintained an active interest in terrestrial physics, and when this subject had a bearing on his experimental work, the interest increased to a passion.

Henry had had some interest in atmospheric electricity and electrical storms before this. He participated in a kite experiment in Philadelphia in 1836, which eventually found its way into "Contributions III" (*Henry Papers*, 3:77–80; "Contributions III: Electro-Dynamic Induction," paragraph 124). He saw Peltier experiment on atmospheric electricity in France in 1837, and observed St. Elmo's fire on his return trip from Europe ("Atmospheric Electricity," Part V of "Meteorology in Its Connection with Agriculture," *Report of the Commissioner of Patents for 1859: Agriculture* [Washington, 1860], p. 493; *Henry Papers*, 3: 514–515). He had variously noted the effects of induction and lateral discharge from lightning and lightning rods (ibid., 3:63, 4:57). Finally, he noted in some detail in his commonplace book the effects of an April 12, 1840, thunderstorm in Princeton (ibid., 4:345–346). But the present long entry, and the next, marked his largest investment of time and effort to date, and started his lifelong concern with explaining storms on physical principles.

In this volume of the *Henry Papers* appears much of his additional work on the phenomena of atmospheric electricity and lightning. Henry twice took note of similar storms in Princeton: July 22, 1842, and May 8, 1843 (see the "Record of Experiments" entries, below). On at least two other occasions he referred to this entry in explaining other electrical effects: entries for October 12 and 28, 1843, below. Henry also became interested in atmospheric electricity, proposing (May 28, 1842) and constructing (June 10) a detector, and considering an automated registering system as well ("Record of Experiments" entries for those dates, and Lefroy to Sabine, October 25, 1842, all below). Finally, his commonplace book for the period is full of references to theory and phenomena of lightning, from Becquerel's "De l'électricité atmosphérique" (*Traité de l'électricité et du magnétisme*, 7 vols. [Paris, 1834–1840], 6:117–222), Peltier's *Météorologie* (Brussels, 1841), Arago's "Sur la tonnerre," *Annuaire du Bureau des Longitudes, 1838* (Paris, 1839), pp. 221–618, and articles from eighteenth-century volumes of the *Phil. Trans.* (Henry Commonplace Book [10615], pp. 10–32, passim, Henry Papers, Smithsonian Archives).

Henry's interest continued. He brought up the subject of lightning in remarks to the American Philosophical Society in 1843 (APS *Proceedings*, 1843–1847, 4:23), 1845 (ibid., pp. 179–180), and 1846 (ibid., pp. 260–268), and to the 1850 meeting of the American Association for the Advancement of Science, in New Haven (AAAS *Proceedings*, 1850, 4:7, 10, 39–42). His large-scale work, "Meteorology in Its Connection with Agriculture," published in five parts by the Commissioner of Patents from 1855 to 1859, was essentially a physics text, and its fifth part (1859), "Atmospheric Electricity," dealt extensively with storms and lightning. In it Henry collected and discussed almost all his observations and thoughts to this time. Even in the year of his death Henry had a letter published on the best and most scientific way of observing thunderstorms (*Journal of the American Electrical Society*, 1878, 2:1–8).

Henry's theoretical speculations on the nature of storms centered on the less generally discussed electrical effects. He considered it well established from experiments of Volta and Peltier that the earth as a whole was negatively charged—a conclusion he saw as no stranger than that it should be magnetic. Thunderclouds, then, being vertical objects of ascending warm vapor and descending condensate—partially conducting—are acted on by static induction by the earth. The portion of the cloud closest to the earth is positively charged, the portion farthest away is negative. As the electrical condition of the cloud changes through condensation, lightning can then travel between the upper and lower portions of the cloud, or between the lower portion and the earth.

In discussing lightning bolts, Henry high-lighted three effects. When lightning passes, it gives "a sudden and violent repulsive energy" to the air and other objects, especially in the direction of its passage. Thus lightning can form holes in walls and splinter trees. Second, the storm cloud, prior to emitting its lightning, strongly induces static charges in the area under it. This explained the apparent attraction of lightning to tall metallic objects. Similarly, the discharge of the lightning releases the inductive effect explosively, giving shocks to all that had formerly been subject to it. Finally, Henry always pointed to the process of lateral discharge, which is the giving off of sparks from a wire discharging a capacitor. Since Henry considered the discharge not to be a simple process, but actually a double wave of deficiency and redundancy of electrical fluid traveling down the rod, sparks could always be drawn from the lightning rod, no matter how large and well-grounded it might be. All three effects appear in Henry's account of this July storm. For the theories in full form, see his "Atmospheric Electricity," especially pp. 478–505.

Henry was often asked for advice about the selection and positioning of lightning rods. See, for example, the letter of Jacobus to Henry, July 18, 1843, and Henry's reply of the following day, both below.

Material from this entry was used in a November 5, 1841, presentation to the APS, published in the *Proceedings*, 1841–1843, 2:111–116. The account of the last two paragraphs, beginning "Between Princeton and Mr Philips . . . ," was omitted; another paragraph, relating to the "Record of Experiments" entry of September 2, 1841, was included.

[2] The dates on this document provide insight into Henry's procedures. The entire entry refers to the effects of a severe storm that swept through the Princeton area on the fourteenth. Henry's narrative of his survey of houses hit by lightning is continuous through the nine-page entry. The entire entry clearly refers to his activities on the fifteenth, and the first three pages are so dated. The next two pages, originally dated the fifteenth, were later changed to the sixteenth, and a small note in the upper margin of the first of these states "Written 16th." The last four pages of this entry lack date and heading. Distinctly separated from this one, the next entry is dated the sixteenth, and refers to activities of that day.

change has been produced since the construction of the canal.[3] Be this as it may, the storm of the 14th was very unusual and nothing like it, it is said, has occurred here in the course of 20 years. The clouds had an unusual direction, there appeared to be two storms, one in the norwest and the other in the south. The clouds came together over Princeton and deluged us with rain. The lighting was almost incessant but the thunder was not very loud except on one or two occassions when it appeared to be very near and then the intensity was not as great as I have heard it in Albany. The storm lasted about 3 hours but not in full force during the whole time.

Several places in the vicinity of Princeton were struck and one in the village namely Mrs Hamiltons[4] house, situated on the main street, about 30 rods to the south west of the college on the opposite side of the street. It appears somewhat strange that this house should have been struck, since it is one of the lowest on that side of the street in the vicinity and on the west of it are a number of high trees. The house is also furnished with a lightning rod but not of very perfect construction or arrangement.

The house stands parallel to the street in a north east and south west direction. It is of br[i]ck covered with a shingle roof two stories high—has a door and an entrance hall on the west and two rooms one front and the other rear above and below with a small room in front over the hall. In the upper storey there are three windows in front and two below—the front

door being under the 1st window. There is a wooden gutter which runs horrizontally along the front of the house under the eaves and at the nor<*west*>east side this is furnished with a tin pipe of about <*4*>3 inches indiameter connecting it with the ground. Both the gutter and the pipe must have been filled or nearly filled with water at the time. The lightning rod is attached to the N-W gable of the house and was probably placed there, rather than on the east on account of the support which the chim-

---

[3] The Delaware and Raritan Canal was constructed through Princeton in 1834. In 1839, a branch of the Camden and Amboy Railroad, running from Trenton to New Brunswick, was constructed along the bank of the canal. This connected Princeton directly with New York and Philadelphia. *Hageman, 1*:252–253.

[4] The reference was to Phebe Hamilton, the widow of James Hamilton (painter and chairmaker, d. 1815) and mother of two sons and five daughters. All the daughters but one married clergymen, including one Reverend Mr. Huntington, from which comes the textual reference to Mrs. Huntington. One daughter remained unmarried, the Miss Hamilton of the entry. One son survived to adulthood, James Hamilton, Professor of Mathematics and Natural Philosophy at the University of Nashville. He appears below in the "Record of Experiments" entry of May 8, 1843. *Hageman, 1*:192–193.

ney would give it.[5] It is made of round iron ⅜th of an inch in diameter and in 5 pieces joined by hook and eye joint. It is terminated above by 3 points which are very blunt but do not exhibit signs of fusion and at the lower end its connection with the earth is very imperfect—it appears to be merely stuck into the ground to the depth of perhaps 2 or three feet. It rises to the hight of about [. . .][6] feet above the roof

The lightning appears to have come from the South perhaps a little to the West and first to have struck the S.W end of the horrizontal gutter. It then appears to have divided into two parts—the one passing along the gutter which was in all probability filled with water as the rain was falling almost in torrents, and then down the pipe to the ground the pipe was also probably gorged with water at the time. The other part passed immediatly down from the gutter—where the stroke was first made—to the casing of the window and then to the jambs of the door beneath to the pavement. Traces of it were observed on each side of the window frame the S W upright was split at the top where the hinge of the window shutter was fastened and

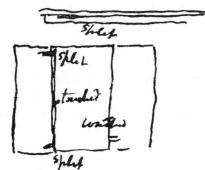

below also on the opposite upright of the frame near the lower hing[e] of the shutter the casing was marked. The gutter was split where the lightning passed down to the window. It made its appearance principally where the nails were inserted. In some case the discharge appeared merely to have touched the <part> wood and gouged out a groove of about the 8th of an inch in diameter. The channel appeared rough but regular in width. After passing down from the window, it is next seen on the jams of the door the casing on each side is marked—that on the SW is split and that on the opposite side marked in several places. The course of the lightning along the gutter was probably principally through the water its course hower is shown by a long splinter <on> near the S end of the gutter and also two splinters thrown off from the wash board or architrave under the gutter at the other end near the tin pipe. No marks of the discharge were observed along the tin pipe <or> at the ground where the electricity was probably discharged. The lightning rod was also examined but no markes about it could be seen which would lead us to supose than any part of the discharge had gone down this

[5] In this sentence, Henry has mistakenly switched west and east; the lightning rod is on the northeast gable, where the chimney is. Compare with the correct account in the APS *Proceedings* (see note 1), and the diagram.

[6] Henry left this blank, but his published account gives the height as six feet.

During the storm there were several females in the house three of these Old Mrs Hamilton and her two daughters were in the front room in the second story. The Old Lady was lying on <*the*> a bead placed near the partition wall between the two rooms her daughter Miss Hamilton was sitting on the be<*a*>d and her Daughter Mrs Huntington was on the floor about 8 feet from the front wall of the house with her face to the same. A[t] the moment of the discharge Old Mrs Hamilton who was looking towars Mrs Huntington as she stood on the floor saw her surrounded with light. Mrs H. herself felt a sensation on her right ear which was nearest the point where the lightning first struck as if it had been touched with a live coal of fire. She also felt a "rushing sensation" down her left side and perceived a brilliant discharge of light at her foot. At the same time a flash or <*long*> forked spark, 8 inches long, appeared between her body and the nearest window. The other two persons in the room felt nothing unusual, or if any effect was produced it was merged in the succeeding alarm. No mark on the ear or the foot was perceptible next day. The shoe was also examined but nothing could be seen. Mrs H at the time was standing on a grass carpet which covered the floor of the room. The window shutter nearest Mrs H. was shut and also the <*windo*> shutter of the window over the door was closed. One valve of the window next the pipe was open. The shutters were of the open kind with slanting slats. Three pains of glass were broken in the window over the door and the glass thrown inward. This window it must be observed was in the little room over the hall and therefore was seperated from the room in which the females were by a partition wall.

These phenomena do not appear difficult of explanation—the long horizontal gutter and the perpendicular pipe, both filled with water, formed a continuous conductor from the place where the lightning struck to the ground at the farther corner of the front of the house. This conductor would be acted on by the approaching discharge and by induction become highly charged if the cloud was + the <*upper area*> end of the gutter would be minus <*the*> its natural electricity would be repelled towards the earth through the pipe and therefore the whole would be in the most favourable condition to attract the lightning, which came in a direction somewhat coinsiding with the direction of the gutter. The effects observed by Mrs H and her mother in the room, were probably owing to induction. If electricity be suddenlly thrown on a pain of glass on one side, electricity will be thrown off on the other by induction and when a powerful discharge passed along the front of the house as in this case the natural electricity of the interior we would suppose would be disturbed and all the effects described by Mrs H produced. She says that an explosion like that of a pistol took place apparently at her foot—the light of which appeared like a ball of about an inch and a half in diameter. I am inclined to believe however that this was the explosion of the part of the discharge from the cloud which struck the house since a similar noise was heard at Dr Macleans[7]

The discharge came from the South and passed over the houses on the opposite side of the street. In one of these two persons were affected with the discharge—one a servant girl of Mr Warner[8] was thrown into convulsions, either by the immediate effects of the lightning or by the fright produced by the thunder—the other Mrs Warner felt at the moment a prickling sensation in her limbs particularly in her arms, which to use her own expression went out at her fingers. A girl in the room below, with the windows closed, thought she saw the lightning on the floor. Much of these effects may have been produced by immagination but still there is a sufficient cause in the principle of induction to account for all these appearances.

On the same day I visited Mr. Henry Philip's[9] house, situated about 3 miles from Princeton on the road to Trenton. This was also struck by the same storm. The house has a lightning rod on the end fartherest from Princeton but it is in a very bad condition the top and for or five feet of the stem is broken off or rather bent down so that no part of the rod rises above the top of the house. The lightning struck the farth[er] gable from the rod on the east end of the house passed down the chimney into the fire of the cellar kitchen scattered the ashes through the room and filled all below with smoke—a strong odour of sulphure was perceptible and this was also the case at Mrs Hamiltons. The smell was so strong around the front door that Mrs H thought the house was on fire. But to return to Mr. Philip's case. A large quantity of suit was thrown down the chimney—the whole charge however did not go down <*the*> into the fire—a part of it passed out through the thick stone wall which formed the back of the fire place and came out opposite the upper iron hoop of a Ley cask which was placed against the wall. It then passed down the cask which was moisted with the ley and burst off three or four wooden hoops which alternated with those

---

[7] Henry retrospectively added here a reference to the next entry in the "Record of Experiments," July 16.

[8] The 1840 census lists five Warner households in Mercer County. Only one of these, however, that of John Warner, was located in Princeton township. Ronald Vern Jackson and Gary Ronald Teeples, eds., *New Jersey 1840 Census Index* (Bountiful, Utah, 1978).

[9] Henry D. Phillips (1793–1873) of Maiden-head Plantation located near Lawrenceville, New Jersey, halfway between Princeton and Trenton. Phillips was a prosperous landowner from a family prominent in central New Jersey. In addition to his stock farm and stable of thoroughbred horses, Phillips owned and operated the Lawrenceville Female Seminary. Francis Bazley Lee, ed., *Genealogical and Personal Memorial of Mercer County, New Jersey*, 2 vols. (New York, 1907), *1*:79.

of iron. The hole in the wall was made between the stone of a triangular △ form the plaster was thrown out and the angles of the stone broken. No sines of fusion were observed—other cases of a passage through a thick wall were observed in the discharges of the same storm[10]

Inductive effects were also noticed in this discharge. Mr P his wife and little son were seated on the edge of <*the*> a bed at the distance of about 20 feet <*from*> or more from the chimney where the discharge passed down. They each felt a shock in the legs. Mr P felt it in his right leg, which was thrown over the other and did not touch the floor. Mrs P felt the shock in both legs and said it resembled precisely that which She had felt from an electrical jar. The boy felt it in his knees also Mr P felt it most sensibly in the same joint. The house was about 60 feet long and from the bad condition of the rod it is not surprising that the farther end of the house should have been struck particularly since it <*came*> there was a fire in the chimney[11]

Between Princeton and Mr Philips at Stony brook we inspected a tree which was struck at nearly the same time. It stood before the door of the house on the <*left*> right hand as you pass over the bridge going from Princeton. The tree was of the kind called Balm of Gilead about 50 feet high—it showed signs of the descharge at the distance of about 15 feet from the ground but the principal effect was produced at about 5 feet above this, where the first larger branches came out. The splitting and scathing appeared to be confined to a length of 5 or six feet—the upper branches were not affected and the lower part of the trunk showed no sines of the passage of the discharge. The <*effect*> action however was so intense on the part about the projection of the lower branches that the tree was nearly severed in two and was unable to withstand the wind which followed the storm. It fell in the wind and had been cut up that is all the upper part before I saw it. The high stump however was standing

The woman was in the entrance hall almost immediatly opposite the tree and about 25 or 30 feet distance from it. She experienced no effect except fright. Her husband was in the garden immediately behind the house and complained of being very sensibly affected by the shock—had a pain in his head all the next day. The tree showed no indications of ignition, the part struck was much splintered and the slivers thrown off as if by an explosive force. The tree was green and quite succulent and this was probably the cause of its not being splintered below perhaps it was hollow

---

[10] Another reference to the July 16 entry, added later.

[11] In light of the fact that heated air, being less dense, conducted electricity better. *Henry Papers*, 3:66.

"RECORD OF EXPERIMENTS"
Henry Papers, Smithsonian Archives

July 16ᵗʰ 1841
{ Effects of lightning
{ Barn struck on Rocky Hill
{ Dʳ Macleans House

Visited this morning with Mr <*George*> Archiᵈ Maclean[1] the bar[n] of Mr <*G*> Leigh[2] of rocky hill which was also struck on the same evening at about 10 oclock. Lightning struck at *a*, the highest peak of the barn,  which consists of two parts one for hay and grain and the other for a horse stable. It passed down each rafter, splintering them in its course, so as to completely destroy the continuity of the wood on the north side. It passed down along the posts and large barn door and then through the foundation wall into a kind of c[e]llar stable. The barn is on ground which slopes on one side so that the entrance to the cellar is even with the ground on the lower side. In this cellar a number of cattle and sheep were collected at the time—3 of the sheep and a heifer were killed. The lighting made a triangular hole in the wall, with the apex inward as if an explosion from within out had produced the effect. The same kind of hole was also observed in the wall at Mr Philip's[3] and also at Dʳ Maclean's.[4] A horse in the stable *c* was also much injured by the discharge.

On the same day, or rather evening, Dr Maclean's house, about 6 miles south of Princeton was struck. The lightning passed down the rod which had been erected but a few days previous. It left the rod at or near the ground and passed through the foundation of the chimney, which is 3½ feet thick, making a solid angular hole as if by a force from within out[5] as in the case mentioned in reference to Mr Philip's wall and the barn on

---

[1] Archibald Maclean (d. 1894), brother of John Maclean, Jr. *Henry Papers*, 4:419. George M. Maclean (*Henry Papers*, 2:100) was another brother of these two.

[2] The only G. Leigh mentioned in the 1840 New Jersey census was Gabriel H. Leigh of Lebanon Township, Hunterdon County. This was far from Rocky Hill, a community in Somerset County, about four miles north of Princeton. So Mr. Leigh's precise identity still eludes us, although four Leighs lived near Princeton, Albert S., James E., Phebe, and Samuel. Ronald Vern Jackson and Gary Ronald Teeples, eds., *New Jersey 1840 Census Index* (Bountiful, Utah, 1978).

[3] See the previous entry.

[4] George M. Maclean.

[5] At this page turn, the text does not resume at the top of the next page, but rather midway down. The entry for September 2, 1841, intervenes.

73

Rocky hill. The connection of this lightning rod with the ground was defective—it probably terminated in dry earth

The natural electricity being driven down into the lower end if it had not a free escape would be repelled off the electricity of the descharged as it descended the rod

I have examined a number of trees struck by lightning and they all present the same appearance that of being most shattered at the place where the larger branches are given off from the trunk.

    1 A tulip poplar, about 4 miles this side of Trenton struck. First and principal effect at the juncture of the body and larger branches slight effects higher up.

    2 High pine tree near <*the*> above struck at the branches

    3 Tree near Mr Comforts[6] struck same man[ner]

    4 Tree on Rocky hill struck the same

    5 Liberty pole without branches struck at the top and splintered to the bottom

[6] Presumably David Comfort of Kingston (*Henry Papers*, 2:376), Trustee of Princeton, and member of the Board of Directors and Trustee of the Seminary.

TO HARRIET HENRY
Family Correspondence, Henry Papers, Smithsonian Archives

[Philadelphia]
Monday afternoon
July 19th 1841

My Dear H.

I arrived safely in the city at about 3 oclock had a plesant passage found Mr Backus[1] of Baltimore on board the steamboat. We took the water at the place next below Trenton. Also I had some interesting conversation with the Physician from Africa who is mentioned in the papers as having addressed a meeting at Newark.[2] He gave me information concerning the

[1] Probably John Chester Backus (1810–1884), pastor of the First Presbyterian Church of Baltimore. Backus studied at the Princeton Theological Seminary and was a Director from 1841 to 1884. Alfred Nevin, *Encyclopaedia of the Presbyterian Church in the United States of America* (Philadelphia, 1884), p. 47. *Princeton Catalogue*, p. 431.

[2] The *Newark Daily Advertiser* of July 13, 1841, reported on a colonization meeting addressed by two colonists from Liberia, a Mr. Brown and a Mr. Harris: "Mr. Brown is an educated man, having studied medicine in Washington city before emigrating to Liberia, and is an influential citizen of the colony." The *Twenty-Fifth Annual Report of the American Colonization Society* (1842), p. 11, notes that James Brown, a member of the Legislative Council of Liberia, had been traveling with an ACS agent in the United

two young men Canfield and Alward who went from Princeton. They and their wives put up at his house. They were in good health and sperits when he left.[3] He is quite an intelligent man has the confidence and bearing of a free-man and says that nothing could induce him to return to the state of degradation of a coloured inhabitant of the United States. On my arrival I immediately called at Mr Vaughans found the Old Gentleman smart but somewhat indisposd with a slight attack of the bowell complaint. I next went to Baches—met on the way William Rogers the Geologist said he and his Brother[4] had just concluded to give us a visit at Princeton. They will perhaps return with me. Found Bache and his little wife preparing for a trip thrugh the State of Pennsylvania on a magnetic tour.[5] Staid at Baches until this morning. Went with Mrs B and Mr B to the Episcopal church. First however in the morning B and myself started to go to Dr Bethunes[6] to hear Dr Ludlow who is supplying Dr B's pulpit but found the church closed and was informed that Dr L[. . .][7] out of town. I have [. . .] as yet to call at [. . .] intend to go there to n[. . .] obliged to write this [. . .] inorder to request you [. . .] if you can find an[. . .] by the cars tomorrow [. . .] the 7[th] vol of Becquere[l . . .] city and the atlass[8] to the [. . .] the Book is in French [. . .] the shelf next the front [. . .] the atlass is on one of the she[lves . . .] under my desk. Direct [. . .] articles to me care of Mr Vaug[h]an Philosophical society rooms above the Atheneum.

I must make haste or I will be too late for the mail.

Kiss the little ones for me and believe me yours

as ever   H

I have purchased the book you requested. I have written this with a villanous steel pen.

States for six months and successfully promoting Liberia. The ACS concluded that "many of the colored people who had considered themselves as privileged above all their race, have been induced to reconsider the subject, and are constrained to admit that their condition and prospects are far beneath what they would be were they to emigrate to Liberia."

Several earlier annual reports mention support of James Brown in Washington during his training and his later position as Colonial Apothecary in Liberia. *Sixteenth Annual Report* (1833), p. 27; *Seventeenth Annual Report* (1834), p. 19; *Nineteenth Annual Report* (1836), pp. 18, 31; *Twentieth Annual Report* (1837), p. 12.

[3] Oren Kasson Canfield (1808–1842) and Jonathan Pennington Alward (1812–1841)

were both graduates of Princeton (1835 and 1836) and had attended the Princeton Theological Seminary. Alward was already dead by this time; Canfield died within a year. *Roberts*, pp. 92, 105.

[4] Probably Henry Darwin Rogers.

[5] During the summers of 1840 and 1841, Bache made a magnetic survey of Pennsylvania. See *Henry Papers*, 4:440n–441n.

[6] George Washington Bethune. *DAB. Henry Papers*, 3:341n.

[7] Because the upper right corner of the third page of the manuscript is missing, this and subsequent gaps occur in our text.

[8] Henry is referring to A. C. Becquerel's *Traité expérimental de l'électricité et du magnétisme*; both volume 7 and the atlas (1840) are in the Henry Library.

TO ALEXANDER DALLAS BACHE

Bache Papers, Smithsonian Archives

Princeton Aug 10th 1841

My Dear Bache

I have been so much occupied with my new course of Lectures on Geology that I have scarcely found time to eat or sleep and have therefore defered until the close of my lectures the overhaling of a lot of old papers to find the *memoranda* of the monuments on which the variation is recorded.[1] I find that I have the places of two of these noted on my old survey books.[2] One is at the place where the Chemung or Tioga river crosses the Pennsylvania line in the county of Tioga. It stands about 4 rods to the east of the river on the north side and is marked as follows one the one side

N York 60 miles and 69 chains

And on the other side

Penn^a Lat 40° [3] var 1°. 50'
1786

The other stone is in the county of steuben Town of Painted Post. It is not on the state line but on what is called the Massachusetts Preemption line.[4] On one side it is marked

8 miles 209 perch var 3°. 20 West
1792

On the other side

Massachusetts Preemption line

You will find no difficulty in finding these stones. Any person in the neighbourhood will inform you more particularly of the position. By following along the Preemption line and also the state line you would probably meet with a number of these monuments. I only noted such as came in the line of the survey on which I was engaged.

---

[1] Bache needed this information on the magnetic variation for his magnetic survey of Pennsylvania and adjacent sections of New York, Ohio and Maryland, which he conducted in 1840 and 1841. A. D. Bache, "Records and Results of a Magnetic Survey of Pennsylvania and Parts of Adjacent States, in 1840 and 1841 . . . ," *Smithsonian Contributions to Knowledge*, 1863, *13*: article 8; *Henry Papers*, *4*:440–441.

[2] The books of levels which Henry kept while a member of the state road survey of July–December 1825. *Henry Papers*, *1*:97–105.

[3] In reality, the latitude of the New York–Pennsylvania border is 42°. However, Henry wrote 40° in his tenth book of levels. We are uncertain whether blame for the error rests with Henry's copying or the boundary stone.

[4] In this case, the southern boundary of the portion of New York in which Massachusetts was granted the right of pre-emption (the privilege to purchase land before others, and at a minimum price) in 1786 in exchange for Massachusetts dropping all claims to sovereignty over this land. Benson J. Lossing, *The Empire State: A Compendious History of the Commonwealth of New York* (Hartford, 1888), pp. 333-335.

I will write by the next mail to my acquaintance Mr H. Pumpelley[5] of Owego and inform him of your intended visit to his village. He is a gentleman of leisure and will be of assistance to you in your survey. I would enclose a letter to him in this but I fear you may possibly have left Erie before it arrives[6] and in that case a doub[le][7] letter would subject you to a large postage.

I see by the papers that the Phil. society has purchased the Museum property for about 37 thousand dollars.[8] It was bid in by Dr Patterson. We will be very happy to see you at Princeton agreeably to your promise on your return. Lyell the great English geologist has arrived and is about meeting the New York State Geologists. The Governor I am informed was to call a special meeting of the corpse to receive him.[9] I am not certain that Mr Lyell will add much to our knowledge of the Philosophy of Geology by his lectures in this country although he will probably do much in the way of identifying our rocks. I think his work is sadly difficient in the principles of physique.[10] You may have seen by the papers that Union college had pre-

---

[5] Henry had met Harmon Pumpelly (1795–1882), a surveyor and wealthy landowner, while on the state road survey. *Henry Papers,* 1:109–110.

[6] The postmarks and changes of address indicate that the letter did miss Bache in Erie. It finally caught up to him in Philadelphia.

[7] A hole in the paper.

[8] The *Newark Daily Advertiser* of August 7, 1841, announced that the American Philosophical Society had purchased the Philadelphia Museum (Peale's Museum) on August 5 for $37,500. Although the price was initially viewed as a great bargain, in fact the acquisition of the Museum property almost destroyed the American Philosophical Society. The purchase had been made in anticipation of the sale of the Society's Philosophical Hall to the city of Philadelphia; and the Society had mortgaged its library, collections, and real property to raise the purchase price for the Museum. When the business depression and intensifying financial crisis of 1841 forced the city to withdraw its offer, the Society was left with two buildings, a large mortgage, and no funds. A vigorous fund-raising campaign by the membership helped pull the Society out of immediate financial disaster, but the Museum property had to be sold at a Sheriff's sale in May 1843.

William E. Lingelbach, "The Story of 'Philosophical Hall,'" APS *Proceedings,* 1950, 94:194; Charles Coleman Sellers, *Mr. Peale's Museum: Charles Willson Peale and the First*

Popular Museum of Natural Science and Art (New York, 1980), p. 302.

[9] In August 1841 Charles Lyell (*Henry Papers,* 2:135) arrived in the United States for a one-year visit. John Torrey had requested that Governor Seward call the New York State Geologists together to meet with Lyell during his swing through New York. Although such a formal meeting proved impractical, Seward issued orders for the geologists to cooperate with Lyell. Lyell did meet three of the State Geologists and spent some six weeks studying the geology of New York. Michele L. Aldrich, "New York Natural History Survey, 1836–1845" (Ph.D. dissertation, University of Texas at Austin, 1974), pp. 282–287; Charles Lyell, *Travels in North America, in the Years 1841–2,* 2 vols. (New York, 1845).

[10] Henry was not alone in finding Lyell's work less than satisfying. Lyell's failure to explain adequately the existence of great mountains, his rejection of the concept of the gradual cooling of the earth as a subject of concern by geologists, and the absence of tectonic complexities from his theory all dissatisfied contemporary scientists. Lyell's opponents argued that the earth's history reflected a progressive development rather than a mere repetition of events. Mott T. Greene, *Geology in the Nineteenth Century: Changing Views of a Changing World* (Ithaca and London, 1982), pp. 70–76, 93–112.

For other aspects of Henry's anti-Lyellian leanings in geology, see Henry Darwin Rogers

---

paired a degree for him (L L D) before his arrival.[11] We are now in the midst of our final examination and I have only had a snatch of time to search for the notes among papers which have been put away for ten years and more.

Yours as ever
Joseph Henry

My respects to Mrs B. I hope she will enjoy the tour very much and particularly the part of it through the state of N.Y. Mrs Henry requests me to say we will certainly expect to see yourself and Mrs B this time at Princeton.

---

to Henry, June 15, 1843, printed below, regarding a theory of mountain formation, and the petition from the senior class of the College of New Jersey, June 25, 1841, printed above, especially footnote 3, which discusses some of the specifics of Henry's lecture course on geology.

[11] Lyell was one of the five recipients of honorary degrees awarded by Union College at its July 1841 commencement. *Newark Daily Advertiser*, August 2, 1841.

TO JOHN TORREY
Private Collection, Albany, New York

Princeton Aug 10th 1841

My Dear Dr

Your letter of this morning was received this afternoon and I hasten to inform you by the return mail that it will not be a favourable time for the commencement of your course on botany until the middle of next week or the beginning of the week after.

We are now in the midst of the senior examination. The class will be dismissed on Tuesday next and until after then it will be impossible to make proper arrangements for your lectures. I have spoken to Mr Maclean on the subject and he is of the same opinion as myself. Tuesday the day on which the seniors are dismissed is holiday and therefore your lectures would be interrupted. Besides this during the senior examination the rooms are occupied with the several divisions of the senior class and those of the other classes.

If it be equally convenient to yourself I think it will be best that you begin say a week from Monday next or at any time after that before commencement. We will then be perfectly settled. If however it would be more convenient to begin sooner you might commence on the Thursday previous to the time above mentioned.

I have finished my course on geology and became very much interested in the subject. I am not however much impressed with philosophising of your friend Mr Lyell. He is an excellent observer but I think not much of a reasoner and deficient in a knowledge of Physique.[1]

Hitchcocks book I consider an excellent one.[2] The mail closes.

Yours as ever

Joseph Henry

All well Respects to Yours   J.H.

---

[1] Henry has half-printed this word, perhaps to give it a slight emphasis and indicate its foreign origin.

[2] Edward Hitchcock, *Elementary Geology* (Amherst, 1840), a copy of which exists in the Henry Library. For a discussion of the role of this work in Henry's course, see the petition of the senior class, June 25, 1841, above.

ROBERT HARE TO A.-A. DE LA RIVE

De La Rive Papers, Bibliothèque publique et universitaire, Geneva

Hotel de Couronne

Augt 11th

1841

My dear Sir

I much regret leaving Geneva without seeing you again and the more so on acct of the distressing nature of the causes which have prevented you from realizing your kind intention of allowing me to see you in town and to enjoy a few hours of conversation with you. Not hearing from you I should have left Geneva this morning but for the Delay of a Trunk which was to follow me here. That impediment being removed and not being enabled to see you I shall proceed to Villeneuve in the morning at eight oclock. I am however happy to have had an opp[y] of making a personal acquaintance with you. In all my peregrinations I have met with no individual so congenial at the same time in his pursuits and in his position in the world with myself as you are. You are a Professor of physical sciences which I also teach. We are both republicans and both reside in Countries where men of science living as we do in the style of gentlemen are among the first in society.[1] In too many instances have I found that those who fill

---

[1] Robert Hare's considerable wealth, estimated in 1846 to be between $250,000 and $1,000,000, was inherited from both parents. His father, Robert Hare, emigrated from England and was a prominent Philadelphia businessman. His mother was Margaret Willing, daughter of Charles Willing and Anna Shippen and sister of the Revolutionary financier Thomas Willing. J. W. Jordan, ed., *Colonial and Revolutionary Families of Pennsylvania*, 4 vols. (New York, 1911), *1*:129–130, and Edward Pessen, *Riches, Class, and Power*

professorships in Europe have but a humble position in life and from want of opportunity in consequence have not the air or manners which designates gentlemen. Of course I make these remarks confidentially.

I was advised on coming upon the European Continent by some experienced travellers to put *"rentier"*[2] after my name neither adding M D nor my title as professor. I have been told that to be a man of fortune living on my means would be more creditable than that knowledge of the sciences which is associated with the idea of a professor of Chemistry.[3] It is indeed

---

Before the Civil War (Lexington, Massachusetts, 1973), pp. 88, 328.

De La Rive's family had been among the Geneva elite for centuries. *DSB.*

[2] i.e., person of property, man of independent means, deriving income from *rentes*, financial instruments yielding regular and periodic revenue.

[3] Hare's interesting comments bear on the social status of scientists, and especially on the status of the professional positions they filled in the early nineteenth century. France and the continental countries developed their scientific institutions in ways very different than Britain or the United States. The stronger statist political culture of the former countries meant that science was first institutionalized in academies, was always closely allied to government, and was bureaucratized at a relatively early stage.

In Britain science was generally the preserve of wealthy gentlemen, and was institutionalized for the most part in universities (also the preserve of the wealthy). Such voluntary organizations devoted to science as the Royal Society or Royal Institution, or even the Manchester Literary and Philosophical Society, were similarly associated with upper-class values, or at least aspired to be. One of the concerns of the fledgling British Association for the Advancement of Science was to maintain a mass organization without losing the gentlemanly quality of the participants.

In the United States, the small scientific community was first found in voluntary organizations of polite culture, such as the American Philosophical Society. But in the 1820s and 1830s the science professoriate expanded, and the colleges became the dominant institutional base. They were attended by the wealthier members of society, and scientists often came from the ranks of the ministry, a relatively prestigious profession in antebellum America. As a result, the title "professor of science" in the Anglo-American context possessed high status: it connoted gentlemanly station and polite culture, and often—especially in Britain—wealth.

In France, "professor" was a term of ambiguous meaning. For example, teachers at French *lycées* (the equivalent of the German *gymnasium* or American high school) were termed professors, as were their more highly trained and regarded colleagues at the universities. The term could therefore evoke a lower-level civil servant in the provinces or a moderately independent and well-regarded faculty member of the Paris branch of the Université de France, or of the École polytechnique. But in addition, the highest status positions for scientists in France lay outside the university system, in the Bureau des Longitudes, or in the first section of the National Institute, the successor of the Royal Academy of Sciences. The term "professor" was not a clear sign of higher status on the continent.

"Rentier," however, had an unambiguous meaning in the kingdom of Louis Philippe, the motto of whose reign was *"Enrichez vous."*

See Maurice P. Crosland, "The Development of a Professional Career in Science in France," in *The Emergence of Science in Western Europe*, ed. idem (New York, 1976), pp. 139–159. Crosland stresses the switch from a "status" to a "merit" ordering of social institutions in France as a result of the Revolution, and the concomitant opening of professional careers in science. For the structure of French science on the eve of the Revolution see Charles Coulston Gillispie, *Science and Polity in France at the End of the Old Regime* (Princeton, 1980), especially pp. 74–184. The social roles of British scientists in the 1830s are explored in Jack Morrell and Arnold Thackray, *Gentlemen of Science: Early Years of the British Association for the Advancement of Science* (Oxford, 1981). The example of the BAAS was not lost on Americans; see ibid., pp. 411–425. See Stanley M. Guralnick, "The American Scientist in Higher Education," in

to be lamented that so little is done for science by those who lavish enormous sums for statues or pictures. How much has science done and is still doing for mankind, yet how meagre has been the patronage afforded to men of science? Amid the greatest extravagance in his expenditures in architecture statuary and painting the king of Bavaria does nothing for science. He is about to ornament one of his palaces with twelve gilt statues in Bronze at the cost of about sixty thousand of our dollars or 300000 franks yet I understood from the best authority that science owes to him no new resource.[4] Almost every where I observe that scavans are pinched for means wherewith to live or to prosecute their experimental enquiries.

I have been looking over your pamphlet on the actuel state of Electrical science.[5] It was quite agreeable to have my memory thus refreshed by a hand so competent as yours. Allow me to say that I am much surprised to learn that you saw a rotary apparatus moving upon the principle latterly reported to by Jacobi and others for the production of a moving power. I was of course aware of the rotary movements contrived by Faraday Ampere Cummings[6] and others, but was not aware that prior to Henrys wonderful improvement of the Electromagnet the idea of the employment of electro-magnetism to propel machinery had originated. Henry himself soon after he had made the improvement alluded to contrived an alternating machine. It seems to me that no essential advance has since been made. I conceive that the power of an electro-magnet cannot be advantageously applied to produce a rotary movement unless through the medium of an alternating one because the magnet can only react in an oblique manner in producing rotary motion directly. As soon as the position producing the greatest force is attain'd it no longer acts tangentially but tends to arrest the motion and retain the rotary magnet in that state of proximity. Under all circumstances I do not think that you should have passed from Richie to Jacobi without any allusion to Henry.[7]

The Sciences in the American Context: New Perspectives, ed. Nathan Reingold (Washington, 1979), pp. 99–141, for the status of American collegial scientists of this period. Clark A. Elliott, in "The American Scientist, 1800–1863: His Origin, Career, and Interests" (Ph.D. dissertation, Case Western Reserve University, 1970), found that the family background of scientists of the period—of which professors of science formed a fifth—was slightly wealthier and definitely more socially prestigious by occupation than the general population.

[4] Ludwig or Louis I (1786–1868), King of Bavaria from 1825 to 1848, is better known for his patronage of the arts and his affair with the dancer Lola Montez than for his support of science.

[5] "Coup d'oeil sur l'état actuel de nos connaissances en électricité," *Archives de l'électricité*, 1841, *1*:5–30.

[6] James Cumming (1777–1861, *DSB*), who produced a rotary motion using thermoelectric currents.

[7] In his article, pp. 27–28, De La Rive wrote that he had seen William Ritchie's rotary electric motor in operation in London in 1828. He then mentioned M. H. von Jacobi's larger motor and noted only in passing that some Italian and American physicists had also designed motors. Henry had published a de-

You seem to have overlooked Faradays recent researches and the doctrines respecting induction conduction and insulation which I have combated.[8] I hope from Bale to send you a pamphlet which I should be glad to have noticed under the head of atmospheric electricity when you again recur to that subject.

With high
Esteem
your friend
Robt Hare

---

scription of his reciprocating motor in 1831 and believed that Ritchie produced his motor only after Michael Faraday had exhibited a motor on Henry's design after reading Henry's article. Henry's concern that Ritchie did not properly acknowledge his prior work dates back to 1834. See *Henry Papers*, 2:162–163. See also Henry's similar comments to De La Rive concerning this priority problem in his

letter of November 24, 1841, printed below.

[8] i.e., in "A Letter to Prof. Faraday, on Certain Theoretical Opinions," *Silliman's Journal*, 1840, *38*:1–11, later supplemented by Hare's "Second Letter to Prof. Faraday," *Silliman's Journal*, 1841, *41*:1–14 (reprinted in L. Pearce Williams, ed., *The Selected Correspondence of Michael Faraday*, 2 vols. [Cambridge, England, 1971], *1*:350–358, 382–392).

FROM THE LECTURE COMMITTEE, MERCANTILE LIBRARY COMPANY OF PHILADELPHIA[1]

Henry Papers, Smithsonian Archives

Philad^a August 21st 1841

Dear Sir

The favourable reception accorded to the public Lectures heretofore delivered before the Mercantile Library Company of Philadelphia and the belief that a course of similar character during the ensuing autumn and winter will be equally satisfactory to the public has induced the Directors to appoint the undersigned a committee to make the requisite arrangements for that purpose.

---

[1] Founded in 1821, the Mercantile Library Company of Philadelphia provided its members with the services of a private library at a reasonable cost. The Company flourished and was reorganized twice between 1821 and 1842, first as a joint stock company, then as a corporation under an act of the Pennsylvania legislature.

A series of lectures on mercantile law, de-

livered during the winter of 1828–1829, led to the establishment of an annual program of lectures. Ten years later, the Company and the Athenian Institute began a jointly sponsored popular lecture series, encompassing a variety of topics. *An Historical Sketch of the Mercantile Library Company of Philadelphia* (Philadelphia, 1850), pp. 1–7.

In performance of the duty assigned them the committee most respectfully ask that you will deliver one lecture of the course at such time as will best suit your convenience and on such subject as you shall select excepting only sectarian tenets of Religion and of Politics.

The lectures are intended to be popular in their character and suited to a numerous audience of both Ladies & Gentlemen.

It is expected the course will commence on the last Friday in October and continue on the evening of each succeeding Friday untill about the first of March.

Your aid is earnestly desired in carrying forward this measure which the experience of past years affords abundant cause to believe is capable of effecting much good.

The undersigned will be glad to receive your reply[2] at your earliest convenience addressed to Isaac Barton No 27 South Second St Philadelphia.

> With great respect
> We are
> Yours &c[3]
> Thos. P. Cope
> Isaac Barton
> Charles S. Wood
> H. C. Corbit   } Committee
> Wm L. Schaffer
> Jno. Fausset
> Joseph C. Grubb

---

[2] No reply by Henry has been found. In light of the exchange printed below of May 21 and June 7, 1842, in which Henry agreed to lecture, we assume Henry did not participate in 1841.

[3] With the exception of Thomas P. Cope (1768–1854), philanthropist, state legislator and President of the Company (*DAB*), William L. Schaffer, a cashier at Girard Bank, and Joseph C. Grubb, suspender manufacturer, the co-signers were all Philadelphia merchants with businesses on High Street. Philadelphia City Directories, 1840–1845.

TO JOHN TORREY
Torrey Papers, Library, New York Botanical Garden

Princeton Aug 2[4][1] 1841

My Dear Dr.

I have made arrangements for occupying the class during the present week and agreeably to the statement of your letter[2] I anounced to the Faculty at their meeting yesterday that you would be in Princeton in time to commence your course on monday or tuesday next. It is probable that arrangements will be made so that the Sophomores can attend your lectures with the Juniors. You will therefore have a respectable audience as far as numbers are concerned. We are glad to learn that Princeton air has been of permanent benefit to Herbert.[3] He appeared to recruit quite smartely while he was here. I hope Mrs. T got home safely and pleasantly. She should have remained until you came out—her visit would have been much more plesant to herself and us had you been of the company.

Tell Dr Ellet that I would be much pleased to see him in Princeton.[4] I have sent copies of my paper to his Institution.

I receved this morning the Journals for Aug. but see nothing relative to the discovery of the transmutation of matter. The whole matter in the present state of the case is not worth much attention.[5] Sturgeon has gravely copied the story which went the rounds of our papers some months since of the wonderful recussitation of a criminal by means of galvanism which was said to have been produced by some persons in St Lewis. The whole you know bears the evidence on the face of it of imposition.[6] The Athe-

[1] Henry erroneously dated this letter "Aug 2nd." The postmark reads August 24. Notes by Torrey indicate it was received on the twenty-fifth and should have been dated the twenty-fourth.

[2] Not found.

[3] Herbert Gray Torrey (*Henry Papers, 4:* 145n).

[4] W. H. Ellet, Professor of Chemistry and Mineralogy at South Carolina College (*Henry Papers, 1:*337n).

[5] The April–June 1841 number of *Silliman's Journal* (*41:*208–209) contained a notice by Benjamin Silliman, Jr., on a discovery claimed by a young Edinburgh chemist, Samuel Brown, "that one element may be derived from another by causing atoms of the *same* element to combine with each other under peculiar conditions, giving rise to bodies dissimilar in all respects to the properties of the original matter, and corresponding in char-

acter with the attributes of some other elementary body. In other words, one element (as we at present consider them) may be transmuted into another, and he conceives that all matter may proceed from one simple elementary body, which by union with *itself* under different conditions, gives rise to other dissimilar bodies possessing characters which have, we think, been considered elementary. He can combine but cannot separate the atoms."

In papers read to the Royal Society of Edinburgh by Robert Christison, Brown claimed to have produced silicon from the carbon portion of paracyanogen (a polymer of cyanogen). Liebig was not able to duplicate his results (*BAAS Report, 1841* [1842], part 2, p. 54), nor was J. K. Mitchell (*Silliman's Journal,* 1841, *41:*382–383, and 1842, *42:*193–195).

[6] Electrical experiments on executed criminals were not unusual. Henry had conducted some himself in 1833 (*Henry Papers, 2:*90–96).

naeum contains very favourable notices of the Travels of Dr Robinson in the east and Stevens in Central America. [I] have as yet seen no further notice of Dr. Grant's book.[7]

I am glad that you have arranged the business you mention since I almost feared that you would let the valuable property slip out of your hands from sensitiveness relative to the proper course to be taken in such matters.

I agree with you in opinion relative to the treatment of an englishman although it would give me much pleasure to reciprocate in some degree the hospitality I receved when in England yet I would not like to have my advances improperly received.

I am now engaged with the junior class on the introductory part of my next years course. I have already gone over with them my lectures on geology in the way of review and recitations.

Yours as ever
J H

The article Sturgeon took from the *Louisville City Gazette* reported the resuscitation by galvanism of a murderer, John White, who was connected to a battery after hanging for twenty-five minutes. Whereas other subjects merely twitched, White sat up, stood up, and jumped into a corner. Although the leap severed his connection to the battery, he was pronounced alive by physicians and lived until overcome by violent convulsions some minutes later. *Annals of Electricity, Magnetism, and Chemistry*, 1841, 7:165–167.

[7] The July 24 issue of the *London Athenaeum: Journal of English and Foreign Literature, Science, and the Fine Arts* (pp. 550–552) contained a review of *Biblical Researches in Palestine, Mount Sinai and Arabia Petraea*, 3 vols. (London, 1841), by Edward Robinson (1794–1863, *DAB*). The reviewer called it "the most important contribution to Biblical geography which has appeared since the days of St. Jerome."

A four-part review, with extensive excerpts, of John Lloyd Stephens, *Incidents of Travel in Central America, Chiapas, and Yucatan*, 2 vols. (London, 1841), appeared in the *Athenaeum* issues of July 31, August 7, August 14, and August 21. Stephens (1805–1852, *DAB*) had briefly practiced law before he started traveling and writing highly popular books about his travels. In 1841 he returned to Central America and described his second trip in *Incidents of Travel in Yucatan*, 2 vols. (New York, 1843). His work stimulated great interest in the area.

Asahel Grant's book, *The Nestorians; or, The Lost Tribes* (London, 1841), was reviewed in the May 22 issue of the *Athenaeum*. Grant (1807–1844, *DAB*) had practiced medicine in Utica, New York, before becoming a missionary to the Nestorian Christians in Persia. The *Athenaeum* reviewer thought Grant's observations were valuable regardless of whether one adopted his hypothesis that the Nestorians were descended from the lost tribes of Israel.

Henry and Torrey may have known all three authors. Robinson was a graduate of Hamilton College and taught at the Union Theological Seminary in New York City. Stephens was a graduate of Columbia College and was elected a member of the American Philosophical Society in January 1841. Grant (*Henry Papers*, 3:50n) was a son-in-law of Henry's old friend William Campbell. His oldest son, Seth Hastings Grant, was raised by the Torreys (see below, Henry to Harriet Henry, August 8–10, 1843).

TO LA ROY SUNDERLAND[1]
The Magnet,[2] *July 1842, 1:39*

Princeton, N.J., Aug. 28, 1841.

Dear Sir:—Your letter,[3] making inquiry in reference to Animal Electricity, was received yesterday, but I fear I can give you but little information on the subject. We are, as yet, in possession of but a few definite facts, belonging to this part of science, and these are so insulated as scarcely to be entitled to the appellation of scientific.

The term polarity, of which you make use, is rather an indefinite expression, derived from magnetism, and sometimes rather loosely applied to certain electrical phenomena, but nothing like these has, as yet, been shown to exist in connection with the brain. Of the electro-magnetism of the human system I know nothing, and I can say, with certainty, that no branch of science bearing this name has an existence in the circle of the positive sciences of the present day.[4]

In reference to the galvanism of the human system, it may be said, that there are some striking analogies between the operations of the nervous influence and those of the galvanic current; but no definite connection has, as yet, been made out between them, although many experiments have been instituted for that purpose. Prevoost and Dumass, two Genevese philosophers, advanced the hypothesis, a few years since, that muscular contraction is the result of a current of electricity from the brain, through the filaments of nerves which surround the bundles of muscular fibres.[5] And Prevoost, just before his death, in 1839, (I think)[6] announced that he had succeeded in imparting magnetism to iron needles by means of the

[1] A Methodist preacher and abolitionist, La Roy Sunderland (1804–1885) credited his success as a revivalist to his hypnotic power. After becoming convinced that religion was a fraud, he turned to mesmerism, faith-healing, and the various reform movements of the antebellum period. He was a prolific writer and lecturer. *DAB.*

[2] Sunderland edited the first volume (June 1842–May 1843) of this monthly journal concerned with phrenology, mesmerism, the influence of electromagnetism on human physiology and psychology, and, more generally, the laws governing human nature. Subsequent volumes of the journal, issued under the title of the *New York Magnet*, were edited by P. P. Good. The last recorded issue was September 1844. *National Union Catalog.*

Sunderland included the following editorial comment at the bottom of the letter: "We were favored with the foregoing letter from Professor Henry, last Fall. His well known scientific attainments entitle his opinions to great weight on this subject; and hence we have given this letter a place in our columns."

The original of the letter has not been located.

[3] Not found.

[4] A garbled version of this paragraph is quoted by Robert W. Gibbes in his *Lecture on the Magnetism of the Human Body* (Columbia, South Carolina, 1843), p. 5.

[5] Jean-Louis Prevost and Jean-Baptiste Dumas, "Mémoire sur les phénomènes qui accompagnent la contraction de la fibre musculaire," *Journal de physiologie expérimental et pathologique,* 1823, 3:301–338.

[6] Henry has confused two different scientists. It was Pierre Prevost, a physicist (1751–1839, *DSB*), who had died.

nervous influence. As yet, however, this experiment has not been verified by any other person, although many have attempted it, and myself among the number.[7] No effect could be obtained, although the directions of Prevoost were observed, and I am almost certain that he was misled by some fallacy in the arrangements of the apparatus or the indications he observed. You will find a notice of this experiment in the *Bibliotheque Universelle de Geneve*,[8] and I believe there is a brief account of the hypothesis before mentioned, given in Melim Edward's Physiology.[9]

A variety of experiments were made by the English and French physiologists by dividing the gastric nerves of different animals, and introducing a galvanic apparatus into the circuit; but it is not certain whether the effects observed were due to the specification of the electricity, or to the ordinary vital action stimulated by galvanism.[10]

In the July number of the London, Edinburgh, and Dublin Philosophical Magazine, you will find the beginning of a paper by Martin Roberts,[11] Esq., on the analogy between the phenomena of electrical and nervous influence.[12] The author, however, appears to have only a very superficial acquaintance with the principles of natural philosophy, and his speculations are, therefore, of little or no value. Philosophical discoveries in the present advanced state of science can only be made by those who have prepared themselves by long study for the purpose, and have served, as it were, an apprenticeship to the business of experimenting. In order to advance any of

[7] See *Henry Papers*, 4:91. For another example of Henry's experimental interest in animal electricity, see *Henry Papers*, 2:90–96.

[8] "Note sur le développement d'un courant électrique qui accompagne la contraction de la fibre musculaire," *Bibliothèque universelle de Genève*, 1837, n.s. *12*:202–204.

[9] H. Milne-Edwards, *Outlines of Anatomy and Physiology*, trans. J. F. W. Lane (Boston, 1841), pp. 237–238. We suspect that "Melim" is Sunderland's misreading of Henry's scrawl.

[10] These experiments were initiated by A. P. Wilson Philip (1770–1847), a Scottish physician, during the second decade of the nineteenth century. After considerable controversy over the validity of the results, Philip's findings were confirmed in the 1820s. Philip argued that galvanic electricity was identical with the "nervous influence." More cautious scientists agreed that there were similarities between nerve impulses and galvanic electricity, but refused to go beyond the view that the electricity acted as a stimulus to the remaining nerve tissue, enabling the nerve to compensate for the damage. William H. McMenemey, "Alexander Philips Wilson Philip

(1770–1847), Physiologist and Physician," *Journal of the History of Medicine and Allied Sciences*, 1958, *13*:289–328, especially 298–301 and 304–310; P. M. Roget, "Galvanism," *Encyclopaedia Metropolitana*, Second Division (Mixed Sciences), 2:198.

[11] Martyn John Roberts (1806–1878) was a Welshman of independent means. Essentially self-educated in science, although he did spend some time at the University of Edinburgh in the late 1830s, Roberts's great passion was the application of galvanism to practical needs, such as blasting, assaying ores, and lighting. His lack of formal scientific training led, in his research and publication, to the rediscovery of already well-known principles and the exhibition of great gaps in his knowledge. He was an active but fringe member of the scientific and technological communities in Great Britain. *Proceedings of the Royal Society of Edinburgh*, 1878–1880, *10*:26–31.

[12] "On the Analogy Between the Phaenomena of the Electric and Nervous Influences," *Phil. Mag.*, 1841, 3d ser. *19*:31–38. The article was continued in 1843, 3d ser. *23*:41–45.

the experimental sciences, we must have a profound acquaintance with all that has been done in the particular branch, as well as with all the collateral ones. We must be familiar with the processes of experimenting, and with the logical methods of reasoning which alone are admissible in science.

Respectfully yours, &c.

JOSEPH HENRY.

P.S. You will find in the Annales de Chimie et de Physique, by consulting the general index to the work, several papers by Marianini on the effects of galvanism on animals, and also on the subject of electrical fish.[13]

[12] e.g., 1829, 2d ser. *40*:225–256; 1833, 2d ser. *54*:366–379.

"RECORD OF EXPERIMENTS"[1]
Henry Papers, Smithsonian Archives

Sept 2nd [1841]

⎰Effects of Lightning induction
⎱at a distance

I am informed by My Friend Dr Ellett[2] that he has observed that one of Dr Hares electrometers is affected by the flash from a cloud at a great distance even miles off[3]

apparatus placed on a window at each flash the leaf will strike the knob

If you take a human hair and draw it across the brass the leaves will diverge

[1] This entry shared a notebook page with the last paragraphs of the entry for July 16, 1841, printed above, which completed Henry's observations of the storm of July 14. Part of the entry found its way into Henry's November 5, 1841, account of that storm to the American Philosophical Society, published in the *Proceedings*, 1841–1843, 2:115–116.

[2] Apparently Ellet visited Henry in Princeton. See above, Henry to Torrey, August 24, 1841.

[3] Henry used this observation in his discussion of inductive effects from sparks in "Contributions V: Induction from Ordinary Electricity; Oscillatory Discharge," last paragraph.

EXCERPT,[1] MINUTES, TRUSTEES, COLLEGE OF NEW JERSEY
Trustees' Minutes, 3:389, 390, 391, Princeton University Archives

September 30th 1841 Eight Oclock A.M.
The Board took up the report of the committee on the *Presidents report*, on the *state* of the *College*. The Committee recommended the adoption of the following *Resolutions*, viz, . . .

6th　That, the *Museum* be put under the care of Professors *McLean* and *Henry*; and, that they be authorised to have the minerals arranged, and labelled; and, that a sum not exceeding $100.00, be appropriated for this purpose.
7th　That Professor *Henrys bills* for procuring and purchasing drawings, on Mineralogy, amounting to $97.25 *be paid* . . .[2]

Whereas, it is highly important to make substantial provision for the purchase of Philosophical and Chemical apparatus, for repairing and improving the same, from time to time:

Therefore *Resolved*, that in time to come, the members of the Senior Class pay, Each *Five dollars ($5.00)* to be appropriated to the enlargement of the *Philosophical* and *Chemical* apparatus.

[1] Omitted from these minutes are other routine actions of the Trustees.
[2] Henry's bill, for drawings for his geological lectures, is located in the Maclean Papers, Princeton University Archives.

FROM T. ROMEYN BECK
Henry Papers, Smithsonian Archives

Albany Oct[r] 4, 1841.

Dear Sir

You will receive with this, a copy of the "Revised Instructions of the Regents to Academies" published this year. By referring to page 53, you will observe that I intend to urge next winter, an appropriation for the purchase of instruments & the establishment of observers in various parts of the State.[1]

[1] Beck had succeeded Gideon Hawley as Secretary of the Board of Regents of the University of the State of New York on May 25, 1841. In a section of notes in the revised instructions, he wrote that he intended to propose improvements in the New York meteoro-

It would afford me great pleasure, if you would give me your views *in extenso*, as to the improvement of our Meteorological Observations—what additional instruments should be provided—what subjects deserve particular notice—& in fine whatever may occur to you to render these observations more scientific & at the same time, applicable to practical purposes.

I have made this application to only four individuals—viz. yourself, M[r] Redfield,[2] A. Dallas Bache & Col M[c]Cord[3] of Montreal. If you will favour me with your views, I intend presenting them with my report to the Regents, who will doubtless send them to the Legislature.

I should be glad to receive your communication not later than the 1st of December.[4]

The Secretaryship of the Institute has for the last two years been in rather a bad way—having been conducted either by M Henry or Horace B. Webster.[5] The former went out of office last January. I doubt whether the latter has ever transmitted the following resolution to you. If he has, there is no harm done in repeating it & it also allows me to ask that you will favour us with a notice of the matter. I have made repeated efforts

---

logical observations to the Regents at their next annual session. Conceding that previous appeals by the Regents to the legislature had failed, Beck urged that certain areas receive particular attention until the system could be improved. In addition to calling for accuracy in the calculations, Beck urged that every thunderstorm be registered, that the wind, rain, and duration of storms be noted, that foul weather following auroras be recorded, and that observations be made on the amount of rain at different heights. *Instructions from the Regents of the University, to the Several Academies Subject to their Visitation, Prescribing the Requisites and Forms of Academic Reports, &c.*, rev. ed. (Albany, 1841), pp. 53–54.

[2] William C. Redfield (1789–1857, *DAB*), one of the two leading meteorologists in the United States. Beck apparently did not consult James P. Espy.

[3] John Samuel McCord (1801–1865), a native of Ireland, was a prominent lawyer, and later judge, in Montreal. A summary by McCord of the weather at Montreal from 1836 to 1840 gives his affiliations as associate member of the London Meteorological Society, member of the Natural History Society of Montreal, and corresponding member of the Literary and Historical Society of Quebec and of the Albany Institute *(Silliman's Journal*, 1841, *41*:330–331). Pierre-Georges Roy, *Les avocats de la région de Quebec* (Lévis, Quebec, 1936), p. 295.

Charles G. B. Daubeny mentioned McCord in his *Journal of a Tour Through the United States, and in Canada, Made During the Years 1837–38* (Oxford, 1843), pp. 28 and 31: "Montreal contains a few individuals addicted to science, especially Mr. M'Cord, who keeps a very exact meteorological register," and "Saw Mr. M'Cord's meteorological instruments—very complete, and of the best kind."

[4] For Bache's ideas about improvements in the New York system and a description of the changes that were eventually made, see his letter to Henry of April 21, 1841, above. We have not found any reply from Henry to Beck. Bache mentions that he was about to send off a reply in his letter to Henry of December 1, 1841, printed below.

[5] Following several years of decline, the Albany Institute ceased operating in 1843. James M. Hobbins places part of the blame on Matthew Henry Webster (*Henry Papers*, *1*:62n) for "an overemphasis on meteorology, combined with Webster's own overbearing performances." Hobbins, "Shaping a Provincial Learned Society: The Early History of the Albany Institute," in *The Pursuit of Knowledge in the Early American Republic*, ed. Alexandra Oleson and Sanborn C. Brown (Baltimore, 1976), pp. 117–150; quote from p. 139. For Horace Bush Webster, see *Henry Papers*, *1*:407n. The Institute did not revive until 1851.

through booksellers here, to obtain Pickering's Address on Dr Bowditch, but have not succeeded.

The Resolution is as follows

"At a meeting of the Albany Institute held April 15. 1841.

A Statement was made to the Institute that in the Hon. John Pickering's eulogium on the late Nathaniel Bowditch, the author had made some remarks, which went to impute some error in the late Simeon DeWitt's Observations on Magnetism whereupon

Resolved that Professor Henry of Princeton be requested to investigate the subject & to furnish his opinion on the same to the Institute."[6]

Give my kindest regards to Mrs Henry, Miss Alexander & Miss Conner also to M^r & Mrs Alexander.[7]

Yours truly

T. R. Beck

NB. Address your answer to me [as] Sec^y of the Regents & it will come postage free.[8]

---

[6] The error was actually alleged by Bowditch, not Pickering, who may have caused confusion by not using quotation marks around material taken almost verbatim from Bowditch's article "On the Variation of the Magnetic Needle," *Memoirs of the American Academy of Arts and Sciences*, 1815, *3* (pt. 2):337–343. Neither Pickering nor Bowditch actually mentioned DeWitt. Bowditch questioned the assertion by "public surveyors" in New York that a retrograde movement of the magnetic needle had begun there sometime between 1804 and 1807, specifically, that the deviation between magnetic north and true north had stopped decreasing and begun to increase. He argued that the changes in declination on which the New York surveyors based their assertion were too small to be conclusive evidence of retrograde movement. From thousands of observations he made in Salem, Massachusetts, in 1805, 1808, and 1811, Bowditch concluded that the declination there was still decreasing at the usual rate.

In 1825 Simeon DeWitt had presented a copy of a table of magnetic variation from 1673 to 1800 to the Albany Institute and then described how he first noticed the retrograde movement of the needle in 1807. *Transactions*, Albany Institute, 1828–1830, *1*:4–7. *Silliman's Journal* linked the two papers by reprinting them together in 1829 (*16*:60–69).

If the Albany Institute members had looked at Pickering's eulogy, they would have seen that although Pickering quoted Bowditch, he

also cited an 1838 paper by Elias Loomis in which Loomis concluded that a retrograde movement of the needle had commenced sometime between 1793 and 1819 and that the change had probably not occurred everywhere at the same time (*Silliman's Journal*, 1838, *34*:290–309). In answer to the Institute, Henry simply called attention to Pickering's citation of Loomis's article, "the results of which, so far as they have a bearing on the point, fully verify the correctness of the late M^r DeWitt's observations." The substance of Henry's reply (which we have not found) is given in the Albany Institute Minutes of July 12, 1842, Albany Institute Archives. See also *Henry Papers*, *1*:96n–97n, 217n–218n, and 428–432. A copy of the eulogy, John Pickering, *Eulogy on Nathaniel Bowditch* (Boston, 1838), is in the Henry Library and is annotated with lines in the margins of the pages in question here (pp. 22–25 and Note G, pp. 92–94).

Henry evidently saw no reason to call the Institute's attention to another part of Loomis's paper in which he discredited the table which DeWitt had presented to the Institute in 1825, proving that some of it was based on calculations rather than actual observations.

[7] i.e., Harriet Henry, her mother and aunt, and her brother and his wife.

[8] This letter is not postmarked and is addressed to Henry in Princeton, "Care of Mr James Henry," who presumably delivered it in person.

FROM THOMAS GRAHAM[1]
Testimonials of J. J. Sylvester, *page 40*[2]

University College, London, Oct. 5, 1841

My Dear Sir,

Allow me to avail myself of the opportunity of communicating with you through my friend and late colleague, Professor Sylvester, who has been appointed, as you have probably heard, to the chair of Mathematics in the University of Virginia.[3]

I have to thank you for your kind recollection of me in forwarding copies of your electrical papers, which in common with other more competent judges here I highly admire. Indeed, it is an opinion not confined to myself, that the reputation of your country in physical science has for some time rested mainly on your shoulders.

Mr. Sylvester is a warm-hearted and most excellent man: his loss is much regretted by his former colleagues. He will, I have no doubt, confer dis-

[1] Henry had met Thomas Graham, Professor of Chemistry at University College, London, in 1837. *Henry Papers*, *3*:324–325, 493.

[2] This pamphlet, a copy of which is in the Library of Congress, was apparently privately printed by Sylvester in 1842. For a description see pp. 91–92 of Raymond Clare Archibald, "Unpublished Letters of James Joseph Sylvester . . . ," *Osiris*, 1936, *1*:85–154. We have not found the original of Graham's letter.

[3] James Joseph Sylvester (1814–1897), considered one of the most brilliant mathematicians of his generation, had been Professor of Natural Philosophy at University College, London, since 1837. Sylvester was a "graduate" of St. John's College, Cambridge; although he placed second in the mathematical tripos in 1837, his degree was not awarded until 1872 because he was Jewish, i.e., non-Anglican.

Several months after his arrival at the University of Virginia in November 1841, Sylvester resigned over an affair concerning an insubordinate student. He was unable to find another position in the States although he had testimonials from the leading British mathematicians and the support of his new American colleagues, notably Benjamin Peirce and Joseph Henry. His unsuccessful application to Columbia is documented below in letters of June and July of 1843. Unable to support himself and rejected by a woman whom he hoped to marry, Sylvester left for London in November 1843.

After working for many years as an actuary for an insurance company, Sylvester became Professor of Mathematics at the Royal Military Academy, Woolwich, in 1855 and also launched the *Quarterly Journal of Pure and Applied Mathematics*. He resigned from Woolwich in 1870 and was later awarded a government pension.

In 1876, on the recommendation of Peirce and Henry, Sylvester became Professor of Mathematics at the new Johns Hopkins University. For the next six years, as a teacher and as editor of the *American Journal of Mathematics*, he had a great impact on mathematics in the United States. He returned to England as Savilian Professor of Geometry at Oxford in 1884, a position he held until his death, although he retired from teaching in 1894.

DSB. For details of Sylvester's first residence in the United States see Raymond Clare Archibald, op. cit., which includes five letters from Sylvester to Benjamin Peirce in 1842 and 1843. Several letters which will be published in volume 6 of the *Henry Papers* concern Sylvester's disheartening experience in the United States and his activities immediately following his return to England.

According to a notation in Henry's address book, p. [37], he wrote to Graham about Sylvester in May 1844; we have not found a copy of the letter.

tinction upon the Mathematical School of the country which has adopted him, and be a valuable addition to its scientific circle.

Allow me to recommend him to your friendly consideration, and believe me,

My dear Sir,
Very sincerely and respectfully yours,
(Signed) THOS. GRAHAM.

"RECORD OF EXPERIMENTS"[1]
Henry Papers, Smithsonian Archives

Wednesday Oct. 6th 1841

Put large bar of iron into large spool—sent charge from 6 cups through the short thick inner coil. Sound at making and breaking battery contact— nearly of the same intensity.[2]

The sound was observed by means of the microphone and appeared the same whether wires were placed in the same line as above or at right angles thus

Next placed rod of small round iron in the coil of about 2½ feet in length sound of nearly the same intensity as with the larger both at begining and ending of the battery current. Then sent the current through the long wire, found the sound at the ending but not at the begining. Next

---

[1] These experiments in electroacoustics inaugurated the fall season of investigations, occasioned by the Princeton school recess. Henry experimented on an almost daily basis until November 5, when he presented findings on magnetic distribution and magnetic screening at a regular meeting of the American Philosophical Society (see below, Excerpt, Minutes, APS). Besides his magnetic experiments, Henry's research included electroacoustics, the direction of induced currents, the standardization of size of electric discharges, the magnetic action of a current in different parts of a long wire, a comparison of a bar magnet and an electromagnet in producing inductive effects, electrical repulsion in a vacuum, light polarization, the effect of magnetism on the chemistry of iron, and the

construction of a new battery. Only a certain portion of the results of a month of experimenting—notably that of the days just before the November 5 APS meeting—showed up in Henry's oral presention there.

[2] Work on electroacoustics first began on April 21, 1838 (*Henry Papers, 4:*34), but earnest effort only commenced some two years later, on April 29, 1840, and continued fairly regularly through May 15 (ibid., pp. 368–388), picking up again briefly in the middle of June (ibid., pp. 414–415). He very briefly experimented on electroacoustics on June 24, 1841 (above), as well. Henry thought of presenting his findings to the American Philosophical Society (letter to Bache, September 28, 1840, ibid., p. 441), but apparently never did so.

joined the ends of the short inner coil. The sound was now intirely imperceptible although the magnetism was as strong as before. Next sent the current through the inner coil and joind the ends of the outer the sound was diminished apparently but not intirely neuteralized.

The apparatus remaining as before, the microphone was removed and the end of a round rod of wood, about 15 feet long, placed against the end of the iron rod and the two pressed together. The sound by this arrangement was conveyed to the large room and appeared as distinct as with the sonometre close to the bar. The far end of rod of wood was placed in the ear which the other meatus was blugged with the finger.[3]

A single wire 18 inches long 1/10 of an inch in diameter, was next placed in the coil and the sound observed by means of a rod. It was not as clear as with the large bar but nearly as loud. The wire was stuck into the side of the rod thus the sound was apparently not quite as loud as before but the difference was very small.

Put a bundle of wires into the hollow axis of the large spool with the single wire. The sound was now almost imperceptible. Repeated this experiment with the same result. Next drew the bundle of wires so far out that the wire and the bundle met end to end in the middle—then the sound was as loud as when no wire was in the spool. Tried this again the sound was much less when the wires were put in.

[3] Meatus is an anatomical term referring to an opening, especially of a bony structure; in this case, the opening of the ear. Henry clearly meant "plugged," not "blugged."

"RECORD OF EXPERIMENTS"
Henry Papers, Smithsonian Archives

Oct 7th 1841

Put in operation 6 cups, arranged as a series of 3. Connected large coil no 1 with the battery. Placed coil no 2 on this with its ends connected with the shorter coil around the inside of the large spool. With this arrangement the sound from the small iron rod was distinct but not loud. This is a repatition of an experiment made about a year ago.[1]

Tried the shock from the current of the third order from the arrangement above, the <iron> bundle of iron wire being inserted and withdrawn alternately but little or no difference could be observed.

Made exp with magnetizing spirals. Placed Coil No 2 on No 1 which was connected with the battery arranged as 3 elements and the circuit of the secondary current closed with four spirals *a b c d* with a needle in each. The connection with the battery being made by means of a file or rather a rasp, the needles were all slightly magnetized except the one in *b*. They all gave the same direction to the current which was in accordance with my previous determinations. The first coil[2] was a compound one and consisted of more than a hundred turns of fine wire. The second *b* was a double spiral, the third was a single spiral the spires in contact—the third[3] a singl spiral with the spires widely seperated.

From this exp (which I have tried before)[4] it would appear that the spiral with a galvanic induced current gives in all cases the same indication of direction. The only circumstance which was unexpected in the result was the non magnetism of the needle in spiral *b*

Repeated this exp. again with the alteration of leaving out the long fine wire spiral *a*. All the other spirals now gave strong magnetism to their needles. I should have mentioned above that the magnetism was weak in all the spirals except *a*. This was probably due to the diminution of the intensity on account of the long fine wire which composed *a*.[5]

Made exp on magnetizing. the out side of small Boston on the inside — magnetism tin in the inside of the coil on out side.

Put piece of tin on coil sprinkled filings exhibited — put the magnetism stronger

[1] Electroacoustics experiments of June 15 and 16, 1840, *Henry Papers*, 4:414–415.

[2] "Spiral" not "coil" is meant.

[3] Henry meant the fourth spiral.

[4] See the experiments of September 24 and 25, 1840, *Henry Papers*, 4:436–439.

[5] A marginal comment "See page 266," referred forward to the May 30, 1842, entry (below), where Henry again investigated the secondary currents from galvanic batteries by means of magnetizing spirals.

"RECORD OF EXPERIMENTS"
Henry Papers, Smithsonian Archives

Oct 8th [1841]

Made an attempt this morning to determine the direction of the currents from galvanism by means of the effect on the nerves but without any definite effect.[1] Neither myself nor Sam gave the same indications in refference to the secondary and tertiary current. Perhaps we were not sufficiently sensitive galvanometers

Took the direction of the ending tertiary current with three sperals— same as those at the top of the page.[2] Each gave the same direction. The result in accordance with all my previous determinations. The tertiary current was one of quantity.

Took the direction of the tertiary current with the galvanometer—noted the first impulse, which was in the proper direction or in that which is given by the needle. The long swing however is in the opposite direction and might be mistaken for the true direction were not attention particularly directed to the fact. Repeated this with the long coil and by passing the current through water. The effect was not however much increased

[1] By having his subject grasp two handles and thus passing the current through the arms and torso, Henry hoped to find the direction of current unambiguously by seeing which side of the body twitched first.

[2] See the last two paragraphs of the previous entry.

"RECORD OF EXPERIMENTS"
Henry Papers, Smithsonian Archives

Oct 9th [1841]
Description of magnetometer also
Batteries—Magnetization of
needles transverse to conjunctive wire

Made arrangements for expermenting with ordinary electricity. Constructed an instrument for determining the intensity of the needles. It

consists of a graduated circle within which is suspended a magnetic needle. The needle to be tested is brought at right angles to the magnetic needle and the deflection gives the intensity required.

To measure the quantity of electricity passed into the battery from the machine, the unit measure of Snow Harris was employed. The slide or gage was placed at the 7th mark on the stem.[1]

The batteries used were th[re]e in number

First of 7 jars each of 10 $\times$ 18, 180 square inches = in all to $8\frac{3}{4}$ square feet afterwards added 5 more jars the whole surface was then *15 feet*

2nd of eight jars 13 $\times$ 12=156 inch = in all to $8\frac{1}{2}$ square feet

3rd consits of 23 bottles each $17\frac{1}{2}$ by $7\frac{1}{2}$ making 131 square inches = in all to 21 square feet nearly. This is the old Dr Franklin battery[2]

Exp. 1st Stretched fine copper silvered wire between the glass posts of the Universal discharger 30 inches long.

needle placed { 1st with 3rd battery charge 50—11 needles in contact mean deflection—	4°	5. hund
at 1st 10 wires { 2nd Same 12 needles in contact mean		
of the magnet. { deflection of the magnetometer	3.	16 hnd

2nd By the same arrangement—25 charge mean deflection
of 4 needles in contact   2? 25 hnd

Charge 50 4 needles   2. 89
Again same arrangement 4 needles in contact
charge 100—deflection   3? 12
Again charge   150 mean deflection   3 —

[1] On Snow Harris's electrometer, see *Encyclopaedia Britannica*, 8th ed., s.v. "Electricity," by David Brewster, p. 622, and *Henry Papers*, 3:177–178.

[2] A collection of Leyden jars, probably received through A. D. Bache, Franklin's great-grandson. See also Henry to O'Shaughnessy, October 30, 1843, footnote 3, below.

"RECORD OF EXPERIMENTS"

Henry Papers, Smithsonian Archives

October 11th Monday 1841

To determine if the same action is exerted alike on every part of the conjunctive wire—eleven needles were placed at equal distances from each other <*and*> along the wire and in contact with it. With the charge of 50 the following were the results the battery remained the same as before

1st 2nd 3rd 4th

3° 3° 4 $4\frac{1}{2}$, 5°, 5°, 6°, 6°, $6\frac{1}{4}$, $5\frac{1}{2}$, 6 farther end of the wire

Again same arrangement

$2\frac{3}{4}$, 3, $2\frac{1}{2}$, 4, $2\frac{3}{4}$, $2\frac{1}{2}$, $2\frac{3}{4}$, $3\frac{3}{4}$, $3\frac{3}{4}$, $2\frac{1}{2}$, 6, $2\frac{1}{2}$ farther end[1]

[1] Henry had eleven needles, but here made twelve entries. It is possible that he mistakenly entered "3 $\frac{3}{4}$" twice, as the second number is slightly smudged, as if it were partially erased.

There appears from the above results to be somewhat of a greater tendency to more intense magnetism at the farther end of the wire ie to the end nearer the out side of the battery. This was probably produced by the position of the balls of the handles of the universal discharger along which the wire was streached

NB In discharging the battery of 6 jars part of battery No 2 through the thin wire used in the above experiments and about a foot in length the wire observed to produce a sound which continued some seconds after the discharge. I must examine this

Platina wire fine 19 inches long 6 jars 1ˢᵗ battery—charge 250 deflection of needles 10. 7. 1 $\frac{1}{2}$ 0 0—needles one inch apart on the stand in a direct line at right angles to the length of the wire

Thin platinum wire again charge 275 needles arranged as before one inch apart—deflection 13. 7. 3. $\frac{1}{2}$ 0 —$\frac{1}{2}$ all the charge did not pass

Wire changed to the silvered coper length the same—charge 375 battery same needles arranged as before, deflections —8 +1 +6 +5$\frac{1}{2}$ +3 +$\frac{1}{2}$ 0. The discharge was loud. The alternation is manifest in this experiment

Wire the same as the last 2 batteries 1ˢᵗ & 3ʳᵈ (6 jars of first) charge 300.

+8$\frac{1}{2}$ +9 +6 +1$\frac{3}{4}$ +$\frac{1}{2}$ +0 +0   1ˢᵗ needle in cont
and each one inch
apart

"RECORD OF EXPERIMENTS"

Henry Papers, Smithsonian Archives

Oct 12ᵗʰ 1841
Magnetism
Axis of Spontaneous Polarity[1]

Battery of 6 jars charge 100—wire thin coper plated used before length 12 inches deflect. +2 +1$\frac{1}{2}$ +$\frac{1}{2}$ 0 $\mp$0. 0

Wire same as in last exp 3 needles first in cont a frame *a* with long wire placed near—battery 6 jars—charge 100

4$\frac{1}{2}$ 3$\frac{1}{2}$ 0 deflect

From this exp no effect is produced by the frame perhaps the wire is too long

---

[1] The heading was moved here from the top of the second full notebook page. It occurs on the following page also.

The machine does not work well to day. The weather is damp and rainy

Turned to the experiments on the galvanic current the weather being unfavourable to the action of the ordinary electrical machine.

Exp stretched fine copper wire between the poles of the universal discharger—sent primary and secondary current through  while the microphone was attached but no sound could be heard.

Attached long copper wire to the poles of Clark's galvanometer then suddenly streached the wire, thinking perhaps by this disturbance of the particles, electricity might be developed but no effect was observed on the needle.

Perhaps if the wire had been stretched in one direction and condensed in another <*that*> a positive effect may have been produced. Try this again.

 Suspended or rather supported on a point a plate of tinned iron, within a coil of copper wire (the Davis coil).[2] I was surprised to find that the <*points*> positions of stable equilibrium were those in which the sides of the square were parallel to the axis of the coil—and that when the square was so turned that its diagonals were parallel to the sides of the coil, then the position was an unstable one and the slightest oscillations would throw it to one side or the other. I should have supposed before this experiment that the plate would have arranged itself with the diagonal in the direction of the axis of the coil.

I supposed at first that the above exper. tended to show that the magnetism of a piece of [iron] was[3] at right angles to the surface and inorder to test this idea I formed a piece of plate thus cutting the edges of a square so that the circles might be at rangles[4] to the surface and also to the diagonal *a b* but when this was supported in the coil the position of stable equilibrium was as before that in which the sides of the square were at right angles to the coil or parallel to its axis. (The reason for the phenomenon is probably that when the one diagonal is parallel to the axis of the coil the other is perpendicular to the axis and near in the extremities to the surface of the inside of the coil and hence it will be powerfully acted on [by] the induction of coil)[5]

---

[2] i.e., one bought from Daniel Davis, Jr. See *Henry Papers*, 4:444–445.

[3] In the margin of the page which begins here is the descriptive title, "Axis of spontan-

eous magnetism of soft iron."

[4] i.e., right angles.

[5] The material in parentheses is **lightly** crossed through in the original.

When the angles *a b* were cut off then the square arranged itself at right angles to the coil in the lines S N [6]

Next cut a circle of tinned iron—supported this horizontally in the coil which was placed vertical. Thus around on the needle point many times fore comming to rest—but as soon as The plate spun in sucession before the circuit was completed with the battery, the whirling ceased. The plate became polar. The polarity was indifferent however as the plate would remain at rest <at> in any position but it required a slight force to turn it into a near position

Next cut a piece of iron into the form of a cross thus with equal arms supported this in the centre of the coil.

It took up a position of stable equilibrium with the axies in the direction NS or with the sides of the square from which the figure was cut parallel to the axis of the coil. The directive force was quite energetic and when the circuit was suddenly formed the cross came to its position by a series of rapid oscillations. The directive force appeared greater than in the case of the square.

The whole of this subject appears to me to be curious and connected with the theory of magnetic distribution and the retentive power of long bars.

[6] Added here with a different pen are the words, "The shorter axis ⟨at right angles to the⟩ in the plane of the coil."

"RECORD OF EXPERIMENTS"
Henry Papers, Smithsonian Archives

Oct 13th 1841

Clear day—good weather for elect.

Tried the induction of the different of plates of tinned iron by a common straight steel magnet. As I had expected the axis of spontaneous magnetism was in all cases through one of the longer axies of the figure. In the case of the square for instance the polar axis passed through one of the diagonals.

The idea occurred to me, that perhaps a motion might be produced by means of the arrangement of the circular plate and the coil. For this purpose the coil was placed vertically, with the plate supported horizontally on a needl point in the centre of the coil—and a bar magnet brought in a line of the tangent to the circle but no motion of a rotatory kind was produced.

Made an experiment to determine if a coil transmitting a galvanic current acted like soft iron in increasing the intensity of the secondary current. For this purpose coil no one was placed on the table, coil no 2 on the last and helix no 1 on these. The ends of coil no 1 connected with the battery by means of the mercury cup—while a perminent current was passed through no 2. When the circuit with the battery was formed with no 1 the needle of the galvanometer was deflected by the secondary current to 15°.

The constant current through no 2 was then stopped and the exp repeated. The deflection was about the same.[1]

The experiment was repeated in the same manner with the exception of changing the direction of the constant current but no difference was perceptible

It would appear from this experimt that in the reaction of the induction of soft iron there is no analogy in an action of a coil transmitting a galvanic current. And on reflection I now think there was no reason to expect an action of the kind since in the case of soft iron the induction is produced at the beginning and ending of the change of magnetic state of the bar—which only takes place at the beginning and ending of the galvanic current—but in the case of the galvanic current the action must be instantaneous both ways like a single wave which instantaneously subsides

Repeated the attempt to reproduce the sound mentioned on page 206[2] and suceded with the battery of six jars and the electrometer (quadrant) at nearly eighty. The sound was quite perceptible. The wire was 15 inches long and of the thin plated kind. The same effect was produced by a wire of about a foot long of the same spool as the last. With a shorter wire the sound was not produced nor with a small discharge of the battery

The same effect was produced with a lowder sound in using the sonometre sending the discharge through the iron wire of the instrument which is 3 feet 8 inches long. The battery was still the same as before. Next the Franklin battery was added and a charge considerably greater but the electrometer only s[t]ood at about 48. The wire was stretchd by a w[e]ight

---

[1] Henry made a marginal reference here to an experiment of October 24, 1840. See *Henry Papers, 4*:445–446.

[2] In the first half of the entry for October 11, 1841, above.

October 15, 1841

I found on inspecting Priestelies History of electricity that he had made experimts on the sound of electricity and at first sight I was of opinion that he had hit on the same phenomenon as the one given above but it appears that the sounds he mentions (see second vol.) were produced by the concussion of the air by the discharge of the battery[3]

[3] In *The History and Present State of Electricity*, 3d ed., 2 vols. (London, 1775), 2:355–356, Joseph Priestley stated that of four batteries he tested, two gave concert F-sharp and two C-sharp, with the batteries of the larger surface area giving the deeper tones. This work is found in the Henry Library.

"RECORD OF EXPERIMENTS"
Henry Papers, Smithsonian Archives

Oct 15th 1841
Made no exp on the 14th

N B Accidentally turned over two pages[1]

In order to determine if the sounds described on the $<last>$ 212th page were not due, as in the case mentioned by Priestley, to the sympathy of the wire with the agitation of the air by the crack of the battery discharge, I made a number of experiments—using the battery of 6 jars—but although the crack was very loud the electrometer at 80° no sound could be observed—unless the discharge was passed through the wire of the sonometer. Also care was taken to prevent any effect from the noise made by the striking of the different parts of the apparatus together

Also the discharge was sent through a thick copper wire placed parallel to the wire of the sonometer and at the distance of about $3/4$ of an inch from it but no sound could be produced in this way. From all these experimts I am sure that the sound must be due to the agitation of the particles of the wire by the sudden repulsive energy of the electrical principle

Attempted to get sound from the sonemetre by means of a galvanic current from the battery of 6 cups arranged as three but no effect was observed neither with the sonometre alone nor by the addition to the circuit of the long coil no 1

N B The idea occurred to me while making this exp. that possibly the conducting power of a wire for electricity might be altered by causing it to vibrate during the passage of the current. Try this[2]

[1] Originally circled in ink. Henry skipped from page 212 of the notebook (the last three paragraphs of the entry of October 13) to page 215. Realizing his mistake, he skipped back to write on pages 213 and 214, and concluded the entry on page 216. We have arranged the material to fit his order of writing.

[2] Henry endorsed this idea in an undated

I have had made by Mr Rowan[3] an ingenious watch repairer now settled in our village a heliostat on the plan given by Dr Young in his Natural philosophy.[4] I have put [it] in its position on a board nailed on the window sill of my little study. I find it answers very well. The instrument was adjusted by calculating the point on the wall of the room where the image should strike and then turning the mirror until it fell on this place. A meridean line was drawn on the board which is on the window by means of concentric circles and the immage of a small hole

Made another experiment on the spontaneous axis of polearization.[5]

Held the streight magnet over the cross found that the induced polarity was still along the arms and not along the resultant as in the case of the induction from the coil.

When the coil was placed with its axis in a line with the support of the cross so as to be at a small distance from the same and to act like the end of a magnet then the direction of the spontaneous axis of polarity was the same as in the case of a straight magnet

Placed[6] a piece of white paper over the face of the small coil (Davis) and passed through a current from the battery of 6 cups arranged as three then sprinkled filings on the paper the arrangment was as shown in the margin. The filings around the margin of the circle were arranged in radii while in the middle they stood perpendicular to the paper

---

jotting found at the end of volume 2 of his laboratory notebook, following the entry of July 22, 1842: "Is the conducting power of a bar for elect. affected by being put in a state of vibration. Perhaps elect may be developed by the vibration of a bar." Henry Papers, Smithsonian Archives. See also "Record of Experiments," October 14, 1843, footnote 2, below.

[3] James Rowand, a jeweler and watchmaker in Princeton. *Hageman*, *1*:320.

[4] See the APS *Proceedings*, 1841–1843, 2:97–98, for Henry's presentation on the heliostat at the American Philosophical Society meeting of September 17, 1841.

The idea that Thomas Young had for a heliostat is sketched in Figure 400, Plate XXVIII of his *Course of Lectures on Natural Philosophy*. The conception was both simple and elegant: a mirror canted to reflect sunlight in a line parallel to the earth's axis of rotation will continue to reflect light in that direction if rotated around this axis to follow the sun. (Of course, this device would not take account of the seasonal variation of the sun's position in the sky and would have to be recalibrated every couple of days.) Thomas Young, *A Course of Lectures on Natural Philosophy and the Mechanical Arts*, 2 vols. (1807; reprint ed., New York, 1971), *1*:425–426.

Henry's earliest known acquaintance with the heliostat came in 1837, on a trip to the instrument shop of Alexander Adie of Edinburgh. Henry observed a heliostat made on Young's principles, and noted that its independent discovery had been made by Richard Potter of London in 1833, a point he reiterated in his APS talk. That presentation also stressed the low cost of Henry's heliostat and its improvement over earlier models: it was adjustable for use at different latitudes. Henry's European Diary, August 5, 1837, *Henry Papers*, *3*:440–441.

[5] Compare the "Record of Experiments," October 12, 1841, above.

[6] In the original, the illustration to the left is smudged over, presumably by Henry.

Next sent current through coil on the out side of tinned iron cylender. The arrangement was as shown in the margin scarcely no magnetism within while it whas highly magnetic on the out side. The filings were drawn away from the rim on the inside and thus left a white line around

Put the coil insid of the tinned iron cylinder we had then no signs of magnetism on the out side but a very beautiful eradiation on the inside, similar to that shown in the figure. In order to exhibit the magnetism of the inside the circle of the section of the iron should be of considerable diameter, 6 inches or more, and the current should be very powerful—perhaps a certain thickness of the iron is necessary. (*Make experiments on these points with a large and more powerful battery*)[7]

Sent charge of galvanism through the inside and out side in same direction—the magnetism on the out side was then strong but no radiation or appearance of polarity was found on the inside. The action within was nutralized by that without

Next passed the current through the coil on the inside and out side but in opposite directions. Now magnetism was apparent within and without. Repeat this with reference to the lifting power

[7] See the end of the entry for November 3, 1841, below, for similar experiments with the stronger Daniell battery constructed on the second. The experiments continued through November 4.

TO CHARLES N. BANCKER[1]
Bancker Papers, Library, American Philosophical Society

Princeton Oct 15th 1841

My Dear Sir

In the prosecution of my electrical experiments I am just now much in want of one of Snow Harris' thermo-electrometers—the instrument which indicates a current of electricity by the heating of a platinum wire in the bulb of an air thermometer.[2] I know of no person in our country except yourself who probably has the instrument. If you have one and are not

[1] Bancker was a member of the American Philosophical Society and had an extensive collection of instruments. *Henry Papers*, 2:160n; 4:223–224.

[2] Henry's description was quite accurate. Though Henry mentioned current electricity, the device was an electrometer, used to measure the static charge on an object. The electricity was discharged through a thin platinum wire, which heated a large air bulb. The expansion of the air was noted by the rise in height of a column of fluid. In all, the

using it you will oblige me much by loaning it to me for a few weeks. Or if you have two of the same kind or if you are in the way of procuring another perhaps you would sell the instrument to me for our college collection. If you can oblige me in this matter may I ask you to send the article directed to me to the care of Dr William Mc.Dowell Mission Rooms Sansom St.[3] Dr McDowell will come to Princeton on monday or tuesday of next week and will take charge of the instrument. It will be well to give the bearer caution in reference to the fragile nature of the article.

I regret to be obliged to trouble you in this way particularly since you have never given me an opportunity of reciprocating your favours.

With much
Respect
Yours truly
Joseph Henry

---

height of the fluid was as the square of the quantity of electricity discharged. For a diagram of the instrument and a fuller explanation, see W. Snow Harris, *Rudimentary Electricity*, 2d ed. (London, 1851), pp. 108–109.

Though Henry claimed that he needed this instrument for his experiments, he made no explicit reference to it in the October and November entries of the "Record of Experiments."

[3] William Anderson McDowell (1789–1851), D.D., Princeton graduate, tutor, seminarian, and variously Trustee of the College and Director of the Seminary. In 1841, McDowell was Corresponding Secretary of the Board of Domestic Missions of the Presbyterian Church, at 29 Sansom St., Philadelphia. *Princeton Catalogue*, p. 122; *Roberts*, p. 2; Philadelphia City Directory, 1841.

"RECORD OF EXPERIMENTS"
Henry Papers, Smithsonian Archives

Oct 16th 1841

Tried this morning the expermt of Snow Harris. Placed an electrometer of gold leaf under the receiver of the air pump—made a vacumm of less than 1/4 of an inch. The leaves still remained in a divergent state. When the air was let in very gently the leaves converged immediatly.

 This result of Snow Harris is due to the small charge of the electrometer and the imperfect vacumm, for when I suspended two peices of cotton thread between two balls thus and the air exhausted no sign of repulsion was exhibited, when the ball on top was connected with the excited machine. But when the air was re-admitted the insulation was produced and the threads were powerfully repelled[1]

[1] See W. Snow Harris, "On Some Elementary Laws of Electricity," *Phil. Trans.*, 1834, pp. 213–245, especially pp. 223–224 and 243–244. The experiment was designed to test

It would not be difficult to try the repulsion of the leaves in a Toricellian vacum

Repeated this morning the experiment with a slip of tin foil pasted on glass.[2] Suspect that the result given as the repulsion of the consecutive parts of the current is due to an explosion of the metal at the point of section, because at each point I observe that there is a stain on the glass of the deflagrated metal. Also observed that when one piece of metal (tin foil) is plac[e]d over another that a hole is made in one or the other. Made the same exp. under the receiver of an air pump repulsion did not appear as great as in the air.

---

whether the repulsion depended on the presence of the atmosphere, as it might in a fluid theory, if atmospheric pressure were necessary to keep the electrical fluid on the surface of the body. In a vacuum the fluid would be expected to disperse, and electrical repulsion disappear (L. Pearce Williams, *Michael Faraday:*

A Biography [New York, 1965], pp. 302, 317–318). Harris found that the absence of air made no difference in the electrical effects, and that a vacuum in fact improved the retention of electrical charge.

[2] "Contributions III: Electro-Dynamic Induction," paragraph 126.

"RECORD OF EXPERIMENTS"
Henry Papers, Smithsonian Archives

Monday Nov 1st 1841

Placed a <glass> tin tube on the two sides of a piece of plate glass, I should say window glass, so that the axes of the two tubes were in the same line on the end of each tube. I then fastened with bees wax a tourmaline, placed with their axes at right angles to each other so that no light passed through the tube. The tube on on[e] side of the glass was attached to the positive side of a battery of six jars and that on the other side was connected with the minus side of the same. The eye was then placed near the end next to the minus side but no effect could be perceived. I thought perhaps depolearization might be produced by a change in the particles of the glass

Connected with the galvanometer two pi[e]c[e]s of iron, plunged both into solution of acid to the depth of quarter of an inch. The needle was deflected sometimes on one side and sometimes on the other. When it became stationary—I brought the pole of a strong magnet incontact with one of the end[s] of one of the pieces of iron so as to render it strongly magnetic but no differ[ence] in the current could be observed the needle remained stationary. Hence the magnetization of a bar does not change the chemical relation to acid.[1] I observed in this experiment that the [needle] always joumped in one direction when the iron was plunged in and then swing widely in the other imediatly after

The following exp shows the delicacy of the galvanometer. I grasped in one hand a piece of zinc connected with one of the wires of the galvanometer and with the other I touched to my tongue the other end of the galvanometer wire the needle was deflected and by timing the touchs to the tongue with the swing the deflection was extended to $45°$ degrees. When the circuit was extended by introducing into it an other person the same effect was produced. In this experiment one person grasped the zinc the other the copper and then the two joined hands the needle was deflected. In these two last experiments the small fine wire galvanometer was used.

[1] Both these experiments try to show "correlation of forces" by looking for the effect of one type of physical force on another: electricity on the polarization of light and magnetism on the chemical properties of iron.

"RECORD OF EXPERIMENTS"
Henry Papers, Smithsonian Archives

Nov 2nd [18]41.

For several days past I have been engaged with *Sam* the *coloured assistant* in constructing a Daniell's Battery on a much larger scale than the one I before used.[1] It consits of 12 elements, each formed of a tube of brass—shut at the bottom so as to form a cup twenty inches high and 3¾ inches in diameter. The zincs are formed of rods 3 quarters of an inch indiameter and 20 inches long. They were cast by driving into a stove-pipe filled with sand a rod of wood of the dimentions of the intended rod and then withdrawing the same—the metal was poured into the hollow. In this way the casting was perfect and completely answered the purpose.

Tried 6 jars of the above battery found the magnetic and electrical effects very powerful. The snap was louder than the one with the great battery of plates described in my first paper[2] when arranged as a series of 8 elements

[1] This in part explains the lack of entries between October 16 and November 1.

[2] "Contributions I: Battery."

Tried the secondary current from the long or rather large reel—4 miles of wire were placed on the reel around the nine strands at the axis. The hollow in the axis was filled with a bundle of iron wire. The secondary shock was so powerful that I felt it through the floor. It passed through nearly half an inch of heated air in the flame of a spirit lamp. When iron filings were placed in a tea sau[c]er and the secondary discharge made through them the effe[c]t was beautiful the deflagration was like the coruscations from the jar coated on the out side with iron filings. With the six jars* a spark was produced at the moment of making contact as well as at breaking

* *mugs*

"RECORD OF EXPERIMENTS"
Henry Papers, Smithsonian Archives

Nov 3$^{\underline{rd}}$ 1841
{ Illustration of the
{ Electrical fish

Made arrangements this morning to experiment with the Daniells battery and while the apparatus was prepairing I repeated some expermts on magnetism of soft iron. For this purpose used first Davis' small coil.

Iron wire placed on the inside became strongly magnetic on the outside also magnet but much less powerful. Where the end projected considerably below the plane of the coil the magnetis[m] was quite feeble. This was probably due to the action of the farther side of the coil unscreaned

Tried the decomposing power of the battery found 5 inches of gas was given off in 20 seconds or 15 cubic inches in a minute—gass come [?out] in large bubles from the wires. Secondary shock quite powerful could be felt in the breast and arms when the feet stood on the damp floor

Placed the two balls which serve as handles into a basin of water while they were connected with the ends of the secondary current from the large spool. When the finger and thumb of the hand were placed in the basin—in the line of the discharge—a shock was felt and also when the finger and thumb were  placed a considerable distance aside as at *a b* but when the fingers were placed cross wise as at *c & a* no effect could be perceved.

When a single finger was plunged in the basin no effect could be noticed provided the body was insulated. This is the repition of the experiment which I have published in my last paper, relative to the hypothesis of the electric eel[1] but I was probably mistaken in reference to the slight shock in the one finger which is probably due to a lateral current.

When salt and water was substituted for the pure water of the last experiment no shock could be felt with the finger and thumb in any position. The salt water is a better conductor than the body and the elect will not leav it to pass into body

 Attempted to get induction from the water through which a current was passing but did not succeed at least by the method of shocks

Sent[2] the secondary shock from the large reel through the wire of the sonometre but could perceve no sound.

Tried to produce sound by sending primary current first through wire around the iron of the large reel and then through the wire of the sonometre. The iron wire of the sonometre became quite hot but no sound was produced.

Made a coil of three layers around a zinc cylinder of about <8>7 inches in diameter and the same in length of axis. Floated in this a piece of iron wire with a cork around it. The wire became powerfully magnetic and invariably sought the side of the tube, so that the position in the centre is one of unstable equilibrium

Next supported on a needle point a small iron needle. This became powerfully magnetic and vibrated with great rapidity. It required a considerable force to put it out of the direction of the axis of the cylinder

Supported a plate of <*tinned*> sheet iron on the point of a needle presented it to the mouth of a coil (the one last mentioned) when out of the coil before the mouth the axis of spontaneous magnetism was in the direction of the longer axis or the diagonal of the square. When

[1] "Contributions IV: Electro-Dynamic Induction," paragraph 30.

[2] Here, at the beginning of a new page in the notebook, Henry had a new heading: "Spontaneous axis of polarity."

the square was put into the coil the axis of spontaneous magnetism was found as before along the middle and parallel to the side of the square

Sent current through long helix described in the old book[3]— wire placed on the out side magnetic when the lower end was near the lower side of the coil as at *a* but when the wire was pushed down so that the lower end was at *c* very little effect the filings dropped off.

Put wire in inside it became powrfully magnetic but went to the side.

Rolled the large ribbon in[t]o a ring 20 inches in diameter—placed piece of soft iron without the coil at the distance of 6 inches. Lifted large quantity of filings near by, which became less and less as the distance was increased. Placed piece of iron on the out-side which became magnetic.

Made the two coils No 1 & 2 into a single ring of 34 inches in diameter and then made a magnetic exploration of the space around for this purpose I used a slip of sheet iron

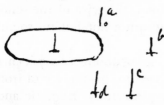

At *a* very little magnetism at *b* which was 13 inches off magnetism very percptible and increased in strength until the iron was placed against the coil. At c the magnetsm appeared stronger than at d.

In passing across the coil the magnetism changed its sign

Repeated last expermt with the apparatus for induction helix no 1 was placed at different distances from the ring. On the outside and above found shock at elevation of 90 inches—and at 15 inches on the out side

Found the magnetism within the ring increase in intensity as the circumference was approached

Placed inside of this large ring of current a large ring of iron one foot in diameter. This became magnet the end face a pole.

Placed the square plate over the ring it took the position shown ie with the shorter diameter across as the spontaneous axis of polarity

---

[3] In the previous laboratory notebook, Henry had described and used a helix of 1,640 feet of fine wire. See *Henry Papers*, 4:7 ("Record of Experiments," February 1838) and "Contributions III: Electro-Dynamic Induction," paragraph 9.

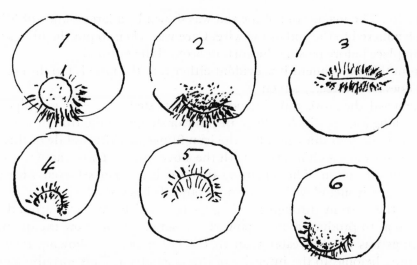

The above figures represent the magnetization of a plate within the large coil. NO complete circle no 2

"RECORD OF EXPERIMENTS"
Henry Papers, Smithsonian Archives

Nov 4[th] 1841
Exp with 12 cylinders
of New battery[1]

{ Imitate the foregoing experiments by means of straps or ribbons of copper
{ Exp[er]iment on the magnetism of hollow bars with soft iron needle.[2]

Put stove pipe into the coil around the zinc and into this a soft iron needle on a needle point. The soft iron was rendered strongly polar. To vary this expermt placed a quantity of iron filings on a paper in the middle of the length of the stove pipe and then introduced a short rod of

---

[1] Four subsequent headings in the entry read: "Distribution of magnetism."

[2] These two notes may have been part of the previous entry. The first clearly refers to the experiments of November 3; and Henry added a citation in the margin to experiments 4 and 5 of June 15, 1840 (*Henry Papers*, 4:412–413), which mention an experimental apparatus similar to the one used that day.

The comment "Exp[er]iment on the magnetism of hollow bars with soft iron needle" referred to the work of November 4. However, Henry quickly—witness the first paragraph below—switched from a needle to iron filings to test the magnetic field.

iron wire. The magnetism of the rod was shown by a large bunch of filings which adhered to the end of the wire. Care was taken to put the filings and rod in place before passing the current around the outside.

From this experiment it is evident either that the pipe is too thin or the iron does not perfectly screen

Removed the stove pipe introduced in its sted a pece of gas pipe—27 inches long and 1½ inch <*thi*> in interior diameter the iron of which is 3/16 of an inch in thickness. Put the iron filings into the middle of this the magnetism was much less than with the stove pipe but still there was considerable attraction. The screaning therefor is not perfect even with this thickness of iron and with a current as powerful as was now used

Sent the current through a <*large*> coil which was close around the iron, so as to produce a more powerful magnetization. Now the quantity of filings was much greater than in the last experimt, showing that the screening belongs to the intensity of the magnetism. This was also shown by passing a smaller current, one from a single jar, the screening was now almost perfect.

Next took the direction of the polarity of the magnetism within and without <*of*> the stove pipe found the polarity within the stove pipe the same as within the coil which showed that the magnetism within was due to the action of the coil through the iron which was not sufficiently thick to act as a perfect screene.

Put stove-pipe into coil and into the pipe put the gas pipe and into the latter iron filings. With this arrangement the screening was much more perfect than with the single iron but still I could perceve a slight attraction of the filings which I put into the rod. The gas pipe was strongly magnetic on the out side. The stove pipe is ½ a 16th thick 7/32 of an inch the whole thickness of iron.

Added another stove-pipe making the whole thickness of iron 3/16 + ½/16 + ½/16 = 4/16 = ¼ of an inch but still magnetism was perceptible in the interior. The filings were attracted but still very slightly.

Put around the gas pipe another iron cylinder of just sufficient <*power*> size to admit the gas pip with its surrounding coil. Placed glass on the top and paper over this on which was strewed iron filings. The result was rather curious. The polarity within was so strong that it acted through the iron so that the outer cylinder showed a different magnetism from that which it really possessed. The appearance exhibited by the filings was like that

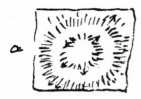

shown in the margin. A space around was u[n]mag-
netized, or the filings were drawn away from it. The
outer cylinder had the same polarity apparently as
the inner, although it should have had a different
polarity as is evident from inspecting fig *b* in the
margin

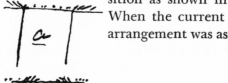

Removed the iron cylinder and supplied its place by one of paste board
found the same polarity as before but some what stronger. The distance at
which filings were made to jump on a paper held above the magnet was a
little greater with the paste board coating than with the iron one.

NB Perhaps the double ring shown in figure *a* above was due to the
drawing away of the filings from the outer circumference as I have found
with the single cylinder

Placed coil around cylinder within the large coil and
around the same coil placed the cylinder of sheet
iron. Noted very particularly the arrangements of
the filings when the current was passed in the two
circuits in the same and in different directions.
When the current was passed on the outside alone the filings took the position as shown in the section of the iron cylinder *a*.
When the current in the inside was passed alone, the
arrangement was as shown in fig *b*

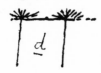

When the current passed through both circuits in the
same direction the arrangement was as shown in Fig C,
probably the action of the coil under neath produced
this result.

When the current was passed through both circuits <*the
arr*> but in different directions the arrangement was as
shown in figure *d* which is precisely the same as is exhibited on the end of a plate of iron placed in a coil.

Yesterday we were much troubled with the breaking of the pasteboard cylinders. They are so long that they cannot withstand the hydrostatic pressure. *Sam* has remedied the defect to day by rolling the pasteboard into a scroll of double thickness.

These exhibit the magnetism on the in and out side on a larger scale. The arrangement of the particles was observed with an eye glass.

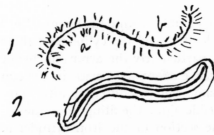

Placed a piece of iron (sheet) bent in the form of an S in a strap of copper, so that the strap would be close on each side of the iron making two complete turns around it. When the current was passed through the strap the filings arranged themselves as in fig 1. This is an experiment proposed by Prof Jacobi, who did not however try it—since he was sure there would be no magnetism in the concave parts, *a* and *b*. The result however is entirely different the magnetism of the concave part is nearly as strong as that of the convex.

See Scientific Memoirs[3]

Scattered filings over the straps fig 2 without the iron the same arrangement of the filings took place but they did not stand up as in the case of the iron—the effect was much feebler

Make a theoretical magnet of a wire coiled in cylindrical and these arranged in circles. Place paper over the end and strew on this iron filings

[3] This experiment was suggested but not tried by M. H. von Jacobi in "Electro-Magnetic Experiments, Forming a Sequel to the Memoir on the Application of Electro-Magnetism to the Movement of Machines, Second Series," Taylor's *Scientific Memoirs*, 1841, 2:1–19, especially p. 16.

FROM RICHARD VARICK DEWITT[1]
Henry Papers, Smithsonian Archives

Albany Nov 4 1841.

My dear Sir,

I know you will both from your love of philosophical advancement in science & art, & personal interest in my success, excuse the trouble these lines propose to you, & therefore make no apology for their intrusion upon your time & patience.

My affairs are so settling down, that I have the hope of commanding for myself & my own schemes, some time during the coming year or years. You know I have always been very desirous to take up the Annesley plan of ship building[2] as a matter of interesting employment—& I might add of humane duty—for such is one of the lights in which I view the matter of its universal introduction could that be effected.

I have to these motives, the hope of gain superadded, for my losses thro' false friends &c have made it a desireable matter for me to employ my abilities in making up these losses if I can do so, by venturing on some safe scheme of business with which I am conversant.

I should like to reintroduce the System to the notice of Government—& obtain the building of a vessel of any size by contract or superintendance. The great obstacle to success lies in the fact that Mr Annesley did once

---

[1] Richard Varick DeWitt (1800–1868) was one of Henry's close friends from Albany. The financial setbacks referred to in this letter were centered upon the collapse of the Ithaca and Oswego Railroad, a victim of the Panic of 1837. *Henry Papers*, *1*:62n.

[2] Originally patented in 1816, William Annesley's technique for ship construction was subsequently protected by a patent on later improvements (1830) and an act of Congress (October 7, 1844) which extended the second patent until 1851. Annesley's idea was to make shipbuilding less expensive by replacing much of the metal and heavy timbers with layers of planks. He also argued that his method resulted in stronger, and hence safer, vessels than those constructed by traditional methods.

The schooner mentioned in the fourth paragraph of this letter was the *Annesley*, built in Belfast in 1817. Not a good sailer, it ran aground on its maiden voyage, raising misgivings about the utility of Annesley's method. Critics also believed that Annesley's boats

would be more vulnerable to decay. There was also great doubt whether larger vessels could be constructed in this manner.

William Annesley was a resident of Albany at the time he took out his patents, although he did reside in Great Britain while securing his English patent and attempting to generate support. He is listed in Albany City Directories as a "patent ship builder." The last listing for Annesley in the Albany City Directories is in 1849–1850.

William Annesley, *A Description of William Annesley's New System of Naval Architecture . . .* (London, 1818); John Langdon Sullivan, *A Commentary on the New System of Naval Architecture of William Annesley, Architect* (Troy, 1823); *Burke's Index*, p. 169; "Specification of a Patent for Improvements on a Mode of 'Building Boats and Sea Vessels,' Patented on the 12th Day of September, 1816. Granted to WILLIAM ANNESLEY, Albany, New York, November 6, 1830," *Journal of the Franklin Institute*, 1831, n.s. 7:175–179, 180–181.

build a misbegotten *Tub* which he called a Schooner & which by the want of sailing qualities so disgusted the naval men connected with her, that they have attributed to the entire System the partial defects of the *"Experiment."*

I have in 15 years experience collected so many *facts* & proven the strength & value of the System so thoroughly that I feel strong in my ability to convince any reasonable man of the value of the *System* & of the undoubted success that would follow its introduction—& I also feel prepared to undertake the construction of any vessel from Pilot Boat to Ship of Line if I have the chance.[3]

I have some thoughts of trying the Gov^nt this winter & as preparatory thereto to canvass the opinions, & get the favourable aid of men of Scientific & personal weight before I take the matter up. It has occurred to me that Capt *Stocktons*[4] good opinion of the matter might be of value, but as I have no acquaintance with him, have thought it best to ask your opinion in regard to the matter. You will probably be able to say to me what are his peculiarities—what motives would weigh with him & whose judgments he would rely on in forming an opinion of the system—& whether he is or is not as frank & liberal in his views of such subjects as he is in character & manners otherwise.

If you sh^d think favourably of my view in this respect, I would, if it would not be putting you to inconvenience, ask you to see him forthwith & talk on the subject with him. If he expects to visit NYork within a fortnight & will name a day for an interview, I will meet him there, & shew him a memoir[5] I have prepared, principally of facts proved under my own eye, & a beautiful model built by Mr Annesley to illustrate the plan & its recent improvements.

If adviseable I would come to *Princeton* with the same.

My western business has kept me away from home till within a few days, & I expect to return to Ithaca by the 25th of this month. It would be de-

---

[3] DeWitt's active involvement with the Annesley method probably dates from the construction of the *DeWitt Clinton*, a hundred-foot steam-powered vessel upon which Annesley based his 1830 patent. The *DeWitt Clinton* was built in Ithaca during the late 1820s. *Journal of the Franklin Institute*, 1831, n.s. 7:176.

DeWitt's father, Simeon, was also involved with Annesley, having publicly endorsed the principle used by Annesley in his construction. Sullivan, *Commentary*, Appendix.

[4] Robert Field Stockton was a naval officer who resided in Princeton. *Henry Papers*, 2:82. While in England in 1838 he had studied improvements in naval architecture and over the intervening years had developed a reputation as an advocate of progressive and novel approaches to ship construction. S. J. Bayard, *A Sketch of the Life of Com. Robert F. Stockton* (New York, 1856), pp. 76–80.

[5] We have been unable to locate either a published or manuscript version of this paper.

sireable therefore for me to see Capt Stockton if at all very soon. I expect to be in NYork Tuesday next & shall be pleased to hear from you there.[6]

Direct to *"Care of W G Bucknor[7] Exchange Place NYC."*

Linn[8] starts this week for IOWA. He goes with two other gentlemen to enter into the Surveying business under Gen Wilson[9] Surv Gen there. It is in my opinion a good move. He will support himself handsomely & have opportunities for purchasing advantageously Lands—whilst his own Ithaca property now unproductive will be at nurse.

I pray you present my respects to Mrs Henry.

Very truly
Your friend
R V DeWitt

[6] Henry's response, if any, has not been found.

[7] William G. Bucknor, a broker. New York City Directories, 1841–1843.

[8] William Linn DeWitt, Richard DeWitt's half-brother, a former pupil of Henry's, and his companion on the European trip. *Henry Papers*, 2:310, 3:passim.

[9] George Wilson (1808 or 1809–1880) graduated West Point in 1830. He resigned from the Army in 1837. At this date he was Surveyor of Public Lands for Iowa and Adjutant for the Iowa militia. G. W. Cullum, *Biographical Register of the Officers and Graduates of the U.S. Military Academy at West Point . . .*, 3d ed., 3 vols. (Boston, 1891), 1:466.

EXCERPT, MINUTES, AMERICAN PHILOSOPHICAL SOCIETY
Archives, American Philosophical Society

November 5, 1841

Professor Henry made an oral communication of results which he had obtained in reference to the distribution of Magnetism.[1] The Professor gave an account of experiments on the magnetism of hollow cylinders, showing the differences between magnetic and electrical inductions; of the inductive effects of coils of metal, through which a galvanic current is passing in producing Magnetism in every direction in reference to the coil; of experiments tending to show and to measure the force of resistance to change

[1] The *Proceedings of the American Philosophical Society* for the November 5, 1841, meeting (2:111) give as an account only this first sentence (slightly altered) and then the notice that a full account would follow, which was intended as the fifth of Henry's "Contributions to Electricity and Magnetism." Henry never dealt with the distribution of magnetism in a major way. "Contributions V: Induction from Ordinary Electricity; Oscillatory Discharge," was on a different topic; it was a truncated abstract of a longer paper on the oscillatory discharge of a Leyden jar.

Henry also presented his account of the thunderstorm of the night of July 14, 1841, for which see "Record of Experiments," July 15 and 16, 1841, and APS *Proceedings*, 1841–1843, 2:111–116.

of magnetization. Professor Henry also stated that his experiments are favourable to magnetic action being the result of a species of polarization of the particles of bodies. He gave the results of his experiments on the spontaneous polarity of soft iron, and the direction of the magnetic axes assumed by bodies of different figures.[2] Professor Henry referred to the history of the subject embraced in his experiments.

[2] Though Henry had a longstanding concern with these subjects, see especially the "Record of Experiments" entries for October 12, 13, and 15, and November 3 and 4, 1841, above.

MICHAEL FARADAY TO ALEXANDER DALLAS BACHE

Bache Papers,[1] Smithsonian Archives

Royal Institution
12 Novr 1841

My Dear Sir

It was with great pleasure I saw your handwriting and read your words,[2] for I have a most pleasant remembrance of your kind feelings towards us here when you came to see us, and I should be sorry to think you forget me altogether. Do you remember the meeting in the Hanover Square rooms? I hope you will represent me kindly to those I saw there, Mrs. Bache and my willing friend her sister, I think.

With regard to the matter you ask me about, I have been searching about, and find that there was a gentleman, James Smithson Esq[r] F.R.S. of 3 Stanhope Place St James Square, who was one of our earliest members.[3] He was elected in the year 1799 and joined according to the formalities in March 1800. We cannot find however his name in the proceedings of the Institution i.e on the committees or otherwise, and in the abscence of any other means of judging, conclude he was no other wise active than as all the members then generally were. Mr Fi[nc]her[4] our assistant Secretary

[1] Along with this letter, marked "Copy," is a copy of a letter to Bache from J. Guillemard, on which it is noted that the originals, both relating to James Smithson, were deposited with the Smithsonian Institution in January 1849. The two originals were probably destroyed in the Smithsonian fire of 1865.

[2] Bache's letter to Faraday has not been found.

[3] Bache had been requested to furnish the National Institute, which had designs on the Smithson bequest, with information about the institutions to which James Smithson belonged. Bache to Francis Markoe, Jr., July 21, 1841, National Institute Records, Smithsonian Archives.

[4] Joseph Fincher (the copyist incorrectly wrote "Fisher") was appointed Clerk of Accounts of the Royal Institution in May 1810. He was made Assistant Secretary in 1821, and designated the Collector in 1827. Fincher was suspended, then dismissed, in 1846, after it was discovered that he had embezzled over £864 in Royal Institution funds. Manager's Minutes, Royal Institution, 5:79; 6:324; 7:106; 9:398.

who has been in the Institution since I believe the year 1810 or before, does not know of any especial activity on Mr Smithsons part or remember any circumstance which might lead to such a conclusion. Persons are often importantly active who are not formally so. Indeed sometimes they are the most valuable but I cannot in the present case recover any indications of activity here.[5]

I send you all our printed documents. The list of Members and the Charters Bye laws &c &c I have [. . .][6] out, also a set of the early Journal numbers. They are very scarce & all are in the packet that were published. As Mr Vaughan[7] wants the packet I may not detain them long enough to give them a decent exterior but I hope you will accept them as they are.

Ever my dear Sir your very faithful Servant

Signed   M. Faraday

[5] Faraday was relating what many others would subsequently discover—information about James Smithson was difficult to obtain. Smithson's papers, brought to the United States in 1838, were destroyed in the 1865 fire.

As Secretary of the Smithsonian, Henry attempted to gather information about Smithson's life and work. As future volumes will show, he was particularly interested in discovering the motives for Smithson's enigmatic bequest to the United States.

Leonard Carmichael and J. C. Long, *James Smithson and the Smithsonian Story* (New York, 1965), pp. 43–44; James Smithson Collection, Smithsonian Archives.

[6] The copyist left a blank here.

[7] Either William or Petty Vaughan.

TO A.-A. DE LA RIVE

De La Rive Papers, Bibliothèque publique et universitaire, Geneva [1]

Princeton College of New-Jersey
United States Nov 24th 1841

My Dear Sir

I have long intended to write to you but have defered doing so from time to time for no good reason, but merely from a habit of procrastination. I am however just now induced to overcome my inertia by a conversation relative to yourself with my friend Dr. Hare who returned about 3 weeks ago in improved health from his European tour. He informed me that when he was in Geneva you were afflicted in your family by an accident

[1] Henry enclosed this letter in a short letter dated November 29 (also in the De La Rive Papers). The second letter introduces the bearer, Robert Baird. See Henry's introduction of Baird to Melloni of November 29, printed below.

A partial Mary Henry Copy of a November 12 draft of this letter is in the Henry Papers, Smithsonian Archives.

which had happened to one of your sons and by the consequent illness of Madam De La Rive. I hope these causes of grief have passed away and that you are again enjoying in your interesting family that happiness which should result from the successful prosecution of science and the possession of an enviable reputation.

Dr Hare showed me the first no. of the Archives of Electricity and I am so much pleased with the work that I have ordered it through M. Berteau of New-York, from your agent M Anselin of Paris. I have sent you since my return from Europe copies of two nos. of my *"contributions to electricity and magnetism,"* which I hope you have received. I am now engaged in preparing for the press the 5th no. a copy of which I hope to be able to send you in a short time. I have but little time for research. My college duties occupy so much of my time that I can only experiment during the vacations and these embrace but a few weeks in the year.

I have little news in the way of science to communicate. There are few persons in the United States who engage in original research, although there are more persons among us interested in popular science than in any other part of the world. Those branches of science which depend on observation, occupy most attention. Geology has become very fashionable among us and the unexplored regions of the great west afford a wide field for its cultivation. A considerable portion of the public lands have been geologically examined at the expense of the government and 17 of the individual states have ordered surveys of their possessions. Mr Lyell the celebrated English Geologist has been called from London, to give a course of lectures in Boston[2] on his favourite subject. His course, which is just now in progress, is to consist of 12 lectures for which he is to receive 500 £s sterling. He intends to remain a year in this country studying the rocky formations and comparing them with those of Europe.[3] We have now two magnetic observatories in operation one in Philadelphia under the direction of my Friend Professor Bache and the other at Boston under the superintendance of a Professor Lovering,[4] of the university at that place. The observatory at Philadelphia is furnished with a complete set of German instruments both for magnetism and meteorology, the other observatory is provided with a set of English magnetic instruments. Both these establishments are supported by private subscriptions but we have some hopes that the general government will make an appropriation of money for the

---

[2] At the Lowell Institute.

[3] For other comments by Henry on Lyell's visit, see his letter to Bache of August 10, 1841, above, and that to Torrey of February 19, 1842, below.

[4] Joseph Lovering (1813–1892), Professor of Mathematics and Natural Philosophy at Harvard. *DAB.*

establishment of several other observatories in distant parts of the country.[5] Two series of meteorological observations of considerable magnitude are kept in our country one under the direction of the officers of the army at the different military posts and the other by the several academies of the State of New-York. These furnish some interesting results in reference to the simultaneous directions of the wind, at distant places, and also in regard to the appearance of the aurora borealis. The mechanic arts however receive most encouragement in the United States. We pride ourselves much on the number, the beauty, and speed of our steamboats; and on the number and extent of our canals and rail-roads.

Some attempts have been made in this country to get up a society similar to the British Association but the success as yet has been but partial.[6] The geologists have formed a society of the kind which has held two annual meetings, and apparently with good effect; but I doubt the propriety of forming an association which should embrace every department of science.[7] We have amoung us too small a number of "working men" and too large a number of those who would occupy the time of the meeting in idle discussion. The British Association has undoubtedly done much good particularly in advancing those branches of science which depend on observation by prescribing the general forms and in furnishing the money necessary to the observations but it appears to me that its usefulness, for the present, is nearly at an end and that its friends would do well to suspend its operations for a while. The last meeting appeared to me little better than a failure.[8]

You have heard of the wonderful accounts from America of the attempts to apply electromagnetism as a moving power in the arts—these accounts

[5] Although the American Philosophical Society had appealed to Congress in 1839 for such an appropriation, the effort was essentially dead by this time. See *Henry Papers*, 4:315–320.

[6] For one such attempt, see *Henry Papers*, 4:114–115.

[7] The Association of American Geologists, "the first viable national association for scientists," grew out of the efforts of geologists working on the New York Natural History Survey. The survey geologists found coordination necessary, and those from rural areas especially appreciated being able to meet and exchange information with their colleagues. The organization began small and with a narrow focus; eighteen state survey geologists from seven states attended the first meeting in Philadelphia in April 1840. The focus gradually broadened, the name being changed to the Association of American Geologists and Naturalists at the 1842 meeting. Although Henry and other scientists had doubts about establishing a comprehensive national scientific organization in 1841, by 1847 they supported the move to turn the still fairly specialized Association of American Geologists and Naturalists into the all-encompassing American Association for the Advancement of Science. See Sally Gregory Kohlstedt, *The Formation of the American Scientific Community: The American Association for the Advancement of Science, 1848–60* (Urbana, Illinois, 1976), especially chapters 3 and 4; quotation from p. 60.

[8] According to John Torrey, Henry characterized the BAAS as a "squeezed lemon." Torrey to J. W. Bailey, August 23, 1842, Bailey Papers, Boston Science Museum.

have all been exaggerations and no advance of any importance what ever has been made. The persons who have been engaged in the attempts are those who have no knowledge of science and were willing to obtain a little notoriety at the expense of truth and honesty. I believe the project at present is entirely abandoned in the United States, at least I have heard, during the last year, of no new attempt of the kind. While on this subject you will pardon me for mentioning that in the first number of your Archives page 27, you have done me the injustice of ascribing to Professor Richie the invention of the first electro-magnetic machine, instead of giving me credit for the same. The invention was made by myself, immediately after my experiments on the construction of large electro-magnetic magnets and published about 6 months after, in the 20th vol. of Silliman's journal for 1831 (page 340). As soon as this no. of the journal was received in England Dr. Faraday (as he informed me himself) constructed a machine precisely like the one I had described, and exhibited it, as my invention at a meeting of the Royal Institution; not withstanding this, I am sorry to be obliged to say that Professor Richie published his account of a machine on the same principle in the transactions of the Royal society without alluding to my previous labours. The affair is not of much consequence but we find in this country that unless we are somewhat tenacious in relation to our rights we are liable to have our discoveries and inventions claimed by others owing to our distance and the want, (before the late triumph of steam) of rapid communication. I shall therefore look in some subsequent no. of your Journal for that correction of the statement (page 27) which on examination you may consider my due.[9]

I invented about two years ago a little machine, of which no particular account has yet been published but which you may consider of some interest since it is moved by a principle which has not as far as I know been applied to produce motion of the kind. I allude to the consecutive repulsion of the several parts of a galvanic current discovered by Ampere. You will readily understand the machine by a reference to the figure. *a b* is a piece of copper wire supported on an axis so as to vibrate freely in a vertical plane and terminated at the two ends by cross wires the extremities of which dip into shallow cups of mercury *c d e f—h i* are cups of mercury connected with the poles of the battery. When the cross wire at *a* is down so that its ends rest in the cups *c d* the current passes through it and repulsion takes place; the ends are thrown out of the cups and the current is closed at the other ex-

---

[9] Henry might have known that Hare had already complained to De La Rive about this. See Hare's letter of August 11, 1841, printed above. In a letter of May 8, 1846 (Henry Papers, Smithsonian Archives), Henry again asked for a correction.

tremity by bringing the other ends in contact with the cups *b c*. Repulsion again takes place and thus the motion is kept up.[10]

It would give me much pleasure to receive a line from you. We were strangers together in England and since then I have been interested in whatever concerns you. Give my kind regards to your Lady and accept the assurance for yourself that I am your

Friend and Serv.

Joseph Henry

Please to give my respects to your friend M Prevost[11] of London. He still lives in my remembrance and the portrait of his Father which he presented to me is now one of the embellishments of our parlor.

[10] For this motor, designed in April 1840, see *Henry Papers*, 4:342–343.

[11] Henry had met John Lewis Prevost (1796–1852) in London in 1837. Son of Pierre Prevost of Geneva, John Lewis Prevost was a London merchant and served there as Consul General of the Swiss government. Prevost was a Fellow of the Geological Society of London and was Treasurer at the time of his death. *Quarterly Journal of the Geological Society of London*, 1853, 9:xxv–xxvi.

TO ALEXANDER DALLAS BACHE

Mary Henry Copy, Henry Papers, Smithsonian Archives

Nov. 28. 1841[1]

Please to put my name to the Report of the committee on the pendulum experiments. I think the offer should be accepted.[2]

[1] The date is clearly indicated as November 28, 1841. The nineteenth, however, was when the report referred to in the letter (and discussed in footnote 2, below) was due at the American Philosophical Society. It is conceivable that Henry wrote Bache on November 18, and that Mary Henry miscopied the date. This fragment is all that apparently remains of what was probably a longer communication.

[2] The report referred to the contents of a letter received by the American Philosophical Society from Charles (Károly) Nagy. Nagy (1797–1868) was a Hungarian mathematician and natural philosopher, and member of the relatively young (f. 1825) Hungarian Academy of Sciences. On a trip to the United States in 1832–1833, he coordinated the opening of correspondence between the Academy and the APS, and on April 19, 1833, he was elected an APS member. Nagy maintained an active correspondence with the Society on subjects such as telescopes and microscopes, charts of Hungary, the Hungarian Academy's yearbook, calendars, and Hungarian arithmetic books. These items indicate the nationalist pride that was evident in the founding within the bounds of the Austrian Empire of an independent scientific society, which established its first corresponding relationship with a non-Germanic, even non-European society located in a country with a libertarian reputation. Constant von Wurzbach, *Biographisches Lexicon des Kaiserthums Oesterreich*, 60 vols. (Vienna, 1856–1891), 20:60–62; Francis S. Wagner, "The Start of Cultural Exchange between the Hungarian Academy of Sciences and the American Philosophical Society," *Hungarian Quarterly*, 1965, 5:90–97; *Poggendorff*, 3:954.

The report to which Henry referred was prepared by an APS committee which consisted of A. D. Bache and R. M. Patterson in addition to Henry. It was acting on a proposal by Nagy contained in a March 10, 1841, letter to the Society. In the letter, Nagy offered the use of his "invariable pendulum" so that the APS could repeat certain of his experiments in Philadelphia. The invariable pendulum was of fixed length, and constructed to minimize variation in length due to climate and use. This instrument could be used for geodesy, by comparing the number of oscillations made in a fixed unit of time at various points of the earth's surface. The oscillation time was a function of the local force of gravity, which in turn depended on the distance of the observation point from the center of gravity of the earth. The variation of the earth's shape from a true sphere could therefore be determined, once disturbing factors such as the extent of swing, air friction, variations in temperature, and local gravitational disturbances (due to large mountains, etc.) were taken into account. Edward Sabine undertook experiments with invariable pendulums in the 1820s, and the report to the APS referred to these experiments. The report maintained that the expense of transporting the pendulum to and from the United States and of prosecuting the experiments would be justified by the results. On November 19, 1841, the committee report—lacking Henry's signature—was read and its recommendations adopted. We have been unable to determine whether the pendulum experiments ever took place under the auspices of the APS. Charles Nagy to John Vaughan, March 10, 1841, and Report, November 19, 1841, Archives, American Philosophical Society; *Proceedings of the American Philosophical Society*, 1841, 2:107–108, 118; Robert Grant, *History of Physical Astronomy* (London, 1852), pp. 151–155.

TO MACEDONIO MELLONI
Henry Papers, Smithsonian Archives[1]

Princeton College of
New-Jersey Nov 29th
1841

My Dear Sir

Permit me to introduce to your acquaintance my Friend the Rev. Mr Baird,[2] an American gentleman of much respectability now residing in Paris. I have requested him to procure for me a complete set of apparatus for the repitition of your interesting experiments, and may I ask as a particular favour that you will inspect the articles before they are sent and see that all are perfect.

The reccollection of my visit to Europe always gives me pleasure and nothing which I saw during my tour is remembered with more pleasure

[1] This is either a retained copy or the copy sent to Baird in Paris with Henry's letter of December 28, 1841 (below), and then returned by Baird when he found Melloni had left Paris.

[2] Robert Baird (1798–1863) was a graduate of the Princeton Theological Seminary and a former principal of the Princeton Academy. In 1829 he began five years of travels in the United States on behalf of the American Sunday School Union. In 1835 he was sent to Paris to study religious conditions in France and Europe. Baird returned to Europe frequently and spent many years abroad. Several of his many publications explored European religion and society. *DAB*.

than the beautiful experiments shown me by yourself.[3] It will give me much pleasure to make your important and interesting descoveries more generally known in America and to place in a clear light before my class in *Physique* your claims of priority.

With the kindest wishes for your continued health and prosperity I remain your

Friend &c
Joseph Henry

I have learned that the best and cheapest instruments are to be procured of Ruhmkorff[4] and I have accordingly directed my Friend to get the apparatus of this workman.

[3] See *Henry Papers*, 3:394–401.
[4] Heinrich Daniel Rühmkorff (1803–1877, *DSB*), a German who worked in England before establishing himself as an instrument maker in Paris. He became known worldwide for the quality of his electrical apparatus, particularly his powerful induction coils.

TO ELIAS LOOMIS[1]
Loomis Papers, Beinecke Library, Yale University

Princeton Nov 29th[2] 1841

My Dear Sir

Your letter[3] making inquiries relative to the management &c of galvanic apparatus was duly received so that I have not the excuse of the fault in the mail for the long silence which has ensued. The truth is that the letter came to hand at a time when I happened to be so much engaged that I could not give it an immediate answer and as is often the case in such instances I defered writing from time to time for no good reason but merely because the necessity of making the effort on any given day was no greater than on the day previous. Perhaps however the delay has been attended with the advantage of enabling me to give you the additional information derived from the experience of the last year. There is no form of the galvanic battery which is not attended with some inconvenience of manipulation and a liability of soiling the clothes with acids and salts. The Trustees of our college have however furnished me with an article which I now find

[1] The Professor of Mathematics and Natural Philosophy at Western Reserve. *Henry Papers*, 3:362–363.
[2] The postmark reads December 27.
[3] Of December 28, 1840. See *Henry Papers*, 4:453–454.

125

indespensible namely with a coloured servant[4] whom I have taught to manage my batteries and who now relieves me from all the dirty work of the laboratory.

The battery to which I give a preference over all others is the one invented by Professor Daniell.[5] I have two of these, the smaller of which and perhaps the simpler is partially described in the 4th number of my contributions. It consists of 30 elements each formed of a copper cylender into which is inserted a rod of zinc the two being seperated by a cylender of paste board on one side of which is placed a solution of sulphuric acid and sulphate of copper and on the other simply sulphuricacid and water. Where a very intense action is not required a solution of sulphate of copper alone may be placed next [to] the copper and sulphate of soda on the other side of the diaphragm a small quantity of acid being added at first merely to start the action which will afterwards be continued by the decomposition of the sulphate. The several parts of this apparatus will be readily under-

stood by a reference to the figures *a b* &c. The first *a* is <*a*> represents a quart mug of earthen-ware to contain the other parts, and which should be made acid tight by a wash inside of cement. Fig *b* shows the form of the copper cylender, which is of such a height and diameter, as just to fit into the mug; it is not soldered but merely bent into the cylendrical form. On the upper edge is soldered a slip of thick copper, to serve as a connection, with the zinc of the next element. Fig *c* is the zinc rod about an inch in diameter and six inches long; from the top of it, a copper wire projects, and on the extremity of this a brass thimble is soldered. The rod is easily formed by driving a rod of wood of the required diameter into a vessel filled with damp sand which has been packed in. While the zinc is still fluid the lower end of the wire, before mentioned, is inserted and inorder to insure a more perfect union the same end of the wire should be previously tinned by means of the soldering iron. Fig *d* represents the paste-board cylender which serves as a diaphragm. It consists of a short cylender of wood which forms the bottom and around which is rolled a parallelogram of paste-board of such dimensions as will form a cylender of double thickness of the paper. The edges of the paste board are secured in place by a slip of cement. The cylender is

[4] Sam Parker.
[5] For the background of the Daniell constant battery see *Henry Papers*, 3:192–193, 4:337–338.

fashioned and brought into proper shape by rubbing it with a piece of wood, on a wooden mandril. The bottom is afterwards cemented into place. Fig *e* represents a simple form of a cullender, or support for holding the crystals of sulphate of copper, so that the salt may be constantly near the top of the liquid and by the greater specific gravity of the solution keep the liquid constantly saturated. This cullender is formed by rolling a parallelogram of copper into a cylendrical form and then cutting the lower half of it into slips, which are afterwards bent out at right angles so as to form radii on which the salt is supported. The cullender is pressed into the copper cylinder so that the radii are about an inch and a half below the upper edge of the copper where it is retained in place by the spring or elasticity of the slips or radii. The several parts having been constructed the battery is put in operation by placing the coppe[r] cylender *b* in the mug *a* and the cullender e in [the] cylinder, then the paste-board *d* in this and the zinc again within the latter. The *thimble* on the rod being amalgamated and filled with mercury receives the end of the rod, also amalgamated, attached to the copper of the next element. 30 elements prepared in this way and charged on both sides of the paste-board with 7 parts of water and one of sulphuric acid to which is added on the outer side the crystals of sulphate of zinc will produce from 8 to 9 cubic inches of the combined gases in a minute. It will ignite fifteen or 20 inches of fine platina wire and produce a beautiful ignition of charcoal points. In short it will be sufficient to exhibit all the experiments usually shown to a class and will continue in uniform activity for six hours by adding a few additional crystals of sulphate of copper. There is considerable trouble in preparing the apparatus and some little in putting it together ready for operation but it is exceedingly convenient when once in action no disagreeable fumes are given off. There is no lifting of the battery from the acid. All the preperations can be made with leisure and the experiments rehearsed before the class assemble. By a few additional slips or straps of copper or thick lead, the battery can readily be transformed from one of intensity into one of quantity and the converse. I have forgotten to mention an important particular namely the amalgamation of the zinc rods. This is readily effected by putting a quantity of mercury in a tea-saucer and over this a solution of sulphuric acid, if the acid and mercury together be now poured over the zinc by dipping them up in a watch glass the metal will be instantly covered with a coating of mercury. I have now given you a sufficiently minute description of the smaller battery to enable you to construct one and manipulate with it and I can recommend it to you as superior to any other battery I have ever used. It must be reccollected however that I have no trouble myself in putting it together this labour being performed by the servant before mentioned. The battery cost but little. It was construct[ed] by my servant from the copper and zinc of a part of my old large battery. I have an other battery on the same principle of the size and construction as that described by Professor Daniell. It is composed of 12 elements and is used for the development of a great quantity of galvanism.

I am now engaged on the 5th no of my contributions but my college duties occupy so much of time that little is left for researches which requires a degree of uninterrupted leisure.

Permit me at this late day to congratulate you on your Philosophical change of condition. When you next visit the east we shall be happy to see Mrs Loomis[6] with you. With much Respect

Truely yours
Joseph Henry

[6] Loomis married Julia Elmore Upson (d. 1854) on May 18, 1840. *DAB.*

FROM ALEXANDER DALLAS BACHE
Henry Papers, Smithsonian Archives

Philad. Dec. 1. 1841.

Dear Henry.

Your P.S.S. are always acceptable, as for the letters they do not contain so much, being full of excuses. If our regard for each other were measured by paper exchanged the intensity & quantity would both be low; luckily we have better instruments. I shall send off a despatch to Dr. Beck in the course of the week, the hints only want a few words about the times of observation.[1] They were written under the pleasant circumstance of being *overhauled* in Common Council.[2] Sufficient glory to be attacked by Thom-

[1] Beck had asked Bache and Henry for their suggestions concerning meteorological observations. See above, Beck to Henry, October 4, 1841.

[2] Bache was still nominally President of Girard College although he had no duties and had stopped drawing a salary over a year earlier. Years of feuding between the Philadelphia city councils and the Girard College Board of Trustees came to a climax on December 23, 1841, when the councils abolished both the office of President and the Board of Trustees. A brief account of Bache's presidency of Girard College is given in *Henry Papers,* 4:156n. See also Cheesman A. Herrick, *History of Girard College* (Philadelphia, 1927), especially pp. 25–29.

as S. Smith[3] & defended by Samuel Breck[4] & Peter McCall.[5] Alas & alack-a-day to have so dirty a bird in our domestic nest. I have been obliged to turn to the humiliating occupation of showing Peter McCall what a distinguished character I am! if you find me more conceited than ever when you come back to Philad. excuse it for a review of the works, & the opinions of these works, of the great unknown has inspired him anew with an exalted sense of his worth! having thus prepared all the materials for a brilliant necrological notice if Providence does not take me just now perhaps it may will that the first act of the drama close. Perhaps when we meet again we may weep together over the green grave of the first President of the Girard College for Orphans. Doubtless you will be one of his executors. Perhaps even a legatee. A pocket thermometer. A well worn copy of Brewsters' Optics. May hap an odd number of the N. Y. review—the North Amer—the Princeton—the Methodist &^c with the passages carefully marked which describe the mental qualities of the great defunct. An autograph letter of Arago. A diploma <of the> Regiae Academiae Taurinensis.[6] I wonder what he will leave me—perhaps a small slice of reputation—Some porcelain—Some red glasses and hock. Our friend Peter caustically informed the President that he "argued himself unknown." Seriously—the mask is thrown from before the battery of those who are anew attempting to abolish my place, & they show that it is pointed at *me* personally.[7] It has done good

[3] In order to keep Bache, the Trustees had proposed operating a preliminary school for several years until Girard College could be opened. Thomas S. Smith was chairman of a special committee of the city councils whose report of September 27, 1840, instead recommended discharging the President and dissolving the Board of Trustees. Smith (ca. 1798–1873) was a lawyer in Philadelphia (John Hill Martin, *Martin's Bench and Bar of Philadelphia* [Philadelphia, 1883], p. 313). The committee, which included Isaac Myer and Charles Gilpin, criticized the original selection of Bache as non-competitive and a precedent for "favouritism and intrigue" (p. 40) and found it hard to believe "that this country does not afford more than one individual who is fully qualified to preside over an institution for educating boys . . ." (p. 25). *Report of the Special Committee Appointed by the Common Council on a Communication from the Board of Trustees of the Girard College* (Philadelphia, 1840).

The relevant Common Council minutes show Smith consistently voting against Bache and the Trustees. See, for example, Philadelphia Common Council, *Journal, 1841–1842*

(1842), pp. 20–21 (November 11, 1841), pp. 32–33 (December 9, 1841), and p. 39 (December 23, 1841). Gilpin led the opposition in the Select Council. Philadelphia Select Council, *Journal, 1841–1842* (1842), pp. 30–33 (December 23, 1841).

[4] Samuel Breck (1771–1862, *DAB*) was a wealthy and prominent Philadelphian who had served in the Pennsylvania Senate and one term in Congress. He was a member of the American Philosophical Society from 1838.

[5] Peter McCall (1809–1880), a graduate of Princeton (1826), was a lawyer in Philadelphia, "where he attained eminence not only as an advocate in cause celebres, but as an extremely learned and conscientious counsellor." McCall was later Mayor of Philadelphia, a professor of law and Trustee of the University of Pennsylvania, and a member of the American Philosophical Society. *National Cyclopaedia*, 4:374.

[6] Bache was a corresponding member of the Royal Academy of Sciences of Turin (notice of election of April 9, 1839, Box 6, Bache Papers, Smithsonian Archives).

[7] A December 23 resolution thanking Bache for his services disguised the nature of the end

when it is known at all—done good in the very council chamber & mayhap may defeat the <*very*> object of planting the said battery. We shall see. L'homme propose, Dieu dispose. Should the movement take effect I intend to embrace the first opportunity of returning to science *as a business*. The magnetic observations were treated as pretty amusements for grown children.[8] In London you have heard Babbage called Cabbage & his calculating machine pronounced a humbug—if the light is pronounced darkness—how thick darkness must the twilight be.

Ency unites with me in the kindest regards to you & yours. I thank you for your reception of my young friends—they are both nice fellows and Lesley[9] has shown himself grateful for *small favours* which is decidedly to his credit.

What do you think of Quimby & his ⧢ conductors.[10]

Yours truly as ever
A. D. Bache.

---

of Bache's presidency of Girard College. As he later wrote, "That connection was dissolved in the most violent way & it was not the fault of those who effected the dissolution that I was not ruined by it." Bache to J. A. Deloutte, September 24, 1849, quoted in Merle M. Odgers, *Alexander Dallas Bache: Scientist and Educator, 1806–1867* (Philadelphia, 1947), p. 140.

[8] The December 23 resolution left Bache in charge of the magnetic observatory and instruments at Girard College, a provision which survived Charles Gilpin's attempt to strike it. With the assistance of John F. Frazer, Bache operated the observatory from 1840 to 1845 with funds provided at various times by individuals, by the American Philosophical Society, and by the Topographical Bureau of the War Department. Most of the observers were students at Central High School. See the preface to volume 1 of *Observations at the Magnetic and Meteorological Observatory, at the Girard College, Philadelphia . . . , 1840–1845*, 3 vols. (Washington, 1847), and Franklin Spencer Edmonds, *History of the Central High School of Philadelphia* (Philadelphia, 1902), pp. 37, 93–95.

[9] J. Peter Lesley (1819–1903), later one of the leading geologists of the United States, attended the Princeton Theological Seminary from 1841 to 1844. Lesley had graduated from the University of Pennsylvania in 1838 and then worked under Henry Darwin Rogers on the Pennsylvania State Geological Survey un-

til it was discontinued in 1841.

Following a trip to Europe in 1844–1845 and several years of pastoral work, Lesley left the ministry in 1852 to commit himself to geology. He wrote two major works on the coal and iron fields of Pennsylvania, served as a consultant to the mining industry, taught mining at the University of Pennsylvania and headed its science department and scientific school, and at fifty-four became State Geologist of Pennsylvania, where he conducted a second state geological survey from 1873 to 1887. Lesley was also an original member of the National Academy of Sciences and Librarian and Secretary of the American Philosophical Society for over twenty-five years. *DAB. DSB.*

[10] According to a student notebook, Henry thought that Quimby's lightning rods, with points projecting every few feet, were dangerous because the points would tend to cause lateral discharge (lecture 54 of John J. Olcott's natural philosophy notebooks, 1842–1843, Manuscripts and Special Collections, New York State Library).

We think the Quimby referred to here is the A. M. Quimby of A. M. Quimby and Son of New York City who published a pamphlet in 1852 advocating the use of "Quimby's Improved Lightning Rods" for residences, churches, schools, etc. The author claimed that his lightning rods had been in use for seventeen years and printed testimonials from satisfied customers and lists of buildings furnished with his rods. Quimby did not describe

About that Pole I am afraid he is a "gay deceiver" I once was guilty of the indiscretion of supporting but the fellow turned out a rogue. If he speaks Latin like a Roman he is *the* man.[11]

---

the rods in this pamphlet or in later 1854 and 1864 editions so it is not known whether he retained the design Henry found so objectionable. A copy of the 1852 pamphlet is in the Henry Library.

Henry mentions a conversation with Quimby in his "Record of Experiments" entry of February 23, 1843, below.

[11] In a letter of December 8, 1841, James W. Alexander of Princeton wrote John Hall in Philadelphia: "Your Pole [a beggar] came here, and in excellent Latin swindled us all out of sundry 'vetera vestimenta,' and money likewise." John Hall, ed., *Forty Years' Familiar Letters of James W. Alexander*, 2 vols. (New York, 1860), *1*:341.

FROM JAMES P. ESPY
Henry Papers, Smithsonian Archives

Philᵃ Dec. 3ᵈ 1841

My Dear Henry,

Yesterday on leaving New York, I ordered my baggage to be put in the Princeton Car; but on arriving at Princeton I found my cold and hoarseness so much increased, that I could not have lectured if I had stopped; so I came on here to rest, determining not to impose my dullness on you while I was sick. I have been entirely well for many months, and a little sickness makes me feel wondrous stupid. I write you these few lines to let you know that it would still give me pleasure to explain my subject before you and your students, before I go to Washington City—which will about the first of January. I shall write to Prof Strong[1] of New Brunswick on the same subject. I will not be able to explain my theory in less than 3 lectures of 1½ hours each—I should prefer 4 lectures. If I do not hear from you immediately nothing can be done on the subject at present as I will make other engagements.[2] I wish to be at liberty to come at any time this month, and lecture every day or evening unless I should be engaged at New Brunswick, when I could lecture alternately at the two places. Mrs Espy will be here from Harrisburg on Monday next. Give our love to Mrs Henry and believe me to be very truly your friend

J. P. Espy

If I should be invited I will expect $100 for 4 lectures or $80 for 3. and if more should be raised by admitting the citizens the students may appropriate it to their own purposes.

---

[1] Theodore Strong, Professor of Mathematics and Natural Philosophy at Rutgers (*Henry Papers*, 2:436n–437n).

[2] We do not know whether Espy lectured on meteorology to Henry's students.

TO JOHN TORREY
Torrey Papers, Library, New York Botanical Garden

Princeton Mond. Dec [20][1] 1841

My Dear D[r]

I have just heard to day in faculty meeting that the house now occupied by Professor James Alexander will be to rent the next year and also the house now occupied by Mr. Dwite[2] the old Voorhees house opposite Mrs Gibsons.[3]

I have thought that perhaps one of these will suit your family better than the Byard house. I informed Mr Dod[4] that you had concluded to take the house but should you think fit to change your mind he would perhaps have no objections to release you from the engagement. I say perhaps because I have not had any conversation with him on the subject.

I am now in the midst of my lectures and have such an arrangement of the course as to give me the principal part of my labour in the winter. The College appears in good condition nearly 70 new students have entered but a number of the old ones have not returned on account of the great commercial depression which is now begining to be felt more severely in the country than before. Princeton has never before known such times in the way of bankruptcy. Mr J. S. [?Hart][5] has been sold out and now leaves Princeton some 6 or 8 thousand dollars worse than nothing and I could mention half a dozen who are on the point of unstable equilibrium and who cannot long support their present condition.

I have heard nothing about the amount of repairs which are to be put on Mr Byards house. Professor Dod will be disposed to accomodate you as far as he can but I suppose he will not feel himself at liberty to do much.

Mr Field[6] expressed himself much gratified with the prospect of having you for a neighbour. I see by the papers that the Gay Lothario Dr Dyonisious Lardner is flourishing in New York.[7] I think it is time for you to leave.

---

[1] Although Henry dated this letter December 21, the faculty meeting was held on Monday, December 20. Faculty Minutes, Princeton University Archives.

[2] Probably Theodore A. Dwight. Sixth Census of the United States, 1840: Mercer County, New Jersey, Record Group 29, National Archives.

[3] Margaret T. Gibson. *Henry Papers*, *4*:328.

[4] Albert Baldwin Dod (1805–1845) was Professor of Mathematics at Princeton. *Henry Papers*, *1*:434. The house belonged to Dod's late father-in-law, Samuel Bayard (1767–1840). *Henry Papers*, *3*:112, *4*:328, 390.

[5] The reading is uncertain. However, in the fall of 1841, a John S. Hart sold his farm and other holdings. *Princeton Whig*, October 8, 1841. This may be John Seely Hart (*Henry Papers*, *2*:172), who closed the Edgehill School, sold the school property, and then left Princeton for Philadelphia in December 1841. *DAB*; *Hageman*, *2*:222–223.

[6] Richard Stockton Field (1803–1870) was a lawyer and politician. *Henry Papers*, *2*:364.

[7] A popular science lecturer and old nemesis of Henry's (*Henry Papers*, *2*:257, *3*:508–510, *4*:100–101), the Englishman Dionysius Lardner had come to the United States in the autumn

December 20, 1841

The Philadelphians have some reason to crow—they gave him no countenance.[8] Our friend Mapes[9] has got quite in with the Learned Gentleman.

I have as you may recollect the barrel and part of the breach of an old air gun which you promised to present to the Philosophical Hall. You promised also to look up the other parts and send them to me. I should like to receve them before I get on the subject of air which will be in about 3 weeks. Nothing new in the Philosophical line I have not visited Phila^d since the begining of the session. I saw Dr Hare at my last visit he appeared much better in health than before he left but much thinner in flesh. He did not do much in the way of science but spent most of his time in travelling. I had some interesting packages through him from De La Rive of Geneva. He is about publishing a periodical on the subject of electricity and its kindred branches.[10]

I received a short time since a very interesting letter[11] from Berzelius acknowledging the receipt of my papers which are to be inserted in the next number of his year book of science.[12] He describes three new forms of gal-

---

of 1840 in the wake of the public scandal which had erupted in England over his affair with the wife of Richard Heaviside. Lardner remained in the New World until Heaviside obtained a divorce in 1845, and he then settled in Paris. The initial American reaction to Lardner and Mrs. Heaviside (later Mrs. Lardner) was extremely negative. Lardner was labeled "the gay Lothario," while Mrs. Heaviside was described as having covered "herself with infamy for the sake of such a stale libel on humanity as he [Lardner]."

Shortly after landing in New York, Lardner settled in Philadelphia for some seven months. He then returned to New York, where he remained another seven months before initiating a three-year lecture tour of the United States. Lardner began the tour with two very successful series of lectures in New York City.

DNB; Philadelphia Public Ledger, October 6, 1840; Dionysius Lardner, *Popular Lectures on Science and Art,* 2 vols. (New York, 1846), *1*:8–14; *New-York Herald,* November 19, 1842; New-York Tribune, *Course of Lectures Delivered by Dionysius Lardner . . . ,* 2d ed. (New York, 1842); J. N. Hays, "The Rise and Fall of Dionysius Lardner," *Annals of Science,* 1981, *38*:527–542.

[8] Philadelphia's resistance to Lardner did not last long. In March 1842 he was lecturing at the Chestnut Street Theatre before an audience of twelve hundred. He returned to speak before even larger Philadelphia audiences during the winter of 1843–1844. Lardner,

Popular Lectures, 1:12–13; *Philadelphia Public Ledger,* March 3, 1842.

[9] James Jay Mapes (1806–1866) was an analytical and consulting chemist from 1834 through 1847 and later manufactured fertilizer and other chemical products. From 1840 until 1842 he edited the *American Repertory of Arts, Sciences, and Manufactures.* During the period 1842–1843 he was associate editor of the *Journal of the Franklin Institute* as a result of the merger of that journal with the *American Repertory.* In 1849 he founded *The Working Farmer,* which he edited until 1863. *DAB; Elliott;* Bruce Sinclair, *Philadelphia's Philosopher Mechanics: A History of the Franklin Institute, 1824–1865* (Baltimore and London, 1974), pp. 283–284.

Mapes had opened the pages of his journal to Lardner (see below, Henry to Torrey, December 29, 1841, footnote 5). In addition, he was a prominent member of the audience for Lardner's lectures (see, e.g., the *New-York Herald,* November 19, 1841).

[10] See above, Henry to De La Rive, November 24, 1841.

[11] Not found.

[12] Henry had enclosed copies of his publications in his letter to Berzelius of April 29, 1841, printed above.

Berzelius did not reprint Henry's papers because he narrowed the scope of his yearbook in 1842. Physics was no longer covered as the *Jahres-Bericht über die Fortschritte der physischen Wissenschaften* became the *Jahres-*

vanic batteries one of which he says occupies but a part of a square foot of the surface of the Lecturer's table and produces more effect than any instrument he has ever seen. It is on the principle of Groves battery the negative element consisting of a preparation of coal. I intend to make one at my earliest leisure.[13]

Yours as ever

Joseph Henry

I was written to some weeks since to edit the new edition of turners chemistry. I informed the publishers[14] that I would have nothing to do with the work unless they would pay me for rewriting nearly the whole of the 1st 120 pages including Heat Light electricity and galvanism. These parts abound in mistakes and errors of principle which could scarcely be corrected without remodelling the whole.[15] They thought this was too much and so the matter ended.

I am pretty strongly inclined to attempt something in the school line and I am most in want myself of a book in mechanics but I fear the one which would answer my purpose would be of little use to others.[16]

Bericht über die Fortschritte der Chemie und Mineralogie. J. Erik Jorpes, *Jac. Berzelius: His Life and Work* (Uppsala, 1966), p. 97.

[13] Henry's description of the compact Berzelius battery appears in his letter to Torrey of February 19, 1842, printed below. From that description it is likely that Berzelius sent Henry an account of the Bunsen battery. Robert Bunsen (1811–1899, *DSB*) replaced the platinum electrode in the Grove cell with one of charcoal. The resulting battery was much cheaper to construct than a Grove cell, gave almost as much voltage and twice the current. Bunsen had just published his idea in a German-language article, a forum which was inaccessible to Henry (as well as a number of other American scientists; see *Henry Papers*, 2:325–326). *King*, pp. 243–245.

[14] Neither the letter from Thomas, Cowperthwait & Company, the American publishers of Edward Turner's *Elements of Chemistry*, nor Henry's reply has been located.

[15] Henry is referring to pages 5–120 of the sixth American edition, edited by Franklin Bache (Philadelphia, 1840), which contain a review of the imponderable substances derived from the fifth London edition (1834). Once a major element in chemistry courses, the imponderables were displaced during the 1840s by organic chemistry. An illustration of this displacement is the seventh American edition of Turner (Philadelphia, 1846). Edited by James B. and Robert E. Rogers, the new edition was considerably expanded, corrected, and revised compared to its predecessor. It incorporated much of Justus von Liebig's recent work in organic chemistry.

Coincident with the displacement of the imponderables by organic chemistry in chemistry courses was the rise in significance of the imponderables in natural philosophy courses. The imponderables were a major subject of research in nineteenth-century physics—electricity and magnetism represented the fastest growing area in the antebellum period. By the 1840s the imponderables were clearly more in the purview of the physicist than the chemist.

Stanley M. Guralnick, *Science and the Antebellum American College* (Philadelphia, 1975), pp. 61, 104; Weiner, "Joseph Henry's Lectures," pp. 83–84.

[16] Despite Henry's unhappiness with available textbooks, he never wrote one himself, although he did print a partial syllabus of his natural philosophy course (including a section on mechanics) for his students. Over the next several years he considered writing a textbook on various occasions. See, for example, Henry to Bache, November 12, 1843, printed below.

December 28, 1841

TO ROBERT BAIRD

Mary Henry Copy, Henry Papers, Smithsonian Archives

Princeton Dec. 28th 1841

My dear Sir.   I send by the packet of the 1st of January a bill on Paris, the amount of which I wish you to expend for me in purchasing the following articles.

1.   A complete set of Melloni's Apparatus for the repetition of the experiments on radiant heat. Professor Bartlett of West Point informs me that these articles can be procured best and cheapest of a private workman named Ruhmkorff no. 6[1]

I send you a letter to M. Melloni[2] the inventor of these instruments, requesting him to call with you on the maker and see that the articles are perfect before they are sent off. You will find him at the meetings of the Institute. He reads English but perhaps it would be as well if you should give him an account of the contents of my letter.

The cost of this set of instruments will be somewhere between fifty and seventy-five dollars.

2.   I also wish to procure a first-rate Atwood Machine,[3] described in the catalogue as follows—"montée sur une grand colonne en bois d'acajou avec pendule ou compte-secondes; règle et poids divisés, addition d'une détente qui laisse tomber le corps." This article in the catalogue of Pixii Rue de Grenelle St. Germain No. 18, is marked at nine hundred francs. Perhaps the article can be purchased cheaper of Ruhmkorff, the private workman. I wish however a good instrument and would prefer to get the article of Pixii with whom I am acquainted and whom I have found a perfectly honest man.

At my suggestion the trustees of the college have levied a tax of five dollars on every student of each senior class[4] and from this source I will have at the beginning of the next Summer term two hundred dollars in addition to what I now send. If Mr. Pixii will send me on the strength of this the articles, I will transmit him the money as soon as the articles arrive in New York.

---

[1] Mary Henry evidently couldn't decipher the rest of the address.

[2] Of November 29, 1841, printed above. Henry also sent Baird his letter to De La Rive of November 24, 1841 (above).

[3] A common piece of demonstration apparatus used to illustrate the laws of falling bodies.

[4] See the Trustees' Minutes of September 30, 1841, printed above.

135

TO JOHN TORREY

Torrey Papers, Library, New York Botanical Garden

Princeton Dec. 29th 1841

My Dear Dr

Your favour of the 22nd came to hand yesterday[1] and I immediately made enquiries relative to your salary. The Dr[2] informed me that he had placed your warrant into the hands of the Treasurer three months ago and supposed that you had received your money a long time since. I called at the Bank this morning and was informed that they could not give New York money under a charge of 5 percent. This I could not allow without an order from you. Mr Maclean however informes me that there are some bank dividends due in New York or will be due the first of Jany. and that if you can wait a few days say a week perhaps we may manage to send you a draft on the city.

I have spoken to Mr Maclean on the subject of the cases but he appears just now afraid of the expense and proposes that the plants be placed for the present in one of the large cases of the Museum.[3] He says he will have one of them prepared for their reception provided you agree to the proposition. The small room of the Library is to be used in the summer as the meeting place of the Faculty. Perhaps the long cases which are now placed horizontally on the floor of the Museum may be widened, set on edge and made to contain the Herbarium.[4] The article however is so valuable that you would be unwilling to have it placed in an exposed position.

I am now as usual at this season of the year much engaged with my college duties. I am making an effort to get through with the principal part of my course during the present session so as to leave the field to you and others the next summer. I have seen the number of Mape's Journal containing the exposition of Dr Lardner[5] but as I made some remarks in refer-

[1] Letter not found.

[2] Dr. James Carnahan.

[3] At the September 30, 1841, meeting of the Trustees (see above) responsibility for Princeton's museum was given to Maclean and Henry.

[4] According to James Alexander, Torrey's herbarium, "equal in bulk to 500 folio volumes, and containing, as I remember, 50,000 species," was placed in the library. John Hall, ed., *Forty Years' Familiar Letters of James W. Alexander, D.D.*, 2 vols. (New York, 1860), *1*:342.

[5] Volume 4 of James J. Mapes's journal, *The American Repertory of Arts, Sciences,* *and Manufactures,* contains an exchange of letters, solicited by Mapes, between himself and Lardner, concerning the latter's remarks at the British Association meetings of 1835 and 1836 on the use of steam power for Atlantic crossings.

Lardner claimed that he denied only the practicality, not the possibility, of uninterrupted steam-powered voyages between Europe and the Americas. "Correspondence between Dr. Lardner and the Editor," *The American Repertory of Arts, Sciences, and Manufactures,* 1842, 4:246–254. See also *Henry Papers,* 4:37–38, footnote 3.

ence to the gay gentleman in my last letter[6] I will not tresspass farther on your time with the same subject.

Nothing of especial interest about Princeton just at present. There is some stir about the Post Office. Mrs Solomons[7] is making an attempt to get the appointment. She started for Washington on monday for the second time. Herself and Perrine[8] the present incumbant are now the principal competitors. I hope she may get it. The small annuity allowed her by her sister has been stopped. The income of Mrs Pintard[9] from the Bayard estate no longer exists and therefore the family are in straitened circumstance. It was at first confidently expected that Robert Horner[10] would get the appointment but the Presidents circular relative to Political Editors[11] cut him off. Mrs. Solomons prospects were then encouraging but lately Mr Perrine has got up a petition signed by many of the citizens to retain him in the office; so that with the unwillingness to appoint a female Mrs. S. now stands but a small chance of success.[12] I see by the morning papers that Bache has been [?reformed] from the presidency of Girard college.[13] He only held on to the office inorder to keep the charge of the instruments and with the hope that something would be done with the Institution. He has received no pay for several years past.

I agree with you relative to the support of the greeks. I would advance something towards sending them home.[14]

Yours
Joseph Henry

[6] See above, Henry to Torrey, December 20, 1841.

[7] Susan Salomans, *Henry Papers*, 2:23.

[8] Major John A. Perrine (d. 1864) was appointed Postmaster of Princeton by Andrew Jackson. Perrine also served as Captain of the company of Princeton Blues, the local militia unit. *Hageman*, 2:340.

[9] Elizabeth Pintard, Susan Saloman's sister. *Hageman*, 2:268.

[10] Robert E. Hornor (d. 1851) edited the *Princeton Whig* up to early 1842. Hornor was known throughout the state for his political activities on behalf of the Whig party. *Hageman*, 2:279–280.

[11] On September 28, 1841, President Tyler instructed the Acting Postmaster General to investigate two incidents of misuse of the office of Deputy Postmaster, ostensibly in an attempt to depoliticize the Post Office Department. Tyler used the occasion to point out the particular impropriety of appointing political editors as postmasters. *Niles National Register*, October 2, 1841, p. 67.

[12] Presidential proclamations notwithstand-ing, the appointment of a postmaster at Princeton appeared to be a political matter. Hornor received a permanent commission as Deputy Postmaster from President Tyler on February 21, 1842. The appointment was for a term of four years, to be served at the pleasure of the President.

Tyler apparently found cause to disagree with Hornor's politics, for Hornor was removed in April 1843. Hornor later claimed his removal was for "being *at heart* opposed to the National Administration."

National Archives, RG 59, General Records of the Department of State, Appointment Records, Commissions, Permanent Commissions of Deputy Postmasters, 1842. Robert E. Hornor, *Uncle Ben's Farmers' and Mechanics' Great Western Almanac, for 1844* (Princeton, New Jersey, 1843), p. 38.

[13] A notice that the city council had abolished the office of the President of Girard College appeared in the December 27, 1841, edition of the *Newark Daily Advertiser*.

[14] Henry may be referring to the Greek students who had attended Princeton tuition

free. See above, James to Henry, March 15, 1841. Many of the Greeks sent by missionaries to the United States for an education had no means of returning home. Clifton Jackson

Phillips, *Protestant America and the Pagan World* (Cambridge, Massachusetts, 1969), pp. 139–140.

TO [JOHN T. ROBINSON][1]
Draft,[2] Henry Papers, Smithsonian Archives

[December 1841][3]

I have just received your communication informing me of my election as an Honorary member of the Mechanics Institute of Princeton. Please to give my thanks to the society and assure its members that I accept with much pleasure the honor they have conferred on me.[4]

[1] John T. Robinson (1811–1862) was Corresponding Secretary of the Mechanics' Institute of Princeton, and wrote to Henry on December 3, 1841 (Henry Papers, Smithsonian Archives) informing him of his election as an honorary member. Robinson was a printer, the editor and publisher of the *Princeton Whig* from early 1842. He was widely respected in the community, serving as judge and mayor, and was a ruling elder of the Second Presbyterian Church. *Hageman*, 2:60; Francis Bazley Lee, *Genealogical and Personal Memorial of Mercer County, New Jersey*, 2 vols. (New York, 1907), *1*:482.

[2] This text is on one side of a torn sheet of paper; an unrelated fragment, perhaps of a letter, is on the other. In the Smithsonian Archives, the notice of election and this document are found together, in Box 39 of the Henry Papers, under "Honors and Awards, Chronological, 1830–1878."

[3] The date was surmised from the notice of election of December 3, 1841, which Henry indicated he had "just received."

[4] Very little has been found out about the Mechanics' Institute of Princeton. It apparently held regular Wednesday evening meetings. The note to Henry said that his election occurred on Wednesday evening, November 24, 1841, and notices of Institute talks appearing in the pages of the newspaper, the *Princeton Whig*, referred to Wednesday night lectures (January 14, 1842; January 21, 1842; January 6, 1843). However, one notice in the *Princeton Whig* referred to regular Saturday night lectures as well (January 14, 1842). The Institute was apparently well-established at the time of Henry's election, for the newspaper announcements of lectures did not indicate a place, implying that either the Institute had its own hall, or that the meeting places were so well known that no reference needed to be made.

Two members of the Institute have been identified: John T. Robinson, Corresponding Secretary, and S. N. Lowrey, Recording Secretary. Two lectures were mentioned in the meeting announcements. Colonel William C. Alexander (d. 1874) was an alumnus of the College of New Jersey (B.A. 1824, A.M. 1827), LL.D. of Lafayette College (1860), active in New Jersey state politics as a Democrat, a lively gentleman and a popular and sought-after orator. He was interested in literary affairs and published a short-lived literary journal in Princeton. His topics for the Mechanics' Institute were the early history of New Jersey and the "rights and liabilities of women." *Princeton Catalogue*, p. 136; *Hageman*, *1*:351–354; *Princeton Whig*, January 14, 1842, and January 6, 1843. The Reverend George E. Hare, D.D., who spoke on the history of the country of the Edomites, was rector of Trinity Protestant Episcopal Church of Princeton from 1833 to 1843. *Hageman*, 2:192; *Princeton Whig*, January 21, 1842. For further information on the mechanics' institute movement in this country, see Bruce Sinclair, *Philadelphia's Philosopher Mechanics: A History of the Franklin Institute, 1824–1865* (Baltimore, 1974), especially pp. 1–19.

⊸{ 1842 }⊱

TO THOMAS SPARROW, JR.[1]
Henry Papers, Smithsonian Archives

Princeton Jan. 10th 1842.

My Dear Sir

I have been informed from a source entitled to full confidence that if you will withdraw the proposition you have made to Young Stockton[2] relative to the settlement of your difference that such an explanation will be made as will be perfectly satisfactory to yourself.

From the confidential manner in which I have obtained information of the quarrel, I do not feel myself called on at present to bring the matter before the faculty; but should the affair be not speedily adjusted I shall be obliged, however unwilling, to take such farther measures in reference to it as will be very disagreeable to myself: you will therefore confer a favour on *me* by making the withdrawel above mentioned and this in my opinion can be done without the least compromise of your honor.[3]

Your Friend
Joseph Henry

[1] A member of the Princeton Class of 1842 from North Carolina.

[2] One of the two sons of Robert Field Stockton who were members of the Class of 1843. Richard (1824–1876) and John Potter (1826–1900) both became lawyers. The latter brother was elected to the U.S. Senate in 1865 and again in 1869. *Princeton Catalogue*, p. 165; Thomas C. Stockton, *The Stockton Family of New Jersey and Other Stocktons* (Washington, 1911), pp. 128, 175–176.

[3] At the bottom of the letter Henry wrote: "Not Sent affair settled." Although Henry's intervention was not required this time, he possessed an acknowledged ability to understand the psychology of students and gain their respect and cooperation. *Henry Papers*, 2:39n.

FROM DANIEL B. SMITH[1]
Henry Papers, Smithsonian Archives

Haverford 1 mo: 11th 1842[2]

Respected Friend
Jos Henry

I learn from Judah Dobson that a few copies of my little compilation on

[1] Smith (1792–1883, *DAB*) was Professor of Chemistry, as well as Moral Philosophy and English Literature, at Haverford. After attending John Griscom's school in Burlington, New Jersey, he returned to Philadelphia to become a pharmacist. Smith was active in the founding and early years of the Philadelphia College of Pharmacy and later served as first President of the American Pharmaceutical Association. Interests outside his profession made him a familiar figure in Philadelphia's educational, cultural, and scientific organizations, including the American Philosophical Society.

[2] This date is in the early Quaker form with

Chemistry[3] are still in thy hands. As I am greatly in want of some—the edition being exhausted—I shall be greatly obliged by thy taking the trouble to look them up, & forward them to me through Judah Dobson.

Allow me to say that I hope thy course of Electro magnetic & Electro Dynamic research is still pursued. The results already published must I think be admitted to be the most brilliant contribution America has yet made to Science at least since Franklin's day.

respectfully
Dan[l] B Smith

---

numbers, rather than names, designating the month and day of the week.

[3] *The Principles of Chemistry for the Use of Schools, Academies and Colleges*, published by Dobson (Philadelphia, 1837); a second revised edition was published in 1842. Dobson supplied textbooks for Princeton (*Henry Papers*, 2:285n).

FROM SAMUEL F. B. MORSE[1]
Henry Papers, Smithsonian Archives

New York Jan[y] 11th 1842.

My Dear Sir,

I am again engaged upon my Electro-Magnetic Telegraph, and using means to induce Congress to pass the bill reported in 1838[2] but suffered to lie by without action upon it. Want of means alone has prevented me from prosecuting the enterprize, and the same cause now operates, (however unphilosophical it may seem,) to turn my attention again to the subject.

The success of Wheatstone's in England for some hundred miles, puts the practicability beyond doubt.[3] I could have wished that the Government of my own country had enabled me long since to have secured that honor to the country, the honor of first putting in practice the Electric Telegraph. The superiority which is awarded by scientific bodies abroad as well as at home to my system, ought at least to have rescued the invention from ne-

[1] This is the first known correspondence between Henry and Morse since May 20, 1839 (*Henry Papers*, 4:221). In the interval, Morse became a professional daguerreotypist and ran unsuccessfully for Mayor of New York City. Carleton Mabee, *The American Leonardo: A Life of Samuel F. B. Morse* (1943; reprint ed., New York, 1969), chapter 19.

[2] On April 6, 1838, the House Committee on Commerce, chaired by F. O. J. Smith, re-ported favorably on a bill which would have authorized $30,000 to test Morse's telegraph. *House Reports*, 25th Congress, 2d Session, 1837–1838, No. 753. See also *Henry Papers*, 4:98, especially footnote 6.

[3] For Wheatstone's telegraph, see *Henry Papers*, 3:218–220. Wheatstone secured a United States patent for his version of the telegraph in 1840. Mabee, p. 248.

glect, and may I not add the inventor from want, by proffering that aid which a government can with the least inconvenience extend.

I have been advised to procure from scientific men and societies, letters expressing their desire that Congress should extend its aid in putting the system into operation for at least fifty miles, (the distance proposed by the bill reported by the Com^tee of Commerce,) that science might derive the benefit of many useful experiments necessarily connected with such a measure.

I know your feelings on the subject, my dear Sir, and may I ask of you a letter expressive of your views, and bearing, in such manner as you may deem advisable, on this subject.[4]

I would also say that if you are not using the 5 miles of wire loaned to you some time since it will *now be of essential service to me.*

> Believe me Dear Sir
> With sincere respect & esteem
> Y^r friend & Servt
> Sam! F: B: Morse.∴

[4] For Henry's endorsement, see below, February 24, 1842.

TO JAMES HENRY

Mary Henry Copy, Family Correspondence, Henry Papers,
Smithsonian Archives

Princeton Jan. 12.[1] 1842

My dear James   . . . We have nothing new of much interest. I spent New Year's day partly in Phil. partly in Princeton. I was invited to the city to attend the funeral of my old friend John Vaughan Treasurer and Librarian of the American Philosophical Society.[2] He was a native of England, the son of a wealthy West Indian merchant who married in Boston. He was one of Dr. Franklin's family when the Dr. was minister in France and became after his arrival in America intimate with the most prominent men who figured at the close of the Revolution. I became acquainted with him on my first visit to Phil. in 1827[3] and after my removal to Princeton he

[1] A questionable dating by Mary Henry; one of the deaths reported here occurred on January 15.
[2] John Vaughan (*Henry Papers*, 2:107n–108n) died on December 30, 1841, at age eighty-five. The APS held a special meeting the next day to pay tribute to Vaughan and arrange for his funeral, which took place in the Hall of the Society. APS *Proceedings*, 1841–1843, 2:131–133.
[3] The earliest trip for which there is documentation was in 1833.

was one of the persons who advocated my election to the Philosophical Society.[4] We have heard today of the death of another old member of the Society, Judge Hopkinson.[5]

A happy New Year from all to all.

[4] See *Henry Papers*, 2:277.
[5] Joseph Hopkinson died on January 15, 1842. APS *Proceedings*, 1841–1843, 2:138–139.

EXCERPT,[1] MINUTES, COUNCIL OF THE ROYAL SOCIETY
Council Minutes, Printed Series, Library, Royal Society of London

January 27th, 1842,
At a Council of the Royal Society:

Present—

SIR JOHN W. LUBBOCK, Bart. V.P. and Treasurer, in the Chair.[2]

MR. BAILY.	MR. PEPYS.
MR. BRANDE.	MR. RENNIE.
MR. CHRISTIE.	DR. ROGET.
MR. DANIELL.	LIEUT.-COL. W. H. SYKES.
SIR WILLIAM J. HOOKER.	MR. WHEATSTONE.

The Minutes of the last Meeting were read and confirmed.

Professor Link, of Berlin, was proposed for recommendation to the Society, as Foreign Member, in addition to the names proposed at the last Meeting.

Resolved,—That the selection of names to be recommended to the Society for election as Foreign Members, be deferred till the next Meeting of the Council. . . .

The names of persons proposed for recommendation as Foreign Members, are the following;[3] viz.

[1] The material not included here dealt with the election of Friedrich Wilhelm IV, King of Prussia, as Member of the Society, in addition to routine business.

[2] John William Lubbock, Bart. (1803–1865). *Henry Papers*, 4:238.

[3] On February 10, 1842, the Council voted to nominate Ohm, Poncelet, Rose, and Link as Foreign Members of the Royal Society. The decision was formally approved by the full society on April 28, 1842. De La Rive was elected in 1846, Chasles in 1854. Colladon, Lamé, and Henry were never elected to that august body, though Henry was nominated again in 1846. *Minutes*, Council of the Royal Society, Printed Series, February 10, 1842; *Proceedings of the Royal Society*, 1842, 4:384.

The Council members who voted on Henry's proposed membership on February 10 were almost the same as those who accepted his nomination on January 27. William Henry Fitton, geologist, and Robert Willis, Professor of

January 27, 1842

Professor Chasles, of Paris.[4]
M. Daniell Colladon, of Geneva.[5]
Auguste De la Rive, of Geneva.[6]
Professor Henry, of Princetown, U.S.
Professor Lamé, of Paris.[7]
Professor Ohm, of Nuremberg.[8]
Professor Poncelet, of Paris.[9]

Mechanics at Cambridge University, were also present and John Rennie was absent. Henry had met all these members of the Council on his European trip (as shown by volume 3 of the *Henry Papers*) with the possible exceptions of Sykes, Hooker, and Willis. However, Henry's notes of the Glasgow portion of his journey were lost (*Henry Papers*, 3:171), and he did visit that city while Hooker was Professor of Botany at the university. Similarly, Henry was in Cambridge while Willis was Professor of Mechanics, and their meeting was certainly possible. Thus Henry had been introduced to the great majority of the members of the Council who voted on his election, and was well-known to some, such as Daniell and Wheatstone.

The Society had but four positions to fill in the election of 1842, for the Council had earlier decided to limit the number of Foreign Members. During Sir Joseph Banks's presidency, there was increasing criticism on the quality of the membership in general. On his death in 1820, the number of Foreign Members was restricted to fifty. Few Americans were represented as Foreign Members of the Society in this period: none were elected between Nathaniel Bowditch in 1818 and Benjamin Peirce in 1852. *Record of the Royal Society of London*, 4th ed. (London, 1940); Dorothy Stimson, *Scientists and Amateurs: A History of the Royal Society* (New York, 1948), pp. 157–158.

[4] Michel Chasles (1793–1880), geometer and historian of mathematics. In 1841 he was made professor of the École polytechnique on the strength of his book *Aperçu historique sur l'origine et le développement des méthodes en géométrie* (Brussels, 1837), an expansion of his prize essay for the Royal Academy of Brussels. In 1865 he was awarded the Royal Society's Copley Medal. *DSB*.

[5] Jean-Daniel Colladon (1802–1893), engineer. From 1835, he was Professor of Mechanics at the University of Geneva. His research involved the compressibility of liquids and the determination of the speed of sound in water. *World Who's Who in Science*, s.v. "Col-

ladon, (Jean-) Daniel."

[6] Arthur-Auguste De La Rive (1801–1873), natural philosopher. De La Rive was Secretary and Professor of Experimental Physics at the Académie de Genève, and editor of the *Bibliothèque universelle de Genève* and the *Archives de l'électricité*. He was generally acknowledged as the leader of the Swiss scientific community until 1846, when he retired from academic and public life due to political reverses in both spheres (he was a philosophical conservative). His primary scientific interest was the voltaic pile. *DSB*.

[7] Gabriel Lamé (1795–1870), geometer and engineer. Lamé was a graduate of the École polytechnique in 1817 and of the École des mines in 1820. After twelve years as a civil engineer in Russia, he returned to Paris in 1832 to become Professor of Physics at the École polytechnique. His greatest contribution to mathematics was in the theory of curvilinear coordinates, of use in problems of mathematical physics and differential geometry from mid-century on. *DSB*.

[8] Georg Simon Ohm (1789–1854), a physicist interested in electricity, about whom an extensive literature exists. See *DSB*; *Henry Papers*, 2:299n–300n. At the time of his election, Ohm was a professor at the Polytechnical School in Nuremberg. In 1841, he had received the Copley Medal from the Royal Society.

[9] Jean Victor Poncelet (1788–1867), geometer and mechanical engineer. A graduate of the École polytechnique, Poncelet was interested in two distinct fields. From 1813 to 1824 he worked on projective geometry; from 1825 to 1840, on applied mechanics and technology. The occasion of the Royal Society's interest may have been the 1841 publication of his large theoretical text on mechanics, *Introduction à la mécanique industrielle, physique ou expérimentale* (Metz, France, 1841). He was a member of the mechanics section of the Académie des sciences from 1834, and offered courses on physical and experimental mechanics at the Faculty of Sciences of the Sorbonne from 1837. *DSB*.

February 2, 1842

Professor Rose, of Berlin.[10]
Professor Link, of Berlin.[11]

(Signed)   J. W. LUBBOCK.

[10] Heinrich Rose (1795–1864), chemist. Rose came from a family of scientist-pharmacists, including his grandfather, father, and his brother Gustav, later Ordinary Professor of Mineralogy at the University of Berlin. He pursued pharmacy intermittently in his early life, but while in Paris during the Prussian occupation of 1815 he became acquainted with the foremost French scientists, such as Berthollet, and turned to chemistry. He worked under Berzelius in Stockholm, producing a dissertation on titanium in 1822. That same year he became Privatdozent at the University of Berlin, rising to ordinary professor by 1835. His scientific work was mainly in analytical and inorganic chemistry, and consisted in the careful analysis of minerals, alkaline earth compounds, and in the study of acid properties of non-metals. *DSB*.

[11] Heinrich Friedrich Link (1767–1851), natural philosopher. Link studied medicine and natural sciences at Göttingen, from which he received the M.D. in 1789. After two short appointments he was made Professor of Botany at the University of Berlin in 1815. Link published papers and books in geology, botany, chemistry, zoology, and philosophy of science. His last major publication occurred just before his election to the Royal Society: *Ueber die Bildung der festen Körper* (Berlin, 1841). *DSB*.

FROM SAMUEL F. B. MORSE

Henry Papers, Smithsonian Archives

New York Feby. 2[d] 1842

My dear Sir,

I dropped you a line I think nearly one month since[1] which, I fear, from not having heard from you in reply has in some way miscarried. It was requesting the return of my reel of wire, if it can be done without inconvenience to you in any present experiments. I am putting my Telegraphic apparatus into a state to show its operation and with a view to induce Congress eventually to adopt it. I think of giving a Lecture upon the subject and thus create a public interest in its favor. Congress seem engaged just now rather in weakening than strengthening the Union,[2] and my proposition of tying it together with wires may not receive so favorable a consideration at the present as at a future session. It was suggested by a Member of Congress that I should obtain the request of scientific bodies that Congress would move in the matter and I in my letter to you ventured to ask a letter from you which would avail me in my suit before the Government.

[1] Morse's letter of January 11, 1842, is printed above.

[2] See a related comment by Henry in the next letter.

Please direct any letter, or the box containing the wire to me at the N. Y. Observer Office 142 Nassau St.

I need not say how happy I shall be to see you when you come to the city and to show you the Telegraphic apparatus in its completeness,

> With sincere respect & esteem
> Dᴿ Sir
> Yᴿ Mo. Ob. Servᵗ
> Samˡ F: B: Morse.ᐧ.

TO JAMES HENRY

*Mary Henry Copy, Family Correspondence, Henry Papers,
Smithsonian Archives*

Princeton Feb. 5. 184[2].[1]

Dear James   Don't scold. Here is a letter although long in coming. . . . We have had thus far a most remarkable winter; the temperature is now that of April. The trees are beginning to swell their buds and the campus has quite a green appearance. The frost is entirely out of the ground and the walks are dry. . . . We have nothing new in this dull place except that our bank bills are ten percent below par in New York. The depreciation is owing to the connection of the institution with the banks of Pennsylvania. There is considerable stir in the legislature of the state relative to causing the banks of west Jersey to resume specie payment.[2] If the banks are forced to resume they will all probably go by the board. . . . What doing we have in Congress! Old John appears to have turned the tables on the brawlers of the South who were a few years ago so fierce for the dissolution of the union.[3] I regret such occurrences but have full faith in the virtue and in-

---

[1] Although dated 1841 by Mary Henry's copyist, the contents clearly indicate that the letter was written in 1842.

[2] The banks in the northeastern half of New Jersey were linked to those of New York City, while those in the southwestern half were tied to the Philadelphia banking community. Although Philadelphia banks suspended specie payment in the wake of the Crisis of 1839, New York City banks did not. New Jersey banks adopted one or the other practice according to their geographical location. In order to ensure uniform practice, the state legislature passed a law on March 5, 1842, requiring all banks to resume specie payment by August 15, 1842.

Eugene E. Agger, "Banking in New Jersey," in *New Jersey: A History,* ed. Irving S. Kull, 4 vols. (New York, 1930), 4:1223–1224.

[3] On January 24, 1842, a resolution was offered in the House of Representatives to censure John Quincy Adams. The symbol of Northern defense of constitutional rights because of his fight for the unrestricted right of petition in the face of Southern opposition to anti-slavery petitions, Adams was attacked in this instance for presenting a petition from residents of Haverhill, Massachusetts, praying for the dissolution of the Union. He was accused by Southerners of insulting the people of the United States by presenting this petition

telligence of the people at large and have no doubt that good men north and south would be found in case of real danger to settle any difficulties which may occur. . . . I see that quite a trade has sprung up between Albany and Boston; the old dutch customs and feelings will soon be entirely swept from our I should say your city. The blood of the Vans will be lost in the floods from Yankee Land. Well the more we are mixed up and mingled into one homogeneous whole the better.[4] The union I trust will be bound together by means of railways too strongly for politics to sever it.

John and Harriet would not belong to the Henry stock if they had not some impetuosity of character. The principle of life is strong within them and unless the steam is sometimes allowed to escape the consequences might be fatal.

If anything interesting occurs in the legislature of the State of New York send me a paper. Love from all to all Your Brother.

---

advocating secession. After violent debate, the censure motion was defeated on February 7. Charles Francis Adams, ed., *Memoirs of John Quincy Adams*, 12 vols. (Philadelphia, 1874–1877), *11*:70–88; Louis Filler, *The Crusade Against Slavery, 1830–1860* (New York, 1960), pp. 100–101.

[4] The Dutch were a distinct minority in Albany as early as 1820. Their position worsened during that decade as New Englanders took advantage of the economic opportunities created by the opening of the Erie Canal to obtain economic and political control of the city. But Henry's hopes for a homogeneous population were shattered by the massive Irish immigration of the 1830s and 1840s. The city evolved into two quite distinct communities: Protestant, Yankee and Dutch, native-born versus Roman Catholic, Irish, immigrant. William Esmond Rowley, "Albany: A Tale of Two Cities, 1820–1880" (Ph.D. dissertation, Harvard University, 1967).

TO SAMUEL F. B. MORSE
Morse Papers, Library of Congress

Princeton [February 8, 1842][1]

My Dear Sir

I am almost ashamed to confess that you[r] letter was received not quite a month since. But I have been so much engaged in extra college duties on account of the illness of the wife of one of the faculty that I have suffered every thing else to remain unattend to. I hope you will pardon the unintentional neglect and accept my thanks for the long use of the wire. I will send the article if possible on saturday next and will then also prepare the letter for congress.[2] Every moment of my time will be occup[i]ed for several

---

[1] Although this letter bears the date "Dec 5th 1841," it seems to be in response to Morse's letter of February 2, 1842. We are printing it under the date of the postmark.

[2] The letter, dated February 24, 1842, is printed below.

days to come. I hope you will not be put to any inconvenien[ce] on account of the delay. The wire is now on two spools but I will set a person to put it on the original one.

In haste with much
Respect yours &c
Joseph Henry

TO JOHN TORREY

Torrey Papers, Library, New York Botanical Garden

Princeton Feby 19th 18[42][1]

My Dear Dr

Your favour of the 12th came to hand at the begining of the week[2] but I am sure you will excuse me for not writing before when I inform you that I have lectured 5 times this week with recitations in the afternoon besides being in Philad. on Monday.

James Alexander left two weeks ago for Virginia before he had worked out his time on account of a letter informing him that his wife was unwell.[3] I took the class for him in addition to my other lectures. The Berzelius Battery[4] is constructed as follows: a cylender of coak is formed by heating in a furnace pounded coak an[d] stone[5] coal until the whole is cemented into a mass. Inorder to give it a proper shape it is moulded in a hollow cylender of sheat iron and heated in this and I think a rod of iron should be placed in the axis of the cylender to preserve the interior in the proper shape while baking although nothing is said about this in the directions. The cylender being formed it is placed in a glass or other vessel and around it a cylender of zinc. Within the coak cylender strong nitric acid is poured and on the outside of the same and in contact with the zinc a solution of sulphuric acid. The zinc forms one element and the coak the other. Also electricity is generated by the action of the two acids which in the pores of the coak come in contact with each other. Several of these arrangements being united to each other by joining the negative element of the one to the positive element of the other by strips of copper the whole is complete.

---

[1] Henry dated the letter 1841. References to John Vaughan's death and Lyell's lectures indicate 1842.

[2] Letter not found.

[3] James Alexander's wife, Elizabeth, had been in Virginia since November 1841. The Alexanders did not return to Princeton until May. John Hall, ed., *Forty Years' Familiar* *Letters of James W. Alexander, D.D.*, 2 vols. (New York, 1860), *1*:340, 346, 348, 355. A letter from Alexander to Henry of March 14, 1842, is in the Henry Papers, Smithsonian Archives.

[4] See above, Henry to Torrey, December 20, 1841.

[5] Perhaps "stove."

I should have mentioned that the copper connector forms a collár which surrounds the upper end of the coak cylender so as to make a broader contact. Berzelius states that this is the most powerful battery he has ever seen. I have not as yet had time to put the article in operation although I have procured coak for the purpose of making the cylenders.

I requested William Dod some weeks since to call and inform you that his Brother[6] would make the arrangement you desired in reference to the house ie he would reduce the rent so that repairs could be made under your own direction.

I called today on Mr Talmage[7] in reference to the remainder of the salary. He informed me that the money due in New York had not yet been received although it was to be paid on the first of the month. He expects to receive a letter in the course of a few days from Mr James Lenox[8] in reference to it. If you can possibly do without it for a short time it will be best to wait, for the Princeton bills are at a discount of 7 or 8 per cent in New York.

Yours in haste
Joseph Henry

P.S. We will expect to see you at our house next week.

I went to Philad. to attend Baches Whistar and also to hear one of Lyells lectures. As a Lecturer he does not make much impression but his matter is highly interesting to the man of science.[9] I found a sad loss in the rooms of the society on account of the absence of our old Friend Mr Vaughan. George Ord[10] has been chosen Librarian in his place but as yet he does not reside in the rooms of the society.

---

[6] Albert Baldwin Dod.

[7] John Vredenburgh Talmage was Treasurer of Princeton from 1839 until 1845. *Princeton Catalogue*, p. 27.

[8] A Trustee of Princeton. *Henry Papers*, 2: 423.

[9] Henry attended Lyell's fourth lecture, part of a series that was widely covered in the Philadelphia press. The *Public Ledger*'s statement following an earlier lecture that Lyell "appeared to want self possession" lends support to Henry's comments. The *Ledger* added however that the lecture room at the Philadelphia Museum was not particularly suited to Lyell's method of lecturing. *Philadelphia Public Ledger*, February 4, 1842.

[10] George Ord (1781–1866), naturalist and philologist, was a close associate of Alexander Wilson's, completing and reissuing *American Ornithology* after Wilson's death. Ord served as Treasurer and Librarian of the American Philosophical Society from January 1842 until January 1848. *DAB*; Minutes, January 7, 1842, January 31, 1842, January 7, 1848, January 21, 1848, Archives, American Philosophical Society.

TO BENJAMIN SILLIMAN, SR.

Mary Henry Copy, Henry Papers, Smithsonian Archives

Princeton [February] 24, 1842[1]

My Dear Sir

... My college duties during the winter season are so arduous that I cannot find the least time for anything else. Last summer I was prevented from making but little advance in the way of research by a request from the senior class that I would prepare a course of lectures in Geology.[2] I was of course obliged to give the subject all my attention, for since the time of my excursion with Prof. Eaton[3] I had attended only in a popular way to the subject. I was however richly paid for my labor by the delightful field of knowledge which it opened to me and although I do not aspire to become an officiating priest within the geological temple yet I shall certainly contrive to be an ardent although humble worshiper without. Hereafter the geological course will be divided between Dr. Torrey and myself. He will attend particularly to the mineralogical part and I to the dynamical principles of the science. The Doctor is about to settle with his family in Princeton. With much respect and esteem I am as ever[4]

Sincerely yours

Joseph Henry

[1] Although the copyist dated this letter July 24, another, less complete version in the Mary Henry Memoir is dated February 24. The references to winter and the impending move of the Torrey family, which occurred in the spring of 1842, indicate that the latter date is correct.

[2] On June 25, 1841, printed above.

[3] A reference to Henry's field trip along the Erie Canal under the direction of Amos Eaton during May and June of 1826. *Henry Papers,* *1*:136.

[4] Silliman replied on September 1, 1842 (Mary Henry Copy, Henry Papers, Smithsonian Archives). Unfortunately, the Mary Henry Copy is incomplete and extremely unreliable.

TO SAMUEL F. B. MORSE[1]
Draft, Henry Papers, Smithsonian Archives

Princeton[2] Feby 24th 1842

Professor Morse

Dear Sir

I am pleased to learn that you have again petitioned congress in reference to your telegraph and I most sincerely hope that you will succed in convincing our Representatives of the importance of the invention. In this however you may perhaps find some difficulty, since in the minds of many, the electro-magnetic telegraph is associated with the many chimerical projects constantly brought before the Public[3] and particularly with the schemes so popular a year or two ago for the application of electricity as a moving power in the arts. All schemes for this purpose, I have from the first asserted, are premature and formed without proper scientific knowledge.[4] The case however is entirely different in regard to the electro-

---

[1] This letter was written in response to Morse's requests of January 11 and February 2, 1842. Henry mentioned it in his letter to Morse of February 8, 1842. All three letters are printed above.

Morse used this letter to help plead his case before the U.S. Congress for adoption of his telegraph, and Henry wrote it with that purpose in mind. The version printed here is from a copy in Henry's hand found in his papers. Our search has not found the original letter he sent to Morse. However, our draft is slightly unusual in that it contains Morse's name and address on the back of the second page. At least eight other copies of the letter exist which differ from this one in phrasing and spelling and are very similar to each other. Two are handwritten; one, in an unknown hand, is in the Henry Papers, Smithsonian Archives, and has a Mary Henry annotation. Another is in Morse's hand and is in RG 233 of the National Archives, Records of the House of Representatives (27th Congress, 1841–1843, Committee Reports and Papers, 3d Session, 1842, Report No. 17). This latter copy was submitted by Morse in support of his telegraphic claims. There are also six printed copies known to us: Appendix A to *House Reports*, 27th Congress, 3d Session, 1842, No. 17, pp. 4–5 (reprinted in Thomas C. Cochran, ed., *The New American State Papers, Science and Technology* [Wilmington, 1973], 8:68–69); Carleton Mabee, *The American Leonardo: A Life of Samuel F. B. Morse* (1943; reprint ed., New York, 1969), pp. 249–

250; *A Memorial of Samuel F. B. Morse from the City of Boston* (Boston, 1872), pp. 62–63; Alfred Vail, *The American Electro Magnetic Telegraph . . .* (Philadelphia, 1845), pp. 87–88; *Shaffner's Telegraph Companion*, 1855, 2:16–17 (in an article written by Morse); and Edward Lind Morse, ed., *Samuel F. B. Morse: His Letters and Journals*, 2 vols. (Boston and New York, 1914), 2:170–172. Because most of the changes from Henry's retained copy to the other eight copies consist of corrections of spelling and elevations of language, we surmise that Henry's copy was a draft, which he then altered before sending to Morse because he knew the letter would be used for public purposes. The last five printed copies were based on the first printed copy, and it was derived from Morse's handwritten version. We do believe that Morse italicized one sentence of that text (indicated in note 5, below); neither Henry's retained copy, nor the copy annotated by Mary Henry, nor the version printed by Morse's biographer-son has that sentence italicized. The latter two copies might have been made from the now lost original letter; a lack of extended emphasis was more in keeping with Henry's rather formal, restrained style; and emphasis would have been entirely in Morse's interest.

[2] "Princeton College" appears in all variants but one.

[3] All variants have ". . . the various chimerical projects brought before the public. . . ."

[4] All variants have "I have asserted from the first that all attempts of this kind are

magnetic telegraph the science is now fully ripe for such an application <*of its principles*>, and I have not the least dout, if proper means be afforded, of the perfect success of the invention.[5] The idea, of <*the transmission of*> transmitting intelligence,[6] by the electrical action has been suggested by various persons from the time of Franklin to the present but until within the last few years or since the discoveries[7] in electro-magnetism all attempts to reduce it to practice were necessarily unsuccessful. The mere suggestion however, of a scheme, of this kind is a matter for which little credit can be claimed, since it is one which would naturally arise in the mind of almost any person familiar with the phenomena of electricity; but the bringing it forward at the proper moment when the developments of science can furnish the means of certain sucess and <*the*> to <*devising of a*> devise plans for putting <*the scheme*> it into practical operation <*offred*> are the grounds of a just claim to scientific reputation as well as to public patronage.

About the same time with yourself Professor Wheatstone of England and Dr Steinheil of Germany proposed plans of the electro-magnetic telegraph but these differ almost as much from your's as the nature of the common principle will permit and unless some essential improvements have lately been made in the European plans I should prefer the one invented by yourself.[8] With my best wishes for your success I remain

With much Respect & Esteem[9]

<*I am as ever*> Yours Truly

Joseph Henry

---

premature; and made without a proper knowledge of scientific principles."

[5] All variants drop the word "the" before "science," and begin a new sentence there. All variants but two italicize this sentence through the word "application." One variant (*Morse Memorial*) in addition italicizes to the end of the sentence. The two variants which lack italicization are the copy annotated by Mary Henry and the Morse *Letters and Journals* copy.

[6] All variants insert "to a distance" at this point.

[7] All variants give ". . . the principal discoveries. . . ."

[8] For Wheatstone's work see *Henry Papers,3*: 218n–219n. For Steinheil's project, see C. A. von Steinheil, "Upon Telegraphic Communication, Especially by Means of Galvanism (Trans.)," Sturgeon's *Annals of Electricity, Magnetism, and Chemistry*, 1839, 3:439–452, 509–520. This volume is in the Henry Library, with Henry annotations.

Karl August Steinheil (1801–1870) studied natural science and astronomy at Göttingen and Königsberg. He received his Ph.D. in 1825, as a student of Bessel. At the time of Henry's writing he was Ordinary Professor of Mathematics and Natural Philosophy at Munich, where he was highly influential in the scientific life of the city. Between 1849 and 1852 he organized the telegraphic communications in Austria. He also worked extensively in optics and scientific instrumentation. *DSB*.

This is the first instance of Henry's oft-repeated statement that Morse deserved credit not for priority of conception, but rather for the ability to realize an efficient system. This point would be of crucial importance later in Morse's legal travails over the telegraph, as would be the interpretation of this letter. See Henry's deposition and Morse's rejoinder in *Shaffner's Telegraph Companion*, 1855, 2:108 and passim.

[9] Many variations of the closing exist; this is the longest and most elaborate.

February 25, 1842

TO CADWALLADER EVANS

Mary Henry Copy,[1] *Memoir, Henry Papers, Smithsonian Archives*

Princeton Feb 25[h] 1842

Dear Sir:

I have deferred answering your letter[2] relative to your safety apparatus until I could find time to make some experiments with the model you sent me, but I have been unable to give the subject any attention until within a few days past.

I have for the last few years been in the habit of mentioning to my class the advantages of using the fusible metal enclosed in a tube surrounded by the steam for the purpose of moving an alarm in case of the undue heating of the boiler, as proposed by my friend Professor Bache, but I was not aware of the fact until I was informed of it by Professor Bache himself that you had independently applied the same principle to set in operation a self-acting apparatus for relieving the safety valve in case of danger.

I have made a number of experiments with your apparatus, the results of which are perfectly satisfactory. To determine if the discharge of steam always takes place at the same pressure, the composition of the fusible metal remaining the same, I attached to the boiler a manometer gauge, and found that in each case the discharge took place at a pressure of 33 lbs per square inch. The indications of the gauge did not vary from this more than a lb on either side in any of the experiments, although the circumstances were not precisely the same in all, in reference to the quantity of water in the boiler.

I have also made some experiments on surcharged steam. For this purpose the water was suffered to get low in the boiler, and then the fire was removed from the bottom to one side so as to heat the metal above the water line and surcharge the steam. Under these circumstances, the fusible metal gave way at a pressure of about 16 pounds.

These results appear so satisfactory that I do not hesitate to state that I consider the plan of using the fusible metal enclosed in a tube exposed to the steam, and your whole arrangement for relieving the safety-valve at the moment of danger by far the best contrivance which has ever been proposed to the public as the means of preventing the disastrous explosions from

---

[1] In the handwriting of W. L. Nicholson, who noted that the copy was made from   Henry's draft.

[2] Of July 12, 1841, printed above.

steam. You have my best wishes for success in getting your invention into general use.

> With much respect, I am
> Yours &c
> Joseph Henry

P.S. If perfectly convenient, you will much oblige me by sending me another copy of your circular.

I hope you will pardon my long silence. I have been so much engaged during the past year that I could not find time to make any experiments with your apparatus, until in the course of my lectures I came to the subject of steam. My lectures on this subject were finished last spring before I received your apparatus.

I have always endeavored to do justice to American inventors, and always dwell on the labors of Oliver Evans in my lectures as the Improver of our corn mills and the introducer of the high pressure steam engine &c.[3]

You are at liberty to make what use you may think fit of the letter on the opposite leaf.[4]

> J.H.

[3] In Joseph J. Halsey's two-volume notebook on the 1841–1842 course (Henry Papers, Smithsonian Archives), remarks on Oliver Evans and his high-pressure steam engine occupy two pages (2:26–27). In discussing steam boiler explosions, Henry told his class: "An engine constructed by M.ͬ Evans' son at Philadelphia is very ingenious & promises to remedy the evil pretty effectually" (2:34).

[4] Evans used Henry's endorsement (everything up to the postscript) almost immediately. It was published in the March 1842 number of the *Journal of the Franklin Institute* (29:210) and in various newspapers. Evans also used it in his *Treatise on the Causes of Explosions of Steam Boilers, with Practical Suggestions for Their Prevention: To Which Is Added a Description of Evans' Improved Safety Guard, or Engineer's Assistant* (Pittsburgh, 1850), p. 36, a copy of which is in the Henry Library.

TO PETTY VAUGHAN

Mary Henry Copy, Henry Papers, Smithsonian Archives

[February 1842][1]

I intended to have written to you an expression of my sympathy for the loss we have experienced in the death of your dear good uncle—John

[1] John Vaughan had died on December 30, 1841. Aside from his attendance at Vaughan's funeral, Henry's next documented visits to Philadelphia were January 7 and February 14, 1842. See above, Henry to James Henry, January 12, 1842, and Henry to Torrey, February 19, 1842; also, Minutes, January 7, 1842, Archives, American Philosophical Society.

Vaughan. I took breakfast with him a few weeks before his death. He was feeble but quite cheerful; said that he had lived a long and happy life and that like Franklin had he to live his days over again he would choose the same life rather than run the chance of a worse. I attended his funeral by a special invitation sent to Princeton by the committee of arrangements.[2] I have been in Philadelphia but once since his death and then found that his absence made a sad difference in the pleasure and profit of my visit. For several years past I have been in the habit of calling immediately on my arrival in the city at the Hall of the Society and of making that place my headquarters and study during my stay in town. Mr. Vaughan always received me with the kindness of a Father and was pleased to assist me to references to scientific papers and to direct my attention to anything new in my line. The change was a melancholy one. I now found the doors of the Philosophical Hall closed and could get access to the Library only at stated times. I loved the old gentleman while he lived and will cherish his memory now that he is dead.

[2] Not found.

FROM SAMUEL F. B. MORSE
Henry Papers, Smithsonian Archives

New York March 5th 1842.

My Dear Sir,

The wire arrived safely, and the letter[1] for which accept my sincere thanks. You will not consider it flattery when I say that I value your opinion on this subject as highly as that of any scientific man living.

In conversation with D[r] Torrey a few days since, he told me he had received a letter from you in which you gave him an account of a new battery you had received from Berzelius, in which a cup formed of coke was substituted for the copper electrode, and which is said to be far superior to Daniel's battery.[2] I feel much interested in this matter, and shall await with anxiety the results of yours and D[r] Torrey's experiments, and shall commence some experiments myself. What is the philosophy of such an arrangement? Supposing that carbon was the main agent in the new ar-

[1] Henry's letter of February 24, 1842 (printed above), endorsing the telegraph, which Morse presented to Congress.

[2] Henry had first mentioned Berzelius's account of a new battery (a Bunsen battery) in a letter to Torrey of December 20, 1841, and then described it in detail in a letter of February 19, 1842 (both printed above).

rangement, I took the dust of anthracite, and mixed with it one fourth plaster of Paris, and cast a cup with a copper rim within the upper part of the cup; within the cup I put dilute nitric acid, around the cup dilute sulph. acid and zinc, there was a very feeble galvanic action. Instead of the dust of anthracite, I used common charcoal dust; all the other parts of the arrangement were as before. *The result was a stronger galvanic action.* These are the only experiments I have had time to make, and I give them to you on the principle that the *record of failures* in certain experiments is valuable to the philosopher.

If anything of interest shall result in my experiments I will communicate it to you, and I should be happy if it is not taxing your kindness, and your valuable time too much, to receive from you any hints which may be of service to me in my Telegraph.

When you are in the city I shall be happy to show you the Telegraph, which with its improved mechanism is now nearly completed.[3] I have devoted myself wholly to it the past winter, and propose to prepare a popular lecture upon it.

> With respect & esteem Dr Sir
> Y^r friend & Servt
> Sam! F: B: Morse .∙.

[3] Henry saw Morse's telegraph for the first time in early July 1842, presumably on the same trip to New York City during which he attended an examination at the Rutgers Female Institute (see below, Henry to Kinney, July 12, 1842). In a letter to F. O. J. Smith of July 16, Morse described Henry's visit:

Prof. Henry of Princeton visited me a day or two since. He knew the principles of the Telegraph, but had never seen it before. He told a gentleman afterwards who mentioned it again to me, that without exception it was the most beautiful and ingenious instrument he had ever seen. He further says that mine is truly the only practicable plan. He has been engaged for some time in experiments & discoveries on celestial electricity, and he says that both Wheatstone's and Steinheil's Telegraphs, must be so influenced ⟨by⟩ in a highly electric state of the atmosphere as at times to be useless, because they use the *deflection of the needle,* while mine from its use of the *magnet* is not subject to this disturbing influence.

F. O. J. Smith Papers, Maine Historical Society.

In another passage indicative of what Henry's blessing meant to him, Morse wrote W. W. Boardman on August 10, 1842:

I have showed its operation to a few friends occasionally within a few weeks, among others to Prof. Henry of Princeton, (a copy of whose letter to me on this subject, I sent you some time since,) he had never seen it in operation but had only learned from description the principle on which it is founded. He is not of an enthusiastic temperament but exceedingly cautious in giving an opinion on scientific inventions, yet in this case he expressed himself in the warmest terms and told my friend Dr Chilton, (who informed me of it) that he had just been witnessing "the operation of the most beautiful and ingenious instrument he had ever seen."

Draft, Morse Papers, Library of Congress. Both of these letters are printed in Edward Lind Morse, ed., *Samuel F. B. Morse: His Letters and Journals,* 2 vols. (Boston and New York, 1914), 2:172–173, 174–176, and Samuel I. Prime, *The Life of Samuel F. B. Morse* (New York, 1875), pp. 434–435, 436–439.

FROM ROBERT BAIRD

Henry Papers, Smithsonian Archives

> Paris, 16 rue de la Ferme des
> Mathurins. March 18. 1842.[1]

My dear Professor Henry.

In a letter which I wrote to Dr Maclean about a fortnight ago, I requested him to say to you that your letter of Dec. 28th came whilst I was a-way in Switzerland, but that as soon as I could do so I would attend to its contents.[2] This I am now able to say that I have done. And I should have done sooner, if it had been possible; but upon my return from Geneva; I had so many things to do, which I could not postpone, that I could take hold of nothing else till they were done. I will now tell you what I have done in your affairs.

1.   I attempted to find Melloni, but he is not here, but at Naples, where he is a professor, & only comes here in his vacation.

2.   I went to Ruhmkorff and engaged him to make the set of Melloni's Apparatus. But I was a little at a loss what to do. Melloni not being here to consult with, I hesitated whether to get such an apparatus as Prof. Bartlette[3] procured, or to get such as R. now makes, with all the late & important improvements & additions which Melloni has made within the last year or two. Mr R. says that they are highly important, and that you would certainly regret not to get them. He further stated that Prof. Bartlette had requested him to send him on any additional machinery which Melloni might from time to time make relating to the same apparatus. After deliberating maturely on the subject I concluded that it would be best to order a *perfect* apparatus, though the cost of every thing, including the *crystal*, is 800 francs. This you will see is just double the cost of the apparatus gotten by Mr B., which had no crystal (which costs 100 frs.), but which he has since ordered. Mr Ruhmkorff has promised me that the whole shall be as complete as possible, & that all shall be made in the very best style. I am sorry to say, however, that the time which he demands is long. I cannot get him to engage to have it done before the 1st of June. I shall do all that is possible to have it sent by the Packet of that day from Havre. He begs me to say to you, to engage the Custom House officers at New York *not to open the box, without your being present.* This you must look after with care. He is fearful that, not being acquainted with such matters, they may break something. I shall go from time to time to see him & urge him on.

---

[1] The letter was postmarked in New York on April 17.

[2] Printed above.

[3] W. H. C. Bartlett.

3.   Pixii has engaged to have *Attwood's Machine* & all the other articles which you wish ready to go by the Packet of the 16th April. I think he will do so, for he has but little to do. The *Machine* is now nearly ready, & so are the most of the other things. I shall have them forwarded by the Packet of the 16th April, & not wait for what R. is making; because I suppose you would like to have them as soon as possible, & I see no advantage in putting them all together, as R. wishes to do. The economy in expense would be of little avail. R. has never made Atwood's Machine. I had therefore to get it of Pixii.

Pixii agrees to wait for the money until you have received the articles. However I shall place with my banker 800 francs for Ruhmkorff, to be paid him when he has done his work, & the remainder I shall pay to Pixii. So that you will know precisely what the balance is when Pixii forwards his articles. The whole will cost somewhere about 25 or 26 hundred francs— the precise sum I can not say, but will inform you by the Packet of the 16th of April.[4]

4.   Lastly, I went to the Post office, paid the postage of your letter (no 3311) and directed it to be forwarded to you—which you will get in due time.

I hope that I have executed your orders to your entire satisfaction. I have endeavoured to do all for the best.

We are all quite well, save Charles,[5] our second son, who is still a sufferer. We think of going to Switzerland in the begining of May. But I will leave your affairs in such a state that you will have nothing to do but to send Pixii his money when I go away. It is probable that we shall return to Paris in the fall.

I thank you for the interest you take in my book. It was written in great haste, but if it does any good I shall be glad. I have a much more important work on hands now.[6] Mrs B.[7] joins me in kindest regards to Mrs H. Ah me, when shall I have the quietness of such a life as you have? I have written enough since I returned from U.S. (which was on the 1st of Jan.) to make a large book.

With great respect
I am yours truly
R. Baird.

---

[4] Baird next wrote on May 3, 1842 (printed below).

[5] Charles Washington Baird (1828–1887), *DAB*.

[6] Baird is apparently referring to his *Visit to Northern Europe; or Sketches, Descriptive,* *Historical, Political and Moral of Denmark, Norway, Sweden and Finland* . . . (New York, 1841) and *Religion in America* (New York, 1844).

[7] Fermine Du Buisson Baird. *DAB*, s.v. "Baird, Robert."

FROM JOHN S. HART[1]
Henry Papers, Smithsonian Archives

Phil[a] March 18th 1842

Dear Sir,

In closing a lecture on British steam vessels last evening D[r] Lardner[2] made some remarks upon their *speed* and in doing so drew particular attention to the point that the vessels of whose speed he was speaking were those used in *salt water navigation*, which point he wished to be borne in mind for fear of misapprehension. For, said he, <*misunderstanding*> hard thoughts often arise from persons not understanding each other. In illustration of this he remarked that a few years since, 1835 I think, at a public meeting in Liverpool, he offered some statements similar to those now made to the gentlemen there assembled consisting of nearly all the distinguished engineers of Great Britain when a stranger, a distinguished Professor from this vicinity and perfectly well known at that time in Europe, though unfortunately not known to the persons there assembled, made some assertions in regard to the speed of American steam boats which, being unaccompanied with any explanations and being understood to refer to salt water vessels with which alone they were conversant, were received with incredulity and raised quite a breeze of dissent.[3] In this he, (D[r] Lardner) took an active part and thereby gave the gentleman serious offence. He regretted the circumstance and thought it an evidence of the importance of persons understanding each other. He took the occasion to make this public explanation because since his arrival he had been told that he had treated that gentleman very badly on the occasion alluded to.

I give you as nearly as I can recollect the very words of D[r] Lardner, supposing you would be glad to know. His tone was rather that of defence than apology though it partook of both. Should I see any report of the Lecture in the papers I will send it to you.[4]

Very Respectfully
Your Obed Sert
John S. Hart

---

[1] John Seely Hart (1810–1877), alumnus and former tutor at Princeton. *Henry Papers*, 2: 172n. Hart had been a resident of Philadelphia since the previous December.

[2] Dionysius Lardner (1793–1859), *Henry Papers*, 2:257n, and Henry to Torrey, December 20, 1841, above.

[3] This was, of course, Henry during his European trip. For Henry's account of the exchange, see his letters to Bache, October 1, 1837, *Henry Papers*, 3:508–510, and August 9, 1838, *4*:100–101.

[4] An extensive account of Lardner's eighth lecture appeared in the *Philadelphia Public Ledger*, March 19, 1842, which shows Hart to be a faithful recounter of the events.

April 12, 1842

FROM ANDREW LANE[1]
Henry Papers, Smithsonian Archives

12 Apl [1842][2]

My very dear Sir,

As a small token of my very great regard, allow me to ask your acceptance of a set of Chessmen.[3] I know of no game more appropriate for a Philosopher; and, as I wish to see you as much as possible like your great prototype, Franklin, who was an excellent Chessplayer, I can think of nothing I possess—for a petit présent—better suited to the occasion.

I have no chessboard, nor can I find one in this place, but the ordinary Backgammon board is just as good.

In chess, each denomination of pieces have their peculiar move; and as soon as you have learned the alphabet, which is very easy, I am sure you will take great delight in the game. Any one at all skilled can show you the moves in a very few minutes.

Professor Dodd[4] I am told is quite au fait. I regret that one of the pieces has been despoiled of its orniment.

> With sentiments of high consideration
> and respect, I am, dear sir, your
> very sincere friend,
> Andrew Lane

[1] Although obviously a man of some learning and culture (or at least with pretensions towards projecting an image of learning and culture), Andrew Lane has escaped our net. No member of the Princeton, Philadelphia, Albany, or New York communities appears to fit the bill. Nor, aside from Henry's reply, is there any other correspondence or known contact between the two men.

[2] From Henry's file notation.

[3] The letter and the chess pieces were apparently hand-delivered. There is no postmark.

[4] Albert Baldwin Dod. Both Dod and Charles Hodge were excellent players. A. A. Hodge, *The Life of Charles Hodge* (New York, 1880), pp. 239–240.

TO ANDREW LANE
Retained Copy, Henry Papers, Smithsonian Archives

Princeton April 13th 1842

My Dear Sir

I accept with much pleasure your very interesting present of a set of chessmen and although I have no hope of emulating the Great American

Philosopher whom you are pleased to style my prototype yet I shall certainly endeavour to become acquainted with the principles of the game if for no other reason than to assure you that I highly value the good feelings which have prompted your kind gift.

With much esteem
Yours truly
Joseph Henry

TO [JAMES HENRY]

Mary Henry Copy,[1] Family Correspondence, Henry Papers,
Smithsonian Archives

Princeton, April. 1842.

We have had quite a busy time in our house the last month. One of the students from the far South was taken dangerously ill with typhus fever.[2] His life was despaired of, and we had him brought to our house. He was not expected to live for several days, but almost against hope, he revived and has now nearly recovered. He still remains in our house and occupies the room over my study. He is a very good fellow and we do not regret the trouble he has occasioned us.

Dr. Torrey has removed with his family to Princeton.

You know nothing of the difficulties which have been experienced by the inhabitants of Philadelphia by the operations of the Banking system.[3]

---

[1] Two incomplete Mary Henry Copies of this letter exist; our text is based on the longer, typewritten, copy.

[2] Possibly John A. Lamar, d. 1865, a sophomore from Montgomery, Alabama. On April 11, 1842, the faculty voted to inform him that he could not continue with classes "having, from continual ill health, been unable to attend upon other than a very few of the exercises of the class. . . ." Lamar graduated in 1844. Faculty Minutes, April 11, 1842, Princeton University Archives; *Princeton Catalogue,* p. 166.

[3] Pennsylvania's economic situation in early 1842 was serious and complex. The banks of the state had suspended specie payment the previous January after a run on the United States Bank of Pennsylvania, the third bank crash in under four years. In addition, there was no revenue to pay the interest on the state debt or for further internal improvements.

A "Relief Bill" designed to solve both these problems was passed by the state legislature in May 1841, but proved ineffective.

Continuing lack of public confidence led to numerous runs on banks in the Philadelphia area during the last week in January 1842. The legislature quickly reaffirmed the state's intention to pay interest on its debt, and forced the banks to resume specie payments in March. After the stronger banks appeared safe from further collapse, public confidence was to a large extent restored.

Charles McCool Snyder, *The Jacksonian Heritage: Pennsylvania Politics, 1833–1848* (Harrisburg, Pennsylvania, 1958), pp. 136–163.

Hundreds of persons have been reduced to poverty and distress. I fear the worst has not yet come; the normal value of all property must come down much lower than it is now before we can be fully settled. We have been a nation of speculators living in habits of extravagance; the only way to retrieve ourselves is to come back to labor and economy. I wish you could arrange your business so as to be independent of state patronage. Politics in our country, and under any circumstances, is a dangerous and unstable business, and the less we are connected with it the better. When once a man becomes imbued with the spirit of party politics, he becomes unfit for the sober duties of life.

FROM ROBERT BAIRD
Henry Papers, Smithsonian Archives

Paris, May 3. 1842.

My dear Sir.

I wrote you some two months ago,[1] to inform you what I had done in relation to the things which you wished me to buy for the College. In that letter I stated that M. Ruhmkorff would require till the 1st of June, if not the last of that Month, to make what he had undertaken, but that M. Pixii would have his done in time to go out in the Packet of the 16th of April. But I am sorry to say that he has not be[en] able to do so. He assures me, however, that every thing is now nearly done, & that without faile, the box shall be delivered to Messrs. Emersom & Co.[2] to be sent by the Packet of the 16 inst.—just a month later than he first engaged for. But you know the French are not punctual. As to Mr Ruhmkorff he will get through his task by the end of June & deliver the box containing his machine & its accompaniments to Mr Emerson who will send it on as soon as possible & advise you by mail. I made a mistake as to the cost of what Mr R. is making. Instead of 800 francs, it is but 630 francs with all the improvements which have been made, & including the box for packing. As I shall leave for Geneva in a day or two, & shall not be here until the fall, I place with Mr Emerson two drafts on my banker, to be paid upon the delivery of the boxes from Mr R. & Mr P.—to the former 630 francs, which is all his bill, & to the

---

[1] On March 18, 1842, above.
[2] Emerton & Co. were the Paris agents for Harnden's Express.

latter 800 which will leave 1036 francs to be sent to him when you shall have received the articles, as you will see from the annexed note.[3] The draft which [. . .][4] sent yield, [?abating] discount, postage[?&c] 1430 f[rancs.] I hope that every thing has been done to your acceptance, and that the things commanded will reach you in due season. M͏ͬ Ruhmkorff is greatly concerned lest the box containing his things may be opened in New York by the custom House officers before you reach there to see it done yourself. He begs you to be careful on this point. You will of course inform the C. H. officers not to touch the box till you arrive. He also wishes to add a piece of machinery which he is just making under the direction of a professor here—which he thinks valuable. I have told him that if the experiment succeeds he may add it, & that I will pay it in the fall, as it will be an additional cost. It may [be] some 50 francs or so. We are all well save Charles, who is [. . .] worse we think. M͏ͬͤ B. joins me in kind regards to M͏ͬͦ H. and all our friends in Princeton.

Yours with great respect.
R. Baird.

[3] We are not printing Pixii's itemized bill of May 7, 1842, for 1,836 francs. The bill is based on Pixii's 1835 catalogue and is the same in format as the bill printed in *Henry Papers, 3*:541–543. The prices, however, are those given in Pixii's 1842 catalogue, which were about 11 percent lower. Henry's copy of the 1835 catalogue (in the Henry Library) is annotated to show the 1842 purchases as well as those ordered in 1837.

Henry bought five pieces of apparatus for demonstrations in mechanics (including At-wood's machine for 800 francs), four for hydrostatics, two for hydrodynamics (including a model of Montgolfier's hydraulic ram for 160 francs), two for pneumatics, a Daniell hygrometer, four for heat, one for electricity, a Wollaston goniometer, and a thirty-six-inch glass plate (180 francs) for the electrical machine he bought from Pixii in 1837.

[4] The original is torn at several places at the bottom of the sheet, resulting in gaps here and near the end of the letter.

"RECORD OF EXPERIMENTS"[1]

Henry Papers, Smithsonian Archives

May 6th 1842

(Induction from Ordinary Electricity)[2]

Magnetize steelplate when straight then bend it into a [?smal] cylindrical form, note the effect

Also magnetize a plate while kept by means of a clamp in a bent condition. Note the effect when the plate is suffered to return to its flat form. In these experiments use iron filings

Make experiments on the slow evaporation of water on heated metal. I found a few mornings ago whiel I was heating water to shave, with a cup on the top of a sheet iron stove, that a drop of the size of a ½ cent would remain perhaps 10 minutes. When the drop was of this size I could plainly perceive that in its centre underneath there was a globule of steam and this globule remained under the water until the drop was diminished to the eight of an inch in diameter. This was evident by watching the gradual and slow diminution of the size of the drop and the appearance of the reflected light from its surface.

A section of the drop was of this form . The part shaded thus represents the steam.

The motion of the drop appeard to be due to the escape of the bubble of steam. As it bust out on one side the bubble was elongated in the direction of the diameter, pasing through the point of rupture and immediatly after the attraction of cohesion would tend to bring the bubble back into its circular form but the moment[um] of the particles would carry them

---

[1] This entry inaugurated a month-and-a-half period of intensive experimentation. Henry made short investigations of some subjects: patterns of magnetization and the mode of evaporation of water (May 6); formation and screening of secondary and tertiary currents induced by static discharge (May 6–7); capillarity and the daguerreotype process (May 13). Most of the research went into determining the direction of currents in wire (May 7 and following), in light of the recurring problem of reconciling his results with Faraday's ("Contributions IV: Electro-Dynamic Induction," Section II) and with Savary's observations of the effect of distance and strength of discharge on magnetization ("Contributions III: Electro-Dynamic Induction," paragraph 134, and "Contributions V: Induction from Ordinary Electricity; Oscillatory Discharge"). Henry looked at the way of measuring the direction of the current—the magnetization of a needle in a small spiral. In the most important work of the early entries, he showed that the magnetization was very sensitive to small changes in the experimental set-up (May 9–10) and spent much of the remaining period working on this observation. One result of this work was "Contributions V: Induction from Ordinary Electricity; Oscillatory Discharge," a June 17 oral presentation to the American Philosophical Society, never published in full form.

[2] A heading moved from the third page of the entry, also repeated on the fourth page, referring to the experiments done after his observations on magnetized steel plates and evaporating water. In the text there is a large blank space between these first subjects and his induction experiments, which lead off a new page.

beyond the point of equilibrium and elongulate the bubble in another direction. I found that by putting a brass pin into the bubble the steam did not escape, so that the temperature of the buble may be ascertained by plunging into it the ends of the thermo-galvanometer. To determine the effect of letting off the bubble of steam a small tube of glass may be plunged into the bubble—perhaps this would permit the steam to escape as through a chimney. Also by means of two platinum wires attached to the galvanometer perhaps a current of galvanism might be detected between the stove and the water of the bubble.[3]

Charged[4] the Franklin battery of 24 jars with 100 sparks of Haris unit measurer ball at the 7th ring on the stem. The ribbon coil No 2 was then placed on the coil with its <strands> spires seperated so as to ensure insulation. <With> Helix no 1 was placed in this and when the discharge

 was made *sam* felt a sever shock up to his sholders. This is the repetition with more precision of an experiment described in my 3rd series.[5]

Repeated this experiment with the variation of placing two persons in the circuit. The shock was again very severe, the smaller person Mr—[6] felt the shock very severely and both complained of its intensity.

Repeated the same again with the strands of the spiral farther apart and also with the circle of greater diameter. The shock was now not as severe as before but still unpleasant

To be more certain of the insulation, I placed the helix within a glass cylinder and the coil around this. The shock was now not as severe as before but still felt in the arms

Repeated again arrangement as before charge *125 spark*—shock more severe felt higher up on the fore arm.

Again *charge 150 sparks* from Haris' unit jar. The shock was still more intense felt <in> up the arms higher

Same arrangement continued with the variation of elevating the plane of the middle of the <coil> helix about 2 inches above the plane of the mid-

[3] Henry would pick up on this phenomenon again in experiments of October 1842 on steam. But his thoughts here probably led to the June 1842 addendum to the "Record of Experiments" entry for May 14, 1840. *Henry Papers*, 4:384.

[4] Immediately above this line, Henry squeezed in the comment, "I here commenced a long series of experiments on the induction from ordinary electricity," outlined it in ink, and placed a footnote to it, "On this subject see exp. page 108," referring to the beginning of the entry for May 20, 1840 (*Henry Papers*, 4:395–396). See also note 2 above.

[5] See "Contributions III: Electro-Dynamic Induction," especially Section VI, paragraph 112.

[6] Henry supplied a dash instead of the surname.

dle of the coil. Effect nearly as strong as the last shock, although the charge was but 100 sparks.

Same arrangement as the last—no effect. The only difference apparently between the circumstances of this and the last experiment was that the handles were grasped by myself and I stood on a chair. Tried the same again with the change of standing on the floor, instead of the chair, now I felt the shock in my arms but not severe.

Lowered the helix to the plane of the coil. Charge 100 snaps or sparks from the unit jar. Felt the shock in both wrists. There appeared in this experiment no cause of error shuch as cutting across of the charge &c.

Substituted for the battery 2 gallon jars with the charge of 25 sparks shock perceptible while standing on the chair

The experiments of this afternoon prove the truth of the account I gave in my 3rd series. A shock from the induced current can be obtained by ordinary electricity as well as from galvanism.

From some considerations of a hypothetical nature I had been lead to think that perhaps some error existed in the account I had published. In making the experiments <*as published*> which were published I had but few conveniences, the apparatus was the small machine and a single large jar sometimes the battery belong to the *Nairn* apparatus[7]

[7] Probably the electrostatic apparatus invented by Edward Nairne (1726–1806, *DNB*) around 1772. The large device consisted of a horizontal glass cylinder brushed by a collecting pad and powered by a hand crank, all placed in a solid mahogany frame. The machine was popular in England. Maurice Daumas, *Scientific Instrument Makers of the Seventeenth and Eighteenth Centuries*, trans. Mary Holbrook (New York, 1972), pp. 220, 240–241. See I. Bernard Cohen, *Some Early Tools of American Science* (Cambridge, Massachusetts, 1950), Appendix III, plate 13 and p. 160, for a similar form of apparatus. The glass cylinder from the Nairne machine formed part of the experimental set-up in figure eleven of "Contributions III."

"RECORD OF EXPERIMENTS"
Henry Papers, Smithsonian Archives

May 7th Saturday 1842
(Induction from ordinary Elect)

Placed helix no 1 within glass receiver and around this passed a single spire of <*the*> copper ribbon. With the 2 jars and about 25 sparks the shock was almost imperceptible. The long coil was next added to the circuit but not so as to act on the helix—the shock was now imperceptible

May 7, 1842

Repeated the expermt as before with the difference of using the battery (Franklins) charged with 100 sparks the shock with the single riband alone was not perceptible. With the long coil added to the circuit it was distinctly felt in the wrists

Repeated the same exp with the same result.

Repeated same experiment with the variation of a break in the circuit of about 1/8 of an inch bet[we]en the balls of the universal discharger. The shock with this arrangement was <much> considerably more <severe> intense

Repeated the same with the single spire around the receiver—shock not perceptible when the long coil was introduced shock was felt in the wrists. The break in the circuit was the same in each experiment.

These results show conclusively the effect of the long circuit in modifying the shock.

Next made arrangements to get currents of different orders from ordinary electricity. Coil No 1 was placed on an insulating stool—coil 2 was placed over this with a dry pine board placed between them and its ends joined to coil No 3 on which helix no 1 was placed

The shock was quite perceptible with 100 sparks passed into the battery—with 150 it was more intense—with 200 the explosion was very loud but the shock was not so severe but scarcely perceptible

The same arrangement being continued the small battery No 2 (see page 205)[1] was added to the Franklin battery with this and 100 sparks the balls of the unit jar being still at the 7th mark the shock from the secondary current was apparently more intense than in the case of the last experiment

The apparatus remaining as in the last exp the plate of zinc which has beefore so often been used was placed between coil no 1 and no 2. The no of sparks was still 100 not the least effect could be perceived the plate perfectly screened the action of the primary current from the secondary conductor. Repeated this ex so that no doubt can remain of the screening influence of the plate

Commenced a series of experiments on the direction of the induced currents with needles in spirals and for this purpose I made 6 spirals all turned from right to left—two were formed of *three* strata of spires close to each other—two of one stratum each of wire also in contact and two of one stratum each of which the several spires were seperated like those of a corks screw

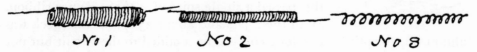

N° 1 N° 2 N° 3

---

[1] The entry for October 9, 1841, above.

166

1st Ep   Made an arrangement with coil no 1. 2. 3 & 4 to get the current of the third order. Then united the electrometers into 2 sets as in the figure at the bottom of the last page[2]—and placed one set in the circuit of the secondary current and the other in that of the tertiary. Each needle was found to be magnetic that in Nos 1 the stronger in no 2 less strong in No 3 feeble and in an opposite direction to that in the other two spirals in both sets of spirals. The directions of the currents as given by spirals no 1 and Nos 2 were as follows

No 1 & 2	Primary ——————————— +	Tolerably
	Seccondary ——————————— +	strong
	Tertiary ——————————— −	

The direction of the currents as given by Nos 3 are

No. 3	Primary ——————————— +	Feeble mag
	Seccondary ——————————— −	
	Tertiary ——————————— +	

It must be observed in this result that the needle in spiral No 3 was magnetized in a contrary direction to those in the other spirals in both the circuits. In this expermt the two batteries Franklins and No 2 were joined as one and charged with 100 sparks from the unit jar

Repeated the same with 150 sparks with the same result. The same series was produced

2nd Exp   Charged the batteries with 50 sparks no 1 and no 2 now gave the same directions of magnetism and the following series of currents namely

Primary ——————————— +	The magnetism
Seccondary ——————————— −	stronger
Tertiary ——————————— +	

No 2[3] gave the following

Primary ——————————— +	Magnetism
Secondary ——————————— +	Weaker
Tertiary —	

---

[2] The illustration immediately above.   [3] Henry clearly meant number three.

"RECORD OF EXPERIMENTS"
Henry Papers, Smithsonian Archives

May 9th 1842 (Monday)
Induction of ordinary Elect.

The experiments given on the last page[1] are just in accordance with an hypothesis I have formed of the cause of the change in the direction of the mag. of the needle as given in Contributions no 3 and as recorded in the old book.[2] I now suppose that there is in reality no change in the direction of the current and that the phenomena may be explained on the same principles I have advanced in no 4 relative to the induction from galvanic electricity.[3] The electrical discharge from a Leyden jar must of necessity give two inductions one at the beginning of the discharge and the other at the ending. The intensity of these may be made to vary by increasing the length of the conductor or by increasing the intensity of the discharge according to the laws I have given in the 1st section of my paper No 4. In this way the shock becomes evident.

The magnetisation of the needle in opposite directions, by a change of distance &c, is readily accounted for by an application of the same principles. When the conductors are placed near each other <*the induction of*> both inductions are sufficiently energetic to <*develop*> more than develope the full magnetism of the needle or to magnetize it to saturation it accordingly is magnetized to saturation by the first induction say — minus and immediately afterwards in an opposite direction + by the ending induction. If the magnetic capacity of needle were indefinitely great then the magnetism induced by the action at the beginning would just neuteralize that produced at the ending. The same effect would be produced were the two inductions just sufficient to magnetize the needle to saturation without any surplus power—but where the inductive action is greater than this, the needle at the end of the experiment will show the magnetism of the ending induction.

If the magnetic capacity of the needle is greater than the inductive influence of the <*current*> beginning induction then the final magnetism of the needle will be that of the more energetic induction. With a short conductor and intensity current the beginning induction is most intense (See No 4 1st sec) and hence in the case last supposed the needle will come

---

[1] i.e., the end of the May 7 entry.
[2] The "old book" was the previous laboratory notebook, running up to September 7, 1839. On his hypothesis, see "Contributions III: Electro-Dynamic Induction," paragraphs 127–132, and "Record of Experiments," October 18–20, 1838, *Henry Papers*, 4:129–137.
[3] "Contributions IV: Electro-Dynamic Induction," Section III, especially paragraph 56.

out of the spiral with the magnetism of the beginning induction but much reduced from its primary strength.[4]

The several experiments given on page 236[5] are <*the*> confirmations of this hypothesis.

N1   To investigate this subject still farther an other spiral was added to each set as described at the bottom of page 235 of two strata of spires.[6] The series will therefore be as follows

No 1 3 strata   No 2 2 strata   No 3. 1 stratum   No 4 Spires apart

These spirals were placed on slips of thin lath in two sets. The ends marked at which the needles were to be always put in and then the direction of the current marked on the wood for the magnetism of the end which was thrust in

No 2   The coils were arranged as in the last exp. (bottom of page 236).[7] The two stets[8] of four spirals were introduced—the needle in each was magnetized by a discharge from the two batteries of 50 sparks of the unit jar.

The series was as follows with all the spirals

Primary ——————————————— $+$ ⎫
Secondary ——————————————— $-$ ⎬ all the spirals
Tertiary ——————————————— $-$ ⎭

The only change in the arrangement of this experiment was the introduction of the additional length of fine wire used in the construction of the spiral—also the needles were larger

3   The[9] same arrangement as before the batteries charged with *100* sparks. Needle in spiral No 1 first series *South,* in No 2 Do *North* in no 3 south no 4 north all feeble

The needles in <*No*> seccond series or that in the circuit of the tertiary current were all north

4   Arrangement the same as before charge *175* sparks Needles in No 1 2 strongly mag in 3 & 4 feebly large needles

---

[4] The first appearance of Henry's explanation of the effect of distance on magnetization that would later form part of "Contributions V: Induction from Ordinary Electricity; Oscillatory Discharge." Compare "Contributions III," paragraph 127, and "Contributions IV," paragraphs 92 and 93.
[5] The end of the last entry.

[6] See the paragraph of the May 7 entry beginning "Commenced a series of experiments . . ."
[7] The end of the last entry.
[8] Meaning "sets."
[9] A new page heading, immediately above, states "Battery no 2 and Franklin battery."

The series with spirals No 1 2 & 3 in each was

Primary ——————————————— + ⎫
Secondary ————————————————— + ⎬ Nos 1. 2. 3.
Tertiary ——————————————— − ⎭ spirals

Primary ——————————————— + ⎫
Secondary ——————————————— − ⎬ spiral
<Secondary> Tertiary——————— − ⎭ no 4

* NB The magnetism of the last was feeble

5 Same arrangement and same charge *175* sparks also the same needles with the exception of softning them in the flame of a spirit lamp. The following series namely

This is the series
of the ending induct ⎧Primary ————— + ⎫
⎨Secondary ————— + ⎬ With spirals
⎩Tertiary ————— − ⎭ Nos 1. 2 & 3

Irregular
series ⎧Primary ——————— + ⎫ very feeble
⎨Secondary —————— − ⎬ with spiral
⎩Tertiary − ⎭ No 4 −

6 Same arrangement charge *150* needls smaller & softened in the lamp— all now gave the same indication

Namely the series
Primary ——————————— + ⎫
Secondary ———————————— + ⎬ all the spirals
Tertiary ——————————— − ⎭

The[10] result in the last experiment was what I expected. The magnetic capacity of the needles was very small so that even no 4 could magnetize them to saturation hence the effects of the beginning induction were intirely neuteralized by the ending induction and the needles exhibited the direction of that due to the ending induction.

The results in the two experiments before the last were approximations towards the last result sinc[e] the magnetism of the needle in No 4 was feeble and most in the exp next to the last where the needle had been heated. It was however a large needle and perhaps not quite soft.

[10] Here at the beginning of a new page, Henry added the heading, "Unit jar at 7th circle on the stem."

7   Same arrangement as before except that a plate of metal (the zinc plate) was placed on the top of coil no 2 so as partially to neutralize the action charge 150 sparks

The following series were produced

Primary	———————————— +	}	series with spirals
Secondary	———————————— +	}	Nos 1. 2. & 3.
Tertiary	———————————— −	}	

Primary	———————————— +	}	
Secondary	−	}	With No. 4
Tertiary	———————————— +	}	

This result is also in accordance with what I anticipated. The plate of zinc would partially nutralize the induction of the primary current and thus cause <*it to fall below*> the 2nd and 3rd currents to fall below the intensity necssary to magnetize the needle in No 4 to saturation and hence the needles <*showed*> in No 4 showed the series due to the beginning induction

8   The same arrangement being made and the charge the same namely 150 sparks from the unit jar the plate of metal removed and small needles used as in the expermnt before the last. All the needles gave the same series namely—

Primary	———————————— +	}	
Secondary	———————————— +	}	all the spirals
Tertiary	———————————— −	}	

10   Same arrangement used large needles charge the same as before 150 sparks all the needles gave the same series. The needl in no 4 of the secondary circuit very feeble or scarcely at all magnetized

Primary	———————————— +	}	
Seccondary	———————————— +	}	all the nedles
Tertiary	———————————— −	}	

11   Same arrangement as the last except that the secondary conductor was seperated from the other or elevated above it to the distance of about 6 inches[11]

[11] A marginal note, probably added later, states "Change of distance in the conductors."

The series were now as follows

Primary	——————————— +	⎫ From spirals
Secondary	——————————— +	⎬ nos 1 2 & 3
Tertiary	——————————— −	⎭

and

Primary	——————————— +	⎫ From
Secondary	——————————— −	⎬ spiral<s>
Tertiary	——————————— +	⎭ No 4 [12]—

12 Same arrangement charge 75 sparks—needles small. The following series

N1	Primary	——————————— +	⎫ From
	Sec<c>ondary	——————————— +	⎬ s[p]irals
	Tertiary	——————————— −	⎭ No 1 alone

and

Primary	——————————— +	⎫ From spirals
Secondary	——————————— −	⎬ NO 3. & 4 [13]
Tertiary	——————————— +	⎭

The needle in Spiral No. 2 in the Secondary circuit was scarcely perceptibly magnetized in the adverse direction to that in No 1 in the same circuit—while spiral no 2 in the tertiary circuit gave a magnetism the same as no 1. The series from this would be therefore

Primary	——————————— +	⎫ From no 2 but very
Secondary	——————————— −	⎬ feeble
Tertiary	——————————— −	⎭

---

[12] Another marginal note: "Change in direction shown by NO 4."

[13] The final marginal note of this entry reads, "Change shown by no 3 & 4 and partially by no 2."

"RECORD OF EXPERIMENTS"

Henry Papers, Smithsonian Archives

May 10th 1842

Induction of ordinary Elect.

The results of the experiments on the last page[1] are also in accordance with my anticipations. By increasing the distance the inductive influence

---

[1] Immediately above.

is diminished and consequently the needles are not magnetized to saturation by the beginning induction and hence as the ending induction is allways feebler than the beginning it cannot destroy all the magnetism of the needles and hence the residue will be that of the beginning induction therefore a change in the direction of the secondary current will be ap[parent][2] in the case of the spirals of a single stratum of spires. The multiplication of the spirals in spirals No 1 & 2 will prevent this result and still give the current in the same direction as the primary. In the first exp the intensity of the charge was such as to show the change only in spiral no 4

In the 2nd exp the intensity was less so that no 3 & 4 exhibited the same. It should be recollected however that by diminishing the intensity of the charge while the quantity remains the same we will diminish the redundancy of the beginning induction over that of the ending

I have not yet considered very attntvely the nature [of] the induction of the secondary current on the conductor of the current of the third order. If the primary current produces two inductions one in one direction and the other in the other then the secondary current must produce 4 inductions two from the adverse current of the beginning of the primary and two from the direct current of the ending of the same. The question which arises is how will these four currents act <*to give magnetism*> in giving magnetism to the needle—there will be two negative currents and two positive ones these may be represented by cur[v]es as <*described*> explained in my last paper thus.[3]

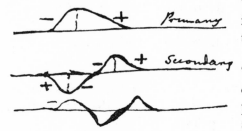

The minus induction whill prevail in this case with a large needle and the plus with a small one

There will here be a <*great*> tendency for the minus induction to prevail with compound <*helix*> spiral

1 The experiment (10) of yesterday repeated. The battery charged with 150 sparks. All the needles gave the same series namely

Primary	————————	+	
Secondary	————————	+	all the spirals
Tertiary	————————	−	

[2] A hole in the paper.
[3] i.e., "Contributions IV: Electro-Dynamic Induction," Section III, and especially paragraphs 60–64.

The [needle][4] in spiral no 4 of the tertiary circuit was scarcely if at all magnetic. This result is the same as that of yesterday.

2   The same arrangement with the same charge with the exception that the coil forming the tertiary circuit was removed. The series was now

$$
\begin{array}{ll}
\text{Primary} \underline{\hspace{3cm}} + \left.\right\} & \text{all the spirals} \\
\text{Secondary} \underline{\hspace{2.5cm}} + \int & \text{strongly}
\end{array}
$$

The[5] object of this experiment was to note the effect of the <*effect of the*> reflex influence of the tertiary current on the secondary—each needle was strongly magnetized No 1 drew small needle 12½ d no 2 10° no 3 6° No 4—5°. The apparatus was used described page 205[6]

3   Same arrangement same charge. Zinc plate placed on the part of the secondary conductor which was occupied by the tertiary or on the 3rd coil. The needles were magnetized thus
     no 1—7°   no 2—7°   no 3—2½°   no 4—1°
By comparing the intensity of the needles in the last exp with this there will perceived a great reduction in the development of magnetism. The sum of the degrees in the last series is 17½° while the sum of the other series is 33½°

4   To determine the effect of a change in the quantity of elect. on the intensity the batteries were charged with 75 sparks. The arrangement being as in the last exp but one magnetism of the needles all the same. Series +
     no 1—4½°   No 2—3½°   no 3—2°   no 4—2°
The sum of the degrees here is but 12 whereas in the other experiment (2) the sum of the deflections was 33½

5   Same arrangement as before charge reduced to the half or 37½ sparks (38). Now all the needles were changed in the direction of their magnetism. They all showed a current adverse to the primary

6   Same arrangement as before charge again <*put at*> 75 sparks. The same result was now obtained in exp. 4. All the needles were magnetized alike and in the plus direction

7   Repeated exp 5 with the same result except that the needle in the compound spiral was slightly magnetized plus while all the others were minus

---

[4] A hole in the paper.
[5] A marginal note at this point, probably

added later, states "Action & reaction."
[6] The entry for October 9, 1841.

Same arrangement as before batteries charged to *200* needles all charged so as to give the series

$$\text{Primary} \quad \underline{\hspace{3cm}} \quad +\ \big\}$$
$$\text{Secondary} \quad\qquad\qquad\qquad +\ \big\} \quad \text{all the needles}$$

No 1—12°   No 2—10½°   No 3 11¼°   No 4 6½°

Same arrangement as before batteries charged to *250*. All the needles magnetized as in the last experiment

No 1—9°   No 2—9°   No 3—12°   No 4—6°

There appears to be in the last a diminution in the magnetism of the needle in the compound coil

"RECORD OF EXPERIMENTS"
Henry Papers, Smithsonian Archives

May 11ᵗʰ 1842 Wednesday
Induction from Ordinary Elect

Made arrangements for experimenting on the apparent change of direction in the secondary current by change of distance in the two conductors. For this purpose I put up a rectangle of wire inside of the electrical case against the glass partition—8 feet high and 6½ feet wide. The wire was insulated from the wood of the window frames by glass tubes. Also on the large frame which I use for the screan in experiments on light I fastened a rectangle of covered wire of the same dimensions as the rectangle on the inside of the glass. The two rectangles were seperated by the glass partition

1 Exp   Rectangles at the distance of 13½ inches. The three batteries were charged with *100 sparks*. The batteres together contain [. . .][1] feet of coiled surface—all the needles were magnetized alike and indicating a + current

Each repelled the needl of the inst[rument] mentioned page [. . .][2] as follows

No 1 1°   No 2—1°   No 3—½°   no 4—½°

---

[1] Henry left a blank space in his account.
[2] Another blank space. The reference is to page 205 of the laboratory book, the October 9, 1841, entry, printed above, where Henry discusses his magnetometer.

2   Distance the same as before charge *150*. All the needles gave as before a *plus* current—magnetism as follows

   No 1—2°   No 2—1½°   no 3—1°   No 4—1°

3   Distance the same charge *250* all the needles gave as before a *plus* current magnetism as follows

   No 1—2°   No 2—1½°   no 3—1°   No 4—¾°

4   Distance same charge *300* all the needl magnetized as before

   No 1—3°   no 2—3½   No 3—1¾°   No 4—1¾°

   Next exp with smaller charges

"RECORD OF EXPERIMENTS"

Henry Papers, Smithsonian Archives

May 12th 1842

Induction from ordinary electricity

1   Arrangement the same as before charge *350* all the needls magnetized *plus* ie indicating a current in the same direction as the primary current. The magnetism as follows

   No 1—<*10*>3°   No 2—3°   No 3—2°   No 4—1¼

2   Also made a seriees of experments with the two rectangles seperated to various distances from that given in exp (1) of yesterday (13½ inches) to 6 feet with various charges from ten to 350 in all the experments as many as 12 the needles in all cases and in all the spirals gave the same results namely a *plus* magnetism. Even when the frames were seperated to the distan[ce] in feet which is equal to the perpendicular height of the rectangle with 200 sparks the magnetism was quite perceptible and still *plus*. I have not thus far in my experiments with the rectangle as thus placed suceeded in getting a single reversion of magnetism although I have employed different amounts of coated surface from 3 jars of battery no 1 <*to*> (page 205)[1] to all the batteres. I am not at present able to interpret these results

3   Next added to the primary circuit coil no 1 loosely coiled and first placed it on the negative side of the rectangle and again on the + side but the result was still the same the needles in all the spirals showed the same magnetism indicating a *plus* current

---

[1] The October 9, 1841, entry, printed above.

4 Next added the coil to the secondary circuit, the charge being 200 and the distance the same as in the last experiment—namely 13½ inches. The result was still the same the needles were again magnetized in all the spirals *plus* ⎱ This coil was very loosely
⎰ coiled

5 Next removed coil no 1 and substituted coil no 2 the spires of which were in close contact—charge *150* distance the same—needle no 1 scarcly at all magnetized[2]

6 The other three needles gave indications of the preponderance of the *minus* magnetism. This is the first result of the kind I have had to day—all the other results were in the *plus* direction
　Magnetism as follows
　<No *1*—*1¾*° 　no *2*—*2¼*°> That of the needles in No 3 & 4 was stronger than that in Nos 1 & 2

7 Repeated the same experiment with a charge of 200 <*while*> all the condidit[i]ons the same as 4 on last Page[3]—except that coil no 2 with spires close together. Result same as the last <*cur*> magnetism *minus*—needle in the first slightly magnetic in the last the strongest. I do not at present see the rational[i]ty of the result of the action of the helix. It probably by its action on itself produces an adverse current which diminishes the intensity of the beginning current and also that of the ending below the point of saturation of the needle

⎧This is an important experiment as it shows the inductive in-
⎨fluence of a part of the seccondary current on itself when this part
⎩is not affected <*with*> by the action of the primary current[4]

8 Placed the rectangles <*with*> at the distance of 2½ inches from each other—charge *20* of *two* jars all the needles + *plus*—magnetism as follows
　No 1—1°+　No 2—1°+　No 3—½°+　No 4—½°

9 In charging the jars again they were filled <*at a*> with a littl more than 30 sparks. Accidentally the jars were attempted to be discharged when the negative end of the primary circuit was not incontact with the coating of the battery the needles were magnetized *minus*[5]

---

[2] Here the page turns; at the top of the next page Henry added another heading to the repetition of date and previous heading: "Experiments with the rectangle on the window of the glass case."

[3] i.e., the fourth experiment of this entry.

[4] Henry added a note dated May 28, presumably 1842, stating: "This should be repeated again with the open and closed coil."

[5] Here at the next page turn, Henry merely wrote the date and the comments, "Continued. Experiments with the rectangle continued."

10   Repeated the last experiment with the two batteries charged to 150. Also with the three batteries chcharged to 200 all gave the inverse direction to the needle. Also 2 batters interrupted circuit by means of 4 inches of water

11   Rectangles at the same distance 2½ inches charge 50 whole of 1st battery—all the needles gave *plus* magnetism. The intensity as follows
No 1—4°   No 2—1½°   No 3—½°   No 4—¼

12   Distance same charge 75 <*two*> 1st battery
No 1—4½°   No 2—3°   No 3—1¼   No 4—½°

13   Distance same charge 100 batteries no 1 <*& 2*>
No 1—4°   No 2—2°   No 3—1°   No 4—¾°

14   Distance same charge 150 batteries 1 & 2
No 1—4½°   No 2—4°   No 3—2°   No 4—1½°

15   Distance same charge 200 <*all the*> no 1 & 2 batteries
No 1—6½°   No 2—5½°   No 3—4½°   No 4—2°

16   Distan same all the batteries charge 200
no 1—6½   no 2—6°   no 3—6°   no 4—4½

17   Repeated exp. 9 & 10 by interrupting the discharge by means of 4 inches of water betwen the ends of a break in the primary circuit near the + end. The needles in all the spirals were *reversed*. Repeated the same with the break and water at the positive end of the circuit—with the same result.

18   Repeated exp. 6, of last page,[6] with the exception adding the coil no 2 to the negative end of the primary current. 2 batter 1 & 2nd. The reversion did not take place although the needles in the 3 & 4 spirals were scarcely if at all magnetic while those in the other two were tolerably strong. Tried again with the same result all the batteries charge *200*[7]

19   Repeated the experiment of introducing the Coil No 2 ⎫ distance
into the circuit of the secondary current. The result was as ⎬ 10 inches
given in 6 page 247[8] needles were again reversed.   ⎭ 200 spar

Made experiment to determ if an induced current could be produced without the jar—for this purpose connected one end of the rectangle with a wire connected with a plate of copper buried in the ground and the other in connection with the prime conductor or rather so near that sparks could

---

[6] i.e., of this entry.
[7] Here Henry wrote "Induction from ordinary elect. continued. (Experiments with the rectangle on the electrical case)."
[8] Experiment 6 of this entry.

be drawn. Passed several sparks—needles all magnetic in a *minus* direction. This result when compared with the others appear to be in accordance with the hypothesis. The comparitively small quantity of electricity passed through the primary current magnetized the needle in the two directions both below the point of saturation of the needle and since the first induction is more energetic, particularly in the case of a discharge from the prime conductor, the predominant magnetism is that of the beginning or — *minus*.[9]

It also appears from the same experiment that a small quantity of electricity is sufficient to produce inductive currents of considerable intensity and that consequently all the discharges which I have passed through the rectangle tended to magnetize the needle beyond its maximum point and hence the whole series of experiments I have made with the rectangles are in accordance with the hypothesis I have adopted[10] that is so far as I have studied them. The experimts on the retardation of the primary and secondary I have not yet sufficiently considered.

The effect of water in the circuit will be to lessen the developement of the current or diminish the length of the ordinates of the curve.[11]

---

[9] In the margin next to this paragraph, Henry wrote "Remarks," as he did for the following paragraph as well.

[10] See the entry for May 9, 1842, above.

[11] i.e., the types of curves described in the May 10 entry.

"RECORD OF EXPERIMENTS"

Henry Papers, Smithsonian Archives

May 13th 1842

Induction from ordinary electricity

Observed this morning a phenomenon which I do not recollect to have seen noticed namely a bubble of air confined in a small bag of lace this was in water and the arrangement happened to be such as to confine the buble. I was surprised to find that it did not escape upwards through the meshes of the lace, although the bag containing it was plunged 5 or six inches under water. Make exp on the Oersteds apparatus for pressure &c[1]

Made a rectangle along the floor of the lecture room 41 feet long and 22 wide. Then under this in the room below I placed a similar rectangle or parallelogram of the same dimentions, the two being seperated by a dis-

---

[1] Henry outlined this paragraph in ink, and wrote a marginal note to it: "Capillarity." On the Oersted apparatus, see letter to Oersted, April 27, 1841, above, note 11.

tance of 7 10/12 feet and the floor of one room with the cealing of the other or two partitions one of wood and the other of lath and plaster.*

Charged the three batteries with 350 sparks of the unit jar—then made the discharge through the parallelogram in the upper room—one of the sticks <*with*> of spirals being introduced into the circuit <*of*> in the room below the needles were all found to be magnetic after the discharge in the *plus* direction, or in such a way as to indicate a current in the direction of the primary current.

N:B The  in the upper room was formed of coils no 5 & 6. In the lower room of a part of wire helix no 3.[2]

This afternoon I was engaged with a Mr Smith[3] in making some experiments on the photogenic principle in reference to the effect produced by connecting the silvered plate with the prime conductor of the electrical machine while in action according to the later announcement of Daguarre.[4] The result was in favour of the electrical process as far as the experiments were prosecuted b[ut] by no means desiceve and therefore we have concluded to repeat them again. The *camera* was not sufficeantly well insulated

[*] The thickness of the floor & cealing together between the rooms is 1 ft. 2 in.

[2] This was a repetition of the parallelogram experiments of the previous two days, but with much larger rectangles.

[3] Not identified.

[4] A reference to "Photographie—Nouvelles découvertes de M. Daguerre," *Comptes rendus*, 1841, *12*:1228–1229, which stated that Daguerre could shorten the exposure time of his plates to light by electrifying them. This article was quickly translated, e.g., Sturgeon's *Annals of Electricity, Magnetism, and Chemistry*, 1841, 7:399–400.

"RECORD OF EXPERIMENTS"

Henry Papers, Smithsonian Archives

May 14th 1842 Saturday
Induction from ordinary elect

1 Repeated the experiment of yesterday with the large parallelogram. The batter<*y*>ies <*was ch*> were charged with—first 200 <*turns*> sparks of the unit jar the direction of the magnetism was *plus*. The charge was next diminished to 100 the needles were still all magnetized *plus*. Next the charge was 50—the needles were again magnetized *plus*

2 Next the batteries were seperated from the circuit of the conductor and the spark taken on one end of the conductor from the prime conductor

while the other end was connected with a wire leading to the rubber and also to the ground with which it had a broad connection by means of a plate of metal buried in the soil

The needle was still magnetized in all the spirals but the direction was now in all *minus*

The capacity of the conductor was increased by connecting with it the hollow globe of about 11 inches in diameter. The result was the same the needles were magnetized in all the spirals and in all *minus*

3 Next the batteries were attached and charged with 100 sparks. The shock however was not sent immediatly through the conductor but through 6 inches of water in a basin the magnetism of the needles was changed by this retardation of the current.

The result obtained by exp (3) is surprising. The effect of a single spark from the machine was sufficient to magnetize the needles at the distance of 7 feet in an other room[1]

Lowered the parallelogram in the lower room about four feet so that the whole distance was increased to nearly 11 feet. The batteries were then charged with 250 sparks—the needles were all magnetized and in the *plus* direction.

Next charged the batteries with 150 sparks and interrupted the primary circuit by about 6 inches of water in a basin. The needles were again all magnetic and all magnetized *minus*.

Next sent a spark from the prime conductor, which, as in exp 2, was increased in capacity by the globe before mentioned. The end of the ribbon was furnished with a ball to receive the spark. In the other exp (2) the spark was received on the thin end of the long riband. The needles were all magnetized *minus*.

The same arrangement being made <*two*> four 4 sparks were passed through the long ribbon, which formed the primary conductor. The needles were again all magnetic except the last which was a very small one in the *minus* direction. It is not improbable that the small needle was magnetized before being put into the spiral. To test this I put into the same spiral, another fine needle, of which the magnetism was previously examined. The result was now as before the needle was magnetized slightly in the *minus*. Repeated the exp with the small needle in the last coil, with the same result *minus*. Repeated again with the same result. The result therefore with the first small needle was in all probability produced by

[1] Here at the turn of the page, Henry repeated the heading and added the words, "Exp. with large parallelograms in two rooms."

previous magnetism and this is rendered more probable from the fact that I had just before found a needle strongly magnetic in the same lot.

"RECORD OF EXPERIMENTS"
Henry Papers, Smithsonian Archives

May 16th Monday 1842
Magnetization in
spiral

1 Berfore making farther experiments on the direction of currents I have concluded to investigate the magnetization of needles in spirals. For this purpose a medium sized sewing needle was placed in the long spiral mentioned [...].[1] The one end of this spiral was connected with the prime conductor of the machine and the other with a wire leading to the rubber and also to a plate of metal buried in the ground. No magnetism was perceptible in the needle after 20 turns of the machine. Next a very small needle was substituted. After 20 turns of the machen this exhibited magnetic polarity in the *plus* direction

2 Again a larger needle was heated to redness in the flame of a sperit lamp and although before it was annealed it exhibited no signes of magnetism, yet now it became descidedly magnetic with the *plus* <*magn*> polarity.

Again placed a needle in the coil mentioned above (1) gave 20 turns— no signs of magnetism—then passed a very small spark from the prime conductor, needle was now polar in the *plus* direction. Also sent very small spark through a coarser wire spiral—needle polarized *plus*

3 Next used a spiral formed of 13 turns of copper bell wire around a glass tube of about ½ an inch in diameter— commenced with single jar

2 sparks— needle plus		made same	
5 do " plus		expermts with	
10 do " plus		large & small	
13 do jar charged		needles same	
to saturat plus		Result[2]	

---

[1] Though Henry left a space for a page number, he did not supply one and his reference remains unclear.

[2] The new page heading reads "Examination of Phenomena of magnetizing spiral—see page 262," the reference—added later—being to the entry of May 27, 1842, below.

4　Same experiments as the last set, with battery no 3.

charge	5	needle mag	*plus*	
	10	" "	*plus*	
	20	" "	*plus*	All made with
	40	" "	plus	a loose single
50 60 70 80 90 100			plus	spiral with
120 150 200			plus	needles of differt
all the batteres 250 —			plus	sizes
Do " " 100			plus	

Attached the coil No 2 to the circuit, but still the needl was
magnetized—　　　　　　　　*plus*

5　Used spiral of 2<2>1 turns in 4 inches around tube of about ⅜ of an
inch <*began*> of wire [. . .][3] of an inch in diameter. Began with a charge
of 2 sparks in single jar—then 5 sparks—then 10 then 13. Then with full set
of batteries at 25 [s]parks and continued to increase the charge up to 250
sparks, at the rate of 25 sparks at a time—but in every case the needle was
magnetized *plus*.

6　Next used a compound spiral which was composed of [. . .][4] turns.
Charge from single jar from 2 sparks to 14 the full charge of the jar,
magnetism constantly + except once which might perhaps been produced
by the previous magnetism of the needle. But about the discharge of 4 or 5
and 9 & 10 there appeared to be a minimum of magnetic developement.
Next used battery No 3 charged with 25 50 75 &c up to 150 but each discharge produced a *plus* developement of magnetism

7　Added the coil to the circuit found the polarity the same

NB　I have made to day with single and double spirals upwards of 60 exp.
and all except one gave *plus* results.

[3] Henry left this blank.　　　　　[4] Also left blank.

"RECORD OF EXPERIMENTS"
Henry Papers, Smithsonian Archives

May 17th 1842
Induction from ordinary
electricity

Returned to the exp[s] with the large rectangles or as I have called them before parallelograms and gradually lowered the wire in the museum[1] until was along the floor the magnetism was still quite evident as was shown by the repulsion of the north end of the small compass. The polarity was still *plus.* This experment was made yesterday afternoon

Made arrangements to get if possible a secondary current from a conductor which was not closed for this purpose I placed two conductors each 12 feet long parallel to the one side of the parallelogram in the upper room and united them by means of the magnetizing spiral thus . But no effect could be observed although the experiment was twice repeated[2]

Next repeated the experiment of producing induced currents by a single spark of the electrical machine. The conductor in the lower room was placed on the floor the spirals furnished with needles. The spark being passed from the prime conductor, the needles were found magnetic in the *minus* direction.

[1] Probably the natural history museum established by the purchase of a private cabinet in 1805. *Maclean,* 2:68. The collection was on the second floor of Philosophical Hall, under Henry's apparatus room. *Henry Papers,* 2:384.

[2] Henry wrote in here: "See exp. page 264 & 5," referring to the entry for May 28, 1842, below, specifically the discussion midway through the entry on rectangular wire loops.

"RECORD OF EXPERIMENTS"
Henry Papers, Smithsonian Archives

May 18th 1842[1]
Induction from ordinary electricity
This morning I enlarged the parallelogram and substituted for the thin ribbon, of coils no 4 & 5 the thicker copper ribbon of coils no 1 & 2.

[1] Henry misdated the three pages of his "Record of Experiments" entry situated between the entries of May 17 and May 26, 1842. The first page was dated May 18, 1840. The subsequent two pages were both dated May 17, 1842. Internal evidence has led us to the conclusion that the three pages constitute a single entry which should be dated May 18, 1842.

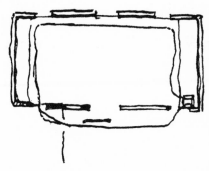

In order to increase the width of the circuit a part of it was passed out of the south east window—through the preparation room and in at the NE window.

The circuit was also removed from the museum and another formed of bell wire substituted in the dining room below. The length of the two circuits was about the same and the one in the basement also passed out of the S.E. lower window, then through Mr Clows kitchen and in at the NE window.[2] The wire below and also the riband above was insulated from the walls and all conductors by means of silk ribb[ons][3] and tubes of glass through which the conductors were passed at points where the electricity might pass off. All the arrangement being complete, battery no 3 was charged with 275 sparks—a needle being placed in a compound spiral of [. . .][4] turns was found magnetized so much as to li[ft][5] quite a collection of iron filings and to make the needle of the small compass whirl entirely round. Next the a new needle was inserted into the spiral and while the one end of the long ribban was in connection with the rubber and the ground and the other brought to the ball of the prime conductor so as to receive sparks. When a spark of $1\frac{1}{2}$ inches in length was thrown on the end of the ribban armed with a ball of $2\frac{1}{2}$ inches in diameter, the needle appeared about as strongly magnetized as before, but in the *minus* direction.

Again the end of the long ribbon in the upper room was disconnected from the rubber and the wire leading to the ground; the sparks being passed as before the needle was not affected. The end of the ribbon being again connected with the rubber, the needle was strongly, comparatively speaking, in the *minus* direction.[6]

With spark from the machine the magnetism with the arrangement described on the last page was always *minus* in all the spirals and an additional one of these was used

The circuit of the secondary current was next interrupted by about an inch of water in a tumbler, while the current was induced by means of the snap. Still the current or I should say the magnetism, remained unchanged.

Next charged the battery (no 3) with 200 sparks of the unit jar—all the needles *direct*

[2] These rooms are depicted in Henry's sketch of Philosophical Hall, printed in *Henry Papers*, 2:384.
[3] The ink is smeared.
[4] Left blank.
[5] A hole in the paper.
[6] The remainder of the entry had been placed under the running head "Induced currents in the basement story—ordinary electricity."

Next introduced into the circuit about an inch of water now all the needles were *minus*

Next charge the battery 120 sparks battery (no 3) the magnetism was as follows circuit complete

No 1 +   No 2 +   no 3 —   no 4 — o

Again charge the [sa]me[7] 120

No 1 +   No 2 +   no 3 —o   no 4 —

Again charge the same 120

No 1 +   No 2 +   No 3 —   No 4 —

Again charge the same 120°

No 1 +   No 2 +   No 3 —o   No   —   minus

Charge 150

No 1 +   No 2 +   No 3 —o   No 4   o This result more +

Charge 175[8]

No 1   No 2   No 3   No 4

Charge 200

No 1 +   No. 2 +   No 3 +   No 4   o

Charge 100

No. 1 +   No. 2 +   No. 3   o   No. 4 —

Charge 75

No 1 —o   No 2 —   No 3 —   No 4 —

Charge 50   1 +   No 2 —o   No 3 —   No 4   o very little magnetism

Next commenced a series with 3 jars of battery no 3, so as to increase the intensity. The following were the results

3 Jars charged 10 sparks			all the needles almost without magnetism			
"	"	"	15	No 1 —	No 2 —	No 3 —	No 4
"	"	"	20	No. 1 +	No 2 +	No 3 —	No. 4 —
"	"	"	20	No. 1 —	No 2 —	No 3 —	No 4 —
"	"	"	30	No. 1 —	No 2 —	No 3 o	No 4 —
"	"	"	40	No. 1 o	No 2 —	No 3 —	No 4 —
"	"	"	50	No. 1 +	No 2 —	No 3 —	No 4 —
"	"	"	60	No. 1 +	No 2 —	No 3 —	No 4 —
"	"	"	60	No. 1 +	No 2 —	No 3 —	No 4

*

* All the variations in this last <*column*> table are to be accounted for by the hypothesis I have adopted in reference to the two inductions and

---

[7] A hole in the paper.
[8] Henry never recorded the results at this level of charge.

the action of the spiral.[9] Any slight variations from perfect regularity is readily accounted for by the different capacities and coercive forces of the needles

All the results with this large arrangement which I have obtained to day are in strict accordance with the hypothesis I have adopted.

The strength of the magnetism of the needles was so great, that the effect would be perceptible I am confident at a much greater distance

[9] For a statement of Henry's hypothesis, see the opening paragraphs of the "Record of Experiments" entry of May 9, 1842, printed above.

TO GEORGE ORD
Archives, American Philosophical Society

Princeton <*April*> May 18th 1842

My Dear Sir

I sent you yesterday by Mr Huntington,[1] (one of the delegates to the general assembly of the Presbyterian church now meeting in your city) the no of the Annales de chimmie et de Physique belonging to the society which I hope you have safely received before the time it was wanted.

Since my visit to the city I have been much occupied and with good success in the extension of my electrical researches. In reference to these I have just now an occasion to refer to XXXIV vol. of the annales de chimie. The vol contains a memoir on magnetization by M. Savary[2] which is directly in the line of my present research. You will oblige me by sending it to me by the bearer of this Mr. Alexander of Princeton.[3] I am informed by Petty Vaughan of London that he has sent a package for the college of New Jersey to care of the american Philosophical society. If the article has arrived please to send it also by Mr Alexander. I have been in the habit of receiving from abroad for several years past packages and papers directed to the care of the society and as this is a very important matter with me in reference to my communications with persons abroad who only know me as a member

[1] Ezra Abel Huntington (1813–1901), pastor of the Third Presbyterian Church of Albany. *Minutes of the General Assembly of the Presbyterian Church in the United States of America* (Philadelphia, 1842), *10*:3. *Auburn Theological Seminary General Biographical Catalogue, 1818–1918* (Auburn, New York, 1918), p. 12.

[2] Félix Savary, "Mémoire sur l'aimantation," *Annales de chimie et de physique*, 1827, 2d ser. *34*:5–57, 220–221.

[3] Next to the address Henry wrote "Favoured by Mr H. Alexander of Princeton." Perhaps Henry Martyn Alexander, a former student of Henry's. *Princeton Catalogue*, p. 157.

of the society I will willingly pay all charges and be thankful for the continuation of the favour if it be not incompatible with present arrangements.

> With much Respect
> Yours truely
> Joseph Henry

FROM THE LECTURE COMMITTEE,
MERCANTILE LIBRARY COMPANY OF PHILADELPHIA[1]
Henry Papers, Smithsonian Archives

Philadelphia May 21, 1842

Dear Sir,

The undersigned, a Committee of the Directors of the Mercantile Library Comp^y, of Philadelphia, appointed to provide a Course of Lectures to be delivered before the Association the ensuing Autumn and Winter, address you with the request that you will consent to deliver one of the series, at such time in the season as will best suit your convenience.

It is desired that the Lectures will be on subjects of general interest, and suited to a numerous audience of both sexes.

The course will commence on Friday evening, 4th November, and will be continued on the same evening of each week until the close, which will be about the first of March.

We trust that this will receive your favorable consideration, and that you will transmit us an affirmative reply to our request, at your earliest convenience.[2]

Address Charles S. Wood, N° 131 Market St.

> Respectfully
> yours &c[3]
> Thos P. Cope
> Charles S. Wood
> Jos. Patterson
> S. H. Brooke
> J. L. Erringer
> Joseph C. Grubb

P.S. The Directors have appropriated the sum of Fifty dollars to defray travelling expenses &c.

---

[1] The lecture committee had made a similar request the previous year. See above, Lecture Committee, Mercantile Library Company to Henry, August 21, 1841.

[2] For Henry's reply, see below, June 7, 1842.

[3] The new members of the committee, S. H. Brooke, J. Livingston Erringer, and Joseph Patterson, were Philadelphia merchants, as were most of the Company's Directors. Philadelphia City Directories, 1840–1845.

FROM ROBERT HARE
Henry Papers, Smithsonian Archives

Philad[a] May 26th 1842[1]

My dear Sir

I have just received your kind letter,[2] recommending the perusal of Doves theory. My essay[3] has been for some time in the printers hands having sent it to my fd Silliman three weeks ago. I do not know where I can get a sight of Doves memoir[4] at present. Miller has orders to send it to me but has only sent the 2nd volume without the number in which the memoir in question is published. If you would entrust your number to the mail I should be willing to bear the cost of the postage coming and returning.

I cannot conceive of any adequate cause of an extensive whirlwind excepting an ascending current at the axis. Nor do I think that even in that way the whirl can reach to the distance which hurricanes are known to reach. But however generated they cannot agreeably to my view of the subject endure without as sustaining force, t[r]avelling as they are alleged to do.[5]

I am well pleased to find that you have come over to my idea of an electrical plenum.[6] I presume you have not forgotten the suggestions ass[o]ciated with the idea of a plenum in my letter to Faraday respecting polarization.[7]

I have just succeeded in fusing some comparatively large specimens of Iridium and Rhodium, 600[8] grains of the one and 77 of the other. The Iridium is of a specific gravity of 21 83/100 the Rhodium is a specific gravity of 11. There is a slight malleability. This quality and their fusibility increases with fusion.[9]

---

[1] The date is unclear in original; possibly May 20.

[2] Not found.

[3] "Additional Objections to Redfield's Theory of Storms," *Silliman's Journal*, 1842, *43*: 122–140.

[4] Henry may have referred Hare to Dove's theory as it appeared in translation in part 10 of Taylor's *Scientific Memoirs*: "On the Law of Storms," 1843, *3*:197–220. Dove, like Redfield, advocated a whirlwind theory.

[5] Later in the year Hare published "Strictures on Prof. Dove's Essay 'On the Law of Storms,'" *Silliman's Journal*, 1843, *44*:137–146. Hare criticized Dove, as well as Espy and Redfield, for neglecting electricity as an agent in storms.

[6] Henry announced his adoption of an electrical plenum in "Contributions V: Induction from Ordinary Electricity; Oscillatory Discharge," presented to the American Philosophical Society at the next meeting on June 17, 1842. For Henry's earlier consideration of a plenum, see *Henry Papers*, *4*:44, 46.

[7] In paragraph 29 of his first letter to Faraday, Hare wrote ". . . it has appeared to me inconceivable that the phenomena of galvanism and electro-magnetism, latterly brought into view, can be satisfactorily explained without supposing the agency of an intervening imponderable medium by whose subserviency the inductive influence of currents or magnets is propagated." *Silliman's Journal*, 1840, *38*:9.

[8] Should read "60."

[9] Hare claimed to be the first to fuse pure iridium and rhodium in a communication to

I am affraid my steel pen is so refractory that you will not find this epistle very legible.

I am with esteem
Yours
Robt Hare

the APS on May 6, 1842. *Proceedings, 1841–1843,* 2:182. Although Hare's finding was later published in *Silliman's Journal* (1846, 2d ser. 2:365–369), the eighth edition of the *Encyclo-*

paedia Britannica (s.v. "Chemistry," p. 499) was still describing iridium and rhodium as infusible.

"RECORD OF EXPERIMENTS"

Henry Papers, Smithsonian Archives

May 26th (Thursday) 1842
magnetization of needles by
ordinary electricity

Since the last date[1] my experiments have been interrupted by the opening of the college, and my lectures on light.

In[2] my experiments on induction on ordinary electricity as given in the old book, I found that when the wire to receive the induction was formed of a compound circuit of several strands then the magnetism of the needles were always *minus*.[3] This fa[c]t at first sight appeared <*quite*> difficult to explain but on a little reflection I find it in strict accordance with the hypothesis I have adopted. By employing a number of strands the same induction which would be exerted on a single wire, is now active through a long wire. The intensity of the disturbance is therefore so much increased and its quantity so much diminished that the power of magnetizing the needles to saturation ceases in precisely in the same manner as the power of the induction in helix no. 1 is not sufficient to magnetize needles in a single spiral in the case of galvanic induction as shown in my paper No 3.[4]

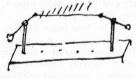

Charged all the batteres with 390 sparks. Placed a number of fine needles above the wire see fig at different distances from contact up to ½ an inch. All were magnetized by the discharge in the *plus*

[1] May 18, 1842, printed above.

[2] There is a marginal notation to this paragraph—"Remarks."

[3] See, for example, the conclusion Henry drew in his July 26, 1838, "Record of Experiments" entry. *Henry Papers,* 4:71.

[4] In paragraphs 30 through 35 of "Contributions III: Electro-Dynamic Induction," Henry discussed how increasing the length of the conductor increased the intensity of the induced current while reducing its quantity.

direction. The length the wire was about 6 inches its thickness [. . .][5] of an inch

Repeated the same increased the length of the wire to 14 inches still the result was the same—the needles were all (10 in number) magnetized *plus*—charge the same in battery 1 & 2

Repeated same exp lengthened the wire to 20 inches—charge the same, distance of the needles from contact to 1¾ inches. All (11) in the same direction magnetized *plus*. Battery 1 & 2.

Again increased the length of the wire to 40 inches charge the same—need[l]es from contact to the distance of 3 inches all (12) magnetic *plus*. No change in direction. The needle in contact with the wire appeared more feebly magnetized than any other.

Again the same arrangement as before, with the exception of 3 jars instead of the 2 batteries. The charge was 55 sparks, all the needles except the first and 3 last were magnetized and in the *plus* direction. Magnetism much more feeble than when the batteries were used.

Again Lengthened the wire to about 6 feet. Charge 250, 2 batteris. All the needles magnetic in the *plus* direction—distance from contact to 3 inches.

Again wire of the same length—charge the same—between three of the 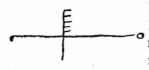 needles and the wire a zinc plate was placed—a thin plate of about 8 inches square, so note if any screaning took place. No effect was observed in reference to the plate, all the needles were magnetized *plus*.

Placed eleven needles on the edge of a lath and then held the article perpendicular to the wire. The magnetism extended up to the sixth needle. Each was magnetized *plus*. No change of direction could be obtained

Magnetized[6] needles by a spark from the machine—only however the needles immediatly in contact with the wire was —

Prepared[7] a battery of 10 elements, the battery of quart mugs. Connected this battery with the rectangle on the inside of the electrical case. Next charged the several spirals of one set with needles and connected this with the secondary conductor. The wires being near together all the needles came out magnetic when the contact was made. The one in the more compound the stronger —. When the needles were replaced and the con-

[5] Left blank.
[6] To the left of this word are three horizontal lines; perhaps an aborted illustration.
[7] This and the succeeding three paragraphs were placed under the heading "Induction from galvanism." However, the last paragraph, on an entirely different subject, was separated from the preceding three by a double line.

tact broken, all the needles except that in the first spiral came out neutral. The action at the ending just neuteralized that at the <*ending*> begining, except in the case of the first needle—this at first was perhapse magnetized to near saturation and consequently <*the same charge*> an equal action would more than discharge the magnetism.

The induction with this arrangement is quite feeble probably the effect would be much greater if a ribbon were used instead of the thin wire.

Next the same spirals were charged with needles and then the contact was made and broken with the battery several times in succession. The needles at the end of the operation came out electrified +, or as if by the ending induction.

A part of this afternoon was occupied in distilling mercury for the use of the photographic art.[8] The mercury was placed in an iron bottle and this placed in the forge. A gun barrel attached at one end to the bottle dipped into water in a wide mouth phial and this was placed in a wash basin filled with water. The mouth of the phial was closed with a wet towel and a part of the same was wrapped around the barrel. This arrangement was made inorder to prevent the regurgitation of the water and the blowing out of the mercury with the steam. Only about one half of the mouth of the barrel was plunged under the surface of the water in the phial so as to let the air in to restore the equilibrum.

---

[8] Mercury was used in the developing of daguerreotypes. *Encyclopaedia Britannica*, 8th ed., s.v. "Photography," p. 546.

"RECORD OF EXPERIMENTS"
Henry Papers, Smithsonian Archives

May 27$\underline{th}$ 1842

Magnetizing spiral   common electricity

1   Placed needle in the axis of the spiral described, bottom page 253.[1] Sent <*dis*>charge through the spiral from 3 jars, needle magnetic in the *plus* direction. Next placed a similar needle in a lead tube, of about ¼ of an inch of external diameter, and 1/20 of an inch thick of metal. The needle with a charge equal in quantity to that of the last, was now unaffected, it showed no polarity. The quantity of the charge was next varied but in no case could I magnetize the needle while it remained in the tube.

2   Next the tube was cut open along <*its axis*> a line on its side parallel to its axis. The needle was now as strongly magnetic as if the metal were not present. The two edges of the opening were next pinched together so as to be in contact but with this I could not suceed in screening or rather in neutralizing the magnetism.

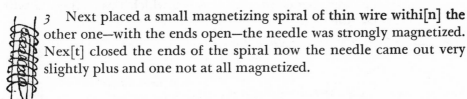

3   Next placed a small magnetizing spiral of thin wire withi[n] the other one—with the ends open—the needle was strongly magnetized. Nex[t] closed the ends of the spiral now the needle came out very slightly plus and one not at all magnetized.

4   The spiral used in the last exp was a single one—substituted for this a compound one. The needle placed in this in the first attempt was also magnetized slightly *plus* when the ends were closed. I then introduced into the circuit a tube of water, so as to pass the charge through about one inch of water. The needle now came out of the inner spiral magnetized — *minus*. This was repeated 6 or 8 times with the same result[2]

---

[1] See the fourth paragraph of the "Record of Experiments" entry of May 16, 1842, above.

[2] According to a notation in the left-hand margin, Henry considered this an "Important exp." His explanation of the experiment's significance is given below in the next "Record of Experiments" entry.

"RECORD OF EXPERIMENTS"
Henry Papers, Smithsonian Archives

May 28th 1842 (Saturday)
Current from the
return stroke[1]

I consider the last experiment on the last page[2] as an important one in reference to the explanation of the change of magnetism observed by Savary in the case of a spiral.[3] I think it probable that the results obtained by him were due to the cutting across of or striking across of the electricity from one spire to the other and thus forming a shut circuit which in certain cases would have more magnetic power than the primary

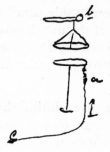 Made an arrangement, such as is shown in the figure, with the plates used for the dancing images. Placed the spiral at *a*. When a spark was drawn from the ball *b* the needle became magnetic by the current of the return magnetism. The direction of the current was upwards. The wire c was connected with another which was connected with the earth.

---

[1] This phenomenon was first recognized by Charles Stanhope, Lord Mahon (1753–1816, *DNB*), in the 1770s. The cause of considerable damage during lightning storms, it was the current produced when lightning removed the cause of previously induced charges. In the laboratory it could be produced using a prime conductor and two metal rods. The prime conductor would be used to induce a charge in the metal rod A. In turn, rod A would induce a charge in metal rod B. If the prime conductor released its charge in the form of a spark to ground (analogous to the strike of a lightning bolt), then a spark would fly from rod B to rod A. This latter spark was the return stroke. Charles Viscount Mahon, *Principles of Electricity* . . . (London, 1779), pp. 76–78, 113–131.

Among Henry's reading notes in Notebook [10615] is a section (pp. 18–22) dated June 23, 1842, entitled "Facts from Mahon's Electricity." His penultimate paragraph refers to this "Record of Experiments" entry: "I must repeat these experiments and vary them. It appears from the experimt I have given at page [. . .] of vol 2nd of my manuscript records, that the return stroke is composed like the discharge from a Lyden jar of a reverberation, or series of oscillations." Concluding this section of the reading notes is a reference to another Stanhope publication: "Remarks on Mr. Brydone's Account of a Remarkable Thunder-storm in Scotland," *Phil. Trans.,* 1787, pp. 130–150.

On January 18, 1845, Henry repeated Stanhope's experiments on the return stroke. "Record of Experiments," Henry Papers, Smithsonian Archives.

[2] The fourth experiment of May 27, 1842, printed above.

[3] Félix Savary, "Mémoire sur l'aimantation," *Annales de chimie et de physique,* 1827, 2d ser. *34*:5–57.

May 28, 1842

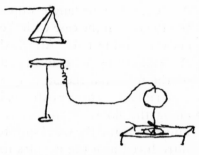

Made an arrangement like that in the margin in which the wire from the lower plate did not form a connection with the earth <*but*> [on] the contrary the end was well insulated by placing it first in the large hollow globe and the latter on an insulating stool. The needl as before was strongly magnetized by an asscending current. The compound spiral was used in thes experiments. I next substituted a single spiral but the result was the same. The needle was again magnetized by an ascending current.[4]

These experiments give me assurance that I can produce results from the clouds by attaching a wire to the tin roof of my house and connecting the lower end of this with the ground or rather with the well. A part of this wire being formed into a spiral will indicate the effect from the flash of a cloud.[5]

Could[6] not a self-registering electrometer be constructed to be used with clock-work which would register the state of the atmosphere at every hour or minute by magnetized needls placed in spirals around the periphery of a wheel moved by the clock work and brought in contact with the end of the exploring wire. The wheel might contain 20 or 30 spirals and the exploring rod might be so arranged as to be pushed against the knob of the spiral when it came near. Or perhaps better the spiral might be thrust out when it came opposite the end of the exploring rod by means of a clamp and a spring.[7]

I must however first determ whether I can get induction from the Heavens by means of the arrangement mentioned at the bottom of the last page.

---

[4] A marginal annotation designates this and the preceding experiment as illustrations of the role of the "Current from the Return stroke."

[5] On June 10, 1842, Henry turned this idea into working experimental apparatus. See the "Record of Experiments" entry of that date, below.

[6] This and the subsequent four paragraphs of the entry were placed under the heading of "Secondary conductor interrupted."

[7] Henry announced his self-registering electrometer in the last paragraph of "Contributions V: Induction from Ordinary Electricity; Oscillatory Discharge," but the published abstract gives no details regarding the design or construction of the instrument.

Arranged the rectangle opposite the one in the case with the ends disconnected.[8] Attached one end to the globe, insulated on the stool and the other to a long ribban of copper extended along the floor. With this arrangement and the set of spirals introduced at *a* the needles in the single spirals were unmagnetized but those in the compound were magnetized in a direction opposite to that of the battery current. From this result it would appear that a primary <*current*> conductor can have a secondary current produced in it although the two ends are seperated by the thickness of the glass in the jar

In this experiment 2 jars No 1 & 2 were used charged with 150 sparks.

With the same arrangement the induction was produced by sparks from the machine. The result was the same the needle was slightly magnetized again in the *minus* direction[9]

Repeated the last experiment with the variation of disconnecting the long <*spiral*> ribban which was extended along the floor—now the needles exhibited no signes of magnetism.[10]

I next attached the end of the wire, which before had been joined to the long ribb[on] to the wire leading to the ground. Now the needle was again magnetic *minus*.

Next I insulated the long ribbon, by suspending it from a silk ribbon.

Also insulated the frame which supported the secondary conductor. With a charge of 150 the needle was scarcely magnetized perceptibly. In spiral no 1—with 200 the magnetism was decided and as before in the *minus* direction. A larger needle appeared to be more affected than a smaller one

Next the same arrangement being continued the discharge consisted of

---

[8] At this point Henry is refocusing on a problem he had explored on May 17, 1842 (see the "Record of Experiments" entry of that date, above)—the existence of an induced current in an open secondary circuit.

[9] The remainder of the entry is under the heading "Induction from ordinary elect. secondary conductor with current interrupted."

[10] In the left margin Henry noted: "In all these experiments the spiral of ⟨2⟩3 turns was used no 1. page 238." The reference is to the entry of May 9, 1842, printed above.

sparks from the prime conductor now the direction of the magnetism was changed an[d] the needle came out strongly *plus*

All these results appear to prove the induction of a current in a secondary conductor with the circuit interrupted.

Next armed the end of the primary wire with a two inch ball, put needles in all the 4 spirals, sent spark from prime conductor—the arrangement same otherwise as shown in the above figure. The needles were magnetized as follows

In spiral No 1 —   No 2 +   No 3 +   No 4 +
Repeated the exp with the following results—
    in spiral No 1 —   No 2 +   No 3 +   No 4 +

"RECORD OF EXPERIMENTS"
Henry Papers, Smithsonian Archives

May 30<u>th</u> Monday 1842
Magnetization with the spirals and
a galvanic battery

The last result I think conclusively proves that an induced current is produced in the open circuit of the secondary conductor since it gives the characteristic property of such a current namely the changes of polarity in the needles in the different spirals. I thought at first that perhaps this induction might be the result of the action of the extra particle or free electricity but this cannot be the case since then the spirals would all give the same indications. *Try to get a change in the different spirals with the battery also make the insulation more perfect*

The weather being rainy and consequently unfavourable for ordinary electricity I have commenced a series of experiments with the battery on the magnetization of the needles.

First a single cup battery was prepaired and a needle placed in the axis of the Boston coil of bell wire of about 4 inches in diameter. The needle was magnetized in the plus direction but more strongly in the same direction when it was drawn along the inner side of the coil. The same experiment was made with a needle placed in one of the larger coils no 3 the inner circle of which was at least *8* inches in diameter. The needle was slightly magnetized in the *plus* direction

These results afford me a means of investigating the magnetism of a coil and a hollow magnet free from the objections of the filings becoming magnetized.[1]

See page 227 & 229[2]

In all the experiments with spirals and the galvanic battery I have never obtained any change of direction. See p. 203[3]

Tried to get a tertiary current with the circuit open as in the case of page 265[4] with galvanism but did not succed with hard needles. Tried this again with needles which had been softened in the flame of the spirit lamp but with the same result. Try this exp with the secondary

[1] There are two parallel horizontal lines in the left margin next to this paragraph, presumably placed there by Henry to emphasize the importance of this experimental technique.

[2] A reference to the experiments on the distribution of magnetism around hollow metal cylinders conducted on November 4, 1841, and recorded in the "Record of Experiments" entry of that date, printed above.

[3] Henry is referring to the "Record of Experiments" entry of October 7, 1841, above, where he had previously conducted experiments with spirals and galvanic electricity.

[4] This is a reference to the final experiments of the preceding entry.

"RECORD OF EXPERIMENTS"
Henry Papers, Smithsonian Archives

May 31st 1842
Magnetization of needles by the electrical discharge[1]

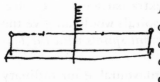

Arranged between the balls of the universal discharger a wire of platina 1/[. . .][2] of an inch in diameter and 14 inches long connected at its two ends with the plated wire 1/4 of a millimetre in diameter.

1 Placed needles so as to be perpendicular to the wire and also perpendicular to the magnetic meridian. Made the discharge from 2[3] sparks. The needles were *plus* magnetized to the 5th needle the distance was 1/2 an inch between each needle

2 Repeated the same experiment with the same result the needles were all magnetized plus to the 5th one after this no magnetism.

[1] In these experiments, Henry is attempting to confirm Savary's findings of reversals in polarity according to the distance of the needle from the wire.

[2] Henry neglected to record the denominator of the fraction.

[3] Given the magnitudes of the discharges in the other experiments, Henry probably meant 200 sparks.

3 Again with a larger charge 275 the platina wire was now deflagrated but the result was the same as the last

4 Next substituted for the fine wire of the last arrangement the plated wire of the same length 4½ feet. The needles were again placed transversely at the distance from each other of ½ an inch. The charge being 200 all the needles *10* in number were found magnetic. The 5th needle was magnetized minus, the others all plus. It is not improbable that the fifth needle was slightly magnetized before the experiment.

5 Repeated the same experimt charge the same arrangement of needles the same now all the needles to the 13th were magnetized and *plus*—no change. The magnetism decreased from the 2nd to the last needle

6 Repeated the same exp with larger needles no 3. The magnetism now extended only to the 8th needle.

7 It is evident from the foregoing experiments that the magnetism is perceptible at a greater distance with fine needles than with coarse and that the second wire gives a greater effect than the first

8 Repeated the same exp. with fine needles found all magnetized to the 13th *plus* beyond this magnetism uncertain—the charge was now 350.

9 Increased the length of the wire to that of [. . .][4] feet procured new needles all of the same size No 10. The needles were all magnetized *plus* to the 12th needle—charge 250

10 Next charged the batteries to the amount of 250[5] sparks all the other circumstances remaining the same as in the last experiment. Needles magnetized to the 10th all *plus*—discharge not good.

11 Next charged the battery to the extent of 275 sparks now found that 15 needles were magnetized—the magnetism gradually increasing from the 2nd needle until the 15th all *plus*. It should be noted in these experiments that the needle in contact with the wire in all cases was very little magnetized and that the second needle was the one which receved the maximum of developement.

12 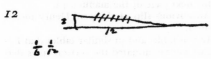 Next inorder to detirmin if there were any changes in the magnetism of the needles between the 1st and 2nd needles

---

[4] Left blank.
[5] It appears that Henry originally wrote "350," then wrote a "2" over the first digit of the number.

of the last experiment I placed the needles along the wire as shown in the figure, 11 in number. They were all magnetized *alike plus*. The first was in contact with the wire and each one 1/12 of an inch above the preceding one

The following are the relative strengths of the magnetism of the needles in exp 11[6]

no 2[7]—o   No 2—9   no 3 9   no 4 9¼   no 5—8°   no 6 9½   n 7—o No 8 4°   9 4°   10 2½°   These are statical deflections see next page. The following are the relative intensities of the needles in the exp 12 last page

No 1—19°   No 2 19°   No 3—17½   No 4—22½   No 5 21   No 6 26 No 7 24°   No 8 23   No 9 25°   No 10 25   No 11 26°

Charge 275   wire 7½ feet long

no[8] of the needle	dist	deflect	no of the needle	dist	deflect
1	0	7 +	13	12	15 +
2	1	23° +	14	13	14½ Do
3	2	27 Do	15	14	13 Do
4	3	22 Do	16	15	13
5	4	27 Do	17	16	12½ Do
6	5	17 Do	18	17	15 Do
7	6	23 Do	19	18	12½ Do
8	7	18	20	19	11 Do
9	8	19 Do	21	20	10 Do
10	9	17 Do	22	21	10¼ Do
11	10	17 Do	23	22	12½ Do
12	11	16 Do	24	23	11

The above results were obtained by placing a series of needles on the same piece of lath at the distance of ½ an inch from each other inclined to the

[6] This data does not match Henry's written account of the eleventh experiment, which reported "the magnetism gradually increasing from the 2nd needle until the 15th." We are uncertain whether Henry meant to write that the magnetism in experiment 11 was gradually decreasing, or that this data belongs to another experiment. In the latter case, it is possible that these are the statical deflection readings for experiment 12, to be compared to the initial deflection readings which follow on the next page of the manuscript.

[7] An obvious slip of the pen. Henry meant needle 1.

[8] In this table, and in similar tables that follow, we have eliminated the vertical rules that appear in Henry's manuscript. In a few cases we have added a horizontal rule to set off a table from the text.

axis of the same wire used in the last experiment.
The first needle was in contact with the wire <*the* 2 in. this [sketch]
second one 1/12 of an inch above the wire>. The
last end of the stick was 2 inches from the wire and consequently the several needles were each 1/12 of an inch above the other

In the above experiment the deflection is the initial deflection. This I
find to be about as accurate as the statical deflection and is incomparably
more expiditious to be used.[9] The small degree of magnetism of the first
needle is shown in the above experiment very conspiciously. Needle placed
against a piece of glass

Charge the batteries with 275 sparks placed the needles on
the lath perpendicular to the meridian and in the same vertical plane. Then introduced into the circuit a tube with about
1/4 of an inch of water between the balls. The tube was
broken into powder and the peces scattered about. The following is the result of the magnetism

Small needles no 10

no of the needle	Dist from wire	deflec	no	dist	deflec
1	0	0	9	4	0
2	½ inch	0	10	4½	0
3	1	15°+	11	5	0
4	1½	0	12	5½	0
5	2	0	13	6	15+
6	2½	0	14	6½	17½+
7	3	5+	15	7	18+
8	3½	10+	16	7½	23+
			17	8	28+

In the above expermt the tube of water was placed on the negative side
of the fine wire. This result is so curious that I will repeat the experiment
again.

[9] Judging by a survey of natural philosophy texts, the terms "initial deflection" and "statical deflection" were not in common use in Henry's day. We believe that Henry used the former to indicate the initial displacement of the magnetometer needle from the zero point. The latter probably refers to the final resting point of the needle. Using initial deflections would be much faster.

Needles the same

no of needles	dist from wire	Deflection	no of needles	dist	deflect
1	0	0+	13	6	0
2	½	17+	14	6½	0
3	1	16+	15	7	0
4	1½	12+	16	7½	0
5	2	10+	17	8	0
6	2½	7+	18	8½	0
7	3	3+	19	9	0
8	3½	2+	20	9½	0
9	4	very slight +	21	10	0
10	4½	"+	22	10½	0
11	5	"+	23	11	0
12	5½	"+	24	11½	0

The place of the tube in this exp. was supplied by a cup of water the crack was louder than before but the magnetic effects quite different from those of the last experiment

Wire 7½ feet long   small needles No 10   charge 275

no of n	dist	defl	No of n	dist	defl
1	0	4+	13	6	12+[10]
2	½ inch	20+	14	6½	feeble +
3	1	16+	15	7	0
4	1½	16+	16	7½	0
5	2	9+	17	8	0
6	2½	8+	18	8½	0
7	3	6+	19	9	0
8	3½	5+	20	9½	0
9	4<½>	4+	21	10	0
10	4½	3+	22	10½	0
11	5	very feeble +	23	11	0
12	5½	"+	24	11½	0

[10] This figure is clearly a slip of the pen.

Here the magnetism diminishes gradually after the second needle. The effect ends with the 12th needle.

{ I have been careful in all the experiments of to day to place the needles perpendicular to the magnetic meridian so as to nutralize or rather prevent any action of the earth.

Next changed the wire, substituted a thicker one of copper 1/[. . .][11] of an inch in diameter same length 7½ feet. Charge 275

No	Dis	def	no	dis	def
1	0	0	11	5	1°+
2	½ inch	20+	12	5½	very feeble +
3	1	15+	13	6	0
4	1½	12+	14	6½	0
5	2	11+	15	7	0
6	2½	10½+	16	7½	0
7	3	8½+	17		
8	3½	7½+	18		
9	4	4+	19		
10	4½	2+	20		

[11] Left blank.

"RECORD OF EXPERIMENTS"
Henry Papers, Smithsonian Archives

June 1st 1842
Magnetization of needles by
elect discharge

From the last experiment it appears that the thike wire does not give as great a developement of magnetism as the thinner. In this experiment [just][1] as in those with the thin wire the needle in contact is not magnetized.

[1] A hole in the paper.

Are not the results obtained by Savary in reference to the change of the direction [of] polarity due to the discharge passing along the air and thus as it were surrounding the needle. Make experime[nt]s with piece of metal placed on opposite sides of the needle also near the wire.

Arranged a number of needles on a lath as in the figure. The magnetism was as follows

No 1 4   No 2—2½   No 3 2½   No 4 3°   No 5 2   No 6. 2°¼   No 7—4°
N 8. 7½   No 9 feeble   No 10 3°   No 11 2½   No 12 very feeble   13 1½
14 3°

No	dis	defl	no	dis	defl
1	0	0+	12		
2	¼	25+	13		
3	½	25+	14		
4	1	24½+	15		
5	1½	24+	16		
6	2	18+	17	no magnetism	
7	2½	13½+	18		
8	3	8½+	19		
9	3½	7+	20		
10	4	very feeble +	21		
11	4½	+	22		

In the above exp a new magnetometer was used constructed with a small needle, the deflections with the same magnetism are large. The needle is screened from agitation of the air. The charge in both the above was 275. Thick wire same as last exp page 271[2]

Charge the same as in the last exp wire also the same and the arrangement of the need[les][3] perpendicular on the lath. A brass rod was held on one side of the needles as at .a .b being the section of the discharging wire.

[2] A reference to the last experiment of May 31, 1842, above.

Henry later added another sentence right after this: "For a description of this instrument see page 176." The description of the instrument actually appears on page 276 (the entry of June 2, 1842, below).

[3] The same hole as above, but on the reverse side of the page.

no.	dis.	defl.
1	0	5°+
2	¼	24+
3	½	28+
4	1	22+
5	1½	20+
6	2	18+
7	2½	12½+
8	3	5½+

Small needles No 9

 Next the brass rod was held between the 6 & 7ᵗʰ needle. Charge the same as the last needles the same

no.	dis.	defl.
1	0	0+
2	¼	23+
3	½	22+
4	1	24+
5	1½	19+
6	2	15+
7	2½	13½+
8	3	8+

Small needles No 9

It appars from all the experiments that the small needle in contact with the wire is magnetized but very feebly

N B Is it not magnetized stronger in its middle.

Next compared large and small needles no 9 & 3

no	dis.	defl.
1	0	37
2	¼	42
3	½	37
4	1	35½

Large needles no 3

no	dis		defl
1	0	<¼>	0
2	¼	<½>	22½
3	½	<1>	24
4	1	<1½>	21
5	1½	<2>	17½
6	2	<2½>	10
7	2½	<3>	2½
8	3	<3½>	1½

Small needles no 9

"RECORD OF EXPERIMENTS"
Henry Papers, Smithsonian Archives

June 2$\underline{\text{nd}}$ 1842
magnetization of needles by
the ordinary discharge

Charge wire and arrangement the
same as in the last experiments large
needles no 3 used

no.	dis.	defl.
1	0	35+
2	1/4	38½+
3	1/2	32+
4	1	34+
5	1½	26+
6	2	24+
7	2½	20+
8	3	12½+
9	3½	9+
10	4	feebly+
11	4½	feebly+

To determ if the same action is produced by all parts of the conjunctive wire 36 needles (No 3) were arranged at the distance of an inch apart on the middle part of the wire 7½ feet long 1/[. . .][1] of an inch in diameter

no		defl.	no		Defl			defl.
1		30	1		36	1		32
2		32	2		38	2		31½
3	charge	25	3	275	27	3	sparks	33
4		32	4		32	4		31
5		32	5		27	5		25
6	all	33	6	in	34	6	contact[2]	24½
7		34	7		32	7		30
8		34	8		32	8		32
9		37	9		26	9		31
11		39	10		29½	10		30
11		38½	11		31	11		15
12		36	12		28	12		

[1] Henry neglected to record the diameter of the wire.

[2] In the manuscript, the phrase "all in contact" is written vertically in all three columns.

The 12 first needles give a mean deflection of 35° the next 12 a deflection of 31 the last 12 of 28 7/12. The intensity would appear to diminish according to this result, from the negative towards the positive end of the conjunctive wire but this effect was what I anticipated on account of the derangement of the apparatus by which the needles next the + pole was passed a little too far over the wire thus

In the magnetization of the needles of the last expermt which were all in contact with the conducting wire a very important fact was noted namely all the needles appeared most strongly magnetized at the section against which the wire was pressed, or in other words there was a strong tendency to form a concecutive point[3] at the spot which was in contact with the needle. This was shown by the deflection of the small needle and a comparison was made with observations on needles magnetized at a <greater> distance from the wire

Repeated the same exp with the fine needles no 9; 13 of these were placed in contact with the wire diagonally so that it was in contact with the eye of the first and the point of the last

number of needles beginning at the postve end													
1	2	3	4	5	6	7	8	9	10	11	12	13	
							Deflection						Charge
12	12½	13	13	15	20	21	8	2	0	feeb	feeb	feeb	275
+	+	+	+	+	+	+	+	+	[. . .]⁴	—	—	—	

The first needles were magnetized strongly with a north polarity at the <north> larger end and this diminished as the series advanced towards the other end and at the 11th needle it became feebly negative, showing the

---

[3] These are the successive points along the length of a magnetic bar or magnetized steel wire at which the direction of the magnetism is reversed. Hence, the bar or wire appears to consist of a series of alternating magnetic poles. In French, the term is "points conséquens," which has been rendered into English alternatively as "consequent points" or "consecutive points." *Oxford English Dictionary*; Félix Savary, "Mémoire sur l'aimantation," *Annales de chimie et de physique*, 1827, 2d

ser. 34:14, is translated in Sturgeon's *Annals of Electricity, Magnetism, and Chemistry*, 1842, 9:262; P. M. Roget, *Treatises on Electricity, Galvanism, Magnetism, and Electro-Magnetism* (London, 1832), "Magnetism," p. 11, "Electro-Magnetism," p. 54.

For Henry's further interest in consecutive points, see below, "Record of Experiments," June 6, 1842.

[4] A hole in the paper.

effect of a concecutive point. The pole appeared to [be] about one four[th] of the length of the needle from the larger end in the last needles. This result appears to give me a clue to the phenomenon recorded by M Savary and which has thus far been a great difficulty in the way of my researches appearing to viciate the results which I have obtained by means of the polarity of the needle in reference to the direction of the secondary currents. (See the paper of M Riess Annales de chimie et de Physique tome LXXIV p 158)[5]

The results given above explain an action which I observed yesterday in testing the strength of magnetism of the small needles which were in connection with the connecting wire. The needle when approached to the magnetometer from a distance would repel the needle of the instrument which would immediatly return and then adhere to the side of the glass. This effect was produced by the following action

Let *a* be the point of the needle of the instrument and b the larger end of the needle to be tested. Let *c* be the concecutive point of the needle then it is evident that at a distance the point *b* and *c* would act with nearly the same mechanical effect the small distance b.c would be merged in the greater distance of the needles apart but when the needles of the instrument in its return vibration comes very near *b* then its influence is felt paramount to that of *b* and attraction is produced

[5] A reference to Peter T. Riess (1804–1883, *Poggendorff*), "Sur le courant secondaire de la batterie électrique," *Annales de chimie et de physique*, 1840, 2d ser. 74:158–185. Riess rejected Henry's correlation in "Contributions III: Electro-Dynamic Induction" of the direction of the secondary current with the distance between the primary and secondary circuits, accusing Henry of circular reasoning. Henry had assumed that changes in the magnetization of a needle gave an accurate accounting of changes in the direction of the magnetizing circuit. However, Riess pointed to Savary's findings that the intensity and direction of the magnetization of the needles varied according to a number of parameters in such experiments, such as the size and temper of the needles. Hence, the needle could not be assumed to be a reliable indicator of changes in the direction of currents. Moreover, Riess's own experiments had demonstrated a variation in intensity and direction of magnetism according to the number of jars in the electric battery and the length of the secondary circuit.

Henry was not alone in appreciating that Riess's interpretation of Savary's work threatened to negate Henry's conclusions about secondary currents induced by ordinary electricity. Carlo Matteucci, who had independently come to conclusions similar to Henry's, acknowledged Riess's attack, but proclaimed his continued faith in his (and Henry's) methodology. "Sur l'induction de la décharge de la batterie," *Archives de l'électricité*, 1841, *1*:136–144 (an annotated copy of this article survives in the Henry Library).

In a draft of "Contributions V: Induction from Ordinary Electricity; Oscillatory Discharge" (Box 23, Henry Papers, Smithsonian Archives), Henry includes in his preliminary discussion paraphrases of Riess's critique and Matteucci's response.

I have mentioned that I had prepaired a new magnetometer and since I have referred to it several times, yesterday to day it will be best before going farther to describe the instrument. It is on the same principle as the instrument described page [...].[6]
The index needle is formed of a slender sewing needle 2 inches long, and ballanced by a piece of wood at the larger end

(thus see margin) and suspended by a fine silk filiment in a paper stirrup. The suspension string is at right angles to the plane of a graduated circle and this is covered by a piece of mica cut out at one corner, so that the needle to be experimented on may approached sufficiently near the end of the index

needle. The sides of the figure are enclosed by glass. The oscillations of the needle are stopped by the glass plate which is placed directly across the zero point. The repulsion of the needles drives the index from its point of rest and the extreme dynamic deflection gives the magnetic force required. The force in this case is the *vis viva*.[7] The operation of this instrument was very satisfactory

Arranged <10>9 needles small no 9 along the wire in contact arrangement the same as before

Charge 275

1	2	3	4	5	6	7	8	9	10
−30°	− −	17°+	14+	17+	12+	12½	13+	11+	

It appears that there are here two needles polarized in the negative direction but I am not sure but the wire may have been on the opposite of these

Repeated the same experiment but was careful to place each needle on the middle of the wire. All the series was magnetized *plus* with the following intensities:

---

[6] Henry left a blank. This is probably a reference to the instrument described in the "Record of Experiments" entry of October 9, 1841, above.
[7] The so-called "living force" of a body in motion is its mass times the square of its velocity. W. H. C. Bartlett, *Elements of Natural Philosophy*, Section I: *Mechanics* (New York, 1850), p. 85.

Charge 275

1	2	3	4	5	6	7	8	9
14+	18+	22+	16+	15+	13½+	10½+	15½+	14+

It would appear from the last result that the needles in the last exp marked — was on the opposite side of the wire

Next tried large needles no 3

Charge 275

1	2	3	4	5	6	7	8	9
35+	27½+	30+	32½+	30+	40+	30+	29+	30+

The needles in the above experiments were placed at the distance of about 4 inches apart along the wire

Arranged 7 half needles no 9 along the wire very nearly in contact

1 Contact	2 not quite contact	3 cont.	4 not cont	6 cont	7 non con	8 non c
0	3+	2±	5+	2±	0	1—

Arranged fine needles each an inch from the other first in contact last 9 inches from the wire whole no 31 3/10 of an inch[8] common difference. The charge batteries and wire the same as in the last expermts

needles no 9.

No	1	2 inches	3	4	5	6	7	8	9	10
Dis	0	.3	.6	.9	1.2	1.5	1.8	2.1	2.4	2.7
defl	13+	31+	25+	26++	25+	20+	19	15	15	11

[8] In the left-hand margin Henry calculated the three-tenths of an inch variation in the distances of the needles from the wire. Henry's arithmetic is quite basic: nine divided by thirty equals three-tenths.

No	11	12	13	14	15	16	17	18	19
dist	3.0	3.3	3.6	3.9	4.2	4.5	4.8	5.1	5.4
defl	8+	7½+	4+	1½+	feeb+	feeb+	0		

The maximum magnetism is here found at 3 tenths of an inch, and the power extended to the distance of nearly 5 inches

Large needles no 3

No	1	2	3[9]	4	5	6	7	8	9	10	11	12
		inches										
Dis	¼	½	1	1¼	1½	1¾	2	2¼	2½	2¾	3	3¼
defl	42	41	38	36½	36¼	32½	29	27	20	16½	15[10] *	11

No	13	14	15	16	17	18	19
Dis	3½	3¾	4	4¼	4½	4¾	5
Defl	10	6	4	feeb	feeb	fee	0

Each needle one inch from the other along the line *a b*. The first needle was not quite in contact the maxim[um] is at ¼ of an inch. All the needles after the 15 and this also exhibited some effects like that of conceccutive points

I find on subsequent examination that the action mentioned here is due to the [?soft] eye of the needle and the induction of the needle of the index. The magnet[ism] how[ev]er appears to stop at about the same distance in both cases *ie* with find and coarse needles

[9] Henry did not take a measurement at three-quarters of an inch.

[10] The meaning of the asterisk is unclear.

June 3, 1842

"RECORD OF EXPERIMENTS"
Henry Papers, Smithsonian Archives

June 3^d 1842

The copper plated wire used was 1/11oth of an inch.

no	1	2	3	4	5	6	7	8	9
				tenths of inches					
dist	0	.2¼	.5¼	.8	1.0¾	1.3¾	1.6½	1.9¼	2.2
Defl	16½+	34	36 +	32	29	24½	23	21	17½

no	10	11	12	13	14		15	16
Dist	2.4¾	2.7¼	3.0¼	3.3¼	3.5¾+			
def	18+	17½	9+	feeb +	very feeble +			

The above table gives the result with a series of fine (9) needles arranged on a lath. The maximum is here at the 3rd needle and the magnetic effect does not extend up as high as in the other cases with the fine wire. This was rather an unsatisfactory exp

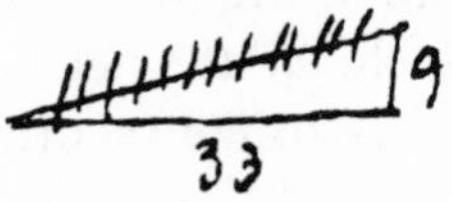

Repeated the same exp smal needles no 9

no	1	2	3	4	5	6	7	8	9
dis	0	¼ inch	½	1	1¼	1½	1¾	2	2¼
def	16½+	37½+	37+	34+	32+	30+	26+	24+	21+

June 3, 1842

The needles were placed along the lath
copper plated wire 1/110[1]

10	11	12	13	14	15	16	17	18
2½	2¾	3	3¼	3½	3¾	4	4¼	4½
17+	15+	12+	10+	5+	2+	feeble +	do +	do +

Charge 275. Here the magnetism ends at 4½ inches. The maximum is at the 2nd needle. The magnetism stopped at precisely the same distance as it did in the exp which stands 1st on the last page[2]

Shortened the fine wire to 3 feet also used needles 15 mill. long wire 1/110th of an inch.

no	1	2	3	4	5	6	7	8	9	10
			tenths							
dis	0	.1	.2	.3	.4	.5	.6	.7	.8	.9
defl	7	26	30	32	31	29½	20	18	21	25

The needles in the last experiment were of the same length as those used by Savary but the thickness was just double that of those used by the same
Repeated the expermt with the needles transverse to the wire but projecting more and more over

 Wire the same 1/110 of an inch 3 feet long

Large needles no 3

no	1	2	3	4	5	6	7	8	9
		all in contact							
defl	22+	38+	50+	48+	32+	29+	30+	12+	feeble +

---

[1] This phrase has been moved from the left-hand margin.

[2] A reference to the next to last experiment of June 2, 1842, above.

In this exp there are no changes in the direction of the magnetism. The ninth needle was scarcely at all magnetized at the larger end which projected over the wire but was strongly at the south end

Repeated same experiment with the small needles no 9

no	1	2	3	4	5	6	7	8	9	10
				No change of sign						
Def	15+	8+	18+	22+	18+	22+	18+	9+	4+	3+

Charge not quite as great as before

no	1	2	3	4	5	6	7	8	9	10	11
		all in contact									
defl	19+	26+	38+	32+	23+		32+	28+	22+	9+	0

Repeated the same exp same charge same arrangement needles fine No 9 and softened in the lamp. No change of sign

"RECORD OF EXPERIMENTS"
Henry Papers, Smithsonian Archives

June 6th (monday) 1842
attempt to get statical
induction through the floor

I have been prevented from repeating the experiments of M Savery in the manner described by him in the Annel de chimie on account of the want of platinum wire of the proper thickness.[1]

Made arrangements to determ at what distance I could get inductive effects by ordinary statical induction. Used for this purpose Dr Hares single

[1] Savary used a wire one-quarter of a milli-meter in diameter. "Mémoire sur l'aimanta-tion," *Annales de chimie et de physique*, 1827, 2d ser. *34*:11. Henry would shortly obtain wire of approximately the proper diameter. See below, Joseph Saxton to Henry, June 9, 1842.

leaf electrometer.[2] The one which he presented me with. Suspended the plate for dancing images from a cross piece of wood by a silk ribbon placed the electrometer under this. Found that the influence was perceptible at the distance of 10 feet horizontally and quite strong at the distance of five feet perpendicularly. I next carried the electrometer into the room below to determine the fact if the induction could be felt through the floor but I was unable to get any positive result although the electrometer was armed with a spirit lamp which very much increased its sensibility

The day was not perhaps very good although the machine gave a long spark but as far as this experiment can be depended on it shows that ordinary induction is by no means as energetic as the current or dynamic induction[3]

Savary states that he found by filings sprinkled over the needles that they had no conseccutive points.[4] I tried this expermnt with some of the fine needles I had previously magnetized by contact but I was unable to determine the polarity by this means even by the aid of the microscope. I begin to doubt the accuracy of Savarys results

In the arrangement shown in the figure above I placed at a a spiral and then drew sparks from the machine found the needle magnetic in a direction indicating a current towards the machine

Next removed the plate *a* and insulated the wire[5] of the spiral still the needle was magnetized in the same direction but not as strongly. Next put a piece of tin foil in contact with the end of the wire so as to increase the surface on the other side of the needle now the magnetism was considerly stronger than in the last experiment.

Made the arrangement shown in the figure—placed needle in the spiral at a found it indicated a current in the direction towards the jar.

[2] Described in Robert Hare, *A Brief Exposition of the Science of Mechanical Electricity, or Electricity Proper* . . . (Philadelphia, 1840), pp. 31–32.

[3] This failure is in contrast with his previous success in inducing static electricity over considerable distances and his ultimate conclusion. For example, see above, "Record of Experiments," May 18, 1842, and "Contributions V: Induction from Ordinary Electricity; Oscillatory Discharge," p. 195.

[4] "Mémoire sur l'aimantation," p. 14. For Henry's earlier experiments on consecutive points see above, "Record of Experiments," June 2, 1842.

[5] The remainder of this paragraph and the subsequent five paragraphs are under the running head "Latteral discharge."

Next repeated same experiment with a set of spirals (see page 238).[6] All gave current in the same direction as the last but I took a spark from the prime conductor accidentally which perhaps interfered with the result for when the experiment was again tried with a heavy charge all the needles were reversed except the last which gave [?same]. In this experiment a spark was seen at *c*

Next repeated the experiment <*by*> seperated conductor from jar so that no spark was perceived at c still the magnetism as the last *adverse*. The needle in no 4 was again not magnetic

Next Repeated the experiment with the difference of making the con-

ductor a part of the circuit. The spirals in this and the last two experiments were attached to the suspended insulated metal plate. The result was now different from the last the needle in spiral no 1 was magnetized strongly indicating a current towards the jar also that in no 2 the same while those in nos 3 & 4 were oppositely magnetized. This effect would indicate what I suspected the action of two currents and it would also appear that the current <*towards*> from the jar was the more intense of the two because it prevails in the <*current*> single spirals[7]

Tried the spirals by a spark from the machine found all the needles magnetized in the *plus* direction. Sent a heavy shock from the single jar through spirals found all the needles powerfully magnetic *plus*.[8]

Repeated the last exp sent shock through all the spirals same result

Next united the two sets of spirals together so that they formed 8 consecutive spirals

needles no 5

	1st set				2nd set				
one jar No 1	2	3	4		1	2	3	4	statical
defl 41½+	42+	35+	29+		41+	41¼+	33½+	30½+	deflection

[6] This is a reference to the spirals illustrated in the "Record of Experiments" entry of May 9, 1842, above.

[7] Henry later added a notation in the left-hand margin to "vol 3 p 59," a reference to the second paragraph of the "Record of Experi-

ments" entry of October 9, 1843, printed below.

[8] The remainder of the entry has been placed under the running head "Investigations relative to the spiral."

In both sets of spirals in this experiment the 2nd spiral gives the stronger magnetism. This probably owing to the imperfect insulation which suffers more electricity to pass between the spires of the compound than the more simple spiral

	1st set		needles No 5		2nd set			
No. 1	2	3	4	1	2	3	4	Statical
Dif. 35½°+	37½°+	28°+	27°+	32½°+	38°+	29½°+	27°+	Deflection

In the above experiment the discharge was somewhat less than the last. The first and second as a mean will give about the same
Repeated the same exp with much stronger charge.

	1st set		needles 5		2nd set			
No 1	2	3	4	1	2	3	4	statical
Defl 38°+	38¼°+	30°+	30°+	38°+	38¼°+	29½°+	31°+	def

This result is of the character as the previous

	1st set		needles No 5		2nd set			
no 1	2	3	4	1	2	3	4
Deflec 38°+	38°+	35°+	31½°+	36½°+	38½°+	33½°+	31½°+

This result was obtained by two jars
NB The above experms must be repeated with needles of different sizes in the two sets of spirals.[9]

[9] Which Henry proceeded to do. See the next "Record of Experiments" entry, printed below.

"RECORD OF EXPERIMENTS"
Henry Papers, Smithsonian Archives

June 7th 1842
Spiral continued

To test by direct experiment the hypothesis I have formed I passed through the two sets of spirals a spark from the machine and then a smaller one in the opposite direction.

The result was as follows[1]

needle in spiral $<No\ 1 + No\ 2 + No\ 3 - o\ No\ 4>$
1st set no 1 — no 2 — no 3 — no 4 +
2nd set no 1 — no 2 — no 3 — No 4 +

This is a beautiful confirmation of the theory.

Next sent a very small charge from two jars through both sets of spirals. The following was the result

	1st set			2nd set			
no. 1	2	3	4	1	2	3	4
defl 28½+	28+	22½+	20+	30	27	23	20

Sent a very small charge from one jar through both sets of spirals.

	1st set			2nd set			
No 1	2	3	4	1	2	3	4
Defl 28°+	25°+	20°+	17½°+	28°+	25°+	20°+	18°+

Next sent single spark from prime conductor through both sets of spirals. The following is the results

	1st set			2nd set			
No 1	2	3	4	1	2	3	4
Defl 13°+	12°+	feeble+	o	12½°	11°	feeble +	o

---

[1] In the right-hand margin Henry indicated that the first eight sets of experiments were made "all by statical defl and needles No 5."

In this case the magnetism of the needles in spirals no 3 and 4 was so feeble that the softness so to speak which I have found at the end of the needle was attracted by the index needle

In all these results it appears that with a heavy charge the magnetism developed in spiral no 2 is greater than that in no 1 and the contrary when the charge is small.[2] This I think is due to the striking across of the discharge from spire to spire the tendancy being of course greater in the more compound spiral.[3]

Next made a new spiral of three strata put in the circuit with spiral no one of one of the sets passed shock of intensity through both from two jars.[4] The new spiral was insulated between the layers by gold-beaters skin still I perceived at each discharge a flash between the ends of the different strata and this appeared to neutralize a considerable part of the magnetic power

new spiral 23°   again   new spir   24½
spiral No 1 35   spiral no 1   36

In the last experiment the spark appeared at the lower extremity of the spiral and in the fi[r]st at the upper. No spark was seen between the spires of the old spiral and it is probable that it passed along from spire to spire through out the two surfaces of spires which were in contact.

Next used a spiral the several spires of which were insulated by coating of cement but a spark appeard between the ends of the layers in this as in the last, and the result was the same.

Sent a smaller spark from 2 jars through the two coils of the above experiment. The result was about the same

Large coil 27   Smaller 32

It is not improbable that the larger coil was injured by the discharge from the two jars of the previous experiments

Passed a small spark from the Prime conductor through the <*machine*> two spirals. The one consisted of 6 spirals with 45 spires in each, the other— 3 strata of spirals

Larger spiral gave deflec 16½
Smaller do   "   "   13

---

[2] The left-hand margin contained a summary of experimental results:

Mean of 2	38⅓
Do of 1	36
Mean of 1s	23⅓
" of 2d	21⅓

The first two means are those of the experiments conducted on June 6, 1842. In the manuscript "Record of Experiments" these experiments are on the page opposite the marginalia. The final two means are those of the second, third, and fourth sets of experiments of June 7.

[3] This conclusion was questioned before the end of the day's experimenting. Two days later, after further probing of the problem, Henry added a parenthetical remark: "another reason reflex wave June 9th 1842."

[4] Henry wrote in the left-hand margin: "N.B. all the experiments on this page were made with needles of no 5."

From this it appears that when there is no cutting across from spire to spire the greater the number of spires the greater is the magnetic development.[5]

Commenced a series of experiments similar to those given in the last three pages[6] with small needles no 12

	1st Set				2nd set			
No	1	2	3	4	1	2	3	4
Def.	15½+	14½+	12+	7¾+	15½+	13¾+	12¼+	6+

The current here was a very small spark the prime conductor

Small charge from two jars

1	2	3	4	1	2	3	4
10	13½	15	15½	9½	14	15	15½

Little larger charge from 2 jars

1st Set				2nd Set			
1	2	3	4	1	2	3	4
6¼	5½	16°	17	21¼	2	15	17½

needles no 9

Litt[le] larger charge from 2 jars   quantity not great

	1st Set				2nd Set			
No	1	2	3	4	1	2	3	4
* Defl	15½+	26½+	10—	13+	26+	26+	10—	7½

needles no 9

[5] At this point Henry began a new page which he ultimately headed: "Investigations of the spiral continued *needles magnetized minus.*" This heading, no doubt, was to alert Henry that buried among the experimental results recorded on this page was the last set of experiments, marked by an asterisk, in which the polarity of the needles was reversed.

[6] i.e., the last four sets of experiments recorded in the "Record of Experiments" entry of June 6, 1842, and the experiments of June 7.

The result of last experiment completely over throws my supposition that the change of direction is accidental. It can scarcely be possible that the needles in the two spirals 3 & 3 should both accidentally and by cutting across of the electricity magnetize just these two minus while all the others are *plus*. This is the first unequ[i]vocal example I have yet found of the change of sign with a direct current <*as in the case of electricity*>.

I must follow out this result with great care.

I thought that perhaps the last effect might have been produced by a spark passing to my fingers but on repeating the experiment with precaution in this respect I found the same result.[7]

After reflection on the cause of this phenomenon I am disposed to atribute it to a series of inductions backwards and forward in the primary conductor[8]

[7] At this point Henry later added a reference to the top of the next page, an allusion to the experiments conducted on June 8, 1842.

[8] On June 8 and June 9, 1842, Henry continued his investigation, varying the charge and the size of the needles ("Record of Experiments," Henry Papers, Smithsonian Archives; because these entries consist almost exclusively of tables of data, we have not published them). His results confirmed this conclusion about the oscillatory nature of the electric discharge. They also demonstrated the dependency of the results upon the size of the needle. He was unable to get a change in the direction of the magnetism when using the larger needles (no. 5), but could when using smaller ones (no. 12). These results became the basis for "Contributions V: Induction from Ordinary Electricity; Oscillatory Discharge."

TO THE LECTURE COMMITTEE, MERCANTILE LIBRARY COMPANY OF PHILADELPHIA

Draft, Henry Papers, Smithsonian Archives

Princeton June 7th 1842

Gentlemen

Your letter[1] inviting me to lecture before the Mercantile Library Company of Philadelphia was received some time since and I regret that engagements which have occupied all my thoughts for <*two*> the last two weeks <*past*> have prevented my giving the subject a more early consideration.

I have <*made it a*> generally <*rule to*> declined all invitations to lecture to a popular audience but as this is the second time I have been honored with <*an invitation*> a request from your Institution I have concluded after some hesitation to accept the <*present one*> your invitation.

[1] Of May 21, 1842, printed above.

The subject which I have chosen for my lecture is the <*Progress and*> Methods and Progress of scientific discovery.[2]

I have the honor to be with much Respect
yours

J——

[2] For a statement of Henry's reluctance, see *Henry Papers*, 3:7. By this date he had had a considerable success with a series of popular lectures before the Mercantile Library Association of New York City (see *Henry Papers*, 4 for the numerous references to that experience).

According to later correspondence with Joseph Patterson (to Henry of August 4, October 14, and November 5, 1842, and from Henry of November 9, 1842, Henry Papers, Smithsonian Archives), Henry delivered his lecture on November 11. Although we cannot identify the text among the surviving fragments of writings in the Henry Papers of the Smithsonian Archives, the subject is a familiar one to Joseph Henry. We assume the views given were like those in *Henry Papers*, 1:380–397, and in Arthur P. Molella et al., eds., *A Scientist in American Life: Essays and Lectures of Joseph Henry* (Washington, 1980), pp. 35–50, 54–70, and 88–98.

TO [?JOHN TORREY][1]
Mary Henry Copy, Henry Papers, Smithsonian Archives

Princeton, June 9th. 1842

I am now much engaged in a series of experiments and have had a month of uninterrupted time to devote to the matter.

Dr. Carnahan says we will be obliged to wait awhile for our salary. The great depression of business, and the derangement of the currency at the South prevents prompt remittances from the parents of the students. And the bank in New York, in which the college funds are placed, has failed to pay its dividends this season.[2]

[1] The recipient is not given. But Henry often wrote of salary matters and experiments to Torrey, the part-time Professor of Chemistry and Natural History at the College of New Jersey.

[2] The depression was one of the most severe in the history of the country. Hugh McCulloch, head of the Second Bank of Indiana and later Secretary of the Treasury, described it in these words: "The depression which prevailed from 1837 to 1843 cannot be well understood by any who did not witness it. It was widespread and all-pervading. It affected all classes, but the greatest sufferers, next to the day laborers, were the farmers. Everything which the farmer had to sell had to be disposed of in barter or for currency at ruinous prices." (Quoted in Margaret G. Myers, *A Financial History of the United States* [New York, 1970], p. 99.) These difficulties for farmers were a fact of life for cotton growers in the South, where financial stability depended upon high cotton prices, which did not prevail. Specie was in short supply, and

after the disestablishment of the Second Bank of the United States under Jackson, there was no central financial institution to moderate financial development. Banks were free to issue their own currency notes, but these fluctuated wildly in value, for many banks were undercapitalized or overextended. The notes also depended for their value on sound state fiscal policy, which was lacking. The general depression was combined with a chaotic financial scene.

Princeton was as hard hit by these poor economic times as any other institution. The College was heavily dependent (90 percent) on student fees for operating income. As 45 percent of the students were from southern states in 1841–1842, financial irregularities there were a problem for the College. (See also Henry to Torrey, March 2, 1840, *Henry Papers, 4*:331–332.) Total enrollment was down that year as well. Moreover, such income as was derived from their endowment—shares in the Bank of New York—was used almost completely to pay interest on outstanding debts.

To compensate, the College was forced to liquidate the holdings in its separate scholarship fund and loan the money to its operating fund. In addition, Carnahan repeatedly took out short-term loans from the Bank of Princeton, in ever-increasing amounts from $3,000 to $5,000. Of course, in the short run the easiest thing to do was to suspend payment of salaries, which made up seven-eighths of the annual expenses of the College. In 1842, the Trustees tried to increase income by increasing tuition, imposing fees on students living off-campus, pressing students for overdue payments, and advertising the College more widely. Yet the financial report of March 1844 showed a continued drain of money from the institution.

Trustees' Minutes, September 1841 to June 1844, Princeton University Archives; *Wertenbaker*, p. 250; Margaret G. Myers, *A Financial History of the United States* (New York, 1970), especially pp. 92–147; *Princeton Annual Catalogues*, 1841–1842; *Henry Papers*, 2:xvii–xviii.

FROM JOSEPH SAXTON[1]
Henry Papers, Smithsonian Archives

Philadelphia 9[th] June 1842.

Dear Sir

Enclosed you will find two piece of wire drawn to the 100[th] of an inch diameter,[2] but not quite so long as you wished—my wire plates not being sufficient[l]y good to draw a piece longer without braking. If they do not answer, let me know and I will try and get somthing better.

I am sorry that there has been so much delay about it but I could not get a piece that would draw till this morning.

Yours Truly
J. Saxton

[1] The Philadelphia inventor, at this time the Curator of Measuring and Weighing Apparatus at the United States Mint. *Henry Papers*, 2:159–160.

[2] Henry's file note reads "Joseph Saxton enclosing platinum wire for my exp." Henry needed this wire to repeat experiments conducted earlier by Savary. See above, "Record of Experiments," June 6, 1842.

"RECORD OF EXPERIMENTS"
Henry Papers, Smithsonian Archives

June 10th 1842

First[1] Induction from a thunder cloud[2]

Agreeably to the suggestion given at the bottom of page 263[3] I connected 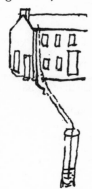 by soldering a copper wire (bell size) to the tin roof of our house and passed the lower extremity into the water of the well. This was effected by fastning a cylender of lead to the end of the wire and passing this through a hole in the cover near the pump of the well. The wire was then divided near the window of the study and a compound spiral inserted. This was formed of 6 strata of wire each consisting of 40 spires and insulated by cement.[4]

After this arrangement was completed (on monday last)[5] I waited with some anxiety for the appearance of a thunder cloud but none appeared until last evening when I observed before going to bed a few very distant and faint flashes of light but too distant to produce any effect: they must have been from a cloud at the distance of 100 miles. I placed a needle no 5 in the spiral and then went to bed. At a little before three o'clock I was awakened by a storm of rain and heard several distant discharges of lightning. I did not rise but in the morning I found the needle strongly magnetic in the direction which indicated a current upwards. This result is precisely in accordance with my anticipations and perfectly analogous to the experiment described page 263.[6]

The deflection of the needle magnetized by the flash was 23½° minus.[7]

Commenced a series of experiments with needles nº 5 and a fine wire spiral (plated) containing about 200 spires. I commenced with 5 spark and increased the charge to 30 when I obtained a *minus* polarity strongly de-

---

[1] This word appears to be a later addition to the heading, probably to distinguish this experiment from that of June 13, below.

[2] On the opposite page is the running head: "experiments with the spiral." This refers to the experiments described in the final paragraph of the entry.

[3] See above, "Record of Experiments," May 28, 1842, fourth paragraph.

[4] An illustrated description of Henry's apparatus for this experiment is contained in his article "Meteorology in Its Connection with Agriculture, Part V: Atmospheric Electricity," *Report of the Commissioner of Patents, 1859:*

Agriculture (Washington, 1860), pp. 477–478.

[5] June 6.

[6] Henry is referring to the experiments described in the second and third paragraphs of the "Record of Experiments" entry of May 28, 1842, above.

[7] Henry reported his success in detecting induced currents from atmospheric electricity in the last paragraph of "Contributions V: Induction from Ordinary Electricity; Oscillatory Discharge." He later drew upon this work when called upon in 1846 to consider the effect of lightning on telegraph lines. APS *Proceedings, 1843–1847, 4:*265.

veloped. I however could get this but once although I experimented several times with the same charge. The weather however is so unfavourable for experiments of this kind that the battery will not hold its charge and therefore there is some uncertainty relative to the exact quantity of electricity which produced the above result

TO W. A. SMITH[1]
Joseph Francis Papers, Division of Naval History,
National Museum of American History, Smithsonian Institution

Princeton June 10th 1842

My Dear Sir

I am just now in the midst of a new series of electrical researches and find myself much in want of a small quantity of copper bell wire. I am therefore obliged to apply to you and ask that you will forward me by the rail way as soon as convenient about 10 or 12 lbs of the article. Please put the bill in the package and I will send the money immediately or pay it to your Brother.[2]

Come on to Princeton & I will show you my new results. In haste yours

Truly

Joseph Henry

I have made magnets by a flash of Lightning from a cloud at the distance of several miles.

J H

[1] William Asa Smith (1820–1894), an 1838 graduate of Princeton, was in the dry goods business with his father in New York City. *Princeton Catalogue*, p. 155. William Edward Schenck, *Biography of the Class of 1838 of the College of New Jersey* (Philadelphia, 1889), pp. 140–142.

[2] Edward B. Smith, a sophomore at Princeton. Schenck, *Biography*, p. 141.

"RECORD OF EXPERIMENTS"
Henry Papers, Smithsonian Archives

June 11th (Saturday) [1842]

Repeated the experiments on the magnetization with the fine wire spiral. Commenced at 30 and went up to 150 the full jar of the jar. The weather is very fine to day for electrical experments and the battery holds the charge well. In the whole series of the experiments I have not obtained a single *negative* result.

Repeated the expermet with the lower charges and also took the lower series found a change at 29 & 30 the same as in the first exp on this page.[1]

The following is the series of deflections obtained

2	4	6	8	10	12	15	20	25	19[2]	30	35	40
27	26	25½	33	25	26	24	27			—25	16	31

45	50	55	60	65	70	75	80			90	100
35	18°	24°	29	27	34	23°	23½°			30½	19½

My experiments are interrupted on account of the illness of the colored servant of the Laboratory *Sam* Parker

---

[1] The last paragraph of the "Record of Experiments" entry of June 10, 1842, above.

[2] We presume Henry meant to write "29," reflecting the shift in direction he noted in the preceding paragraph.

FROM ALEXANDER DALLAS BACHE AND WILLIAM H. C. BARTLETT[1]

*General Manuscripts, Rare Book Collection,
University of Pennsylvania Library*

West Point. June 11, 1842.

Dear Henry,

Do come to West Point, and stay a few days with Bartlett & me & the apparatus. It will be so interesting to form a trio in the Philos. Academy & see the new polariscope & all such matters: then as you have been experimenting lately in that line[2] your knowledge will all come into play. Do come. Mrs. Ency Bache comes on on Monday, join her in the cars & add to the pleasure of her visit that of your company. I was much amused by her proposing that you should come to Philad. to put her in the W. Pt. boat at New York. My brother Geo.[3] is to meet her but I am sure she will be glad to *bring you* along. With best regards to Mrs Henry.

Yours very truly A. D. Bache.

---

[1] Bartlett added his note directly beneath Bache's.

[2] The only recent experiments Henry had conducted involving polarization were the Experiments in Optics of May 1841, and the entry in the "Record of Experiments" for November 1, 1841 (both above). He had done work on polarization in the late summer of 1839. See *Henry Papers*, 4:253–255.

[3] George M. Bache (1811–1846). A. D. Bache's younger brother received his education in Philadelphia prior to joining the U.S. Navy.

June 13, 1842

My dear Sir

I take it for granted that you will not be able to withstand the temptations presented to you in the note of our good friend above, & I shall therefore have a bed & plate in readiness for you at my house, where Mrs: B & myself shall expect you. I have now got into my new room,[4] & have much to interest us, & perhaps the opportunity of having Bache & yourself here together may not in a long time again occur. Now do lay aside whatever you may be engaged in & give a few days to the gratification & benefit of your friends. If you acknowledged military authority I should put an order on you.[5] With kind rememberance to Mrs: Henry I remain

Most sincerely yours
Wm H. C. Bartlett

Attached to the Coast Survey, Bache participated in surveying the shoreline of much of the Mid-Atlantic region. By 1846, Bache was a lieutenant, commanding the brig *Washington*, assigned to survey the Gulf Stream. He was washed overboard and drowned during a storm off Virginia. *Niles National Register*, October 10, 1846; James Dallas, *The History of the Family of Dallas* (Edinburgh, 1921), pp. 513–514.
[4] Bartlett returned from a tour of European observatories late in 1840, having purchased various optical and astronomical instruments.

He then supervised the construction of a new observatory and library at West Point, with four towers designed specifically to house the astronomical apparatus. Jacob W. Bailey to John Torrey, February 27, 1841, Torrey Papers, Library, New York Botanical Garden; William H. C. Bartlett, "On the Instruments of the Astronomical Observatory of the United States Military Academy, West Point," *Transactions of the American Philosophical Society*, 1846, n.s. 9:191–203.
[5] Henry was unable to leave Princeton. See below, Henry to Bache, June 24, 1842.

"RECORD OF EXPERIMENTS"
Henry Papers, Smithsonian Archives

June 13th
Monday 1842
Second
Induction from a thunder cloud[1]

A thunder storm occurred again to day at about 7 oclock P.M but as is usual in this village the lightning was at a distance. There were two reports; at the time of the first no needle happened to be in the spiral. Before the next one came the rain was falling in great quantity; but notwithstanding this the needle was magnetized by the second flash. The distance of the thunder must have been between 3 and four miles, as indicated by the interval be-

---

[1] The first was reported in the "Record of Experiments" entry of June 10, 1842, printed above. As in that entry, the ordinal appears to be a later addition.

tween the flash and the report. The inductive effect was the same in this case as in that of the morning of the 10th the needle was magnetized with the end in the spiral a south pole indicating a discharge upwards.

Since the arrangement of the wire and the spiral I have examined more attentively the insulation of the tin roof of the house and I am somewhat surprised that I have been able to get any results. I find that on the rear of the house is a gutter made by a ridge of tin along the lower edge of the roof and to this is soledered at the corners tin conductors, one of which passes along the side of the house to the front and then connects with the front gutter which is agan conected with an iron pipe which leads into a stone cistern, so that the roof is in connection with the earth and a large quantity of water through the medium of a tin gutter pipe.

The deflection of the needle was considerably less in this case, than in the last, it was about —18°.[2]

[2] This is an ambiguous reading. Henry might have written "—10."

"RECORD OF EXPERIMENTS"
Henry Papers, Smithsonian Archives

June 14th 1842 Tuesday.
Currents by induction from the machi[ne] return stroke and statical induction
Unfavourable weather
for electrical expermts

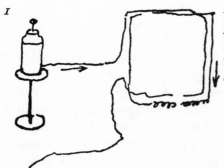

Attached a wire to the out side of a jar connected with the rectangle page [. . .].[1] Found an induced current which magnetized all the needles as if by a current in the *plus direction.*

[1] Henry neglected to record the page number. This is a reference to the second piece of apparatus pictured above in the "Record of Experiments" entry of May 28, 1842.

2 While the apparatus remained the same, the jar was fully charged and then discharged. The secondary current was now in the adverse direction the needles were magnetized *minus*.

3 Small no 10 needles were next used with the conditions the same as the first exp. the needles were all magnetized but the one in spiral no 1 of the second set of spirals this was magnetized *minus*. The same experiment was repeated with needles still smaller n° 12 and with the same result, the needle in spiral n° 1, 2ⁿᵈ set was again magnetized *minus*.

4 Next removed the jar received the sparks from the ball of the prime conductor immediately on the end of the primary wire the needles were all magnetized in the *plus* direction. When the frame of the rectangle was moved a little farther off, say to the distance of a foot, then with a medium spark the needle was magnetized *minus* when the spark was larger the needle was *plus*.

For corresponding exper. see page 249[2]

5 Repeated the experiment n° 1 while the frames were at the last distance. Now the current in the secondary circuit was such as to magnetize the needle *minus*.[3]

---

[2] A reference to the last experiment of May 12, 1842. See above.

[3] This is the last "Record of Experiments" entry prior to the presentation of "Contributions V: Induction from Ordinary Electricity; Oscillatory Discharge" to the June 17, 1842, meeting of the American Philosophical Society.

TO ALEXANDER DALLAS BACHE
Mary Henry Copy, Henry Papers, Smithsonian Archives

Princeton June 24ᵗʰ 1842

My dear Bache . . . . I was much disappointed in not meeting you in Phil. You were expected home on Saturday night but did not make your appearance. We passed each other on the railway a little after you left the Princeton point. I caught for an instant a glimpse of Mrs. Bache as the cars flew past but my eyes did not rest on your goodly person although I naturally concluded that you were not very far from your good wife.

I gave a verbal account of my last series of experiments to the Society on Friday night and presented my record of the same for reference to a committee of which you were chosen chairman.[1] I was obliged to bring my book home with me in order to make out an account of my verbal communication for the Bulletin[2] and unless you will come to Princeton and pay your long promised visit I shall be obliged to make another trip to your city. The book contains a record of all the experiments placed under their proper dates. I wish these inspected by the committee as my vouchers for the time these were submitted to the society.[3]

I sent you by Mrs. Bache, the first needle which I magnetized by an electric flash from the clouds.[4] When it was first taken from the spiral it was sufficiently strong to make a small needle such as is found in a watch-key turn entirely around by the single repulsion of a single approach. I also gave Mrs. Bache an ordinary unmagnetized needle for comparison with the other but in the confusion of the moment I neglected to give her a proper account of it. I have since had an opportunity of magnetizing two other needles in the same way, but we have not had as yet any thunder at Princeton nearer than three or four miles.

I regret that I could not have joined you at the Point. I know that I would have been delighted with the visit. . . . Mrs. Henry joins me in respects and love [to] Mrs. Bache and yourself.

Yours
Joseph Henry

[1] The other members of the committee were Robert M. Patterson and Isaiah Lukens. Manuscript Minutes, June 17, 1842, Archives, American Philosophical Society. Verification of Henry's presentation of the "Record of Experiments" to this committee appears just above the "Record of Experiments" entry of July 17, 1840, opposite the verification of June 19, 1840. For the background of Henry's policy of submitting the "Record of Experiments" to the American Philosophical Society, see *Henry Papers*, 2:217–218.

[2] i.e., the *Proceedings of the American Philosophical Society*, 1841–1843, 2:193–196. This was "Contributions V: Induction from Ordi-

nary Electricity; Oscillatory Discharge." A complete text was never published in the *Transactions*. Some years later Henry implied that the failure to publish in full was due to some incomplete aspects to his experiments. He never found the time to complete the work to his satisfaction. "On the Phenomena of the Leyden Jar," *Proceedings of the American Association for the Advancement of Science*, 1850, 4:377–378.

[3] We are uncertain whether Bache came to the "Record of Experiments" or the "Record of Experiments" came to Bache.

[4] See above, "Record of Experiments," June 10, 1842.

"RECORD OF EXPERIMENTS"

Henry Papers, Smithsonian Archives

June 26th [1842] Sunday
Electricity from a Thunder
shower

A thunder storm passed over Princeton at 4 o'clock this afternoon. The cloud was in our verticle at about 20 minutes past 4. It came from the west inclining to the north and passed off to the South East. As usual with thunder clouds when it passed over this village it was very high. The rain and wind were very violent and were accompanied by hail. The thunder was very low not loud but constant and accompanied [?but] by 5 or 6 perceptible flashes of lighting and these by counting the interval between the appearance of the light and the perception of the reports, were found to be at the distance of from 5 to 8 miles. These flashes were attended with thunder a little louder tha[n][1] that which was unaccompanied [by] visible lightning.

During the storm I made observation on the magnetization of the needles in the spiral before described (page 293).[2] The needles appeared to be little affected with the continued low thunder, of which no flash was perceptible, but at each distinct flash a needle was rendered magnetized <*with*> [the] flash of one of these was at the distance of 8 miles since 40 seconds elapsed before the report was heard. In another the sound was about 25 and another 30 seconds in reaching the ear.

Each needle was magnetized so as to indicate a current upwards. Before and immediatly after the storm, there was scarcely any wind and although the gust was very violent it appeared to advance comparitively speaking quite slowley. During the storm 5 needles were magnetized.[3]

---

[1] This and the subsequent insertion were necessitated by a hole in the paper.

[2] See above, "Record of Experiments," June 10, 1842.

[3] Across from this entry Henry had tipped in two newspaper clippings. The top article is a reprint of an account of a lightning strike which killed nine people. It originally appeared in the July 22, 1840, issue of the *Charleston Mercury*. The bottom article is a reprint from the *New York Journal of Commerce* reporting the impact of a June 19 lightning storm on an iron works in Trenton, New Jersey; the date of the original publication is unknown. In neither case have we identified the date or the newspaper from which the clippings were obtained.

FROM JAMES P. ESPY[1]

Henry Papers, Smithsonian Archives

Day	Hour	Barometer	Thermometer whole	Wet bulb scale	Dew point	Course of Wind	Force of Wind	Number of Clouds	Course of lower Clouds	Course of upper Clouds	Beginning of Rain	End of Rain	Quantity of Rain	Time of max of Barometer	Temp of Mean of Barometer	Rise and fall of Rivers	Rise and fall of Lakes	Observations
Mean at O'clock																		

Month   *and*   *Year.*

Washington City July 2ᵈ 1842.

Dear Sir,

It is my wish to have a great many simultaneous observations on the weather made over a wide extent of territory, and sent monthly to the Navy Department—care of Professor James P. Espy.

My chief object is to try, by collating these journals, to find out something more of the nature of storms, than is yet known. Will you, Sir, have the goodness to co-operate with me in this undertaking. If you will send me a copy of your journal kept either in your own way or according to the form given above, I will send to you the results of this investigation from time to time as I may find any thing worth communicating. This system, to be of much value, must be continued for several years. It is confidently expected that the interest in the subject will become more general; and the number of observers greatly increase, as soon as it is known, that their labors are not likely to be in vain, as thousands of insulated observations have heretofore been.

I request you also as soon as you have carefully read the contents of this "Circular" to send it to some one in your state or elsewhere, who will be likely to take an interest in the subject—and let him do the same, and thus very many will become acquainted with the plan in time to co-operate, at the very beginning. It is my intention also in a few months, to have a pam-

---

[1] This is a handwritten, lithographed circular sent under the frank of Henry White Beeson, Member of Congress from Fayette County, Pennsylvania. Only the last few lines (beginning with "I expect") are in Espy's hand and addressed to Henry personally.

phlet of more particular instructions printed, and sent to all who co-operate with me in this undertaking.[2]

I have also an Epitome of the "Philosophy of Storms," which shall be put to press as soon as a sufficient number of subscribers shall offer, to bear the expense of publication.

The work will contain about 300 pages, price $10 for 11 Copies.[3]

No other effort than this notice will be made to obtain subscribers. Until particular hours are fixed on hereafter let all choose the hours they please, three times a day at least when no storm is passing—but when a storm is passing much more frequently—particularly noting the time when the wind changes and the moment when the barometer is the lowest. The force of wind may be noted by the figures 1, 2, 3, 4, 5. 1 being a very gentle breeze— 2 a fresh breeze—3 a strong breeze 4 a very strong wind, and 5 a heavy gale.

To complete the knowledge of some storms which have already been investigated in part, journals are much desired—especially on the night of the 10th of Nov. 1835 on the northern shore of Lake Ontario, and on the 11th 12th 13th 14th & 15th of May 1833. in the same region, on the 16th 17th & 18th of March 1838 in Virginia and N. Car; on the evening and night of the 3d Sep. 1821 in the western part of Massachusetts and Connecticut; on the 15th & 16th Nov. 1839. in the Atlantic Ocean from 100 to 600 miles east of the U. States.

Information concerning this last storm and that of 1821 is particularly desired, and will be highly valuable, as will appear to any one who will read an account of them in Espy's Philosophy of Storms.[4]

Finally I am resolved to prosecute this subject to the full extent of my means (and my ventilator will probably furnish me the means[5])—whether

---

[2] This is the second of three circulars Espy sent out in 1842 in his effort to form the national network of weather observers he had been advocating for several years (see *Henry Papers*, 2:196n, 3:369n–370n, 535–536). By the end of August, Congress had authorized a position in the War Department, and Espy had received the appointment.

After his initial success in Congress in 1842, Espy received small appropriations (usually $2,000 a year in the Army and then Navy budget) for his salary and operating expenses. Although he cooperated with the more comprehensive system Henry set up at the Smithsonian in 1849, the separate appropriations continued until the late 1850s. Espy's national meteorological work, including his four reports to the government, is discussed in David M. Ludlum, *Early American Tornadoes, 1586–1870* (Boston, 1970), pp. 169–178. See also

Bruce Sinclair, "Gustavus A. Hyde, Professor Espy's Volunteers, and the Development of Systematic Weather Observations," *Bulletin of the American Meteorological Society*, 1965, *46*: 779–784.

[3] Espy's *Philosophy of Storms* (Boston, 1841), was closer to 600 pages; no such abridgement is listed in the *National Union Catalog*.

[4] Espy and Redfield had been arguing over the storms of September 1821 and December (not November) 1839 for some time. See *Philosophy of Storms*, pp. 183–187, 209–228, and 535–543.

[5] In 1833 Espy patented a "*Chimney cap* for increasing the draft in furnaces of steam-boats and locomotive engines." Franklin Institute *Journal*, 1833, n.s. *12*:402. In the 1840s he petitioned Congress several times to purchase rights to his "conical ventilator" for the purification of air in ships and public buildings.

Government aids me or not, provided I obtain a sufficient number of simultaneous observations to enable me to determine the Shape or Size of all storms, and the direction and velocity of their motion over the surface of the earth, and thus enable us to predict their approach, in time to answer the purposes of the Farmer, the Mariner and all Mankind.

Lend me your assistance, and much greater discoveries will be made than we can now anticipate.

Yours very respectfully
James P. Espy

P.S. If observations of temperature are taken constantly at the same hour throughout the year the mean temperature may be known as is shown by John S. McCord Esq. of Montreal.[6] For example 9 A. M will give a temperature one degree too low—and 10 A. M. 0.91° too high.

Moreover the mean temperature derived from each pair of hours such as 1 A. M and 1 P.M., 2 A. M and 2 P. M &c never differs from the true mean of the year as much as 9/10 of a degree.

You are particularly desired if you have not already done so, to send me a journal of the weather immediately for the first four days of Febr. and also for the 15,^th 16,^th 17,^th 18,^th 19,^th & 20th of Febr. 1842.

It is hoped that many of those who wish to co-operate in this undertaking will, if convenient, furnish themselves with a barometer, as from the fall of that instrument alone, the direction which storms take over the surface of the earth and their velocity may be ascertained. Let not those however who have no barometer be discouraged—their journal of the Winds and rains and snows will be of great importance. Those who have a barometer will of course note the attached thermometer.

I expect to succeed here in obtaining aid from Government to carry out my views. Will you please to have this "Circular" published in some paper, with such remarks as will be likely to induce many to send me journals as requested?[7]

With respects to Mrs Henry

I remain your *friend*
J. P. Espy

How did the wind blow at Princeton on last Friday evening &^c &^c?[8]

Although Congress at one point appropriated $250 to install the ventilator in the Senate chamber, it is not known how much income Espy received from his invention. Clark C. Spence, *The Rainmakers: American "Pluviculture" to World War II* (Lincoln, Nebraska, and London, 1980), p.144, and Ludlum, *Early American Tornadoes*, p. 170.

[6] For whom see above, Beck to Henry, October 4, 1841.

[7] Henry's copy of the circular is not marked in any way to indicate he complied.

[8] We have not found a reply. Espy asked again for this information and for Henry's assistance in a letter of August 20, 1842, printed below.

TO JAMES D. FORBES
Forbes Papers, Library, St. Andrews University, Scotland

Princeton College of New Jersey
July 2nd 1842

My Dear Sir

My young friend Mr Cuyler[1] starts for Scotland in a few days and I embrace the opportunity of sending to you a package containing all the numbers of the meteorological reports I could procure in Princeton.[2] They will complete your set with the exception of one number and that I will endeavour to get for you when I next visit Albany.

Your letter of Janr[y] was received nearly three months ago[3] and I would have answered it long before this time but that I wished to give you some definite information in reference to the prospect of being able to furnish you and your friends on the continent with complete sets of the Reports. Bache and myself had petitioned to have the back numbers reprinted[4] and I was wating to learn the result of our pitition but as I have heard nothing from Dr Beck on the subject I have concluded that the Legislature of the State of New York did not act on it at their last session. Although I do not despair of an appropriation of funds being granted for the printing yet on account of the great depression of the times and the debt of the state for

[1] Theodore Ledyard Cuyler (1822–1909) graduated from Princeton in 1841 and spent the following year traveling in the British Isles and France. He entered Princeton Theological Seminary in 1843. After graduating in 1846 he served in a series of churches, until 1860 when he became pastor of the Lafayette Avenue Presbyterian Church of Brooklyn, New York. During a ministry of thirty years, Cuyler built the church into one of the largest Presbyterian congregations in the United States, published extensively, took an active role in the temperance movement and traveled widely. He then resigned to take a ministry-at-large. Theodore L. Cuyler, John T. Duffield, and Edward W. Scudder, comps., *Record of the Class of '41* (Princeton, 1891), pp. 19–20. *DAB*.

Cuyler reminisced about his trip in his *Recollections of a Long Life: An Autobiography* (New York, 1902). Although most of what Cuyler recalled had to do with literary and political figures, including meeting with Wordsworth, Dickens, and Carlyle, and seeing young Queen Victoria and Napoleon's tomb, he also included a vignette on Faraday: "When, soon after [I graduated from the Col-

lege, Henry] gave me a note of introduction to Sir Michael Faraday, Faraday said to me: 'By far the greatest man of science your country has produced since Benjamin Franklin is Professor Henry'" (p. 10). Cuyler also recounts that his friendship with Henry continued long after his accession to the Secretaryship of the Smithsonian, and Cuyler "found a home with him whenever I went to Washington" (ibid.).

[2] Bache had written over a year before requesting that Henry procure a complete set of the New York State meteorological reports for Forbes. (See above, Bache to Henry, April 21, 1841.)

[3] A letterpress copy of Forbes's letter to Henry of January 3, 1842, is in the Forbes Papers at St. Andrews. The original has not been found.

[4] The petition has not been found. The meteorological reports were not reprinted until 1855 when a compilation of the reports from 1826 to 1850 was authorized by the New York legislature. Franklin B. Hough, comp., *Results of a Series of Meteorological Observations* (Albany, 1855).

works of internal improvement I fear nothing will be done in the matter for a year or two to come.

I am much obliged to you for the copy of your last report on meteorology.[5] I have studied the article with much interest and profit. Permit me to assure you that I think your reports on this subject among the most important which have been presented to the British Association and that they have been of much service in improving this branch of science.

In the progress of my electrical research I have been brought to the subject of atmospheric electricity and I think I have hit on a method of observation relative to this branch of Meteorology which will prove of some importance.[6] I will send you a copy of my contributions N° 5 which contains an account of these results as soon as it is published.

I have ordered from Romkorff of Paris a set of apparatus for the repitition of the interesting results of Melloni and yourself and should I meet with many difficulties I may perhaps tax your kindness for some particular directions in reference to the manipulation. I have received assurance that the articles will be shipped on the 16th of this month. I have found however that there is but little confidence to be placed in the promise of a French workman.

> With much Respect
> I am Truly Yours &c
> Joseph Henry

P.S. Since writing this letter I have received a communication from Dr Beck[7] in which he states that he has good hopes of getting the appropriation for the reprinting of the Reports and expresses his regret that you have not received the reports since 1837 free of expense. He says that he has done better this year in sending a package by a passenger in one of the Packets.

> J. H.

[5] A presentation copy of Forbes's "Supplementary Report on Meteorology," reprinted in 1841 from the report of the British Association for 1840, is in the Henry Library.

[6] Henry is probably referring to his self-registering electrometer. See "Record of Experiments," May 28, 1842, above.

[7] T. R. Beck's letter has not been found.

NOTES ON LETTERS SENT WITH
THEODORE LEDYARD CUYLER

Henry Papers, Smithsonian Archives[1]

[July 2–6, 1842]

Letter to Sir John Robison[2]   By Cuyler   July 1842

1   Introduction of Mr Cuyler gentlem[an] of respect connections graduate of our colleg[e] &c

2   Agreeably surprised to find Sir Johns Father had rec^d degree from Princton[3]

3   Some account of the col[l]ege Dr Witherspoon[4]

4   He has recd my paper. Intend to send him 5th n^o of the same

5   Respects to Mother and Daughters

To J D. Roberton   Royal society[5]

1   Introduction of Cuyler

2   Obliged for copies of several papers

3   If any expense has been occurred call on O. Rich[6]

To Prof Stevelly[7]

1   Introduction of Cuyler

2   Can give an account of his own country

---

[1] These are précis of letters sent with Theodore Ledyard Cuyler (see above, Henry to Forbes, July 2, 1842, note 1). We are printing three of the letters from this list, Henry to Forbes, to Henslow, and to Gregory (see the letters of early July 1842 in this volume). One other letter of this type that we have found, to Quetelet (July 4, 1842, below), was not mentioned on this list. Henry's address book gives a further letter, to Thomas Murray, for which see his letter of November 18, 1842, below.

This manuscript is found in Box 17 of the Henry Papers, Smithsonian Archives. On the back of the last page, continued in the brown ink of the end of the previous page, are notes of letters of October 4, 1842, to John Stevens Henslow (for which see below under the date of October 3), and October 5, presumably to Thomas Exley (1775–1855, British mathematician, *DNB*; letter not found). These notes have not been printed.

[2] John Robison, Jr., General Secretary of the Royal Society of Edinburgh and founding member of the Royal Scottish Society of Arts. *Henry Papers*, 3:444.

[3] This phrase refers to John Robison, Sr. (1739–1805), a Professor of Natural Philosophy at Edinburgh University, and author of the well-known treatise, *A System of Mechanical Philosophy*, 4 vols. (Edinburgh, 1822), David Brewster's edition of Robison's articles from the *Encyclopaedia Britannica*. In 1790, Robison received an honorary degree of Doctor of Laws from Princeton. He was in fine company for this: he shared the symbolic dais with David Hume, the Marquis de Lafayette, and Jacques Necker, as well as James Kinsey, Chief Justice of the New Jersey Supreme Court. *Princeton Catalogue*, p. 402.

[4] John Witherspoon (*Henry Papers*, 2:80) was a "laureate" of the University of Edinburgh (1739), and President of Princeton, 1768–1794, when Robison received his degree.

[5] Assistant Secretary of the Royal Society, London. *Henry Papers*, 3:188–189.

[6] Obadiah Rich, an American bookseller residing in London, and Henry's agent there. *Henry Papers*, 3:266; 4:9–10.

[7] John Stevelly, Professor of Natural Philosophy at the Belfast Royal Academical Institution. *Henry Papers*, 4:104. Henry met Stevelly at the Liverpool meeting of the British Association in 1837, where Stevelly was Secretary of the Mathematics and Physical Science Section. As Henry's diary account for that portion of his trip is lost, we have few impressions of Henry's reaction to the man.

3   Always recollect our meeting in Liverpoo[l]. Sorry could not accept his invitation to visit Irelan[d]

4   Will send the 5th no of my researches as soon as it is printed

To Prof Lloyd[8]

1   Introduction Cuyler

2   Will give me much pleasure to reciprocate favor in referen[ce] to friend of his who may visit USA

3   Obliged for several copies of <*books*> papers

4   Bache and myself 40 miles apart b[y] railway. I frequent visit Phil. Hope soon to able to send you copy of <*4*>5th no.

5   Last researches have lead me to atmosph. elct. While almos[t] writing this letter to magnet[i]ze needles at the distance of 6 or 7 miles[9]

To Baden Powell[10] oxford

1   Introduction of Cuyler

2   Sending small package hope not entirely without interest[11]

3   Subject of oxford tracts interest of in america. Your opins known in this country as will be found by the package. Notic[e] of pamphlet in Princeton Review.[12]

---

[8] Humphrey Lloyd of Trinity College, Dublin. *Henry Papers*, 3:329.

[9] Compare Henry's note in the "Record of Experiments," September 2, 1841, and his experiments with magnetizing needles during electrical storms, June 10, 13, and 26, 1842, above.

[10] Baden Powell, Savilian Professor of Geometry at Oxford. *Henry Papers*, 3:238.

[11] Henry's address book often noted the contents of packages sent abroad. He indicated that he sent to Powell, through Cuyler, copies of "Contributions III" and "Contributions IV: Electro-Dynamic Induction"; the *Regents' Report* (presumably of the State of New York) for 1842; a copy of the review in the *Biblical Repertory and Princeton Review* of Powell's *Tradition Unveiled*; and *An Examination of the Essays Bacchus and Anti-Bacchus* (Princeton, 1841), by John Maclean. This 140-page book, a copy of which is in the Henry Library, was a discussion of two English temperance books, *Bacchus*, by Ralph Barnes Grindrod, and *Anti-Bacchus*, by B. Parsons. Maclean was incensed by the claim that no fermented wines or intoxicating drinks were used either by the Jews at Passover (both past and present) or by Jesus in his ministry, and by the authors' use of this claim to support abstinence on scriptural grounds. He proved, in great detail, citing both scripture and the church fathers, that "in the institution of the Eucharist, the Savior used the fermented juice of the grape" (p. 118), and that "the scriptures do not condemn the moderate and temperate use of wine and other drinks" (p. 125). But with a nod toward the temperance movement, he also said that voluntary abstinence was acceptable, and at certain times the proper thing to do.

Henry evidently thought highly of this book, sending copies to no less than three of his correspondents whom Cuyler was to meet: Henslow, Powell, and Murray.

[12] The review in the July number of the *Biblical Repertory and Princeton Review* (1842, 2d ser. *14*:598–630) of Powell's *Tradition Unveiled: or, An Exposition of the Pretensions and Tendency of Authoritative Teaching in the Church* (Philadelphia, 1841), an American reprint of a London publication addressing the Tractarian controversy. The Oxford "Tracts for the Times" were written between 1833 and 1841 by Anglican clergymen under the leadership of Edward Pusey, John Keble, and John Henry Newman. They attacked the prevailing Protestant notion of the sufficiency of the Bible as a basis for the Christian religion. As the review article stated: "The turning point in these controversies is the Rule of Faith. Are the Scriptures of the Old and New Testaments the only infallible rule of faith and practice? If so, Romanism and Puseyism, are confessedly without any ade-

4 Bache has presented me with a copy of connect[io]n of <*Phis*> natural and divin[e] truth. Pleased with particularly the part on induction. Only correct account of the actual process I have ever seen[13]

---

quate foundation" (p. 599). The Tractarians maintained that scripture and tradition—by which they meant the practices of the church handed down from generation to generation—properly constituted religious worship and guaranteed religious truth. The position was very close to that maintained by the Church of Rome, and in 1845 the Tractarians' most famous controversialist, John Henry Newman, converted to Roman Catholicism, on the strength of his conviction that the English Reformation had broken the necessary ties of traditional continuity. The Presbyterian reviewer, of course, would have none of this position: "It is virtually admitted by traditionalists that their system cannot be found in scripture, nor in the first three centuries of the church. We believe, say they, what the fifth century believed and because the church of that age believed. The reason for this is obvious. Priestly power was not fully established before the fifth century. . . . Where the Spirit of the Lord is there is Liberty. The men who read the Bible and hear there the voice of God, cannot but be free" (p. 629).

The distinction between Powell's tract and its review could not be more marked. In place of the polemic of the review, Powell provided closely-reasoned argument. He allowed that there could be but two types of churches: those which accepted private judgment in matters of interpretation, and those which were authoritative, persecutive, and ostensibly infallible. The former based themselves on reason, the latter on mystery. His objection to the latter type, that of the Tractarians and the Catholics, was that they stripped away solid rational reasons for faith. Thus they must be seen to equate the doctrines and miracles of the Church with the rules or stories of a merely human system or mythology, according to the judgment of any rational, thinking person. The rise of ceremony and rite, which the Tractarians championed, did not bother him, for these had their utility if properly conceived. His opposition came rather to the Tractarians' denial of the rights and responsibilities of private judgment of scripture in the determination of religious truth.

[13] Henry's annotated copy of Baden Powell's *The Connexion of Natural and Divine Truth; or, The Study of the Inductive Philosophy Considered as Subservient to Theology* (Lon-don, 1838) still exists in the Henry Library.

Powell was a religious latitudinarian, and wrote the book as a response to the high church Oxford Movement. Powell's work has four sections: induction, causality, natural theology, and revelation, presented as leading from one to the other. His exposition was a forceful restatement of the argument for natural theology: study of the natural world leading to the demonstration of a wise and good Creator. Natural theology's conclusions were "limited in extent and demonstrative in proof" (p. 273). They did not supplant revelation, which was a unique dispensation whereby God made His nature known to man, but they were independent means by which man, through his reason, could know God and His attributes. Powell called upon the Protestant tradition of the revelation in two books, the Bible and the Book of Nature. His work attempted to clear a rational path between the growing evangelical movement, with its desire for strict accommodation of physical events and laws with Biblical interpretation, and the Tractarians, with their emphasis on the body of the church and the teaching authority of her elders as the only legitimate interpreters of the truths of religion. Powell maintained that the inquiries of physical science, properly understood, could have a bearing on these truths as well.

Powell's section on induction clearly interested Henry, who had no patience with simple-minded schemes where facts magically coalesced under the weight of intense comparison to form general laws of nature (*Henry Papers*, 3:473–475). Citing Herschel's *Preliminary Discourse on the Study of Natural Philosophy*, Powell affirmed that a mechanical comparison of a large number of cases was not how science proceeds. "This certainly would imply no exercise of reasoning, and would hardly be worthy the name of induction" (p. 15). He looked to the natural tendency of the mind to generalize and to the implicit belief in the uniformity of nature to provide the basic material out of which one could construct an inductive philosophy. These both acted in the historical framework of previous work: "We shall find that the models by which we must be guided, are to be found in the careful and extended study of already established natural relations" (p. 21). Analogies between different physical phenomena provided the clues by

5 Highly gratif[i]ed with visit to England. Regret not having seen more of you and others in whom I am interested

Henslow[14]

1 Introduct of C 2 Much obliged for papers on diseas[e] of wheat &c sent to Publishers for repr[int]ing

2 An apology for long silence. Guilty of procrastina[tio]n with tolerably good intentions. Delayed with hope of being able to send promised specim[en]s. Cannot procur snakes nor allig. die on the way to Eng. 3 Send allegator eggs Horned frog of Texas remaining no of the Flora

4 Dr Torrey moved to Princeton an accession to [?circle]. Mr. Jager resi[g]ned gone to Washington dut[i]es by Dr Torrey

5 You are not much interested in elect but I send 4 numbers of contr hope soon to for[d] 5 no 6[15] Difficulty of getting works noticed in general. I have little to complain of since return from Eng. 6 Subject of copy right

6 Dr Lardner thanks for alter[ing] his account. His progress in America. Lectures in theaters. Object of pity rather than resentment. Wants essential ingr[e]d[ie]nt of phil character honesty

M De La Rive[16]

1 Introduction of Cuyler regards to Madam

which previous work was extended to new areas, arguing against any "other authority than simply that of natural analogies" (p. 65). On this basis, he rejected Cartesian vortices, phlogiston, and the Neptunist hypothesis as the products of deluded minds. "If we confine ourselves to arguing from the known to the unknown by rational induction; and pursue only the real analogies which are everywhere traceable in the operations of nature," we find that "the results of science . . . are yet not only rational and logical, but absolutely unavoidable and undeniable" (p. 70).

Henry relied heavily on Baden Powell's book for his introductory lecture in natural philosophy, which was traditionally devoted to scientific method. Henry paraphrased large sections of the book—with attribution—in his discussion of induction and the nature of causality. Though his comments show a clear appreciation of the Scottish Common Sense philosophers, such as Thomas Reid and Dugald Stewart (who are also quoted, as are Newton and Euler), his ideas came primarily from Powell. Interleaved annotated syllabus of lectures in natural philosophy, Henry Papers, Smithsonian Archives (undated, but early 1840s). See also Joseph Henry, "The Philosophy of Inductive Science: Excerpts from Lectures to the Peabody Institute of Baltimore," and "Geology and Revelation," in *A Scientist in American Life: Essays and Lectures of Joseph Henry*, ed. Arthur P. Molella et al. (Washington, 1980), pp. 88–98, 23–29; and Theodore Dwight Bozeman, *Protestants in an Age of Science: The Baconian Ideal and Antebellum American Religious Thought* (Chapel Hill, 1977).

[14] For a draft copy of Henry's letter to Henslow, see below, July 5, 1842.

Henry's address book notes that, in addition to the items mentioned in the letter, Henry sent Henslow the *Regents' Report* (probably of New York State) for 1842, a college catalogue (presumably for Princeton), Maclean's *Bacchus and Anti-Bacchus*, and copies of "Contributions IV" for William Whewell, George Peacock, and Henslow.

[15] The sixth item of this list, not a proposed sixth contribution. Compare the doubling of "2" above, with Henry's tripling of "6" here.

[16] Henry did not have more to say to De La Rive because he had written him at length the previous November, covering most of the topics that he addressed to the other correspondents on this list. See Henry to De La Rive, November 24, 1841, above.

Prof Forbes[17]

1   Introd. of Cuyler 2 Send Package cont[ain]ing all noms except one of the meteor. Reports will [?furnish] that when I next go Albany[18] Letter received nearly 3 months ago. Wished to give some definite information relative to reprint of work reprint. Note from Dr. Beck hopes to get appropriation for reprinting. Much obliged for copy of report on meteorolog compliment for same. I have be[en] led to the subj of atmospheric elect. Think I have hit on a method observation will be of some importance. Will send an account of this. Apparatus expected from Paris. I will call on him perhaps for directions in the way of manipulation

Prof Gregory[19]

Introduction thanks for letter to Brother

Dr Arnott[20] Introduction of C

E^d Solley[21] Introduction

Young Thomson[22] Introduction

---

[17] See the full letter of July 2, 1842, above.

[18] Henry's address book indicates that the reports for 1837, 1839, 1840, and 1841 were sent, while he was to send that of 1838. The notes also show that he sent "Hasleres Report," probably the *Tenth Annual Report of the Coast Survey*, for 1841, by Ferdinand R. Hassler, Superintendent of the Coast Survey, which was, in addition to being the annual report, a progress report on the project.

[19] See the full letter of July 6, 1842, below. Henry switched from blue to brown ink for the rest of this document.

[20] Neil Arnot, London physician and amateur physicist. *Henry Papers*, 3:245.

[21] Edward Solley, London chemist. *Henry Papers*, 3:249.

[22] The reference to "young Thomson" seems to refer not to Thomas Thomson, the Glasgow chemist whom Henry met on his European trip, who was almost seventy, but to his son, Thomas Thomson. The younger Thomson at the time of Henry's writing was in India, but it is probable that Henry did not know this. *DNB*.

TO ADOLPHE QUETELET

Correspondance d'A. Quetelet, Académie royale de Belgique[1]

Princeton College of New Jersey
July 4th 1842

My Dear Sir

Although I had not the good fortune to find you at home when I visited Belgium for almost the sole purpose of making your personal acquaintance[2]

---

[1] The Quetelet Papers are temporarily deposited in the Bibliothèque royale Albert Ier in Brussels.

[2] When Henry visited the Brussels Observatory in 1837, Quetelet was in Ostend. Quetelet wrote Henry in July 1838 via Bache to express his regret at missing him and to ask Henry to inform him of his research (*Henry Papers*, 4:73).

yet I am so familiar with your character from the representations of our friend Bache that I take the liberty of introducing to your acquaintance my young friend Mr Cuyler of the United States. He is on a tour of self improvement previous to the commencement of the study of the Law and I beg leave to ask for him your kind attention during his short visit to your city. Please accept my thanks for the several interesting papers you have sent me.[3]

> With sentiments of much
> respect I am my Dear
> Sir very Truly yours
> Joseph Henry

[3] Henry's Library contains several pre-1842 Quetelet papers on meteorological observations, shooting stars, and terrestrial magnetism.

On the back of this letter is a letter from Cuyler to Quetelet of October 6, 1842. Cuyler wrote that he was unable to deliver Henry's letter in person and that he regretted not meeting Quetelet.

TO [JOHN STEVENS HENSLOW][1]
Draft, Henry Papers, Smithsonian Archives

Princeton Colege of New Jersey
July 5th 1842

My Dear Sir

My young friend and late Pupil Mr Cuyler sails for Liverpool in the Packet of the 7th and I embrace the opportunity of sending you a package which he will deliver after a short excursion into Scotland.[2] I beg leave to request that if it be perfectly convenient you will show him some litle attention in the way of his becoming acquainted with the objects of interest connected with your venerable Institution. You will find him an amiable and intelligent youth and in reference to moral character I can assure he is worthy of your full confidence.

I am much obliged to you for the copies of the papers on the diseases of wheat <&c>. I have sent them to the editor of one of our agricultural

[1] We identify the recipient as Henslow on the basis of Henry's record of letters sent by way of Cuyler. See above, July 2–6, 1842.

[2] The Henry address book (p.[32]) lists material sent with Cuyler to Henslow. In addition to the items indicated below in this draft, these include the *Regents' Report* (of the State of New York) for 1842, a college catalogue, and a copy of John Maclean's *Examination of the Essays Bacchus and Anti-Bacchus*, for which see above, Notes on Letters Sent with Theodore Ledyard Cuyler, July 2–6, 1842, note 11.

journals for republication.[3] I owe you an apology for my long silence. The truth is that with tolerably good intentions I am often guilty of the sin of procrastination and in addition to this in the present case I have been induced to defer writing from time to time with the hope of being able to send you the promised specimens of natural history. I have made a number of unsuccessful attemps to procure specimens of Rattle snakes and alligators. The first are very scarce in the more thickly [inhabited] parts of our country or at least in the State of New Jersey and the second are only found in the southern states. Three of the young men who have graduated at our college have promised that they would forward an alligator for you but as yet they have failed to keep their promis. I am informed by one that it is a difficult matter to send one alive to England although they are frequently sent apparently in good health to New York.[4]

One of my young friends has sent me instead of the alligator itself a few of its eggs and also a specimen of the Horned Frog of Texas. These you will find in the package, the latter in the tin box. I also send you all the remaining nos. of the Flora of North America which have yet been published. These will complete your set up to this time.[5]

Dr Torrey has taken up his residence permanently in Princeton and has moved his great herbarium to this place; he forms quite an addition to our little scientific circle. Professor Jaeger has resigned his Professorship in this Institution and gone to reside in the city of Washington.[6]

You are not much interested I suppose in the subject of electricity but I send you a copy of the 4th n° of my contributions to that branch of science

[3] According to the *Royal Society Catalogue of Scientific Papers*, Henslow published at least four papers on wheat diseases in 1841 and 1842. Henry forwarded two papers, "Diseases of Wheat" (*Agricultural Society Journal*, 1841, 2:1–25), and "On the Specific Identity of the Fungi Producing Rust and Mildew" (ibid., pp. 220–224), to the *Cultivator*, an Albany agricultural journal previously edited by Jesse Buel (1778–1839, *Henry Papers*, 4:250n). An abstract of the articles appeared in the September 1842 issue of the journal (9:143).

[4] Henry reiterated his desire to send an alligator to Henslow in a letter of April 27, 1844 (Miscellaneous Manuscripts H, New-York Historical Society).

[5] *Flora of North America*, by John Torrey and Asa Gray, was published in New York between 1838 and 1843 in two volumes comprising eight parts. The most recent publication that Henry referred to was part 2 of volume 2, the seventh part issued. Andrew Denny Rodgers III, *John Torrey: A Story of North American Botany* (1942; reprint ed., New York, 1965), pp. 124, 127, 156. See also Henry's letter to Henslow, October 3, 1842, below, where he fears he may have forwarded two copies of the same part, and his letter of April 27, 1844 (see note 4), which accompanied the last part of the *Flora*.

[6] Torrey moved to Princeton so "that he might live more cheaply than in New York." Torrey to Bailey, August 23, 1842, in Rodgers, *Torrey*, p. 136. After Benedict Jaeger's departure, Torrey taught botany as well as his usual course of chemistry.

Jaeger, the entomologist and Professor of Modern Languages and Lecturer on Natural History at Princeton (*Henry Papers*, 2:56n), resigned abruptly in September 1841 and became involved in the fledgling National Institute in Washington. Harry B. Weiss, "Professor Benedict Jaeger, Early Entomologist of New Jersey," *Proceedings of the New Jersey Historical Society*, 1922, 7:196–207.

and hope to be able soon to forward you the 5th n° of the same. We find great difficulty in this country in getting our labours properly noticed in Europe but in reference to my last papers I have had little to complain of on this account. They have met with a very favourable reception in France and Germany and have been immediately republished in England.[7]

We are very disagreeably situated in this country in reference to the prosecution of science. The unrighteous custom of reprinting English books without paying the authors has a most pernicious and paralizing influence on the effor[t]s of native literary talent. The American author can get no remuneration for his labours for why should the book seller pay for the copy right of an American work when he can get one on the same subject which will sell better, from England for nothing.[8] Besides this the man of science can scarcely hope to get proper credit for his labours since all his reputation must come from Abroad through the medium of the English republications and it is not in the nature of things that the compiler of a scientific work should be as much inclined to give as full credit to a stranger in a distant count[r]y as to a neabour at his elbow.[9]

It is surprising how much noterity such <*men as Dr La*> the compiler of pop English popular works get in this country. Dr. Lardener[10] was before he came to <*this country*> here was a much greater man than Herschell.

Speaking of Lardner reminds me that I have to thank you for the alteration that was made in <*the report*> his account of my communication

---

[7] The republications of Henry's last two major papers in England were Sturgeon's *Annals of Electricity, Magnetism, and Chemistry*, 1840, *4*:281–310 ("Contributions III: Electro-Dynamic Induction"), and 1841, *7*:21–56 ("Contributions IV: Electro-Dynamic Induction"); and *Phil. Mag.*, 1840, 3d ser. *16*:200–210, 254–265, 551–562 ("Contributions III"), and 1841, 3d ser. *18*:482–514 ("Contributions IV").

[8] Copyright laws in this country did not protect foreign authors until 1891. *Encyclopedia Britannica*, 15th ed., s.v. "Copyright Laws," by Barbara A. Ringer. See also Henry's letters to John White Webster, August 17 and September 2, 1842, below, and *Henry Papers*, 4:105.

[9] The text breaks here. The following paragraphs are a continuation of this letter, probably in an earlier draft, from a scrap of paper inscribed "Jesse Buel Esq Publisher of the Agricultural Paper, Albany" (Henry Papers, Smithsonian Archives). The pages have been attributed to the Henslow letter from the abstract of contents Henry kept of his overseas letters. See note 1, above.

From this point the text is hard to reconstruct, as it is written in a very poor hand with many corrections, on two sides of one sheet of paper, alternate sections upside down. The material divides into four parts; we have supplied the order of the sections, and have distinctly separated them from each other to indicate this.

We had previously identified this section incorrectly as part of a letter to Jesse Buel, the younger (*Henry Papers*, *3*:509), on the basis of the center inscription.

[10] Dionysius Lardner. See Henry to John Torrey, December 20, 1841, above, note 7.

to the mechanical section of the British association in 1837.[11] You may reccollect that he gave me the Lie in reference to the speed of American boats before the whole section and afterward made <*some*> rather a disparaging <*remark*> insinuation in reference to the nature of my communication.

I do not [?exult] in <*his*> the misfortune he has brought on himself but regard him rather <*as an*> as <*the*> an ob[j]ect of pit[y] than of <*anger*> resenmt. <*He has met no*> He has met with no encouragement from scientific men of any standing in our country. He has adopted the [?*position*] of an itineran[t] lecturer and during the past winter has managed to <*get*> draw tollerably large audiences in the theaters of New York by <*alternating*> occuping the stage on <*different*> alternate nights with jugles and public dancers at from 6^d to a shilling sterling per head,

and with this as an indication of the state of morals among us I am pleased.[12] He is certainly a very interesting writer and a man of considerable talent but he has <*always*> sadly been wanting in <*one*> an essential element of <*the*> a <*Philosoph*> scientific character <*the*> a sacred regard to truth. I hold that no person can be trusted as the historian of sci[ence] who could be guilty of the crime of which he is charged.[13]

Perhaps I have now said to much in reference to this paramour yet I do assure you that although I dislike his character I regard him as an object of pity.

He gave an account in one of his Lectures in Phil^d of his treatment of me at the British association and attributed the whole to a mistake. Although his lecture was published in the papers[14] I took no notice of it. If I were so disposed I could easily [have] caused him to be [?passed][15] even from the stage since there is in this country with very little claims to science.

Since writing this letter I have received a communication from Dr Beck. He informs that he[16]

[11] Henslow's role in having Lardner's account changed is not known.

[12] Henry was apparently pleased that Lardner was accorded no higher status than that of common entertainer.

[13] A reference to Lardner's adultery.

[14] See John S. Hart to Henry, March 18, 1842, above, note 4.

[15] One illegible word, apparently ending in "ssed."

[16] T. Romeyn Beck. These two lines are very similar to ones in the postscript of Henry's letter to Forbes, July 2, 1842, above. They may represent a draft of that letter.

TO WILLIAM GREGORY[1]
Warren Collection, Buffalo and Erie County Historical Society

Princeton College of New Jersey
July 6th 1842

My Dear Sir

Allow me to introduce to your acquaintance my young Friend the bearer of this letter Mr Theodore Cuyler and to ask for him your kind attention should he chance to visit your city. He is a graduate of our college and intends travelling for selfimprovement in Europe previous to commencing the study of a profession.

I forwarded to you last winter by a Person visiting Scotland a copy of the 4th number of my contributions to electricity and I hope to be able soon to send you the 5th number of the same. I regret that I had not an opportunity of delivering your kind letter of introduction to your Brother when I visited cambridge it was a time of vacation.[2]

I hope you find your present situation a pleasant one and that you are in the way of prosperity of every kind.

With much esteem I am
my dear Sir Truely
yours &c
Joseph Henry

[1] Henry had met Gregory in Glasgow in 1837, if not earlier at the British Association meetings (*Henry Papers*, 3:507). At this time Gregory was Professor of Medicine and Chemistry in King's College, Aberdeen.

[2] Duncan Farquharson Gregory (1813–1844), a mathematician, was an undergraduate at Trinity College in 1837. *DNB*.

TO JOHN P. GASSIOT[1]
Retained Copy, Henry Papers, Smithsonian Archives

Princeton College of New Jersey
July 11th 1842[2]

My Dear Sir

I am much obliged to you for the copy of your interesting paper on the spark from a galvanic circuit.[3] I have read the article with much pleasure and beg <leave in return to ask your acceptance of a copy of my last paper> consider it an important addition to our knowledge of the phenomenon of

[1] John Peter Gassiot of London, an experimental physicist. *Henry Papers*, 4:264.

[2] There is a draft of the first paragraph of this letter, dated July 4, 1842, in Box 23, Henry Papers, Smithsonian Archives.

[3] "An Account of Experiments Made with the View of Ascertaining the Possibility of Obtaining a Spark Before the Circuit of the Vol-

electrcy. I send you with this letter an account of my last research on elec-trcy. It is not among the least pleasures of science that it offords the means of a community of feeling between persons the most widely seperated. Its tendencies are republican in the proper sense of the term and those who honestly labour to advance its cause should be recognised as Brothers in what ever <climb> part of the wor[l]d they may be found.

With much Respe[c]t I am
Your very obt serv
Joseph Henry

---

taic Battery is Completed," *Phil. Trans.*, 1840, pp. 183–192. The presentation copy survives in the Henry Library.

This paper questioned the generally ac-cepted identity of static and voltaic electricity. If the two were identical, then one should be able to obtain sparks from a voltaic battery before the circuit was completed. Gassiot, however, failed to obtain any sparks from a fairly large Daniell battery.

Gassiot returned to the problem a few years later, and in "A Description of an Extensive Series of the Water Battery," *Phil. Trans.*, 1844, pp. 39–52, described his success in ob-taining sparks from an incomplete voltaic cir-cuit. He used a battery with three times the cells of the one described in the 1840 pub-lication. More importantly, he was extremely careful in insulating the individual cells, pre-serving their electrical tension.

Henry's pleasure in receiving Gassiot's 1840 paper was no doubt increased by Gassiot's mentioning "Contributions III: Electro-Dynamic Induction," and describing Henry as "the celebrated experimentalist" (p. 191). Gassiot had read Henry's paper in the hope that Henry had examined this question. Al-though disappointed that Henry had gone off in another direction, Gassiot did find Henry's conclusions suggestive.

TO WILLIAM B. KINNEY

Kinney Family Papers, New Jersey Historical Society,
and Mathematics in Female Education: Abstracts from the Archives of the
Rutgers Female Institute *(New York, 1860), pages 7–8*

Princeton July 12th 1842

My Dear Sir

Enclosed I send you the sketch of the Report I have prepared for our committee of the Rutgers Institute.[1] Please touch up the several parts or what will be better do the whole article over in better style since I have merely attempted to give in simple language the ideas which should be in-troduced into the report.

[1] Henry, Kinney, and the Reverend Gardiner Spring attended the 1842 mathematics ex-amination of the Rutgers Female Institute, a school for girls in New York City. Although the enclosure has not been found, an excerpt from their report was printed in 1860 and is reprinted below.

The Institute, which opened in 1839, be-came the Rutgers Female College in 1867. The College went out of business in June 1895 fol-lowing several years of financial problems in-volving shortages in the accounts of the princi-pal and property manipulation by a trustee. Daniel S. Martin, "Rutgers Female College," *University of the State of New York, Board of Regents' Report for 1877*, pp. 644–654. Sidney

I did not leave New York until Saturday evening and therefore I was obliged to defer my visit to your city.

> With much Respect
> Yours Truly
> Joseph Henry

PS Send the report as soon as convenient to Mr West.[2]

. . . "The subjects on which the young ladies were prepared for examination were the following: 1st. The general principles of Algebra, including the management of fractions and of surd quantities; the investigation of the binomial theorem; the rules of involution and evolution; arithmetical and geometrical progression, and the doctrine of equations of the first and second degree. 2d. The application of the foregoing principles to a great variety of problems, particularly of such as involved the reduction of a quadratic equation. 3d. Plane and Solid Geometry. 4th. The use and construction of Logarithms. 5th. Plane Trigonometry.

"The examination was conducted in a manner to put the knowledge of the pupils to the severest test. The numbers of the problems in Algebra corresponding to those in the text-book, were written on folded pieces of paper, and from the pile formed of these and placed upon the table before the examiners, each pupil drew one at random, so that previous to opening the paper she must have been entirely ignorant of the numbers of the problem she would be called upon to solve. The numbers of the propositions in Geometry were drawn in the same way, and each pupil was required to enunciate from memory the text of the proposition which had fallen to her

---

Sherwood, *The University of the State of New York* (Washington, 1900), pp. 466–467. *New York Times*, November 29, 1891, and December 16, 1891.

[2] Charles Edwin West (1809–1900), an 1832 graduate of Union College, was Principal of the Rutgers Female Institute from 1839 to 1851. West considered himself a pioneer in higher education for women. He was particularly interested in determining whether girls could be taught higher mathematics and abstract science. Assessing his students' performance at the mathematical examinations he wrote:

Noble girls! What honors did they not achieve for themselves and their sex! The miserable subterfuge of lies which man had set up for his own self-aggrandizement, that he alone was to "the manner born," that he, the self-styled lord of creation, could alone revel in the mysteries of science, that

to him alone belonged the aristocracy of learning, was forever swept away!
Celebration of the Twenty-Fifth Anniversary of the Rutgers Female Institute (New York, 1864), p. 13.

In an autobiographical sketch, West wrote that Henry used his lab in New York for experiments on atmospheric electricity in 1842 and that Henry frequently wrote him on scientific subjects. An exchange in March 1843 is printed below. West was a founding member of the American Association for the Advancement of Science. After leaving the Rutgers Female Institute, he was Principal of the Buffalo Female Seminary, 1851–1860, and the Brooklyn Heights Seminary, 1860–1889.

Charles E. West, *An Address on the Fiftieth Anniversary of the Class of 1832 . . . Union College* (Brooklyn, 1882). *National Cyclopaedia, 8:325. Columbia Alumni*, p. 292.

lot. Also in the progress of the solution or demonstration, as the case might be, the several steps of the progress were required to be fully explained.

"The examination was continued until the Committee declared themselves fully satisfied with the evidences of proficiency which had been exhibited. They were surprised and delighted with the rapidity and precision with which the exercises were conducted, and although they have frequently attended examinations of males, yet they are free to say that they have never been present at one which surpassed this in the evidence given on the part of the pupils of a thorough acquaintance with the subjects.

"The Committee were pleased to find that the text-book used in Algebra was one which abounds in difficult problems, affording full exercise in the more abstruse parts of the subject, and that the principles of the science had been taught verbally by competent teachers as often as the progress of the pupil in practical expertness required a new explanation. It will be perceived by this remark, that the Committee are in favor of the old method of teaching called *drilling*, provided it be connected as it is in this case with frequent explanations of the principles.

"In the course of the examination the Committee have been strongly impressed with the importance of the Mathematics as a branch of female education. A philosophical course of instruction is one which tends to develop in harmonious proportions all the faculties of the mind, and since from the constitution of the female, and her peculiar position in civilized society, she is prone to an undue exercise of the imagination, the Committee believe that she requires just that training which the proper study of the mathematics is so well calculated to give. Algebra, as it is taught in this Institution, affords an admirable exercise of the attention and the invention; and Geometry has ever been celebrated for the strength and precision it imparts to the reasoning faculties. The Committee are, moreover, convinced that there is nothing incompatible with all that is amiable and interesting in the female character, and the highest attainments in literature and science. Indeed there is an example of this at the present day. Mrs. MARY SOMERVILLE, although the learned authoress of a Mathematical exposition of the Celestial Mechanics of LA PLACE, is well-skilled in music and in painting, and in the acquisition of her profound attainments, she has lost nothing of that sensibility and sweetness of character which ever made her the admiration of her acquaintances, and now render her the loved as well as respected of her family."[3]

[3] Mary Somerville was probably a favorite example for proponents of science education for women. Deborah Jean Warner cites Theodore Strong's similar invocation of Somerville in "Science Education of Women in Antebellum America," *Isis*, 1978, *69*:58–67, and mentions other examiners who were as "surprised and delighted" as Henry's committee with the proficiency of young ladies in mathematics and science.

July 19, 1842

"RECORD OF EXPERIMENTS"
Henry Papers, Smithsonian Archives

July 19th Tuesday 1842

Since the last date I have given an account of my experiments to the american Phil society[1] and have informed some of my Friends abroad of the most prominent results.[2] But my time has been so much occupied in college duties, writing letters, drawing up a report for an examination of a school[3] and examing old papers in the Transactions of the Royal society relative to electricity, that I have done nothing in the way of experiment except to make some observations on the electricity of the thunder cloud.[4]

The first expermt this morning was made with the mug susta[in]ing battery. 19 pots or mugs were arranged by Sam the action was quite energetic. The magnetizing spirals were introduced, first into the secondary circuit with the helix no 1 but as in the old experiments no effect was produced the electricity was too small in quantity to effect the magnetism of the needles with spirals employed.

Next the coil no 2 was substituted for the helix then the needles were magnetized as follows:

no 1 2 3 4   That is the fir[s]t one in the largest spiral was
    o — + +   not magnetized, the 2[nd] in the next spiral was —
minus that in the third plus, in the 4[th] plus

While the same needles remained in the same spirals the current was again passed by means of the file so as to give the beg[in]ning and the ending induction the needles were now magnetized as follows

no 1 2 3 4   I should have mentioned that in this expmt I
    — — + +   change[d] the direction of the current[5]

Attempted to get induced currents from galvanic current when the secondary circuit was open but did not succede. Used for this purpose the coil no 1 for the battery coil no. 2 on this and coil no. 3 under. The sperials were then placed between the two ends of no 2 and 3, while the other two were seperated but no effect was observed on the fine needles

---

[1] Henry's last experiments were on June 14, shortly before his presentation of "Contributions V: Induction from Ordinary Electricity; Oscillatory Discharge" to the American Philosophical Society on June 17.

[2] These letters are printed above.

[3] Rutgers Female Institute.

[4] Recorded in the "Record of Experiments" entry of June 26, 1842, above.

[5] At this point Henry began a new paragraph. All he wrote, however, was a single word—"These"—before breaking off. He then resumed writing on the top of the next page of the "Record of Experiments" with the sentence beginning "Attempted."

James Joseph Sylvester (1814–1897), ca. 1841, by George Patten (1801–1865). Courtesy of Alain C. Enthoven, Stanford, California; photograph by Greg Webb.

Jöns Jacob Berzelius (1779–1848), n.d.
Courtesy of the Smithsonian Archives.

Charles Lyell (1797–1875), 1849, lithograph by T. H. Maguire (1821–1895).
Courtesy of the Smithsonian Archives.

John Stevens Henslow (1796–1861),
1849, lithograph by T. H. Maguire
(1821–1895).
Courtesy of the Smithsonian Archives.

Hans Christian Oersted (1777–1851),
n.d., lithograph by C. A. Jensen
(1792–1870).
Courtesy of the Smithsonian Archives.

Robert Maskell Patterson (1787–1854),
posthumous, by James Reid Lambdin
(1807–1889).
Courtesy of the American
Philosophical Society.

John Ludlow (1793–1857), ca. 1833–1838,
by Samuel Sexton.
Courtesy of the University of
Pennsylvania Archives.

John Kintzing Kane (1795–1858), 1859,
by Thomas Hicks (1823–1890).
Courtesy of the American
Philosophical Society.

Henry Darwin Rogers (1808–1866), n.d.
Courtesy of the Smithsonian Archives.

Ferdinand Rudolph Hassler (1770–1843), ca. 1830–1840, by William G. Williams (1801–1846). Courtesy of the National Ocean Service, National Oceanic and Atmospheric Administration; photograph by Eugene L. Mantie.

Samuel F. B. Morse (1791–1872), ca. 1845, photograph.
Courtesy of the National Museum of American History, Smithsonian Institution.

Joseph Henry, 1843, silhouette by
Auguste Edouart (1789–1861). In the
original, Henry is paired with
Dr. Nathaniel William Cole of
Burlington, New Jersey.
Courtesy of the National Portrait
Gallery, Smithsonian Institution,
Washington, D.C., lent by an
anonymous owner.

Detail of multi-color chalk drawing
by Russell Smith (1812–1896), 1843,
enclosed in letter of Henry Darwin
Rogers to Joseph Henry, June 15, 1843.
Courtesy of the Smithsonian Archives.

"RECORD OF EXPERIMENTS"
Henry Papers, Smithsonian Archives

July 22nd 1842
Account of House struck by
Lightning July 9th 1842[1]

Visited this afternoon in company Arch^d Alexander M D[2] a house struck with lightning near the plain Tavern about 4 miles south east or perhaps nearly east of Princeton on the morning of July the 9th at about 10 o'clock. I regret that I did not go soonner to inspect the building <since> because the house has been since partially repaired although the greater effects are still visible.

The house is a tall narrow two story one with a kitchen on the west side. It stands on the road with a small court yard in front nearly east and west. The lightning struck the chimney of the house part of the lightning passed into the chimney and down it about 3 feet and then burst through to the front <corner> edge down which was a tin water conductor. The principal part of the discharge passed down the corner post of the frame of the building and almost completely destroyed it, throwing some parts of it into the yard to the east to the distance of 20 yards and even pieces of the clap boards were thrown off with such force as to fall on the house to the east at the distance of 35 yards. The principal part of the discharge passed down the corner post and perhaps along the gutter and then appears to have scattered in every direction along the surface <which> of the ground which was flooded with water at the time. Around the house, in every direction, to the distance of 20 yards, marks on the vegetation of its passage were visible. At the distance of about 22 yards to the NE of the house, two pigs

---

[1] This heading has been moved from the top of the following page of the entry.

[2] A resident of Princeton, Archibald Alexander, Jr. (d. 1882) was the son of the Reverend Archibald Alexander (*Henry Papers*, 2:437n– 438n). He had received his medical degree from Jefferson Medical College in 1836, the same year that Princeton granted him an honorary Master of Arts. *Princeton Catalogue*, p. 415; *Hageman*, 2:348.

were killed out of seven in a pen. A part of the discharge passed along the ceiling of the garret or rather of the floor of the garret of the main building and then through the garret of the kitchen—in which some pieces of stove-pipe were placed at the time—to the chimney of the kitchen. In its passage it threw off <*all the*> a great part of the plaster from the ceiling of the upper room.

Either the explosion of the main discharge or the part which passed to the kitchen excited such an expansive influence on the air in the small garret that the whole roof was lifted from its place and all the rafters unloosened the shingles were torn up and the whole effect resembled the operation of a quantity of confined gun-powder. Nearly all the panes of glass in the house were broken.

At the time of the stroke the house was occupied by a man and his wife and two children. The woman was in the lower room, standing near the door which was closed or nearly closed. The man was in the corner of the kitchen in the rear and next to the house part on his bench making shoes. The two children were at the kitchen front door one had climbed up on a chair and was looking over the half door. The other was climbing up at the time. The woman heard nothing of the report and must have been stunned at the moment. The man says that his head fell on his breast as if he had suddenly lost the power of sustaining it. He thinks that he raised it immediately but cannot be certain. When he looked up the children were both jumping up and down on the floor but did not exhibit any signs of having been affected by the lightning. The woman did not complain of any effect and the man was affected so slightly as to suffer but little inconvenience although he thinks his head has not been as steady since the time of the accident.

A small part of the discharge passed down the well since a small hole was observed on the crib.

There was a stove in the fire place of the kitchen, with a pipe reaching up about a foot into the flue of the chimney. There probably was fire in the stove at the time but the heated air from this must have been very small and overpowered by the falling rain. A small quantity of plastering is knocked off in the inside of the kitchen chimney opposite the top of the stovepipe.

The most surprising part of this exhibition of the electrical discharge, is the fact that the corner post of the buiding was destroyed although the tinned iron gutter which was parallel to it <*and*> was at the distance of less than a foot. I am not sure however that that part of the post was as much injured which was opposite the gutter as that above and below the extremities of the metal. The gutter was burst open at top in a hole of about 3/4 of an inch in diameter with a large bur outward. The white paint on the tin was not disturbed on the foreside of tine tube but app[e]ared to be allittle blackened on the back side or that nearest the house.

The discharge app[e]ars to have been <*an*> excedingly powerful and to have spread in every direction over the surface of the ground. A small quantity entered the cellar but not as much as in the cases of the house I examind last summer.[3]

The people in the next house perceved the lightning on the hearth in the form of a ball as large as a water pail according to the account of the shoemaker

We also visited a tree which was riven by electricity about a week after the house was struck. It was about a mile from the Plain Tavern on the farm of Mr Grundiker.[4] It was a red oak tree and stood on the west <*side*> edge of the wood and was the largest in the vicinity. All the other trees were of the same kind. There was nothing very particular in this case the branches as in the trees I have before examined were but little scathed and the <*whole*> principal force of the discharge was on the main trunk, at about 12 feet from the ground. It was broken off at this point although nearly 18 inches thick. The splinters were thrown to the distance of 75 yards.

For an account struck with lightning see Edinburgh Phil Jour vol VI 379.[5]

[3] See the "Record of Experiments" entries of July 15 and 16, 1841, printed above.

[4] Not otherwise identified.

[5] A reference to an account of the effect of lightning upon a house in Geneva. *Edinburgh Philosophical Journal*, 1822, 6:379–380.

Henry subsequently added two additional paragraphs to this entry, summarizing the account of lightning striking the Cathedral of Strasbourg on July 10, 1843, published by A. Fargeaud under the title "Note sur les coups de tonnerre qui ont frappé la cathédrale de Strasbourg le lundi 10 juillet 1843, à une heure et demie après midi," *Comptes rendus*, 1843, 17:254–260. He had read this account on October 28, 1843. See the "Record of Experiments" entry of that date, below.

TO [ALEXANDER DALLAS BACHE][1]
Draft,[2] Henry Papers, Smithsonian Archives

[Late July 1842][3]

I have just learned <*by*> from Mr [?Alexander][4] of the <*change whi*> resignation which has taken place in the university and of the perplexing position which you are placed in regarding the acceptance of the vacant chair. I needle[ss] scarcely inform you what my feelings would be in such a condition <*I would*> and perhaps what I may say will only tend to give <*you*> but s[t]ill I will venture to give you my impressions and feelings rather a sober judgment drawn from an attentive a consideration of all the facts of the case. In the first place you have now given seven of the best years of your life to the subject of general education you have become interested in this and doubtless fear that <*all*> your labours in a measur[e] in this line will be thrown away by returning to the university. You have now got the high school under successful operation and even should this fail you have the prospect of establishing an <*ind*> private school which in probability would give you a competence in a few years added to this your income from the high school would be much greater than from the university and money is a matter of importance to us all.

---

[1] On July 8, 1842, Roswell Park (1807–1869, *DAB; Henry Papers,* 3:87) submitted his resignation as Professor of Natural Philosophy and Chemistry at the University of Pennsylvania (Trustees' Minutes, University Archives, University of Pennsylvania). The professorship was offered to Bache, who had been Park's predecessor. Bache accepted the position, but remained only a little more than a year before accepting the superintendency of the Coast Survey. During this second tenure at Pennsylvania Bache never taught. Stanley M. Guralnick, *Science and the Ante-Bellum American College* (Philadelphia, 1975), p. 173.

[2] This draft was written on the reverse of a portion of a draft of the full version of "Contributions V." It is in Box 23, "Researches and Lectures."

No outgoing copy of this letter has been located, although Henry did send one to Bache, since there is an apparent response dated July 29, 1842 (printed immediately below).

[3] We have arbitrarily placed this letter between the date of Park's resignation and that of Bache's response.

[4] The reading is uncertain.

FROM ALEXANDER DALLAS BACHE
Henry Papers, Smithsonian Archives

Bordentown Friday aft[n]
[July 29 1842][1]

My dear friend[2]

The fates appear to lead me gently back to the feet of that divine mistress, so long neglected, for that homespun damsel with whom the destinies of Columbia are so closely connected &[c] &[c] &[c] I have not written to you to ask advice because I knew before hand the $x + y + z = x$, would not afford you the means of sending the value of x. Will you be ready to give those lessons on the last days of August—dog days. If so I shall be tempted to stop. Write to me about it to Newport. I have been *reluctantly*, I confess, brought to the conviction that my present position is too precarious to allow me to decline the University offer. Of that more some other time.

To morrow I shall pass you in the 7 o'clock (Philad.) line & beg you to be at the depot if practicable. To say 1. if in your opinion M[r] Hart[3] will do for Principal of the High School, the man must have tact in management of men as well as boys, firmness, conscienciousness—these chiefly. 2. If he has will he be likely to come there for $1600 & take charge. 3. If both, then can you spare the time & have you the feelings which would induce you to go to Philad. to see Geo. M. Wharton, Geo Emlen Jr., Jno. Miller, Jac Heyberger, Henry Leech[4] & any other Controllers whom M[r] Wharton may think you should see?

Tell me about this to-morrow.

Love to Mrs H. & to you from Mrs. B & me.

Yours ever truly
A. D. Bache

---

[1] The date is from Henry's file notation.

[2] This is an apparent response to Henry's letter of late July 1842, printed immediately above.

[3] John S. Hart.

[4] George M. Wharton, George Emlen, Jr., John Miller, and Jacob Heyberger were members of the Committee on the High School. Henry Leech was President of the Controllers. *Twenty-Fourth Annual Report of the Controllers of the Public Schools of the City and County of Philadelphia* ... (Philadelphia, 1842), pp. 52–53.

Hart did succeed Bache as Principal of Central High School. The next report noted the "strong recommendations which were given in favor of Mr. Hart, especially from the Professors of Princeton College." *Twenty-Fifth Annual Report* ... (Philadelphia, 1843), p. 8.

TO JOHN WHITE WEBSTER
Mary Henry Copy, Henry Papers, Smithsonian Archives

Princeton Aug 17. 1842

My dear Sir. Your letter relative to Liebig's animal chemistry was received a few days ago.[1] I have been so much engaged with our senior examination that I have had no leisure before this morning to answer it. . . . I am strongly opposed to the [?unrighteous] system of publication which is carried on in this country in reference to English books. It does gross injustice to the foreign authors and paralyzes national effort. We can never hope to take rank with other nations in the lines of literature and science so long as we are supplied with English books at the cost of mere printing and paper. There would be no manufactory of cloth in our country if the consumer could get his garments for the mere price of making up.[2] I was so fortunate in my tour in Europe to make the acquaintance of Liebig and Gregory. I met them at Dr. Thomson's in Glasgow and made a short excursion with them and the Doctor to the Highlands. Kane of Dublin was also of the party.[3]

With much respect, yours truly   Joseph Henry

[1] We have not found the letter. Webster, Professor of Chemistry at Harvard (*Henry Papers, 1*:330), was on the verge of publishing an American edition of Justus von Liebig's *Animal Chemistry, or Organic Chemistry in Its Application to Physiology and Pathology* (Cambridge, Massachusetts: John Owen, 1842), translated and edited by William Gregory. The work was based on the second part of Liebig's report on organic chemistry which was presented to the British Association for the Advancement of Science in June 1842. Webster had already published an American edition of the first part of the report: *Organic Chemistry in Its Application to Agriculture and Physiology* (Cambridge, Massachusetts: John Owen, 1841). Margaret Rossiter notes that although Webster was not the most obvious American editor, he probably needed the money. "Justus Liebig and the Americans: A Study in the Transit of Science" (Ph.D. dissertation, Yale University, 1971), p. 18.

[2] The issue of literary piracy arose when an unauthorized edition was published by Wiley & Putnam in advance of Webster's edition, which was authorized by Liebig and Gregory. Wiley & Putnam claimed that Liebig had no right to authorize the publication because he had been paid for preparing the work by the British Association. Webster denied this, asserted Liebig's right to authorize publication, and made a plea for international copyright in *Reply to a Notice of Messrs. Wiley & Putnam* (Boston, 1842). For other comments by Henry on international copyright, see his letter to Henslow of July 5, 1842, above. See also *Henry Papers, 4*:105.

[3] See *Henry Papers, 3*:507.

FROM JAMES P. ESPY

Henry Papers, Smithsonian Archives

Washington City Aug. 20th '42

My Dear Sir,

On reading the Proceedings of the A. P. Soc. of the 17th June I was much struck with some of your discoveries in electricity, and one in particular, it appears to me, promises to be of great use to the meteorologist. It is the self-registering electrometer, which you propose, connected with an elevated exploring rod.

It is my wish to have one of these electrometers immediately in operation in Washington, and beg you to take an early opportunity to describe it to me in such a plain manner that I can have one constructed.[1] Perhaps also many of my meteorological correspondents will adopt it as soon as they may be informed of use.[2] I hope it is destined to throw a flood of light on the mysterious subject of atmospheric electricity. The "bill" appropriating $3000 for the purposes of Meteorology,[3] only wants now the signature of the President to become a law, and I therefore hope that I shall be able to devote myself exclusively to this subject for some years, without embarassment. I solicit your aid so far as your other highly interesting pursuits will permit.

On the evening of Aug. 18th I had the pleasure at 7[h] 50[m] to see a luminous Meteor—called shooting star—pass between me and some clouds in such a manner as to leave no doubt that this meteor at least was below the clouds.[4] The clouds were broken—and part of the meteor's path, had clear sky for its back ground, and part was cloud dense enough to conceal entirely stars of the first magnitude, and yet the luminosity of the meteor and the streak of light left behind it was uniform.

It passed from the middle of Corona Borealis to near the hand of Serpentarius. I shall be glad to have any suggestions from you concerning my future operations in Meteorology.

---

[1] "Contributions V: Induction from Ordinary Electricity; Oscillatory Discharge" mentions the existence of the self-registering electrometer but gives no details on its construction. If Henry sent Espy a description, it has not survived.

[2] Espy's published meteorological reports do not mention Henry's invention.

[3] See above, Espy to Henry, July 2, 1842.

[4] Fundamental to Denison Olmsted's theory of the extra-terrestrial origin of meteor showers was his belief that meteors had been observed falling through the atmosphere from great heights (approximately 2,200 miles). Espy had countered that the observations of meteors proved the contrary—that these were a relatively low altitude phenomenon—and argued that meteors originated in the atmosphere. For the background to and further references for this dispute, see *Henry Papers*, 2:302, 478–481.

What do you think of my answer to Olmsted's Objections?[5] or have you read them?[6] I wish much to know how the wind blew at Princeton on the evening of the 1st July.

Mrs Espy is now at Harrisburg, and if she were here she would join me in kind remembrances to you and Mrs Henry.

Write soon to yours very truly

James P. Espy

[5] Olmsted had attacked Espy's theory of storms in a public lecture in New York City. He claimed that there was no strong empirical basis for Espy's theory. Perhaps more seriously, he accused Espy of appealing to the general public for approval when the scientific community rejected the theory.

Espy argued that Olmsted had either misunderstood his theory of storms or misinterpreted the data. There was no way to supply empirical evidence for the theory which would convince Olmsted because Olmsted's prejudices blinded him to the facts. As to appealing over the heads of his peers to the populace, he accused Olmsted of twisting his words. James P. Espy, *The Philosophy of Storms* (Boston, 1841), pp. 429–452.

[6] Although Henry's reply, if any, has been lost, we can state that all the leaves in Henry's copy of Espy's book (in the Henry Library) from page 429 to page 452 have been cut. This is not true for other sections of the book.

FROM ALEXANDER DALLAS BACHE

Henry Papers, Smithsonian Archives

Newport R.I. August 22nd 1842.

My dear friend.

I have been unexpectedly called upon to leave Newport so as to be in Philad. on Friday morning at furthest: now my plan is this: to leave here on Wednesday afternoon, & New York by the 10 o'clock line on Thursday. I want you to join me in passing & to go on with me to Philad. in return for which unless circumstances which I am not now acquainted with should come up to derange the plan, I will go up with you to Princeton on Friday aft.ⁿ or Saturday & stay until Tuesday. Do not fail me for I have need of *advice*: there is no use of attempting on paper to say all for I do not find it possible to make myself fully understood by so doing. I spared you in the High School & University matter, but now I *cannot*, & you *must* give me the time. I am tempted to the University of Virginia & besides want you to be present at one or more *talks* which I must have with the dignitaries of the Univ. Penna The affairs of others too are at stake.[1] Remain on the plat-

[1] Following a long illness, John Patten Emmet (*Henry Papers*, 2:388n–389n) died on August 15, 1842, and left vacant the Chair of Chemistry and Materia Medica at the University of Virginia. Bache was one of several of Henry's friends who considered applying for the job. Although he was back at the University of Pennsylvania after serving as Presi-

form & I will get out of the cars as I can easily find *you* while I shall be like a needle in a haystack. Should the steam boat fail to take us to N.Y. in time to see Courtenay[2] before 10 o'clock, I shall come on in the afternoon mail line at 4½. Kindest regards to you & yours, from me & mine. Make some exertion not to disappoint me.

Yours as ever truly
A. D. Bache

---

dent of Girard College and then as Principal of Philadelphia's Central High School, he was not satisfied with his position, particularly his salary of $2,300. Faculty compensation at the University of Virginia was higher than average and depended in part on how many students enrolled in a course. In 1835, Emmet received $4,075 as Professor of Chemistry (*Henry Papers*, 2:420). According to a letter from John Torrey to Jacob Whitman Bailey of August 27, 1842 (Bailey Papers, Boston Science Museum), Bache intended to use the Virginia vacancy to bargain with the University of Pennsylvania and to go to Virginia if the bargaining failed. Although Bache was not successful in get-

ting a higher salary, he remained at the University of Pennsylvania for over a year until he became Superintendent of the Coast Survey. Henry and Torrey eventually supported Bailey for the Virginia position. See Bailey's letter to Torrey of September 17, 1842, printed below.

[2] Edward H. Courtenay (*Henry Papers*, 2:32n). In 1842 he worked as an engineer at the Brooklyn Navy Yard and then went to the University of Virginia as Professor of Mathematics. Bache may have thought Courtenay would be especially knowledgeable about the situation in Charlottesville.

CHARLES GODFREY LELAND[1] TO ELIJAH R. CRAVEN[2]
Leland Collection, Firestone Library, Princeton University

Aug 25 1842. *Philadelphia!* ! ! !

Mein Lieben.

Look at the *date* & read my *fate*. Yea and verily the Faculty (may the World-Soul never bless them) have triumphed and I am now an exile from the classic shades of Princeton! ![3]

[1] Charles Godfrey Leland (1824–1903; *DAB*), a freshman from Philadelphia, became a prominent if idiosyncratic poet, humorist, and man of letters, known for his comic use of literary allusion. Leland's thorough mastery of gypsy lore and the Romany language was an example of his more esoteric accomplishments. His *oeuvre* also included textbooks on crafts and industrial arts, which he endeavored to introduce into the Philadelphia schools. Already evident in this student letter were Le-

land's characteristic fascination with the occult and the metaphysical, his deep love for Germany, where he went to study after Princeton, and his remarkable erudition. Despite the disciplinary actions currently preoccupying him, Leland went on to graduate in 1845.

[2] Craven was a senior from Washington, D.C. Unless otherwise noted, the names appearing below belonged to students listed in the *Princeton Annual Catalogue*, 1842.

[3] Leland (and most of the rest of his class)

Having blown off my steam, I will now go ahead correctly and mathematically. The day on which you left as you may remember our situation—
(not quite so agreeable a one as that of the pig who was shut up by mistake
in the corn-granary,) we were up in arms. I had old Dod[4] after me five times
that day. They sent Gassey[5] up to hear recitation and Taylor was the only
man there, then came a *scene* which you should have *seen!* (oh Lord).
There was Johnny[6] & Dod & Henry all in the campus begging and
threat'ning and scolding—some of the students were crying—some swearing
like devils—some vowing that they would'nt stir a step to save themselves
from ———— expulsion &c. But it was no use, the Sophs & Junr's had all
gone to a man (no! Burton did'nt go) and so we went. I was nearly fainting
by the time it was all over and can faintly remember that I roared out a tall
interjection, as I took my seat,—Then Howard got up and staid up & per-
sisted in telling Gassey (who had come again) that he was no gentleman
which in my private opinion was pretty near the truth!—But the squall
was'nt over yet, they had gone to recitation & just one man recited (Cromartie). In the afternoon they went—and stumped to a man (Cromartie
excepted). For this they had us up before the Faculty the next morning and
we were dismissed—not for saying "not prepared" but for *conspiring*! ! But
I told them that I had not agreed not to recite (that was true) but they (a
nigger has just brought me up a card from Geo Boker)[7] said that (here he is
again) although I had not agreed with 'em before hand not to recite, yet
that I had conspired in not reciting, was'nt that a damn piece of sophistry?
I suppose you can recognise Dod's hand or rather *heart* in it? Well they told
me to mosey and by that time the next day I was O.P.H.

Dod told me that I was less to blame than anybody and they would have
let me off if I would plead "non preparation" whereupon I said to old Boss[8]
(for it was him and not Dod) that as for that matter I had not been prepared
on that lesson for a month, but that I would not have recited if I had been
ever so well prepared. "That's enough" said old Boss (I thought so too) "I
admire the honesty of your confession" (so did I) but you must be off by

---

had been sent home for participating in a
"rebellion" in which the underclassmen
skipped recitation in protest of an abruptly
cancelled holiday. Nathaniel Burt, "Student
Life at Nassau Hall," in *Nassau Hall, 1756–
1956,* ed. Henry Lyttleton Savage (Princeton,
1956), p. 130. Faculty Minutes, August 17,
1842, Princeton University Archives.
[4] Leland was to develop an especially close
relationship with his math professor Albert
Baldwin Dod, whom he memorialized in his
1893 *Memoirs.*
[5] The nickname suggests the chemistry professor, John Torrey.
[6] John Maclean.
[7] Like Leland, George Henry Boker (1823–
1890) went on to literary fame, as the author
of the tragedy *Francesca da Rimini* (1855). He
later served as minister to Turkey and Russia.
DAB.
[8] College President James Carnahan.

tomorrow (hal-lo-o-o!! thought I). Dod told me the next day that if the Sophs did'nt keep up the rebellion any longer we should be recalled in a week. I recieved a letter from the editor of the Nassau Monthly[9] yesterday [? rowing] me up for my piece. He concluded with telling me not to despair, that Tully and Demosthenes and Aristides and Beelzebub had all been exiled from their homes—and advised me to read "Thoughts on exile" and advised me to sing "The exile of Erin." I did sing it—listen!! hark to the low melancholy tones! ! ! ! ! ! !

"There came to the city an exile from Princeton"
"But he had not a sorrow his bosom to chill"
"I saw him adown to the Library steering"
"And he walked into folios & quartos to kill"
Oh my! ! hold my hat Elijah! ! till I take my coat off—I am now writing to you with Kants Critic of pure reason on one hand and Jacob Behmen[10] on the other. (Dod advised me to study while gone) . . . .
. . . . . . Oh Elijah, since the last word (ie gone) was written, an interval of several hours has elapsed and now I sit down in my room (the same room that we both occupied) to tell you what has happened, after visiting Boker, I went to the Library and who think you I saw there? why _____ Professor Henry! ! ! ! ! ! ! ! ! He shook hands *mit mir=* "Mister Leland" says he "when do you intend to write so as to come back," upon which I told him that Dod told me that I should be recalled. "But" says he "you must say in a letter that you were wrong in signing a paper in the first instance." "Did'nt sign any sir" whereupon he looked *"rayther aback"* "well" says he "'you may back to Princeton as soon as you like and tell the President that I told you you might go back"—then we had a grand talk all about philosophy, and metaphysics= (N.B. he believes in progressive improvement in the human-race). I astonished him with a slight allusion to Paracelsus[11] and got a thundering big compliment for it. We were looking in a book about popular delusions where a long list of the different arts of divination was put down—such as chaomancy, necromancy, aeromancy, pyromancy, geomancy, hydromancy and so forth (just to fill out a line). Says he "I did'nt know that there were so many. "Oh sir" says I *"if you remember*, Paracelsus has many more in his Naturarerum." "What" says he, how shall I describe the tone of that *"what"* let it stand as follows, imag-

---

[9] The senior class literary magazine, begun in 1842. The editor and contributors were anonymous.

[10] The German mystic, also known as Jacob Boehm (1575–1624).

[11] Theophrastus Bombastus von Hohenheim (1490–1541), the Swiss chemist, physician and natural philosopher. *DSB.*

ine the blank space filled with notes of admiration [12] ———————————————
"WHAT" ! ! ! ! ! ! ! ! ! ! ! ! !

Lord knows that I have got plenty of them in this letter! ! ! ! ! If he expects this child to be off *right away* he's green, he told me that I had better *eventuate* this week.

"The transcendental conception of reason at all times only looks to absolute totality in the synthesis of the conc[eption?] and never terminates except in the *absolutely*," Kants "Critic"

Translate the above ——————————— and the following, Mathematics afford a shining example of a pure reason extending itself successfully, of itself, without the aid of experience.

Kant [13]

Do not apply any arguments disfavourable to the second for 'tis without a context or note given you. Translate the following "The light and glory of the Son goeth into all the powers of the Father, and the Holy Ghost moveth Eternally in all, which in the Deep of the Father, is like a Divine Soliter or Sol[. . .]itium to be likened to the Earth, &c.

J. Behmen

I do feel it to be my duty to say Elijah Craven, if you do'nt pass judgment upon me for a lunatic after reading the above letter—you must be lunatic yourself—thar's manners for you—I have become very impolite ever since I have been deprived of your urbane and gentlemanly presence! ! ! !

Write soon (i.e. instanter)
Yours "nunc et sempiterner" Carl the mystic

Let me beg of you to present my respects to the first (white) young lady that you may meet after reading this, whoever she may be, tell her that I am desperately in love with her—tell her to—to—to—acknowledge my devotion and—and—and reply to me— —dont forget to tell me who she was,— Man I am in earnest by the Animus Mundi I am, I should like mighty well

---

[12] Whether Henry's reaction was astonishment or admiration, Leland's precocious erudition was recognized at Princeton, at least according to Leland: "Professor Dodd had said that at seventeen there were not ten men in America who had read so much, while Professor Henry often used words to this effect. . . ." Charles Godfrey Leland, *Memoirs* (1893; reprint ed., Detroit, 1968), p. 90.

[13] Compare Norman Kemp Smith, trans., *Immanuel Kant's Critique of Pure Reason* (1929; reprint ed., New York, 1965), pp. 318 and 46, respectively. These are denoted in Smith's notation for the first and second editions of the *Critique* as A 326, B 382, and A 4, B 8. We have been unable to determine which edition of Kant Leland used.

to see you just now— —Find me an inamorata dont forget, you may show her
this picture as a specimen.

Address,   { Carl Göttfried Leland,
           { care of Amos Leland,
or—you may Latinise it and call it Carolus Gotto-
fredus Leland.

{ Some Germans (gentlemen) are singing to night under }
{   my window   }

The *Duc* D'Orleans.

TO [?JOHN STEVELLY][1]
Draft, Henry Papers, Smithsonian Archives

Princeton Aug 29th 1842

My Dear Sir

Mrs[2] Beattie[3] a former pupil of yours who has been connected for a short
time with our Institution starts this evening for New-York with the intention of sailing in the next ship for Ireland and I embrace so favourable
an opportunity of sending you a small package. You will find the articles
of little value in themselves but I am sure you will receive them with some
interest as testimony of my kind regard.

Our friend Bache is now in Princeton on a short visit with his wife at
our house. We have been enjoying ourselves in a scientific gossip and we
have only to regret that he is obliged to return to Phil[d] tomorrow morning. We were speaking of you this morning before Mr Beattie gave us the
information of his intention of starting so soon. I have but little to com-

[1] Henry's address book (Box 17, Henry Papers, Smithsonian Archives), p. [12], contains
the notation that he sent a letter to Stevelly
via a student. John Beatty is a likely candidate.

[2] A slip of the pen.
[3] John Beatty of Belfast College joined the
senior class at Princeton in May 1842. Faculty
Minutes, May 20, 1842, Princeton University
Archives.

municate in the way of science. I have just received the Atheneum containing the report of the association[4] but have not yet had time to read it attentively. I have seen however by a glance that you were as usual faithful to your duty[5] and with unabated zeal assisting in the good cause.

You will see by a leaf from the procedings of the American Phil. Society that I have again been engaged on the subject of electricity.[6] Some of my results have a bearing on your favourite science Meteorology and I send you a needle which was magnetized, this very afternoon in my study by a flash from a thunder cloud, at the distance of several miles. The polarity is not very strong in the needle I send but very decided and indicates an upward current. You will be able to test the magnetism by approaching the larger end of the needle to one extremity of a small compass, such as is sometimes worn in a watch key, or by an other needle slightly magnetized and suspended by a very fine fibre of silk. The arrangement of apparatus is a simple wire of copper soldered at one end to the tinned-iron roof of our house and dipping at the other end into the water of a deep well. This wire is divided near the middle of its length and a spiral of about a hundred convalutions inserted into the opening. The needle is inserted into the axis of this spiral and at each flash the induction from a distance produces a current in the wire which passing round the needle developes the magnetism. The spiral and the middle part of the long wire are brought into the window of my study.[7]

[4] Each of the weekly *Athenaeum* issues from June 25, 1842, to July 23, 1842, contained reports of the British Association meeting in Manchester.

[5] Stevelly was one of the secretaries of Section A (Mathematical and Physical Science).

[6] Henry presumably enclosed "Contributions V: Induction from Ordinary Electricity; Oscillatory Discharge."

[7] The draft ends here; we have not located the copy sent Stevelly. This document has markings from the biographical and editorial labors of Mary Henry.

TO [JOHN WHITE WEBSTER][1]
Draft, Henry Papers, Smithsonian Archives

Princeton Sept 2nd 1842

My Dear Sir

Your favour of the 27th ult[2] was received last night and I called this morning on one of the editors of the Princeton Review[3] and stated to him your

[1] Although Webster's name does not appear on this draft, the content indicates he was the intended recipient.

[2] Not found, but probably a response to Henry's letter of August 17, 1842, above.

[3] Probably Charles Hodge.

request to be allowed to circulate your answer to Wiley and Putman[4] within the cover of the Review. His <*answer was*> reply was that a general rule had been made not to admit of any thing of the kind on account of the increase of the postage which was already so large as to be complained of and also on account of the abuses the custom is liable to besides in the present case should your antagonist desire to circulate a rejoinder in the same way it would not be proper to refuse him the same privalege. He promised however to insert any notice of your book that might serve to point out the superiority of it over that of the edition published by Wiley and Putman and as this might contain a reference to your pamphlet I think your cause would be equally well served by this method.[5] The fact of the payment of Liebig by the B.A. for the preparation of the Report can be ascertained I should think by referring to the appropriations of money for different objects and also to the treasurers accounts as given in the several volums of the transactions or Reports as they are called of the association.[6]

I hope you will not bring forward the authority of Lardner[7] to establish any of your positions and that for the sake of the cause of good morals in our country he will receve the countenance of no Person of your standing amoung us. It is true that we are all liable to be misled by our passions and therefore it may be said we should be charitable in regard to <*the errors of our fellows*> those who may have given way to temptations but it should

---

[4] i.e., *Reply to a Notice of Messrs. Wiley & Putnam* (Boston, 1842), which Webster wrote on August 29.

In a circular of June 26, 1842, Webster had accused Wiley & Putnam of publishing an unauthorized, incomplete, and incorrect edition of Liebig's *Animal Chemistry.* Wiley & Putnam responded with an advertisement in the *Boston Daily Advertiser* of August 16, claiming they had legitimately acquired a corrected copy of the work, the property of the British Association, at a London auction. Webster wanted to have his August 29 reply printed in the *Biblical Repertory and Princeton Review.*

[5] An unsigned review of Liebig's *Animal Chemistry* did not appear in the *Princeton Review* until October 1843. Not only was Webster's pamphlet not mentioned, the reviewer utilized yet another, and cheaper, American edition, that of James M. Campbell and Co., of Philadelphia, published in 1843. *Biblical Repertory and Princeton Review,* 1843, *15*:611.

To complicate matters, still another American edition had been published in October 1842 as an extra of the *New World* (volume 2, numbers 25 and 26), edited by Benjamin Park and published by J. Winchester. This edition sold for twenty-five cents a copy. In a note to the reader, Winchester remarked "two American editions have already been published, but at a price about five times the amount of that which is demanded for this. . . . The people at large are thereby excluded from the benefits of instruction which they confer. This should not be, and we intend to remedy the evil."

The appearance of this cheap edition was to give Webster additional problems with his own publisher, John Owen, who had not yet paid Webster for the work done on his edition. John White Webster to Eben N. Horsford, September 28, 1844, Horsford Papers, Rensselaer Polytechnic Institute.

[6] In his pamphlet, Webster asserted that an examination of the British Association's annual reports and Treasurer's annual statements proved that "not a shilling appears to have been appropriated for defraying the expense, or to have been paid to Professor Liebig." John White Webster, *Reply to a Notice,* p. 3.

[7] Dionysius Lardner. For other comments on Lardner, see Henry to Henslow, July 5, 1842, printed above.

be reccollected that just in proportion as we are in danger of <*falling into any crime*> vices the greater is the necessity of visiting <*it in*> every case <*of it*> with the more severe condemnation. I am should be glad to join any association of scientific men in our country for the purpose of expressing our approbation of an international copy-right law. Nothing however but a full copy right woul[d] satisfy me.

TO JAMES HENRY COFFIN[1]
Henry Papers, Smithsonian Archives[2]

Princeton Sept 9th 1842

Dear Sir

Your favour of the 2nd ult[3] was duely received by mail but I have not found it convenient to answer it before to day. I was once much interested in astronomy but for seven or eight years past I have given it no attention except so far as occasionally to take part with my Brotherinlaw Professor Alexander in some of his observations.

[1] An 1828 graduate of Amherst, Coffin (1806–1873) was a tutor at Williams College. He was later Professor of Mathematics and Natural Philosophy at Lafayette College in Easton, Pennsylvania (1846–1873).

Coffin avidly gathered and published meteorological data and became one of the earliest and closest collaborators in the work of the Smithsonian Institution. Henry gave Coffin all of the meteorological data gathered by the Smithsonian network and Army observers from 1854 to 1859 for reduction and analysis. The Smithsonian also published his two major works: *Winds of the Northern Hemisphere* (1853) and *Winds of the Globe*, posthumously published in 1875.

Henry's respect for Coffin's work and character is evident in a statement he prepared for use in a eulogy:

In attentively studying the result of Prof. Coffin's labors, we cannot but be struck with his conscientious regard for accuracy, and his devotion to truth . . . .

. . . we cannot refrain from endeavoring to impress upon the mind of the general public that men of his character, who do honor to humanity, ought not to be suffered to expend their energies in the drilling of youth in the mere elements of knowledge, and with a compensation not more than suf-ficient to secure the necessaries of life; that they should be consecrated as officiating priests in the temple of knowledge, be furnished with all the appliances and assistance necessary to the accomplishment of their objects, namely, the extension of the bounds of human thought and of human power.
Popular Science Monthly, August 1873, 3:507, 508.

DAB. John C. Clyde, *Life of James H. Coffin* (Easton, Pennsylvania, 1881). According to Clyde (Coffin's son-in-law), Coffin and Henry became acquainted when Coffin published a meteorological register in 1839. Henry sent Coffin a copy of his "Contributions III: Electro-Dynamic Induction," with the inscription:

To James H. Coffin, author of the interesting report on the Meteorology of Ogdensburg, just published in the abstracts of the Regents of the University of New York. With the respects of Joseph Henry.
Clyde, *Coffin*, pp. 42–43.

[2] One box of the Henry Papers contains correspondence to and from Coffin dating from 1842 to 1873. The Smithsonian Archives also has a small collection of Coffin Papers, as well as Coffin correspondence in other record units.

[3] Not found.

I have examined your pamphlet[4] and think it will be of much value to the teacher of astronomy and it appears to me to be precisely such a work as was required in our colleges. I fully agree with you in the opinion that with the limited time of our college course we should aim at giving clear views of general principles rather than attempt to make adepts in the practical application of any science. The details should and indeed can be <*profitably*> no farther dwelt on than is necessary to impress more thoroughly the general principles on the mind. According to the theory I have adopted of education we should begin with pure art and end with pure science.[5] The boy may be occupied with committing rules and indeed should be drilled into an expert use of all practical processes, but the young man should be principally occupied with purely intellectual studies and nothing can be farther from these than the calculation of eclipses from elements taken from the nautical almanack or from tables the principles of which have not been clearly explained to him.[6]

I have shown your pamphlet to Professor Alexander and he has promised to examine it carefully as soon as he gets through with some investigations which now occupy all his time not devoted to college duties.

There are no meteorological observations at present made in Princeton except a register of the Thermometer kept by Dr Hodge of the Theological seminary. I commenced a series of observations when I first came to this place but while I was abroad they were discontinued and amidst my other engagements I have thought I could not attend to them.

I am just now considerably interested in one part of meteorology namely the phenomena of thunder storms although I am not very favourably situated at Princeton for observing them. The thunder cloud scarcely eve[r] passes directly over the village. It generally divides into two parts as it approaches us from the west one part going to the north of us and the other to the south. You will see by a copy of the account of my last communication to the American Philosophical society* that I have succeeded

* I will mail with this letter a copy of the article[7] refered to.

[4] *Astronomical Tables Adapted to the Theory of Astronomy, as Taught in New England Colleges* (New Haven, 1842).

[5] Henry gave a full exposition of his views on education in an 1854 address to the American Association for the Advancement of Education. See "The Philosophy of Education" in Arthur P. Molella et al., eds., *A Scientist in American Life: Lectures and Essays of Joseph Henry* (Washington, 1980).

[6] Coffin designed the tables in his small pamphlet to be used with the astronomical treatises of Olmsted and Herschel. He later expanded the work and published it as *Solar and Lunar Eclipses Familiarly Illustrated and Explained, With the Method of Calculating Them According to the Theory of Astronomy as Taught in New England Colleges* (New York, 1845).

[7] "Contributions V: Induction from Ordinary Electricity; Oscillatory Discharge."

in getting induced currents from discharges from the clouds at a great distance and I hope to be able with this new method of studying the phenomena to arrive at some interesting results.

Feby 25ᵗʰ 1843

This letter was written shortly after the receipt of your letter and pamphlet but by some accident I neglected to send it at the time and it has since laid in my portfolio.

I have received a letter from my friend Professor Hopkins in reference to you which I have answered to day.[8] I have suggested in my letter to Professor H. that it might be advisable for you to apply for a Professorship of mathematics in the Navey and this I should think could be best done through the members of Congress from your District.

With much Respect I am yours &c

Joseph Henry

[8] Neither letter has been found. Albert Hopkins (*Henry Papers*, 2:212) was Professor of Natural Philosophy at Williams. He and Coffin worked together even before Coffin became a tutor at Williams, and at Williams they were close friends. Clyde, *Coffin*, pp. 48, 232.

JACOB WHITMAN BAILEY TO JOHN TORREY
Torrey Papers, Library, New York Botanical Garden

West Point Sept 17th. 1842

My dear Friend

The exceeding kindness of you and Prof Henry ex[c]ites my warmest gratitude, and although it is now too late to take any steps with regard to the appointment in Virginia, I shall always remember with heartfelt pleasure, the spontaneous offer of assistance from you and Henry.[1] Such acts as

[1] The appointment was to the Chair of Chemistry and Materia Medica at the University of Virginia, made vacant by the death of John Patten Emmet (*Henry Papers*, 2:388n–389n).

Emmet had been dissatisfied with the position and resigned even before his death. His position was filled temporarily by Robert Empie Rogers (1813–1884, *DAB*), formerly chemist to the Pennsylvania Geological Survey and brother of Henry Darwin and William Barton Rogers.

Although the chair paid well, Charlottesville was isolated from the scientific community, whose southern extremity rarely reached below Philadelphia, and this dis-

these show one who are his true friends. Before receiving your letter I had heard from two sources worthy of credit, that the election was to take place on the *19ᵗʰ inst*, consequently when I got your letter[2] on the morning of the 16th, there were but 3 days left to act in. Of course it would have been worse than useless to attempt to do any thing.

I had indeed previously made up my mind that Bache or Rogers would succeed, and having also heard that none but an M.D would be appointed, I had given up all thoughts of applying, for I did not relish the idea of rejection. I felt also very doubtful about the propriety of going to the U. of Vᵃ even if I could have got the appointment. I felt that *lecturing* to large classes would be new business to me, and that if I should fail to render myself popular, I might be ruined.[3] There being also so little prospect of success, I had previously to the reception of your letter given up all thoughts of the subject. Yet your letter unsettled me again, and had it not been too late, I believe I should have been tempted to let you and Henry "*go* it as strong" as you pleased in my behalf, and even now, should it prove that there is any mistake about the date of the election, I am not unwilling to become a Candidate. But I suppose it will be all settled ere this reaches you, and it will not be worth while to bother ourselves any more about the affair.

I have been so much of a nurse lately, in consequence of the long continued illness of Mrs Bailey that I have had no time for scientific observations. I hope to go to work again this winter and think I shall continue a course of expᵗˢ in the micro-chemical examination of cry[s]tals in plants. I have already a number of facts which I believe quite new and interesting. I forget whether I have mentioned to you the occurrence and predominance

---

suaded many. Henry urged Torrey to apply for the position (Torrey to Bailey, August 23, 1842, Bailey Papers, Boston Science Museum), and Torrey, declining, in turn urged Bailey, adding Henry's heartfelt support (ibid.). Bailey thought that nothing but the financial advantage—and possibility of better climate for his invalid wife—would induce him to make the move (Bailey to Torrey, August [24], 1842, Torrey Papers, Library, New York Botanical Garden). His incipient plans were interrupted by A. D. Bache's decision to apply for the chair, probably to put pressure on University of Pennsylvania officials. Torrey wrote Bailey, "You would, of course, not be a rival candidate to Bache, especially when he has almost been promised the appointment." (Torrey to Bailey, August 27, 1842, Bailey Papers, Boston Science Museum). The ploy worked; although Bache did not receive a higher salary, he did receive permission to have another salaried position in addition to his professorship. (Torrey to Bailey, September 13, 1842, Bailey Papers, Boston Science Museum). But by this time it was too late for Bailey, even with Torrey's and Henry's promptings. (Henry had endorsed no other candidate, reserving his recommendation for Bailey.) Rogers succeeded to the permanent post, strongly helped by the campaign of his two prominent older brothers.

[2] Torrey's letter of September 13, 1842, cited above.

[3] The salary at Virginia was in part based on students' lecture fees. Medical students were required to take the course, others could choose it or not. Thus an unpopular lecturer could expect straightened circumstances.

of *macled* crystals of this form[4] Pomeae and Amygdalae which I They appear to be like the single Hickory, composed of Oxalate of of crystals in bark of Chesnut and but they are exceedingly minute.  in bark of all the have yet examined.[5] crystals in bark of Lime. The number locust is enormous,

In the leaves of many plants one or more rows of these crystals accompany the spiral vessels or rather the vascular bundles in all their ramifications through the leaves and may be seen beautifuly when the *burnt* leaf is carefully fixed in Canad[a] Balsam. I am sure that this is a rich field for research, but it will require a deal of time.[6] As for the Algae, what shall I do? I consider all my observations on these as your property. I can either send you a list of such as I have determined, with occasional remarks, or I can get Silliman to publish it. It is time that a beginning was made in this department of American botany. How shall I return your valuable collection of Algae. If you wished I could rearrange the whole according to the manner adopted by Harvey in his recent work on British Algae.[7] I have been afraid however to meddle with your genera papers, although several of them include plants now referred to different groups. Let me know whether I shall return them as they are or without altering the old labels, or write in pencil the new names, and put them under their new genera. I have 4 N[os] of the Linnea[8] belonging to you, and will return them by first opportunity.

I lately received a small package from N. B. Ward of London with a kind note inviting me to send papers and specimens to the Microscopical Soc. of Lond., he also send me a copy of his work on the growth of plants in Glazed Cases and several copies of the 1st and 2[d] Reports of the Mic. Soc.[9] I believe

[4] Macled crystals are twinned crystals of the type in Bailey's illustration. The term also means a spotted or speckled mineral.

[5] The term Amygdalus refers to the family of trees and shrubs including plums, peaches, and almonds. Ellen R. Farr, Jan A. Leussink, and Frans A. Statler, *Index Nominum Genericorum (Plantarum)* (The Hague, 1979). Pomeae (now obsolete) referred to pomes: apples, pears, etc. Asa Gray, *Lessons in Botany and Vegetable Physiology* (New York, 1857), p. 147.

[6] Bailey's researches resulted in the paper "On the Crystals Which Occur Spontaneously Formed in the Tissues of Plants," read at the Association of American Geologists and Naturalists meeting on April 27, 1843, abstracted in *Silliman's Journal*, 1843, *45*:149–

151, and printed in full in ibid., 1845, *48*:17–33.

[7] William Henry Harvey (1811–1866), Irish botanist and Keeper of the Herbarium and Professor of Botany at Trinity College, Dublin, published *A Manual of British Marine Algae* ([London?], 1841). Harvey later assisted Bailey in categorizing the algae collections from the Wilkes Expedition.

[8] *Linnaea, Ein Journal für die Botanik in ihrem ganzen Umfange*, published in the 1840s in Halle by D. F. L. von Schlechtendahl.

[9] Nathaniel Bagshaw Ward (1791–1868, *DNB*), British botanist, member of the Royal Microscopical Society, and author of *The Growth of Plants without Exposure to Air* (London, 1836). See also *Henry Papers*, *3*:297.

I sent you a copy of the 2[d] Report. I have one of the 1st at your service if [you][10] have not got one.

What a grand time you and my friend Henry must have together, two such congenial spirits must add much to each others happiness, and the sympathy $<and>$ advice and suggestions to one another must be of mutual benefit. Are you making a Botanist of him. I hope he still continues to attend to Geology. He had made good progress when I last saw him. I should think he would be somewhat taken with the undulatory theory started by the Rogers to account for our parrallel Appalachian and Alleghany ranges. The amount of it I believe is this. They suppose a line of igneous action—outbreak of volcanic gases, and a starting line for earthquake waves to have existed from Canada to Alabama either at, or a little East of the great primary range. The earthquake waves propagated along this line have thrown up the earths crust into parallel waves, which as in all imperfecly elastic media die off as the distance from the starting point increases. These waves connected with a "vis a tergo"[11] have produced first the inverted dips along the E. margin of the Appalachian Vally, then the sharp waves W of the Shawangunk and finally broad undulations of the far West, thus

What ever may be thought of this theory, it serves well to connect in the memory the leading facts with regard to the position of the rocks of a vast extent of our country.[12] A mathematical investigation of the effect of suc-

---

[10] A tear in the page.

[11] A force of impulse. The term was derived from scholastic natural philosophy; cf. James Clerk Maxwell, "Action at a Distance," *The Scientific Papers of James Clerk Maxwell*, ed. W. D. Niven, 2 vols. (Cambridge, England, 1890), 2:313: "a force of the old school—a case of *vis a tergo*—a shove from behind."

[12] Henry Darwin Rogers and William Barton Rogers read a paper, "On the Physical Structure of the Appalachian Chain, As Exemplifying the Laws Which Have Regulated the Elevation of Great Mountain Chains Generally," at the third meeting of the Association of American Geologists and Naturalists in April 1842 in Boston, a meeting which Bailey attended. The paper was also presented at the June 1842 meeting of the British Association in Manchester, and its contents summarized in the London *Athenaeum* (July 2, 1842, pp. 591–592). Bailey's short summary is accurate except that the Rogers brothers placed the greatest local rupture at the southeast of the Appalachian Chain. The theory generated less interest in the United States than in Britain, where it clashed with that of Élie de Beaumont, which relied only on the horizontal stresses of the cooling earth to provide the force to buckle mountains. The Rogers brothers' theory used vertical forces as well, arising from subterranean gases coming to the surface. W. B. and H. D. Rogers, "On the Physical Structure of the Appalachian Chain . . . ," *Reports of the First, Second, and Third Meetings of the Association of American Geologists and Naturalists* (Boston, 1843), pp. 474–531; "Abstract of the Proceedings of the Twelfth Meeting of the British Association for the Advancement of Science, Section C, Geology and Physical Geography," *Silliman's Journal*, 1843, *44*:359–365; Patsy A. Gerstner, "A Dynamic Theory of Mountain Building: Henry Darwin Rogers, 1842," *Isis*, 1975, *66*:26–37.

cessive earthquake waves, connected possibly with cross waves would throw much light on this subject. Just think of the possibility of the earths crust having undulated under the influence of laws similar to those governing the subtle medium of light! Mrs Bailey sends her kindest regard to you all, including Prof Henry and family. She would be delighted to see any of your here this fall and it is so long since we met, that I trust we may see each other before long. What a disappointment I met with last spring, when on calling at your old quarters and expecting your usual kind welcome, I found the house stripped of all its furniture and no familiar face to greet me. I have not a specimen of Udora to look at the remarkable structure you describe. Can there be an interior set of Carpels.[13]

I like Grays Book[14] very [much][15] and I hope as he publishes new editions that he will gradually add new figures of illustration of the Nat. families. I have recommended his work to several young students who appear much pleased with it.

Believe me ever with kindest regards
Yrs J. W. Bailey

[13] Udora was a genus now referred to as Anacharis. There are eight American species of this aqueous flowering plant. J. C. Willis, *A Dictionary of the Flowering Plants and Ferns*, 8th ed., rev. H. K. Airy Shaw (Cambridge, England, 1973), s.v. "Udora." In his letter of September 13 (cited above), Torrey had asked Bailey to look at the ovary of Udora.

[14] Asa Gray's *Botanical Textbook for Colleges, Schools, and Private Students* (New York, 1841).

[15] Written on the outside sheet of the folded letter, this word was obscured by the wax seal.

FROM JOHN W. DRAPER[1]

Henry Papers, Smithsonian Archives

683 Broadway. N. York
[September 1842][2]

Dear Sir,

Dr Daniel P Gardner[3] a friend of mine is a candidate for the vacant Professorship of Chemistry in the University of Va. He will shew you a letter

[1] John W. Draper (1811–1882) was Professor of Chemistry at New York University. *Henry Papers, 4*:207–208.

[2] The date is from Henry's file note. Apparently Gardner presented the letter in person; it was not mailed.

[3] Daniel Pereira Gardner (d. 1853) was Draper's brother-in-law. The son of the physician to the Emperor of Brazil, Gardner was a practicing physician with an interest in botany. Biographical information supplied by Daniel Draper (nephew) to University of Pennsylvania, J. W. Draper and Draper Family Papers, Library of Congress.

which I have written to the Visitors of that institution in his behalf.[4] I am anxious to fortify his claims as much as I can and if you can say any thing in his favour based upon those facts it will be received by me as a deep obligation. He has very strong recommendations from an extensive circle of Scientific friends.

Yours truly
Jno W Draper

[4] The University of Virginia Archives has been unable to discover any material dealing with Gardner's candidacy for the Professorship of Chemistry. No record of a letter of recommendation from Henry has been found, but then it was unlikely that Henry would have supported Gardner, as Bache had been a candidate. When Bache withdrew, Henry endorsed J. W. Bailey. See above, Bache to Henry, August 22, 1842, and Bailey to John Torrey, September 17, 1842.

TO [JOHN STEVENS HENSLOW]
Draft,[1] Henry Papers, Smithsonian Archives

Princeton College of NJ
Oct 3rd 1842

My Dear Sir

I forward to you by my young Friend Mr Cuyler about two months ago[2] a few articles of natural history and two nos of Torrey and Gray's flora. I have found to day in one of the drawers of my study a copy of the 2nd no of the 2nd vol of the flora with your name written on the cover and the idea has occurred to me that I have by mistake sent to you two nos of the same kind. Please to inform me what nos of <*the flora*> you have received and I will endeavour to complete your set as soon as the work is published. [. . .][3] new in the way of science. This is the season of our college vacation and I am about commencing to day a new series of experiments on electricity. My last labours in this line produced a series of interesting results. I was enabled to magnetize needles by an induced current at the distance of 30 feet from the primary current in the cellar of the Philosophical cabinet by a single spark from the electrical machine placed in the third story of

[1] Henry made brief notes on the content of this letter to Henslow, the final version of which was written on October 4, at the end of his Notes on Letters Sent with Theodore Ledyard Cuyler, July 2–6, 1842, above (see note 1). The notes do not indicate any subjects not covered in this draft.

[2] Henry's letter of July 5, 1842, is printed above.

[3] The second page of this draft, on the back of the first, begins in mid-sentence. Mary Henry may have discarded some of the middle of the draft when she copied an extract from it.

the same building without any connection by mere induction or disturbance of the <*elec*> equilibrium of the electrical plenum and also <*magnetize*> to produce similar effects in my study by flashes of lightning at the
distance of seven and eight miles.[4]

[4] Henry had reported both of these results
at the end of his June 17, 1842, communication to the American Philosophical Society
(*Proceedings*, 1841–1843, 2:195–196). This is
all that survives of the draft.

"RECORD OF EXPERIMENTS"[1]
Henry Papers, Smithsonian Archives

Oct 5th 1842
Phenomena of a drop of water
on heated metal

Made to day a few experments on the slow evaporation of water from the
surface of heated metal[2]

1 Supported a silver spoon over a spirit lamp with a large wick. Then after
the metal was heated poured in water from a pipe until the spoon was
nearly or quite half full. The water was considerably aggitated but remained without boiling and very slowly evaporated.

2. Made the same experment with alcohol the effect was produced at a
lower temperature than with water—also repeated the same with eather.

3 Placed a quanty of brass filings in the spoon these were much agitated
and gathered up into the drop of water and there floated, as it were at some
distance from the metal until the whole of the liquid was evaporated. It appears evident from this experiment that the water is not incontact with the
surface of the metal. There is also no attraction of cohesion betwen the
water and the metal or if any it is very small for when a stick or piece of
wire is thurst into the drop, the water adheres to the wire or stick.

4 A piece of thin metal (plate) was thrown into the drop. The metal remained suspended and moved with the gliding motion of the drop show-

[1] This is the first entry of the third and last
manuscript volume of the "Record of Experiments."

[2] These experiments are a follow-up to those
reported in the "Record of Experiments"
entry of May 6, 1842, printed above.

ing as in the case of the filings that the drop is not in close approximation with the surface of the metal.[3]

5   Next tried mercury on a slip of platina found that the same phenomenon was produced the platinum was heated to a white heat nearly. The globule remained a few moments stationary or in motion with the gliding motion of the drop of water and then suddenly disappeared with something like an explosive action

6   Tried on the same piece of platinum small globules of melted lead and tin but no effect like that produced by the mercury and water was observed. The substance was incapable of giving off a vapour

7   Small drops of water were thrown on to a small cup formed of thin plate platinum, heated to whiteness in the spirit lamp. The water remained some minutes unevaporated, slowly however diminishing in bulk and when it got to the size of about that of a pin's head, it disappeared at once with a kind of an explosion. Sometimes an explosion took place which seperated the small drop into two parts. All the time the drop was diminishing the little cup of platinum which contained it was at a low red heat but the moment that the drop disappeared, the metal became white hot. This shows the constant evaporation which is going on

8   When a drop of water is taken up on the end of a rod of bad conducting matter (for heat) and then held in the midst of the flame of a spirit lamp the drop does not instantaneously disappear, but it remains several minutes and gradually disappears. It would appear from these experments that the slow evaporation of a drop of water on heated metal is due to the *constant* generation at the lower surface of the drop of a quantity of steam, which by its elastic force prevents the drop from coming in contact with the heated metal. The heat necessary for the constant production of the steam is conveyed to the water by eradiation from the heated metal

Also it would appear that inorder to the sudden evaporation which produces the phenomenon called boiling it appears necessary that the water should be in physical contact with the metal and if this be correct, boiling will not take place at the same temperature in vessels which are not capable of being infilmed with the liquid. Hence I should infer that mercury will boil in a vessel of which the inner surface is amalgamated sooner than in one of glass which has no attraction or litle for the metal

[3] Henry annotated both this and the preceding experiment with marginal references to the "Record of Experiments" entry of June 5, 1845 (Henry Papers, Smithsonian Archives), where he recorded his examination of capillary phenomena.

8[4] Could not produce the same effect with a glass plate. This substance appears to be[5] so bad a conductor of heat that the upper surface on which the drop is thrown almost instantly cools and lets the water down to the glass. The sudden evaporation then takes place

Put the drop upon a piece of platinum into which a hole was made of about the 1/20 of an inch in diameter. Placed this over the lamp, and when the heat was up to that of redness a drop of water would not pass through until the diameter was so much reduced as to be less than that of the hole; it then fell through as if it had been a piece of lead.

If a large ladle be heated red hot and water poured cautiously into it, the liqud will not pass through holes of 1/10 of an inch in diameter. The cause of this is evident the cohesion of the water remains nearly as strong as before the heating, while the stratum of steam prevents the water from wetting or infilming the iron

[4] An obvious slip of the pen.
[5] The remainder of this entry is on a page dated "Oct 6th." Given the relationship between these experiments and those preceding them, and the quite different topic of the entry of October 6, we presume the "6" is a slip of the pen.

"RECORD OF EXPERIMENTS"
Henry Papers, Smithsonian Archives

Oct 6th 1842
Arrangement of Long wire
from Phil Hall to my study

I made an arrangement a few days since of a long wire, extending from the electrical machine in the philos. Hall to my study on the opposite side of the campus. The wire passed diagonally across the large lecture room to the southwest window facing the Library and thence to the south<*erly*> most window of the two upper ones of the east end of the old college then through the long upper college hall to the southerly window of the west end of the college to the door of my study. The whole length of this wire is [. . .] feet.[1] It is supported by silk ribbons fastened to the sides of the windows.

This morning I completed a circuit with this wire and the ground by plunging the end next my study into the well, or rather by connecting it with the wire which is already in the well, for the experiments on atmo-

[1] Henry never recorded the length of the wire, but one visitor stated that it was 400 feet. See below, J. H. Lefroy to Edward Sabine, October 25, 1842.

spheric elect (see last book)[2] and by placing the end of a copper wire with a plate of lead on it into Mr Clow's well and then connecting this last with the wire first mentioned. When a small galvanometer of fine wire was placed in the circuit in my study and a small electrometer, consisting of a plate of zinc of about a tenth of an inch in width and the end of the wire (1/20 of an inch) for a negative element the needle was deflected, showing that this small galvanic arrangement was sufficient to send a current through [. . .] feet of wire and [. . .] feet[3] of earth[4]

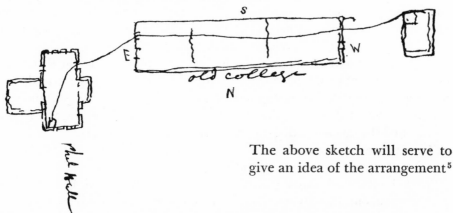

The above sketch will serve to give an idea of the arrangement[5]

[2] See above, "Record of Experiments," June 10, 1842.

[3] Again, Henry failed to record the length of the wire, as well as the distance between the wells.

[4] It was this experiment Henry had in mind when, while giving testimony regarding the invention of the electric telegraph, he claimed to be the first in the United States to repeat Steinheil's experiment using the earth as a portion of the electric circuit. See, e.g., United States Circuit Court, Eastern District of Pennsylvania, *Benjamin B. French, et al. versus Henry J. Rogers, et als.: Respondents' Evidence* (Philadelphia, 1851), p. 254.

[5] The building in the center labelled "old college" is Nassau Hall. The building on the right is Henry's house.

"RECORD OF EXPERIMENTS"
Henry Papers, Smithsonian Archives

Oct 7th 1842
Experiments on the induction of the long wire on another parallel wire[1]

Made a number of experiments to day with the wire above described and another placed parallel to it. A discharge of electricity from 3 jars of the

[1] In the original notebook, this entry begins in the middle of a left-hand page and continues on a right-hand page. This descriptive phrase is the running head of the left-hand

French battery was passed through the wire and a needle placed in a helix connected with the secondary wire was magnetized. The arrangement was as follows. Two poles supported by tripods formed of long slats of boards were placed upright in the back campus and over the tops of these a part of a wire was stretched parallel to the wire through the old college, and of a length equal to the whole breadth of the campus. This wire was continued backward on each side until it extended to the two halls[2] it then crossed over with the two ends united so as to form a complete parallelogram. In the first experiment the distance of the nearst and parallel parts of the two wires was 60 feet and with this the needle placed in the helix used in the study for atmospheric electricity, was strongly magnetized.

The parallel part of the second wire was next removed to the distance of 90 feet from that of the wire through the old college and again at this distance several needles were magnetized to a degree scarcely less than in the case of the last distance. In the experiments previous to the one now to be mentioned the electrical discharge was from three [. . .][3] jars.

The charge was now reduced to that from one jar, the needle again came from the hel[i]x strongly magnetic.

Next the jar was removed and a single spark thown on to the suspended end of the conducting wire while the other end was connected with the rubber. The needle with this was also magnetic but apparently not quite as strongly as before.

After this the second wire was removed from the long poles and the parallel part stretched between the two upper windows of the first entry of the two parallel colleges.[4] By this arrangement the distance between the parallel parts was increased to 165 feet but notwithstanding this great distance, the needle from the induction of a discharge of 3 jars was strongly magnetized. The experiment of a single spark was not attempted on account of the lateness of the hour. It would appear from the strength of the inductive action at this distance that the space between the two wires can be farther increased.

The needles in all the above mentioned experments were magnetized in the same direction, indicating a current in [. . .][5] of the primary current.

---

page. The running head on the right reads: "Induction of ordinary electricity at a great distance."

[2] The American Whig and Cliosophic Society Halls.

[3] Henry left a space, presumably for the later addition of the size of the jars.

[4] East and West Colleges.

[5] Henry left a blank. Apparently he forgot to record the direction of the magnetization.

October 8, 1842

"RECORD OF EXPERIMENTS"
Henry Papers, Smithsonian Archives

Oct 8th 1842

Removed the secondary wire to the farther entry of the parallel buildings. Sent through the primary wire a charge from three jars. The needle placed in the helix mentioned before was again magnetic and in the same direction as in the expermts of yesterday and the day before.

Next sent a charge from a single jar the needle was in this case magnetized in the same direction as before but not to the same degree of intensity.

In these experiments the whole paralelogram formed by the secondary wire, was carried backward, so that the fartherest side was in the field beyond the society halls.[1] The experiments were not continued this day on account of the dampness of the weather. In the morning a very heavy fog rested on the ground until about 10 oclock AM.

[1] On October 21, 1842, Henry reported to a meeting of the American Philosophical Society that with only a single spark from the electrical machine he had succeeded in magnetizing a needle by an induced current when the primary and secondary wires were separated by over 220 feet. APS *Proceedings*, 1841–1843, 2:229. He later included a brief account of these experiments in his letter to Samuel B. Dod of December 4, 1876, on his scientific researches at Princeton. Samuel B. Dod, *Discourse Memorial of Joseph Henry* (New York, 1878), pp. 54; reprinted in *Memorial of Joseph Henry* (Washington, 1880), pp. 151–152.

"RECORD OF EXPERIMENTS"
Henry Papers, Smithsonian Archives

Oct 15th 1842

Spent the forepart of this day with Lieut Lefroy[1] of the Royal Artillery in determing the dip and intensity of terrestrial magnetism at this place. The

[1] Commissioned in the Royal Artillery in 1834, John Henry Lefroy (1817–1890) began demonstrating an interest in science in 1837. From 1839 until 1842 he conducted a magnetic survey at St. Helena Island. In the latter year, after a short stay in England for further training, he took command of the magnetic observatory at Toronto, Canada, one of the colonial observing sites for the Magnetic Crusade. While in Canada, where he remained until 1853, he directed an expedition to the Northwest from April 1843 to November 1844. Lefroy remained in the army until 1870, resigning with the rank of major general. John Henry Lefroy, *In Search of the Magnetic North: A Soldier-Surveyor's Letters from the North-West, 1843–1844*, ed. George F. G. Stanley (Toronto, 1955), pp. xi–xxviii; *DNB*.

Presentation copies of two of his publications survive in the Henry Library. A copy of the monograph resulting from his expedition, *Magnetical and Meteorological Observations at Lake Athabasca and Fort Simpson . . .* (London, 1855), was given Henry by Edward

station was that at which my observations were made on the intensity several years ago, namely in Mr Clows field south of the west college.[2] The spot may be known by a depression in the general level of the ground the station was the middle of this.

Sabine. Lefroy himself sent Henry a copy of his circular letter, "Second Report on Observations of the Aurora Borealis, 1850–1," subsequently published in *Silliman's Journal*, 1852, 2d ser. *14*:153–160.

For more specific information on Lefroy's surveying activities in North America and his meeting with Henry, see below, Lefroy to Edward Sabine, October 25, 1842.

[2] Perhaps a reference to the observations Henry made in the summer of 1838. *Henry Papers*, 3:412.

FROM ROBERT M. PATTERSON

Henry Papers, Smithsonian Archives

Philadelphia.
Oct. 17, 1842.

My dear Sir,

You look upon us occasionally at Philadelphia: can you not make Saturday next one of your days? The Wistar party will be at my house, and you will meet a score of your friends. Besides, you can see the exhibition of the Franklin Institute,[1] and can, if you give a few hours more, attend the A. P. Soc. on Friday evening.[2] If Prof. Alexander & Prof. Torrey would accompany you, my pleasure would be much increased.

I have not yet been able to make my promised visit at Princeton, but I will do so in a few days.

Very truly your friend,
R. M. Patterson

---

[1] The Franklin Institute began holding an annual exhibition of American industrial products in 1824. The exhibitions not only served to encourage manufactures through a prize system, but also to increase interest in the Institute. After 1829, exhibitions were held biannually. However, as the fairs were among the few financially successful programs of the Institute, after 1842 they were again held every year, for two weeks. Alexander Bache delivered the opening remarks in 1842. Bruce Sinclair, *Philadelphia's Philosopher Mechanics: A History of the Franklin Institute, 1824–1865* (Baltimore, 1974), pp. 39–41, 100–103, 237–239.

[2] Henry attended the October 21 meeting of the American Philosophical Society, where he gave an account of his latest work in induction over great distances. *APS Proceedings*, 1841–1843, 2:229.

J. H. LEFROY TO EDWARD SABINE[1]
Sabine Papers, Records of Kew Observatory, Public Record Office, London

Toronto.
Oct:. 25. 1842.

My dear Colonel.

I have great pleasure in acquainting you with my arrival here yesterday, the 24th, after spending a sunday at the Falls of Niagara, and visiting all the places named in your list excepting Hudson, Ohio.[2] My visit to the States was so productive in pleasure and profit to myself that I feel some difficulty in finding where to begin in my account of proceedings. I wrote to you last from Drummondville. I went on thence to Kingsey, 9m N of Richmond, on the St Francis, thence to Stanstead, to St John's, and so to Montreal.[3] I observed on St Helens,[4] every thing, the weather being very unfavourable however, sent Bombr Henry[5] on to Toronto, where he reported himself 27 Septr, and started myself for N. York on the 20th Septr. I called on Professor

---

[1] This long third party document is being printed because it tells us not only about Henry and his projects, but also about the state of physics and geology research all through the eastern seaboard, and about the incipient geomagnetic survey in Canada. Thus it provides a quick overview of the range of scientific activities which concerned Henry, both centrally and peripherally, at this time of his life.

This document comes from section BJ3/35 of the Sabine Papers. Transcripts of Crown-copyright records in the Public Record Office appear by permission of the Controller of H. M. Stationery Office.

[2] Following Sabine's instructions, Lefroy visited numerous cities in the United States through September and October, 1842. He took dip and intensity readings in Manhattanville, New York (September 26), Providence (September 28), Dorchester, Massachusetts (October 1), Cambridge, Massachusetts (October 3), Philadelphia (October 6), Baltimore (October 8), Washington (October 10), Princeton (October 14), New Haven (October 18), West Point (October 19), and Albany (October 21, 1842). J. H. Lefroy, *Diary of a Magnetic Survey of a Portion of the Dominion of Canada Chiefly in the Northwest Territories* (London, 1883), pp. 52–53.

Hudson, Ohio, was the home of Elias Loomis. In September 1839, with Sabine's urging, A. D. Bache had suggested the forma-

tion of a magnetic survey team in the United States. Loomis was invited to participate, as were Henry, James Renwick, Sr., W. H. C. Bartlett, and John Locke. See *Henry Papers*, 4:265–266.

[3] Lefroy had been traveling in southeastern Quebec. The route of his quick tour, September 10–20, 1842, formed roughly a triangle. Beginning at Drummondville, he moved east to Kingsey, then south to Stanstead, and finally west to St. John's and Montreal. Lefroy, *Diary*, p. 52.

[4] St. Helen's Island, in the St. Lawrence River, Montreal, was the first choice of a site for the Canadian observatory. The rock formations around the city made the area unsuitable, however, and the location was changed to Toronto in 1839. John Henry Lefroy, *In Search of the Magnetic North: A Soldier-Surveyor's Letters from the North-West, 1843–1844*, ed. George F. G. Stanley (Toronto, 1955), p. xv.

[5] Bombardier William Henry (ca. 1818–1881) assisted Lefroy throughout his year-and-a-half-long expedition through northwest Canada (1843–1844) and in the early years of Lefroy's tenure at the Toronto observatory. Leaving Canada in 1846, he went on to serve in the Crimea (1854–1856), retiring a Lieutenant-Colonel in 1877. Brigadier R. J. Lewendon (Retired), Assistant Secretary (Historical), Royal Artillery Institution, personal communication.

Renwick[6] and he went out with me the day following my arrival to the
\<*orphan*\> Lunatic Asylum at Bloomingdale[7] where we observed the dip
& Intensity with Fox,[8] and the Absolute Intensity. I have seven magnetism-
Stations, viz. Quebec Montreal New York Boston Philadelphia West Point
Albany, \<*and*\> Kingston will be an eight[h], of which the five in the States
form a very good group. No Intensity observ$\underline{^{ns}}$ have been made at Philadelphia, so I get no comparison there, but shall do so at Boston. Of all the
American magneticians I have formed acquaintance with none seems so
much in earnest as Prof^r Bartlett of W. Point.[9] I landed there on my way to
N. York merely to see the establishment, was introduced to him, and at his
request stopped there again on my way back. He was much pleased with the
instrument,[10] but still more so with Fox's circle and in this every one who
has seen \<*him*\> it agrees with him. I think it likely that three or four of
them will be ordered. I made a set of observ$\underline{^{ns}}$ there but it is a bad spot,
notorious for local attraction. I observed at Albany because it makes such
an excellent group with N. York and Boston. Mr Henry also asked me to
observe there on account of a disagreement between his Dip results and
those of Dr Bache. Their places of observ$\underline{^n}$ were not the same, I took his, and
my result is a dip 7' less than his taken about 9 years ago, but 4' more than D^r
Baches taken in 1834, therefore confirming his.[11] At Dr Baches request too

[6] James Renwick, Sr. (1792–1863), Professor
of Natural Philosophy and Experimental
Chemistry, Columbia College. See *Henry Papers, 1*:59.

[7] The Bloomingdale Asylum for the Insane
opened in June 1821 as a branch of the New
York Hospital on lower Broadway. Located on
Harlem Heights between what is presently
Riverside Drive and Columbus Avenue, 107th
and 120th Streets, the complex covered approximately seventy acres, a third of which
were used for gardens, playgrounds, and open
spaces. Lefroy did his work in a grove behind
the hospital building. See Pliny Earle, *History,
Description, and Statistics of the Bloomingdale Asylum for the Insane* (New York, 1848),
pp. 9–11; *A Psychiatric Milestone: Bloomingdale Hospital Centenary, 1821–1921* (New
York, 1921), pp. 12–16; and Lefroy, *Diary*,
p. 173.

[8] Robert Were Fox's dip circle. Designed to
measure the dip and intensity of terrestrial
magnetism, the circle consisted of a dipping
needle, the axis of which moved in jewelled
holes, mounted on a concentric disc. See Robert Were Fox, "Notice of an Instrument for
Ascertaining Various Properties of Terrestrial
Magnetism, and Affording a Permanent Standard Measure of Its Intensity in Every Latitude," *Phil. Mag.*, 1834, 3d ser. *4*:81–88.
Though Lefroy attested to the circle's accuracy, he claimed it was "easily put out of
order." Lefroy, *Diary*, p. 23.

[9] William H. C. Bartlett. *Henry Papers*,
2:311n–313n.

[10] An instrument to measure absolute magnetic intensity, most likely a portable declinometer, which determines absolute declination and absolute horizontal intensity.
This instrument and Fox's circle would provide the readings of inclination (dip), declination, and intensity that the survey made.
C. J. B. Riddell, *Magnetical Instructions for
the Use of Portable Instruments . . .* (London,
1844), pp. 6, 9.

[11] Henry remarked on his April 1833 observations in various letters (*Henry Papers*,
2:59–66). The 11' discrepancy with Bache's
August 1834 observations is noted in the summary of results: A. D. Bache and Edward H.
Courtenay, "Observations to Determine the
Magnetic Dip at Baltimore, Philadelphia,
New York, West Point, Providence, Springfield
and Albany," *APS Transactions*, 1837, n.s.
5:209–215.

I observed at <*Alb*> Baltimore, where some local effects have been observ$\underline{d}$, the results at two of three stations were identical with Mr Nicollets,[12] and at third differed <2′. I am very glad to have stopped at Baltimore, it gave me the acquaintance of Mr Nicollet, and of Dr Ducatel, State Geologist of Maryland,[13] one of the pleasantest people I have met. Mr N. is extremely ill, entire prostration of bodly strength, has not left his bed for two months and seems scarcely to expect to leave it again: they all speak very highly of him.[14] Like Dr Bartlett he is a most modest and unassuming man, enthousiasitic in the field; his map of upper valley of the Mississippi and Missouri is now being engraved on a very large scale at Washington, I saw the MSS, and a noble map it is, but the geological account will be delayed until his recovery; his minerals and fossils are not even arranged. Nothing could be more kind and hospitable than the reception I have received everywhere, particularly from Prof^r Henry at Princeton, to whom Dr Bache gave me an introduction.[15] I never met a person who united such simplicity and bonhommie with high talents, I think him one of the most clearheaded men, entirely absorbed in his particular branch of Electricity, and a perfect Enthousiast in it. Some of his experiments are very surprizing. One in particular he shewed me, I must preserve a mysterious silence as to its nature, which I verily think will prove one of the most instructive and interesting of recent discoveries in that subject.[16] He has not had leisure to do more than look into the new door it opens: these are surprizing enough. He leads a wire 400 ft from his Physical Cabinet to his house, where it joins an helix, and is conducted into a well. At the other end he forms a diminutive battery

---

[12] Joseph Nicolas Nicollet (1786–1843), French astronomer and explorer. Having immigrated to the United States in 1832, he led several surveying expeditions to the upper Mississippi. The last years of his life were devoted to preparation of a map of the region, published posthumously in 1843. *DAB*; Martha Coleman Bray, *Joseph Nicollet and His Map* (Philadelphia, 1980).

[13] Julius Timoleon Ducatel (1796–1849), naturalist, was the son of a leading Baltimore pharmacist. He studied in Europe, chiefly in Paris, between 1818 and 1822, and taught at the Mechanics' Institute of Baltimore and the University of Maryland, where between 1830 and 1839 he held the Chair of Chemistry in the Medical Department. Ducatel, along with J. H. Alexander, was appointed by the legislature to survey the state of Maryland, a task he gave up in 1841 when funding ceased. Ducatel accompanied Nicollet on his expedition in the upper Mississippi valley in 1842,

and visited the region around Lake Superior in 1846, which expeditions broke his health and led to his death in 1849. "Obituary," *Silliman's Journal*, 1849, 2d ser. *8*:146–149.

[14] Nicollet died September 11, 1843. *DAB*.

[15] Not found.

[16] In a letter to Mary Henry, dated February 24, 1887, Lefroy recalled his first meeting with Henry: "The first is ever connected with an experiment he shewed me under pledge of secrecy, namely the production of a musical note on making and breaking the circuit of a large Electro-magnet, shewing the molecular vibrations produced by the particles assuming a state of polarity. It interested me extremely." Lefroy reiterated the nature of the experiment and the request for discretion in a second letter to Mary Henry, February 7, 1888. Both are found in Miscellaneous Correspondence File, Harriet Henry Correspondence, Box 57, Henry Papers, Smithsonian Archives.

of about halfinch plates, also communicating with another well there. In <*making*> immersing the plates a <*circuit*> current is transmitted which magnetizes the needles in the helix, the circuit being completed only through the *dry soil* (compact shale) between the two wells. He finds that every *machine spark* he makes in his cabinet, magnetizes a needle in an helix formed in a wire entirely unconnected with the machine, or the building, and about 600 ft distant. In fact he appears to think that in attending chiefly to cabinet experiments Electricians have wholly lost sight of the facts, as to the distance to which any disturbance of Electricity is propagated: he finds that the most distant flash of summer lightning magnetizes a needle in the aforesaid helix which communicates <*directly*> with the metal in the roof of his house. He <*shewed me*> explained to me a plan he has thought of for a self registering Electrometer, So simple that I wish to try it, and mean to erect two masts for conductors at any rate.[17]

I found on my arrival here that none of the difficulties the storekeeper has made have been cleared up. He will not give my extra pay or that of the N.C. officer, or meet travelling charges, or defray contingent expenses. I therefore got from him an explanation of his position and have addressed at letter to you on the subject. I have left blanks in one place because I do not know either the amount of the contingent last granted, or the date and authority. I cannot proceed with the comparisons you wish with the transportables for there is no place to establish them in, the room commenced by Younghusband[18] some months ago, 29 x 18 ft, stands in frame, unroofed and had better be begun again. I shall proceed with it immediately. There is no outbuilding that I could make use of. The dip house is a very rough shed at a corner of the fence, too small for any other purpose. I met with a very kind and pleasant reception from Younghusband, who is looking uncommonly well, and have established myself in a very short space of time. The last steamer for Chicago, bottom of L. Michigan, starts on the 2^{d} Nov^{r}, I proposed to him that he should go round in her, and this he pro-

---

[17] For Henry's account of the meeting with Lefroy, see "Record of Experiments," October 15, 1842, above. The experiment Lefroy described is in the "Record of Experiments" entries of October 6, 7, and 8, 1842, above. Henry and Lefroy took their magnetic measurements in "Mr. Clow's Field," two hundred yards southwest of the college (Lefroy, *Diary*, p. 173), the same field in which Henry's electrical experiment was set up.

On December 2, 1842, Lefroy wrote to Henry, asking for help in obtaining an electrometer. Henry responded with detailed instructions on its construction on December 22, 1842. (See below.)

[18] Lieutenant Charles Wright Younghusband (1821–1899) served as assistant to Lieutenant Charles J. B. Riddell, first director of the Canadian observatory, and as temporary director when Riddell returned to England in 1841. The Royal Society's first choice to head the northern magnetic expedition, Younghusband was replaced by Lefroy in the same year. Lefroy, *In Search of the Magnetic North*, p. xix; Lewendòn, personal communication; and Frederick Boase, comp., *Modern English Biography*, 6 vols. (1892–1921; reprint ed., London, 1965), 3:1582.

poses to do. It is about three weeks trip, and will give opportunity of observ$\underline{\text{g}}$ at about four or five stations, among them is Mackinaw,[19] where M. Nicolett has also observed I believe, but his observ^n are not yet reduced, and Dr Bache appeared to think no intensity observ$\underline{\text{ns}}$ of value have been made in that district, at Mackinaw it should be greater than any observed in this country as yet. He will take Hudson in his way, going or returning. And as soon as he starts I start also for Kingston, which will take about three days, to see about a N. C. Officer for whom Younghusband applied several weeks ago to replace one whom he sent back to his duty, the man sent did not answer, and one for whom he applied was refused by Col. Campbell[20] because in the Batteries, Col. C. told me very plainly that he will give anyman who has not gone through the battery, but will not give up one who has, without his Captains consent: the matter has been at a standstill ever since. I have also to find out a box of copper nails left there many months ago, and since missing. Unless they can be recovered we must complete the new shed with Iron ones, which will do quite as well for all comparative observ$\underline{\text{ns}}$.

I will forward to you the Intensity observ$\underline{\text{ns}}$ by the next mail, if possible, and at the same time will send Captn Beaufort[21] the observ$\underline{\text{ns}}$ of Variation made on the voyage out, but both these require to be looked over, and I have not had time hitherto for it. There are so many things which require attention here that it be a work of some time to get free from all the past observ$\underline{\text{ns}}$. Dr Bache was alarmed when I mentioned the idea of giving up the regular term days,[22] and trusting to the extra observ$\underline{\text{ns}}$ of disturbances, he can always get assistance for the Term days, while it is doubtful whether he can even keep up his observ$\underline{\text{y}}$ to the close of the present year. It costs $100 a month, and it is difficult to raise this sum, for every body in the States seems to share the embarrasment of the country. He was suffering from severe sick headaches, faceaches and so on. I saw a good deal of Capt$\underline{\text{n}}$ Wilkes[23] at Washington, saw his charts, &$\underline{\text{c}}$. He has been hardly used. I have

---

[19] Lefroy was referring to Mackinac Island, in the straits between Lakes Michigan and Huron. The island had an army post since 1781. Willis F. Dunbar, *Michigan: A History of the Wolverine State*, 2d ed. (Grand Rapids, 1980), p. 97.

[20] Possibly Colonel Frederick Campbell (1780–1866) of the Royal Artillery, who was stationed in Canada from January 1838 to October 1847. Lewendon, personal communication.

[21] Sir Francis Beaufort (1774–1857), Hydrographer to the Navy from 1829 until 1855. *DNB.*

[22] Twelve term days annually were set aside for all observatories to take simultaneous magnetic readings at short intervals, thus giving comparative measures. *Henry Papers,* 4:411.

[23] Charles Wilkes (1798–1877). As head of the Depot of Charts and Instruments from 1833 to 1836, Wilkes helped establish the Naval Observatory in Washington, D.C. His command of a round-the-world expedition (1838–1842) brought him international attention. *DAB* and *Henry Papers,* 2:87.

Upon his return, Wilkes was brought before a court-martial on numerous charges and

a copy of his defence for Captn Beaufort, and a synopsis of the results of his expedition. When these are better known, and when the real amount of the work he has executed comes to be seen by the country, I dont doubt a re-action in his favour. He attributes his reception to political motives, he being a Northerner and the President and Secretary to the Navy, both Virginians.[24] He said that the best fortune that ever happened to him was the meeting with Capt$^{\underline{n}}$ Belcher at the Fijii Islands,[25] for though he was reputed a Tartar in his own expedition before, when his officers came to compare notes with Belcher's, he came out as an angel of light. They estimate the expense of the Expedition at $500.000, and the publication is to cost $200.000. more. I visited the observ^{y}, at Washington, it hardly deserves the name. They have a Var$^{\underline{n}}$ transit Instrument, and Mr Lloyd's vert. force Mag$^{\underline{r}}$, but no H. F. Mag$^{\underline{r}}$:[26] the V. F. is too close to the Var$^{\underline{n}}$ transit for comfort, the building is a shed about 10 x 6 feet, liable to extreme changes of temp$^{\underline{re}}$.[27] I will not add to the length of the letter but by sending my kind rememberance to Mr$^{\underline{s}}$ Sabine. Beleive me

Yours very faithfully
J H Lefroy

---

finally reprimanded for severely punishing some of his men.

[24] President John Tyler was from Charles City County, Virginia. Abel Parker Upshur (1791–1844), his Secretary of the Navy from 1841 to 1843, was from Northampton County, Virginia. *DAB*.

Beyond the North-South split lay differing party allegiances. The expedition set out under Democratic auspices, but returned to a Whig administration. William Stanton, *The Great United States Exploring Expedition of 1838–1842* (Berkeley, 1975), pp. 282–283.

[25] Sir Edward Belcher (1799–1877) sailed on numerous survey expeditions for the Royal Navy. In November 1836, he was assigned to the survey ship *Sulphur*, then in South America. The *Sulphur* began its return voyage in 1839, taking in several of the South Pacific island groups in the next three years.

On June 13, 1840, Charles Wilkes, then at the Fiji Islands, visited Belcher aboard the *Sulphur*. In his *Narrative of the United States Exploring Expedition*, 5 vols. (Philadelphia, 1844), *3*:191–192, Wilkes recounted Belcher's inability to deal with the islanders. The Fiji kings, Wilkes concluded, thought "Captain Belcher was a wrongheaded and bad man." In subsequent voyages, Belcher would gain a reputation as an incompetent commander, making his final expedition, a disastrous Arctic trip, in 1852. *DNB*; Stanton, *Expedition*, p. 195.

[26] The instruments are described in detail in J. M. Gilliss, *Magnetical and Meteorological Observations* (Washington, 1845), pp. x–xviii. The variation transit, or declinometer, measures deviation from true north, while Humphrey Lloyd's vertical force magnetometer measures change over time in the vertical component of magnetic force. The horizontal force magnetometer measures the horizontal component.

The magnetometer was donated to the observatory by A. D. Bache in 1841. Its influence on the variation transit was immediately recognized, and various efforts were made to compensate for the change.

[27] The U.S. Naval Observatory was in a transition period in 1842. Lefroy conducted his observation at the original structure built by Charles Wilkes in 1833–1834. Located almost twelve hundred feet northwest of the Capitol, the structure was nothing more than a small frame building, fourteen feet by thirteen feet.

It soon became apparent that the building was inadequate, and a Congressional act of August 31, 1842, cleared the way for construction of more suitable quarters. The new observatory opened in late 1844 between 23rd and 25th Streets, and E Street and Potomac Park, N.W., and included a separate underground magnetic observatory. Since July 1, 1842, all instruments and charts had been stored in a rented building, which may explain why Lefroy saw so few of the observatory's instruments. For a contemporary account see J. M. Gilliss, *Astronomical Observations Made at the Naval Observatory, Washington* (Washing-ton, 1846), pp. viii–xi. See also Gustavus A. Weber, *The Naval Observatory* (Baltimore, 1926), pp. 12–13 and 16–17, and J. K. Herman, "Home of BUMED: The Maury Years (Part Two)," *U.S. Navy Medicine*, March 1982, 73(3):10–21.

TO PETER BULLIONS[1]

Gratz Collection, Historical Society of Pennsylvania

Princeton Tuesday Nov 1st 1842

My Dear Sir

I have had an interview with the Professors of the Seminary relative to the admission of your son[2] of which the following is the result. They regret that he had not joined the institution at the beginning of the present term sinc he will now be about two months behind the class in the study of Hebrew and consequently will labour under considerable difficulty on this account but rather than that he should remain a year unemployed they think it best that he come on immediately.

In reference to the expense, no charge is made by the seminary except 10 dollars for warming the public rooms keeping building clean &c. The students board themselves and the expense is divided among the whole. Dr Miller[3] thinks the necssary expenses exclusive of books cloathing &c. is about 100 dollars per year.

But you need be under no apprehension on the score of expense since Dr Hodge informs me that your son can be put on the list of the education board; or in all probability will be able to get one of the scholarships of the seminary.[4] He is not sure that any scholarships are vacant at present but vacancies will probably occur in a short time. He says that for his own part he would have no hesitation to accept assistance of this kind and that there

[1] Bullions (1791–1864) was the Professor of Latin and Greek at the Albany Academy. *Henry Papers, 1*:129.

[2] Alexander Blyth Bullions (1822–1882) was a student at the Princeton Theological Seminary from 1842 until 1844. Ordained in 1846, he held a number of pastorates in New York and Connecticut. *Roberts*, p. 128.

[3] The Professor of Ecclesiastical History and Church Government at the Seminary, Samuel Miller (1769–1850). *Henry Papers*, 2:438n.

[4] Financial support for Seminary students was available from the Presbyterian Board of Education and through the Seminary's endowed scholarships. In 1838 there were twenty-six scholarships available from the Seminary. *Catalogue of the Officers and Students of the Theological Seminary, at Princeton, New Jersey, 1841–1842* (Princeton, 1841); *A Brief History of the Theological Seminary of the Presbyterian Church, at Princeton, New Jersey* (Princeton, 1838), pp. 30–32.

is no moral obligation to repay the money provided the individual continues in the service of the church. He puts it on the same footing as the receiving of a salary by the students of West-Point. They devote their time to the acquisition of knowledge which will be of service to the country.

Mr Maclean starts this morning for a short tour through the southern part of the state of New <*York*> Jersey. He is anxious that I should accompany him and I would do so but that I have agreed to lecture in Philadelphia next week[5] and am just at this time busily engaged in preparing for the occasion.

John Newlands[6] is now at our house but intends to return to New York on thursday. He expects to meet Mrs Patchin[7] in that city and to accompany her to the south. He will receive a number of letters from Gentlem[en] in this place introducing him to Persons in the south.[8]

My Brother has sent on the first vol. of the Natural history of the state of New York. It is a beautiful volum so far as the mechanical execution is concerned and I presume the zoological part by Dr DeKay[9] is well done but I am out of all patience with the "small potatoe" introduction of the governor. It would make a very proper introduction to the natural history of Little Pedlington but it is not quite the thing for the State of New York.[10]

On my return I found all well and glad to meet us in safety. Mrs H joins me in respects to Mrs Bullions, Miss Margaret, Jane[11] and all the others.

In haste Truly yours
Joseph Henry

PS. I am not sure that I have informed you that I made inquires of a friend relative to the probability of procuring a midshipmans warrent for

---

[5] See above, Lecture Committee, Mercantile Library Company of Philadelphia to Henry, May 21, 1842, and Henry's response of June 7, 1842.

[6] One of Henry's former students at both Albany and Princeton, John Newland (1820–1880) had become an attorney. *Henry Papers*, 2:467.

[7] Presumably the wife of Aaron D. Patchin, the Cashier of the State Bank. Albany City Directories, 1840–1843.

[8] We have no idea why Newland was traveling south.

[9] James Ellsworth DeKay (1792–1851). *Henry Papers*, 1:75.

[10] William H. Seward's introduction (*Natural History of New York* [New York, Boston, and Albany, 1842], separate pagination) was an uncritical and essentially unanalytical history of the intellectual activity in the Colony and State of New York. It was not an original essay by the Governor, but rather a compilation of information obtained from experts within the state. The treatments of individual topics were very uneven in length and depth, depending upon the quantity and quality of the information supplied by the expert. Michele L. Aldrich, "New York Natural History Survey, 1836–1845" (Ph.D. dissertation, University of Texas, 1974), pp. 259–261.

Henry was not alone in his unhappiness over the introduction. One reviewer believed "it would be more appropriate for a gazetteer than as the introduction to the *Natural History*." *Silliman's Journal*, 1843, *44*:188.

[11] Bullions's daughters.

George[12] and that I was informed that the list of applicants was so large that there was but little hope of success at the time.

J.H.[13]

[12] George H. Bullions (1826–1852), Peter's third son. His occupation is unknown to us. Hun, "Albany Academy."

[13] Bullions's response of November 8, 1842, is in the Rare Book Collection, University of Pennsylvania Library.

TO [THOMAS MURRAY][1]
Retained Copy, Henry Papers, Smithsonian Archives

Princeton Nove 18ᵗʰ 1842

My Dear Sir

Your letter of the 22ⁿᵈ of June[2] and the accompanying package have just been received. I am surprised at the long passage they have had and know not what has caused the delay. The academic honors of our college are confered by the Board of Trustees at their meeting in September at the close of the college year and the law requires that the candidate for a degree shall be placed on nomination six months previous to the time of the election. The next election for degrees will take place on the last Wednesday of Sept 1843. It will give me much pleasure to present your letter and the other testimonials relative to the character and acquirements of your friend Mr Dunnett to the Board of Trustees and to solicit for him the honor you ask but as to the result of the application I cannot at present speak with much confidence. The Trustees have adopted the opinion that honors of this kind in our country have been too liberally bestowed and for the last few years they have rather erred on the other extreme. I will however press the claims of your friend and hope the result will be favourable.

I am confident that I can procure for him the degree of *master* of *arts* and I shall be obliged to you if you will inform me if this would be acceptable

[1] Although the recipient's name is not given, the last paragraph indicates that he gave Henry a copy of *Letters of David Hume*. An inscription in Henry's copy of the 1841 Edinburgh edition by Thomas Murray reads "to Joseph Henry from the editor Edinburgh June 1842."

Thomas Murray (1792–1872, *DNB*) was a prominent Edinburgh publisher and writer.

In a letter of February 7, 1844, to Thurlow Weed (Weed Collection, University of Rochester Library) Henry refers to him as "my friend and distant kinsman Dr. Murray of Edinburgh." Murray was born in Kirkcudbrightshire, the same county from which Henry's grandfather, James Henry, emigrated to America.

[2] Not found.

provided the higher degree cannot at present be obtained.[3] I have no doubt of the merits of Mr Dunnett but perhaps the Trustees may require further time to consider in reference to his claims and to ask to see the entire work of which you send a specimen. Please to write me in reference to this point as soon after the receipt of this letter as conven[ien]t. By the new mail regulations the intercourse between this country and Great Britain is much facilitated. A letter from Edinburgh will reach me in the course of three weeks and cost about sixpence sterling. You will be obliged to pay the postage to Liverpool.

I have been interrupted in the writing of this letter by the arrival of a package from the post office which contains amoung other things a letter from my young friend Mr Theodore Cuyler[4] dated at Sheffield Oct 28th. In this he speaks with much satisfaction of the kind and hospitable reception he received from you while on his visit to Edinburgh. Please to accept my warmest thanks for your attention to my young friend and also for the several unrequited favours <*for which I am still your debtor*> to my self while in Edinburgh in 1837.

I receive with much pleasure the valuable present of the letters of Hume. <*they*> I have not yet had an <*opport*> leisure to read it but I am sure it cannot be otherwise than an interesting addition to the literary history of the past age. <*I was delighted with my tour in Europe and reccollect the several acquaints with much pleasure. Since my return my time has been much occupied in my research*>

---

[3] Princeton gave William Dunnett an honorary M.A. in 1843. Although two LL.D. degrees were awarded in 1841, none were given in 1840, 1842, or 1843. For a discussion of the awarding of M.A. degrees by American colleges in this period, see *Henry Papers*, 2:213n.

A testimonial by William Steven of May 21, 1842 (Henry Papers, Smithsonian Archives) describes Dunnett as Classical Master in George Heriot's Hospital, Edinburgh.

[4] Not found. According to a notation in Henry's address book, p. [34], he had given Cuyler several publications for Murray, including his "Contributions IV: Electro-Dynamic Induction," and John Maclean's *Examination of the Essays Bacchus and Anti-Bacchus* (Princeton, 1841).

TO FRANCIS PRESTON BLAIR, JR.[1]

Retained Copy, Henry Papers, Smithsonian Archives

Princeton Nov 25th 1842

My Dear Sir

I have just learned almost accidentally and for the first time that you did not receive your degree at the last meeting of the Board of Trustees. I regret

---

[1] (1821–1875). A member of a notable political family of the ante-bellum and Civil War period. *DAB*.

this excedingly for although I still think as I have before told you, that your conduct was highly improper in the first act and very imprudent in returning to Princeton in violation of the express directions to the contrary of the Faculty, yet I do not think it proper under all the circumstances of the case that your degree should have been withheld.[2]

Some remarks were made on the subject before the faculty at the meeting previous to the commencement and I supposed that it was fully understood by the members that you and Bowen were to be recommended for a degree. Mr Maclean was also under the same impression but I suppose some mistake was made in placing the business before the Trustees. Dr Carnahan is now in the city and I have as yet had no opportunity of speaking with any member of the Faculty on the subject except Professor Maclean.

I regret the occurrance and will endeavour to get the matter adjusted at the next meeting of the Board by a personal appeal. In this I will be joined by Professor Maclean.

I had as you may recollect considerable conversation with you after your difficulty at Princeton and expressed my sorrow at the occurrence and my hopes that it would eventually be of service to you in the way of stimulating you to proper exertion in the acquirement of your Profession and of cautioning you in reference to future conduct. These expressions I trust you considered as prompted by a sincere regard for your welfare and an earnest desire that you might so exert your talents as to do honor to yourself and to your country. You have talents which with well directed industry and the cultivation of high moral principles will enable you to perform an important part in your day; and I most sincerely hope that you will resolve to inflict on the College of New Jersey the noble revenge of rendering her anxious to claim you as an alumnus.[3]

With kind regards I
remain your Friend
Joseph Henry

[2] Blair and Edward H. Bowen, members of the Class of 1841, had a "personal conflict ... at a house of refreshment" in August 1841. The faculty minutes of August 17, 1841 (p. 229), record the recommendation to withhold the degree. On August 31 (pp. 233–234), the faculty agreed to consider a degree for the 1842 commencement. This occurred for Bowen (d. 1848) who also received the A.M. in 1847. *Princeton Catalogue*, p. 160.

The Trustees approved the faculty recommendations on September 29, 1841 (Trustees' Minutes, p. 388), and at the April 1843 meeting gave Blair his degree in his original class.

Both sets of minutes are in the Princeton University Archives.

For Henry's account of the affair and his subsequent successful effort on Blair's behalf, see his letter to Carnahan of April 10, 1843, below.

[3] Blair served in the House of Representatives for Missouri, 1856–1858, 1860–1862. He was in the Mexican War and rose to the rank of Major-General of Volunteers during the Civil War. From 1871 to 1873, Blair represented Missouri in the U.S. Senate. During the interval between his fight and the award of the degree, Blair was studying the law.

P.S. I do not know where you are to be found and I therefore enclose this letter to your friend Charles Abert[4] who as I have been lately informed received some communication from you at the close of the last college session relative to your degree. I regret that he had not confered with me on the subject.

J H

[4] Class of 1842, A.M. 1845, d. 1897. *Princeton Catalogue*, p. 162. See *Henry Papers*, 4:220.

FROM J. H. LEFROY
Henry Papers, Smithsonian Archives[1]

Toronto.

2 Dec⁻ 1842.

My dear Sir.

I am under the necessity of troubling you again,[2] to ask of you the favour of ordering me a Gold leaf Electroscope from Philadelphia or New York, for which I will forward the amount with many thanks as soon as I know it. Such a thing is not to be procured here nor can I succeed in making one of anything like delicacy. I dont know how to attach the slips of Gold leaf without the use of some gum or cement which is a nonconductor, and for want of it cannot test the new apparatus.[3]

Believe me yours sincerely

JH Lefroy.

[1] Joseph Henry Papers, Box 50, Folder "Film as supplement and then interfile." For Henry's response, see below, December 22, 1842.

[2] Perhaps a reference to Lefroy's visit to Henry that October. See "Record of Experiments," October 15, 1842, above.

[3] The electrometer or electroscope was part of the meteorological apparatus of the station, used for testing the electrical state of the atmosphere. The circular letter sent by the Royal Society on the Ross expedition and colonial magnetic and meteorological observatories mentioned "an apparatus for atmospheric electricity" as part of the permanent meteorological instrumentation. *Henry Papers*, 4:244. Henry and the American Philosophical Society reiterated this in their Congressional request of December 20, 1839. *Henry Papers*, 4:318. The 1840 report of the Royal Society on the Ross expedition was specific about the form of the apparatus, an "electroscope . . . connected with a lofty insulated wire." A gold-leaf electrometer was one of the four types of registering instruments mentioned. *Report of the Committee of Physics and Meteorology of the Royal Society Relative to the Observations to be Made in the Antarctic Expedition and in the Magnetic Observatories* (London, 1840), pp. 71–72. Lefroy himself in a letter to Sabine (October 25, 1842, printed above) stated that "[Henry] explained to me a plan he has thought of for a self registering Electrometer, So simple that I wish to try it, and mean to erect two masts for conductors at any rate." Another source of information is the Smithsonian report for 1855. In it were published instructions for electrical observations of the atmosphere during auroras (pertinent because the Report stated that the instructions were derived from those in use in Toronto): "the end of a long insulated wire suspended from two high masts or two chimneys by means of silk threads, may be placed in connexion with a delicate gold leaf electrometer." S.I., *Ann. Rep.*, 1855, p. 249.

Curiously, Sabine's report on the Toronto

observatory did not mention the electrical apparatus; the observations were not a routine part of the institutional procedure. Edward Sabine, *Observations Made at the Magnetical* and *Meteorological Observatory at Toronto in Canada, 1840–1848,* 3 vols. (London, 1845–1857).

FROM THOMAS W. CATTELL, JR.[1]
Henry Papers, Smithsonian Archives

Bentivoglio Albemarle Co
Virgin—Dec 6[11] 1842

Dear Sir

The gentleman with whom I am engaged at this place is much troubled with a smoking stove, for which none of those around him can suggest a remedy. I have therefore ventured with his permission to send a brief description of the circumstances in which the stove is placed and to ask of you some hint on the subject. The stove was purchased for his parlour and there it drew very well as the pipe could go into the chimney. But the additional comfort in warming the room could not compensate for the cheerful blaze

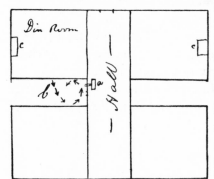

of the open hearth & the stove was soon removed. He now wishes to place it in the hall—the situation of which you can best understand by a diagram,—a marks the position of the stove in the Hall,—c, c of the chimneys of the Dining room & parlour. He wishes the pipe to go out into the open space b. Now when the wind comes over the dining room it strikes against the side of the house be hind it and makes a kind of whorl around the opening of the pipe. Dr Page[2] tried a knee—or rather a ⌐ on the end of the pipe but it smoked as badly as ever. If Prof Henry ⌐ will suggest some method

<hr/>

[1] Thomas Ware Cattell, Jr. (1823–1887), graduated Princeton in 1842. He spent the following academic year teaching at the Keswick School, a small institution in Albemarle County, Virginia. In 1844 he returned to Princeton to enroll in the Theological Seminary but left the Seminary four years later without graduating. For the next quarter century he served alternately as a pastor or school principal in New Jersey. From 1874 until his death he was Professor of Sacred Geography and Biblical Antiquities at Lincoln University. *Roberts,* p. 146; *Princeton Catalogue,* p. 162; Edward C. Mead, *Historic Homes of the South-West Mountains Virginia* (Philadelphia and London, 1899), pp. 225, 228.

[2] Dr. Mann Page (1791–1850), educated at Hampden-Sydney College and the Medical School of the University of Pennsylvania, had run Keswick, his wife's estate in Albemarle County, since their marriage in 1815. He had established the Keswick School in 1831 to insure the quality of the education of his sons. Cattell was just one of a long line of recent

of obviating the difficulty,[3] he will confer an obligation on Dr Page as well as on one of his pupils who will ever remember with gratitude the kindness of his instructor & highly prize what he has taught him. The three years which I spent under the genial influence of your college I shall alway consider the most interesting of my life. And as the cares of life crowd around me & the duties of that station to which I may be called press upon me I shall cast many a thought back to college days, drop many a tear over the associations of college life and offer many a fervent prayer for the increasing prosperity & usefulness of my alma mater.

Yours Very Obediently
Tho[s] W Cattell Jr.

---

college graduates from such schools as Princeton, Bowdoin, Yale, and Harvard who were brought to Keswick over a twenty-year span to teach the sons of the leading families of the neighborhood. Mead, *Historic Homes*, pp. 221–230.

[3] No response has been located.

"RECORD OF EXPERIMENTS"
Henry Papers, Smithsonian Archives

Thursday Dec 15th 1842

Mr Welsh[1] the engineer of the Raritan canal called on me this morning and gave an account of a series of not very extensive but very interesting experiments at which he had been assisting relative to the velocity range and elevation of a ball, shot from Capt Stocktons large gun of wrought iron.[2]

[1] Ashbel Welch (1809–1882) had been one of Henry's students at the Albany Academy. He then went on to a distinguished career as a civil engineer, serving, among other posts, as Chief Engineer of the Delaware and Raritan Canal, Engineer of the Philadelphia and Trenton Railroad, Vice-President of the Camden and Amboy Railroad, and President of the American Society of Civil Engineers. In the fall of 1845 he assisted Henry with telegraphic experiments. *Henry Papers, 4:332;* John Bogart, "Ashbel Welch, President Am. Soc. C.E.," American Society of Civil Engineers, *Proceedings,* 1883, *9*:137–144.

[2] Robert F. Stockton had been engaged at Sandy Hook in testing two twelve-inch bore guns destined for the Navy steam frigate *Princeton,* one of wrought iron, manufactured by the Mersey Iron Works near Liverpool, and one of cast iron from the West Point Foundry. The wrought-iron gun was judged superior, and Stockton ordered a second, this time from an American manufacturer.

Mounted on the *Princeton* in January 1844, the American wrought-iron gun, named the "Peacemaker," exploded on February 28, 1844, killing six men, including two members of the Cabinet. Lee M. Pearson, "The 'Princeton' and the 'Peacemaker': A Study in Nineteenth-Century Naval Research and Development Procedures," *Technology and Culture,* 1966, *7*:163–183. The explosion and subsequent investigation will be discussed in the next volume of the *Henry Papers.*

Welch's role in the Stockton tests is difficult to ascertain from the official reports. His biographer credits him with having "superintended the experiments in gunnery instituted by Commodore Stockton." Bogart, "Ashbel Welch," American Society of Civil Engineers,

This gun throws a ball of 212 lbs and is found to hit the mark with great precision, at the distance of 2730 feet. Mr Welsh has devised a very simple method of getting the velocity approximately by means of the deflections from a straight line. Thus he measures the fall of the ball by means of a series of screens placed at regular distances, through which the ball passes and from these falls or deflection aa' bb' cc' &c he gets the times.[3]

The object of making this memorandum is to record my own idea of getting the velocity [of] the ball at different distances, by means of a current of galvanism.[4] Mr Welsh had thought that some method might be de-

---

Proceedings, 1883, *9*:138. However, Stockton's report of December 23, 1842, does not mention Welch. *House Reports*, 28th Congress, 1st Session, 1842–1843, No. 479, pp. 32–40. This omission may be another example of Stockton's reputed reluctance to share credit. Pearson, p. 175.

[3] Stockton briefly described this apparatus in his letter to William M. Crane, Chief of the Bureau of Ordnance and Hydrography, of November 21, 1842, Box 1, Letters from Naval Officers, Records of the Bureau of Ordnance, RG 74, National Archives. The results appeared in *House Reports*, No. 479, pp. 36–39.

[4] The device in common use for determining the velocity of a projectile was the ballistic pendulum, invented by Benjamin Robins (1707–1751, *DSB*) prior to 1742. Based on the principle of the conservation of momentum, the ballistic pendulum was simply a large, suspended mass. When struck by a projectile, the resulting inelastic collision displaced the pendulum a small distance. There was a relatively simple relationship between that displacement and the velocity of the projectile at impact. See, e.g., Alfred Mordecai, *Report of Experiments on Gunpowder Made at Washington Arsenal, in 1843 and 1844* (Washington, 1845), pp. 12–31.

Charles Wheatstone first devised a method of measuring the velocity of a projectile by the application of electricity. His chronograph was mentioned by L.-A.-J. Quetelet at an October 1840 meeting of the Royal Academy of Sciences of Belgium. Subsequently, Wheatstone refined and modified his instrument, although he did not supply a detailed published account until spurred by a priority claim by Louis F. C. Breguet (1804–1883, *DSB*). L.-A.-J. Quetelet, "Télégraphes électriques," *Bulletins de l'Académie royale des sciences et belles-lettres de Bruxelles*, 1840, *7*:134; L. Breguet, "Note sur un appareil destiné à mesurer la vitesse d'un projectile dans différents points de sa trajectoire," *Comptes rendus*, 1845, *20*:157–162; Charles Wheatstone, "Note sur le chronoscope électromagnétique," ibid., 1845, *20*:1554–1561.

There were a number of differences in the methods applied by Wheatstone and Henry (Henry's set-up underwent a number of modifications, such as those mentioned in the "Record of Experiments" entry of December 28, 1842, below; the ultimate version is discussed in "On a New Method of Determining the Velocity of Projectiles," APS *Proceedings*, 1843, *3*:165–167). For example, Wheatstone broke a circuit upon firing a gun, but established one when the projectile hit the target. The time of flight equaled the period when there was no current in the circuit. In Henry's version, the projectile broke two circuits in succession. The velocity was determined from the length of time between breaks. But the basic principles behind the two forms of apparatus were the same.

None of the early applications of electricity to ballistics proved completely acceptable. The accuracy of the apparatus was insufficient. Even as late as 1861, preference was given to data obtained through the ballistic pendulum. Not until 1867 was a chronograph created which truly met the needs of the ballistics community. G. Mackinlay, *Text Book of Gunnery, 1887* (London, 1887), pp. 119, 237; Francis Bashforth, "Description of a Chronograph Adapted for Measuring the Varying Velocity of a Body in Motion through the Air, and for Other Purposes," *Minutes of the Proceedings of the Royal Artillery Institution*, 1867, *5*:161–192.

vised for using electricity for getting the velocity of the ball but as he said his knowlege of the agent was not sufficient to enable him to devise any means. The idea first occurred to me of using the revolving mirror as a means of determing the velocity, but the electrical method which almost immediately suggested itself appears preferable.

The general arrangement will be something like this. A number of

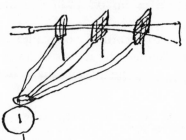

screens being erected at equal distan[ces] a circuit of wire is mad[e] from each screen to a galvanometer placed tangent or nearly so to a large graduated wheel, which is made to revolve once in a second or oftener. Suppose the wheel revolves once in a second and the needle of the galvanometer be made to carry a bar on its end so as to make a dot on the revolving cylinder at the moment the current is stopped by breaking the circuit. In this way the time may be noted to the 1/1000th part of a second. All the registers may be made possibly by one galvanometer, by using a current of less intensity than the one connected with the screens to deflect the needle constantly against a fixed pin.

The counter current may also be used if the register be made with a number of galvanometers. The same circuit may be continued around each. If it should be found necessary to use several galvanometers then the inertia of each needle and the resistance of the point may not be the same. In this case it would be necessary to test the accuracy of the register and this could be effected by causing another wheel graduated like the first to revolve with two pins on it at intervals along its circumference. These could be made to interrupt two circuits by striking against two wires in mercury and as the distance of the pins apart are know, they would give the elapsed time which should also be given of the same duration by the other revolving wheel. The difference of the result given by the index wheel and the other would probably be constant, or at least it could be made approximately so. If one of the needles were a little heavier than the other, then the time noted would be a little later comparatively and the interval would be shorter than the truth if the heavier needle were the first to move. If the heavier were placed behind the other on the register then the interval would be lengthened.[5]

The wheel may be made to revolve by means of a weight with thread

---

[5] Henry added the following marginal annotation: "To test the truth of the indications of the needles two sets of wires may be attached to the same."

over a pulley or cylindrical part of the axis and the same axis furnished with two pairs of centrifugal balls to regulate the motion.[6]

If the wheel were a foot in diameter, and revolved one in a second, then the $1/100^{th}$ of second would indicate by about .4 of an inch and the $1/1000^{th}$ part of a second by .04 of an inch[7]

[6] This and the following paragraph were written with a different pen. They may represent later additions.

[7] In the top margin of this entry is an annotation dated October 1843. Henry wrote: "I have improved the plan of this apparatus and published an account of it in the proceedings of the Phil Society."

FROM ROBERT FIELD STOCKTON

Stockton Family Miscellany, New Jersey Historical Society

22^d D^{ec} 1842

Dr Sir

It may not be uninteresting to you to look over the results of my late experiments in Gunnery. I send to you my report[1] which you can have for Two Hours[2] when my son[3] will call for it that I may enclose it to night for Washington.

Yrs truly
R. F. Stockton

[1] Stockton's report on the tests (see above, "Record of Experiments," December 15, 1842) of the guns for the frigate *Princeton*, complete with tables and charts, was sent to William M. Crane, Chief of the Bureau of Ordnance and Hydrography. In it, Stockton contended that formulas previously applied to gunnery were demonstrated to be erroneous by his experiments. *House Reports*, 28th Congress, 1st Session, 1842–1843, No. 479.

[2] The number is unclear and may be "Four." Lack of a postmark indicates this note was delivered by hand.

[3] Either Richard or John Potter Stockton. See above, Henry to Thomas Sparrow, Jr., January 10, 1842.

TO [J. H. LEFROY]

Retained Copy, Henry Papers, Smithsonian Archives

Princeton Dec 22nd 1842

My Dear Sir

Your favour of the 2nd inst[1] came to hand about a week ago but I have been so much occupied since then in college duties that I have been unable

[1] Printed above.

to make the visit which I had premeditated to the city and to get your electrometer. I think I shall be able to leave home next week but on reflection I have concluded to advise you to attempt the construction of an electrometer for yourself. The article is very simple and it can be made of the materials to be found in almost every part of the world. The only difficult part of the manipulation is that of attaching the gold leaves to the stem and this you can have done for you by a book-binder if there be one in Toronto. The leaves being cut to the proper size can be stuck to the end of the stem with the white of an egg which is used by the binder for attaching the gold to the back of the book. It is of little consequence whether the cement be of a conducting material or not since it will be very easy to bring the gold into metallic contact with the stem by the touching of some of the filiments or angles of the leaf with the metal of the stem; but even if no contact of this kind exists the effect of a small charge of electricity will be the same. The leaves will then be electrified at there lower ends with the same kind of electricity given to the top of the instrument by *induction*. The upper end of the leaves will be *minus* and the lower ends plus if the top of the instrument be electrified positively. The other parts of the instrument are easily constructed of such materials as even Torronto cannot fail to furnish. First procure a glass cylinder (see *a* Fig 1)[2] of from 2½ to 3 or more inches in diameter—the cylindrical glass chimney of a common lamp will answer or the cylindrical part of a large phial which you can procure at the druggists. To this attach by melted sealing wax a wooden cover and bottom. These can be fashioned by the turner or the cabinet maker or by yourself with a pen knife—care being taken to round the edges well and to smooth the wood with sand paper. They should be made of wood that has been well dried, by the fire or by being placed for some hours on a stove; and covered with a coating of sealing wax dissolved in alcohol or strong whiskey. The solution can be readily made by placing the alcohol in a phial and putting into this a quantity of sealing wax in a pulverized state. The solution will take place more readily if the vessel be gently heated and this can be effected by placing the phial in a dish containing some sand or water and heating the whole on a stove. The heat in this way is so gradually communi-

cated that the phial is in no danger of breaking. The sealing wax may be applied by means of a camel's hair pencil. It prevents the wood from imbibing moisture and renders its surface a nonconductor. For the stem to which the gold leaf is attached, a piece of tolerably thick wire of any metal will answer, provided it is

[2] Henry left a space for this figure in his retained copy but did not draw it.

sufficiently stiff and smooth; a top for it may be found in a large bell or ball
button such as is worn or was worn by Artillery men or you can
find a knob of polished brass of some kind by calling at any country
store among the articles of hard ware intended for the cabinet
maker. This ball or knob may be attached to the stem by soft solder
or if this cannot be procured the attachment may be effected by
pouring melted sealing wax around the end of the stem while it rests in
the hollow of the inverted ball—See fig.—care being taken to press the stem
down on the ball so as to make metallic contact. But there must be
a watch repairer in a place like Toronto and therefore you can
readily get the ball soldered on. The ball at all parts should be
smooth so as to prevent the escape of electricity. The stem can be
passed tightly through the cover as is shown in fig. but it will be best
to make the hole in the wood a little larger than the stem and then fill it

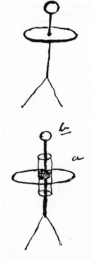

with sealing wax so as to prevent the metal from coming in
direct contact with the fibres of the wood which would tend
to conduct it to the circumference of the couver and thus
favour its escape. A more perfect plan of insulating the stem
is to first fasten it in the axis of a glass tube which is several
times its diameter and then pass this tube through the axis
of the cover. It may be thus fastened by a piece of cork (*a*)
placed in the middle of the tube or still more perfectly in
reference to insulation by wrapping round the stem at the
part *a* a quantity of silk and then soaking the same in the
liquid sealing wax or in other words by making a cork of
silk stiffened with sealing wax. The object of this arrangement is to prevent any communication of electricity from
the stem to the wood and to effect this still more perfectly
the tube should be covered inside and out with a thin coating of the sealing wax varnish. The electricity can only
escape by passing up the inside of the tube and then down the outside to
the wooden cover. Unless a very delicate instrument be required and one
which will retain its charge for a long time this precaution of the glass tube
may be neglected.

If you wish to make a condensing electrometer then the ball *b* must be
replaced by a plate of metal 4 or 5 inches in diameter.[3]

---

[3] The surviving text ends here.

"RECORD OF EXPERIMENTS"
Henry Papers, Smithsonian Archives

Dec 28th 1842

I have been studying for some days past capillarity and in connection with the subject I have made to day a few experiments. First to determine the effect of heat on capillarity. I wetted a tube of about 1/50 of an inch internal diameter with water, found the elevation of the liquid when the tube was withdrawn from the water. I then plunged the same tube with its contained column of water into a kettle of boiling water when the glass was withdrawn the column was observed to be the tenth of an inch or about this quantity below its former level. This was repeated several times and always with the same result.

Reflecting on this experiment, which in principle is an old one the thought occurred to me that if a column of water were placed in a tube in a horizontal position thus and heat applied to the one end a motion should be produced in the column towards the other. The column will be equally attracted by the 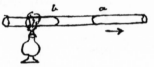 cappillarity in each direction, namely towards *a* and *b* therefore if we lessen the attraction at one end, the column will move in the direction of the other. When the experiment was tried the result was as I anticipated. The motion of the column was quite rapid and could be moved several inches by the cautious application of the heat of a spirit lamp.

This experiment explains very satisfactorily the fact mentioned by Kane in his chemestry of the motion of <*heat*> oil along a wire by applying a lamp to the wire on one side of the oil. The effect is given as an illustration of the repulsive power of heat.[1]

Another idea has occurred to me in the course of my reflection on this subject in reference to the theory of capillarity of Poisson—namely that the liquid is rarified and condensed by the action of the capilliary force.[2] If this

---

[1] An examination of both the Dublin (1841) and New York (1842; edited by John William Draper) editions of Robert Kane's *Elements of Chemistry* has failed to uncover the source of Henry's reference.

We have discovered one experiment which does resemble the one Henry mentions. In 1824, G. B. Libri applied heat to water resting upon fine wires. He argued that the resulting movement of the globules of water along the wires demonstrated the repulsive power of heat at sensible distances. Contemporaries, however, thought Libri's experiments to be inconclusive. *Encyclopaedia Britannica*, 8th ed., s.v., "Heat," p. 268.

[2] A reference to the ultimately unsuccessful effort of Siméon-Denis Poisson (1781–1840; *DSB*) to improve Laplace's treatment of capillarity. Poisson, *Nouvelle théorie de l'action capillaire* (Paris, 1831).

Albert Dod presented a copy of this book to Henry. It survives in the Henry Library.

hypothesis be correct should not the top of a capillary column depolarize light?[3]

I have since writing the account of the machine for determing the velocity of a cannon ball, by means of electricity,[4] conversed with Mr Saxton on the subject and learn from him that there would be but little difficulty in constructing the revolving disc, it could be rendered sufficiently uniform in motion by means of a fly wheel or by its own momentum. He advises however a wheel or rather cylinder of not more than 4 or 5 inches in diameter and says on this spaces corresponding to the 1/100 of a second could be marked out.

I have since thought of a method of adjusting the several needles so as to obviate the difficulty attending the different degrees of inertia and this consi[s]ts in deflecting the different needles to different distances by means of pins, moved backward and forward by means of fine screws. The needles could all be proved by attaching all the wires or the wire from each to the same screen and when this was broken through, each needle should mark the same moment on the revolving disc, if they did not then the deflecting pins should be so adjusted that the desired result would be produced.[5]

---

[3] In the left-hand margin is a reference forward to the "Record of Experiments" entry of April 24, 1843, where Henry describes an experiment testing this hypothesis. Henry's thoughts about the results of the April experiment are summarized in a sentence he subsequently squeezed between this paragraph and the succeeding one: "Tried this by means of the polarizing apparatus of a microscope but without success."

[4] See above, "Record of Experiments," December 15, 1842.

[5] Subsequent paragraphs added later describe improvements in the apparatus. The first reads: "Another improvement was made in this machine by causing the electri[cit]y to make its own mark—see my paper Proceedings Phil. society centenary." This was a reference to the Henry publication "On a New Method of Determining the Velocity of Projectiles," APS *Proceedings*, 1843, 3:165–167. The second paragraph reads: "N.B. An other improvement in the arrangement consists in making the earth perform the part of half the conductor."

⊰{ 1843 }⊱

TO ROBERT M. PATTERSON
Mary Henry Copy, Henry Papers, Smithsonian Archives

Princeton Jan. 31.ᵗ 1843

My dear Sir. Your favor of Saturday[1] was received on Monday night. . . . It will give me much pleasure to furnish you with any articles for your lecture in my possession. . . . I am much pleased with your project of obtaining the relative velocity of sound in air and water[2]. . . .

I heard on Saturday of the loss of your daughter. I am no stranger to the feelings of a parent and can sympathize with you in your sorrow for the untimely departure of your loved one. But strong as may be the feelings of a Father they are less tender than those of a Mother and I am sure your loss must be felt as a very sad bereavement by Mrs. Patterson.[3] There are however I believe in every event of this kind some considerations which are calculated to give consolation. We receive the gift of life with the annexed condition of death and since this condition must be fulfilled, it may be considered a merciful arrangement, in order that our attachment to life may not be too strong, that we should suffer affliction and thus be taught how temporary and unstable are all things of earth. If continued youth and constant prosperity were our lot during life how dreadful would be death but every sorrow seems to loose the cords which bind us to earth and aids in fitting us for the great inevitable change. It is not in our nature not to mourn for the loss of those we love but our grief is for our own loss, not theirs. We may feel and deeply sorrow for the misfortunes of a living child but the dead one, however loved in life, is beyond our sympathies; it has entered on a new state of existence and its destinies are in the hands of a just God. With much respect and esteem

Yours, Joseph Henry

[1] Letter not found.
[2] We have not found any information concerning Robert M. Patterson's method of determining the relative velocity of sound in air and water.

[3] Helen Hamilton Leiper Patterson (1792–1871). Lawrence Buckley Thomas, *The Thomas Book* (New York, 1896), p. 438.

FROM ALEXANDER DALLAS BACHE[1]
Henry Papers, Smithsonian Archives

Philad. Feb. 22ᵈ 1843

My dear Henry

I want you to come down to my Wistar on Saturday next, come and bring Mrs Henry with you. We will give her a bed of an oyster.

You promised to write me about Niccolet, and have not done so. After a consultation with Washington Smith[2] it is decided that you had better write to Sir David Brewster. Dʳ Bache V.P. thinks so also. Let me have a copy of your letter to Sir David.[3]

I shall expect to see you on Saturday.

Ever Yours
A. D. Bache

[1] This letter is in the hand of his wife, Nancy Clarke Fowler (Ency) Bache.

[2] George Washington Smith (1800–1876), alumnus of the College of New Jersey (A.B. 1818, A.M. 1822), was the author of several tracts, written in the 1820s and 1830s, on internal improvements and in defense of the Pennsylvania system of solitary confinement of prisoners. Thomas P. Cope, a leading merchant of Philadelphia and fellow member of the American Philosophical Society, described him as "one of our distinguished literati." Smith became an APS member in 1840; he studied law, but may have been a merchant. Eliza Cope Harrison, ed., *Philadelphia Merchant: The Diary of Thomas P. Cope, 1800–1851* (South Bend, Indiana, 1978), p. 550; Philadelphia City Directory, 1843; W. Stuart Wallace, *A Dictionary of North American Authors Deceased before 1950* (Toronto, 1951); S. Austin Allibone, *A Critical Dictionary of English Literature and British and American Authors*, 3 vols. (1872; reprint ed., Detroit, 1968), 2:2136.

[3] We have found no reference to letters to Brewster or Nicollet from this period, either over Henry's signature or that of the officers of the American Philosophical Society. We surmise that Bache was promoting plans for the centennial celebration of the APS, due to take place in May 1843. Both A. D. Bache and Smith were on the committee on arrangements, and Franklin Bache was the active senior officer of the Society in the frequent absence of President Duponceau. *Proceedings of the American Philosophical Society, 1841–1843,* 2:255.

Nicollet and Brewster were natural choices for the Society to contact about its centennial meeting. Nicollet's brainchild, the great map of the West, was just then nearing completion. The geographer had recently been elected to the Society and did read a paper on his project at the May centennial celebration. *Proceedings of the American Philosophical Society,* 1843, 3:140. Brewster was an eminent British scientist, active in the British Association and the Royal Society of Edinburgh. Informing him of the proposed celebration would have been both considerate and politic. Though not on the arrangements committee, Henry would have been a good choice to write to Brewster, for Henry knew Brewster as a result of his European trip. *Henry Papers,* 3:473–483.

"RECORD OF EXPERIMENTS"
Henry Papers, Smithsonian Archives

Feby 23rd 1843
Information from
Mr Quinby[1]

Mr Quinby informes me that with an insulated lightning rod of copper 90 feet in height, terminated at the top by several points and connected with an insulated conductor below—and near the latter a ball connected with the ground to receve the discharge, he <*with*> has observed several times that when the pith balls connected with the <*pith balls*> end of the rod exhibited no signs of electricity and when a flash was observed at the distance of several miles a spark passed between the end of the rod and the communication with the ground. In some cases two sparks were observed in rapid succession with the same flash. He observed this for the first time in 1837.

The fact of the two sparks is in accordance with my new views of the action of the discharge of a Leyden jar.[2]

In connection with this subject the idea has just occurred to me that the several discharges in succession which may be observd in the discharge of a cloud may in part at least be due to the reflex action of the electrical induction.

[1] A. M. Quimby. See above, Bache to Henry, December 1, 1841.
[2] i.e., the oscillatory discharge.

ASA GRAY TO JOHN TORREY
Torrey Papers, Library, New York Botanical Garden

[February 28, 1843][1]

Dear Doctor

Yours of the 21ᵗ reached me duly, as al[so] Hooker's letter. I make brief memoranda of your enquiri[es]. I have not yet looked at the seeds of the Ruellia. These things are noticed in *very many* Acanthaceae by Don and Kippist in Linn. Trans, a few years back.[2] In the breaking up of the genera,

[1] From the postmark and internal evidence. Gray may have put the date only on an accompanying letter addressed to Jane Torrey.
[2] The 1840 article by Richard Kippist, communicated to the Linnean Society by David Don, is "On the Existence of Spiral Cells in the Seeds of Acanthaceae," *Linnean Society Transactions*, 1845, *19*:65–76. Acanthaceae is a family of chiefly tropical herbs, shrubs, and trees.

I believe we have neither Justicia nor Ruellia left in U.S. It *is* in the Linnaea that you saw some Amer. Acanthaceae described by Nees.[3]

Buckley's paper must be *ready* soon, if it is to go in the July no. of Silliman.[4] The April is already printed, all but, and is so crowded as to have no miscellanies. If Buckley will send an advertisement-shaped offer of his *bones* for sale, I will insist upon its insertion.[5] Silliman is here. I have heard him lecture—organic chemistry—*small potatoes!*[6] Benny[7] says you may get Endicott[8] to lithograph the Buckleya,[9] as cheap as you can—& strike off 1250 copies for him, & as many extra as you want extra copies of the article, & send the bill to New Haven. I hope of course that Baily will write on raphidic crystals.[10] Has he not the 3ᵈ vol. of my Meyen?[11]

Presl's figure is not *Ragiopteris obtusilobata*, but *R. onocleoides* & from Willd. Herb.—the hist. of which you know.[12] You must send to Hooker, & let his man Fitch[13] copy Schkuhr's figure; for the work is not in this country.[14]

---

[3] Probably C. G. Nees von Esenbeck, "Observationes in Acanthaceas horti Vratislaviensis," *Linnaea*, 1842, *16*:289–308.

[4] i.e., volume 45, number 1, covering April to June 1843. Torrey was helping Samuel Botsford Buckley arrange and describe materials he had collected the previous year in the Southeast (Buckley, "Description of Some New Species of Plants," *Silliman's Journal*, 1843, *45*:170–177). Buckley (1809–1883, *DAB*) was a graduate of Wesleyan University in Connecticut (1836). He did some additional field work in the South in the late 1850s after spending many years on the family farm. Before and after the Civil War, Buckley was with the Texas Geological Survey. During the war he worked with the U.S. Sanitary Commission.

Torrey's biographer notes that although Torrey was willing to work with Buckley and considered him a determined collector, he found him "illiterate and vulgar." His personality apparently kept him from joining Audubon's and Frémont's expeditions. Andrew Denny Rodgers III, *John Torrey: A Story of North American Botany* (1942; reprint ed., New York, 1965), pp. 173–174.

[5] Buckley was trying to sell a collection of fossil bones described in "Notice of the Discovery of a Nearly Complete Skeleton of the Zygodon of Owen (Basilosaurus of Harlan) in Alabama," *Silliman's Journal*, 1843, *44*:409–412.

[6] Silliman was lecturing at the Lowell Institute for the fourth consecutive year. From a study of his course materials, Margaret Rossiter has concluded that he felt uneasy lecturing on organic chemistry. Rossiter, "Benjamin Silliman and the Lowell Institute: The Popularization of Science in Nineteenth-Century America," *New England Quarterly*, 1971, *44*:622.

[7] Benjamin Silliman, Jr.

[8] Probably George Endicott (1802–1848), a New York City lithographer, or his younger brother William (1816–1851). George C. Groce and David H. Wallace, *The New-York Historical Society's Dictionary of Artists in America, 1564–1860* (New Haven, 1957).

[9] A new genus of Santalaceae collected by Buckley which Torrey established and dedicated to Buckley. Buckley's paper in the July issue included only a brief descriptive note and Silliman's promise, apparently never fulfilled, of a full description and illustration in a future issue. *Silliman's Journal*, 1843, *45*:170.

[10] Bailey had been examining needle-shaped crystals in the bark, wood, and leaves of various types of trees and found them to be composed of oxalate of lime (calcium oxalate). See his letter to Torrey of September 17, 1842, printed above.

[11] Probably Franz J. F. Meyen, *Neues System der Pflanzen-Physiologie*, 3 vols. (Berlin, 1837–1839).

[12] Gray is probably referring to K. B. Presl's illustration of a species of fern in the Willdenow herbarium in Berlin in his *Testamen Pteridographiae, seu Genera Filicacearum* (Prague, 1836), plate 3, figures 9 and 10.

[13] Walter Hood Fitch, a botanical draftsman (*DSB*, s.v. "Hooker, William Jackson").

[14] Probably a reference to Christian Sch-

Have you yet reported on Fremont's plants?[15]

I laid before *Benny* a plan for collaborating Sill. Journal, entirely on my own responsibility, naming to him Henry[16] & Bache for Physical Science, Dana[17] for Mineralogy, Peirce[18] for Mathematical Science, Wyman[19] for Zoology, &c.—insisting on these 3 points—1. that no new collaborators should be introduced but by the consent of these. 2. That original communications in these several departments should pass thru the hands of the proper collaborator, and be rejected at his discretion. Their reviews &c. shall be signed by their initials, &c. 3. They shall be supplied with such journals as they want by the Editors. I have seen him but for a moment since he has laid it before the Father. I see, I think, that they are disposed to catch at so much of the plan as suits them. I suspect they think that the rise in the character of the Journal, co-incident with the appearance of these names on the title-page, would be so much glory taken from them.[20] Benny merely said that they thought the plan might be adopted in part, or its advantages secured, & says he will write to Henry & Bache on the subject. I wish you therefore to speak to Henry and say *two* things, 1st That in mentioning his name as the person desirable to be secured for this purpose, I disclaimed having any authority or permission to use his name, or Bache's, but did it simply on my own responsibility, suggesting merely that these

---

kuhr's *Botanische Handbuch* . . . , 8 vols. (Wittenberg, 1791–1803). Schkuhr (1741–1811) designed and etched the plates himself. George C. Williamson, *Bryan's Dictionary of Painters and Engravers*, 5th ed., 5 vols. (New York, 1964), 5:41.

[15] Torrey was finishing a catalogue of plants collected by J. C. Frémont on his first major expedition in 1842 which explored between the Missouri River and the Rocky Mountains. He later described Frémont's collections from subsequent expeditions. Rodgers, *Torrey*, pp. 151–171.

[16] Years earlier, Benjamin Silliman, Sr., had proposed to Henry that he take charge of the subject of electromagnetism for the journal. See *Henry Papers*, 1:461.

[17] Following the return of the Wilkes Expedition in 1842, James Dwight Dana spent two years in Washington working with the expedition collections. In 1846 he became a co-editor of *Silliman's Journal*. *Henry Papers*, 3:126n–127n.

[18] Benjamin Peirce (1809–1880), Perkins Professor of Mathematics and Astronomy at Harvard. Peirce had already published a number of math texts and edited the short-lived *Cambridge Miscellany of Mathematics, Physics,*

and Astronomy. In his works and teaching, he demonstrated a mastery of the literature in his fields. *DAB. DSB.*

[19] Jeffries Wyman (1814–1874), a graduate of Harvard (1833) and the Harvard Medical School (1837), became the leading anatomist in America. In the early 1840s he served as Curator of the Lowell Institute, studied anatomy and physiology in Europe, and was Curator of Reptiles and Fishes at the Boston Society of Natural History. After five years as Professor of Anatomy and Physiology at Hampden-Sydney Medical College, Wyman returned to Harvard as Professor of Anatomy. *DAB. DSB.*

[20] Although Asa Gray was already largely responsible for the botanical matter which appeared in *Silliman's Journal*, the Sillimans did not formally institute a system of assistant editors with responsibilities for various fields until 1851. See *Henry Papers*, 4:326n. The elder Silliman felt that "the unity of purpose and action so essential to the success of such a work were best secured by *individuality*," a position not threatened by adding first his son and then his son-in-law (Dana) as co-editors. *Silliman's Journal*, 1847, 50:xiii.

gentlemen might accede to such plan, if properly presented. 2ⁿᵈ That what-ever Silliman may propose different from the above essentials, is not *my* plan. If he makes any proposition which they like, and will accept, very well.[21] If not, and the right men feel inclined to start a new Journal, on a comprehensive plan and of high tone, I will be glad to collaborate in it. I think the best part of the *real* science of the country can be concentrated in some shape or other, and its weight be felt.

Adieu, Yours affectionately
A. Gray

[21] Torrey replied on March 6:
You may be sure that the Sillimans will not agree to your plan respecting collabora-tors—& sooner or later we shall have a new journal. I will endeavour to see Henry in the morning & communicate to him your message.
On March 26 Torrey wrote that a letter from the Sillimans failed to mention the subject and that they hadn't written to Henry yet. In a letter of April 14, Torrey mentioned the plan of collaborators again and wrote that Henry was going to Philadelphia soon with a letter to Bache asking his opinion. Torrey to Gray, March 2–6, 1843, March 26, 1843, and April 14, 1843, Historic Letter File, Gray Herbarium Library, Harvard University.

Henry had mentioned a need for collabora-tors to Silliman five years earlier (*Henry Papers, 4*:99–100). See also the correspondence between Henry and Bache of November 6 and 12, printed below.

"RECORD OF EXPERIMENTS"
Henry Papers, Smithsonian Archives

<Feby> March 5ᵗʰ 1843[1]

Made a number of experiments to day on the phosphorogenic emination[2]

1ˢᵗ   Found that it would pass through a cup of water the bottom of the cup was formed of a plate of quartz and the sides of bees wax

[1] Henry originally dated all the March 1843 "Record of Experiments" entries incorrectly, recording them as February 1843. He subse-quently revised some of the entries, either writing over or crossing out the original date.

[2] Henry had become interested in the phe-nomenon of phosphorescence through his knowledge of the work of A.-C. and Edmond Becquerel and Biot. His repetition and ex-pansion of those experiments was briefly re-ported to the American Philosophical Society on April 16, 1841. See above, Henry Notebook Entry, February 17, 1841; "Record of Experi-ments," February 25, 1841.

After a lull of two years he returned, at first intermittently, to the problem. The initial motivation may have been simple curiosity. However, the opportunity to address the American Philosophical Society at their cen-tennial meeting (see below, Bache and John Ludlow to Henry, April 26, 1843, and Henry to Bache, May 15, 1843) was a strong incentive to perform research which would lead to clear and rapid results. From May 3 through May 17 Henry conducted a series of experiments which culminated in his paper entitled "On Phosphorogenic Emanation," delivered to the American Philosophical Society's centennial meeting on May 26, 1843 (published in the APS *Proceedings*, 1843, *3*:38–44).

Although an accurate empirical study of the effects and characteristics of the emanation—

2nd It also passes through salt—a plate of this mineral, nearly half an inch thick, was placed over the paper box or tray in which the phosphorous was placed—the luminosity was as intense as if only air intervened between the spark and the substance

3rd A plate of thin transparent mica was next interposed the phosphorous remained dark

4th Next a plate of sulphate of lime was interposed the emination passed freely through this

5th Alcohol was next tried and with the same result as that of the last experiment

6 A t[hi]ck[3] (one inch) crystal was next interposed the phosphorescence was as vivid with this as without it

---

ultraviolet light—Henry's paper did not prove to be an important contribution to the development of optics. His work was overshadowed by the more exquisite contemporary experiments of Edmond Becquerel, published in "Des effets produits sur les corps par les rayons solaires," *Annales de chimie et de physique,* 1843, 3d ser. *9*:257–322, especially pp. 314–322. E. Newton Harvey, *A History of Luminescence from the Earliest Times until 1900* (Philadelphia, 1957), pp. 350–352.

Henry's experiments also played a role in confirming his belief in the wave theory of light. Responding to questioning by Robert Hare after the delivery of the paper, Henry declared that a greater number of the observed phenomena were more understandable in the framework of the wave than the particulate theory (Manuscript Minutes, November 1842–January 1846, p. 78, Archives, American Philosophical Society), expanding upon his remark in the paper that under the wave theory, all the emanations can "be considered as the results of waves, differing in length and amplitude, and possibly also slightly differing in the direction of vibration." APS *Proceedings,* 1843, *3*:42.

[3] A hole in the paper.

"RECORD OF EXPERIMENTS"
Henry Papers, Smithsonian Archives

<*Feby*> March 10th 1843

7 The emination did not pass through a specimen of white carnelian which was pelucid but not transparent

8 Passed through smoky quartz—an inch thick

9 Placed a quantity of the phosphorous between two plates of quartz and then wound wire around the whole and passed a shock from the jar through the wire, but no effect could be perceived. The phosphorous did not become luminous

Prepared phosphorous paper by first moist[en]ing or rather wetting the paper with gum water and then sprinkling by means of a sieve the powdered sulphuret of lime over the wet surface

The sulphuret of lime was prepared by first calcining a quantity of powdered oyster shells for at least an hour in an intense fire then mixing with this powder $1/8$ part by weight of flow[e]rs of sulphur, and lastly heating the mixture for an hour in a crucible. This preparation is very sensible to the electrical emination. With a discharge from a single jar, the spark appearing between the points of two blunt wires, the phosphorous became luminous when placed at the distance of 54 inches from the spark.

I observed one fact which may lead to some interesting result namely that the emination which produces the phosphoro[. . .][1] light looses more by being reflected from a surface of glass or of metal than ordinary light does under the same circumstances.[2] The phosphorous was so placed as that the direct emination could not reach it. The arrangement was as shown in the margin *a* is the mirror *c* the spark *b* the phosphorous *s* a screen. The light was more feeble from the mirror than from the direct radiation, although in the case of the latter, the phosphorous was placed at 4 times the distance

I at first thought this was peculiar to the glass but found the same result with a metallic mirror

[1] A hole in the paper.

[2] In the published paper, Henry's emphasis is much different. Discussing his efforts "to determine whether the emanation obeys the laws of the reflection of light," Henry concluded that the answer was in the affirmative, but that "glass neither reflects nor transmits the phosphorogenic emanation, except in a very small degree" (APS *Proceedings*, 1843, *3*: 40–41). It was the reflective power of a metallic mirror compared to a glass mirror which Henry focused on in his publication, not the general loss of intensity suffered by the emanation upon reflection.

"RECORD OF EXPERIMENTS"
Henry Papers, Smithsonian Archives

<Feby> March 11th 1843
Phosphorogenic Emination[1]

Made a number of experiments with the object to polarize the phosphorigenic emination but was not successful.[2] I however established the fact that the emination does not produce the phosphoresence when it is passed

[1] This heading has been moved from the top of the second page of this two-page entry.

[2] Henry reported his initial difficulties in polarizing the phosphorogenic emanation and his eventual success through an indirect method in his published paper. "On Phosphorogenic Emanation," APS *Proceedings*, 1843, *3*:41.

through a Nichols eye piece composed of two pieces of calk spar, so arranged as to reflect aside the extra ray. The light is much more vivid under two pieces of spar, making a thickness of 4 inches, than under an eye piece of one inch in thickness.

The substance which is most impervious to the phosphorogenic emination which I have as yet tried is tourmaline. I can determine with some approximation to accuracy the comparitive transpar[ency][3] by making two holes in the same card and covering one with one substance and the other with another the same powder being placed under each the comparitive brightness gives the comparitive transmitting power

Part of the effect in reference to the non luminous result, when a Nichol's prism was used, may be ascribed to the fact that onely half of the incidental light passed through the crystal, the other half was reflected aside but the result was so intense <*when*> under the crystal and so feeble under the eye piece, that the difference cannot be attributed entirely to this cause.

It appears to me that a single polarized beam does not produce as much effect as a beam of ordinary light of the same quantity and intensity.

I next placed a crystal of carbonate of lime above and again below the eye piece with the idea that the depolarization of the light makes a difference in the result but no peculiar effect was observed

The sulphuret of lime has been exposed to the air for several days and is not quite as sensible as at first or as it was yesterday but by illuminating it several times by the discharge it increased very much in sensibillity but it did not appear to remain luminous as long as it did yesterday.

Found that the same phosphorescent light was produced by a coal of stone coal, intensely heated in the anthracite stove. The sulphuret of lime was defended from the direct heat by a thick crystal of sulphate of lime. The same substance is rendered luminous by a small degree of heat.

The emination is screaned by carnelian and this substance, as I am informed by Dr Torrey, is supposed to be fused quartze or it is quartze with a glassy structure[4]

The action appears to diffuse itself. If a paper be placed over the tray with a hole in it and another paper at some distance above also pierced with a small hole, then the ray will not diverge but the whole surface of the

---

[3] The last few letters of this word are covered by an ink blot.

[4] Carnelian was indeed considered a variety of quartz. But as one expert noted, "no mineral species assumes a greater variety of characteristics" than quartz. Not only did the carnelian screen the phosphorogenic emanation, but it was only translucent to light. In contrast, pure quartz crystals were transparent to both forms of emanation. James Dwight Dana, *A System of Mineralogy* (New Haven, 1837), pp. 340–343 (the quote is from p. 340); APS *Proceedings*, 3:44.

mineral powder will exhibit the phosphorescence the most intense light is confined to the centre of the hole but still there is light all around and over the whole surface.

I find on comparing my experiments with those which are given in the Encyclopedia Britanica on the subject of phosphorescence that those substances which I find do not transmit the phosphorigenic principle are also incapable of being made phosphorescent by a discharge of electricity[5]

[5] This is a reference to the summary of William Skrimshire's experiments. *Encyclopaedia* *Britannica*, 7th ed., s.v. "Electricity," pp. 633–634.

FROM CHARLES E. WEST[1]
Henry Papers, Smithsonian Archives

New York March 14th 1843.

My Dear Sir.

I wish your opinion upon an exceedingly interesting subject. In the town of Rome in this state, a lambent flame was observed at night a few years since playing on the surface of a sand-bank some 70 or 80 feet high forming one of the banks of Fish Creek. This excited the curiosity of the neighbourhood which resulted in a search for the cause. After removing some 12 or 18 inches of the soil, they discovered a coarse glass tube evidently formed from the sand bank, which they traced for more than 40 feet in an almost perpendicular line, when it turned off abruptly & passed deeper into the bank. From fear of being inhumed they gave up the search after having dug 5 feet more in a vertical direction. There were two bifurcations from the main stem. Associated with the stem were strata of indurated sand lying in an almost vertical position between which loose sand which ran out under the action of the shovel leaving the strata like the leaves of an open book. The stem was irregular in shape, flattened more in some places than in others: The inside of it was highly <*flattened*> glazed as though it had been exposed to the action of fire—the outside was rough, having particles of sand adhering to it.

Now may I ask the favour of your opinion with regard to the probable

[1] Principal of the Rutgers Female Institute, New York City, and Henry's friend; see above, Henry to W. B. Kinney, July 12, 1842. The envelope to this letter bears the inscription "By Dr. Chilton," a reference to the New York City instrument maker and chemist, James R. Chilton. *Henry Papers*, 2:20n.

cause which formed this tube. I am aware that accounts of short tubes, some two or three yards in length, have been communicated to the world, and that lightning has been considered by some as the agent which produced them. Others have supposed them to be the work of insects; others again, to be a deposition of lime held in solution around vegetable stalks. The two last have no claim to attention in the present instance being utterly inadequate to produce such a result. With regard to atmospheric electricity we would be led to suppose from its diffusive tendency on coming in contact with moist bodies that it would not pass for 50 feet or more in a continuous line through moist sand. And yet the tube appears to have been formed in this way.[2] Any information on this subject will be gratefully received. Another enquiry, from what source was the gas derived?

It would give me great pleasure to receive a visit from you. My kind regards to Mrs Henry.

> I am, Dear Sir, your friend &
> Servant—
> Cha[s] E. West

[2] West wrote a letter dated March 21, 1843, which appeared in *Silliman's Journal*, 1843, 45:220–221, using much the same phrasing as in this letter to Henry. The editors identified the tube as a "fulgurite," by which name it was known in the contemporary literature. For example, Mary Somerville in *On the Connexion of the Physical Sciences*, 5th ed. (London, 1840), p. 314, mentioned a "fulgorite [sic] of forty foot length." Today the term survives in the *Oxford English Dictionary*, *Webster's Third New International Dictionary*, and the *Grand Larousse de la langue français*. Henry cited a competing French usage in explaining the phenomenon to West, using the now archaic "fulminary tube," following Becquerel. ("Des tubes fulminaires," in Antoine-César Becquerel, *Traité expérimental de l'électricité et du magnétisme*, 7 vols. [Paris, 1834–1840], 4:137–139.) Henry's explanation, based on Becquerel's, is found in his March 22 letter to West, printed below.

Attributing the cause of the tubes to lightning was common at the time. *Silliman's Journal*, for example, in making the index for its first forty-nine volumes, ascribed all sand tubes to the agency of lightning, whether that cause was discussed in the individual articles or not. (*Silliman's Journal*, 1847, 50:93, s.v. "Fulgurites.")

West's other two discounted theories for the formation of sand tubes referred to quite different causes, yielding far smaller tubes. The deposition of lime around plants was mentioned by at least one contemporary geology book. Henry T. de la Beche, *A Geological Manual* (Philadelphia, 1832), pp. 78–79, discussed cylindrical bodies found on a beach whose "vegetable origin immediately suggests itself.... They are really incrustations formed on vegetables which have afterwards decayed." In the same author's *How to Observe Geology* (London, 1835), p. 108, he mentioned the agglutination of sand around vegetables through the action of silicious waters, though he did not explicitly refer to the formation of tubes.

A possible interpretation of West's comment that insects could be the cause of such tubes hinges on the sense of the word "insect." One could take it to mean "worm," as in the trumpet worm, *Pectinaria*. This animal lives in a conical shell of sand, buried up to its top. In reference to this order of animal, in the same division as the insects proper, Cuvier remarked: "Some of the Tubicolae form a calcareous, homogenous tube,...others construct one by agglutinating grains of sand, fragments of shell, and particles of mud, by means of a membrane." Georges Cuvier, *The Animal Kingdom*, 4 vols. (London, 1834), 3:128.

"RECORD OF EXPERIMENTS"
Henry Papers, Smithsonian Archives

[March][1] 16th 1843
Experiments on Mesmerism[2]

Agreably to appointment I made some experiments to day on a Mesmeric subject, inorder to test the truth of the assertion which had been made that by throwing a person into what is called the mesmeric state, magnetism could be imparted to soft iron by a touch of his hand and that his body would exhibit electrical phenomena.[3]

The subject was a young Negro—in the employment of a Mr Anthon,[4] a lecturer on mesmerism. He appeared to be about 20 years old—not very intelligent and was perhaps a good subject to be wrought upon, in the way of exciting his immagination. The magnetizer appeared to be an honest man and fully convinced of the reality of the phenomena of animal magnetism.

Before Mr Anthon performed his operations on the boy the frequency of his pulse was noted and found to be 65 per minute—also a thermometer was placed under his tongue, inorder to determine the temperature of his body. On being asked if he perceived any peculiar feeling when the instrument was in his mouth he declared that he did, that it made him *numb*.

---

[1] Another of the series of entries which Henry incorrectly dated "Feby."

[2] After a brief appearance just after the Revolutionary War, mesmerism or animal magnetism was successfully reintroduced into this country from Europe in 1836. Originally conceived as a therapeutic device in medical treatment, mesmerism underwent a major transformation, becoming swept up in a broader enthusiasm for science-based reform movements and efforts to establish a science of human nature. Among the other fields of study and reform movements sharing in this enthusiasm were phrenology, homeopathy, spiritualism, prison reform, and women's rights. Robert C. Fuller, *Mesmerism and the American Cure of Souls* (Philadelphia, 1982); Taylor Stoehr, *Hawthorne's Mad Scientists: Pseudoscience and Social Science in Nineteenth-Century Life and Letters* (Hamden, Connecticut, 1978).

Henry was quite cautious in his dealings with these movements. He was skeptical, demanding empirical verification of assertions, but careful not to reject the claims of these movements out of hand. The good scientist keeps an open mind but insists on evidence. For another example of Henry's dealings with these movements, see his letter to La Roy Sunderland of August 28, 1841, printed above.

[3] Mesmerists claimed a number of relationships between electricity, magnetism, and the mesmeric force. For example, the mesmeric force of a subject would increase if he or she were electrically charged. Subjects would also show reactions if exposed to magnets, even to the point of demonstrating the polarity of the human body. A mesmerist's "passes" of the hand could magnetize a needle. Magnets could even be used to produce the mesmeric state. See, e.g., Chauncy Hare Townshend, *Facts in Mesmerism with Reasons for a Dispassionate Inquiry into It* (London, 1840); Robert W. Gibbes, *A Lecture on the Magnetism of the Human Body . . .* (Columbia, South Carolina, 1843).

[4] Unidentified. According to one contemporary estimate, in 1843 there were more than twenty lecturing mesmerists operating in New England, while there were more than two hundred "magnetizers" just in the city of Boston. Fuller, *Mesmerism*, p. 30.

After this he was placed on an electrical stool[5] and made to touch a delicate gold leaf electrometer but he gave no signs of free electricity.

After these experiments he was thrown into what the operator called, the mesmeric sleep. Of the nature of this state I can say nothing from my own observation, although I am inclined to believe that the condition was not intirely feigned. The eyes were closed or nearly so and the countenance assumed or rather exhibited, a stupid expression resem[bling] that of a troubled sleep. At the command of the operator he stood up and walked about the floor stumbling against the benches and chairs.

He was first brought to the electrical stool and ordered to stand on it, but he did not obey the Magnetizer and finally we were obliged to lift him on by main strength. The electrometer was then placed in communication with his hand but it exhibited no signs of excitement, although the instrument was so dellicate that the least touch of his coat with a silk handkerchief would make the leaves strike the side of the glass. This fact may perhaps have given rise to the assertion that by making what are called the passes down the body it would become electrical. A slight touch of the magnetizer's hand would be sufficient to produce the effect by the ordinary action of friction.

Next his hands were placed in contact with the wires of a delicate electro magnet and then passes made along them, but the soft iron exhibited no signs of magnetism although it was tested very carefully with iron filings. The boy appeared very reluctant although in the mesmeric sleep to approach the apparatus.

I next placed in his hands two poles of a magneto-electrical apparatus the shocks of which were very severe and could scarcely be indured by an ordinary individual. When the machine was put in operation, the muscles of his arms were thrown into <*violent*> convulsive motions and he exclaimed "I want to be waked up," "I want to be waked up". He however still kept his eyes closed and retained the same stupid and sleepy appearance and as soon as he was released from the machine he wandered, as it were, as far from the apparatus as the room would permit. When he was at <*about*> the distance of about 18 feet from the operator and his back to the same, it was proposed by Mr Anthon himself that he should take the shocks inorder to test if the negro—by sympathy—would exhibit any signes of uneasiness. At the first shock given Mr Anthon, the face and neck of the Negro were observed to be spasmodically affected. I was my self working the machine and giving the shocks and therefore did not myself see the face of the subject

[5] Presumably an "insulating stool," a stool with glass feet, which allowed the experimenter to electrify a human just like any other insulated conductor. Denison Olmsted, *An Introduction to Natural Philosophy*, 2 vols. (New Haven, 1832), 2:146–147.

but I did observe the twitching of the body. The experiment was by no means satisfactory, the boy could hear the snap of the machine and could perceive the start of the person shocked. When Professor Maclean took the shock instead of Mr A the effect was said not to be produced. I can say nothing inreferen[ce] to this observation since my position at the machine prevented my observing the effect.

In order to avoid all perception of the ordinary kind by the boy in reference to the shocks given Mr A, the latter with the machine was placed in an adjoining room with the door open but so that the sound would not be perceptable as before and nothing could be seen. With this arrangement no effect was produced on the boy however severe the shocks might be which Mr Anthon endured. Next the door between the two rooms was shut and the boy placed close up to it so that Mr A and himself were seperated by only the thickness of the door, but in this case as in the last, no effect could be observed, although shocks of great intensity were given to the operator.

I forgot to mention in its proper place that the boy was brought near a large and powerful electro-magnet when in full activity and also when the contact with the galvanic battery was broken but no effect could be observed, although the mesmerizer had informed me, and probably believed what he said, that a magnet powerfully affected his subject.

After this Mr A. attempted to restore the boy to his natural state by a seriees of *"passes"* motions with the hands upwards while the boy was in the outer room and the operator in the inner but he appeared to make no progress. He next came in to the outer room and commenced making the passes but still the boy remained in the same state. At length by coming in contact with him he restored him to his natural state, the pulse was then at 75 but this accelaration was probably due to a violent fit of coughing with which the boy was seized just before waking. The result of these experiments prove nothing in favour of Animal magnetism and do not even establish the fact that a person can be thrown into an unnatural state by the manipulations of the Mesmerizer, although from the testimony of many respectable persons I am inclined to believe that the immagination can be so operated on as to induce a state resembling catalepsy or hysteria, in case the subject is of a proper temperament [or] of sufficient credulity.

The subject is just now attracting great attention in our country and in England and although it would require a considerable amount of positive and definite experimental evidence to induce me to believe in the sympathy of mind on mind such as is contended for by the magnetizer, yet I do not think it philosophical to declair that the whole matter is too ridiculous to merit the least attention—since in this case we assume that nothing can exist but what is already known to us. The probability in favour of the fallacy of the whole is certainly very great but there may be notwithstanding this something in it and at least it is a curious cycological phenomenon that so many intelligent persons are at this time firm believers in the truth of the principles of this most improbable of all sciences, if it can be so called.

TO CHARLES E. WEST

Mary Henry Copy, Henry Papers, Smithsonian Archives

Princeton March 22nd 1843

My dear sir. Your favor of the 14th came to hand some days since but my engagements have prevented my answering it before this time.[1] The phenomenon you mention is a very interesting one although by no means uncommon. I think there is but little doubt of the electrical origin of the fulminary tubes, as they are called. According to Mr. Becquerel these tubes were described for the first time by a clergyman of S[. . .] in 1711[2] and since then they have been found in almost every quarter of the globe. They are found in sand banks and generally descend nearly perpendicularly to the moist earth beneath although they sometimes take an oblique direction and are often divided into several branches, at their lower extremity. They are found from 20 to 40 feet long with an internal diameter of two inches and sometimes more. . . .

The conditions necessary to produce the phenomenon according to my views of the subject would be the following. *First* a bank of siliceous sand, under which is a stratum of moist earth, of water, or of any conducting substance. Secondly a cloud highly charged, say with plus electricity, driven by the wind towards the sand bank: when sufficiently near induction would take place through the air and sand and at a distance repel the natural electricity of the moist earth down into the earth, the unsaturated matter thus produced would strongly attract the cloud; its free electricity would be accumulated in its lower surface, the attraction would increase, the cloud would be arrested in its course, would descend towards the bank until the action would become so great between the unsaturated matter below and the redundant electricity of the cloud that a discharge would take place

---

[1] See West to Henry, March 14, 1843, above.
[2] A blank space followed the "S." Antoine-César Becquerel, "Des tubes fulminaires," *Traité expérimental de l'électricité et du* *magnétisme,* 7 vols. (Paris, 1834–1840), *4*:137–139, attributed the first description, occurring in 1711, to Pastor Herman of Silesia.

through the air and the sand into the negative surface below. The condition of things would be the same as in the case of a charged square of glass, coated with tinfoil. The cloud would represent the charged surface in connection with the machine; the glass would represent the air and sand, the other coating the negative surface below. If the glass were thin and the charge powerful, a discharge would probably take place directly through the intervening non-conductor by a perforation through it, as is often the case in the spontaneous breaking of a jar by an overcharge of electricity.

I should think that the lambent flame you mention, was something entirely unconnected with the fulminary tube and unless I had a full account of all the circumstances of its appearance I would not hazard an opinion in reference to the matter.[3]

[3] Mary Henry wrote "unfinished letter to Charles E. West" at the bottom of the page, referring to the state either of her copying or of Henry's composition.

"RECORD OF EXPERIMENTS"
Henry Papers, Smithsonian Archives

March 23[d] 1843

Made an experiment to day on the "pasivity" of iron. A piece of iron wire was heated and then suffered to cool. On plunging this into strong nitric acid no action was perceptible and this state is called pasivity.[1] The idea has occurred to me that perhapse if the wire were magnetized and demagnetized while in the acid, the natural state would return. On making the experment however the effect was not produced. The iron remained in the acid unaffected. The experiment consisted in surrounding the glass tube containing the acid and into which the wire was dipped with a coil.

When the passive wire was made the negative element of a galvanic couplet, the passive state was destroyed and action produced

[1] The "passive condition" of iron was thought to be an electrochemical phenomenon. Other metals—including cobalt and nickel—would also become passive under similar conditions. William Allen Miller, *Elements of Chemistry: Theoretical and Practical*, 2d ed., 3 vols. (London, 1860–1862), 2: 542–543.

FROM THE AMERICAN PHILOSOPHICAL SOCIETY[1]

Henry Papers, Smithsonian Archives

Hall of the American Philosophical
Society, Independence Square
Philadelphia, 31 March, 1843

The American Philosophical Society has determined to celebrate the hundredth anniversary of its organization under that title,[2] on Thursday, the twenty fifth of May next.

A Discourse on the objects of the Society, its history, labours and prospects, will be pronounced on that day, at noon, by D̲r̲ Robert M. Patterson, one of the Vice Presidents, and a meeting will be held on Friday, the twenty sixth, at which communications will be received, on topics of Scientific interest, from members and correspondents.[3]

The committee, which has been charged with the arrangements for the celebration, respectfully invites your presence and co-operation.

Nathaniel Chapman.
John K. Kane.
John Ludlow.
Robley Dunglison.
Frederick Fraley.
Alexander Dallas Bache.
Geo. Washington Smith.
Committee.[4]

[1] This is a lithographed circular.

[2] The qualifying phrase reflected uncertainty over the date of origin of the APS. The May 1843 centennial assumed Benjamin Franklin's proposal of 1743 to be the origin of the Society. The Society has sometimes been traced, however, to Franklin's Junto of 1727; the bicentennial was celebrated in 1927. The 1769 merger of the APS and the American Society Held at Philadelphia for Promoting Useful Knowledge provides a third possibility. It is a mark of the American Philosophical Society's breadth of vision and refusal to stoop to petty pedantry that it now celebrates all three "foundings." Ralph S. Bates, *Scientific Societies in the United States*, 3d ed. (Cambridge, Massachusetts, 1965), pp. 4–9. Whitfield J. Bell, Jr., and Murphy D. Smith, comps., *Guide to the Archives and Manuscript Collections of the American Philosophical Society* (Philadelphia, 1966), p. 20.

[3] The response to this and a later circular (of April 26, printed below) soliciting papers to be read at the meeting was so favorable that the celebration was extended to four days. The entire third volume of the APS *Proceedings*, 1843, is devoted to the centennial.

[4] Nathaniel Chapman (*Henry Papers*, 2:109n) was a Vice-President of the Society. John K. Kane (*Henry Papers*, 1:159n) and Robley Dunglison (*Henry Papers*, 3:369n) were Secretaries. John Ludlow (*Henry Papers*, 1:106n) was Provost of the University of Pennsylvania. Frederick Fraley (*DAB*) was a founder of the Franklin Institute and a prominent merchant and banker. For George Washington Smith, see above, Bache to Henry, February 22, 1843.

April 10, 1843

TO JAMES CARNAHAN
John Maclean Papers, Princeton University Archives

Princeton April 10ᵗʰ 1843

Dear Sir

You will oblige me by presenting to the consideration of the Board of trustees of the College the following communication relative to the case of young Blair of the class which graduated in 1841. It will probable be recollected by the trustees that on account of some gross misconduct on the part of Francis P. Blair and Edward H. Bowen, at the close of the senior examination in 1841, the faculty decided not to recommend these persons for the first degree in the arts with their classmates, but that if they conducted themselves properly and did not return to the approaching commencement they should be recommended for that college honor at the end of the next year. Blair notwithstanding the prohibition of the faculty did return to Princeton and was seen by <*many*> several persons on the day of commencement and on this account as I have since been informed the degree was with held from him at the last <*commencemen*> meeting of the Board although it was confered on Bowen.

Some circumstances connected with this affair came to my knowledge which if presented to the trustees may perhaps induce them to reconsider the subject and grant to Blair the degree at their present session. Blair did not return to Princeton with the intention of treating the authority of the faculty with disrespect but because he had been advised by his friends to seek an interview with the members of the Board of trustees and thus endeavour by personal solicitation to obtain a degree with his classmates. Immediately on his arrival in Princeton he reported himself to me and stated his reasons for returning—said that his friends were exceedingly anxious that he should graduate with his class and that if his name did not appear with those of his companions he would be for ever disgraced. He requested me to introduce him to some members of the Board that he might have an opportunity of pleading his own cause: or that at least I would present to the Trustees a written petition from him. I stated in reply that he had acted very imprudently in returning as he had done and that he could effect nothing for himself in the way he proposed; but that to satisfy him I would speak to some of the Trustees and get an expression of their opinion. The first person I happened to meet after this conversation <*happened to be M*> and to whom I mentioned the case was Mr Southard. He requested me to say to Blair that he had done wrong in returning to Princeton but notwithstanding this if he would conduct himself properly he should have the de-

319

gree at the next commencement and that he (Mr Southard) would advocate his cause before the Trustees.[1]

With this assurance Blair left Princeton started for Lexington; commenced the study of the law; joined the temperance society and as I have been informed from three different sources has conducted himself with great propriety and has been industriously engaged in the acquisition of his profession. Although he was considerably disappointed after the contrary assurance of Mr Southard, in not receiving the degree at the last commencement yet his feelings on the occasion as expressed in the following extract of a letter to me[2] are of a very proper kind. "I entertain no unkind feelings towards any of the Professors connected with the College of New Jersey and all recollection of any immaginary injuries received at their hand has given place to feelings of high and warm regard. If the Trustees should hereafter think proper to grant me a degree I desire to be placed with my classmates on the triennial catalogue.[3] I hope to obtain my license to practice law this spring and doubt not my success will be equal to my deserts."

In concluding this communication I would respectfully state to the Trustees my belief that the whole affair has had a happy effect on the character of the young man and that in my opinion neither justice nor the interest of the college require that the degree should be longer with-held.[4]

> With much Respect I have
> The honor to be Yours &c &c
> Joseph Henry

[1] Samuel Lewis Southard, LL.D. (1787–1842), A.B. Princeton, 1804, and Trustee, 1822–1842. *Henry Papers*, 2:282. Southard died before the September 1842 Trustees' meeting at which Bowen's degree was approved, and thus could not have plead Blair's case.

[2] Not found.

[3] The general catalog of the college, listing presidents, trustees, faculty, and alumni, published in Princeton from 1770–1886 under the title *Catalogus Collegii Neo-Caesariensis.* Blair was missing from the 1842 edition, but present as an alumnus of the Class of 1841 in the 1845 edition.

[4] See the letter of Henry to Blair, November 25, 1842, above.

TO [?JAMES HENRY][1]

Mary Henry Copy, Family Correspondence, Henry Papers,
Smithsonian Archives

Princeton April 15th 1843

Princeton will soon be dressed in its most beautiful garb. We have almost been able to see the grass grow for the last two or three days.

[1] The recipient's name is not given on this Mary Henry fragment of a letter. Another hand has added "Poss. to James."

Stephen has been much engaged for a month past in calculating the path of the comet. It appears to be a difficult gentleman to understand. No less than four orbits have been published no two of which agree.[2]

[2] Visible during the day, endowed with a huge tail, the Great Comet of 1843 was a spectacular sight from February 28 through early March 1843. It was also a major astronomical headache. The comet was a sungrazer, approaching closer to the solar surface than any comet to date. Because of the small perihelion distance, the comet also exhibited tremendous velocity. Accurate observations were difficult to obtain and the computed orbits varied considerably. The computed perihelion point, for example, was placed anywhere from a point well within the solar interior to a point over one million miles beyond the sun's surface.

Among those who found the perihelion in the solar interior were Sears Cook Walker and E. Otis Kendall of the Philadelphia High School Observatory. Realizing that such an orbit was extremely difficult to justify physically, they turned to their colleagues in the American astronomical community for assistance. In a letter dated May 20, 1843, Stephen Alexander responded to Walker and Kendall's plea for help. He accepted their orbit as correct, implying that his computations gave similar results. He also formulated an explanation for the apparent paradox of a comet which either entered, rolled along, or bounced off the solar surface. Alexander argued that the center of gravity of the comet, which defined positions in the orbit, was at some distance from the nucleus, which astronomers had assumed to be the center of gravity when making their observations and computing the orbit. Hence the true orbit of the comet deviated considerably from the orbit based on observations of the nucleus. This deviation was greatest at perihelion.

Walker and Kendall found Alexander's explanation, which was independently developed by W. H. C. Bartlett, to be quite satisfactory. However, most of the world astronomical community rejected the Walker and Kendall orbit in favor of orbits which placed the comet about sixty to ninety thousand miles beyond the solar surface at perihelion.

S. C. Walker and E. O. Kendall, "On the Great Comet of 1843," *Silliman's Journal*, 1843, 45:188–208 (Alexander's letter appears on page 195); Robert Grant, *History of Physical Astronomy from the Earliest Ages to the Middle of the Nineteenth Century* (London, 1852), pp. 290–292; Elias Loomis, *The Recent Progress of Astronomy; Especially in the United States* (New York, 1850), pp. 80–91.

FROM JAMES C. FISHER[1]
Henry Papers, Smithsonian Archives

New York April 15th 1843.

Dear Sir

Some time since you mentioned to Prof Morse that you had used a small hand machine for covering wire with silk or cotton thread. We wish to make a number of experiments on the best form of magnets for the telegraph, & the size of wire &c. & a machine of the kind you spoke of will be very useful to us. Could you inform us where we can procure such a machine & whether you think it will be such as will answer our purpose. We are now receiving proposals for the different parts of the work & will be very glad to receive

[1] James Cogswell Fisher, an assistant of Morse. See *Henry Papers*, 4:227n. Henry's reply is immediately below.

such suggestions from you as you may think will be of service to us. Your intimate acquaintance with the subject of Electro-magnetism, in all its relations, may enable you to give us such hints as will be of very great service to us & save us the trouble of going over ground that has been trodden before. Prof Morse desires me to add that as we shall have 160 miles of wire well covered & put in reels of two miles each before placing in the pipes, if you should wish to make *any experiments* he will be most happy to afford you every facility for so doing. Prof Gale[2] wishes to know whether in your opinion it will be better to fill the vacancy between the pipe & the wire with resin or to leave it open & force dry air through the whole line so as to preserve the most perfect insulation between the wires.[3] We shall all be most happy to have you call & see us whenever you come to the city. The office is at 136 Nassau St. in the 3ʳᵈ story. Profs Morse, Gale, & myself desire a kind remembrance to Dr Torrey. <&> With great respect I remain

Yours &c

James C Fisher.

[2] Leonard Dunnell Gale, former Professor of Geology and Mineralogy at New York University, and Morse's partner from the summer of 1837. At this time he was also Morse's paid assistant. *Henry Papers*, 2:94.

[3] For the first operative telegraph line, which connected Baltimore and Washington, Morse's original plan was to lay underground pipe to protect the two wires comprising the different legs of the circuit. The concern of this letter was with preventing a short circuit between the wires. The discussion became

moot, however, because Fisher's failure sufficiently to test the waterproofing of the pipes led to the abandonment of the technique, to Fisher's dismissal for incompetence, and to Morse's placing the wires on poles. He later dropped the use of one of the wires altogether, by using the earth to complete the circuit. Carleton Mabee, *The American Leonardo: A Life of Samuel F. B. Morse* (1943; reprint ed., New York, 1969), pp. 262–275; *Shaffner's Telegraph Companion*, 1855, 2:18–21.

TO JAMES C. FISHER
S. F. B. Morse Papers, Library of Congress

Princeton April 17ᵗʰ 1843

Dear Sir

A friend of mine in Trenton has a machine for winding wire of which he promised to give a description. I will write to him on the subject and send you a copy of his answer.[1]

The greatest practical difficulty you will have to contend with, I should think, will be the insulation of the wires. Twine is a partial conductor and by making the surface of contact sufficiently extended lateral transmission will take place to some extent. The loss however on this account can only

[1] Neither letter has been found.

be determined by direct experiment with extended wires. It will probably increase with an increasing ratio; first on account of the greater surface of contact and secondly because electricity of greater tension will be required to send the current through the longer wire.

In order to diminish the number of points of contact it might perhaps be well to wrap around each wire besides its continuous covering an extra strand of coarser twine with the several turns at a distance from each other. Thus a _____ a & b representing the two wires. The b _____ contact instead of being continuous will only exist at the points where the outer strands of twine touch each other.

Galvanic electricity has never been made to project itself through a statum of air of the ordinary density so as to exhibit a spark, although the experiment has been tried with a battery of several hundred plates and with the poles approached within the 1/1000 part of an inch.[2] I should therefore conclude that it would be of little importance to fill the space betwen the wires with cement provided the metal can be as well secured from contact by less expensive means.

I shall probably visit New York sometime during the present college vacation and shall not fail to accept the kind invitation of Professor Morse to visit your establishment and perhaps make some experiments with your long wires.

Respectfully yours &c
Joseph Henry

[2] Henry may have been thinking of John P. Gassiot's failure to get a spark before completion of a circuit even with a powerful battery. Gassiot, who discounted earlier reports of a spark, had sent Henry his paper reporting this in 1842. In 1844, however, Gassiot reported producing a spark in an uncompleted circuit. See Henry to Gassiot, July 11, 1842, printed above.

TO HARRIET HENRY

Mary Henry Copy, Family Correspondence, Henry Papers,
Smithsonian Archives

Phil. April 22. 1843

My dear Harriet   I have just concluded after much hesitation to remain until Monday. I am very sorry to deprive you of the pleasure of greeting my return this evening but there is some business of importance before the society relative to the doings of the members of the Society for the last hundred years and as some of the views I have brought forward have found favor with Dr. Ludlow, Bache and others it is thought advisable that I remain to attend a meeting of a committee which will take place this evening.[1] My time has passed very pleasantly. I have slept two nights at Bache's. I dine today at three o'clock with Dr. Mitchell.[2] I am to call this morning at Dr. Goddard[3] to get my likeness taken with the daguerreotype.[4] Yesterday Dr. Goddard took Dr. Mitchell and myself while sitting together in a discussion of mesmerism. The likenesses were good but on account of the light on my eyes it appears as if the Doctor were magnetizing me. It was shown at the Society last night and considered a very good [. . .][5]

Kiss the children for me and receive for yourself the assurance that amid all my pleasures in Phil. my heart is with my dear little wife at home.

I send a note to Stephen.[6] I have engaged to induce him to make a communication to the Society on the 25th of next month at which there is to be a gathering of all the members at the centennial celebration.[7] Your H.

[1] Henry is referring to a special committee in charge of arrangements for the centennial celebration of the American Philosophical Society. See above, American Philosophical Society to Henry, March 31, 1843.

[2] John Kearsley Mitchell, Philadelphia physician, *Henry Papers*, 3:325.

[3] Dr. Paul Beck Goddard (1811–1866), chemist at the University of Pennsylvania, had discovered four years earlier that vapor of bromine on silvered plate would greatly accelerate Daguerre's process, thus enabling daguerreotypists to take successful portraits. Goddard regularly reported his researches in photography to the APS. *DAB*; APS *Proceedings*, 1841–1843, 2:144, 150.

[4] Although he had experimented with daguerreotype plates in his lab (see above, "Record of Experiments," June 19, 1841, and May 13, 1842), this is the first record of Henry sitting for a portrait. The daguerreotype may be one of the two early daguerreotypes of Henry which are printed as the frontispieces of this and the previous volume.

[5] One illegible word. This daguerreotype has not been found.

[6] Not found.

[7] Stephen Alexander presented "On the Physical Phenomena Which Accompany Solar Eclipses" at the APS centennial celebration. APS *Proceedings*, 1843, 3:183–211.

"RECORD OF EXPERIMENTS"
Henry Papers, Smithsonian Archives

April 24th 1843

Being in Phil[d]. I was requested, or I should say invited, to call and see a new microscope lately imported by Dr Beck[1] (son of P. Beck[2] esq) from

[1] Charles F. Beck (d. 1859) was educated at the University of Pennsylvania, receiving his M.D. in 1827. He was elected to the American Philosophical Society in 1845. W. J. Maxwell, comp., *General Alumni Catalogue of the University of Pennsylvania* (Philadelphia, 1922), p. 15; APS *Proceedings*, 1843–1847, 4:138.

[2] Paul Beck, Jr. (1760–1844) acquired a fortune in the wine trade which he used to support the arts in the United States. Among the recipients of his largess were the Philadelphia Academy of Fine Arts, the Historical Society of Pennsylvania, and the Apprentices' and Mercantile Libraries. *Herringshaw*, p. 96; Charles Morris, ed., *Makers of Philadelphia* (Philadelphia, 1894), p. 221.

England—this is the most perfect instrument of the kind which has yet reached this country.[3] It is furnished with all the arrangements for ease of use as well as for exhibiting every thing at present known inreference to the microscope.

With this instrument, I made two original observations or at least two which I do not know to have been previously made. The first was in reference to starch. This substance is contained in minute membraneacious bags which when wet swell and burst—the starch has therefore been considered a kind of organic substance. Each particle under the microscope presented an appearance similar to the nodules of indurated clay found about Albany of the appearance of the figure. The idea occurred to me to view this by means of polarized light—the effect was beautiful—each particle of starch showed the action called depolarization of light and exhibited the black cross similar to that shown by a crystal of carbonate of lime when viewed parallel to the optical axis.

This fact proves that the starch within the bags is in a state of segregation approximating crystalization. The black cross was not perfet but the arms were curved somewhat irregularly. The centre of the cross in each case was the same as that of the concentic circles which were observed on the surface of the particle without the aid of polarized light.[4] (See the figure)

The other observation with this microscope was in reference to capillarity. According to the theory of Poisson, the fluid which comes in contact with the plate of glass suffers a change of density. The idea occurred to me sometime ago that if this were true to any appreciable degree it might

[3] Beck's microscope was the first Powell and Lealand instrument to arrive in Philadelphia and one of the first to be imported into the United States. Products of the 1841 British partnership of Hugh Powell (1799–1883) and his brother-in-law, P. H. Lealand, these compound achromatic microscopes were considered among the finest made. However, they were also expensive compared to the popular French microscopes more frequently imported into this country. In 1842 a Powell and Lealand microscope cost approximately forty-five guineas (over $220). A typical French import could be bought at less than half the price. APS *Proceedings*, 1843, 3:90; G. L'E. Turner, "Powell & Lealand: Trade Mark of Perfection," *Essays on the History of the Microscope* (Oxford, 1980), pp. 119–130; James H. Cassedy, "The Microscope in American Medical Science, 1840–1860," *Isis*, 1976, 67:82; *Catalogue des instrumens d'optique, ... qui se fabriquent et se vendent chez l'ingénieur Chevallier* (Paris, 1834), p. 6.

[4] Although Henry was not the first to notice the quasi-crystalline structure of starch, he may be forgiven for missing the initial announcement. Biot had announced this evidence for the regular structure of the starch molecule in some remarks made after a paper delivered by Anselme Payen (1795–1871, *DSB*) on starch and dextrin. *Comptes rendus*, 1837, 5:905. It was another seven years, a full year after Henry had made his observations, before Biot offered a fuller discussion of the phenomenon in "Note sur les phénomènes de polarisation produits à travers les globules féculacés," *Comptes rendus*, 1844, 18:795–797.

Eventually, this interaction with polarized light was found to be a characteristic of potato starch, but not wheat starch. It was suggested as a test to discover adulteration of wheat starch. William Allen Miller, *Elements of Chemistry: Theoretical and Practical*, 2d ed., 3 vols. (London, 1860–1862), 3:98.

be rendered evident by means of the transmission of polarized light.[5] The effect was as I anticipated when a small quanty of water was placed between two glass plates, seperated by a frame of thin writing paper, and this submitted to the action of polarized light. The apparatus being so arranged as to produce a dark field, the glasses with the contained liquid being introduced a line of light was observed along the edge of the water. The effect appeared to be that of depolarization but I should desire to make a number of experiments before asserting positively that the phenomenon was the one which I anticipated. Colours were also observed which were probably due <*I was about to say*> to the curve of the water. <*but this could not be the case since*> The ray as it <*entered one side*> passed from the second side of the first curve of the meniscus would be refracted from the perpendicular and as it entered the first surface of the 2nd limb of the same would be bent in the same direction, so that both limbs of the meniscus would act as a prism to refract the light and produce colours but I do not see that a bright line of light could be produced in this way so as to exhibit the appearance of depolarization. The only defect in the experiment which strikes me at present is that the field was not perfectly dark. The polarization was effected by one of Nichol's prisms or rather Nichol's polarizing eye pieces. I intend to repeat the experiment with a darker ground produced by the polarization of a tourmaline[6]

[5] See above, "Record of Experiments," December 28, 1842.

[6] In a memorandum dated May 29, 1847 (Henry Papers, Smithsonian Archives), Henry recorded his repetition of this experiment. In the later attempt, Henry utilized a ring of wire similar to that of his soap bubble experiments (see, e.g., his "Record of Experiments" entry of April 22, 1844, Henry Papers, Smithsonian Archives). Once again, the results were positive, but Henry decided that publication at this point would be premature. He felt additional experimentation was necessary. Either he was never satisfied or never repeated the experiment, because he never published his results.

FROM ALEXANDER DALLAS BACHE AND JOHN LUDLOW

Henry Papers, Smithsonian Archives

Hall of the Am Philos Society
Philadelphia April 26th 1843

Sir.

The undersigned beg leave to call your especial attention to the accompanying circular[1] in reference to the celebration of the Centennial Anniversary of the Am Philos Society.

[1] Of March 31, 1843, printed above. Two copies of the circular are in the Henry Papers; one is attached to this letter.

We would respectfully urge your attendance at the meeting & knowing your interest in the cause of science would further ask you to present a communication upon the subject which we have taken the liberty to indicate in the margin,[2] or any other which you may prefer. Interesting papers on different branches of science will be presented at the meeting, the proceedings of which with a full notice of the communications which may be made, will at once be published in the Society's Bulletin. The Society will hope to receive you as their guest at the house of one of their members, during your stay in our city.

Should it not be possible for you to be with us in our city we shall be happy to receive from you the communication above asked to be read at the anniversary meeting.

We shall be obliged by as early an answer to the several points in our letter as may consist with your convenience, addressed to the chairman of the committee, designating the subject upon which we may expect to hear from you, that it may find its appropriate place in the programme of the meeting.[3]

Very respectfully
Yours
A. D. Bache ⎱
John Ludlow ⎰ Com.

[2] Nothing is indicated in the margin.
[3] Henry's reply to Bache of May 15 is printed below.

"RECORD OF EXPERIMENTS"
Henry Papers, Smithsonian Archives

April 27th 1843

Commenced to day to experiment with the apparatus of Melloni, made for me by Rumkhorff of Paris.[1] The cost of this set of articles, including a pile of a single row of elements for determining the heat of the different parts of the solar spectrum was 690 francs. The galvanometer is furnished with an article for increasing its sensibility consisting of two magnets to be placed on the tope of the glass cover and which by being seperated at their lower extremities act with increasing power on the compound needle below and thus render it approximately nearer a perfect [. . .][2] state.

[1] See above, Henry to Macedonio Melloni, November 29, 1841.

[2] One word is missing because of a hole in the paper.

The result of the experiments made with this apparatus are very satisfacory.[3] It exhibits polarization of heat by means of two bundles of mica, also depolarization by placing between the bundles a plate of mica.

Also the different transmissive power of different substances, particularly those of alum and common salt.

I was much surprised at the effect produced by one of the articles. It consists of a pile of mica plates movable around an axis and adjustable to any angle by means of a graduated arc. When the pile of mica was placed perpendicularly to the beam of heat, the needle stood at about 4°, but when it was placed so as to make an angle with the beam, of about 33°, then the needle stood at 13 or 14°. This phenomenon is mentioned by Melloni in his article on polarization translated into the scientific memoirs.[4] The explanation appears to be that the heat which passes the first lamina of mica is partially polarized and is then in a proper condition to pass the next plate, which is placed at the polarizing angle. The same effect is produced by the transmission of light, if the article of apparatus by held before a beam of light at right angles to the same and afterward <bent> turned into an angle of 33° with it a great increase will be perceived in the quantity of transmitted light.

[3] While in Paris, Henry had observed Melloni experiment using this type of apparatus. *Henry Papers*, 3:394–401.

[4] Melloni, "Memoir on the Polarization of Heat," Taylor's *Scientific Memoirs*, 1841, 2:151–165.

"RECORD OF EXPERIMENTS"
Henry Papers, Smithsonian Archives

April 28th–29 1843[1]

Repeated some of the other experiments of Melloni and gained some experience in the use of the apparatus. Tried with the Mellony galvanometer the thermo-pile which I purchased in London[2] found this nearly as sensitive as the new one from Paris. Also tried the single pair of plates which I constructed some year or two ago[3]—found that the approximation of the hand to this produced a wide deflection of the needle.

[1] Appears in the original as two separate dates.

[2] Purchased from John F. Newman. Folder of Accounts with Various European Instrument- and Apparatus-Dealers, Joseph Henry for the College of New Jersey, 1837, Princeton University Archives.

[3] Perhaps a reference to the apparatus discussed in *Henry Papers*, 4:362.

Placed a small cup of platina on the face of the London pile [. . .][4] poured into this a few drops of water the evaporization of the liquid produced a permanent deflection of 30°. The pile was supported by passing it perpendicularly through a disk of paste-board which rested on the rim of a glass tumbler.

When a crystal of muriate of soda of the size of grain of rice was thrown into the water in the little cup, a deflection of 20° degrees was produced by the reduction of temperature due to the solution of the salt. It is on this principle that M Peltier of Paris has formed an hygrometer which gives the rapidity of evaporation by the deflection of a needle connected with a cup, contain[in]g water and placed on the thermo-pile.[5]

Some experiments were also made relative to the solution of tin foil in mercury. This gave cold although the mere contact of mercury with lead appeared to produce a slight increase of temperature. Of this result at present I am not confident farther experiments will be required inorder to establish it.[6]

[4] A hole in the paper. One small word, or perhaps an ampersand, is missing.

[5] Peltier's hygrometer is described in "Nouvel hygromètre," *Comptes rendus*, 1837,

4:767.

[6] We have no evidence that Henry pursued this problem any further.

"RECORD OF EXPERIMENTS"
Henry Papers, Smithsonian Archives

May 1st 1843
Heat from the magnetization
of Iron

Attempted to get an indication of an increase of temperature in the act of magnetizing a small bar of soft iron. For this purpose two long wires were attached to the galvanometer inorder that the polarity of iron might not affect the position of the needle. The magnet was suspended from a lamp stand, with the thermo-pile placed under it, and across this was laid the small bar of soft iron; the whole apparatus was suffered to obtain the temperature of the room and then the thermo pile with the cross bar of soft iron was raised up by moving up the ring of the brass ring stand until the iron touched the magnet, care being taken not to impart sensibly any heat to the several parts of the arrangement. When the experiment was made the needle was observed to move slowley from rest at Zero to 15°. This effect was produced 3 times in succession: the motion of the needle was not as if by a single impulse as in the ordinary cases of the action of the pile when affected by radient heat but as if from a sourse of heat gradually conducted through or from the interior of the iron.

If there be no falacy in this experiment, it shows the evolution of heat by the change produced in a bar by the process of magnetization.[1] There are however several sources from which the heat may be derived as well as from the magnetization of the iron. 1st It may come from the percussion of the iron and the magnet. 2nd from the condensation of the air which takes place when the bar is suddenly brought in contact with the face of the horse shoe.

I must make farther experimts on these points tomorrow. The experimt may be made with the horse shoe in a vacuum and by bring the iron gently in contact with the face of the horse shoe the sources of heat before mentioned will be obviated.

In the afternoon of this day I made some experiments with the thermo pile exposed with its reflector attached on the radiation of distant objects.

I had at first concluded to place a small sheet iron stove in an open field and endeavour to determine the distance to which the stove might be carried and still its heat be sensible to the Thermo apparatus. The idea afterwards ocurred to me to try the effect of a distant cloud. The thermoscope was at first directed towards the clear sky when the needle moved to the side indicating a reduction of temperature and stood at 48°. The tube or rather coni[c]al reflector was then directed to a bright cloud which was in the same part of the heavens and but a few degrees distant from the point to which the cone was first directed, the needle now stood at 25°

The experiment was made after the sun had left the cloud with the same result except that the difference was not now as great as before, the needle moved from 48° to 34°.

When the mouth of the conical reflector was lowered, so as to take in the rays from the distant horizon, then the needle advanced rapidly towards the warmer side, indicating an increased eradiation from the ground.

These experiments lead me to suppose that the instrument may be improved for meterological observations by using a much large cone and

[1] Henry later added a footnote to this sentence: "Repeated these experiments on 2nd of may (page 32) found no Result of the kind." In the "Record of Experiments" entry of that date, printed below, Henry recorded the source of error which had led to these fallacious results.

connecting this with a str[a]ight tube blackened on the inside and highly polished on the out.[2]

Make a large cone so as to fit the end of the "large reflector" use this for heat of moon.[3]

---

[2] For later experiments with the modified apparatus, see below, "Record of Experiments," October 3, 1843. Henry made a brief report of his work to the American Philosophical Society. APS *Proceedings*, 1843–1847, *4*:22.

[3] Henry's initial plan to measure the heat of the moon was not carried out. See below,

"Record of Experiments," May 12, 1843. He returned to the problem of lunar heat in 1846 and 1847 in response to European experiments. These later activities will be documented in subsequent volumes of the *Henry Papers*.

"RECORD OF EXPERIMENTS"
Henry Papers, Smithsonian Archives

May 2nd 1843
Attempt to get heat from
capillary action

1. Repeated the experiment with the magnetization of the bar of soft iron and with the same result as stated page 29.[1] The needle passed gradually from *minus* 2° to *plus* 14°. The same experiment was tried again and with the same result.

The needle was next suffered to come to rest and then the bar was seperated from the magnet. After the whole had attained the temperature of the room the needle was slightly disturbed and passed through an arc of about 3°.

While the articles used in the last experiment were slowley attaining the temperature of the room, I next tried an experiment with a thermo-pile of a single pair for the purpose of determining if any change of temperature was produced by cappillarity. The thermo pile was inserted into the neck of a flat bottle and the whole orifice closed with a cork, so as to prevent the evaporation of the liquid contained in the phial. In this exp. I found considerable difficulty in bringing the extremity of the[2] within the phial to the same temperature as that without. When the needle came to rest and then the phial was shaken so as to throw the water up on the end of the pile the needle moved to 22°

---

[1] See the first three paragraphs of the "Record of Experiments" entry of May 1, 1843, printed above.

[2] Henry left out a word, perhaps "thermo-pile."

degrees and then settled at about 12° on the side of the zero which indicated an increase of cold instead of heat.

Repeated this and found that the needle moved fi[r]st to the *cold* side and then by throwing up the water so as to wet the end of the pile the motion took place in the opposite direction but I afterwards found that this return was due to the heat of my fingers acting by conduction through the glass. The causes of error in these experiments are very numerous and must be guarded against with great care.

Connected the coil with Pages machine which was kept in action for nearly an hour but the heat of the bar was very slightly increased

Made[3] a new arrangement of the apparatus for seperating the small bar from the Keeper this consisted in fasting the bar across a hole in a small board, and placing this on the magnet inverted. The board is elevated or depressed when the bar is to be brought in contact with or seperated from the magnet. When the bar was seperated from the magnet the needle moved about 2½° to the *Cold* Side.

Also when the needle was again suffered to come to rest and the bar was suddenly brought into contact with the magnet, the needle again moved to the *cold* side about 2° degrees. These experiments would appear to show that no heat is produced by the magnetization of the bar and that the effects I obtained before were due to the friction of the pile on the surface of the bar. The last arrangement was such as to prevent any rubbing and also to lessen the effect of percussion.

[3] Henry's running head over this section of the entry reads: "Heat from the Magnetization of Iron."

"RECORD OF EXPERIMENTS"
Henry Papers, Smithsonian Archives

May 3rd 1843

When the same exp.[1] was repeated this morning the needle again moved to the *cold* side about 10°. These changes appear to be owing to the difference of temperature in the thermopile and the magnet, the latter being large and consequently requiring considerable time to assume the temperature of the circumambient while the former being small soon feels each change of temperature.

Try this exp. with a long bar and a coil, one end of the former being thurst into the latter, the pile at the further end

[1] Of the day before. See above.

May 3, 1843

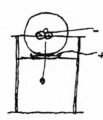 Made an experiment to day to determine the polarization of a conductor, when a current of galvanism is passing through it. It is well known that when a current is passed from the circumference to the centre of a wheel or in the opposite direction that motion will be produced in the wheel, provided a magnet be placed on each side of it.[2] Now this effect could not take place according to my view of the phenomenon unless there was a degree of persistance in the direction of the current. It was with the intention [of] measuring this persistance that this experiment was instituted. The apparatus was however too heavy to exhibit any effect even if it existed, since no motion was produced by placing a powerful horse shoe magnet on the plane of the axis of the plate.

I intended to give motion to the plate, supported as it was on friction rooles by means of a small weight <passing over> suspended from a string suspended over an axle. The friction was so great that no difference in the velocity could be observed wether a current was passing or not. When however the magnet was placed with its legs on each side of the wheel, the force of persistance was sufficient to stop the desent of the weight.[3]

[2] Henry is referring to an experiment described in most standard texts as a demonstration of the effect of the poles of a magnet on a conductor. A cistern of mercury was placed between the poles of a horseshoe magnet. Over the cistern was suspended a metallic wheel so that its edge just dipped into the mercury. When a current was sent through the mercury and the wheel, the wheel would begin to rotate. See, e.g., P. M. Roget, *Treatises on Electricity, Galvanism, Magnetism, and Electro-Magnetism* (London, 1832), "Electro-Magnetism," pp. 30–31.

[3] The phenomenon of the rotating wheel was one which bothered Henry for over twenty-five years. On April 27, 1837, after watching William Ritchie lecture at the Royal Institution in London, Henry recorded his unease in his European Diary (*Henry Papers*, 3:327–328): "On the same principle I do not clearly see why a wheel not notched on its edge should revolve in mercury since the metal is a conductor. The line of electricity would be thrown out and move as there is nothing to prevent it without giving motion to the wheel." Henry had no problem with the rotation of a notched wheel (actually, a spur)—each spur would act as a separate conductor, to be displaced by the magnetic field, and its place taken by the next spur. However, he apparently saw no reason why a metallic wheel with an unbroken edge should share the displacement of the current running through it. Why shouldn't the current be displaced within the wheel, leaving the wheel motionless? In 1837, Henry thought there had to be some sort of external force operating on the wheel.

Now, six years later, his explanation rests upon the concept of the "degree of persistance in the direction of the current." The current has some sort of inertial property which enables it to resist displacement through the wheel. Rather, each radius of the wheel acts as a distinct conductor, carrying the wheel about its center. Henry's experiment tests what happens when the wheel is already spinning when the current is sent through. He initially sets the wheel in motion by dropping a weight which is attached to the wheel. Then a current is sent through the wheel in a direction which would normally rotate the wheel counter to the motion produced by the weight, resulting ultimately in no net motion. He apparently believed that if the wheel continued to act as if it were composed of a great number of distinct conductors, even when the wheel was rotating at high speed when the current was sent through, then he had demonstrated the existence of this persistence.

Nineteen years later, Henry repeated this experiment, although the theoretical framework within which the experiment was con-

Next tried to get indications of heat from the magnetization of a bar of soft iron. For this purpose the bar was placed in the Lecture room at the distance of 27 feet from the galvanometer; yet at this distance the needle was slightly affected with the polarity of the bar and in the direction which would indicate heat when the pile was connected. The result of the exp. was very unsatisfactory the heat if any was developed could not be eliminated from that of the galvanic current around the iron and the difference of temperature of the bar and the pile

Next prepared some of the sulphuriet of calcium, by mixing pounded calcined oyster shells with 1/3 of their weight of sulphur.

First tried if this would become luminous by the galvanic spark, or rather from the coil with a rod of iron in its axis. The effect was apparently as great in proportion to the size of the spark as in the case of the discharge from the Leyden Jar. The powder was supported on a plate of rock crystal, inorder to hold it immediately over the mercury from which the spark was taken.

I next tried if the emination from galvanic spark would pass through glass. The powder was removed to a plate of glass of the same thickness as the plate of rock crystal but although the same number of sparks were taken the powder remained quite dark. It would appear from this that the spark from mercury gives the same emination as that from the electrical discharge.

Tried the comparative transmissive power of glass and allum, found that *alum* was nearly the same as rock crystal.

Next tried the polarizable capacity of the phosphogenic emination, found that it was polarizable, by placing one of the small trays which I made of

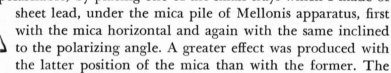 sheet lead, under the mica pile of Mellonis apparatus, first with the mica horizontal and again with the same inclined to the polarizing angle. A greater effect was produced with the latter position of the mica than with the former. The effect was not however as great as in the case of light[4]

---

ducted had changed. He again wrote of external forces. "Record of Experiments," May 8, 12, and 13, 1862, Henry Papers, Smithsonian Archives.

[4] An earlier attempt to discover if the phosphorogenic emanation was polarizable had failed. See above, "Record of Experiments," March 11, 1843. This successful effort is discussed in "On Phosphorogenic Emanation," APS *Proceedings*, 1843, *3*:41.

"RECORD OF EXPERIMENTS"
Henry Papers, Smithsonian Archives

May 4th 1843

Next arranged the apparatus for ascertaining the reflectability of the phosgenic emenation. A *metallic* mirror was arranged so 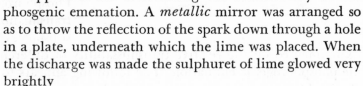 as to throw the reflection of the spark down through a hole in a plate, underneath which the lime was placed. When the discharge was made the sulphuret of lime glowed very brightly

Found a source of error in the last experiment the light direct from the spark was not sufficiently s[c]reaned—remedied tried the experiment again but the same result was produced. The lime was luminous and not much less so than by the direct discharge[1]

Tried the same experiment with a peace of black glass. The result was the same but the amount of reflected light much less than from the mirror of speculum metal.[2]

Repeated the experment of the polarization of the Phos emination and from the result there can be no doubt of the fact of the polar capability of the emination. The mica pile was placed horizontally then the discharge made. The lime was dark. The pile was next inclined in an angle of about 33° with the [horizontal].[3] The spark again pass the lime now was luminous. The light was then suffered to disappear the pile was returned to its horizontal position no effect. The pile again inclined at the polarizing angle, now the lime exhibited a shining surface.

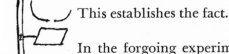 This establishes the fact.

In the forgoing experiments I used the apparatus for supporting the little pans which is represented in the margin

---

[1] Although Henry does not include the information in this "Record of Experiments" entry, he measured the angle of reflection of the phosphorogenic emanation and found that it obeyed the optical law of reflection. "On Phosphorogenic Emanation," APS *Proceedings*, 1843, *3*:40–41.

[2] According to his published paper, Henry's efforts to reflect the emanation off glass failed. Glass, he concluded, "neither reflects nor transmits the phosphorogenic emanation, except in a very small degree." Ibid., p. 41. That conclusion appears to be in contradiction with this experiment, where Henry achieved clearly positive results. Perhaps he later discovered that once again the incidental light of the spark was not screened.

[3] Henry left a blank in the manuscript. His meaning is clear, however.

May 8, 1843

"RECORD OF EXPERIMENTS"

Henry Papers, Smithsonian Archives

Monday May 8th 1843
Phosphorogenic Emination
transmissibility of different
substances for

Experimented on the relative transmissability of different substances for the phosphorogenic emination. The following appears to be the order as obtained by comparing one with another[1]

1[st] Series of exp	2[nd] Series	
Rock crystal	Rock crystal	
Calc spar	Calc spar	very little
Sulphate of Barita	Salt	difference
	Alum	

3[rd] Series

Sul barita
White glass
<Red> Viol[e]t glass
Red glass
Mica

4[th] Series

White glass
Mica
Tourmaline

5[th] Series

Rock crystal
Sulphate of Lime
Calc spar

6[th] Series

Fluor spar
Calc spar
Sulphate of Barita

Transmitted the emination through quartz cut perpendicularly to the axis and obliquely to the same but could not perceive any difference in the intensity of the light.

Tried the same experiment with Calc spar but no difference in the result was observed although the difference in thickness of the two pieces of spar was [. . .][2]

---

[1] These experiments and those published below in the "Record of Experiments" entries of May 10, 13, 15, and 16, 1843, are summarized in the table which concluded "On Phosphorogenic Emanation," APS *Proceedings*, 1843, 3:44. Twenty-two transparent solids and twenty transparent liquids were listed according to their relative permeability by the phosphorogenic emanation.

[2] Henry failed to supply this information.

May 9, 1843

On Sunday the 7th—There was a thunder storm which as usual came from the south west and passed at a great elevation above Princeton. Several needles were magnetized in my study by the flash, with the same apparatus which failed a few days since to give any results when it was connected with the long wire. It was on the 7th connected with the roof of the house.

Mr Professor Hamilton[3] informes that within the last three years he has observed 5 or 6 cases of houses struck with lightning and in each of these the discharge was on the end of the gutter or in the vicinity of the same. He knows of but one exception to this and then the whole house was surrounded by water as if the building were on an island. It was struck at the chimney. The house was in a hollow—does not know if the chimney had fire in it at the time. This fact in reference to the gutter is in accordance with the explanation I gave of the phenomenon of the striking of old Mrs Hamiltons House (see last vol)[4]

[3] James Hamilton (d. 1849) was a Princeton native who had graduated from the College in 1814. He was Professor of Mathematics and Natural Philosophy at the University of Nashville from 1827 to 1829, again from 1831 to 1835, and finally from 1839 until his death. His first resignation was due to ill health. The second was necessitated by the ill health of his mother. *Princeton Catalogue*, p. 126; Kenimer Houze Morgan, "The University of Nashville, 1825–1850" (Ph.D. dissertation, George Peabody College for Teachers, 1960), pp. 712–713. Hamilton apparently published no scientific articles.

[4] See above, "Record of Experiments," July 15, 1841. The "old Mrs Hamilton" in question was the mother of James Hamilton.

"RECORD OF EXPERIMENTS"
Henry Papers, Smithsonian Archives

Tuesday May 9th 1843
Chemical Emination

Commenced to day with the manipulations of the Daguerrotype process inorder to study the chemical emination in connection with that of the P[h]osphorgenic.

 A prepaired plate was placed under a block of wood, through which holes were cut as represented in the figure, and over these holes were placed plates of different transparent substances, *viz* over N° 1 mica N° 2 glass—No 3 calc spar—No 4 Salt—N° 5 Quartz—No 6 alum. The plate was then exposed to the diffuse Light of the sky for about 2 minutes and then removed to the mercury. While the process was going on the iodized plate underneath could be distinctly seen and it appeared to change colour under each but under the cal spar the tint appeared diff[er]ent.[1] The final result of the experiment was not satisfactory the whole effect was overdone—the spots no 1 2 & 3 were more solarized than those marked 4 5 6.

Tried the same experiment, but the time was again too long to indicate any difference of result. The plate under each opening in the wood was marked as before.

Tried the last experiment again. The plate with the different substances as before was exposed to the diffuse light of the sky for 25 seconds all the openings produced spots on the plate but those under the mica and salt appeared a little less intense. The experiment must be repeated several times, inorder to bring out the facts relative to the specific influence of the different screening substances.

Repeated the same experiment again with the same arrangement—the plate was exposed however during 12 seconds instead of 25. The result was that no difference could be perceived in the intensity of the impressions from the different openings. The impressions were as vivid as in any of the other experiments although the light was gradually declining.

Repeated the same experiment, the time of exposing the plate to the light being 7 seconds. The spots were well developed on the plate but no difference or very little could be observed. One & 4 *ie* the salt and the mica appeared rather more blue than the others.

In the foregoing experiments the plate has been coated first with the vapour of iodine and then to render it more sensible has been placed over the vapour of the clo[rett]e[2] of iodine. Inorder to decrease the sensibility of the plate the exposure to the clorette was omitted and the plate exposed during about 10 seconds to the light of the sky. The impressions all came out as strong as before the one under the glass being the more intense if anything.

Repeated the experiment with the plate prepaired as in the last experiment the time was shortened to 6 seconds. The light however is gradually diminishing. The plate again received an impression from each opening the one under the glass was apparently the most intense although they were all faint.

---

[1] A hole in the paper.
[2] A hole in the paper. This is probably a reference to "chloruret" (chloride). See the *Oxford English Dictionary*.

May 10, 1843

The light at the last experiment was quite faint the sky was cloudy the clock struck 6 at the time of the experiment.

From all the results obtained this afternoon it would appear that the Phosphorogenic emination and the chemical are as distinct as the Luminiferous and the calorific.[3]

---

[3] These experiments, as well as those conducted on May 11 and May 15, 1843 (below), led Henry to the tentative conclusion "that the phosphorogenic emanation is distinct from the chemical, and that it exists in a much greater quantity in the electrical spark, than either the luminous or the chemical emanation." "On Phosphorogenic Emanation," APS *Proceedings*, 1843, *3*:42. He had determined from other experiments that the phosphorogenic emanation differed from light or heat. Ibid.

"RECORD OF EXPERIMENTS"
Henry Papers, Smithsonian Archives

Wednesday May 10th 1843
Permeability of electrical
Light[1]

It is well known that when a discharge of electricity is passed through an orange, an egg, or an apple and even through the thumb, the whole interior of the substance becomes illuminated by a phosphorescent red light. Made some experiments to day, or rather this morning, on the penetrating power of the light from the electrical discharge.

1 Four cakes of about one 4th of an inch in thickness of white wax was placed on a stand, before the spark from a Leyden jar, as in the arrangement of the margin and then the light observed through. The effect was beautiful and brilliant, the whole surface of the wax appeared to be illuminated with a white light. The experiment is a good class exhibition.

I next placed a tube of paste-board in front of the wax and the eye at the other end—the effect with this was still more striking. The result could be seen without closing the windows

---

[1] This heading was moved forward from the succeeding page.

The white wax was removed and its place supplied with a cake of common beas-wax unpurified was substituted in its place. The light still appeared through this although it was just an inch and a half thick and apparently impervious to the light of the day. The light was not however perfectly excluded from the inside of the tube as a small quantity entered between the end <*of the*> and the surface of the wax. The two lights howere were not confounded with each other that through the wax from the machine was red while the other was the white light of day.

 The defect in the arrangement mentioned in the last paragraph was remedied by fitting to the end of this tube a short cylinder of copper and pressing the latter into the beas wax. With this all extraneous light was cut off and the discharge appeared through, of a beautiful red colour like that of the sun through the fingers. The points in this experiment were placed at the distance of ¾ of an inch from each other and ¼ of an inch from the surface of the wax.

Next the points were joined by a piece of wax softened so as to bury them in the substance of the mass but the effect was not as great as with the <*wax*> points at a small distance from the surface.

The points were now removed to the distance of about two inches from the surface the light through was still perceptible but very faint[2]

To compare this with the light of the clouds <*a hole was*> the same cake of wax with its tube was placed before a hole in a window shutter and the light observed through. The effect was much stronger than I expected the wax appeared of a beautiful crimson, and the light was as intense as that from the discharge of the jar. From this result it appears that there is nothing peculiar in the permeability of wax for the electrical light. Whether the same is the case in reference to other substances remains to be seen by experiment.

Next placed a piece of wax a little yellower and thicker before the end of the tube. The electrical light did not appear through this although the light of the cloud was faintly perceptible.

Resumed the experiments on the chemical rays. Placed a prepared plate under the piece of wood pierced with holes and brought over this the points used in the last experiments, but no impression could be produced on the

---

[2] The next five paragraphs were placed under the dual heading of "Electrical Ligh" and "Chemical Emination." The initial heading refers to the first two paragraphs; the second to the remaining three. Between the two groups of paragraphs Henry had drawn a horizontal line.

plate from the electrical light although the machine was turned for 5 or 6 minutes. The light from the clouds gave an impression on the same plate in the course of 20 seconds. This experiment combined with that of the phosphorescence produced under the same circumstances mark a strong distinction between the chemical and phosphorogenic eminations.

A series of different coloured glass was nex[t] placed over the openings in the wooden block before mentioned and these again over a prepaired plate. The impressions were very different. The order was as follows *white, violet, blue* (distinct), *green, salmon,* & *red* no impression

The transparency of the green and blue was very nearly the same[3]

Contrasted the effect of the light in the last experiment with that of the electrical spark in the production of phosphorescence. The same glasses resting on the wood block were placed over a shallow box conta[in]ing the sulphurette of lime and the spark from a single phial passed over them. The only plates under which the lime became phosphorescent was the thin clear glass and the violet but under the latter it was much less intense than under the former.

All coloured glasses appear to lessen the transmissability of the phosphoregenic principle.

The refrangibility of the phosphorogenic emination was very prettily exhibited by placing the larger lead box containing the sulphurette of lime under a plate with a slit in it and then passing the discharge over the slit at the distance of about an inch the lime being at about the same distance below the slit. The image of the slit was depicted on the surface of lime in a well defined <*broad*> narrow line. The same experiment was repeated with the difference of placing a prism of salt over the slit. The impression was now increased 5 or 6 times in width and the whole impression thrown to the other end of the box by the refractive power of the salt prism.

I next made some experiments on the relative transmissability of this emination through different liquid substances.

The liquid was placed in a cup made of the cylindrical part of a 4 ounce phial to which a bottom of a plate of rock crystal was cemented.[4] The first series was with *Water Bichromate* of *Potassa* and *clored* of *Lead*. The water is not perfectly trans[parent] for phorescent. The Bichromate is less so and the perfectly transparent chlored of Lead is almost as impervious as glass or mica.

---

[3] Beginning with the next paragraph, Henry has placed his work under the heading "Phosphorogenic Emination."

[4] The remainder of the entry is under the heading "Order of Phosphorogenic transmissability of Liquids."

1st series

The order is as follows[5]

1 Transparent Water

2 Brown Solution Bicarb pottassa

dark   3 Transparent chromate of Lead—dark

formed this a solution of acetic acid

2nd Series

1 Water

dark   2 Nitric acid   } all transparent

dark   3 Chlorate of Lead)

3rd series

Water

Solution of alum   } all transparent

Sulphate of Magnesia } all transmit like water

Muriate of ammonia

X   Camphor   water[6]

4th series

Sulphate of copper } coloured blue

Nitrate of copper } Transmit much more feebly than water

5th series

Sulphat of Zinc } Transparent but

} transmits badly[7]

[5] This does not match the paragraph above.

[6] To the right of the word "water" is a reference to the entry of the following day, probably to the second paragraph.

[7] At a later date Henry added an additional paragraph to this entry:

The bad transmitters according to these expermts are as follows: *nitric acid, (chlorate of Lead)* sul acid p. 47, *Sulphate of Zinc, acetate* of *Lead* (page 44), annisseed p. 47, *acetate* of *Zinc* (p 46), *Sulphate* of *Lead* (p. 46), alcohol p 47.

The page references are to the experiments in which he demonstrated that these substances were poor transmitters of the phosphorogenic emanation. Pages 44 and 46 refer to the "Record of Experiments" entry of May 11, 1843, while page 47 refers to the entry of May 13, 1843.

"RECORD OF EXPERIMENTS"

Henry Papers, Smithsonian Archives

Thursday 11th May 1843.

Procured this morning a transparent solution of acetate of Lead. The acetate is often of a milky colour but it may be rendered transparent by the adition of a small quantity of the pure acetic acid. This salt of lead like the other salts of the same metal which I have tried is nearly impervious to the phosphorogenic emination

Next tried a plate of transparent camphor—found this nearly as impervious as mica more impervious than glass and inded I am not sure but that it is to be classed with mica[1]

The plate of camphor was next submitted to the influence of the chemical emination, over a sensible plate in connection the acetate of Lead and a plate of common glass. The plate under each became blackened without any apparent difference

The time of exposure was 10 seconds

Next tried the transmissability of camphoretted water found this about as permiable as water

Next prepaired a sensible plate and placed over it a thin plate of mica and over this again the pointed wires or rather the blunt ends of wires from the electrical machine. After turning the machine for about 10 minutes the plate was impressed with the effect of the chemical emination.[2]

Repeated this experiment with a lens of small focus (one inch)—the ends of the wires connected with the machine were about $2\frac{1}{2}$ inches from the plate—with the lens interposed with this arrangement no effect was produced

Repeated the last experiment with the same arrangement as in the first case and with the same result. The impression was very distinct. The time was about 10 minutes.* This establishes the fact that the electric spark can produce the effect[3]

In making the last experiment a fact was observed of some interest apparently. When the thread of light of the electrical machine was vewed

* The same effect would have been produced by the light of the clouds in 5 or 10 seconds

[1] Henry had placed an asterisk in the left-hand margin next to this paragraph.

[2] Henry had previously tried to produce an impression on a photographic plate with an electric spark but failed. See above, "Record of Experiments," June 19, 1841.

A cross was placed in the left-hand margin next to this paragraph, probably for emphasis.

[3] These results were reported in "On Phosphorogenic Emanation," APS *Proceedings*, 1843, 3:42.

through a glass coloured deep red it appeared as if cut into two by a black line through the middle thus _____ ~~~~ _____ as in the figure except that the space which appears ——— _ + ——— white in the drawing is black in the spark. It appears from this experiment that the middle part of the electrical spectrum is absorbed by red glass

The transparent plate of camphor mentioned on the last page was next tested in reference to its *thermacy*. For this purpose it was compared with salt alum & glass.

alum gave	$4\frac{1}{2}$ degrees of deflection		
Camphor —	$4\frac{1}{2}$		Repeated this
glass (trans)	$38°$		with the same general
glass (ground)	$28°$		result. Camphor
Salt —	$90°$		scraped let pass a few
			more rays

From this result it appears that camphor is as thermal as alum. The experiment must however be repeated with a perfect polished plate of camphor.

Tried this afternoon the transmissability of sulphat and acetate of zinc. Found that they should be classed with nitric acid and the other substances which have little transmissability

Made a comparitive experiment on the effect of the exposure of a quantity of the sulphuret of lime to the reflected sun light and the electrical spark. The effect was much more brilliant with the electrical discharge [?once] made from a single jar than from the reflected sun light for 60 seconds. By reflected sun light is here understoon the ordinary reflection of bright sun shine from buildings and other objects

The phosphorescent light becomes quite brilliant after a few moments exposure of the sulphuret for a few moments to the direct action of bright sun shine

"RECORD OF EXPERIMENTS"
Henry Papers, Smithsonian Archives

Friday May 12th 1843

Examined the plate of camphor used in the last experiment[1] in reference to its action on light; found that it possessed the polarizing structure as indicated by its depolarizing power between the tourmalines

I was occupied during the remainder of this day in preparing a frame to

---

[1] Actually the experiment in question took place the previous morning. See above.

support a tube on the end of melonies pile[2] to study the radiation from the moon and the sky. Did not however succeed in getting the apparatus arranged in time for the experiment

[2] i.e., Melloni's thermoelectric pile. See the "Record of Experiments" entry of April 27, 1843, above.

"RECORD OF EXPERIMENTS"
Henry Papers, Smithsonian Archives

Saturday May 13th [1843]

Prepaird a plate for the chemical emination submitted it to the electrical spark screaned by a plate of glass and a plate of carbonate of lime placed side by side. I could perceve however very little impression and no difference in the action on the plate under the two substances

Tried alcohol, acetic acid & ether, sul acid.

The order of transmissability was as follows

	Water	
Coloured less	⎧acetic acid⎫	All nearly opaque
Transparent	⎨Ether ⎬	the posgenic emination
Solutions	⎩alcohol ⎭	
	Suphuric acid	
	anniseeeded	

Next tried oil of anniseede found it more opaque than alcohol

acetic acid

acetate of Zinc

Found that *Icee transmitts* the emination as readily as water

Also Rochelle Salts transmits

copal
& Saltpetre⎬ opaque to the emination

Next tried spirits of turpentine found it in comparison with water almost opaque

Horn depolarizes light but it transmitts the phosgenic emination about as glass.

Tried relative transmissability of flint and crown glass found little or no difference[1]

[1] Henry summarized this day's experiments as part of a table which concluded his article "On Phosphorogenic Emanation," APS *Proceedings*, 1843, *3*:44.

TO ALEXANDER DALLAS BACHE
Archives, American Philosophical Society

Princeton May 15th 1843.

My Dear Bache

I received a few days since a letter from our old friend Mr W Vaughan[1] informing me that he had forwarded to your care a package for me. You will oblige me by sending the same to the Book store of John Pennington[2] in Chesnut St near 5th and I will direct a person to call for it there.

I have been engaged since my return with many interruptions on the subject of the Phosphorogenic emination and have succeeded in obtaining some new results which I intend giving to the society on the grand occasion of the 25th. It is by no means however a very easy matter to get up an original scientific paper to order. The secrets of nature must be coaxed from her at auspicious moments and these cannot be produced at any time by the will of the philosopher however gifted. Something however can be done with dogged perseverance even in the course of a week or two.[3]

Besides my results on the phosphorogenic emination I purpose giving an account of the machine I mentioned to you for the determination of the velocity of the cannon ball by electricity.[4] I may also give a scrap or two on something else which at present I cannot specify.[5]

I hope you will have your paper prepared on the thermometer of contact and besides this cannot you join with Saxton in some farther experiments on the subject of the " *'invisible' rays*" and bring them with those Saxton has already made before the society. He will not do the talking part himself and I made a brief of what he had done with the intention of incoporating it with some suggestions of my own and of presenting it to the society but if you will join with him the result will be the same and any additional matter I may collect on the subject can be given as an appendix or in the way of strengthening the position which you will assume. If you do not wish to join with Saxton let me know and I will prepare an article on the subject.[6]

[1] Perhaps Vaughan's letter of March 6 (Henry Papers, Smithsonian Archives).

[2] John Penington (1799–1867), a Philadelphia book importer and fellow member of the American Philosophical Society. *Herringshaw*.

[3] Henry's communication "On Phosphorogenic Emanation" was the first paper presented at the meetings. APS *Proceedings*, 1843, 3:38–44.

[4] "On a New Method of Determining the Velocity of Projectiles," ibid., pp. 165–167.

[5] Henry also read a letter sent to him by Captain Thomas Lavender of Princeton on waterspouts. Ibid., pp. 135–136.

[6] Saxton had been repeating experiments reported by Ludwig F. Moser which Moser claimed proved the existence of a new form of radiation, invisible or latent light. Moser concluded from images left by objects placed

Mr Stephen Alexander is busily engaged on a paper to be entitled the physical phenomena accompanying solar eclipses which I think will be an article of much interest. He is somewhat pleased to find that for a model[7] man he has come nearer the true orbit of the comet in his elements than any other person in this country. I have been engaged in repeating some of the experiments of Melloni with my new apparatus and am delighted with the performance of the instrument. It gives me a new sense for the appreciation of new truths and considerably widens my sphere of research. I wish you could spend your next vacation here in going over the subject of heat—the gleanings which may still be gathered will afford a rich harvest. Dr Torrey will attend the meeting but he is so much engaged in the preparation of his report[8] that I fear he will not be able to prepare an article for the occasion.

Yours
J H.

P.S. Send the package to Pennington's before Wednesday evening. Send package to Penningtons before tuesday afternoon.[9]

---

on or near polished plates that all bodies were self-luminous. Saxton concluded that the images were caused not by invisible rays but rather by "the evaporation of some greasy substance from the surface of the object forming the image."

P. B. Goddard mentioned his own and Saxton's experiments on the phenomenon at the session of May 30. A discussion followed in which Saxton, Henry, and James Rogers took part. At this point in the *Proceedings* there is a detailed description of Saxton's experiments which may have been drafted by Henry; a draft of Goddard's remarks (APS Archives) ends with the note "wait for Henry." Whoever authored the description noted that Saxton reached his conclusion independently of the similar conclusion which Hippolyte Louis Fizeau had reported to François Arago in November 1842: "the investigations of Mr. Saxton were entirely independent of any knowledge of the French experiments, and his explanation of the phenomenon had been communicated to Professor Henry and other members of the Society, before any account of the experiments of M. Fizeau reached this country." APS *Proceedings*, 1843, 3:179–181.

A convenient summary of other investigations of the phenomenon, including citations to articles by David Brewster, John W. Draper, J. F. W. Herschel, and an extract from Fizeau's letter to Arago, is in Taylor's *Scientific Memoirs*, 1843, 3:488–489, following translations of three related papers by Moser (pp. 422–487).

The October-December 1842 issue of *Silliman's Journal* contains the *Athenaeum* account of the 1842 British Association meeting at which Brewster and F. W. Bessel publicized Moser's work (1843, 44:159–160), and John W. Draper's claim of priority over Moser (1843, 44:202–203). To the latter the Sillimans added a note that the discovery "promises to be of as much interest as the original observations of Daguerre."

[7] Although the word looks like "model" Henry frequently didn't cross his t's and may have meant "modest."

[8] Probably his *Flora of the State of New York*, 2 vols. (Albany, 1843).

[9] In the original, this appears above the address.

"RECORD OF EXPERIMENTS"
Henry Papers, Smithsonian Archives

Monday May 15[th] 1843
Phosphorogenic emination
under water &c

Tried on saturday ev[en]ing at the time of full moon to produce the phosphorous glow on sulphuret of lime by means of moon light but I did not succeed.[1] The experiment however was not decisive the lime may not have been in proper condition although when I tried it this morning with the electrical discharge it answered very well

Tried this morning a number of substances in reference to the transmissability by the phosgenic emination among others the sulphate of potassa a transparent salt this gave a beautiful violet coloured light as well as transmitted the influence to the lime below.[2] The phosphoresence was more brilliant than with the lime but did not continue so long nor was it acted on at so great a distance. This is an interesting fact

Exposed the same substance, sulphate of potassa to the direct light of the sun for about a minute then removed it into the dark—found it phosphorescent but much less so than when exposed to the discharge of the Leyden Jar

I next discovered the remarkable fact that the phosphorescence of the sulphate of potash was produced as brilliantly under water, *ie* when the substance was immersed in water as when in the air. Tried the same experiment with the sulphat of lime found the same result both with the sun light and that of the electrical discharge.[3]

When the sulphate of potassa is powdered it gives a beautiful effect with the electrical discharge more brilliant but less durable than the sulphuret of lime

---

[1] A photographic plate exposed under similar conditions would have shown a reaction. This experiment was part of Henry's comparison of photographic, luminous, and chemical emanations. "On Phosphorogenic Emanation," APS *Proceedings*, 1843, *3*:42. See above, "Record of Experiments," May 9, 11, and 15, 1843.

[2] In the left-hand margin Henry drew attention to the "Remarkable effect of sul pot."

[3] Henry's published paper presents the result of this experiment as being "at variance" with the theory that "the phosphorescence of the lime is due to the disturbance of the electricity of the mass of the substance, and the continuance of the light to the subsequently slow restoration of the equilibrium." APS *Proceedings*, 1843, *3*:43. This is a reference to the concept of Edmond Becquerel (see E. Newton Harvey, *A History of Luminescence from the Earliest Times until 1900* [Philadelphia, 1957], p. 364). In Henry's view, placing the lime in a conducting medium like water should have produced a noticeable effect on the results if the phenomenon was electrical.

Made a series of experiments on different substances relative to their transmissibility. The following is the result[4]

Solids	Borax Sulphate of potassa Sulphate of soda Citric acid Rochelle salt *<Hyposulphate of soda>*	Powder under these Brilliant
Solids	Salt petre Tartaric acid Hyposulphate of soda	Powder dark under these
Trans Solutions	Muriate of Barreta Ammonia (doubtful)	Powder light
Trans Solutions	Muriatic acid Spirits of turpentine Arceneous acid Ammonia Phosphoric acid	Powder dark under these

[4] Some of these results are included in the table at the conclusion of Henry's article. APS *Proceedings*, 1843, *3*:44.

"RECORD OF EXPERIMENTS"
Henry Papers, Smithsonian Archives

Tuesday May 16th 1843

Repeated the experiment of rendering the sulphurrette luminous under water. After the substance had stood thus immersed 30 hours and more it appeared as brilliant as that which had not been thus placed.

Submitted the sul of lime to the light of a candle and then examined it in the dark; found it phosphorescent. The phosphorogenic emination therefore exists in the light of a candle

I have before found that alcohol is a bad transmitter of the phosgenic emination to test this again. I placed in a shallow glass vessel a few crystals of sulphate of potassa and over these about ¾ of an inch of alcohol. The crystals <*however*> remained dark when the discharge of electricity passed over them, although when they were steaped in water in the same way they glowed with great brilliancy.

Tried the transmissibility of white wax found that the lime became luminous faintly below a plate of white wax ¼ of an inch thick

Found that common chalk became quite brilliant by a discharge of the jar at the distance of 4 or 5 inches[1] also that the same screening influence was exerted by glass and other substances. Also the screaning took place in the case of the light from the candle. This was not however as fully proved as it might be

[1] From his success with common chalk, Henry inferred that the chalk cliffs of England might become phosphorescent during a thunderstorm. "On Phosphorogenic Emanation," APS *Proceedings*, 1843, 3:43.

"RECORD OF EXPERIMENTS"
Henry Papers, Smithsonian Archives

Wednesday May 17th [1843]

According to Becquerel there are three substances which give light during a change of form from the liquid to the solid state sulphate of potassa, arcenious acid & muriate of ammonia.[1] Since the Sulphate of potassa is phosphoresent I thought that perhaps the other substances might be so also—tried the arcene but got no result. It should have been however the crystallized transparent arcenic and not the ordinary kind (Kane)[2]

[1] A.-C. Becquerel, *Traité experimental de l'électricité et du magnétisme*, 7 vols. (Paris, 1834–1840), 6:280–283. Henry was incorrect about one of the substances—Becquerel credits calcium chloride, not ammonium chloride, with the creation of light during solidification.

[2] Robert Kane, *Elements of Chemistry*, ed. John William Draper (New York, 1842), p. 377. Oxide of arsenic initially forms transparent crystals which become opaque over time. Only the transparent crystals will, when dissolved in hydrochloric acid, produce a phosphorescent light while recrystallizing.

TO ISAAC W. JACKSON[1]

Joseph Henry Collection, Firestone Library, Princeton University

Princeton May 22[d] 1843

My Dear Jackson

Your very acceptable present to Mrs. Henry[2] was duely and safely received and produced quite a feeling of exultation in the breast of the little woman. She will be the envy of the whole village. They have all been put into the ground according to your directions and are apparently doing well.

It will give us, as you know, much pleasure to see yourself and all your family in Princeton in August or at any other time you can make it convenient to come, only make your arrangements so that you can give us a good visit and that we may have a long "crack" about times past and to come. I am sorry to learn that your mother[3] is so ill as to require most of your attention; but amid this affliction you have the consolation of feeling that you are in the way of your duty when you are administering to her comfort, however great may be the sacrifice of time, convenience, or even health to yourself.

Any information I possess relative to the business of scientific manipulation is at your service and as to the optical instruments I would advise you to purchase the apparatus of Babinet and Gearand for interferance of light and that of Norumberg for polarization. You can get them of Soleil fils, Optician Rue de l'Odeon No 35 Paris.[4] Enclosed I send you his card. I have found him an honest man and if you write to him say you do so on my recomendation. Tell him the money will be paid on the delivery of the articles.

---

[1] Isaac Wilbur Jackson (1805–1877), Professor of Mathematics and Natural Philosophy at Union College. *Henry Papers, 1*:254.

[2] Jackson's gift, a "package of flowers," was preceded by a letter, which has not been found. Henry to James Henry, May 16, 1843, Henry Papers, Smithsonian Archives.

[3] Phebe Townsend Jackson (1768–1859) married William Jackson in 1803. Isaac W. was the elder of two sons. *Proceedings of the Sesqui-Centennial Gathering of the Descendants of Isaac and Ann Jackson . . .* (Philadelphia, 1878), pp. 120–121, 128.

[4] Henry purchased these two pieces of apparatus from Soleil during his stay in Paris. *Henry Papers, 3*:543–545. For Nörremberg's polariscope, see above, Henry's Experiments in Optics, May 1841, footnote 14. Learning more about the interference apparatus has proven difficult. Although Babinet's scientific apparatus are well known, and a M. Guérard invented a form of polarizing apparatus (P.A. Daguin, *Traité élémentaire de physique,* 4 vols. [Paris, 1862], *4*:499), we have neither correlated the latter with Babinet's collaborator nor located any literature on the interference apparatus. Still another possible candidate for the role of Babinet's collaborator is H. Guinand, the son of Pierre Louis Guinand (1745–1825; *Nouvelle biographie générale*). Guinand had the reputation for manufacturing "the best glass for optical purposes which is now offered to the public," especially glass for achromatic telescopes. Elias Loomis, *The Recent Progress of Astronomy; Especially in the United States* (New York, 1850), pp. 251–252; the quote is from p. 252.

You can transmit the payment through Harndens express line, and the agent of the company in Paris will attend to the business for a small commission. The articles I have mentioned will cost about two hundred dollars and you can restrict him to this sum. The whole business can be transacted by letter and with little trouble to yourself.

There is to be a gathering of the friends of science and the members of the american philosophical society in Ph^d on the 25th inst. to which you have an invitation. I hope to see you there at the time. My friend Bache [is][5] to deliver an address at your college in July.[6] You will find him a man after your own heart and well desposed to cultivate your acquaintance.

If it were not that I am a very bad correspondent I would inflict many communications on you but whether I write or not be assured that I remain

As of old your Friend
Joseph Henry

[5] A tear in the paper.
[6] The previous November Alonzo Potter requested, on behalf of the literary societies of Union College, that Bache deliver the annual discourse on the evening before the next commencement. Potter's urgings, which included a plea for "men of sense & learning to occupy a place too often filled by the shallow & grandiloquent," apparently were successful. Alonzo Potter to Alexander D. Bache, November 18, 1842, Rhees Collection (RH 2069), Henry E. Huntington Library and Art Gallery.

FROM ALEXANDER DALLAS BACHE
Henry Papers, Smithsonian Archives

Philad. May 22. 1843.

My dear friend.

Your package went as you requested on Wed. afternoon. As you will see I took the *liberty* to cut Daniell's leaves. He has not forgotten you, if he does not understand you.[1]

Saxton agrees with me that you are the proper person to go on with the phosphogenics & I have put you down accordingly. Nature as you justly observe is a difficult jack to woo—B.G.[2] Walker's attempts to find when[3] the Comet has been & why.[4]

[1] Apparently a reference to the second revised edition of J. F. Daniell's *Introduction to the Study of Chemical Philosophy* (London, 1843), two copies of which are in the Henry Library. Daniell referred to Henry on pages 565, 590–591, 593, and 594. On page 269, however, Daniell took material from Henry's paper on lateral discharge without citing Henry, who annotated the passages: "These facts are taken from my paper to the British association in 1837...." Elsewhere Henry made such comments as "The proper explanation is not given" (p. 270), and "All this proves nothing inreference to the induction in curved lines..." (p. 256).
[2] The abbreviation is unclear; perhaps "E.G."
[3] Possibly "where."
[4] Sears C. Walker and E. O. Kendall presented a long letter to the American Philo-

You are down also for the galvanometric mode of ascertaining vel. projectiles.

About the thermometer of contact. I will *put it down* & if you think right, when the time comes *bring it up*. Also results of met¹ & mag¹ obns. of first two years of the Observatory.⁵ May be a historical notice.

Mr. Alexander is down for his interesting subject. We shall have a real feast. We reckon now more than [?38] papers on different subjects. Grandmama shows vigour at her advanced age.

Dr Ludlow expects you & Mr. A. to stay with him so I say nothing for once. Dr. Torrey must come to me & I have written him to that effect.

We have two gems of historical papers fr. Rev. Alonzo Potter of Schenectady.⁶ Cannot Princeton come out in this line.

Brunswick has sent two math¹ papers.⁷

Love to Mrs. Henry & your family

Ever Yours
A. D. Bache

---

sophical Society anniversary meeting on the identity and periodicity of the Great Comet of 1843. APS *Proceedings*, 1843, *3*:67–85.

⁵ Bache's two presentations, one on a variation of Fourier's thermoscope of contact, and one on observations at the Girard College Observatory, are given in ibid., pp. 90–92, 132–134.

⁶ Alonzo Potter wrote a letter on the career of Robert Livingston and accompanied it with an 1811 letter from Count Rumford to Livingston and an 1806 letter from Livingston. The two autograph letters are printed in ibid., pp. 105–108. Potter (1800–1865, *DAB*) was an Episcopal clergyman and Professor of Rhetoric and Moral Philosophy at Union College.

⁷ John Fries Frazer presented two mathematical papers by Theodore Strong, Professor of Natural Philosophy at Rutgers. APS *Proceedings*, 1843, *3*:49–50, 138–140.

TO HARRIET HENRY

Mary Henry Copy,¹ Family Correspondence, Henry Papers, Smithsonian Archives

Philadelphia May 27, 1843

My dear Harriet   I find I cannot return this evening and that I shall probably be detained until Tuesday.² The number of communications to the Society is much greater than had been anticipated, no less than forty-one are on the list. . . . I opened the ball yesterday with an account of my

---

¹ There are two Mary Henry Copies of this letter in the Family Correspondence, Henry Papers, Smithsonian Archives. Both are incomplete. The alternative copy differs considerably in its reading of the opening two sentences: "Will be detained until Tuesday. The number of communications to the Society unusually great no less than 41 are on the list."

² Henry was attending the centennial meeting of the American Philosophical Society. It was not until Tuesday, May 30, that he delivered his communication, "On a New Method of Determining the Velocity of Projectiles." APS *Proceedings*, 1843, *3*:165–167.

last labors on the subject of the phosphorogenic emanation. It was well received by a large and of course learned audience. Dr. Patterson's address[3] on Thursday was delivered in Musical Fund Hall[4] to a very large assembly. The Old School General Assembly attended in a body.[5] At the conclusion of the address the speaker in order to prove his position that the Society was never before in so flourishing a condition alluded to the labors of the active members and gave such an account of my communications that I felt glad I was in a very obscure position in the room and could not be seen by the audience.[6] Dr. Hodge and Dr. Maclean appeared to enjoy the compliment to me as a professor of Princeton very much since it was given before the clergy from every part of the United States.[7] Stephen is busily engaged with his paper and will probably make his appearance today. He has obtained some fine results and his communication will be an interesting one.[8]

[3] Robert M. Patterson, one of the Vice-Presidents of the American Philosophical Society, presented a long discourse on the founding and early history of the Society during the opening ceremonies of May 25. APS *Proceedings*, 1843, *3*:3–38.

[4] Opened to the public in 1824, the Musical Fund Society Hall, on Locust Street above Eighth, was for many years considered the fashionable location for lectures, balls, and concerts. Thompson Westcott, *The Official Guidebook to Philadelphia* (Philadelphia, 1875), p. 198.

[5] The General Assembly of the Old School Presbyterian Church met in Philadelphia from May 18 to May 31, 1843. On May 23 it received an invitation to attend the centennial meeting. *Minutes of the General Assembly of the Presbyterian Church in the United States of America*, Volume 10: *1842–1844* (Philadelphia, 1842–1844), pp. 167, 179, 203.

[6] Rejecting the thesis that the American Philosophical Society had degenerated since the glorious years of Benjamin Franklin and David Rittenhouse, Patterson argued that the Society presently contained many members whose zeal for and success in scientific endeavors were equivalent to those of its early members. Among the examples he presented was Henry, who was compared quite favorably with Franklin. While admitting that Franklin's contributions to electromagnetism were on a level of their own, Patterson contended that Henry's task had been more difficult than

Franklin's due to the increasing complexity of the science. Patterson described Henry's publications as "filled with the most curious and interesting discoveries, and the most sagacious theories; the results of great and continued personal labour and patient thought." APS *Proceedings*, 1843, *3*:32–35; the quote is from p. 33.

Henry continued to believe Patterson's praise to be excessive, asking the editor of the *Newark Daily Advertiser* to omit the reference when reporting the publication of the proceedings of the centennial meeting. See below, Henry to William B. Kinney, October 21, 1843.

[7] This sentence is not in the version we have selected (an ellipsis appears instead), but does appear in the alternative version.

[8] Stephen Alexander's communication, "On the Physical Phenomena Which Accompany Solar Eclipses" (APS *Proceedings*, 1843, *3*:183–210), not delivered until May 30, was the last paper presented at the meeting. It consisted of a detailed listing of various optical, magnetic, and thermodynamic phenomena associated with eclipses of the sun, occultations of planets and stars, the lunar disk, transits of Venus and Mercury, and the disk of Venus. Focusing on optical phenomena accompanying eclipses and occultations, Alexander concluded that many could be explained by assuming that the moon affected beams of light which pass near its limb, although he would not commit himself to a physical cause of the lunar influence.

FROM J. J. SYLVESTER[1]

Henry Papers, Smithsonian Archives

Tuesday June 6 1843
M[rs] Cadell's 691 Broadway

My dear Sir,

When I last parted from you you were kind enough to express your desire to serve me by the influence of your name and recommendation should any vacancy occur where they might admit of being brought effectively into play.

Such a contingency has just fallen in through the resignation of Professor Anderson of Columbia College, which he sent in yesterday and which will in all proba[bi]lity be accepted as final. Of this however there is some doubt as the trustees suggest that he might make his resignation partial and temporary; he appears however himself to be averse to this; but is apparently not sure of his own mind. He resigns in consequence of his wife's illness which is of so serious a nature that the physicians place their sole hopes of her recovery in the advantages that may accrue from a change of air and residence in Europe.[2] At all events whatever may be the nature and limitations of the vacancy my intention is to apply for the place and make all possible interest without delay. I am sure you will be willing to render me the assistance of your powerful recommendation and I will in due time write again or come out to see you on the subject. A great deal will be decided by *private influence*, and if possible (consistently with common decency) the trustees will contrive to screw in an Alumnus of the college or at all events a New Yorker and probably a churchman;[3] notwithstanding

[1] Although Sylvester had arrived in the United States with a letter of introduction from Thomas Graham to Henry (of October 5, 1841, printed above), this is the first evidence of contact that we have found. Sylvester and Henry may have met at the centennial of the American Philosophical Society in late May. Sylvester is listed on the program to deliver a paper although he did not read it at the meeting (*Silliman's Journal*, 1843, 45:232).

This letter and others printed below document Sylvester's unsuccessful attempt to be elected Professor of Mathematics and Astronomy at Columbia College. Sylvester candidly expressed his feelings and gratitude to Henry, who later wrote "I considered you somewhat under my care while you were in America that is after I came to know you for before this time I was somewhat prejudiced against you." Retained copy, February 26, 1846, Henry Pa-

pers, Smithsonian Archives.

[2] Henry James Anderson (1799–1875) was Professor of Mathematics, Analytical Mechanics, and Physical Astronomy at Columbia from 1825 to 1843. Although his wife died soon after they left for Europe, he did not return to the United States until 1851. While abroad he collaborated with Arago, converted to Catholicism, and participated in Lieutenant Lynch's expedition to the Holy Land. In 1874 Anderson set off for Australia to observe the transit of Venus. He died in India where he had gone to explore the Himalayas. *New Catholic Encyclopedia*, 15 vols. (New York, 1967), *1*:489. *New York Times*, December 14, 1875, p. 5.

[3] The successful candidate was an honorary graduate of Columbia, a New Yorker, and an Episcopal minister. See footnote 8.

Most American colleges in the first half of the nineteenth century were associated with

I shall make the attempt, fully conscious at the same time of the manifold disadvantages as well of birth[4] as those growing out of recent occurences under which I labour.[5]

It is my intention also to solicit the good offices of our excellent friend Professor Tod,[6] to testify to my mathematical and general qualifications. Subjoined is a list of the trustees, with the exception of such as may have been very recently elected to fill up vacancies occasioned by deaths.

I tender you and Mrs Henry my very warmest thanks for your kind reception which made my time pass so agreeably when with you in Princeton and beg you to believe me my dear Sir

Yours faithfully and with much respect,
J. J. Sylvester

Clement C. Moore L.L.D	Dr Berrian
David B. Ogden.	Ogden Hoffman
William Johnson, L.L.D	S. B. Ruggles
Edwd. W. Laight.	D^r. Knox (Revd.)
Beverley Robenson	Thomas L. Wells.
Thomas L. Ogden.	Rev. D^r. Williams
David S. Jones.	William H Harison
Bishop Onderdonk.	D^r. John B. Beck.
Philip Hone.	Hamilton Fish
D^r. Gardiner Spring	William Bard.
James Campbell.	
John L. Lawrence	
William A. Duer	

---

a particular denomination; Columbia was Episcopalian. Andrew D. White, President of Cornell University, referred to the period as "the regime of petty sectarian colleges." Frederick Rudolph challenged White's characterization because it "did not accommodate the paradox that while most colleges of the period were founded by denominations, they were also forbidden either by charter or public opinion to indulge in religious tests for faculty or students" (p. 69). In Sylvester's case, a provision in Columbia's charter prohibiting discrimination on the basis of religion did not prevent the Trustees from rejecting him primarily because he was a Jew, as he learned in private conversations with individual trustees. Despite the charter, it may have been common, as Sylvester's comment indicates, for Columbia's Trustees to consider the religion of candidates for the faculty. Ten years later Columbia rejected another superior applicant, Oliver Wolcott Gibbs, because he was a Unitarian (see below, West to Henry, July 4, 1843, footnote 2).

Frederick Rudolph, *The American College and University: A History* (New York, 1965), especially pp. 68–69. Horace Coon, *Columbia: Colossus on the Hudson* (New York, 1947), especially pp. 38–41, 58, 74. Donald George Tewksbury, *The Founding of American Colleges and Universities Before the Civil War* (1932; reprint ed., New York, 1969), especially pp. 138–139, 146, 157–158.

[4] i.e., being Jewish and a foreigner.

[5] Probably a reference to Sylvester's dispute with a student at the University of Virginia which led to his resignation and to rumors that he was unable to keep order in his classes. See his next letter to Henry of June 10, below.

[6] A. B. Dod, Professor of Mathematics at Princeton.

Among the candidates already declared are a brother of Anderson,[7] a Mr Hallett(?)[8] formerly professor in the University of N.Y. *and* Professor Renwick! ! ![9]

[7] Unidentified. Sylvester may have been mistaken about the relationship.

[8] Charles William Hackley (1809–1861), the successful candidate. Hackley was a graduate of the U.S. Military Academy (1829) and an ordained Episcopal minister. He had taught mathematics at West Point and at New York University, and served briefly as President of Jefferson College in Mississippi. Hackley remained at Columbia as Professor of Mathe-matics and Astronomy until 1857, then as Professor of Astronomy until his death. *Cullum, 1:425–426. Herringshaw. Columbia Alumni,* p. 291.

[9] James Renwick, Sr., had been Professor of Natural Philosophy and Experimental Chemistry at Columbia since 1820 and retained the position until he became emeritus in 1853. *DAB.*

TO WILLIAM BUELL SPRAGUE[1]
Rumford Collection, Dartmouth College Library

Princeton June 7th 1843

My Dear Sir

Permit me to remind you of the promise you made me while in Phila[d] to send me a copy of the unpublished letters of Count Rumford which you have in your valuable collection.[2] I hope you reached home in safety and found family and friends in good health.

With much Respect
I remain yours truly
Joseph Henry

[1] For Sprague, see *Henry Papers, 1:*464n.

[2] Sprague had an extensive collection of autographs and antiquities. On several occasions, Henry helped Sprague in adding to his holdings. (*Henry Papers, 2:*79–80, *4:*10, 59, 103–104, 215).

We are not certain why Henry wished to have Rumford material. The American Philosophical Society printed a letter from Rumford to Chancellor Livingston in its hundredth anniversary volume; Henry may have been looking for information or additional letters. APS *Proceedings,* 1843, *3:*105. Faraday and his wife collected pictures and autographs, primarily of European scientists (see *Henry Papers, 3:*277, 281). Henry may have decided to do the same; however he only asked Sprague for copies.

Sprague had already sent a copy of the letters. They are enclosed with a note dated June 1, 1843 (Henry Papers, Smithsonian Archives), in which Sprague says he has sent all his material "in the hand writing of Count Rumford" and hopes it is of use to Henry.

Sprague sent copies of three items—a personal letter dated June 24, 1785, in which Rumford describes the events of the last few years; a letter to a General Armstrong dated June 5, 1809, explaining how to prevent iron from rusting, and an undated note to President Washington which accompanied the gift of a book.

"RECORD OF EXPERIMENTS"
Henry Papers, Smithsonian Archives

Friday June 9th. [1843]

Since the last date I have been engaged in lecturing to the senior class and have also attended the centenary aniversary of the american Phil[a] society. At this meeting I made a communication of the results of my investigation of the phosphorogenic emination. Also gave an account of the method I have proposed for determining the velocity of a canon ball. The meeting was well attended 45 communications were made but I was not much impressed with the importance of this method of advancing science. The temptation to make a display and to bring forward communications merely to produce an effect for the moment is very strong and while the mere declaimer on the foundation of other mens labours producs quite an effect the man of true science who modestly brings forth the result of his labours is scarcely noticed provided he has arranged nothing for effect. These reflections are not made inreference to my own case since I was more complimented than I deserved but they are the sober inferences from an attentive watching of the result of the meeting. I am not sure that the British association has much advanced the cause of science except in the case of meteorology and magnetism[1]

The idea occurred to me while in Phi[d] that possibly the emination from the electrical spark was not of the same intensity throughout the whole line of the discharge and perhaps it might be confined to the poles of the discharging wires. To test this a <hole> slit was made in two plates and these slits were placed transversely to the path of the spark so that the lime under neath could not be reached by the emination except from a single point of the spark. With this arrangement it was found that the light was produced from every part of the line of the discharge but that it was much more intense at the two ends

To test this more accurately another arrangement was made by which the impression from the lime could be made at once from several points and the intensity of the action from each compaired at once with one another. For this purpose three holes were cut in a plate of mica so that one hole would be directly under each pole of the discharger and the other be midway between the other two. When the discharge was made close to the plate of mica so that the emination <from> through each hole might make its impression on one spot without any effect from other parts of the spark; the impression at the middle hole produced a faint phosphorescence which

---

[1] Henry's dissatisfaction with the British Association is not new. See, e.g., his letter to A.-A. De La Rive of November 24, 1841, printed above.

continued a few seconds and then disappeared while those at the two ends continued to glow for more than a minute.[2] I have called the openings holes they were rather slits so that the impression from the whole width of the spark might be received on the lime through each slit

[2] This experiment was incorporated into the published version of the paper. "On Phos- phorogenic Emanation," APS *Proceedings,* 1843, *3*:40.

FROM J. J. SYLVESTER
Henry Papers, Smithsonian Archives

New-York
June 10th/43.[1]

My dear Sir,

It would be of *great consequence* to me, that you should speak to the three gentlemen whose names you advert to,[2] but I can scarcely reconcile it to my sense of propriety to ask of you to incur so much trouble on my behalf.

If however you could come up without much inconvenience, it would be conferring upon me a most essential favour,—for I have ascertained that [*it*] is only by bringing private influence to bear upon the trustees *in detail* that a candidate has any chance of success.

Dr Anthon[3] informs me that certain parties have spread abroad a report that "I am unable to keep order in my class and on that account was *compelled* to leave the University of Virginia." and adds that this is the ground of opposition that will be taken up against my claims.

It may be necessary for me to correspond with the authorities of the University, perhaps to go on there in person, to obtain an official refutation of this calumnious charge.[4]

[1] According to the postmark, Sylvester did not mail this letter until June 13. On June 10, presumably after writing Henry, he heard a rumor that Benjamin Peirce was a candidate for the position at Columbia, and he wrote Peirce the next day to say he would certainly step aside if this were true. Sylvester to Peirce, June 11, 1843, printed in Raymond Clare Archibald, "Unpublished Letters of James Joseph Sylvester and Other New Information Concerning His Life and Work," *Osiris,* 1936, *1*:85–154; letter on pp. 123–124.

[2] Possibly in a letter we have not found. Ac- cording to letters printed below, Henry consulted Charles West, Principal of the Rutgers Female Institute, and Gardiner Spring, a Trustee of Columbia with whom Henry had served on an examination committee a year earlier. The third gentleman may have been John W. Draper, whom Henry also saw in New York. See West's letter of July 4 and Sylvester's letter of July 13, printed below.

[3] Charles Anthon (1797–1867), an eminent classical scholar and Professor of Greek and Latin at Columbia. *DAB.*

[4] Sylvester resigned from the University of

Perhaps Ballard would feel disposed to make a fair statement of what actually occurred and if he be as you suppose of an ingenuous disposition, and feels that in the heat of passion he was betrayed into a course of conduct which in his cooler moments he is inclined to regret and which has eventuated in serious injury to me, he would not object to express so much in writing.[5] At least I can say for myself that under similar circumstances, I should feel a pleasure in making what reparation I could.

This is a matter of very serious importance to me. Anthon says he believes my election may turn upon this point. All with whom he has conversed acknowledge my capabilities as a mathematician but add "He cannot keep a class in order". Renwick has been very active in his canvass & I have rea[son][6] to believe has propagated if not originated th[is] calumny: Let my four years trial as a public lecturer in the University College of London speak for me to the contrary; if *a one disturbance*[7] took place in my class at Virginia, it is nothing more than what all there have been habitually subject to, more especially my own predecessor[8] for years past, and the fault must be laid to the door of the defective discipline or organization of the Institution itself & not to me for refusing to sanction a principle of disorder: but that I was not able to maintain order in general is a direct untruth; my fault if any was in preserving order too well.

With many apologies and [?ineffable] thankfulness for your kind dispositions I remain

Most truly yours
J. J. Sylvester.

The election takes place on the 26th Instant. I intend writing to Professor Dod for the valuable letters you advert to; if you should come to this city, I hope you will do me the favour of staying with me:

Virginia near the end of March 1842, only a few months after his arrival the previous November. Although there are various speculations as to why he resigned, the immediate cause was an affair involving a student, William Henry Ballard, whom Sylvester reported for being unruly and insolent in class. He resigned when the faculty failed to support him to his satisfaction. Raymond Clare Archibald reviewed the literature concerning this episode in "Unpublished Letters of James Joseph Sylvester" (cited above), especially pp. 97–100. See also R. C. Yates, "Sylvester at the University of Virginia," *American Mathematical Monthly*, 1937, *49*:194–201.

Sylvester was successful in getting the faculty at Virginia to state that he left voluntarily; both of the above sources print the statement.

[5] William Henry Ballard (d. 1892) spent his sophomore year at the University of Virginia but attended Princeton the other three years and graduated in 1844. *Princeton Catalogue*, p. 165. *Princeton Annual Catalogues*, 1841, 1843, 1844.

[6] Here, and later in this sentence, the original is torn where the letter was sealed.

[7] The *"one"* is an interlineation in the original.

[8] A reference to Charles Bonnycastle (*Henry Papers*, 2:419n–420n), although William B. Rogers had served as interim professor following Bonnycastle's death in October 1840.

FROM HENRY D. ROGERS
Henry Papers, Smithsonian Archives

Philadelphia June 15. 1843.

My Dear Friend

I send you the promised sketch just received from Russell Smith[1] of my Earthquake picture.[2] Every part of it I doubt not will be understood by you. In some respects I like the design better than the original.[3] Permit me to renew my request that you do not allow any copy of it to be made, beyond what you may make yourself for illustrating the principle of our Theory.[4] For should it get into the hands of Lecturers the interest of *freshness* in my forthcoming Lectures would be lost and injustice be done to both the artist and myself. I am pleased that you deem the theory of importance enough, to make it a topic in your course.[5] Natural Philosophers, too generally I think in devoting their attention to their own closet experiments, overlook the often much more instructive and sublime experiments which *Nature* of herself is daily performing before their eyes.

With true esteem & respect,
sincerely yours &c.
Henry D Rogers

[1] Russell Smith (1812–1896) was a theatrical scene painter, as well as an illustrator for geological surveys. *DAB.*

[2] This letter is written on the back of the sketch (see detail, facing page 251). A multicolor rendition in chalk, the sketch shows the progressive power of the lava flow.

[3] The original illustration, now lost, was prepared by Smith for Rogers's lectures at the Masonic Temple in Boston in late 1843 and 1844. James B. Rogers to William B. Rogers, October 15, 1843, William Barton Rogers Papers, Archives, Massachusetts Institute of Technology. For this reference and other information on Henry Darwin Rogers's lecture series, we wish to thank Patsy A. Gerstner of the Howard Dittrick Museum of Historical Medicine.

[4] Discussed in detail above, J. W. Bailey to John Torrey, September 17, 1842.

[5] On geology. See below, Henry to Harriet Henry, August 3–4, 1843, especially footnote 13.

FROM J. J. SYLVESTER
Henry Papers, Smithsonian Archives

691. Broadway
New. York.
[June 18, 1843][1]

My dear Sir,

I cannot adequately express my sense of your unheard of kindness and zeal for the interests of one having no claim save the general comity of science and your own good feeling, for drawing upon your friendly services. Freely as these are tendered believe me, I feel a compunction of shame in accepting your proposal—it is so much beyond what I have any right to demand. My present object is to request you will do me the favour of accepting a room at my temporary home here (Mrs Cadle's 691 Brd^wy) during your stay in town. If possible I will meet you on your arrival at the cars.

Most truly and respectfully,
J. J. Sylvester

[1] From postmark.

FROM JOHN LUDLOW
Henry Papers, Smithsonian Archives

Uni^y of Penn^a
June 24th/43

My Dear Sir,

You are one of a Com^e to consider the expediency of making a report of the doings of the A.P.S. for the 1st Cent. & perhaps also (as the Com^e may judge) of the plan of the report.

I will state the circumstances. The General Com^e of arrangements for the last anniversary (of which Dr Chapman is Chair^n) met on the 16th inst just before the meeting of the society and adopted their final report. In reference to the resolution which you had offered during the meetings at the anniversary they recommended the appointment of a Com^e to consider as to the propriety of future anniversaries. They said nothing in regard to a report of the doings of the Society (to which your resolution also referred)[1]

[1] Henry's resolution, presented at the May 30, 1843, meeting of the American Philosophical Society, stated: "Resolved, That in the opinion of this meeting it is desirable that a report should be prepared, by an appropriate committee, on the Scientific labours of the Society and its members during the past Century, to be submitted to a future anniversary meeting." The Committee of Arrangements split Henry's resolution, presenting as

thinking it better as a matter of delicacy to the secretaries (of whom three were on the Com^e) that a resolution to prepare such a report should come from an individual. That duty was devolved on me. Accordingly when the report and resolution of the Com^e had been adopted by the society I rose and adverting to your resolution upon the minutes & your absence <*begged*> asked leave to call it up and as a part had been acted on in one of the resolutions adopted made the simple motion That a Com^e be appointed to prepare a report of the doings of the A.P.S. for the 1st cent. of its existence—it was at once seconded by Dr Dunglison. But ho! what a hub-bub! Dr Patterson made opposition[2]—surprised all his friends Kane Dunglison Bache &c showed pep & passion & indeed behaved very strangely. I could tell you more about this, perhaps I ought not to have said so much and I should certainly not except to one whom I consider a second self in these matters and who might wish to know some particulars. I will not say any thing of the reason of all this except that in my innocence I made such an *honorable* motion that some one more honorable was deprived of making. Alas! poor human nature. In all this I write for your own eye. The result of the whole was that a Com^e consisting of Ludlow (very unwillingly), Bache,[3] Rogers,[4] Henry, Smith[5] were appointed for the purpose mentioned in the beginning of this letter.

Now my object is to know whether you can meet the Com^e and when? Can it be next week or later.[6] It will all be determined by your convenience. As to the expediency of such a report the Com^e of arrangements were unanimous. You I thought were decided and I believe that we agreed perfectly that it was the most important of all. The need of such a Com^e seemed to me strange and doubtless it was owing as I think to the flurry into which we were thrown. Be this as it may we are a Com^e—so let me hear

---

their fifth resolution a proposal to appoint a committee of five (Henry and the four secretaries of the Society were eventually selected for this committee) to evaluate the idea of future anniversary meetings. No resolution was offered regarding Henry's proposed report, although the Committee of Arrangements endorsed the idea in the body of their report (where they referred to Henry as "one of our members from a neighbouring State"). Manuscript Minutes, November 1842–January 1846, pp. 117, 145, Archives, American Philosophical Society; APS *Proceedings*, 1843, 3:216–218.

[2] Having made, at the request of the Society, a long historical address during the centennial meeting, Patterson probably believed that Henry's resolution and the committee's en-

dorsement of it represented implicit criticism of the address. That Henry thought Patterson's address was too adulatory is quite evident. The thoughts of the Committee of Arrangements may be gleaned from their call in their report for an objective history of the Society, free of local boosterism, untainted by nationalism, and accurate in its attributions. APS *Proceedings*, 1843, 3:3–36, 216–217; Henry to Harriet Henry, May 27, 1843 (printed above).

[3] Alexander Dallas Bache.

[4] Henry Darwin Rogers.

[5] George Washington Smith.

[6] Henry went to Philadelphia to discuss this issue almost immediately. See below, Henry to Harriet Henry, June 28, 1843.

from you and with kindest regards for you and yours I am your affectionate friend

J. Ludlow[7]

My wife is not in the Un^y but tell Mrs H. that she loves you all so much that I am sure she would reproach me if I did not say this much to her.

[7] At the October 6, 1843, meeting of the Society, Ludlow's committee filed its report, which included four recommended resolutions. An amended version of the first resolution, calling for "a report of the Scientific labours, during the past century, of the American members of the Society" was adopted at this meeting. Henry neither attended the meeting nor signed the committee report.

The following week, on October 13, the Society took up the remaining resolutions proposed by Ludlow's committee. Ultimately, the resolutions were tabled, a set of substitute resolutions proposed by J. K. Kane were adopted, and the whole issue was sent back to Ludlow's committee. Debate had centered over the issue of control of the proposed report. Ludlow's committee had wanted a small committee to write the report; Kane countered with the idea of dividing the volume by subject area, with a different committee responsible for each area. Kane also wanted the Society as a whole executing editorial responsibility over the report; Ludlow's suggestion that one individual have editorial control was rejected.

Although the minutes of the meeting are not sufficiently explicit to be sure, one reason for this debate may have been the fear of exclusion—the more members involved in the project, the less likely any individual would be left out. Robert Hare had responded to the committee's resolutions by proposing an appeal mechanism if "any member of the Society may conceive that due attention has not been given to the labours of any member." Kane's substitute resolutions were actually amendments to Hare's proposal.

Ludlow's committee reported back to the Society on November 3. This time, Henry did sign the committee report, although Rogers's signature is absent. Facing reality, the committee found "the task imposed on them by the Society to be attended with so much difficulty and delicacy, that they beg to refer the whole matter back to the Society, and ask that the Com^e be discharged." So ended Henry's (and the Society's) efforts for a centennial retrospective.

Manuscript Minutes, November 1842–January 1846, pp. 159, 161–162, 165–167, 175, Archives, American Philosophical Society; the committee reports, as well as Kane's resolutions, are also in the Archives. An abbreviated version of the controversy appeared in the published APS *Proceedings*, 1843–1847, *4*:16, 17–18, 23.

TO HARRIET HENRY
Mary Henry Copy,[1] Family Correspondence, Henry Papers, Smithsonian Archives

Phil. June 28th 1843

There is to be a meeting tonight where it is hoped the matter I came in for will be amicably adjusted. I find that my name had occupied a very prominent place in the debate—that it was proposed a publishing committee should be appointed to superintend the making of the great report of the

[1] A second, less complete Mary Henry Copy survives in the Henry Papers, Smithsonian Archives. This second version also contains minor variations in the opening sentence and one phrase (see footnote 3, below) not included in the copy we are publishing.

doings of the Society for the last hundred years and that I was to be the chairman of the same.[2] In order to stand in the way of no one who might desire the honor of such a position I have declined acting in that capacity.[3] I am writing this at Bache's. You will receive it after our dear little ones are asleep. May peaceful slumbers await my dear little wife.

[2] For the background and ultimate resolution of this proposal, see above, John Ludlow to Henry, June 24, 1843.

[3] In the other Mary Henry Copy, there is a phrase at this point which concludes the copy: "and by a talk this morning with several members of the society I think...."

FROM J. C. SPENCER[1]
Henry Papers, Smithsonian Archives

Washington June 28, 1843.

Dear Sir

When in Princeton on the 13th inst. Mr Scudder[2] represented himself as being in very necessitous circumstances and urged the payment of a bill he had against Ambrose.[3] I told him to write me, which he has done. While I am desirous to protect myself, I am unwilling that a poor man should suffer by the misconduct of my son. But as I have always considered the College interested only in the proper adjustment of these demands, and as I am ignorant of Mr Scudder's character and circumstances, I beg leave to refer this matter to you. I have accordingly sent his letter herewith[4] and in it thirty dollars, the amount of his bill. I would respectfully request you, in addition to the many favors you have conferred, to attend to this affair, and do what you deem just and right.

Permit me to remind you of the Elgin marbles[5] and to say that I am ready to do whatever may be in my power to promote your liberal and patriotic views.

Very respectfully yours
J. C. Spencer

[1] John Canfield Spencer (1788–1855) was a New York lawyer and politician whom Henry may have known in Albany. Spencer was Secretary of War from October 1841 to March 1843 and Secretary of the Treasury from March 1843 to May 1844. *DAB.*

Later in the year Henry was asked to use his personal acquaintance with Spencer in the campaign to make Bache Superintendent of the Coast Survey. See below, Kane to Henry, November 20, 1843.

[2] Unidentified.

[3] Ambrose Spencer attended Princeton as a sophomore in 1835 and as a junior in 1836. *Princeton Annual Catalogues,* 1835 and 1836.

[4] Not found.

[5] See *Henry Papers,* 3:530–532, for Henry's project of getting a copy of the Elgin Marbles in the British Museum for the United States.

FROM CHARLES E. WEST

Henry Papers, Smithsonian Archives

New York July 4ᵗʰ 1843.

My Dear Sir,

I owe you an apology for not giving an immediate answer to your letter[1] respecting Sylvester. I learned soon after its receipt that you were coming to the City when I expected to see you. Indeed I was invited to meet you at Dr Draper's, but unfortunately you did not call on the Dr till the day after, as I was informed by him last Evening on my return from Massachusetts. It would give me pleasure to espouse your cause in behalf of Sylvester. I have called upon one of the Trustees of Columbia College & spoke of Sylvester's remarkable mathematical talents. I think however from all I can learn that there is little chance for any one except an Episcopalian or one who *favours* Episcopacy.[2] I had thought of applying for the place myself but the circumstance I have just mentioned and more particularly the fact that you were so much interested in Sylvester deterred me. I believe Sylvester a clever fellow & deserving of patronage in this country. That he was abused at the South is too true. I shall be happy at any time to render him all the aid in my power.

I was much pleased with your letter on "Fulminary Tubes."[3] It cleared up the matter & made the Electrical Theory respecting them very plausible, I think satisfactory. I had sent a paper on the subject to Prof. Silliman for his Journal, which will probably appear this month.[4] I have thought, if you have no objection, of preparing another paper in which I would embody the substance of your letter acknowledging the source from which I derived my information.[5] Such an article may be interesting. If you prefer to write

[1] Not found.

[2] The use of this criterion at Columbia was vigorously challenged in 1854. Oliver Wolcott Gibbs, a Columbia graduate, had been nominated for the Chair of Chemistry, but was opposed by the clergymen on the Board of Trustees because he was a Unitarian. Samuel Ruggles, a personal friend of Gibbs and a Trustee, responded with a resolution before the Board specifically excluding religious tenets as a selection criterion. Both the motion and Gibbs were rejected by the Board, although by a narrow margin, despite strong support for Gibbs among both the New York press and the Columbia alumni. Animosity between the supporters and opponents of Gibbs was so high that plans for the celebration of the College's centennial that year were cancelled. There was, however, one positive result of the controversy. In its wake Ruggles began sustained and ultimately successful efforts to turn Columbia into a university. D. G. Brinton Thompson, *Ruggles of New York: A Life of Samuel B. Ruggles* (New York, 1946), pp. 80–89; Horace Coon, *Columbia: Colossus on the Hudson* (New York, 1947), pp. 74–75.

[3] See above, Henry to West, March 22, 1843.

[4] "Notice of Certain Siliceous Tubes (Fulgurites) Formed in the Earth," *Silliman's Journal*, 1843, *45*:220–222. West questioned the generally accepted role of lightning in fusing the sand into a glass tube.

[5] To the best of our knowledge, this proposed paper was never published.

on the subject yourself I beg you to inform me for this would give me greater satisfaction.

I trust I shall have the pleasure of seeing you at our house when you next visit the City. You need give yourself no anxiety about returning my book I have no use for it at present. Mrs W unites with me in kind regards to yourself & Lady.

Very truly yours
Chas E. West

FROM HENRY JAMES[1]
Henry Papers, Smithsonian Archives

New York 21 Wash. Place
July 9, 1843

My dear friend:

On returning home a few days since, I found to my great regret that you had called in my absence. I am heartily sorry to have missed you, as I have wanted very frequently within the past year to hold communication with you. At such times I should have run over to Princeton, had it not been for the awkwardness of meeting people there who *will not talk with* one on equal terms, about those matters which necessarily form the only staple of discourse *with them*. I cannot so far stultify my understanding of the divine order as to suppose any human being or set of beings entitled by their attainments in philosophy or devotion to pass an *a priori* judgment upon those who chance to differ from them. The disgusting narrowness of church people afflicts my spirit with as palpable an asphyxia as charcoal vapour produces in my body; and effectually forbids all hope of pleasant or profitable intercourse with them. My recollection of the Princeton people is that they are virtuous, agreeable people up to a certain pitch: were it my lot to be thrown much with them I should suffer from a constant apprehension of that pitch becoming transcended, and of their turning out something quite otherwise.[2]

---

[1] Previously published in Ralph Barton Perry, *The Thought and Character of William James*, 2 vols. (Boston, 1935), *1*:16–17, with some deletions from the second paragraph. Henry's reply of August 22 is printed below.

[2] Henry James had attended Princeton Theological Seminary from 1835 to 1837 but left without graduating (*Henry Papers*, 2:35n).

My time has been closely occupied with study, and it was to get some furtherance in this that I desired to meet you. Again and again I am forced by scriptural philosophy to the conviction that all the phenomena of physics are to [be] explained and grouped under laws *exclusively spiritual*—that they are in fact only the material expression of spiritual truth—or as Paul says the visible forms of invisible substance. Heb. 11.3.[3] When I have been feelingly on the brink of some clearer apprehension of the connection between them, I have had deeply to lament my ignorance of any connected view of physics—even of the facts of any one branch: and I have wanted to know from you whether some book did not exist exhibiting the *fundamental unity* of the different sciences; that is exhibiting the presence and operation in *all* the sciences of great leading and fundamental principles which make all *one* at bottom, spite of their superficial diversities. I wish a qualified person would write a book shewing to the ignorant all those phenomena for instance in all the sciences which attest the principle called gravitation, or grouping together all those facts in all science which acknowledge the influence of heat, electricity &c &c. I am perplexed by the barrenness of such scientific books as I have found level to my comprehension, which give one nothing but bewildering heaps of facts peculiar to one branch of science, and never attempt to shew the brotherhood of these facts to every other fact of nature. Surely there must be the closest family relation among all the facts of true science, and to trace this it appears to me would be the sole interest of the natural philosopher. How can a man separate one branch of science from another, without perceiving that he is in so far belittling and dishonouring it, and that it is only by making it connect itself in some manner with *all* other science that it becomes worthy of his pursuit. But—do you know of such a book as I want—that is if I have made my want intelligible, which I think doubtful. I dread too to hear of one, lest when found it should exact more preliminary science from its readers than I could readily muster.

I am advertising my house for sale—and shall be guided by circumstances connected with its sale as to whether I shall go into the country or go for a couple of years to Europe. My health has got unsteady from deprivation of fresh air and confinement to my chair. I think it likely we may go over to France for the winter, and afterwards to Germany. When do you next come hitherwards? Much I should like to know what you discover in those deep waters where you sail, if your discoveries bear any relation to my knowl-

---

[3] The verse reads: "Through faith we understand that the worlds were framed by the word of God, so that things which are seen were not made of things which do appear."

edge. In your researches into the physical, have you yet come to the *moral*? Hand and glove is a poor similitude of the union which to my conviction exists between these things. Cause effect—parent & child—fountain & stream —such rather is their intimacy. However I had no idea of troubling you to this extent when I began.

> Remember me very kindly to your wife & believe
> Me Every faithfully Yours   H James

FROM J. J. SYLVESTER
Henry Papers, Smithsonian Archives

July 13 1843
New York

My dear Sir,

In compliance with your kind request, I write to inform you of the result of the election as far as at present ascertained.

Mr D. S. Jones,[1] Mr T. L. Ogden[2] and Dr Spring[3] were appointed a committee to report on the rival claims and have come *unanimously* to a descision to recommend Ross[4] exclusively for election.

T. L. Ogden only *intimated* but Jones declared in express terms that my profession of faith was the cause of my rejection.

The latter went so far as to say that they the committee were assured that the election of such a person "would be repugnant to the feelings of every member of the board" and gave me liberty to repeat the substance of our conversations, adding in answer to my inquiry that "they went not at all on the ground of my being a foreigner but would have acted the same, had I been born of Jewish parentage in this country." From Virginia I have received the most handsome treatment and the whole affair of my resignation

---

[1] David Samuel Jones (d. 1848) received a B.A. from Columbia in 1796, held a variety of public offices, and was a Trustee from 1820 until 1848. *Columbia Alumni*, p. 117.

[2] Thomas Ludlow Ogden (1773–1844), a graduate of Columbia who became one of New York's most successful corporation lawyers, served as a Trustee from 1817 until 1844. *DAB; Columbia Alumni*, p. 113.

[3] Reverend Gardiner Spring (1785–1873) received a B.A. and M.A. from Yale and a D.D.

from Hamilton in 1819. Spring was a Trustee of Columbia from 1830 until 1873, serving as Chairman from 1858 until resigning in 1859. *Columbia Alumni*, p. 85.

[4] Probably Edward C. Ross (1801–1851), at this time Professor of Mathematics and Natural Philosophy at Kenyon College. *Henry Papers*, *1*:186. Despite what Sylvester says here, the post eventually went to Charles W. Hackley.

put in such a light by D[r] Harrison[5] (the former Chairman) Judge Tucker,[6] & Col. Woodley[7] the proctor & the Faculty at large as to make to the advantage rather than to the injury of my character for efficiency and skill as a teacher.

D[r] Spring on my questioning him and expressing some little surprize that after his conversation with you & the impressions left by his manner on my own mind during an interview I had with him after your departure, stated that "he had overcome his scruples to the extent of resolving not to *originate* objections on grounds of religious difference but being brought forward by others he could not but concur:" in fact he durst not stand out as the champion of tolerance for fear of his church being down upon his back.

There is little doubt that the Trustees will be governed by this decision, so that I now look upon the gates of Columbia College as effectually shut against me, and have only to make up my mind to endure this disappointment with Christian fortitude.

I feel as much obliged to you my dear Sir, as if your generous efforts had been crowned with success, and deem myself happy or at least consoled by the reflexion of there being anything in me capable of eliciting so singular a proof of disinterested kindness & friendship.

My life is now pretty well a blank and my only effort is to sustain existence. Thank in my name Professor Dod for his kind exertions to serve me, and let him understand that I am truly grateful for his good feeling. Please to present my regards to M[rs] Henry and all my Princeton friends and believe me

My dear Sir,
Your faithful friend and obliged Servt
J. J. Sylvester

[5] Gessner Harrison (1770–1862), Professor of Ancient Languages at the University of Virginia from 1828 until 1859. *DAB*.

[6] Henry St. George Tucker (1780–1848). After a career which included service as a Virginia chancery judge and President of the Supreme Court of Appeals of Virginia, Tucker became Professor of Law at the University of Virginia in 1841. He taught until 1845. *DAB*.

Both Tucker and Harrison, the former chairman of the faculty, were on the faculty committee appointed to investigate the incident between Sylvester and Ballard.

[7] "Colonel" Willis H. Woodley was the popular Proctor of the University of Virginia from 1837 until 1845, when he was asked to resign. Philip Alexander Bruce, *History of the University of Virginia, 1819–1919* (New York, 1921), pp. 192–193.

FROM SAMUEL F. B. MORSE
Henry Papers, Smithsonian Archives

New York July 18th 1843.

My Dear Sir,

I think from present appearances that some time next week I shall have my wire in such a state, that the experiments we propose may be made, but I will write you definitely next week *the days* which can be devoted to them.[1] Have you heard from Mr Sexton in regard to the instrument which I authorized to be procured?[2] It should be ready by the beginning of the week, and it would give me great pleasure to see Mr Sexton with it, should he feel at leisure to accompany you. I hope Dr Torrey will find it convenient also to be present, and please say to him that I hope he will not wait for a more formal invitation. If in the arrangements making for the Telegraph, any experiments in furtherance of scientific research, suggest themselves to you or to any of your scientific friends, I shall be exceedingly happy to give every facility during the few days that can be devoted to that purpose.

When last in Washington my friend Mr Robert Greenhow[3] informed me that he had met, in some late proceedings before the French Academy, with a notice of a method of increasing the power of the electro magnet. His information was not definite, but as this is a point of importance to me, I wish to ask if you have met with anything of the kind?[4]

Believe me With great respect
and esteem Yr Mo. Ob. Servt
Saml F: B: Morse.·.

[1] See below, Morse to Henry, July 31, 1843.

[2] An instrument to measure the velocity of electricity had been requested from Joseph Saxton. See below, Morse to Henry, July 31, 1843.

[3] Robert Greenhow was a translator and librarian for the State Department. Washing-ton City Directory, 1843.

[4] Henry was unable to locate such a reference. See his response on August 22, 1843, below. Our own efforts lead us to question the accuracy of Greenhow's information. We have found nothing resembling the notice Morse describes.

July 18, 1843

FROM M. W. JACOBUS[1]
Henry Papers, Smithsonian Archives

Brooklyn July 18ᵗʰ 1843.

Very respected & dear Sir,

On the lofty and exposed location of Brooklyn Heights, it is wise doubtless, to seek a safeguard to our Church edifice from lightning. And in this day of *'doctrine'* touching all *"Divine Agencies"* the multitude are hardly sure whether the element is *'from above'*, or *'from beneath.'*[2] For myself, I have only to ask your favorite species of *rod*. Our edifice is mounted with 4 small pinnacles capped with tin & sheated. The tower (Gothic) say 120 ft high. If you can possibly furnish me a reply by return of Mail it will doubly oblige

Your already indebted & obt
pupil—M. W. Jacobus.

[1] Melancthon Williams Jacobus (1816–1876), A. B. Princeton 1834, attended Princeton Theological Seminary from 1835 to 1838, taught Hebrew there for a year, and was then called to the First Presbyterian Church of Brooklyn (Old School), where he was pastor from 1839 to 1850. The rest of his life he taught at Western Theological Seminary in Allegheny, Pennsylvania. He wrote numerous books of biblical interpretation.

In accordance with the theology of Princeton Seminary, Jacobus was a member of the Old School branch of the Presbyterian Church. In 1869 he was Moderator of their General Assembly, and eased the way toward reunion of the Old and New Schools the following year. *Biblical Repertory and Princeton Review: Index Volume, from 1825 to 1868*

(Philadelphia, 1871), pp. 217–219; *Princeton Catalogue*, p. 146.

[2] Jacobus's language here neatly reflects the split, mainly theological, between the conservative Old School wing of the Presbyterian Church and the more evangelical and liberal New School faction. Old School Presbyterians were orthodox Calvinists, believing in predestined salvation, grace being dispensed "from above" according to God's own reasons. New School Presbyterians held Arminian views, believing in the universality of God's offer of salvation, and man's free choice to respond "from below" to the divine call. Timothy L. Smith, *Revivalism and Social Reform: American Protestantism on the Eve of the Civil War* (1957; reprint ed., Baltimore, 1980), pp. 26–28.

TO M. W. JACOBUS
Mary Henry Copy,[1] Henry Papers, Smithsonian Archives

Princeton July 19, 1843

My dear Sir, Your favor of today came to hand a few minutes since and I hasten to answer it in time for the next mail. The rod I prefer is that recommended by a committee of the French Institute appointed to report on

[1] Mary Henry evidently cut out Henry's sketch before discarding the rest of his draft or retained copy. We have used fragments of text surrounding the sketch and on the verso to correct errors in her transcription.

the best form of lightning rods, for the protection of the government buildings of France in 1824. As these gentlemen took into consideration all the
known laws of electricity I see no reason to deviate essentially from the
form they proposed.[2] The rod consists of round iron at least 3/4 of an inch
thick terminated at the top by a single point tipped with platina. The several parts of the rod are joined together by screwing or by lapping so as to
make a perfect metallic contact of the surfaces as possible. To prevent rusting the rod is covered with a coating of black paint—pieces of zinc attached
to the rod for this purpose are ineffectual, although they have been lately
recommended by some persons. The connection with the earth should be
as perfect as possible and for this purpose the end may be plunged into the
water of a well, where the circumstances will permit of such an arrangement, but where this is not practicable, the French savants reccomend that
the lower part [of the] rod should be placed in a horizontal ditch about
fifteen feet long, directly from the building and terminated at the farther
end by a perpendicular hole of four or five feet deep into which the farther
end of the rod is plunged. The whole space around the rod is then filled
with pounded charcoal or ashes from the baker's oven. The object of the
charcoal is to form a broad contact of conducting matter with the earth and
to preserve the metal from rusting.

I regret that you have not been more explicit in reference to the position
of the pinnacles and the tower and the material of which the roof is composed. I suppose however the arrangement is of the ordinary kind namely
a pinnacle at each corner of the building and the tower on the middle of
one of the gables thus

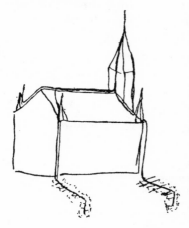

If this is the arrangement I would recommend for the most perfect protection one
long rod from the top of the steeple with
two branches terminating in the earth at the
two ends of the building; one branch passing
along the roof and down the same to one of
the far corners on which a pinnacle is placed
and the other passing down to a corner on
the other end of the building. The wire
on each pinnacle should be placed in metallic contact with this rod or its branches
by means of connecting rods of iron. If the
building is covered with metal it will be

---

[2] Henry had previously endorsed this form
of rod in his August 1, 1838, letter to the editor of the *Newark Daily Advertiser* (*Henry
Papers*, 4:81-83).

sufficient to form a metallic connection with the tin of the pinnacles and the metal of the roof, and the latter with the lightning rod. If the building be covered with slate and furnished with a metallic gutter, the latter should be connected by a metallic communication with the rod. I have known cases in which a building has been struck at the nearest corner to the cloud although it was furnished [with] a lightning rod at the farther end

FROM SAMUEL F. B. MORSE
Henry Papers, Smithsonian Archives

New York July 31st 1843.

My dear Sir,

We have been delayed a little in our arrangements, but on Tuesday the 8th of August (one week from tomorrow,) I shall leave my office in Nassau Street at 9 o'clock A.M. in the Bloomingdale Stage for Mr Chase's ropewalk at the junction of 8th avenue and the Bloomingdale road, about 6 miles from the city Hall. I hope that Professor Torrey & yourself will be able to go out with me at that time. If by any accident you should not be with me in season, you can reach the same spot by the *Knickerbocker* stages, which are passing in Broadway every few minutes; They go as far as 21st Street, whence every half hour they proceed to Manhattanville on the 8th Avenue, passing the above mentioned ropewalk. I am expecting quite a reunion of the scientific men in our vicinity, Profrs Silliman, Renwick, Ellet, Draper &c. &c. I shall have a continuous line of insulated wire 160 miles in length, with which I invite such experiments, as you may deem useful.[1] I hope Mr Saxton with the instrument for measuring the velocity of electricity, will also be with you.[2] In haste but with sincere respect

and esteem Yr Mo. Ob. Servt

Saml F: B: Morse.

[1] Morse reported on the day's experiments in his monthly report to the Secretary of the Treasury and in a letter to *Silliman's Journal.* Although Silliman, Henry, Torrey, and Chilton were unable to attend, Morse was joined by Renwick, Draper, Ellet, G. C. Schaeffer, and his assistants Fisher and Gale. Using a Grove battery of one hundred pairs, they tried both lifting power and decomposition at various distances. Success with the 160 miles of wire led Morse to conclude "that a telegraphic communication on the Electro-Magnetic plan may with certainty be established ACROSS THE ATLANTIC OCEAN!" Morse to J. C. Spencer, August 10, 1843, in Samuel I. Prime, *The Life of Samuel F. B. Morse* (New York, 1875), pp. 480–481, and *Silliman's Journal,* 1843, 45:390–394.

[2] See Henry's reply of August 22, printed below.

July 1843

TO [JOSEPH OWEN][1]
Draft, Henry Papers, Smithsonian Archives

[July 1843][2]

I have been engaged for a few days past in putting up a box of apparatus for you which I have give[n] in charge to Mr Walch.[3] It contains an electrical machine and several articls <*of apparatus*> for electrical expermts. The machine was purchased by money I received from the missionary socety of the college. The accomping articles are such as I have had constructed in Princeton and you will please accept them as a small testimony of my esteem for you personally and my interest in the great and important cause in which you are engaged. I regret that I have suffered so long a time to elapse since the receipt of your kind and highly interesting letter of the [. . .][4] 1841 without answering it but I expected some further communication from you relative to apparatus.[5]

[1] Although Henry's draft does not give the recipient's name, we believe this letter was to Joseph Owen (1814–1870), a former student of Henry's who was a missionary in northern India.

After graduating from Princeton in 1835, Owen tutored students in mathematics at the College while attending the Princeton Theological Seminary. In 1840, the Board of Foreign Missions of the Presbyterian Church sent him to join the mission at Allahabad, some five hundred miles northwest of Calcutta. In addition to preaching and preparing works for the mission press, Owen devoted much of his time to organizing and teaching in the schools of the mission, particularly a high school which opened in 1843 and a college which opened in 1846. Although some of his fellow missionaries stayed in India only a few years, Owen remained there until shortly before his death in Edinburgh while en route to the United States for a visit. *Roberts*, p. 99. *The Foreign Missionary*, 1871, *29*:233–234.

The only letter we have found from Owen to Henry from India, is dated February 15, 1853 (Henry Papers, Smithsonian Archives). In it Owen thanked Henry for sending apparatus, especially an "admirable magnet" which had "astonished the natives" as had "galvanic and electric shocks."

Two presentation copies from Owen to Henry of books published by the Allahabad Mission Press are in the Henry Library: *Sermons: Doctrinal and Practical, by Several Authors* (Allahabad, 1846) and Joseph Owen, *The Creation, Fall, and Flood* (Allahabad, 1855); both are in Urdu.

Other Henry students who became missionaries in India included John H. Morrison (class of 1834), John Edgar Freeman and Levi Janvier (class of 1835), and Archibald Alexander Hodge (class of 1841). *Maclean*, 2:348–349.

[2] The date is based on the date "Mr. Walch," of the first sentence, left for India.

[3] Presumably Owen's fellow graduate of the Princeton Theological Seminary, John Johnston Walsh (1820–1884), who left for northern India in July 1843. *Roberts*, p. 119. *Foreign Missionary Chronicle*, 1843, *11*:243.

[4] Left blank by Henry.

[5] We have not found Owen's 1841 letter to Henry. An earlier letter of August 5, 1840, sent on the eve of his departure, is in the Henry Papers, Smithsonian Archives. In it Owen wrote that he "should have been very happy in receiving the philosophical instruments . . ." and that Walter Lowrie, Secretary of the Board of Foreign Missions, was "anxious to purchase a philosophical apparatus for Allahabad" and "will be very glad of your assistance . . . in selecting the articles."

Lowrie had sent a set of philosophical apparatus to another mission with some of the first Presbyterian missionaries to India almost ten years earlier, reportedly with the hope that "by the blessing of Heaven it might prove the means of undermining the false systems of philosophy adopted by the heathen, and consequently their false systems of religion, with which their philosophy is intimately, if not inseparably connected." *Historical Sketches of the India Missions of the Presbyterian Church in the United States of Ameri-*

The box of minerals which you sent me from Mr Frazer[6] came safely to hand about six weeks ago. They are very beautiful and interesting specimens and are highly esteemed by me not only on account of their comparitive rarity but also on account of their locality. Please give Mr Frazer my kind regards and ask him if I can be of any service to him in this country in the way of science or otherwise. I will send him by the next opportunity some scientific articles. The <hasty> sudden departure of Mr Walsh prevents my <doing so> making up a package at this time.

---

ca ... (Allahabad, 1886), p. 107.

One of Owen's fellow missionaries and teachers at Allahabad, John Wray, echoed that motivation when he wrote Lowrie on April 20, 1844:

> Mr Owen has been lately lecturing on Astronomy to the Orphan Boys & Girls in Urdu & English, using the Apparatus which has been sent out to the mission. The scholars appear delighted with the Lectures. Correct views of science is of great importance to the natives, as it will tend to overturn many of their false views of religion.

John Wray to Walter Lowrie, April 20, 1844 (Presbyterian Historical Society, Board of Foreign Missions of the Presbyterian Church in the U.S.A., Mission Correspondence, India volume 4, Allahabad Mission, 1838–1846; microfilm reel 5).

In a letter in which he explicitly mentions the apparatus sent by Henry, Owen described how he also found the apparatus useful in catching the interest of his students:

> Some two months ago, on the eve of a great holy-day, when we were greatly persecuted with entreaties to close our operations during the next day, and I was followed half way home by a clamorous crowd of about fifty or sixty, I gave permission to them all to be absent if they wished, but promised that those present should see a splendid *tamasha*, (show.) They all went off with a loud salam, and the next morning we had about sixty, when I showed them the solar microscope magnifying a variety of small objects, which filled them with wonder and delight. This succeeded so well that I have done something of the kind ever since, so that they have now learned to expect a *tamasha* every holy-day. Hitherto I have not been at a loss for variety, the magnet, the prism, the convex and concave mirrors, and the electrical machine have entertained them abundantly. With the latter they are astonished beyond measure, and their only name for it is *bijli*, (lightning.) You would laugh to see them electrified, and to hear them describe to each other in their own way the sensation that has passed through their elbows and breast. One shock usually satisfied them. I had, however, an old faqir the other day who volunteered to take a second, and in my anxiety to do him justice I so disturbed his equilibrium that he broke a handsome Leyden jar that Prof. Henry had very kindly sent me with the electrical machine. Some of the young fellows, who wish to observe the holy-days and to see the experiments too, beg and entreat to have the *tamasha* on other days, and the young brahmans of the straiter sect are by no means pleased with the operations performed on their festivals by the philosophical apparatus.

Owen to Lowrie, April 19, 1847, printed in the *Foreign Missionary Chronicle*, September 1847, 15:258 (original in the Presbyterian Historical Society, as cited above, India volume 6, Allahabad Mission, 1847–1851; microfilm reel 9).

In the same volume as Owen's letter to Lowrie (Volume 6; microfilm reel 10), there is an 1847 catalog of the Allahabad Mission College which lists mathematics, mechanics, astronomy, natural philosophy, chemistry, anatomy, and natural history among the subjects taught. There are also an 1851 list of apparatus for the College and specific requests of Owen, including one to "Get us also, with the advice of Prof Henry some of the latest & best works on science, mechanical, astronomical & physical" (sheets 450–451).

[6] Perhaps the G. Frazer who is mentioned in annual reports of the Allahabad mission as "a warm friend of the missionary cause" and a patron of native schools. *Annual Report of the Board of Foreign Missions of the Presbyterian Church, in the United States of America* (New York, 1838), p. 10, and *Second Annual Report ...* (New York, 1839), p. 12.

You will find in the box some college catalogs by which <*you*> it will be seen that few changes have taken place in our faculty since you left. Mr Jager[7] resigned his professorship and has settled at Washington D C as a Teacher of languages and I believe is doing very well considering his habits in refer[ence] to economy.

<*Mr Topping still*>[8] Dr Torrey has removed his family to Princeton and occupies the house <*occupied*> formerly owned by Mr Beard.[9] The other members of the faculty remain about the same as when you left. Mr Dr Maclean I should say[10] still continues in a state of single blessedness. Mr Dod & Stephen Alexander have had an increase of family which James Alexander and myself remain about the same. The college has fallen off a little in numbers but not more so than the depression of the times had lead us to anticipate.

Our country for the last three years has suffered much <*on account of*> from the commercial revultions which had commenced before you sailed

[7] Benedict Jaeger, who left Princeton in 1841.

[8] Evert M. Topping, Adjunct Professor of Ancient Languages from 1839 to 1846, had been a tutor at Princeton at the same time as Owen (*Henry Papers*, 4:201n).

[9] i.e., the late Samuel Bayard.

[10] John Maclean had only recently received an honorary D.D. (1841) from Washington and Jefferson College. *Princeton Catalogue*, p. 128.

TO HARRIET HENRY

Family Correspondence, Henry Papers, Smithsonian Archives

Princeton Thursday night 10 o'clock
Aug 3rd [–4] 1843

My Dear Wife

We are all well and all things thus far have gone on well since your departure.[1] The litle one has appeared happy and contented. Helen has taken quite a motherly charge of her. When Will and myself returned from the Rail-way we found the house quite lonely the little girls did not return from Uncle's[2] until the afternoon. Puss said she had taken care of the baby[3]—had held it on her lap and that she would take care of father. Helen gave her a ride in the waggon last evening in the campus and the two were

[1] Harriet had taken Mary on a trip to up-state New York to visit family and friends, leaving Henry and the remaining three children in Princeton. As this letter makes clear, Henry was able to draw upon the extended family and friends to help him during this brief period of single parenthood.

[2] Stephen Alexander.

[3] Perhaps the Alexanders' youngest daughter, Charlotte Meads Alexander. Unfortunately, neither baptismal nor cemetery records have been located for her.

stopped several times by the students. I sent Ben the servant to tell Puss to keep on her bonnet, she appeared however very indignant at the message, and ordered Ben off. She appeared to think that the bonnet did not become her and could not be prevailed to put it on. Just before going to bed she met with an accident, of the gastronomical kind which required a change of linin and which for a time was a source of great grief to her—but on going up stairs in the course of half an hour after I found both Helen and herself fast asleep in my bed; the former across the foot, and the latter at the head. There was considerable kicking and turning over during the night but neither became awake. I did not sleep very soundly until near morning and was awakened <near> about 7 o'clock by the chattering of the little girls. Just before breakfast there was a slight storm between the two girls relative to a picture book which was however disipated by a story I told them ab[out][4] the starting of Mother and Mary from the Depot and the pro[. . .] arrival of the two travellers at Uncle James' the joy of John Platt[5] &c &c. I have been engaged in the hall to day in be[. . .] hearing recitation and getting drawings made since 8½ o'clock this morning until 6 this evening except a few minutes at dinner. I believe however that all things have gone on smoothly. When I came home for tea at 6 o'clock Catharine had taken the children for a walk—they first went to see the new library.[6] Helen spoke in high terms of the beauty of the building and Puss said oh! grandmother it is splendid! On their return they called at Mr Waggoner's[7] and had each a saucer of ice cream. They also brought home a tumbler full for Mother and Will. The last named person has conducted himself very well since your departure—he spent a considerable time with me yesterday in the Library and has been much engaged to day while not in school in reading Froissarts annals[8] a book I permitted him to take from the library. He has however met with a misfortune, which has caused him considerable sorrow—the new knife given him by Mr. Halsted[9] by some unaccountable means disappeared from the pocket in which he had, as he thought, safely deposited it. This happened yesterday and as yet no tidings have been heard of it.

---

[4] This insertion and the subsequent two indications of missing material are necessitated by rips in the paper.

[5] James Henry's son, John Platt Henry (1836–1905). *Henry Papers*, 3:44.

[6] Erected in 1843, the library of the Princeton Theological Seminary was a Gothic structure donated by James Lenox. It was designated Lenox Hall. *Hageman*, 2:337.

[7] Presumably Daniel B. Wagner, who was Steward of Nassau Hall during 1845–1846.

Princeton Catalogue, p. 81.

[8] According to the 1843 college library catalogue (General Manuscripts Collection, Princeton University Library), the edition Will read was John Froissart, *Chronicles of England, France, Spain, and the Adjoining Countries, from the Latter Part of the Reign of Edward II to the Coronation of Henry IV*, trans. Thomas Johnes, 2 vols. (London, 1839).

[9] Perhaps Mina B. Halsted, a member of the Class of 1843. *Princeton Catalogue*, p. 164.

Miss Prevost[10] has purchased the black *slave* for 500 dollars[11] and has given him a liberal <*opportunity*> offer of working out his time. Such is the rumour of to day. Mrs Taylor[12] called this evening to enquire how we were getting along and requested as a privalege that she might be called in if any thing happened to Mother or the children during your absence. The children are now all asleep. Catharine has shut the house—all is silent. Not a whisper is heard from the College and since I am obliged to lecture to-morrow I must for the present bid you good night.

1½ O'clock on Friday I have just returned from my lecture. Had quite a large audience. I have been obliged to work very hard for two days past in the preparation of my lectures and in superintending the construction of diagrams.[13]

Puss appears quite cheerful. She and Helen are playing in the little room over the hall. I told her just now that I was about to write to Mother and asked her what I should say for her. "Tell mother she must come home next week and bring me a *tumbler* and bed board" was the answer. The weather to day is quite pleasant. The temperature is at the most pleasurable <*degree*> point and I hope you are enjoying yourself amid friends and acquaintances. I received a letter yesterday from John Newland[14] requesting me to send him a catalogue and informing me that Councellor Dean has got a young son.[15] Please to give him my congratulations on the occasion. Mother appears to be very anxious to keep the children in good condition and on the whole I think they will receive rather more indulgence whil you are from home [t]han[16] they usually do. I have been so much engage[d] in my lectures that I have heard nothing of the affairs of the village since you left. Mother and the children are going to visit Aunt Luiza this afternoon and I am to go over after recitation. William has gone regularly to school and appears very well he says however that his head aches some. Dr Torrey informed that *Mrs T* is better but is still very feeble. I have just

---

[10] Theodosia Ann Mary Prevost (1801–1864) was one of the major philanthropists of Princeton. *Henry Papers*, 2:57.

[11] An escaped Maryland slave, recognized by one of the students, had been arrested under the Fugitive Slave Law. The right of the owner to reclaim his slave was upheld by a Princeton jury, but the owner accepted $550 from Miss Prevost in lieu of the slave. *Hageman*, *1*:267–268.

[12] Perhaps Julia Taylor, a friend of the family. See, e.g., Julia Taylor to Harriet Henry, December 5, 1845, Family Correspondence, Henry Papers, Smithsonian Archives.

[13] Henry was lecturing on geology. As he noted to his brother, "I have lectured only once on this subject and that several years ago. I find the labor of preparing arduous in this hot weather." Henry to James Henry, July 29, 1843, Mary Henry Copy, Family Correspondence, Henry Papers, Smithsonian Archives.

[14] Not found.

[15] Presumably one of the two children of Amos Dean (1803–1868; *Henry Papers*, 2:26–27) who died in infancy. Amos Dean, *The History of Civilization*, 7 vols. (Albany, 1868–1869), *1*:xxii.

[16] A hole in the paper is the cause of this and the following insertion.

been to the Post Office and with surprise and pleasure receved your letter of yesterday.[17] It has come with unusual dispatch. The post masters must have known how anxious we were to here from you and have expedited its passage. When I came near the house Puss was on the stoop. I held up the letter. She immediately asked is that a letter from *my* mother. I said yes. Then let me take it to grandmother was her prompt reply. The family being assembled in the study with the exception of Will who has gone to school your letter was read. Carray was very attentive—said she would take good care of father. While I am writing this I can [not][18] make progress for the number of questions relative to the arrival of mother. Why did she not tell more said Helen—why did she not tell more echoed Puss—Oh Puss don't push me so says Helen rather crossly—I will says Puss—shall I tell mother that you and Helen are speaking crossly to each other says I. No no says Puss. The storm giving way to sun shine. The time for meeting the class having nearly arrived I must be off.

5¾ O'clock The mail will close in a short time and I can now only say that I have just returned from prayers & the lecture room & find the house deserted. Mother and the chickens have gone to the other house and as soon as I can deposit this letter in the office I will follow them. I will write you again in a day or two and shall be delighted to hear again from you as soon as possible. Give love and respects to all friends and receive for yourself the ass[urance] which is unnecessary that I remain as ever your devoted husband

J H.

[17] Not found.
[18] Tears in the paper.

TO [HARRIET HENRY]

Family Correspondence, Henry Papers, Smithsonian Archives

[August 8, 1843][1]

Tuesday[2] *12 O'clock* I did not [get] my letter finished by [the] closing of the mail and therefore I will add another pa[ge or] two. I have just been at the Office. The northern mail has a[rrived] but it contains no letter from

[1] The letter has been dated from internal evidence, the date of Archibald Alexander's return from Virginia (John Hall, ed., *Forty Years' Familiar Letters of James W. Alexander*, 2 vols. [New York, 1860], *1*:377), and the dates of Harriet's trip to New York State (see above, Henry to Harriet Henry, August 3–4, 1843).

[2] The preceding portion of this letter has been lost. In addition, the letter is ripped both on top and in one corner. We have inserted appropriate text in brackets.

you. Why don't you wr[ite]. You are a naughty girl! So you are! This is a tru[ly] hot day and very moist. The Senior examination is going on. Dr Shippen[3] is in attendance. He was quite sho[cked] at the result of the examination in geography.[4] This is not taught in the college, but the students are required to be prepaired on it. He is staying as usual with Mrs. Rice.[5] I met the Lady just now as I was leaving the Post Office. [She] has heard from Mary[6] who says she thinks she will get eno[ugh] of the springs in the course of a week. Mrs Rice has requested me to dine with Dr Shippen the day after tomorrow. Dr Cabble[7] has been in Princeton and taken his sister Mrs J. Alexander to New Port. Mrs Meads[8] and someone with her have just arrived at Stephen's. Will commenced a letter to you last night but did not finish it. He is now much engaged with the piano and is endeavouring to learn to play a simple piece of music from his book. Dr Alexander has just returned from Virginia in good health. He has been gone 64 days and made 32 addresses. I said in good health this requires some qualification. The rail road car was thrown from the tracks on his way home and he was considerably bruised. According to the last Princeton Whig it appears that the poetical son of the shoemaker, the editor of the garland of the west is about to open a watchstore in Princeton.[9] I presume the garland has faded; its flowers could not be kept alive in the arid soil of the west. I have now almost exhausted my store of the scraps of news which have accidentally fallen in my way and which may serve to amuse you although they are not of the first importance to the historians of the present age.

[. . . min]utes before 6 o[clo]ck P M

Do you know that tomorrow will be Wednes[day] and that then you will then have been gone a whole [w]eek or one half of the time we gave you

---

[3] A physician in Philadelphia, William Shippen was a Trustee of both the College and the Theological Seminary. *Henry Papers*, 2:461.

[4] Final examinations for the senior class commenced on August 7. Faculty Minutes, August 14, 1843, Princeton University Archives. According to the Trustees' Minutes of September 26, 1843 (Princeton University Archives), the class did well in all subjects "except geography, in which, there was a lamentable display of ignorance."

[5] Martha Alexander Rice (d. 1844) was the wife of Benjamin Holt Rice and the sister of Archibald Alexander. *Hageman*, 2:134, 141.

[6] Possibly Martha Rice's daughter Mary, who later married the Reverend Drury Lacy. Ibid., 2:143.

[7] James Lawrence Cabell was on the faculty of the University of Virginia. Henry had met him during his 1837 European tour. *Henry Papers*, 3:407.

[8] Louisa Crane Meads, Stephen Alexander's mother-in-law.

[9] Edward Young, a former resident of Princeton, was one of the publishers of a monthly literary magazine established at Southport, Wisconsin, entitled the *Garland of the West*. Combining original contributions with reprints from other magazines, the *Garland* initially appeared in June 1842. According to the *National Union Catalog*, only two numbers survive. "Prospectus," *Princeton Whig*, July 1, 1842. We have been unable to locate a copy of the issue of the *Princeton Whig* referred to by Henry.

liberty [for] absence. We will expect you at the end of the promised time but if you are enjoying yourself very much and improving as I hope you are in health and spirits you may stay another week.

I hope Mary is a great comfort to you that she conducts herself with much propriety & behaves properly at the table and keeps her nasal process in a due state cleanliness. Puss said to day dear Mary she must come home next week. Helen has been a very good girl and but on one occassion only has she been otherwise than kind and generous towards her little sister. Puss has had a few storms particularly with Catharine on going to bed but these have generally passed over and have been suceeded <*with*> by sun shine.

I fear I have said so much about the little ones that you will begin to turn the tables on me in reference to talking about the children but you should of course impute the minuteness of my account to the desire I feel to accomodate myself to the peculiarities of my wife. The office will close I fear in a few moments and there[fore] I must close with the assurance that I am devotedly yours.

Love from all to all.
J.H.

TO HARRIET HENRY[1]

Family Correspondence, Henry Papers, Smithsonian Archives

Tue[s]day evening 10 O'clock
[August 8–10, 1843][2]

My Dear Dear H.

I have just been left alone in my study by the departure of Stephen who has been engaged for some 10 or 15 minutes with the evening news paper. He has been engaged all day in examination my turn comes tomorrow. I went to the office this evening with the full expectation of receiving a letter from you but was disappointed and now I am almost inclined to scold you— have you forgotten us? If you do not behave better we will put a veto on your going away again. You are a naughty girl—so you are—yest you are. No letter! that's too bad is the general exclamation. I went over to the other house this evening after tea and saw Mrs Meads and her youngest daughter they look very well and were quite pleasant. Charlotte regretted that her mother had left albany at the time of your arrival since she otherwise would

---

[1] This letter begins on the back of a letter from William Henry to his mother.

[2] This letter is postmarked August 10 and was apparently written during the 1843 senior examinations, which took place from Monday, August 7, through Monday, August 14.

have paid you much attention. She said that Orlandow and his wife how-ever were there and would be attentive to you. Louiza, as I told her, looks very well but the old Lady (I hope she will pardon the name) said she thought she looked very much debilitated and that the care of a family was really too much for her. Louiza has been very kind since you left and has several times sent to ask me to come over to her house to beguile the lone-liness of a wifeless man. From Uncle's I went with *Uncle* to the Whig So-ciety and was there interested with a communication, the nature of which, I am not allowed to reveal.[3] The exercises were interesting but the close-ness of the room gave me a fit of shortness of breath an attack of which I have been labouring under for several days past.

I received a visit this afternoon from young Whitney of New-Haven who as you may recollect graduated two years ago and who made me a present of the model of the Cotton gin.[4] I have invited him and Henry Alexander,[5] who accompanied him, to breakfast. I have spoken to Sam to prepare some-thing and he appears quite pleased with the commission.

By this time you are amoung your old friends in Schenectady with those who have know you long and who love and appreciate you for all your good qualities of head and heart. You may perhaps think I am beginning to flat-ter you but this is not the case. The absence of those we love has a wonderful effect as I can testify in exalting their good qualities.

Wednesday evening   I have been all day engaged in the examination and have had no opportunity of adding anything to this letter. The break-[fast] went off very well. Young Alexander did not come and I sent for Blevan's[6] to meet Whitney. Sam did as well as coud be expected but he and Catharine had quite a blow up below stairs about the size of the plates which were to be put on the table.

---

[3] At a special Whig Society meeting on August 8, President Carnahan presented a history of the Society. Minutes, American Whig Society, Princeton University Archives.

[4] After graduating from Princeton in 1841, Eli Whitney, Jr. (1820–1895) entered his late father's arms manufacturing firm where he engaged in the design and manufacture of firearms as well as the financial side of the business. He was also active in New Haven civic affairs, particularly in the construction of the New Haven waterworks. *Princeton Catalogue*, p. 162. *Record of the Class of '41* (Princeton, 1891), pp. 60–61. F. C. Pierce, *Whitney: The Descendants of John Whitney* (Chicago, 1895), p. 437.

A 1930s discussion of the extant models of the cotton gin does not mention any that was once owned by Henry, nor did Eli Whitney, Jr., mention giving one to Henry in correspon-dence relating to his gift of a model to the U. S. National Museum in 1884. F. L. Lewton, "Historical Notes on the Cotton Gin," S.I., *Ann. Rep.*, 1937, pp. 549–563. Accession 15499, Accession Records, Smithsonian Archives.

[5] Probably Henry Martyn Alexander, an 1840 Princeton graduate (*Princeton Cata-logue*, p. 157).

[6] George Phillips Blevins, a senior (*Prince-ton Catalogue*, p. 164). Blevins had apparently stayed with the Henrys when he was ill the previous year (Stiles French to John Maclean, March 11, 1842, Maclean Papers, Princeton University Archives).

Thursday morning

We have had since saturday almost continually rainy weather. On Tuesday night the water fell in torrents. Yesterday was foggy in the morning and rainy at intervals through the day and the weather this morning is damp and gloomy. Mrs Taylor called last evening before dark. Will gave her an invitation to spend the day with us. She said perhaps I had better move here entirely had I not? Your things are upstairs said Puss already so that you will not have to move. This remark Mrs T thought very wonderful for so little a thing. I call last night at Uncle's but did not see Mrs Meads she had gone to bed with a sick head ache. I afterwards went to Mr Maclean's and spent the evening with him. When I came home all except Catharine were asleap.

Yesterday at noon Will came home from school and said that he had call at the office but nothing was there. I however went over and found a letter. It was from you. I therefore hastened home assembled the family in the study and read the important communication. Read more says Puss when I had finished your short epistle—is that all said Helen. That's a very small letter said Grand mother—why did she not give us more about our friends in Schenectady. She intends to give us all the news when she returns and we must be content with small favours said I. We were all glad to hear from you and the letter though short was sweet.

Aunt looks very feeble—she has had an attack of dioreah but said she was better last evening.

Helen has not been at school since you left but mother thinks of sending her this morning and inorder to make the going more cheerful she is to have a penny. Puss is to go with her in the afternoon if the weather is favourable.

There is just now quite a noise on the part of Puss. Helen has started for school under the charge of Will and Puss is very indignant that she has not been permitted to accompany her. She has no clean *pampas* and the weather is unfavourable.

Yesterday morning I was much surprised to receive a visit from Dr Torrey. He had gone on to New-York by the way of New-Brunswick and ordered Hastings[7] to send his baggage to New York by the rail road. The

[7] Seth Hastings Grant (1828–1911) was a son of Asahel Grant (1807–1844, *DAB*), physician and missionary to Persia, and his first wife, Electa S. Loomis. He apparently lived with the Torreys when his father was in Persia (the entire time from 1835 until his death there in 1844 except for a brief return to the United States) and after his father's death. Torrey's biographer refers to Hastings Grant as Torrey's adopted or foster son.

Grant attended Princeton from 1843 to 1846 as a freshman, sophomore, and junior, but did not graduate. From 1846 to 1849 he was a clerk with New York booksellers and publishers Wiley & Putnam, and with John Wiley, and was then Librarian of the Mercantile

articles however did not arrive and he was obliged to return to Princeton without going to albany. I made an exchange with him in reference to the examination of the class so that he could start again. He left yesterday at 10 o'clock and intends to return on saturday. Mrs. T. is better. The pine apples were sent to her. Puss is now quite cheerful—Will has returned to bring her a peach. By the by I have not informed you that peaches came to town the day you left and have been for sale almost ever since—they are small however and not as yet very good. As ever yours

J.H.

Library Association from 1849 to 1866. He held various editorial positions until 1871 and engaged in various business enterprises from 1866.

Andrew Denny Rodgers III, *John Torrey: A Story of North American Botany* (1942; re-print ed., New York, 1965), p. 168. *Princeton Annual Catalogues*, 1844–1846. Arthur Hastings Grant, *The Grant Family* (Poughkeepsie, 1898), p. 227. Frank and Elihu Grant, eds., *Report of the Sixth Reunion of the Grant Family* (Westfield, Massachusetts, 1914).

TO JAMES HENRY

Family Correspondence, Henry Papers, Smithsonian Archives

Friday Aug 18[th] 1843

My Dear James

The good woman whom you so unexpectedly received in albany arrived at home safely on wednesday the day she was expected. The little one before her eyes were open on the mor[n]ing of the important day said Father is 'this' Tomorrow why do you ask said I because mother is comming home. Dr Wing[1] put the two travellers into a cab which conveyed them safely to Mr. Irelands.[2] They spent Tuesday in New York and devoted most of the day to shopping with Lucinda McMullen.[3] On Wednesday all the children and myself went down to the railroad and after waiting for some time with some doubt of the expected arrival they at length came and were greeted with a hearty welcome. There was however some little disquietude at the moment. H. had purchased a quan[t]ity of crockery which was packed in two large baskets and these she had given into the care of the conductor but nothing could be found of them when they arrived at Princeton. They had either been stolen taken by mistake or left at New York. The conductor on the Princeton part of the line promised to make enquiry and if possible

[1] Joel A. Wing, an Albany physician (*Henry Papers*, *1*:50n).
[2] William H. Ireland (*Henry Papers*, *2*:250n).
[3] *Henry Papers*, *1*:7n.

recover the lost articles. In the evening they arrived in the New York train and as they could not inform us of their adventures we concluded that they had been left at the depot, at Jersey city. All the articles were safe not even the handle of a tea cup broken. All is well that ends well. H. found us all in good health and had she not written that she would be with us on Wednesday we would not have expected her until the end of the week. I was so much engaged with the senior examination that I could not leave home or I would have gone to New York and perhaps albany to meet her. She was well pleased with her visit and was gratified with the kindness with which she was greeted. Mary does not appear to have been as much benefited by the trip as her Mother—she does not appear very well but is not very ill. The weather is quite warm this week and bids fair to continue so for some days to come.

I have scarcely a scrap of news to send you. The grades of the senior class have just been made out and young Olcot comes out the 4th in the class.[4] This is a very good standing particularly when it is considered that there are 63 members in the class and a considerable number of these are very industrious and *"talented"* young men. I have heard that Olcot has failed— is this true?[5]

Gibson's son intends returning to college in the Autumn had he remained he would probably graduated 1st or 2nd so that albany thus far has been well represented in the College.[6] John Newlands stood amoung the very first in his class.[7]

Love from all to all
Your Brother

H. says she has forgotten to pay you for the collars which she purchased of you.

[4] John J. Olcott (d. 1899) was from Albany. *Princeton Catalogue*, p. 164. His notebooks on Henry's natural philosophy course at Princeton are in the New York State Library.

[5] John J. Olcott's father was Thomas W. Olcott (1795–1880), President of the Mechanics and Farmers Bank of Albany. Any setback must have been minor as none is mentioned in the sketch of the bank in *Howell and Tenney*, p. 530, or in a biographical sketch in the *National Cyclopaedia, 18*:204.

[6] William J. Gibson (d. 1902), son of Henry's friend John Gibson of Albany (*Henry Papers*, 2:74n), graduated from Princeton in 1844 after taking a year off. *Princeton Catalogue*, p. 166. *Princeton Annual Catalogues*, 1841–1844. His notebook on the first part of Henry's course is in the Princeton University Archives.

[7] Newland, also from Albany, was an 1837 graduate of Princeton.

TO HENRY JAMES[1]
James Family Papers, Houghton Library, Harvard University

Princeton Aug 22[d] 1843

My Dear James

I have delayed from time to time answering your interesting letter of the 9th ult with the hope of being able to visit you. I have however been prevented from leaving home but I now think it not improbable that I may go to New York in the course of next week and if I do so we can then have a long talk on the subject of your letter. I fear I cannot give you within the compass of a letter an idea of my views of the conexion of the different branches of physical science with each other and with truths of a higher nature. The book you inquire after has not yet been written and indeed the development of physical science is not sufficiently advanced for the production of such a work. Science properly so called does not consist in an accumulation of mere facts but in a *Knowledge of the Laws of Phenomena;* in such a knowledge as will enable us to predict what will take place at any epoch when the circumstances are known. In this sense astronomy is the most perfect of all the branches of physical science since all its phenomena have been refered to the simple laws of gravitation and motion and by an application of these laws we are able to say what was or what will be the particular phenomena exhibited at any given time past or present. Besides the astronomical there are several lesser groups of phenomena which have been traced to the operation of simple laws. Of these we have one group which is classed under the head of the *luminous*—another which may be called the *thermanous*—a third the electrical and a fourth the magnetical. A few years ago these groups were entirely isolated and apparently had no principle of generalization in common, but even within my own time great changes have taken place in this respect; the electrical and the magnetical phenomena have been refered to one law, or to the agency of the same principle operating under different circumstances. Also light and heat have been united in the definite conception of waves of different lengths of an all pervading etherial medium. The connexion between the electrical phenomena and those of light and heat has not yet been made out although there are many facts which lead us to believe that a connexion does exist particularly between the agents of heat and electricity. For example an indefinite development of heat can be produced by the transmission of an electrical current through a platinum wire and conversely the greatest amount of electrical disturbance is produced by a small quantity of heat ap-

---

[1] Previously published in Ralph Barton Perry, *The Thought and Character of William James*, 2 vols. (Boston, 1935), *1*:17–18.

plied to the point of juncture of two bars of different metals. Still we are as yet ignorant of the *key fact* which is necssary to teach us *how* the phenomena of heat are connected with those of light[2] to enable us to say whether they are connected as cause and effect or whether they are both effects of some more general cause. Such a fact however I have little doubt will be discovered in the course of a few years and then the four imponderable agents of nature as we now call them will be reduced to one. The tendancy of science is to higher and higher or rather I should say wider and wider generalizations and could we be possessed of sufficient intelligence we would probably see all the phenomena of the external universe and perhaps all those of the spiritual reduced to the operation of a single and simple law of the *Divine* Will. I cannot think that any fact relative to mind or matter is isolated. On the contrary I believe that every phenomenon is connected with every other. Thus could we cause the polarity of the needle to cease we would by so doing change the whole order and dependance of the material universe. Our elementary books are entirely destitute of the true scientific spirit and generally inculcate the idea that science consists in a mere accumulation and arrangement of facts. The reason of this is that works of this kind are generally prepared by compilers who have no knowledge of the subject beyond the mere facts they collate. Those who are actively engaged in the discovery of new truths are unwilling to stop in their career to teach the mere elements of the knowledge which has been produced by the labours of their predecessors.

With much Respect & Esteem
Yours as ever Joseph Henry

Should I fail to see you in the city it would give me much pleasure to receive a visit from you at Princeton—come with your family. We can give you quarters and will be most happy in doing so. You need not meet any persons but those of our family. J. H

[2] Henry evidently meant "electricity."

TO SAMUEL F. B. MORSE

Samuel I. Prime, The Life of Samuel F. B. Morse *(New York, 1875), page 486*[1]

Princeton, August 22, 1843

My dear Sir: I hope you will pardon me for not before acknowledging the receipt of your kind letters of invitation to attend your galvanic exhibition.[2]

[1] A Mary Henry Copy of this letter, devoid of the postscript and with minor variations in the punctuation, is in the Mary Henry Memoir, Henry Papers, Smithsonian Archives.

[2] There were two invitations issued: on July 18, 1843, and on July 31, 1843. Both letters are printed above.

My time has been so much occupied during the last three weeks, with an extra course of lectures, and our senior examination, and so little at my own disposal, that I was unable to say whether I could be in the city on the day you mentioned or not. I did hope, however, to get away, but the examination prevented. Dr. Torrey was also engaged, and could not leave. I do not know, however, that I could have done much in the way of original experiments in the course of a single day. I am not quick in the process of inventing experiments, unless my mind is thoroughly aroused to the subject by several days' exclusive attention to the work, and then I am often obliged to pause between each effort. I have not been able, since I last saw you, to devise a satisfactory process for determining the velocity of *galvanic* electricity, and, on reflection, I did not think it worth the expense which would be incurred to have a machine constructed for the mere repetition of the experiments of Wheatstone.[3]

I think it probable that I shall visit the city next week, as I shall be unemployed from this time until a week from next Monday. If there is any prospect of your repeating any of your experiments previous to that time, I will be with you on any day you may appoint.[4] With much respect and esteem, yours truly,

Joseph Henry.

P.S.—I have found no mention in my number of the *Comptes Rendus*, of the French Academy, of the proofs you mention relative to the increasing of the power of the electro-magnet, and do not believe that any thing new of any importance has lately been published on that subject.

J. H.

[3] Henry later devised a method of measuring the velocity of galvanic electricity. See the "Record of Experiments" entry of October 16, 1843, printed below.

[4] There was no repetition. See Morse's reply of August 26, 1843, printed below.

FROM SAMUEL F. B. MORSE
Henry Papers, Smithsonian Archives

New York Augs^t 26th 1843

My Dear Sir,

I received your favor yesterday, and would say that my wire being partly removed to the lead pipe manufactory, and my apparatus also being returned to my Office, I shall be unable to repeat the experiments made on the 8th I had already made to myself your apology, for I know that gentlemen in your station have not their time always at their disposal. I regret that the state of the preparations of my wire, which enabled me to make the experiments, occurred at a time which deprived me of the presence of yourself Dͬ Torrey & Dͬ Silliman.

You have seen Prof. Ellet since, who was present,[1] and doubtless learned from him the results which were highly satisfactory and verified the calculations of yourself and other scientific gentlemen.

If you are in the city next week, I hope you will do me the favor to call. With sincere respect and esteem, Dear Sir,

Yͬ Mo. Ob. Servͭ
Sam! F: B: Morse .⋅.

---

[1] W.H. Ellet, a New Yorker, often returned north from South Carolina in the summer vacation. For example, he visited Henry in the summer of 1841 (see Henry's letter to Torrey, August 24, 1841, and "Record of Experiments," September 2, 1841, both above).

Ellet was "desirous ... of quitting the South," as he wrote Henry on February 29, 1844 (Henry Papers, Smithsonian Archives), part of his campaign to succeed Bache at Pennsylvania. His northern proclivities led him back permanently to New York in 1848.

TO CHARLES FOLSOM[1] AND GEORGE B. EMERSON[2]
Archives, American Academy of Arts and Sciences[3]

Princeton College of New Jersey
Aug 29ᵗʰ 1843

Gentlemen

I have received, through Harnden's express, a diploma of membership of the American acadͬ of arts and sciences,[4] for which permit me to request that you will present my sincere thanks to the society.

---

[1] Charles Folsom (1794–1872), Librarian at Harvard and later at the Boston Athenaeum, was Corresponding Secretary of the American Academy of Arts and Sciences from May 1839 until May 1844. *DAB*; AAAS *Memoirs*, 1882–1888, n.s. *11*:64.

[2] George Barrell Emerson (1797–1881), a Boston educator who served as Recording Secretary of the Academy from 1840 until 1843. *DAB*; AAAS *Memoirs*, ibid., p. 65.

[3] A retained copy of this letter, misdated October 29, 1843, is in the Henry Papers, Smithsonian Archives.

[4] Henry was unofficially informed of his election, which took place in 1840, by Enoch Hale in a letter of April 19, 1841, printed above. The diploma does not survive in the Henry Papers.

At this time, the Academy, founded in Boston in 1779, was still a small and exclusive association. Most of the members were socially prominent Bostonians or on the faculty at Harvard. The Academy was largely dormant during the 1830s. Beginning in 1843, interest of the members in the new Harvard College Observatory led to a revival of activity within the Academy.

Membership was a recognized honor; for Henry and other corresponding members, however, the Academy provided few tangible benefits. Sally Gregory Kohlstedt, *The Formation of the American Scientific Community: The American Association for the Advancement of Science, 1848–1860* (Urbana, Illinois, 1976), pp. 29–30, 36, 40–41.

I receive this honor, confered on me by one of the oldest and most respectable institutions of the kind in our country, with much gratification since I am induced to consider it as an expression of approbation of my humble labours in the way of science; and I beg leave to assure the society that this testimonial of their favourable opinion will be a new inducement to renewed effort in the same line.

> With much Respect I
> have the honor to be
> Yours &c
> Joseph Henry

FROM MARY H. GILL[1]
Henry Papers, Smithsonian Archives

> September 1st 1843
> Chestnut Street Philaᵃ

Dear Sir

The enclosed[2] was written, as you will see by the dates, after returning from my first evening at your house. My excitement was such that I could not sleep as early as usual that night or the next. I saw no suitable occasion, during my stay, for handing this to you; but now, upon reperusing it & finding it all sincere & *true*, I send it—though I feel that in doing so I may be throwing away with my own hands the good which Providence has brought me. However I would willingly incur ninetynine chances of such a result, distressing as it would be to me, for the sake of one in favour of what I earnestly desire.

> Respectfully
> Mary H. Gill

[1] Not identified. The Chestnut Street address leads us to believe she was a relative of the "B. Gill, gent., Chestnut opp. Mint," who is listed in the 1843, 1844, and 1845 Philadelphia City Directories, the last two years as a commission merchant with a business address at 15 Commerce. Other Gills on Chestnut Street include a Sarah Gill at 504 Chestnut (1845 directory) and a Sydney P. Gill on Chestnut opposite the Mint (1846 directory). A. D. Bache's address before leaving for Washington was 502 Chestnut.

This note was folded, sealed, and apparently hand-delivered. The address reads "Professor Henry. *Private.*"

[2] Not found.

"RECORD OF EXPERIMENTS"
Henry Papers, Smithsonian Archives

Tuesday Oct 3ʳᵈ 1843

Heat of a thunder cloud

Since the last date[1] I have been engaged in college and other duties an I am now for the first time since then enabled to resume the business of experimenting. This being our Autumnal vacation I hope to have a few weeks of uninterrupted leasure. I must however make the best use of this since on account of the new arrangements of college vacations, during the next year my time will be more than usually occupied.[2]

 Agreeably to the suggestion given at page 30[3] during the summer I have had attached to the thermo pile of Melloni's apparatus[4] a tube of pasteboard covered on the outside with gilt paper inorder to reflect the heat from the outside. The object of the tube is to screen the pile from all radiation except such as proceeds from some circumscribed portion of space. The instrument thus furnished gave very satisfactory and interesting results. When turned towards a cloud of a white appearance it indicated an increase of temperature over that of the blue sky the needle traversing in some cases an arc equal to 50 degrees.

As the instrument was lowered towards the horizon the heat was increased—the experiment being repeated in the forenoon and afternoon but perhaps the result would be different were the observation made early in the morning or late in the evening or rather after sundown

When the instrument was directed to a dark thunder cloud it indicated a diminution of temperature. This is in accordance with the theory of Peltier.[5]

[1] The last entry in the notebook was June 9, 1843, printed above.

[2] For the last time, the first session of the college year was begun in the second week of November. The last faculty meeting of this term is given as March 19, and eight days later the second session was begun, lasting through June 1844. Thereafter, Henry's breaks from college duties would be Januaries and summers, instead of Octobers and springs. Minutes of the Faculty of the College of New Jersey, Princeton University Archives. See also *Henry Papers*, 4:433.

[3] The last half of the May 1, 1843, entry, above.

[4] See "Record of Experiments," April 27, 1843, above. The Melloni apparatus was a sensitive device for measuring small quantities of heat.

[5] [J. C.] A. Peltier, *Météorologie* (Brussels, 1841), part 1, chapters 12 and 13 (an annotated copy is in the Henry Library). Peltier studied the role of electricity in meteorology, not merely lightning, but the effect of free and latent electricity in the formation of clouds, rain, and especially waterspouts and tornadoes. One of his assertions was that electric action in clouds enhances evaporation and consequently leads to cooling (p. 86). Hence, dark storm clouds would be cooler than white ones. There were many sources for the electric action—one was earth induction, on the analogy of contemporary theories of terrestrial magnetism. Henry's high opinion of Peltier's ideas was shown by their extensive treatment in "Meteorology in Its Connection with Agriculture: Part V. Atmospheric Electricity," *Report of the Commissioner of Patents for 1859:*

Found the heat decreased towards evening from the zenith downwards[6]

Made a series of experiments to determine whether ordinary electricity in passing through a conductor passes on the surface or through the entire mass. For this purpose a spiral was made of a number of turns of a piece of bell wire and this was placed with a needle in it in the axis of a hollow iron tube and a shock from a single jar sent through the tube but the needle exhibited no signes of magnetism

The same wire and spiral were next placed on the outside of the tube the shock again passed and now the needle was found to be magnetic

The experiment was repeated by substituting a tube of tin foil around a paper cylinder the needle spiral and connected wire being placed in the inside. The needle exhibited no signes of magnetism but when the needle and spiral were arranged on the outside magnetic effects were produced. The intensity of the charge of the battery was about the same in the different experiments. The discharge was from a single jar highly charged. With a larger battery less highly charged the effect would probably be different (See American Enclycopedia Dobsons edition)[7]

Repeat this exp with battery of several jars less highly charged. Also with galvanism the wire soldered to the tube (See exp of Mr Kenedy, I think in the Phil Mag Irish Academy)[8]

Agriculture (Washington, 1860), pp. 461–524, especially pp. 487–503.

[6] On November 3, Henry made an oral presentation of these meteorological results to the American Philosophical Society: *Proceedings, 1843–1847, 4*:22–23.

Immediately below this, at the turn of the notebook page, Henry wrote a new heading, "Does ordinary elect. pass along the surface?"

[7] Thomas Dobson published *Encyclopaedia, ... The First American Edition*, 18 vols. (Philadelphia, 1798), and a *Supplement to Encyclopaedia*, 3 vols. (Philadelphia, 1803), reprintings of the third edition of the *Encyclopaedia Britannica*, edited and supplemented for American audiences. This work contained the article, "Electricity," by John Robison, Professor of Natural Philosophy at the University of Edinburgh (1739–1805, *DSB*), reprinted in *A System of Mechanical Philosophy*, ed. David Brewster, 4 vols. (Edinburgh, 1822), *4*:1–204, which work included Robison's other articles on natural philosophy as well. An annotated copy of this series is in the Henry Library; why Henry cited Dobson and not the Robison work is not known.

Henry apparently referred to Robison's observation that a residuum of electrical fluid would lodge in non-conductors, such as the paper tube underlying the tinfoil. Hence the discharge from (or through) a combination of conductor and non-conductor (tinfoil and tube) would be slower and milder than from a conductor alone. Compare paragraph 165, where imperfectly silvered glass bulbs are used to treat patients by means of electrical discharges: "Small shocks, which convey the same quantities of fluid [as] the sharp pungent and alarming spark from a large surface, are quite soft and inoffensive, ... and will not alarm the most fearful patient." See also paragraph 180.

[8] Henry almost surely meant George J. Knox's experiments described in the *Transactions of the Royal Irish Academy*. In the first paper of two, "On the Direction and Mode of Propagation of the Electric Force Traversing Interposed Media" (1843, *19*:147–153), Knox used wires hooked to galvanic batteries and terminating in tubes of water to investigate whether a current passes through or on the surface of water. A second paper in the same volume, "Supplementary Researches on the Direction and Mode of Propagation of the Electric Force and on the Source of Electric Developments" (pp. 257–263), investigated similar topics. Knox postulated that solids conduct electricity on their surfaces, while liquids do so through their body, because the strong

The surface alone is not however to be considered in erecting lightning rods

Made an other experiment. Put sulphate of Pottassa in cup of water introduced under the surface of the same two insulated ends of wires sent shock through water from single jar. The salt became luminous and was broken by the concussion of the water

Water appears to conduct electricity badly and when a large quantity is to be transmitted the effect is the same as that of sending a discharge through the air

Try if the same noise and projection of the water would be produced which I observed in this experiment when the discharge is made between two plates of metal

---

directive forces holding one particle to another in solids exclude action by electrical forces, except at the boundaries. Liquids are more susceptible to electric action, because their forces are much less directed. This position was closely akin to Henry's in "On the Cohesion of Liquids," APS *Proceedings*, 1843–1847, *4*:56–57, 84–85.

Henry probably confused Knox with C. J. Kennedy, who presented a paper, "On the Theory of Electricity," to the British Associ-

ation in 1840, reprinted in Sturgeon's *Annals of Electricity, Magnetism, and Chemistry,* 1841, *6*:235–243. The paper was not concerned with Henry's subject, however.

Henry cited Knox on the mode of carrying an electric current in the "Record of Experiments" entry for January 27, 1845 (Henry Papers, Smithsonian Archives). Though Henry had the journal ("Ir. Acad."), volume number, and page number correct, he listed the year of publication as 1829.

"RECORD OF EXPERIMENTS"
Henry Papers, Smithsonian Archives

Wednesday Oct 4th 1843
Lateral Induction. Ordinary Electricity

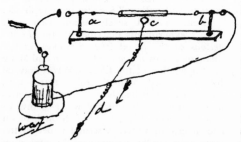

Sent charge through the horizontal wire *a b* while a ball *c* was placed at a small distance from the circuit and seperated from it by a tube of glass which surrounded the wire. The jar was insulated so that the inside or outside could be rendered redundant[1] at pleasure. In all cases <*the*> induction was produced in the wire *c d* which was connected with the earth at its lower end or rather was united to a wire which passes out of the window and is soldered to a copper plate buried in the earth. The current was

[1] That is, with an excess of the electrical fluid.

from the horizontal wire towards the earth both when the outside had the redundant electricity and when it was deficient

In one experiment the most compounded[2] of the three spirals used gave the needle the least degree of magnetism of the three and this would seam to indicate that action consits of an oscillatory motion or that there is an action and a reflex action[3]

In another experiment a spark passed from the horizontal wire to the ball *c* and then the current as indicated by the magnetization of the needles was towards the horizontal wire of this however I am not very sure. To prevent the passage of the electricity from the wire to the ball the glass tube was employed

Made the same experiment as described on the last page[4] with the exception that the battery of Dr Franklin was substituted for the jar with this the effect was not as great as with the jar. The needles were not as strongly magnetized and those in the spirals less compounded were more intensely magnetized than the others. This result would also seam to indicate a wavey motion in the disturbance of the electrical plenum which as I suppose fills all space.

[2] More tightly wound or with more loops of wire.

[3] Compare the experiments of May 7–10, 1842, above, and "Contributions V: Induction from Ordinary Electricity; Oscillatory Discharge." This topic was a persistent one throughout the next few days' work.

That the fact that the most compounded coil gives the least net magnetization should imply a *reflex* action is explained thus: a more compounded coil will develop a stronger magnetic field, which will more easily tend to neutralize the initial magnetization.

[4] The beginning of this entry.

Immediately above this line, Henry added a second heading, "Transverse Induction Continued," a different choice of words than usual.

"RECORD OF EXPERIMENTS"
Henry Papers, Smithsonian Archives

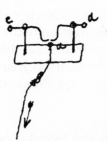

Thursday Oct 5th 1843

Induction Continued

Placed a ball with the wire leading to the earth inconnection with it opposite the points of the French descharger[1] to determine if the electricity passing through the air would produce the induced current in the long wire. The result was as I expected a strong current was exhibited by the magnetization of the needle in the spiral

[1] The discharger is drawn in Henry's illustrations, here and below, but we have been unable to find where he obtained it. The bills of the apparatus Henry ordered from Pixii, Paris, in 1837 (*Henry Papers*, 3:541–543) do not mention it; neither do the later bills of 1842 (Robert Baird to Henry, May 3, 1842, footnote 3, above).

Next the two ends of the wire of the discharger were placed in contact so that the discharge might pass without making an explosion in the air the same effect was produced as before but the needles appeared a little more strongly magnetised. In the above experiments the ball was seperated from the conductor by a plate of glass put between them

The direction of the induction was not altered by changing the direction of the descharge through the discharger *c d*. I have not yet however proved that this induction is independent of the free electricity of the jar

 Fastened by a little wax a piece of thread to the ball of the Leyden jar and another piece to the outside. Then after charging the jar the inside was touched so as to draw off the electricity until the two threads stood at about the same angle with the axis of the jar, indicating that the quantity of free electricity in each was equal. When the discharge was made the needle in the spiral was made magnetic but not as strongly as with[2]

That the effect does not principally depend on the redundant electricity of the jar is evident <*that*> from the fact that when the jar was removed and the sparkes from the machine passed through between the points no magnetism was imparted to the needle.

 When the jar is descharged while standing on a cake of wax and a wire is placed near it the needle [in] the <*hel*> spiral becomes magnetic the current being from the jar. Also a single spark thrown into the inside of the jar magnetizes the needle with the same arrangement as in the last experiment. N.B. To prevent any direct communication of electricity from the outside of the jar a plate of window glass was placed between the jar and the ball

When an arrangement like that shown in the figure[3] was made the needle became magnetic and indicated a current in the adverse direction to that of the jar. The magnetic effect was feeble and this is what was to be expected since the return current in the same wire would obliterate the direct at least in part

---

[2] This word ended the manuscript line, but Henry did not continue his thought. Instead he scored two strokes at the left margin and indented to start the next paragraph.

[3] A note in the sketch refers forward to the last diagram of the entry of October 28, 1843, below.

"RECORD OF EXPERIMENTS"
Henry Papers, Smithsonian Archives

Thursday Oct 6th 1843[1]

If a wire were attached to the <*circuit*> conductor *a b* connecting it with the earth an other effect would probably be produced and perhaps this would be different if the attachment were made at the top or the bottom of the conductor.

Tried the experiment when the wire connected with the conductor was placed at *a* the bottom no magnetism was developed in the needle—but when the same wire was connected with the upper part of the conductor as at *b* a powerful developement took place showing a current upwards. Also when the discharging wire was removed a current was produced as in the exp above

The effect in the last experiment may be explained by considering that the induction down the wire when placed at the bottom tends to invert the current by induction in the vertical conductor

With the arrangement shown in the anexed figure no current was produced or at least I should say no developement of the magnetism took place. When however the circuit was opened and the discharging wire attached to the[2]

The weather to day is so unfavourable for electricity, that I have directed Sam to charge four of the Daniel batteries.

Placed around the room a strap of copper and over this at the distance of three feet a wire of three spires into which a set of magnetizing spirals was introduced but no effect was produced when a current was passed through the strap or ribbon from a Daniels battery of 4 elements. Hence the induction from galvanism in a short coil is much less intense than from the discharge of Leyden jar

---

[1] Henry meant Friday.
[2] He broke in mid-sentence.

"RECORD OF EXPERIMENTS"
Henry Papers, Smithsonian Archives

Monday Oct [9, 1843]

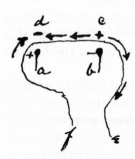

1 Repeated the experiments given at top of last page[1] found the result as shown in the diagram. *a* and *b* are two balls connected with the outside and inside of a jar. When the discharge is made <*a*> currents <*is*> are produced towards *d* from each direction and <*towards c*> from c in each direction. When the discharging wire connected with the earth is connected with the point *e* the current is downward but when it is connected with *f* it is also down[wa]rd[2] but this effect is due in all probability to the action on the part of the wire between *d* & *c* the sum of the actions tend to send the current in the direction of *c d*[3]

2 When the arrangement was made which is shown by the anexed figure the current was <*up ward*> downward <*and this was probably due to the action of the releving of the tension of the redundant electricity of the inside.*>[4]

---

[1] In the last entry, just before Henry conceded to the weather.

[2] A tear in the page.

[3] Probably a later addition, a marginal note here says, "This result cannot be obtained by the discharge of a jar but by two balls one + and the other minus."

[4] A marginal comment, added later, states, "See vol. 2. p. 282," which refers to the middle of the entry for June 6, 1842, starting "Made the arrangement shown in the figure...." Henry had concluded there that there were two currents of lateral discharge, a stronger one away from the jar, another towards it.

3 Next arranged the apparatus with the wire leading to the earth at top but contrary to my expectation the current as indicated by the needle was towards the earth. Tried this many times in succession with needles no 5, in all the spirals of the set the result always the same[5]

Thinking the effect was due to the return wave I used needles of a larger size no 1 and placed these in the least compound part of the set of spirals but the effect was the same the needle was still magnetized so as to exhibit a current downwards

After several attemps to discover the cause of the anomaly which was exhibited in the last experiment I found it due to the charging of the pane of glass which I interposed between the two balls to prevent the transfer. When this was removed and the balls seperated to the distance of two inches the needle in the spiral *b* indicated a current in an upward direction or in accordance with my previous hypothesis and also my previous experiments. The effect of the glass was to produce such an arrangmnt as was given in the experiment above the last on the <*opp*> last page.[6] The one side of the glass was charged + and the other (the one next the receiving ball of the induced current) was negative hen[ce] the result. In all the subsequent experiments the use of glass must be resorted to with a knowledge of the effect[7]

I was mistaken in the last result the glass being removed the needle still indicates a current down tows the ground and no arrangement I have yet been able to make will produce a contrary result

---

[5] Henry added a comment here, "This result is in accordance with the exp on top of page 61—the whole charge passes through the knob." The reference is to a later part of this entry, beginning "Arranged the apparatus. . . ."

[6] Experiment 3 above.

[7] This entire paragraph was marked by a left-margin brace and labelled "Error."

October 9, 1843

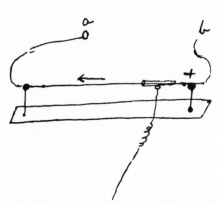

1 When the jar was removed and an insulated plate hled[8] over the ball the current was upward at the moment a spark was drawn from the dist. end of the machine. The effect cannot therefore be due to the redundant or free electricity for this would tend to produce a different result[9]

1 Arranged the apparatus as in the figure—placed the receiving ball near the plus end made the discharge. The needle indicated a current from the wire. The receiving ball was then moved—towards the negative end—the result was the same, the needle still indicated a current towards the earth or from the wire. The induction therefore through the whole wire appears to be due to an accumulation of the fluid in the wire and not to its being in a polar state the one end being + and the other minus and this is in accordance with the puzzling results I have obtained in the experiments of this morning.

2 Next attached a <*wire*> ball to the end of the wire *a* while the other end was placed in connection with the conductor of the machine. When a spark was drawn from the ball a current was produced in the discharging wire from the earth, or contrary to the direction of the current I have before obtained

3 Next connected the ball *a* with the earth and then threw sparks on *b*. The needle was now magnetized as if a <*spark*> shock had passed through

[8] A slip of the pen.

[9] Henry here later added a line, "NB The fact that a current is sent off in every direction from a wire transmitting a discharge will explain the induction produced in thunder storms," and a reference to the article on lightning striking the Cathedral of Strasbourg, for which see the "Record of Experiments," July 22, 1842, above.

the wire or in such a manner as to indicate a current from the wire to the earth

Experiment 2 was varied by connecting the end b with the machine and then drawing sparks from the same end the needle was magnetised by an ascending current

The results obtained in experiments 3 page 59[10] are in accordance with the facts here obtained. The jar is charged and the electricity as it passes out of the ball sends a current in the direction towards [. . .][11] much stronger than that produced by the transision of the ball from the plus state to the nutral. Or in other words the induction is due to the sudden passage through the ball of all the electricity of the jar which for a moment produces a greater effect than the discharge of the ball as in the case of exp 1 page 60[12] with the insulated plate

All the experiments would seam to indicate that the wire acts as though a quantity of additional electricity were added to it for a moment. Perhaps this may not be the case in a very long wire

In reflecting on the subject of the passage of electricity along the surface of a body I am led to conclude that it does not follow that a greater conducting power will be given to a conductor of metal by flattening it so as to increase the surface. The opposite sides which by this process are brought into more near approximation will cause a greater repulsion of the electricity and thus increase the resistance[13]

The tendancy to spread must be greater in a long than in a short conductor because the attraction for the negative surface <for> to which the discharge is tending will prevent a wide deviation from the direct path but this tendancy to spread will be greater in proportion to the length of the conductor.

 Faradays proposition relative to the equality of the amount of negative induced electricity and the positive is correct[14]— the negative ball will not be as strongly electrified but the difference will be made up by the induction on the screaning objects

---

[10] The first experiment 3 of this entry.

[11] Henry did not indicate the direction as he wrote here at the bottom of a notebook page, but started a new page by discussing the force.

[12] The second experiment marked 1 for this entry.

[13] In the margin, Henry wrote "See Snow Harris' paper," probably a reference to "On Some Elementary Laws of Electricity," *Phil.* *Trans.*, 1834, pp. 213–245, especially pp. 232–236, where Harris discussed the effect of shape on the distribution of static electric charges, and specifically contrasted round and flat bodies.

[14] See, for example, Faraday's answer to Hare's first letter, published in the *Phil. Mag.*, 1840, 3d ser. *17*:54–65.

"RECORD OF EXPERIMENTS"

Henry Papers, Smithsonian Archives

Tuesday Oct [10] 1843

The spreading of the electrical discharge from a prime conductor is shown in the experiment of passing the spark through a vacuum. The beams fill all the bulls eye receiver.[1] Try this experiment in the dark with the discharge from an insulated Leyden jar.

The experiments of Priestly on the lateral discharge are not indiscordance with the results I have obtained. A spark passed from the outside of the jar to a neighbouring conductor and back again without imparting but a very small charge to the conductor[2]

---

[1] A glass bulb drawn out at two ends, with embedded metal rods. The bulb can be evacuated and electricity discharged through it, producing electrical light. A sketch of the apparatus appears in Henry's laboratory notebook, in the entry for February 1, 1845, which we expect to print in the next volume of the *Henry Papers*.

[2] Joseph Priestley, *The History and Present State of Electricity*, 3d ed., 2 vols. (London, 1775), 2:336-342.

Priestley hypothesized that the lateral force was *not* due to the electrification of the surrounding bodies and their subsequent repulsion from the electrical fluid and similarly electrified bodies. Instead he attributed the action to the explosive displacement of air by the electrical spark as it passed through space. To support this claim, he stated that small insulated bodies were found to remain uncharged even though they were affected by the lateral discharge. An electrical explosion near a long insulated brass rod did not alter its electrical condition even momentarily, as shown by the small pith balls placed in contact with the rod (pp. 338-340; Henry annotated this last experiment in his copy of Priestley's book).

Henry's theory of the lateral discharge was not compatible with Priestley's, in that he supposed the force to arise from sparks of "free electricity." (*Henry Papers*, 3:53n.) But the amount of this electricity was minute in comparison with the primary discharge, so that Priestley may not have detected it, for Henry found only "a very small charge" imparted to his conductor.

"RECORD OF EXPERIMENTS"
Henry Papers, Smithsonian Archives

Wednesday Oct [11] 1843

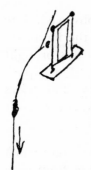

Charged a pane of glass coated with tin foil on the two faces with the idea that the direction of the induction with this apparatus might be different from that with the jar: but the result was the same the direction of the current as indicated by the magnetisation of the needle was constantly from the glass whether the receiving ball was in contact with the negative or positive side of the plate. The experiment was repeated many times in succession and always with the same result.

It appears that the induction is produced by the sudden transfer of the electricity from one side to the other of the glass and that the effect is felt through the glass the distance or rather difference of distance may be considered as nothing. When the discharge of the plate was produced by drawing off the electricity from the + side of the plate, the receiving ball being on the minus side, the needle was magnetized by an ascending current, as might have been expected.

That the suggestion I stated above is true is shown by the fact that when the jar was discharged slowly attaching to the discharging rod a needle so as to make the transfer by degrees the needle was magnetized in the opposite direction or so as to indicate an ascending current towards the *plus* side of the plate

Repeated the above experiment with the different side of the glass and found that in all cases when the discharge was made either rapid or slow the needle on the negative side was <elec> magnetized by a<n> descending current while that in connection with the plus side of the glass with a sudden discharge was downwards while with a slow discharge upwards

The discharge was upwards or towards the positive side of the glass even when a spark passed between the needle point and the tinfoil of the glass

I find it is not invariably the case that a slow discharge gives a current downwards from the *minus* side of the glass. Sometimes the result is different—but this may result from the spark drawn first by touching the side

The change of the direction in the above experiments depend principally on the extra spark being drawn from one or other side but all the experiments I have thus far made indicate that a sudden discharge of the glass plate sends a current from the plate from both sides to the ground

Made an experiment of the haphazard kind on the fringes produced by light. Sent charge from jar through two wires, which formed the apparatus of the two openings in diffraction but no effect could be observed. The

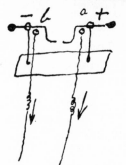

apparatus was formed by cementing a wire as in the figure on the surface of a pece of mica, and the two ends of this brought into contact with the opposite sides of a charged jar. The experiment must also be tried with galvanic electricity. The wires pass in opposite direction and may on this account vary the result since the induced currents may nuteralize each other.

Arrange the discharger as in the anexed figure first took the induction from *a* and then from *b* on each side of the break. The result however was the same the needle was magnetized by a desending current in each case. See Priestley on Lateral discharge[1]

Made an arrangement of wire similar to that represented in the figure—connected one end with the machine *a b*—parallel to this I placed a wire *e f* which was joined at its two ends at *g*. When the machine was turned so as to charge, *h i* and then the electricity drawn off at *a* a current was produced in *e f*. The needle in the spiral no 1 gave a current — those in no 2 & 3 gave a current +

Repeated the last experiment with needles in all <*the set of*> spirals of the set. That in no 1 gave a — current all the others gave + currents. In these two experiments needles no 5 were used

Tried the same experiment with larger needles no 2 the result however was the same the needle in no 1 gave a — current in the other spirals a +. It must be recollected that spiral no one is more complex than the others

[1] See the last entry.

Repeated the same experiment with the exception of drawing off the electricity from the end fartherst from the machine. Now the current as indicated by all the needles was adverse. The condition of the two exper[imen]ts was not precisely the same the whole descharge through the wire of all the electricity of the machine took place but this was not the case in the other case

"RECORD OF EXPERIMENTS"
Henry Papers, Smithsonian Archives

Thursday Oct [12] 1843
Shock passed through wire in water

The sky la[s]t night at 10 oclock was perfectly cloudless and yesterday was delightful. This morning a thick fog covers the face of the earth so as to obscure the sun and the phenomenon of *rain under* the trees is exhibited. I have directed an assistant to take the temperature of the air and also that of the trees by swing[ing] the thermometer first in the air and next placing it amid the leaves of the trees

Temperature of the air   58°
of the leaves   56½.

This was however at the time the air was rising in temperature and when the trees had almost ceased to rain[1]

 Placed a wire in a basin of water and sent shocks through it, while the finger was immersed in the water. A sudden concussion was fe[l]t by the finger as from a shock from the jar passed through it and this happened at each discharge

The effect was the same with a large wire also when the conducting wire was grasped by the hand a severe concussion was felt when the discharge passed through and this is not produced as has been supposed by the redundant electricity according to the explanation of Biot but by the transfer of the electricity of the jar and the consequent induction.[2] It was the

---

[1] Henry circled these meteorological observations in ink, and added in the margin: "Observation on Rain under trees during fog." See also the "Record of Experiments" for June 25, 1841, above.

[2] See *Henry Papers*, 3:53–54, "Record of Experiments," May 6, 1836. Biot thought that these types of shocks were due to free or "redundant" electricity, that amount in excess of the strictly balanced amounts of electricity in a charged capacitor. Henry accepted Biot's explanation for lateral discharge, per se, but gave a different cause—induction—for the shocks he felt in these experiments.

same action in all probability which produced the electrical phenomena within Mrs Hamiltons house at the time the discharge passed along the outside of the building (See vol 2nd page [. . .]) (See also the proceedings of the Amer Phil Society[3]

When the finger is placed in the water and the conductor interrupted quite a severe electrical concussion is felt and this is the case when the finger is placed at the end of the dish at *a*

According to the experiment of Wheatstone, the electrical action whatever may be its nature, arrives last at the middle of the length of the conducting wire. This is in accordance with the theory of one fluid; the moment a spark starts from the knob an equal quantity of the electricity of the end of the wire incontact with the outside of the jar is released and rushes into the jar so that a wave of rarefaction runs along the wire from the negative end <*in one direction*> towards the middle and one of condensation from the other. These waves pass each other at the middle and oscillate backwards and forwards several times[4]

The weather is unfavourable for experiments with the electrical machine and I have therefore directed Sam to put in operation four of the cups of the Daniell's battery

Attempted to get a current between two coils with the ends open but did not succed

Made some rough experiments on the heat produced in a conducting wire by the transmission of an electrical current the result however was not very satisfactory the time required for the long bell wire to arrive at its maximum temperature was much greater than I had supposed

I devised the following apparatus for the purpose of deter[min]ing the heat namely:

A copper wire is passed backward and forward over the face of a *pile* with a single row of elements and over this is placed a plate of polished

[3] Though no page number was given, Henry meant the entry for July 15, 1841, edited and published in the APS *Proceedings*, 1841–1843, 2:111–116.

[4] Charles Wheatstone, "An Account of Some Experiments to Measure the Velocity of Electricity and the Duration of Electric Light," *Phil. Trans.*, 1834, pp. 583–591, an article of some importance to Henry: he took extensive reading notes on it (portions are in the *Henry Papers*, 2:491–493), and had brought it up as recently as the March 14, 1841, "Record of Experiments" (above), and a June 24, 1842, note (Henry Papers, Smithsonian Archives).

Wheatstone used a stroboscopic apparatus to see that sparks jumped spark gaps near either end of a long conducting wire before jumping a gap in the middle of the wire. Henry reiterated here the point of his 1835 observations: though Wheatstone saw his experiment as support for the two-fluid theory, Henry considered it to be consistent with the existence of only one electrical fluid.

or gilded metal to reflect all extraneous heat. This apparatus is introduced into the circuit at different points and the effect noted

On this subject See Peltiers exp Annals de Chim vol [. . .][5]

[5] No volume given, but probably "Nouvelles expériences sur la caloricité des courants électriques," *Annales de chimie et de physique*, 1834, 2d ser. 56:371–386, the article in which the Peltier effect was announced.

Like the first paragraph of the entry, these last paragraphs—on the electrical production of heat—were circled in ink.

"RECORD OF EXPERIMENTS"
Henry Papers, Smithsonian Archives

Saturday Oct 14th 1843

Made an experiment to get electricity by a change of the molecular arrangement of a metallic wire. For this purposed I introduced into the circuit with a copper wire and the French galvanometer[1] a *thermo pair* so that the electricity might pass with more difficulty in one direction than the <an>other and thus a current be exhibited. But when the wire was stretched no effect was observed, although the wire became quite hot. Why should the streatching of a wire thus increase the temperature? The fact is in opposition to the general law that heat is absorbed when the density of a body is lessened. The wire when stretched occupies more space than before.[2]

Tried an experiment on the heat produced by streatching a pece of india-rubber. When the rubber was stretched it produced a great increase of temperature and when it was worked backward and forward there was a permanent increase of the heat. When a piece was broken and the fresh

[1] Probably the galvanometer associated with the Melloni apparatus. See above, Henry to Baird, December 28, 1841, and "Record of Experiments" entry, April 27, 1843.

[2] Henry supplied a note, "See Philosophic Magazine for year 1845," a reference probably to William Sullivan, "On Currents of Electricity Produced by the Vibration of Wires and Metallic Rods," *Phil. Mag.*, 1845, 3d ser. 27:261–264. Sullivan detected very small galvanometer readings in a circuit in which he set the wire vibrating, attributing the production of electrical force to molecular rearrangement. Vibrating an antimony bar in the circuit gave similar effects. His results were tentative, however.

William Kirby Sullivan (1820–1890) was born in Cork, educated in Dublin, taught at Catholic University, and was President of Queen's College, Cork. He was interested in technical and university education in Ireland. J. S. Crone, *A Concise Dictionary of Irish Biography* (New York, 1928).

formed surface applied to the thermo-pile an increase of heat was indicated[3]—(give this under the head of cappillarity)[4]

[3] Henry had observed an entropic effect. The greater regularity of the strands of rubber in their extended state, according to the laws of thermodynamics, implies an increase of temperature of the material. See, for example, Frederick T. Wall, *Chemical Thermodynamics: A Course of Study*, 2d ed. (San Francisco, 1965), pp. 311–325. These concepts, of course, were not worked out until well after Henry wrote.

[4] A marginal comment notes: "Molecular action." Henry's interest in this subject was the reason he classified these observations under capillarity. He subscribed to the theory of Young and Poisson that capillarity and surface tension were phenomena explained by the presence of powerful short-range forces between molecules which are at the free surface of a liquid. His intent in his 1844 communication to the American Philosophical Society was to show that these were of the same magnitude—and perhaps the same nature—as the forces holding together solids. The experiments in this entry bore on that last idea. Compare APS *Proceedings*, 1843–1847, 4:56–57, 84–85.

FROM ROBERT HARE
Henry Papers, Smithsonian Archives

Philad[a] Octr 14th 1843

My dear Sir

Will you do me the favour to inform me whether you consider your self as the author of any new Theory and if so to inform me in what page of our Transactions it has been stated. Not recollecting any & observing that D[r] Patterson alleges our transactions to be filled with your sagacious theories as well as observations[1] I wish to do you that justice in respect to the former which I have always striven to render you in respect to the latter. I am about to republish my treatises of galvanism[2] and electromagnetism[3] and should be glad to introduce any theretic views which may have emanated from you without my knowledge.

I remain
Your friend
truly
Rob[t] Hare

[1] A reference to Patterson's address to the centennial meeting of the American Philosophical Society, recently published in the APS *Proceedings*, 1843, 3:3–36. Patterson had referred to Henry's "series of contributions . . . filled with the most curious and interesting discoveries, and the most sagacious theories" (p. 33).

[2] *On the Origin and Progress of Galvanism,* or *Voltaic Electricity* (n.p., n.d. [post-1836 from internal evidence]). The revised edition of the treatise is entitled *Of Galvanism, or Voltaic Electricity* (n.p., n.d. [post-1844 from internal evidence]). There are copies of both publications in the Henry Library.

[3] In Hare's earlier version of the treatise *On Electromagnetism* (n.p., n.d. [post-1838]), Henry is mentioned (pp. 56–60) in connection

I wish you to say whether you approve at all of the suggestions respecting the existence of an imponderable plenum and that to its opposite polarization the two electricities may be due as stated in my letter to Faraday.[4] Also whether the Faradian currents are not more easy to account for by supposing a reaction such as I have suggested there agreeably to the Franklinian idea of electrical currents.

I wish to know whether you go with Ampere in supposing two fluids to revolve about the atoms of a magnet and in fact whether you lean to the doctrine of Franklin or that of Dufay.

Please to reply to the first part of this letter forthwith and to the postscript as soon as convenient.[5]

---

with his electromagnet and the discoveries announced in "Contributions II: Spiral Conductor" and "Contributions III: Electro-Dynamic Induction." In all cases, Hare discussed Henry's work in terms of "observations," implying an empirical approach.

The revised edition of the treatise, entitled *Electro-Magnetism* (n.p., n.d. [post-1844]), contains (pp. 111–115) a much more detailed account of the results presented in "Contributions III." However, Hare ignored the more theoretical aspects of Henry's work, especially "Contributions IV: Electro-Dynamic Induction," concluding his discussion of Henry with the words (p. 115): "It is not possible to do full justice to the speculations, experiments, and observations of Henry, in an elementary treatise: I therefore forbear to extend this account of them further."

Copies of both publications survive in the Henry Library.

[4] In the concluding paragraph of "A Letter to Prof. Faraday, on Certain Theoretical Opinions," *Silliman's Journal*, 1840, *38*:1–11 (reprinted in *Phil. Mag.*, 1840, 3d ser. *17*:44–65; and Faraday's *Experimental Researches in Electricity*, 3 vols. [New York, 1965], 2:251–261), Hare theorized that "an electric current may be constituted of an imponderable fluid in a state of polarization, the two electricities being the consequence of the position of the poles" (p. 11). He would expand upon this theory in his treatise *Of Galvanism*, explaining there that an electric current was "a succession of polarizing impulses" (p. 1), while rejecting both the two-fluid theory of electricity of Dufay and the single-fluid theory of Franklin.

Hare had presented his theory of an electric current in the context of an attack upon Faraday for apparent inconsistencies in Faraday's development of the concepts of polarity and

electric discharge in a vacuum, an attack Hare continued in his "Second Letter to Prof. Faraday," *Silliman's Journal*, 1841, *41*:1–14 (*Phil. Mag.*, 1841, 3d ser. *18*:465–477). As L. Pearce Williams has pointed out (*Michael Faraday: A Biography* [New York, 1965], pp. 306–311, 372–373), Hare's criticism assumed that Faraday had been using the terms "polarity," "force," and "vacuum" in their traditional senses, resulting in contradictory statements about charged particles. Confusion arose because Faraday neither used these terms in the traditional way nor fully or clearly articulated his new meanings for these concepts. Even in his immediate responses to Hare ("An Answer to Dr. Hare's Letter on Certain Theoretical Opinions," *Silliman's Journal*, 1840, *39*:108–120 [Faraday, *Experimental Researches*, 2:262–274], and "M. Faraday's Answer to Dr. Hare's Second Letter," *Silliman's Journal*, 1842, *42*:291), Faraday did not clarify his position, due in part to the poor state of his health.

Williams (*Faraday*, pp. 374–375, 506–507) has argued that Faraday's obfuscation served to dampen possible controversy. In rejecting electrical fluids in favor of a field theory, Faraday was challenging all electrical orthodoxy. Yet Hare was the first, and for some time the only, scientist to directly attack Faraday's theoretical construct. The rest of the scientific community had not yet recognized the radical nature of Faraday's thought. Not until 1843, with his health improving, did Faraday begin answering Hare's criticisms (in "On Static Electrical Inductive Action," *Phil. Mag.*, 1843, 3d ser. *22*:200–204). It would be a few more years before Faraday would unambiguously set forth his theoretical position.

[5] Henry's reply of October 18, 1843, is printed below.

I will put another query to you. You will no doubt remember that I informed you that a calorimotor consisting of only one pair and having from fifty to a hundred square feet of surface in each of its metals would not ignite a very fine wire at which you were much surprised and interested.

I wish to learn whether you can explain that fact consistently with Ohms formula and calculations whether also he is aware of it either from his mathematical reasoning or observations.[6]

I enclose a copy of my 1st letter to Faraday containing the theory alluded to in the last pages.[7]

[6] Hare is referring to a phenomenon he had noted in the earlier edition of his treatise on galvanism: the lack of a correlation between the size of the battery cells—and hence the quantity of current (amperage)—and the ability of a battery to ignite thin wires. Larger cells did not necessarily serve as better igniters. (*On the Origin and Progress of Galvanism,* pp. 9–10.) Having been assured by Henry in his reply (see below) that Ohm's Law did not offer an explanation, Hare inserted a theoretical discussion of his own in the revised edition of his treatise. He argued that there was a relationship between the ratio of the area of the battery cells and the diameter of the wire, and the efficiency of the production of an electric current by the cells. If the ratio were too large, then the production of the current would be very inefficient, and the battery would produce only a fraction of its potential power. (*Of Galvanism,* pp. 11–12.)

[7] This reprint has not survived in the Henry Library.

TO JAMES HENRY

Mary Henry Copy, Family Correspondence, Henry Papers,
Smithsonian Archives

Princeton Oct 16th 1843

The news of the arrival of the little stranger[1] at your house was received with much interest. It is certainly a very important event this being born. The beginning of a being which is to last as long as time. What is to be the destiny of the little woman is it weal or woe. Whatever it may be, we give her a hearty welcome into this breathing world and many wishes for her success in life and her happiness hereafter. I am almost inclined to join little John in the wish that *she* had been a *he.* The feminine predominates in our families and although there seems little danger of the blood running out in our line, there is not the same chance of the continuation of the name.

As usual at this time of year I am engaged with experiments and hope soon to add a new number to my researches.

[1] Agnes Henry (1843–1923) was born on September 27. Death certificate, New York State Department of Health, Albany.

"RECORD OF EXPERIMENTS"
Henry Papers, Smithsonian Archives

Monday Oct 16th 1843

I have thought of a plan by which the velocity of the galvanic current can be measured. For this purpose the wire should be wound <*and*> at intervals around a bundle of fine wire and over this a long wire to produce a secondary spark at the moment of breaking the primary current. The sparks might be inspected by means of the revolving mirror or by means of the revolving cylinder according to the plan I have proposed in my new method of determining the velocity of a projectile.[1] The plan of making a hole with the spark.

The experiment of Wheatston should be repeated and various partial conducting substances interposed, such as a tube of water—alcohol sulphuric acid &c. Also the intensity of the discharge as well as its quantity should be varied and the effects carefully noted.[2]

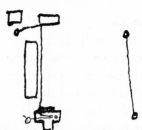

Arranged this afternoon a wire across the campus for transmitting a discharge of electricity from the Phil Hall to the well opposite our house and back through the ground <*from*> to Mr Clow's well at the end of the Phil Hall. The same wire had been stretched across the campus from the time of my lectures last winter[3] until the present but it was taken down to day and insulated at the windows of the Hall and library by placing a tube on a round stick and over this the wire, the stick was then fastened across the window.

Also another wire for receiving the induction was stretched across the campus from Mr Macleans well to Dr Carnahan's.[4] The circuit of each of these was tested by means of the galvanometer with a small single battery the negative element of which was formed of a silver thimble and the positive of a single point of zinc plate. At first with the wire near the old col-

---

[1] First set down in the entries of December 15 and 28, 1842, above, described in his talk at the American Philosophical Society centennial meeting, May 30, 1843, and published in the APS *Proceedings*, 1843, *3*:165–167.

[2] See the October 12 entry for the reference to Wheatstone's article. The experiment also provided a way of measuring the speed with which the electrical disturbance moved along the wire. Henry proposed varying the conditions of the experiment and seeing how this affected the speed.

[3] See the "Record of Experiments," Oc-

tober 6, 1842, above.

[4] In the illustration, the wire runs from Philosophical Hall, the T-shaped building at the bottom, adjacent to the "old college" (Nassau Hall), to the Library (top right), and then to the well in front of Henry's house (top left). On the right in the diagram, Maclean's well is indicated at bottom, Carnahan's at top. Compare the sketches in Henry to James Henry, February 9, 1833 (*Henry Papers*, 2:46), and "Record of Experiments," October 6, 1842, above.

lege, I found some difficulty in completing the circuit, there appeared a break somewhere and after considerable search, it was found at our house at a point where the wire passed behind the window shutter. When the circuit was completed the needle was violently agitated by the mere touching of the point of zinc to the surface of the acid. This result which is a repetition of what I obtained last Oct[5]—is still a matter of surprise. That <*the*> electricity of such feeble intensity should pass through such a distance of partially conducting matter could scarcely have been expected

[5] "Record of Experiments," October 6 through 8, 1842, above.

"RECORD OF EXPERIMENTS"
Henry Papers, Smithsonian Archives

Tuesday Oct 17th 1843
{ Induction at a distance
{ Long wires across the campus[1]
An opening was made in the same circuit and a basin of rain water was introduced the points of the wire being about 8 inches apart. It was thought that in as much as the current had passed through several hundred feet of water or moist earth that it would exhibit but little additional diminution but in this I was much mistaken the effect appeared to be reduced at least one half by the small addition to the resistance of the water. This result is curious and deserves further investigation[2]

The deflection of the needle of the same apparatus was considerably less when placed in the circuit between the wells of the President's and Vice President's houses.[3] From this it is probable that the two wells are not in aqueous connection[4]

The first experiment in induction with this arrangement was by sending

[1] Found at the tops of the next two pages in the original.

[2] Henry added the note, "In accordance with the law the earth offers little or no resistance Dec 1845." Henry may have been led to this comment, and to the one of footnote 4, by his contemporary work on the telegraph. See Henry to Harriet Henry, December 24, and John F. Frazer to Henry, December 29, 1845, Henry Papers, Smithsonian Archives, to appear in the next volume of the *Henry Papers*.

[3] Carnahan and Maclean.

[4] Another Henry note is inserted here: "Important result unless difference in the length of wire caused the difference in the effects. Dec 1845."

a current through the first circuit and magnetizing a needle in the second. The magnetizing spiral was placed near the President's well and was the same which I have used before both \<from> for induction from an arrangement of this kind and the electricity of the clouds. The needle was strongly magnetized by a current *adverse* to that of the battery current

Same experiment was several times repeated with the same result each discharge gave indications of an *adverse* current

Attached to the secondary circuit described yesterday one of the sets of spirals of different convolutions and also the compound spiral used yesterday.

The following was the result:[5]

1st *	With one jar highly charged				
Spirals	No a	No 1	No 2	No 3	No 4
Dynamic defle.	—22	—12½	—17	—5	—3

2nd	One jar				
Spirals	No a	No 1	No 2	No 3	No 4
Dynam defl	—20	—3	—15	—3	—1

3rd	One jar				
Spirals	No a	No 1	No 2	No 3	No 4
Deflec	—20	—10	—18	—3	—1

4th	One jar 2 sets of spirals (stronger charge loud snap				
Spirals 1st set	No A	No 1	No 2	No 3	No 4
Defl	—45	—45	—40	—20	—4
Spirals 2nd set	No A	No 1	No 2	No 3	No 4
Defl		—45	—38	—23	—2

* I have designated by no *a* the spiral used yesterday and also last Oct.[6]

---

[5] The dynamic deflection referred to below was the measurement of the magnetometer described in the "Record of Experiments" entry, October 9, 1841, and used extensively with different magnetizing spirals in May and June 1842.

Many of these readings are ambiguous with regard to direction: often they seem to have first been written with a plus, and then marked over with a minus sign, which we have kept, as these induced currents are said all to be opposite to the direction of the battery current.

[6] That is, in the experiments of October 7 and 8, 1842, above.

5th

spirals 1st set	No A	No 1	No 2	No 3	No 4
Def	—25	—12	—18	—4	—0

spirals 2nd set	No A	No 1	No 2	No 3	No 4
Defl		—17	—12	—3	—0

NB All the results give an induced current opposite to that of the battery

1st		2 jars			
Spirals	No A	No 1	No 2	No 3	No 4
Defl.	—20	—3	—7	—11	—0

2nd		2 jars			
Spirals	No A	No 1	No 2	No 3	No 4
Deflec.	—20	—20	—3	—12	—2

Suspended Large conductor
one spark

With this arrangement the needles came out unmagnetized—(Weather changed more damp)
Next used Dr Franklin's battery of 24 jars—charge 100 units
Air to damp for the jars without warming to retain the charge

TO ROBERT HARE

Hare Papers, Library, American Philosophical Society

Princeton Oct 18th 1843

My Dear Sir
Your favour[1] of the 14th was received yesterday and I now embrace almost the first leisure moment to answer the first part of it. The remainder of it I hope to discuss with you in person in the course of a week or two.

[1] Printed above.

Your question relative to the theories propounded in my papers at first sight appears something like sarcasm but as I have from a knowledge of your character no right to interpret it as such I will give it a candid answer. The term theory is often used to express a generalization in which we refer a number of particular facts to a law assumed as true.[2] It is used in this way when we speak of the theory of universal gravitation and in accordance with this acceptation of the term I may say that my papers *do* contain a number of theories. My communications are not a mere collection of facts without an attempt at classification or explanation; on the contrary in almost every section an attempt is made to refer the facts to some law of action.

In the last section of the 4th no I have given an explanation of all the phenomena I have descovered in galvanism; and have given the title to this section of *"theoretical considerations."* Also in my last series[3] on the induction of currents from a Leyden jar I have explained all the complex phenomena which have presented themselves in the course of my investigations and this explanation I should not hesitate to call the *theory of the phenomena.*[4] It is indeed but a partial theory or an expression for a limited generalization yet in the authorized use of the term I think Dr Patterson was right in saying that my papers contain theories. Whether they are entitled to the denomination of *profound* is not for me to decide.

I have not had time to bring my mind to the subject of your other questions but I will answer some of them on the spur of the moment

1. I do adhere to the theory of Franklin of one electrical fluid and I know of no well established fact that is better explained on the theory of two fluids,[5] either by ordinary logic or the more precise methods of mathematics.*

2. I have adopted the hypothesis of an electrical plenum believing that some of my late results cannot be explained without this hypothesis.[6] I am

---

* I do not say that this theory is absolutely true but that it is a true expression for all the facts of statical electricity.

---

[2] In his 1866 lectures to the Peabody Institute of Baltimore Henry provided a clearer definition. A theory was simply a hypothesis which proved comprehensive enough to embrace all known facts and phenomena and powerful enough to enable the investigator to deduce a vast array of new results. Henry's views were quite derivative; he especially utilized John Herschel. Arthur Molella et al., eds., *A Scientist in American Life: Lectures and Essays of Joseph Henry* (Washington, 1980), pp. 95–98; John F. W. Herschel, *A Preliminary Discourse on the Study of Natural Philosophy* (London, 1830), pp. 190–220.

[3] "Contributions V: Induction from Ordinary Electricity; Oscillatory Discharge."

[4] An uncertain reading. Henry may have written *"phenomenon."*

[5] Henry had been an advocate of Franklin's one-fluid theory of electricity since at least the mid-1830s, although rarely was he as emphatic and explicit as in this letter. *Henry Papers*, 2:492–493; Weiner, "Joseph Henry's Lectures," pp. 171–173.

[6] Note that Henry carefully classifies the existence of the plenum as a "hypothesis," while terming Franklin's concept of electricity a "theory." This differentiation is not merely

also inclined to think that this ethereal plenum is identical with that to which is attributed the phenomena of Light and heat—Heat and light being the results of vibrations while most of the electrical phenomena are produced by a condensation of the ether in some portions of space and a transfer of it in other cases.

I do not think that the interesting phenomenon which you mentioned to me some years ago relative to the heating of a small wire can be accounted for on the theory of Ohm. It deserves investigation.

Perhaps I may be at the next meeting of the society and if so I shall remain several days in the city and thus have an opportun[it]y of a long confabulation with you on our favourite subjects.[7] In the mean time permit me to assure you that I remain with much esteem yours truly

Joseph Henry

a matter of semantics, but a reflection of Henry's perception of real qualitative differences in the explanatory power and track record of the two concepts. Franklin's work had stood the test of time and experiment;

the plenum was still only a useful concept.

[7] Henry attended the meeting of November 3, 1843, but we have no evidence of an extended visit with Hare. APS *Proceedings*, 1843–1847, *4*:22–23.

"RECORD OF EXPERIMENTS"
Henry Papers, Smithsonian Archives

Wednesday Oct 18th 1843
{ Experiments on parallel
wires across the campus[1]

St[r]eatched two wires across the campes from Phil Hall to library. Return of one through the Wells of the President and Vise President, the other (the descharging wire) through the other two wells.

Wires at fi[r]st about 18 inches apart.

One jar

Spirals	No A	No 1	No 2	No 3	No 4
Defl	65	+33	+26	+6	0

Current in the direction of the discharge

[1] The descriptive heading is at the top of the second page of the notebook, below the first data table below.

1 Arrangement the same as before

One jar higher charge

Spirals	No A	No 1	No 2	No 3	No 4
Defl needles No 5	+50	+25	35	+37	+42

2

One jar
2 sets spirals

Spirals 1st set	No A	No 1	No 2	No 3	No 4
Defl	+60	−46	−55	−56	−52

Spirals 2nd set	No A	No 1	No 2	No 3	No 4
Defl		−45	−50	−50	−45

This result is due to a much stronger charge

3 Tried the same with larger needles in one and small in the other set

Spirals 1st	No A	No 1	No 2	No 3	No 4
Defl (needls 5)	+65	+58	+45	+ 28	−22

Spirals 2nd set	No A	No 1	No 2	No 3	No 4
Deflect (Large needles No 2)		+56	−0	+6	−18

This result is in perfect accordance with my previous results and anticipations

Wires at the distance of about 18 inches[2]

4

One jar

Spirals	No A	No 1	No 2	No 3	No 4
Def (needles No 5)	+35	+40	−32	−40	−38

Spirals	<No>				
Defl. *dar[n]ing need.*		+38	−33	−40	−40

This charge was very heavy
jar warm

[2] In the manuscript, this is a marginal comment next to the last three experiments.

One jar   small charge

spirals	No A	No 1	No 2	No 3	No 4
Small needles					
Defl No 5	+55	+47	+38	+33	+24
Defl Darni[n]g		+55	+38	+34	+18
needles					

One jar charged to 60° of electrometer

Spirals	No A	No 1	No 2	No 3	No 4
small needles 5	+55	+45	+44	+35	+32
darning needles		+50	+44	+42	+25

One jar charged to 60

Spirals	No A	No 1	No 2	No 3	No 4
Small needles no 7	+45	+40	+37	+28	+2
Darning needles		+58	+42	+40	+30

Pint jar

Spiral	No A	No 1	No 2	No 3	No 4
Small needles No 7	+45	+38	+33	+17	+0
Darning needles		+50	+42	+30	+2

Jar removed   Spark from the machine (number of sparks)

Spiral	No A	No 1	No 2	No 3	No 4
Smal needles No 7	+33	+25	+2	−2	−2
Darning needles	+45	+45	+22	−2	−0

Single spark (from mach[in]e)

Spiral	No A	No 1	No 2	No 3	No 4
Smal needles No 7	+31	+30	+30	0	0
Darning needles	<35>	35	+32	−2	0

Wires at same distance[3]

[3] This marginal comment is written sideways on the last page of the entry; it could refer to all experiments from number 4 to the end. Clearly Henry used the same distance, eighteen inches, in all experiments of this day.
    In the last five tables, Henry's description did not line up with his data. We have correctly aligned these for publication.

"RECORD OF EXPERIMENTS"

Henry Papers, Smithsonian Archives

Thursday Oct 19th 1843

When the two end of the long secondary conductor were grasped quite a smart shock was felt in each hand

I next tried the method of determining the direction of the current which was used by the Italian Philosopher Matteucci (see Annals de chimie 1841) which consits in piercing a hole in a thin piece of writing paper.[1] The perforation as it is well known will be nearer the negative point and hence the direction may be determined. The experiment was perfectly successful and gave a current in the adverse direction to that of the battery discharge

Made a galvanometer of about 300 turns well seperated by cement suspended a needle in the centre and connected this with the <coil> circuit at the same opening where the needles were placed yesterday. When the current was sent through the long conductor across the campus the needle was moved and indicated a current in an *adverse* direction to that of the battery current.

With three jars charged nearly to 90° the effect was the same except the needle was more moved. To be sure that the effect was due to the action of

[1] Carlo Matteucci, "Sur l'induction de la décharge de la batterie," *Archives de l'électricité*, 1841, *1*:136–144, reprinted in *Annales de chimie et de physique*, 1842, 3d ser. *4*:153–164, and translated in Sturgeon's *Annals of Electricity, Magnetism, and Chemistry*, 1842, *9*:28–33. Henry is mentioned in the article, and an annotated copy (the *Archives* version) is in the Henry Library. Matteucci found that if he pasted two pewter points to a piece of paper, two millimeters apart, one point above the paper and one below, and then passed a spark between the points, a perforation always appeared at the negative point. A second characteristic which frequently appeared was a black stain near the positive point. See Sturgeon's version of the paper, pp. 31–32, or p. 141 of the *Archives* version, where Henry marked the passage which detailed Matteucci's process, especially the comment, "L'appareil est très-simple, très-sensible, et constant dans ses résultats." Matteucci alluded to this method, without giving details, in "On Secondary Currents," Sturgeon's *Annals*, 1841, *7*:374–376, a translation of a *Comptes rendus* article, "Sur les courants secondaires," 1841, *12*:342–344.

Henry's results of this and succeeding days' experiments were presented and discussed at the November 3, 1843, meeting of the American Philosophical Society. (See their *Proceedings*, 1843–1847, *4*:23.) He alluded there to difficulties that the Matteucci paper gave to his results in "Contributions V: Induction from Ordinary Electricity; Oscillatory Discharge." Matteucci claimed that the galvanometer showed a steadily increasing deflection in measurements of the secondary current for higher charged batteries and closer placed circuits. He claimed to support this conclusion—especially on the constancy of direction of the secondary current—with his pierced card experiments. Henry had found that this direction alternated with the oscillating discharge of the Leyden jar. He devoted the experiments of October 19 to trying out Matteucci's method, and then investigated and confirmed the results of "Contributions V" by using a galvanometer as testing device, rather than needles; these trials extended to the twentieth. For several days thereafter, he experimented with Matteucci's method, varying the distance between the points, and the thickness and orientation of the paper, to show that these affected the results. In his presentation to the APS, he affirmed that his conclusions in "Contributions V" were still valid.

the current the direction of the current as regards the electrometer was changed or in other words the current was sent through the galvanometer in an opposite direction but it still indicated a current *adverse* to that of the battery discharge

Made today an apparatus for getting the perforation in a paper more conveniently. *a* & *b* are two glass tubes supporting two corks through which a needles are passed. By s[h]oving the needles more or less through the corks and by elevating one of them the adjustment can be readily made

Also prepared two webs of wire <*for*> to serve as coiles. With these and others like them I intend to repeat the experiments on successive induction from the Leyden jar

"RECORD OF EXPERIMENTS"
Henry Papers, Smithsonian Archives

Friday Oct 20th 1843
{ Repetition of Matteucci's
{ Exp with galvanometer

Repeated the experiment of Matteucci in reference to obtaining the current by means of a galvanometer. Found the result the same as given in his paper.[1] Repeated this exp with the same result

Three jars were used tolerably highly charged

When the experiment was first tried and the jars highly charged a spark quite loud was heard in the galvanometer.

With a single jar the discharge gave a current sometimes in one direction and sometimes in the other

When *three* jars were so charged that they did not produce a snap in the galvanometer the needle remained unaffected. But when the charge was about 60 of the galvanometer then a snap was heard in the galvanometer

[1] Matteucci's "Sur l'induction de la décharge de la batterie" (see the note of the preceding entry).

and the needle was very sensibly move[d] several degrees by a current in the *direction* of the *primary*

When the direction of the discharge was changed in reference to the conductors the result was still the same

When the snap did not appear in the galvanometer then the needle was affected with a mere tremulous motion.

One Small jar charged with 10^{sp} of the unit jar[2] the needle moved 3 or 4 degrees current *direct. Snap in galvanometer*

3 Jars charged with 10 sp of the unit jar no spark—*direct* 4°

3 Jars charge 20^{sp}—no spark; *Adverse*
3 Jars charge 15 — no spark *direct*
3 Jars charge 25   "   "   No motion
3 Jars charge 30   a spark   Direct 5° *

3 Jars charge of unit jar						
"	"	"		5	no spark in galvanometer	*no effect*
"	"	"	"	10	"	*Direct*
"	"	"	"	15	"	Adverse
"	"	"		20	"	Adverse
"	"	"	"	25	spark	Adverse
				30	Loud Spark	*Direct*

3 Jars charge of unit jar							
"	"	"	"	"	5	No snap in galvanometer	o
"	"	"	"	"	10		o
"	"	"	"	"	15	Do	Direct strong
"	"	"	"	"	20	Do	*Adverse*
"	"	"	"	"	25	Do	*Adverse*
"	"	"	"	"	30	Snap	Adverse strong
"	"	"	"	"	35	Snap <*(strong)*>	Adverse
"	"	"	"	"	40	Strong snap	Direct strong
"	"	"	"	"	45	Loud spark	Direct feeble
"	"	"	"	"	50	" Do	Adverse feeble[3]

* NB In this series the shock might have and probably did cut across in some cases either wholy or in part

[2] That is, ten sparks of the unit jar.
[3] A Henry note, "See bottom of page 91," referred forward to the later experiments of October 25, beginning "Matteucci's experiments with the galvanometer...."

From the above series of results it is evident that the changes in the direction of the galvanometer are as great as with the magnetization of steel needle and hence the result obtained by Matteucci the Italian are not to be considered as absolutely[4]

All these results are in conformity with the supposition that the induced current is not a simple disturbance of the electricity of the wire in a single direction, but that it consists[5]

The secondary current may be represented by a curve in reference to its axis thus:[6]

The beginning induction of the discharge of the jar will give an intense current which will be of very short duration—the ending of the jar current will give a wave in the + direction but since the ending takes place more gradually the than the begin[nin]g the wave will not be so intense. Again the rebound of the jar current will produce another wave adverse to itself and hence in the + direction and the stoppage of this another in the same direction with itself and hence adverse to the primary wave and there[fore] minus. This is represented by *d* the others by *c b* and *a*. The next rebound will produc[e] an other which will again be on the same side with the first induced current and so on

The fact that more than one hole is pierced in a card is mentioned by Mr Etrick, Annales of Electricity, Vol 2, p 39[7]

---

[4] A break in mid-sentence.

[5] Again, Henry did not complete his thought.

[6] Compare the curves in the entry of May 10, 1842, above.

[7] W. Ettrick, "On the Two Electricities, and Professor Wheatstone's Determination of the Velocity of Electric Light," Sturgeon's *Annals of Electricity, Magnetism, and Chemistry*, 1838, 2:39–49. The paper was read to the 1837 British Association meeting at Liverpool, but not published in its *Report*. Henry most likely heard Ettrick present the paper, as he was in attendance.

This sentence is at the bottom of the notebook page, separated from the rest of the text by a large space.

October 21, 1843

TO WILLIAM B. KINNEY

Kinney Family Papers, New Jersey Historical Society

Princeton Oct 21st 1843

My Dear Sir

I know from past experience in my own case that you are ever ready to sound the praises of your friends and I therefore write this morning to request that you will not republish the article relative to the American Phil. Society which appeared in the Princeton Whig of yesterday. Or at least that you will omit that part of it which relates to myself. I was it is true much gratified with the compliment given me by Dr. Patterson on such an occasion but there were several other names mentioned with commendation as well as my own, and it is not in accordance with my feelings that I should be thus singled out by a partial extract made by a writer in the *Princeton* paper.[1]

Perhaps some may think I am rather fastidious in such matters but I think it best to err if at all on the safe side.

Give my kind regards to Thomas[2] and accept for yourself the assurance that I am with much Respect

& Esteem Your's
Truely,
Joseph Henry

[1] Although the October 20 issue of the *Princeton Whig* is apparently no longer extant, a clipping in the front of Frederick S. Giger's notebook on natural philosophy in the Princeton University Archives seems to be the article Henry refers to. The writer announces the recent publication of the APS *Proceedings* of the hundredth anniversary and notes, "we are pleased to see the names of some of our fellow-townsmen bearing an important part." After mentioning communications by Captain Thomas Lavender and Stephen Alexander, the writer quotes Robert M. Patterson's laudatory mention of Henry's work in electricity and magnetism which Henry had found somewhat embarrassing at the time (see his letter to Harriet of May 27, 1843, above). The Princeton writer failed to note that Patterson also praised the achievements of other members in astronomy and those of Bache in terrestrial magnetism. APS *Proceedings*, 1843, *3*:33.

We could not find any notice of the APS *Proceedings* in the *Newark Daily Advertiser*.

[2] Kinney's son, for whom see above, William Burnet to Thomas T. Kinney, February 3, 1841.

"RECORD OF EXPERIMENTS"
Henry Papers, Smithsonian Archives

Monday Oct 23rd 1843
{ Exper. on the holes pierced
{ in cards by the secondary current[1]

Commenced this morning the Repetition of Matteucci's experiments to determ the direction of the induced current by means of the pierced card.

The points were placed ¼ of an inch apart, with one *jar* charge 60 <*three*> two small hol[e]s near the — *minus* point current adverse.

Charge 80 *three* holes nearer the minus pole. The larger hole was ragged—one jar distance same

Charge 90. Distance same *three* holes neare the minus side. When these holes are exami[n]ed with a magnifying class the larger appears ragged and triangular

All things remaining about the same with the same charge a large irregular hole was formed neare the — minus end

Small cha[r]ge elect 30° hole near the minus side

Distance ½ an inch single hole near the *minus* pole

At this distance a brilliant spark appared between the points of the needle. When the points were removed to a greater distance so that the spark could not pass a singular hollow sound was produced as if the discha[r]ge from the battery met with an interruption.

Distance rather more than ½ an inch one hole of a ragged appearance near the minus pole.

NB all the larger holes appear double and sometimes triangular.

In repeating the forgoing experiments the position of the points must be attended to. If they have relative to the paper the position shown in the figure—the whole is made at *a* opposite the negative point but neare[r] the + point

When the paper occupies the position shown in the figure the hole is mid way between the two points

---

[1] Variants of this heading, none as complete as this, occur on the succeeding pages of this long entry. Near the end of the entry, Henry switched from secondary to primary current, and duly noted this.

M Matteucci says that if the two points are farther seperated than from 3 to 6 millimetres or from about an 8ᵗʰ to the *quarter* of an inch the hole is no longer found at the negative end but near the middle as if we had made the experiment in rarefied air. The result obtained by the Italian was probably due to the position of the paper

Repeated the last experiment with the same result the hole was mid way

Repeated the exp with the paper touching the needle-points on the two sides hole single but ragged on the *minus side*

In these experiments the paper was placed thus

Dist *one* eight 3 holes near the minus end

Distance the same 4 holes were made one and the largest directly at the point two below the point and one mid way between Elect 70°.

Distance same charge 30° one ragged hole near *minus* point

Distance 1/20 of an inch charge high 70° ragged hole in the middle

Distance 1/20 of an inch charge feeble 30 <*three*> one large hole<*s*> largest near the + pole

Distance same small charge one hole neare plus point

Distance same 1/20 charge 20° *three* fine hole near negative pole

| | " | " | " | charge 30 *one* hole mid way |

| | " | " | " | charge 20° one fine hole mid way |

| | " | " | " | " | 30 3 holes as per fig. |

| | " | " | " | " | 40 2 holes |

| | " | " | " | " | |

| | " | " | " | " | 60 single ragged hole |

| | " | " | " | " | |

	"	"	"	"	65 large triangular hole near the middle inclined to one side
	"	"	"	"	<60> 70 two small holes

One jar used in all these experiments

Experiments continued with 3 jars instead of *one*

Dist 1/20 of an inch   Charge 10°   two large holes at — point

	"	"	"	20°	thre holes near + pole
	"	"	"	25	three holes as in figure
	"	"	"	30	two holes " " "
	"	"	"	40	4 holes " " "
	"	"	"	60	one large irregular hole near the negative pole
	"	"	"	4°	one hole
	"	"	"	5°	one hole mid way
	"	"	"	6°	two holes

Exp continued with 3 jars   Distance 8/40th = 1/5

	Charge	10°	3 holes as in the figure
		11°	2 holes as in figure
		20	one large irregular hole at the — p[ole]
	<25>	30	one small hole as in fig.
		35	one large irregular hole as in fig.
		40	single hole at negative pole
		50	three holes near negative pole
		60	one large hole near the middle

426

⁓ ⁓ Charge with 3 jars   Distance 17/40th of an inch
 Charge

− •− 10° One hole large near minus pole

− •− 20° Do do   Do   do

− :− 30° Two small holes near — pole

⁓ • − 40° One hole middle little neare[r] —

− ⸴− 50° Two holes at minus pole

⌐ •− 60° One hole at the minus pole

− ⸝− 60° One large 2 small holes at minus pole

− ⁓ In all the last experiments with the 3 jars except one the hole has
⸱ — been nearer the *minus* pole
  In making the foregoing experiments I observed that when the wire of
the secondary current came in contact with my leg at the time of the discharge a spark was given off which produced a prickling sensation. With
this an electrometer might be charged

 Experiments with the Franklin battery
  Charge 20 snaps of unit jar no perforation at the distance of 4/40 = 1/10
of an inch

⸴ᵎ ⸗	40 snaps		one hole near plus side
⸴ • ⸗	50 snaps	elect 4	Double hole in the middle
⸩− ⸲⸱ ⁓⁓	60 snps	" 10	one large hole two small neare[r] +
⸩− • ⁓⸜	70 "	" 14	one hole middle
⸩ ⸰⸲⸲⸱⸱⁻⸜		20°	Four holes from point to point
⸩⁻ᵒ ⸗		25	Large hole near plus

  Distance 1/5 of an inch   Frank[lin] battery

⸱ •− Electrometer

⁓ •⸜ 10° One hole near minus

⸝ •⸳⸜ 20° Three holes neare the minus

⸝ ⸳⸶⸜ 30 One large hole two small near minus

⸝ ⸫⸜ 40° one large hole at minus

All these results give holes near the minus pole

427

Experiments with primary current[2]

Passed spark from the machine through paper between two needle points the perforation was very minute and directly opposite the *minus* point

— ··•— Sent charge of one jar elect 90 through paper perforation near <*the middle and*> at one *minus*. Two holes very fine compaired with those of the secondary discharge— the paper was different

— •—— Repeated the same with other paper. One hole & larger near the minus pole

— •—— Same distance in all these experiments ⅜ of an inch. One hole near minus side

—⁺ •— Distance increased one hole at minus ⅝ of an inch
 ⁻

One jar charged each time to 90°

— ·——
—— ·•— Distance diminished to ⅛th of an inch 2 holes *minus*

➔· ·· ◄— Distan 1/10th of an inch
This gave a very beautiful result four perforations each smaller than the other. The largest near or at the minus end the nex at the middle the third a little farther on, and the third[3] at the plus end

—ƒ ·— Distance 1/15 of an inch   2 holes at plus   one at minus holes at plus ragged as if by several discharges

——— ·•— Distance 1/10th of an inch two holes one near the minus end the other near the middle

One jar charged to 90°

In all these experiments with the primary current the perforation was no larger than with the secondary current

Exp with smaller charge points about 1/15th One jar charged to

— •— 30° One fine hole at minus end

—— ·•— 30 Two holes 1 near minus

—· •· → 20 Two holes together near the middle

— ·•— 20 Near the minus one hole

---

[2] Perhaps added later, this phrase was in-tended as a heading.   [3] The fourth is meant.

"RECORD OF EXPERIMENTS"
Henry Papers, Smithsonian Archives

Tuesday Oct 24th 1843
{ Experiments with the pierced card
{ Primary current

Sent shock from single jar through a thick card on the class apparatus with blunt points which were about ¾ of an inch apart *three* holes were made about one third way from the minus pole as in the figure

The points were next removed to the distance of an inch one hole at the minus pole

Repeated the same one hole at minus pole distance of points ½ an inch

In these exps the jar was charged to 90° but it was cold.

    one jar Thick paper[1]

Repeated same one hole at minus

Do   "   "   " "   "

Do   "   "   " "   "

Do with elect at 40° points near 2 holes

Repeated same in all respects one hole at minus

Points ¼ of an inch apart One jar. Thick paper
Charge of elect

20°	— ←	one hole at minus pole
25	— •—	Do do near do
40	— ••— <two>	Do do do do do
50	◡ ••—	two do do do do
60	— :—	one do do d do
70	—• —	one do at the plus pole
80	— ◡—	one do at " minus pol
90	— ←	one do " " " "

[1] Here and in two succeeding tables of results, Henry wrote "Thick paper" sideways in the right margin; a fourth set of experiments was similarly labelled "Thin paper," a fifth in the left margin with "Fine needle points." In all these cases we have placed the comment at the heads of the tables.

Points one inch apart *one jar*
Charge elect

20			did not pass
40	+	+	do „ „
50	–	•—	one hole near minus pole
60	–	•—	„ „ „ „ „ little farther from pole
70	–	•—	„ „ „ „ „
80	–	•—	one hole at minus pole
85	–	·ᵢ—	four holes near each other and the *minus* pole
90	–	·· ·:·—	six holes as in the figure
	+	—	

Points same distance 3 jars. Thick paper
Charge elect

40	–	•—	one hole near the minus pole
50	–	•—	„ „ „ „ „ „
60	–	•.—	two holes near minus pole
70	–	.•—	two holes „ „ „
80	–	⌇—	„ „ „ „ „
	━	—	80 was about as high as I could charge three jars.
	━	—	
	━	—	

Repeated the experiment with one jar and distance one inch with thin paper the following is the result
charge by elect.   Thin paper

50	–	—	one hole at minus point
60	–	•—	one hole near „ „
70	–	—	one hole at „ „
80	–	⸴ —	two holes nearer „ „
85	–	•—	one hole near „ „
90	–	⸴ ᴵᴵ—	two large holes and several small ones

The general result of this set of experiments is the same as that of the thick paper on the last page

Next made a series of experiments with fine sewing needle points. *One jar*

First the distance apart is one inch, perhaps a little more

The charge was from 40 to 90 with the same result the perforations were all at the minus pole and single with one exception—the hole with the charge of 80 was double but near the *minus* pole

Next the points were ¼ of an inch apart

Charge by the electrom[eter] Fine needle points

20	▬ ▬	one hole near minus pole
40	▬ ▬	three " " " "
50	▬ ▬	one " " " "
60	▬ ▬	" " " " "
70	▬ ▬	thre holes one in the middle two near minus pole
80	▬ ▬	two holes near minus pole on[e] very small
85	▬ ▬	one " " " "
75	▬ ▬	five holes across the whole space

When several holes were thus made it appeared that the discharge took place in *parts* and not in a single discharge[2]

Made a series of experiments on the suggestion from the remark at the bottom of the last page[3] with the spark from the prime conductor. The holes were generally single and always at the minus pole although the sparks were double and treble. The fact that a hole previously existed did not interfere with a new hole since when a hole was perforated at the *plus* pole an other was made at the *minus* as if the first did not exist

---

[2] Henry later noted: "For other exp on this point see page 129," a reference to the "Record of Experiments" entry for January 3, 1845, to be published in the next volume of the *Henry Papers*.

Henry observed there that "when the paper was placed obliquely between the points . . . it was pierced with several small holes and one larger, but when the paper was placed directly at right angles to the line joining the points, but one large hole was made."

[3] The sentence immediately above.

"RECORD OF EXPERIMENTS"
Henry Papers, Smithsonian Archives

Wednesday Oct 25th 1843
{ Exp with pierced card
{ Primary current

To test the last experiments result still the jar was so arranged with a conductor with a rounded end as to discharge itself when the intensity arose to a given height. The results however with this were about the same as with the other arrangement. The paper was pierced sometimes with a single hole sometimes with two and more

When the interval at *a* was ¾ of an inch and the points ¾ also the perforation was at the negative pole and single but when the points were brought within 1/5 of an inch all the perforations were double and some of them [...][1]

Repeated last exp. distances same—found *three holes* produced twice and one large hole once all near the negative end

From these results it does not appear that the repeated discharges which I suspected might have some influence in producing the holes [h]as much effect

The weather is not very favourable for elect exp to day the wind is now southerly

Repeated the exp with pierced card and the secondary current with the self discharging apparatus described on the last page.[2]

[?Stuck pair] needl points 1/10 of an inch apart distance of ⅜ of an inch. Results as follows

7 holes perforated at the *minus* pole and single
2 singles near the middle
4 double holes 2 near the *plus* pole 2 with one at each pole

Dist 14/40 = 7/20 of an inch the balls
The points 3/40 = 1/13 of an inch
1 one hole near the negative
2 two holes one at negative small one near middle
3 Three holes near middle nearer plus pole
4 Two holes on a line mid way
5 Two holes „ „ „ „ „
6 one hole at negative pole

---

[1] A hole in the paper.
[2] This entry, immediately above. These words started a new notebook page, headed with "Pierced card with 2nd current," indicating Henry's switch from primary to secondary current experiments.

These results are similar to those obtained Monday 23 inst

NB I observed a fact of some importance in these experiments that although the spark did not pass through a hole which was pierced near the card at the plus pole, yet it passed a considerable distance out of its course to go through a hole near the minus end. Thus + & — representing the points and *a*   the hole the discharge passed through *a* rather than perforate   a new hole—this shows the influence of the perforation of one current in determ[in]ing that of the other.

In[3] one of the last experiments when from the sound of the discharge it appeared evident that the electricity cut across from one part of the primary conductor to the other the perforation was in the middle and not at the negative end.

Made an arrangement for the current of the *third* order—when the two ends of the conductor of the third order were placed near each other a spark was produced ¼ of an inch long with the mere snaps of the machine and without the jar

The perforations in the paper placed at *a* were on the negative side occasionally three very fine holes were made near the same pole but this was by a sucession of sparks.

Placed the apparatus of the pierced card in the circuit of the Secondary current and then threw sparks on the conductor without the jar. The points were 1/20 of an inch apart. The perforation was generally near the negative side but sometimes and often near the middle inclining to the negative side.

The spark appeared on one case to be double but in general but one hole was perforated by a single spark

Matteucci's experiments with the galvanometer were made with the battery.[4] To make parallel exps the Franklin battery was charged as follows Charge per elect.

10° Secondary current per galvanometer Adverse —

12°	"	"	"	"	direct +
20°	"	"	"	"	*direct* +
30°	"	"	"	"	*Adverse* —
40°	"	"	"	"	direct +

With the last a loud snap

---

[3] Two new headings here read, "Tertiary current. Secondary current with galvanometer."

[4] See above, "Record of Experiments," October 20, 1843.

The motion of the galvanometer in these experiments was as if it were acted upon by more than one current

Charged the battery to 30° current *Direct*

Made various attemps this afternoon to get a reversal of the poles of a needle by the direct discharge but did not succeed.[5]

First sent charge from Franklin battery through copper bell wire about 18 inches long. Needles placed at different altitudes above, from contact to one inch all magnetized +. The needles were small no 9.

 Next wrapped long piece of thin wire around a block of bees' wax, placed needle transverse sent through charge from single jar needle always magnetized +

The needles in the case of a single jar highly charged were more highly magnetized than with the battery in the experiment with a straight wire

[5] Henry marked his switch in experimental topics with a new heading: "Magnetism of Needles by the primary current."

"RECORD OF EXPERIMENTS"
Henry Papers, Smithsonian Archives

Thursday Oct 26th 1843
{ Magnetization of Needles by the
{ primary current

Needles no 12.[1] Repeated the last exp with the battery charged to 60°. The needles were all magnetized *plus* except the one nearest the wires which was about one tenth of an inch distance this was magnetized scarcely at all

Repeated same battery charge 45°

Needles No 12		
Needles	distance from wire	Deflect
1	1/10 of an inch	0
2	.2	0
3	.3	—0
4	.4	+5°
5	.5	+15
6	.6	+19°
7	1.0	+17°

[1] Originally written in the left margin sideways next to this paragraph. Throughout this entry, such marginal comments—referring to needle size and temper and to beeswax coils— have been incorporated into the text.

From the last experiment it is evident that the feeble magnetism of the needles as given vol 2 p. 271 272 &c[2] is not due to the action of the wire being confined to the middle of the needle since in this case it is under the whole length and yet the needle is not at all magnetized or in the adverse direction

Same coil around beas wax used in this exp.

Needles	Repeated Battery charge 60° Needles No 12[3] distance	Deflect
1	.1 of an inch	o
2	.2	o
3	.3	o
4	.4	+2°
5	.5	+15°

NB In these experiments care was taken to place the needles at right angles to the magnetic meridian so that no influence from the earth might affect the result

Needles	Needles with temper drawn to bluness Battery 60° needles No 12 temper blue distance	Deflect
1	.1½ᵗʰ of an inch	o
2	.3	o
3	.4½	+13°
4	.6	+18°
5	.7½	+18°
6	.9	+19°

The softness of the needle gives it a more intense magnetism

Made some very small needles from the hair spring of a watch arranged three of these above each other at the distance of ⅛ of an inch

Needles	distance	Deflect	Small compass
1	⅛	+5°	
2	¼	0°	
3	⅜	−1°	

[2] The last part of the entry of May 31, and the first part of June 1, 1842, above.
[3] Beside this table and every succeeding one of this entry but the next, Henry placed an asterisk.

In the last experiment the result was a little doubtful because the needles were slightly magnetic by cutting of the length from the spool of steel wire

Repeated the same great care being taken to demagnetize the needles— the result was as follows

Wire coiled around beas wax   Battery 45°

wire needles

Needles	distance	deflect
1	⅛ of an inch	0
2	¼ "	—5
3	½	+slightly

Small compass

Battery 45°

Needles No 11 over coil around beas wax

Needles	distance	Defl.	
1	1/7 of an inch	—2	*Minus*
2	2/7	+0	
3	3/7	+17	
4	4/7	+19	
5	5/7	+½ 23	
6	6/7	+22½	
7	7/7	+22	
8	8/7	+20	
9	9/7	+17½	
10	10/7	+17	
11	11/7	+14	

Larger compass

Battery 45

Needles No 11

Needles	distance	Defl	
1	⅛	—½	*Minus*
2	¼	+3	
3	⅜	+14	
4	½	+20	

Battery 48°

Needles	dist	Defl	
	Needles No 11		
1	⅛	0	
2	¼	−½	Minus
3	⅜	+20	
4	⅝	+22	
5	⅚	+25	
6	1⅛	+24	

Large globe placed on the end of the wire or rather I should say introduced into the circuit on the side next the positive pole

It is evident from the foregoing experiments on the magnetization of needles that by increasing the number of wires the change of polarity may be produced in <smaller> Larger needles. And this result is what I expected in making the arrangement

In this arrangement however the diminution of force and change of direction is probably influenced by the currents in the spires on the under side of the bea's-wax

Evening 8 o'clock. I made some experiments to night on the electrical light. The discharge through a vacuum is continuous ◄══► and larger in the middle but when small sparks were pass beams of electricity diverged in all derections towards the glass and particularly when the hand was brought near and this is undoubtedly owing to the lateral induction of the hand. When a negative conductor is placed at a little distance from a positive one the induction is principally directed to the negative but all the distant objects around allso receve the induction so that the sum of the negative and the positive electricities <are> is the same[4]

The negative conductor has however less negative electricity than is equal to the positive in the other on account of the distance but the remainder is made up by the induction of the other bodies in the room around but at a distance. The two electric[itie]s must be equal for the same reason that the attraction of gravitation may be said to be the same at all distances when we consider the increasing spherecal surface which surrounds the attracting body[5]

---

[4] See the last paragraph of the "Record of Experiments," October 9, 1843, above.
[5] A marginal note directs the reader to the beginning of the entry for February 1, 1845, to be printed in the next volume of the *Henry Papers*.

437

When the two bodies are near to each other they act on the distant bodies as one and tend to neutralize each other. From this consideration we may perhaps get a more intimate acquaintance with the phenomenon which is exhibited by electri[c]al light in a vacuum

I noticed one fact which I have not seen described *viz* spots of light in the beams of electricity as they were given off from the upper ball they were about a fourth of the distance (6 inches) downwards

I also passed the secondary spark through the vacuum and observed that it produced the same coloured appearance as the ordinary spark

The experiments I have made this evening have a bearing on the spread of electricity in passing along a wire. See page 54.[6]

[6] The part starting "Made a series of experiments . . ." from the October 3, 1843, entry, above.

"RECORD OF EXPERIMENTS"
Henry Papers, Smithsonian Archives

Saturday Oct 28th 1843[1]

We cannot explain all the phenomena of electricity I think without admitting the existance of a plenum of an etherial medium the atoms of which repel each other and are possessed by inertia.[2] When a Leyden jar is grasped by the hand and a spark from a long conductor is [?thrown] on it the induction takes place with such intensity as to give a very unpleasant shock to the hand. When the out side of the jar is connected with an insulated ball the jar being also insulated at the moment the jar receives a spark the electricity is propelled from the outside of the jar to the connected insulated ball and immediately afterwars a return wave is produced which may be exhibited by the effect produced on the needles of the two sets of spirals. The equilibrium in this experiment is evidently produced by a series of

[1] Immediately preceding the beginning of this entry, Henry noted: "Friday rain weather unfavourable for elect exp."

[2] Compare Henry's remarks to the American Philosophical Society, November 6, 1846, on the constitution of matter, APS *Proceedings*, 1843–1847, 4:287–290, where the necessary properties of ordinary and electrical matter are given as passive inertia and active forces. See also his earlier speculations on the existence of the plenum, "Record of Experiments," May 8, 1838, *Henry Papers*, 4:47–48, "Contributions V: Induction from Ordinary Electricity; Oscillatory Discharge," read to the APS in June 1842, and his letter to Robert Hare, October 18, 1843, above.

oscillations. The return wave is not as strong<*er than*> as the direct wave and when the wire conveying the wave to and from the jar is connected with the earth instead of the insulated ball the needle is always magnetized by a current from the jar

The return waves <*or the d*> should perhaps be increased or the direct waves diminished by the [?reflection or] repulsion of the end of the conductor at the moment of the discharge but this is not sufficient to neutralize the current particularly when it is drawn from the out side of the jar near the bottom[3]

The fact of the evolution of oxygen and hydrogen from both poles of the decomposing apparatus in case of ordinary elect. noticed by Wolaston is probably due to the oscillations[4]

My attention has [been] particularly drawn to the subject of the last page from having read last night the Letter of Dr Faraday to the Secretary of the East India House on the question of defending the powder houses of India from thunder.[5] The Dr does not think that there is any danger from the

---

[3] This summary looked forward to the communication of November 7, 1845, on electrical discharge, APS *Proceedings*, 1843–1847, *4*:208–209. Henry further pursued these topics in the winter of 1844–1845.

[4] William Hyde Wollaston, "Experiments on the Chemical Production and Agency of Electricity," *Phil. Trans.*, 1801, pp. 427–434, especially p. 432: "It appears that decomposition of water may take place by common electricity, as well as by the electric pile, although no discernable sparks are produced. . . . I observed that each wire gave both oxygen and hydrogen gas, instead of their being formed separately, as by the electric pile." (From its physical context, this short paragraph might have been a later addition.)

[5] The letter, not published, is dated June 9, 1841, and addressed to James C. Melvill, Secretary of the Court of Directors of the East India Company in London (Board's Collections, Vol. 2099, No. 98202, Draft 668, February 14, 1845, pp. 115–134, India Office Records, Foreign and Commonwealth Office, London, copy). Henry may have received a copy from William Brooke O'Shaughnessy the previous summer, among the papers which Henry mentioned returning to O'Shaughnessy (see Henry to O'Shaughnessy, immediately below). Or the Faraday letter may have been included in correspondence of October 8, 1843, from O'Shaughnessy to Henry (not found), men-

tioned in the "Record of Experiments" entry for January 27, 1845 (Henry Papers, Smithsonian Archives).

Faraday's letter was part of a long, three-way exchange among O'Shaughnessy, J. F. Daniell, and himself, on the practicality and means of erecting lightning rods to protect the powder magazines of India. Her Majesty's Government requested the Military Board of India to investigate the question; the Board relayed the request to O'Shaughnessy (1809–1889, *DNB*), Assistant Surgeon, Bengal Medical Service, who was well-versed in the subject of electricity (see the following correspondence from Henry, note 1). In a letter of December 27, 1838, O'Shaughnessy rejected using lightning rods on the buildings at all, noting that the low buildings were unlikely to be hit, that small lightning conductors could not adequately convey the bolt, which would then disperse into surrounding objects, and that, even if the conductor did conduct the entire charge, lateral discharge in adjacent metal in the magazine could cause sparks—and occasion disaster.

Not receiving its expected answer, the East India Company invited expert opinion and submitted O'Shaughnessy's letter to Faraday and Daniell. In doing so, it placed O'Shaughnessy and the powder magazine question in the middle of an ongoing debate on lateral discharge (see the exchanges between

William Sturgeon and William Snow Harris in Sturgeon's *Annals of Electricity* ..., 1839–1840, vols. 4 and 5, passim, and Sturgeon to Henry, September 23, 1839, *Henry Papers*, 4:263). Faraday and Daniell both rejected the idea that lateral discharge could be dangerous. As Faraday wrote, September 5, 1839, "I have no fear of lateral discharge from a *well arranged* conductor. As far as I understand lateral discharge, it is always a discharge from the conductor itself; it might be very serious from a badly arranged conductor ... but with a good lightning rod it can be but small, and then not to badly conducting matter, as wood or stone, but only to neighbouring masses of good conducting matter.... I am not aware that lateral discharge can take place *within* a building when a lightning conductor outside is struck, except there be portions of metal, as bell wires, or bolts, &c., which may form an interrupted conducting train from the conductor to the interior." Daniell made the same assertion (August 24, 1839).

On June 22, 1840, O'Shaughnessy responded to these two men's comments, and made two points. First, even though a lightning conductor be large enough to pass easily a charge equal to that of a bolt—if *slowly* discharged—such a bolt would be explosive if discharged quickly. Second, he explicitly denied the claim that lateral discharge occurred only if better conductors were found close by. Mentioning Henry by name (referring to, though not citing, "Notice of Electrical Researches—The Lateral Discharge," *British Association Report, 1837* [1838], part 2, pp. 22–24), O'Shaughnessy said that lateral discharge was the effect of the "induction"—not further specified—of the conductor on adjacent bodies. He claimed that "the success of each attempt at obtaining the lateral spark [was] increased by increasing the mass of the prime conductor" (so that larger lightning rods would have a greater, not lesser, ability to produce lateral discharges), and that it was "always easy to obtain this spark to the knuckle, and to many other imperfect conductors." Further, even if sparks did not pass from the rod to the magazine, inductive effects of the lightning on the metal inside—for example, on the copper lining of the powder barrels—could cause sparks.

Faraday responded to O'Shaughnessy's second report on June 9, 1841, with the letter to which Henry referred. As far as can be ascertained from Henry's reading notes, Faraday apparently took O'Shaughnessy's demonstration of lateral sparks as a call to arms, and provided experimental evidence for his own position. He found nothing to change his opinion that a good conductor would be sufficient to transmit safely a stroke of lightning, and that inductive effects would not occur. (To this, Henry noted that "Dr F has here no idea of the induction which I have found in the rod itself.")

The two prevailing opinions on the possible damage caused by the lateral discharge—O'Shaughnessy's and Henry's cautious view against Faraday's and Daniell's dismissal of the problem—were reflected in the different schemes for arranging the rods. O'Shaughnessy was not convinced of the need at all, yet if there were to be rods, he preferred several of them, evenly spaced in a circle at least twenty feet from the building. The rods should terminate twenty feet higher than the building, be dug in down to the water level, and be connected one to the other by ground level metal conductors. By placing the rods as far away from the building as he could, lateral effects would be greatly reduced. For cost's sake, he proposed iron conducting rods. In his second report, O'Shaughnessy reduced the distance away from the building to "six to ten feet," but otherwise scarcely changed his recommendation. The report did not sit well with the military authorities, as often other buildings were closer to the magazines than the distance he specified.

Faraday, seeing no need to guard against lateral discharge, recommended one or two rods only, of copper, and placed only three feet from the building. Reputation implied authority: Faraday's plan was adopted by the Court of Directors of the East India Company.

William Brooke O'Shaughnessy, "Official Correspondence on the Attaching of Lightning Conductors to Powder Magazines. Communicated by Permission of Government," *Journal of the Asiatic Society of Bengal*, 1840, 9:277–310 (wherein are contained O'Shaughnessy's first and second reports, Government responses, and Faraday's and Daniell's letters); Henry Commonplace Book [10615], pp. 45–57, Henry Papers, Smithsonian Archives, quote from p. 56; Mel Gorman, "Faraday on Lightning Rods," *Isis*, 1967, *58*:96–98, which contains a discussion of the entire affair.

induction of a rod near the house but he appears to have no idea of the induction produced by a conductor at the moment it is connecting a discharge which I have discovered. (See page 65 of this vol.)[6]

The effects I have described as witnessed in the case of Mrs Hamiltons House are of this kind[7] and yesterday I found in the Comptes Rendus for Aug 7th 1843 an account of the Steeple of the Strasbourgh cathedral being struck and at the moment of the flash every part of the shop of a tin man situated near the foot of the rod or rather where the rod entered a deep well was illuminated by spark of electricity although no person was hurt[8]

In the paper of Dr Faraday (for an abstract of which see common place book)[9] an account is given of some experiments on lateral discharge one of which consits in throwing sparks on a thick wire C W aside of which a wire E is placed 10 or 12 feet long. An induced or rather lateral spark is seen at *a* and *b* and this is a fine illustration of the fact that I have been contending for that one part of the wire is + (plus) to the other

The nature of the sparks at *a* and *b* in the experiment of the bottom of the last page[10] ought to be examined it is probably a double one

There is also some objection to the experiment as giving a simple result since the primary current would produce in the lateral wire as it is placed in the figure an induced current or rather two induced currents[11]

---

[6] The entry for October 11, 1843, beginning: "Arrange the discharger as in the anexed figure...." Henry came to a similar conclusion on May 28, 1842. Both entries are printed above.

[7] "Record of Experiments," July 15, 1841, above.

[8] Henry's October 27 reading of the *Comptes rendus* was the source for the retrospective comment on the striking of the Cathedral of Strasbourg in the "Record of Experiments," July 22, 1842 (where the paper is briefly abstracted), and for that of October 9, 1843, both above.

[9] Notebook [10615], pp. 45–57, cited above, note 5.

[10] Immediately above.

[11] A marginal note beside these two paragraphs, "Conjecture proved true p 158," referred to experiments of January 17, 1845, where Henry proposed two inductive currents. This entry will be published in the next volume of the *Henry Papers*.

Battery charged to 48° Needles No 10[12]

Needles	distance	defl	
1	1/8	34	
2	1/4	31	
3	3/8	27	Magnetization
4	1/2	25	of needles by
5	5/8	24	the battery
6	6/8	21	discharge
7	7/8	22	
8	1	23	
9	1 1/8	24	
10	1 1/4	23	NB in the case of
11	1 3/8	23	a needl placed on
12	1 1/2	22	the ribband in an
13	1 5/8	20	other exp of same
14	1 3/4	22°	charge the def. was 36.

In this experiment instead of a single wire the discharge was passed through a copper ribbon 1 1/2 of an inch in width and 2 feet long

1/2 Needles No 10

	Needles	Dist.	defl	
Middle	1	on	23	21 1/2
Middle	2	"	20	
N Side	3	"	22	21 3/4
N Side	4	"	22	
S Side	5	"	23	
S Side	6	"	20	

See top of next page[13]

In the last experiment several half needles were placed on different sides and in the middle of the copper riband in order to ascertain if there was any difference in the magnetizing power of the plate at the edges and in the middle. The result would appear to give a greater intensity at the sides but

[12] As in previous entries, we have moved sideways marginal comments referring to needles and batteries to the tops and bottoms of the tables.

[13] Immediately below.

the difference is not sufficiently great to render it certain that such a result was to be depended on.

The induction at a distance, which produces the changes in the small needles would interfere with this result

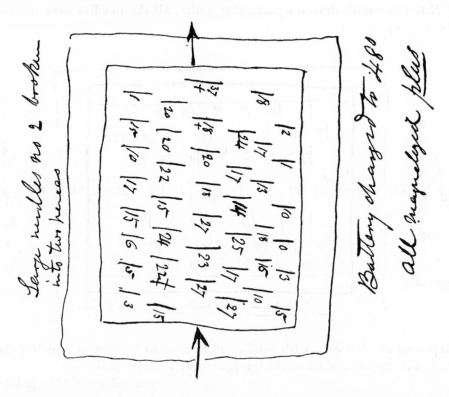

In the above drawing the position of a number of half needles no 2 are shown as they were placed on the surface of the tin foil on the coated pane of glass called the square of Franklin.[14] Every needle on the tin foil was magnetized. The irregularity is due in part to the different magnetic capacity of the needles some of them were shorter than others as it was impossible to break them all of the same length. Also the tempre of the whole lot was not quite the same since some of them could be bent much more than others.

The numbers annexed to each needle indicate the deflection or relative magnetic intensity of each and from these it will be seen that the electrical action extended to every part of the tin foil

[14] A capacitor invented by Franklin, consisting of two sheets of tinfoil attached to opposite sides of a pane of glass. *Encyclopaedia Britannica*, 8th ed., s.v. "Electricity," p. 612.

This experiment is interesting and must be varied in reference to the thickness of the sheet, also by seperating it into parallel sheets to acertain what part of the effect is due to the magnetization at a distance from the discharge.

N B One result deserves particular notice, all the needles were magnetized by a *plus action*.

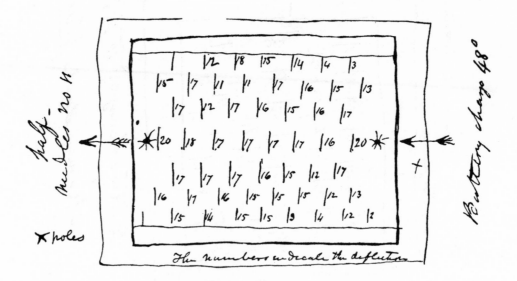

Repeated the last exp. with smaller needles—also broken in two but the parts were nearer alike and the tempres more nearly equal

extend around the pole![15]

The experiment on the last page must be repeated with other needles and with the tin foil seperated. Also with thick plate[16]

---

[15] A note written immediately to the right proclaimed, "Have done so. p 180": "Record of Experiments," January 29, 1845, where Henry again experimented with needles placed on electrified plates. This will be published in the next volume of the *Henry Papers*.

[16] The last phrase appears to have been written at another time; though in Henry's hand, the script is different from what precedes.

Immediately below this, written in the hand of John Kintzing Kane, is: "A.P.S. 3 Nov. 1843. Referred to the Comm. to whom the former papers of Prof. Henry were referred, viz. Dr. Patterson, Prof. Bache, Mr. Lukens. J.K.K. Sec^y." To the left, in Bache's hand, is written "Examined therefore Nov 4/43 A.D. Bache." On Henry's practice of submitting his notebook, see *Henry Papers*, 2:217–218.

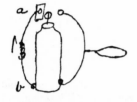

In this arrangement the return or rebound takes place in *a b* instead of in the conductor. See page 57 of this vol.[17]

[17] These comments and sketches are in Henry's hand, but in pencil and on the facing page to the previous material. They are written on an otherwise blank page dividing this run of experiments from that which started the following January. The page reference is to October 5 and the beginning of October 6, 1843, above, where similar sketches are found.

TO WILLIAM BROOKE O'SHAUGHNESSY[1]
Retained Copy,[2] Henry Papers, Smithsonian Archives

Princeton Oct 30th 1843

My Dear sir

I excedingly regret to find that owing to an accident which was the result of my own carelessness <*that*> your papers have not yet left this country. The delay how[ev]er has given me an opportunity of placing in the same package a copy of the Report of the procedings of the Am Phil society which I beg you to accept as a small testimony of my esteem.

[1] O'Shaughnessy (1809–1889, *DNB*) was a surgeon with the East India Company who is best known for his advocacy and construction of a telegraph system in India. Authorized to begin construction in 1853, within two-and-a-half years he had superintended construction of four thousand miles of telegraph over difficult terrain.

O'Shaughnessy published on medical, chemical, and electrical subjects, and was a leader of British scientific circles in India. Elected a Fellow of the Royal Society in 1843, he was knighted in 1856 during a visit to England, to which he retired permanently in 1861.

Mel Gorman has investigated O'Shaughnessy's work in various fields and considered him particularly as a case study in the transfer of European science to a colonial environment. See, for example, "An Early Electric Motor in India," *Technology and Culture*, 1968, *9*:184–190, "Sir William Brooke O'Shaughnessy: Pioneer Chemist in a Colonial Environment," *Journal of Chemical Education*, 1969, *46*:99–103, "Sir William O'Shaughnessy, Lord Dalhousie, and the Establishment of the Telegraph System in India," *Technology and Culture*, 1971, *12*:581–601, and "Sir William B. O'Shaughnessy, Pioneer Chemical Educator in India," *Ambix*, 1983, *30*:107–116.

[2] The copy looks as if it were made in haste and contains numerous misspellings.

Since your visit to Princeton which I shall always reccollect with plea-sure[3] I have made a series of expermts which have a bearing on the subject of Ligh[t]ning rods. The results of these which I hope to get published in the next no of the transactions of our society will tend to support your plan of protecting powder houses by a number of rods at some distance from the building.[4]

With my best wishes for the health of yourself and family I rem[ain] sincerely

Your &– Joseph Henry

[3] According to a presentation copy in the Henry Library of O'Shaughnessy's *Notes of Lectures on Natural Philosophy. First Series. On Galvanic Electricity* (Calcutta, 1841), O'Shaughnessy was in Princeton on June 13, 1843. In a letter written many years later, O'Shaughnessy recalled getting off the train in Princeton, identifying Henry by spotting a copy of the *Comptes rendus* in his hands, and accompanying him home where he was treated to experiments on induction, a gift of one of Franklin's Leyden jars, and an evening of socializing. (Mary Henry Copy of O'Shaugh-nessy to Henry, 1869, Henry Papers, Smith-sonian Archives.)

Prior to their meeting, O'Shaughnessy had mentioned Henry's work in several of his pub-lications, e.g., in "Memoranda Relative to Ex-periments on the Communication of Tele-graphic Signals by Induced Electricity," *Journal of the Asiatic Society of Bengal*, 1839, 8:720 and 729, in "Official Correspondence on the Attaching of Lightning Conductors to Powder Magazines," ibid., 1840, 9:304 and 308, and in his *Notes of Lectures*, pp. 63, 90, and 92.

O'Shaughnessy's trip to the United States is not mentioned in the *DNB* account and we don't know if he had a specific purpose. A letter of August 9, 1843, nominating him as a corresponding member of the National Insti-tute described him as temporarily attached to the staff of the Governor General of the Canadas (Aaron H. Palmer to Francis Markoe, Box 5, Records of the National Institute, Smithsonian Archives).

[4] Henry's communications to the next American Philosophical Society meeting on November 3, 1843, included one on this sub-ject:

Professor Henry described several experi-ments on the direct and return stroke, show-ing that equilibrium was restored by the same succession of oscillations; large and small needles placed in spirals forming part of an electrical circuit, being magnetized in different directions. The disturbance of the electrical plenum by a discharge of elec-tricity was referred to, as explanatory of the induction which takes place; and the sub-ject was applied to the explanation of va-rious phenomena; among others, the light appearing in well authenticated cases about persons and objects in the neighbourhood of a discharge of lightning in its direct passage; and suggestions were made as to the most effectual mode of protecting powder houses, &c., from the effects of lightning.

Professor Henry examined in the same connexion, whether currents of ordinary electricity pass actually at the surface, or, like galvanic electricity, through the mass of the conductor; and he concluded that the law of conduction developed by Ohne [*sic*] cannot apply to the case of surface passages, as these are indicative of ordinary elec-tricity.

APS *Proceedings*, 1843–1847, 4:22–23.

For O'Shaughnessy's plan, see the "Record of Experiments" entry immediately above.

Although we have not examined an August 24, 1844, report by O'Shaughnessy on a system to protect a powder magazine, he re-ferred therein to "personal discussion . . . with Messrs Faraday, Wheatstone, Apjohn, Davy, Draper of New York and Henry of Phila-delphia" (page 16; page 4 of original pagina-tion according to the depository, the India Of-fice Records). After appealing to Faraday, who again found O'Shaughnessy's system faulty, the Court of Directors adopted Faraday's recom-mendations instead. The report is discussed in Mel Gorman, "Faraday on Lightning Rods," *Isis*, 1967, 58:96–98.

FROM ALEXANDER DALLAS BACHE

Henry Papers, Smithsonian Archives

Philad. Nov. 6. 1843

Dear Henry.

I received to day from Prof. Silliman & B.S Jr. a letter[1] which he mentions has been also sent to you & to Dr. Gray, & I presume has been sent to Dr. Torrey also. The amount of it appears to me as well as I can separate it from the very many words in which it is wrapped, that he wishes the influence, exertions & time, study & whatever else some of the leading men of science of the country are disposed to contribute,—in return for which—money is out of the question because the journal will not pay, influence will be given as far as the distance which separates the editors from the collaborators will admit & as may be consistent with the editors retaining the control of all departments, some copies of the journal may be given, & the privilege of inserting articles with initials or better still with entire names will be freely accorded. Do I interpret rightly? Talk over the answer we are to give with Dr. Torrey. I am inclined to run him (S) a little by stating what we think to be the wants of the times, how, at what periods, & where a successful journal might could would or should be got up, the changes which Am. Science has undergone &c. Then to strip his proposition of its verbiage & set it, still, however, with a lace veil over it, before him. And finally if you think it will do to make a counter proposition on a specie basis, none of your paper & ink promises in return for substantial service.[2] What a privilege to appear in connexion with the Joule's & the Sir Graves Houghton's once a quarter![3] Let me hear from you soon,[4] for respect to the veteran general demands an early reply. Mrs. B. who has a right to know says the letter is "downright Yankee."

Col. Abert means to help me further with the Observatory[5] on the first good opportunity.

Kindest regards to Dr. Torrey & to yours

Yours truly
A. D. Bache

[1] Not found.

[2] For an earlier proposal of collaborators for *Silliman's Journal* by Asa Gray, see his letter to Torrey of February 28, 1843, printed above.

[3] Evidently a reference to the physicist James Prescott Joule (1818–1889, *DSB*) and the orientalist Sir Graves Haughton (1788–1849, *DNB*). Bache's choice of this pair for his sarcastic comment is a mystery; perhaps Silliman mentioned them as contributors in his letter. Silliman was aware of a need for better coverage of foreign science and in 1846 announced "the kind aid of several [foreign] gentlemen eminent in their several departments." See *Silliman's Journal*, 1844, *46*:404, and 1846, n.s. *1*:99.

[4] Henry's reply is immediately below.

[5] In May 1843 Bache began receiving funds for the Girard College observatory from the Topographical Bureau of the War Department, headed by J. J. Abert. See *Henry Papers*, *4*:319n.

TO ALEXANDER DALLAS BACHE
Bache Papers, Smithsonian Archives

Princeton Nov 12th 1843

My Dear Bache

As soon as I received your letter[1] relative to the propositions of Professor Silliman I commenced an answer but I was interrupted at the time and amid the bustle of the examination of 70 new students, an attempt to re-model our course of study and the begining of a course of lectures I have not found time to resume my answer until this evening.

Previous to the receipt of your letter I had succeeded in evolving from the Professor's communication precisely the same ideas you have so briefly and conspicuously set forth. Dr. Torrey has removed with his family for the winter to New York. I have however sent him my copy of the letter[2] and have requested him to write me on the subject.

I think the Professor should be answered kindly but candidly; all the points you mention should be placed before him in a clear light particularly that which relates to the change in the character of American science which has been going on for several years unperceived and unsuspected by the good people at New Haven.

He should be informed of the opportunity there now is of making his journal the best publication of the kind in the English language and per-haps the best in any language of the world. By admitting such a set of col-laborators as can now be readily selected from men in different departments in our country the science of the world may be posted up and the readers be apprised of every thing of importance which is ocurring.

A new series of the journal might be commenced with an historical sketch of the progress of the several departments within the last 20 years to serve as a starting point for the succeeding quarterly posting up: Sketches of this kind while they would be of great importance to the more profound student of science might be so prepared as to be interesting to the general reader. This plan however cannot be carried out except by a board of col-laborators who should have the principal if not the entire controll of the different departments so that no article would be inserted that could derogate from the high character of the publication. I think unless Professor Silliman adopts some idea like this his journal will experience a falling off. Our intercourse with England is becoming every day more intimate and Wiley and Putnam will now furnish the Phil. magazine for about the same

---

[1] Bache's letter of November 6, 1843, is printed above.
[2] Not found in either the Henry Papers or the Torrey Papers at the New York Botanical Garden Library.

price as that of the American journal. Indeed I have learned indirectly from a Nephew of Mrs. Silliman a student in the theological seminary[3] that the subscriptions have very much fallen off and that a new effort is about to be made for again increasing the list.

If the Professor will agree to place our names on the title page and give us the charge of the departments afixed to the names, then I think we may consent to a connection with the journal. For the present and as long as the subscription list is no larger than at present we would not ask for compensation in the money line but if the list increased on account of our labours then it would be no more than just that we should be paid. I think a connection of the kind with Sillimans journal would be of some importance to us individually and be of more to the cause of American science.[4]

Our text book has occupied my mind considerably since my last visit to Phil^d.[5] When you last spoke to me on the subject in your room in the University I thought that your sketch related to the labour of this winter and that the whole work was to be hurried through in the course of a few months. I was how[ev]er much relieved by your subsequent explanation.

I am engaged this evening on an addition to my Syllabus[6] and shall con-

---

[3] Probably David Trumbull (1819–1889), studying at Princeton Theological Seminary after his graduation from Yale in 1842. After his ordination in 1845, Trumbull sailed to Valparaiso, Chile, under the auspices of the Foreign Evangelical Society. He served there as a missionary for most of his life. *Biographical Record of the Class of 1842 of Yale College* (New Haven, 1878), pp. 194–197. *Roberts*, p. 128.

[4] We have not found a reply to the Sillimans. Reflecting on the first series of *Silliman's Journal*, Benjamin Silliman, Sr., noted that he had refused "overtures for editorial cooperation ... made to him by gentlemen commanding his confidence and esteem" (1847, 50:xiii). As Henry, Bache, and Gray suspected, he was not ready to share editorial control with anyone outside his family.

Silliman did realize, however, the need for timely reports and analysis of recent advances and publications in the sciences. In the new series, which began in 1846, the old "Miscellanies" section was replaced by a section of "Scientific Intelligence" divided into various departments: chemistry, mineralogy and geology, zoology, botany, general physics, miscellaneous, bibliographical notices, and obituary. In a prospectus for the new series, the editors announced that "the assistance of several gentlemen eminent in different departments has been secured, each collaborator being credited, at his option, for his own contributions," i.e., contributions of notices to the "Scientific Intelligence" section of the *Journal*, not editorial control over everything pertaining to a particular branch of science. Silliman had, in fact, asked Henry to perform this much more limited role as early as 1832: "I should be very glad if you would keep watch of the whole subject of electro dynamics electro-magnetism etc. & favor me with notices of its progress ... to have you take charge of this department & I will pay for the communications" (*Henry Papers*, 1:461). Asa Gray was already collaborating in this sense in botany. It was clearly not what the reformers had in mind.

[5] Bache and Henry had agreed to collaborate on a two-volume text on natural philosophy. However, it was never completed, probably because of Bache's move to Washington.

[6] Henry's *Syllabus of Lectures on Physics* was printed in two parts in Princeton in 1844. The first dealt with somatology, the second with mechanics. Each part also included introductory lectures. A revised version of a portion of the syllabus appeared in the S.I., *Ann. Rep.*, 1856, pp. 187–220. Further reference to the syllabus will be found in the next volume of the *Henry Papers*.

tinue to work on the several parts during the winter. We are all nearly *down* sick with the Influenza. We are in good spirits in reference to the large increase of students. This result shows that the public do not decide against the change we have made in the vacations.[7] I do not think we have any new ones from Phil[d]

Yours as Ever
Joseph Henry

[7] Maclean's proposal for changing the academic calendar at Princeton (see *Henry Papers,* 4:433) had been implemented. Enrollment continued to increase.

FROM JOHN K. KANE
Henry Papers, Smithsonian Archives

Phil[a] 20 Nov. 1843.

My dear Sir,

Mr. Hassler is lying at the point of death in this city, and the superintendency of the coast survey may perhaps be vacant before this letter reaches you.[1] The appointment, in its scientific relations the most important that the Government can confer, is with your friend Mr. Secretary Spencer.[2]

There is one man singularly fitted to hold the office, your friend and mine, Dallas Bache,—and there is no other in the country, his equal or his neighbour. Besides mind and acquirements a century beyond Hassler, he has that which Hassler wanted so much, the administrative talent, and with it every other recommendation. The descendant of Franklin, a democrat always and of the best sort, allied to our Pennsylvania democrats Dallas[3] and Walker[4] and Wilkins[5] and Irwin,[6] a graduate of West Point and there-

[1] Ferdinand Rudolph Hassler had been Superintendent of the Coast Survey since its inception in 1816. The Survey was, however, suspended between 1818 and 1832.

[2] As Secretary of the Treasury, J. C. Spencer was responsible for the Coast Survey. For Spencer, see his letter to Henry of June 28, 1843, printed above.

[3] George Mifflin Dallas (1792–1864) was Bache's uncle. Son of former Secretary of the Treasury Alexander James Dallas, George Mifflin Dallas was a former U. S. Senator and Minister to Russia. *DAB.* Through his mother and sisters, Bache was related to many important politicians. See James Dallas, *The History of the Family of Dallas* (Edinburgh, 1921), pp. 513–516.

[4] Bache's sister Mary was the wife of Robert John Walker (1801–1869), a native of Pennsylvania who was serving as U. S. Senator from Mississippi. Walker became Secretary of the Treasury in 1845. *DAB.*

[5] Bache's aunt Matilda Dallas was the second wife of William Wilkins (1779–1865), who was at this time a U. S. Congressman. In February 1844 Wilkins became Secretary of War. *DAB.*

[6] Bache's sister Sophia was married to Wil-

fore in favour with the army, professor of our University, president of the Girard College while it had the promise of vitality, the leading mind of our Mechanic Institute and Philosophical Society, in a word, the nucleus around which science gathers in Philadelphia, and one of the best known of our Scientific men abroad,—he is withal so gallant a gentleman, and so good a fellow, that every one here will think of him for the place before all others.

Now, there is I apprehend no time to be lost. Probably even now letters may be on their way to the Secretary for all sorts of pseudo-scientifics, who may be willing to occupy Hassler's shoes. Write to him therefore at once. You can speak with authority on a question like this: for you are almost the only man except Bache whose appointment would secure the confidence of scientific men in the success of the great enterprize.

The survey will need such a man as he is to sustain it. In one year he would make it popular, by stripping the work of its mysteries and all the other paraphernalia of quackery that have encumbered it till now. We should have reduced expenses, greatly increased efficiency, and intelligible reports. In a word, the work would be done rapidly and well. It wants this change much; for you know better than I do, how ridiculously Congress has been humbugged in this matter, and how unanimous those are who are capable of judging as to the foolery of Mr. H's proceedings at the public cost.

Write therefore to Mr. Spencer, without delay,—and if credentials are wanted at Washington, we will send them on *au comble*.

> Very truly and always
> yours,
> J. K. Kane

10 o'clock P.M.—I have just heard that Mr. Hassler died this evening. Every moment therefore is precious.[7]

---

liam Wallace Irwin (1803–1856) of Pittsburgh. Irwin was a former Mayor of Pittsburgh and U. S. Congressman. *Biographical Directory of the American Congress.*

[7] Hassler's death set off an intensive campaign by Bache's friends. Calling on scientific and political contacts, Bache and his backers produced numerous individual and group testimonials. By mid-December Bache had received his letter of appointment from President Tyler.

Bache's papers in the Smithsonian Archives contain many background strategy letters (Box 3) as well as copies of the testimonials (Box 6).

November 21, 1843

TO J. C. SPENCER
*Letters Received Relating to the Coast Survey, Office
of the Secretary of the Treasury, Records of the Coast and Geodetic Survey,
RG 23, National Archives*

Princeton Nov 21st 1843

Dear Sir

When you were last in Princeton you were so kind as to say that you would be pleased to receive any communication from me on the subject of science and on the strength of this assurance I now beg leave to offer some suggestions relative to the appointment of a successor to the late Mr Hasler on the Coast Survey. The work over which Mr Hasler presided is one of the most important in a scientific point of view which our government has ever undertaken and the manner of its completion will either reflect lasting credit on us, or be a source of continued disgrace in the eyes of the whole world.

While I had the highest respect for the attainments of Mr Hasler I fear he did not possess that common sense practical talent which with his scientific acquirements were necessary to qualify him in the best manner for the situation he held.[1] I fear he has left the work in great confusion and that the person who may succeede him will find great difficulty in verifying that which has been done and in extending the triangulation in connection with the points already established. The appointment of a successor to Mr H. in its scientific bearings is the most the government can be called on to make and in consideration of all the circumstances I do think there are few persons to be found perfectly qualified for conducting the work. It does not consist alone in making a trigonometrical survey of our coast on the plan adopted by European governments a work which in itself requires peculiar skill and attainment but in continuing a survey which has been commenced on a particular plan, all the principles of which have never been fully given to the public and of which probably no record exists. I know from the habits of Mr H that no Person without great patience, labour, and sagacity, will be able to decipher the intricacy of his calcu-

---

[1] Hassler was hardly a model administrator, either uninterested in or unable to deal with administrative detail and office routine. Even those who admired his scientific accomplishments questioned his accounting and business procedures. Complicating the situation was the rapidly deteriorating relationship between Hassler and his first assistant, Edmund Blunt, who accused Hassler of withholding necessary information from him. Harold L. Burstyn, *At the Sign of the Quadrant: An Account of the Contributions to American Hydrography Made by Edmund March Blunt and His Sons* (Mystic, Connecticut, 1957), pp. 42–43; Florian Cajori, *The Chequered Career of Ferdinand Rudolph Hassler* (1929; reprint ed., New York, 1980), pp. 217–218.

lations or to become acquainted with the details of his processes. His work will all require to be carefully examined—not hastily condemned nor precipitately adopted.

The person selected to succeed him should not only be thoroughly acquainted with the theoretical principles of Natural philosophy, mathematics and astronomy but also practically familiar with the use of instruments and the methods of scientific research, inorder that he may be fully qualified for the manual operations of the work. He should also have established a character for science not only in this country but in Europe so that he might have much to loose should he prove unfit for the undertaking. His scientific character should not rest as is too often the case in our country on the mere favourable opinion of his friends in reference to what they imagine he is capable of doing but on what he has actually accomplished. The question *what has he done?* should be asked in reference to every applicant for the office of superintendance of the coast survey. Besides his scientific qualifications he should be able to govern and direct men and by his address and manner tend to render the work more popular than it now is. To a person properly qualified the office is one of much interest although connected with difficulties enough to cause the best men to hesitate in accepting it.

I am well acquainted with the scientific claims of every one in our country who can justly make pretensions to a scientific reputation and I am particularly acquainted with one who above all others I think best qualified for the situation. I allude to Alexander Dallas Bache of Philadelphia late president of Girard college and now Professor of astronomy and natural philosophy in the Unversity of Penns[a]

The letter which informed me of the death of Mr Hasler stated that some of the friends of Mr Bache had <*proposed*> spoken of him as a candidate. I am not certain however that he would accept the appointment were it offered to him since I happened to have a conversation with him a few weeks ago on the subject of the coast survey in which he spoke of the difficulty in carrying on the work in such terms that I think he would hesitate in accepting the appointment. If however he should become a candidate I beg leave to assure you that there is no man in our country as well qualified for the situation as he is. I do not make this assertion on account of any partiality I may have for him but from a firm conviction of its truth founded on what he has already accomplished in the line of science and a Knowledge of his character as derived from an unreserved intimacy of several years. I regret that I have made this communication so long. Nothing but the deep interest I feel in the appointment of a proper Person for the prosecution of so important a work as the coast survey would induce me to trespass thus long on your patience and time.[2]

> With the highest esteem and respect I have the honor to be your &c
> Joseph Henry

[2] On the last page of the letter there is a file notation in the margin which reads "Mr. Morris acknowledge kindly and file." The acknowledgement, dated November 24, 1843, is printed below.

FROM ALEXANDER DALLAS BACHE
Henry Papers, Smithsonian Archives

Philad. Nov. 21. 1843.

Dear Henry.

The newspapers announce to day the decease of Mʳ Hassler. Some time ago my name was mentioned as possibly to be brought forward in the event of a reorganization of the Survey. I of course wish my scientific friends to judge for me whether I am likely to do justice to the place & if they think this is the case to go in for me—if not—the thing is settled. I would much prefer my present position if it were liberally endowed, but it is a hard task to make two ends meet & requires so much self denial as to more than counterbalance its agreable points. You remember I was frank on taking the place, in saying that if the Trustees wished to *fix* me they must give me enough to live on.[1] We agreed in regard to a man's being worth what he would bring, rather than a Professorship being a constant quantity with out regard to the incumbent. They would not depart *then* from their system & I suppose would not now, so I feel free to move wherever I can better myself. Write & say what you think. Mʳ Spencer can now show your real influence with him. Best regards to Mrs. H.

> Yours truly
> A. D. Bache.

[1] Bache's salary at the University of Pennsylvania was $2,300 a year. The Superintendent of the Coast Survey received $4,500 a year, as well as a $1,500 allowance for expenses.

FROM ALEXANDER DALLAS BACHE
Henry Papers, Smithsonian Archives

Philad. Nov. 21. 1843.

My dear friend.

I find that the matter of the Coast Survey is to be gone into [. . .][1] & out. I write to beg you to sit down at *once* & write to Capt. Stockton[2] such a letter[3] as he may acquire your opinions from to transmit to the Pres[t] If you have friends to be called on in Albany who have influence of the scientific sort, or who are friends of any one at Washington ask them to write. Will your Colleagues aid me?

Yours as ever truly
A. D. Bache

[1] One illegible word.   [3] Not found.
[2] Robert F. Stockton.

TO ALEXANDER DALLAS BACHE
Bache Papers, Smithsonian Archives

Princeton Nov 22nd 1843

Dear Bache

Your favour was received this morning. I received last evening a letter from Kane informing me of the death of Mr. Hasler and suggesting you as a candidate for the vacant office. I immediately commenced a letter as Mr Kane requested to Mr Spencer which was mailed this morning and is now on its way to Washington. I gave Mr S. my views of the importance of the work in reference to our scientific character &c. I stated that while I had the highest respect for the talents and acquirements of Mr H. I did not think that he possessed that practical common sense necssary to the proper prosecution of such a work—that probably the affairs of the survey would be found in great confusion—much labour and sagacity would be required to decipher the plans and calculations which Mr H. may have left behind— that the continuation of the work would be more difficult than the organization of a new survey—that the work already done would require verifying &c.

I stated that the person selected to succ[d] Mr H should not only be theoretically well acquainted with the principles of Nat. Phil. Astron. and

Math. but also familiar from long practice with the methods of scientific investigation so as to be fully qualified for the manual operation. That he should also be a man of established reputation known as well in Europe as in this country inorder that he might have much to loose did he fail in his undertaking—That his reputation should not rest on the mere opinion of his Friends as to what he might be capable of doing but on what he had actually accomplished—the question *What has he done?* should be asked in reference to every candidate for the office of the superintendant of the coast survey—that besides his scientific qualifications he should be able to govern men and by his manner and address tend to render the survey more popular than it now is—that the situation was a desirable one for a person properly qualified but that it was at present surrounded with so many difficulties that <*many would*> some might be deterred from accepting it should it be offered to them.

I farther stated that I am well acquainted with the scientific character of all the men of any prominence in the way of science in our country and that I was particulary acquainted with one who above all the others was best qualified for the office. I then mentioned your name but stated that I was not certain that you would accept the appointment. But if you became a candidate I begged leave to assure him that you were the *best* man that could be [?selected]—that I did not make this assertion from any partiality to you but from a firm conviction of its truth—a conviction founded on what you had already accomplished in the way of science and a knowledge of your character accquired from several years of unreserved intimacy &&—

I as one of your Friends have no hesitation in saying to yourself as I will say to others that if any person in our country can disentangle the work and carry it successfully through *you are the man*. My only objections to your accepting the appointment is that it will again unsettle you in reference to the more peaceful persuits of experimental investigation and dissipate the schemes we have formed of joint labour &c. These objections are of a personal nature and should not be taken into consideration for a moment. The coast survey is an object worthy of your ambition and one in which I am sure from your habits of mind <*and body I am sure*> you are well qualified to suceed in prosecuting.

I fully agree with your proposition that a professorship should *not* be a constant quantity who-ever may fill the chair and I do not think therefore that you are in any respect bound to the University. I shall regret however the change on account of my friend Dr Ludlow.[1] With respects to Mrs B and my best wishes for your success I remain as ever yours

Joseph Henry

[1] Ludlow was Provost of the University of Pennsylvania (*Henry Papers, 1*:106n).

FROM J. C. SPENCER
Retained Copy, Letters Received Relating to the Coast Survey,
Office of the Secretary of the Treasury, Records of the Coast and Geodetic
Survey, RG 23, National Archives

Washington
Treasury Department
Nov 24. 1843.

Dear Sir

I am truly obliged to you for the valuable suggestions contained in your letter of the 21ˢᵗ inst on the subject of the appointment of a suitable person to succeed the late Mʳ Hassler as Superintendent of the Coast Survey. It is very important that his successor should combine the necessary qualifications to carry out the plans of his predecessor; the selection of such a person will, I fear, be attended with much difficulty. Professor Bache's name has already been mentioned as eminently qualified to fill that situation.

With great respect
Your obᵗ Servᵗ
J. C. Spencer

MEMBERS OF THE AMERICAN PHILOSOPHICAL SOCIETY
TO PRESIDENT TYLER
Copy, Bache Papers, Smithsonian Archives[1]

Hall of the American Philosophical
Society, 24 Nov. 1843.

We beg leave most respectfully to recommend to your Excellency, Alexander Dallas Bache, Esquire, of Pennsylvania, as a gentleman eminently qualified to fill the position of Superintendent of the U. S. Coast Survey, now vacant by the death of Mr. Hassler.

[1] This copy is in the hand of J. K. Kane. One other copy of this petition exists in the folder of recommendations of Bache in the Bache Papers, Smithsonian Archives. It is in the hand of Francis George Cummings, a student at the University of Pennsylvania (*General Alumni Catalogue of the University of Pennsylvania* [Philadelphia, 1917], p. 46). Another copy, done by John S. Hart, is in the J. K. Kane Papers, American Philosophical Society Library. The original has not been found. Many of the Bache recommendations exist in multiple copies; through this duplication, his promoters could keep track of their campaign and apply political pressure as needed. As J. G. Totten, an important APS contact in Washington, wrote: "I have advised Mʳ Bache to arm the hands of his friends who take political ground, each with a roll of such documents...." J. G. Totten to J. K. Kane, November 28, 1843. Bache Recommendations, Box 6, Bache Papers, Smithsonian Archives.

In doing so, we testify, from an intimate personal acquaintance with Professor Bache, to his elevated rank as a man of general and practical science, his experience and skill as an observer, his large attainments as a mathematician, his singular administrative talent, his quickness of apprehension and habitual industry, and his signal worth in all the relations of life.

To

   The President of the ⎱
   United States.   ⎰

     John Ludlow
     Clement C. Biddle
     Thoˢ Biddle
     Henry D. Rogers
     Robt. Hare
     Chaˢ D. Meigs
     Thoˢ Sergeant
     B. W. Richards
     H. Vethake
     Isaac Lea
     J. J. VanderKemp
        11

Peter S. DuPonceau
N. Chapman
R. M. Patterson
Franklin Bache
J K Kane
Robley Dunglison
G. Ord
Isaac Hays
Thoˢ P. Cope
Samuel Geo. Morton
Franklin Peale
Joseph Henry
———
Is. Lukens
M. W. Baldwin
Jos. Saxton
Ch. B. Trego
John Downes
Wm. Peter
S. C. Walker
Jno F Frazer
F. Fraley[2]

(32)

[2] The order of the names was significant. Duponceau was President of the Society; Chapman, Patterson, and Franklin Bache, Vice-Presidents; Kane and Dunglison, Secretaries; Ord, Treasurer and Librarian; and Hays, Curator. Cope was a leading merchant of Philadelphia; Morton, an anthropologist and the author of *Crania Americana*; and Franklin Peale, the son of Charles Willson Peale, an APS Curator and Coiner at the U. S. Mint.

The second, slightly less-prestigious block of names on the left comprised Ludlow, Provost of the University of Pennsylvania; the Biddles of the prominent Philadelphia family; Rogers, Pennsylvania State Geologist; Hare, Professor of Chemistry at the University of Pennsylvania Medical School; Meigs, Professor of Medicine at Jefferson Medical College; Sergeant, Associate Justice of the Pennsylvania Supreme Court; Richards, former Mayor of Philadelphia; Vethake, teacher and administrator at the University of Pennsylvania; Lea, a prominent conchologist; and Vanderkemp, agent of the Holland Land Company.

Lukens, Baldwin, and Saxton, who lead off the third tier of signers at bottom right, were mechanics and instrument makers; Trego, a member of the Pennsylvania legislature and amateur geologist; Downes, a calculator for the *United States Almanac* and former member of the Northeast Boundary Survey; Peter, British Consul in Philadelphia and former member of Parliament; Walker, director of

$$\left\{\begin{array}{l}\text{copy of document, mailed by me, 26 Nov. 1843,}\\\text{under address to J. G. Totten, Col of Engr̃s,}\\\hfill\text{Washington}\end{array}\right\}$$

J. K. Kane[3]

the Philadelphia observatory at Central High School; Frazer, Professor of Natural Philosophy at the same institution; and Fraley, a member of the Pennsylvania State Senate.

Information may be found on most of these men in this or previous volumes of the *Henry Papers*. On Sergeant see the *DAB*; on Vanderkemp, the Philadelphia City Directory, 1843; on Trego, see Bruce Sinclair, *Philadelphia's Philosopher Mechanics: A History of the Franklin Institute, 1824–1865* (Baltimore, 1974), pp. 254–258; on Downes, *The United States Almanac for 1844* (Philadelphia, 1844); and on Peter, *DNB*.

[3] J. K. Kane, Secretary of the Society, transmitted the original of this petition to Totten, Chief of the Army Corps of Engineers. Totten had previously served as intermediary for the Society in December 1839, when it petitioned Congress for magnetic and meteorological observatories (*Henry Papers*, 4:315–320). Sent with the Bache recommendation were a descriptive list of the signers (omitting Vander-

kemp) and four other petitions—from the Princeton science and mathematics professors (see below); from Sears C. Walker and E. Otis Kendall of the Philadelphia Central High School Observatory; from Judge Edward King, presiding judge of the Court of Common Pleas of Philadelphia; and from Colonel Henry Leech, President and Controller of the Philadelphia Public Schools. Also included were four cover letters, two to Totten and two to Tyler.

Totten acknowledged receipt of the testimonials, writing that the disposition would be decided by political persuasion, for he judged that Bache's scientific ability had been well-endorsed by that time. "Signers of the A.P.S. Recommendation"; J. K. Kane to J. G. Totten, two letters (copies), November 25, 26, 1843; J. K. Kane to President John Tyler, two letters (copies), November 25, 1843; J. G. Totten to J. K. Kane, November 28, 1843; all in Box 6, Bache Papers, Smithsonian Archives.

MEMBERS OF THE FACULTY OF THE COLLEGE OF NEW JERSEY TO [PRESIDENT TYLER][1]

Copy,[2] Bache Papers, Smithsonian Archives

College of New Jersey.

Princeton. Nov. 24th 1843.

The subscribers take pleasure in expressing their sense of the eminent fitness of Professor A. D. Bache, to succeed Mr Hassler in the charge of the

[1] No addressee is given. This petition was part of a package of supportive material for Bache sent by J. K. Kane to J. G. Totten. See above, Members of the American Philosophical Society to President Tyler, November 24, 1843, footnote 3.

[2] This is one of five extant copies—four in the Bache Papers, the fifth in the J. K. Kane Papers, American Philosophical Society. Each copy had been verified against the original (which has not been found) and signed by an examiner. Three were examined by F. G.

Cummings. A fourth was checked by John S. Hart, Bache's successor at the Philadelphia High School, and also signed by J. K. Kane. The fifth copy—our text, chosen for clarity of writing—was verified by Hart. Despite the assurances of Hart that these were "true" copies and of Cummings that the copies were "found correct," there are minor variations in punctuation and the treatment of titles (in some copies titles are abbreviated, in others not). There is also one word, noted below, which was read two different ways.

Coast Survey, believing him to possess, in a high degree, the talents and attainments necessary to conduct that work to a successful issue. Of the ample sufficiency of Prof. Bache's scientific acquirements, there can be no doubt, and in addition to the requisite acquaintance with abstract and experimental science, we believe him to possess, in combination with this, an uncommon degree of that practical ability, which is necessary for the accurate and effective application of Scientific truth. We are fully confident that the coast Survey, in his hands, would not, on the one hand, be deficient in the most rigid accuracy, nor, on the other, overloaded by useless refinements—that it would be prosecuted with all the despatch compatible with exactness,—and be, in all respects, so far as his agency would[3] reach, wisely and successfully conducted. Being thus confident in our belief that Prof. Bache possesses in a preeminent degree, that happy combination of speculative, practicable, and administrative talent, which is necessary for the highest success in the management of this great work, we earnestly desire that his services may be secured—and we therefore prefer our request for his appointment to the proper authorities.

(signed) John MacLean.
Vice President, & formerly
Prof. of Mathematics.
Albert B. Dod.
Professor of Mathematics.
Stephen Alexander,
Prof. of Astronomy, and
Adj. Prof. of Mathematics.
Joseph Henry,
Prof. Nat. Phil.

I have compared the foregoing with the original & certify it to be a true copy.

John S. Hart
Principal of the Phil[a] High School

---

[3] In two copies, one by each examiner, this word reads "could."

TO BENJAMIN PEIRCE
Peirce Papers, Houghton Library, Harvard University

[November 25, 1843][1]

This part of my letter is intended exclusively for your own eye.[2]

P.S. I regret that on your way to Philad[a] last summer you did not stop at Princeton. It would have given me much pleasure to have received you at our house and to have exhibited to you the objects of interest connected with our village. I have been engaged during my leisure time for some months past in a new series of experimts on induction and have been so fortunate as to develope some new and apparently interesting facts. I have just commenced to repeat the experiments of Melloni on radiant heat and thus far have succeeded beyond my expectation. I see by the papers that your coleague Professor Lovering has published a new vol on Natural Phil. I have not yet seen the book but intend to send for a copy.[3] Do any of your faculty intend to be present at the meeting of savants at Washington? I do not like the plan of uniting science and party politics and I cannot acknowledge the right of the Political Gentlem[en] at Washington to call a meeting of the cultivators of science in our country.[4]

J H.

[1] From the postmark and internal evidence.

[2] The first part of the letter (not found) presumably concerned Bache's candidacy for the Coast Survey. A Harvard endorsement of December 8, 1843, signed by Peirce, Daniel Treadwell, Jared Sparks, Josiah Quincy, Asa Gray, Joseph Lovering, and John Pickering, is in the Bache Papers, Smithsonian Archives. Peirce wrote to Bache on November 28 to offer his support and to inform Bache that Josiah Quincy would write to John Quincy Adams. Bache Papers, Smithsonian Archives.

[3] Perhaps Lovering's edition of John Farrar, comp., *Elements of Electricity, Magnetism, and Electro-Dynamics* ... (Boston, 1842), although Henry had expressed an opinion of this work as early as February 1843. On February 23 (Bailey Papers, Boston Science Museum), John Torrey wrote J. W. Bailey:

Prof. Henry is very severe on him [Lovering] for his new edition of Farrar's books.

You know very well that Farrar in a small advertisement (not in the title page, nor on the lettered back of the volumes) admitted that the matter was translated from Biot. In the new ed[n] the advertisement is omitted, & Prof Farrar stands as the author.—But the text betrays the negligence (as I would rather call it) of Lovering—for he makes his friend speak of his ascending in a balloon with Gay Lussac!

[4] The National Institute for the Promotion of Science was planning a "Scientific Convention" to be held in Washington in April 1844. Henry's comment typified the response of much of the scientific community, many of whom either declined the invitation or, like Henry, did not respond at all. See Sally Kohlstedt, "A Step Toward Scientific Self-Identity in the United States: The Failure of the National Institute, 1844," *Isis*, 1971, *62*:339–362.

FROM ALEXANDER DALLAS BACHE
Henry Papers, Smithsonian Archives

Nov. 26. 1843

Dear Henry.

We go on famously. Col. Abert writes a manly letter[1] going all lengths. Davies[2] ditto to Mr Spencer. The Am. Philos Soc's documents,[3] Observatory,[4] Renwick &c. have gone. The President says he is with me in feeling but is determined to go for the *scientific character of the man.* Let us intermit nothing, to satisfy him on that score! I hope you have seen Capt. Stockton & M^r. James S. Green[5] & that they are heartily with us. Do not forget to write to Silliman, to Rutgers College, to M^r. Aycrigg[6] again to M^r. Spencer telling him of how the thing is moving, to Jackson of Union, to Pierce[7] of Harvard, to Ferguson,[8] to W. B. Rogers, the more evidence we can pile the better. The Soc's paper was admirably done. If we fail, the successful man is to be pitied for he will have the science of the country pledged before hand to another.

Love to your wife from mine & me. Regards to your family. We shall send on documents from the Frank. Inst. & Acad. of Sciences &c. within a day or two.

Yours ever. A. D. Bache.

[1] Among the letters of recommendation in the Bache Papers, Smithsonian Archives, are copies of letters from all the institutions and individuals mentioned here except Abert, Stockton, Rutgers College, Aycrigg, and Ferguson.

[2] Charles Davies (1798–1876), formerly Professor of Mathematics at West Point, was at this time a major in the Army serving as paymaster for West Point. *Henry Papers, 1:*280.

[3] The recommendation of the American Philosophical Society of November 24, 1843, is printed above.

[4] Central High School Observatory.

[5] James Sproat Green (1792–1862) was a Trustee of Princeton. *Henry Papers, 1:*440.

[6] Possibly John Bancker Aycrigg (1798–

1856), an 1818 graduate of the College of Physicians and Surgeons of the City of New York. A physician in Paramus, New Jersey, Aycrigg served as a member of the House of Representatives from 1837 to 1839 and again from 1841 to 1843. He was a Whig. After leaving Congress he returned to the practice of medicine. *Biographical Directory of the American Congress.*

[7] Except for a portion of the letter to Benjamin Peirce, dated November 25, 1843 (printed above), none of Henry's letters on behalf of Bache mentioned in this letter have been located.

[8] One of the First Assistants of the Coast Survey, James Ferguson (1797–1867). *Henry Papers, 2:*15n–16n.

TO JOHN TORREY

Torrey Papers, Library, New York Botanical Garden

Princeton Dec 1st 1843

My Dear Dr

Our friend Bache of Phil[a] is a candidate for the office of superintendant of the coast survey and he is desirous of getting an expression of opinion as to his fitness for the situation from as many persons of scientific reputation as possible.

I know that he would be gratified if you would send him such a letter as your conscience will permit you to write in his favour. Let it be addressed to the President of the United states and forwarded under cover to Bache in Philad.[1] If any of your colleagues are acquainted with Bache's character it would be well to get their signatures along with your own.

I think that he is just the man for the situation. All his habits are in accordance with the power of prosecuting such a work and in acquirements he is inferior to no other person in the country.

I am glad to learn that you are quite prosperous in the medical college and hope that your prosperity will increase until you surpass in numbers your most palmy days.

Hastings has got into the harness and from the accounts which I have heard of him is doing well. I will make inquiry relative to him from time to time and let you know the result.

I am over head and ears in business. I am lecturing almost every day and hear a recitation every morning before breakfast. Nothing new in Princeton. All things going on as usual—Dull times in the winter—the best for study. My respects to Mrs T and the Girls

In haste yours
Truly
Joseph Henry

[1] Torrey had already written a strong recommendation of Bache to President Tyler in a letter of November 29, 1843, which he sent to Bache in a letter of November 30. Torrey noted that Bache had been one of his students at West Point. Bache Papers, Smithsonian Archives.

TO WILLIAM C. REDFIELD[1]
Redfield Papers, Beinecke Library, Yale University

Princeton Dec 4th 1843

My Dear Sir

Professor A. D. Bache of Phil[d] is a candidate for the office of Superintendant of the Coast Survey and his friends are anxious that he should receive testimonials in his favour from all the men of scientific reputation in our country who may be acquainted with his character and acquirements.

Will you be so good as to send on to Bache in Phil[d] a letter addressed to the President of the United States giving your opinion of his fitness for the office &c.

He will have the support of most of the scientific men of the country and in my opinion there is no person among us who can compare with him in all qualifications for the situation. The Coast Survey in its scientific bearings is the most important operation ever undertaken by our government and the manner of its completion will either redound to our credit or be a source of lasting disgrace.

> With much esteem I remain
> Yours Truly
> Joseph Henry

[1] At the bottom of the letter, Henry indicated the recipient as "W. H. Redfield Esq". For the reply, see Redfield's letter of December 21, 1843, below.

TO ALEXANDER DALLAS BACHE
Bache Papers, Smithsonian Archives

Princeton Dec 6th 1843

My Dear Bache

Yours of yesterday[1] came to hand last night and I am rejoiced to learn that our prospects are still so bright. I will write again to Mr Spencer and urge him to your appointment. I have no acquaintance with J Q Adams but I may venture to address him on the subject.[2]

I have received a letter from Professor Strong[3] regretting that he is so little acquainted with you that he cannot conscientiously give you such a

[1] Not found.
[2] We have not found another letter to Spencer or one to J. Q. Adams.
[3] Theodore Strong, Professor of Mathematics and Natural Philosophy at Rutgers. We have not found the letter.

letter as would be of much service to your cause. The letter appears to be written in good feeling and gives the true reason for the Professors not complying with the request which I made him.

From Albany as yet I have heard nothing although I do not doubt that Dr Beck has written to Spencer on the subject.[4] On Thursday (tomorrow) we have Thanksgiving in our state and this will give me a day of leisure on which I will send off a batch of letters.

I did think of *Professor* Mapes[5] of New York who figures largely in the Mechanics Institute of that city but I do not know how you stand related to him in regard to the transactions of the Franklin Institute. If you think it best to condesend to ask a letter from him drop me a line. I have thought of some gentlemen at the South to whom I will write and whose letters may have some weight.[6] I wish you would get some person of your acquaintance to write to Millington. He is intimate with the President and his opinion might have some weight.[7]

I wrote to Redfield[8] and thought at the time that perhaps he might be committed to Blunt.[9] I am not sorry that Blunt is a candidate for if the coast surveyors are rivals among themselves your cause will be strengthened by the dissention. I have made this remark because I gather from your letter that Mr Blunt is a candidate.

The class are pressing me for the continuation of my Syllabus. I have now

[4] T. R. Beck wrote Robley Dunglison on December 4, 1843, that he had already enthusiastically responded to a solicitation from Henry. Bache Papers, Smithsonian Archives.

[5] J. J. Mapes. See above, Henry to Torrey, December 20, 1841.

[6] Henry wrote Lewis R. Gibbes of the College of Charleston the same day (printed below) and W. H. Ellet of South Carolina College. Ellet replied that he had already recommended Bache (February 29, 1844, Henry Papers, Smithsonian Archives).

[7] John Millington (*Henry Papers*, 2:28n–29n), formerly of Philadelphia, wrote Bache from the College of William and Mary on December 4 to tell him he was on friendly and social terms with President Tyler and would write him a confidential letter supporting Bache's candidacy. Millington also announced his intention of applying for Bache's chair at the University of Pennsylvania. Bache Papers, Smithsonian Archives.

[8] On December 4, printed above.

[9] Edmund Blunt (1799–1866), son of Edmund March Blunt and brother of George William Blunt, was appointed First Assistant of the Coast Survey in 1833 and remained with the

Survey until his death. As Hassler's First Assistants, both James Ferguson and Edmund Blunt were obvious candidates for the superintendency. Blunt was one of the foremost hydrographers in the United States and had served on the committee whose plan of reorganization of the Survey was adopted by Congress in 1843.

Originally an intimate of Hassler, Blunt later became a close friend of Bache. Harold Burstyn describes the mutually beneficial relationship between the Coast Survey and the firm of E. & G. W. Blunt in New York City, in effect a New York branch of the Survey. G. W. Blunt also became intimate with Bache and frequently used his extensive political connections and forceful personality on behalf of the Survey.

Harold L. Burstyn, *At the Sign of the Quadrant: An Account of the Contributions to American Hydrography Made by Edmund March Blunt and His Sons* (Mystic, Connecticut, 1957). Burstyn (p. 94) points out an error in the *DAB* entry on G. W. Blunt which describes him (instead of Edmund) as the Coast Survey employee from 1833. The error also appears in *Henry Papers*, 2:466n.

in press the last part of somatology and have got through with that most crabbed of all subjects capillarity.

Yours as ever
Joseph Henry

Respects to Mrs. B.

TO LEWIS R. GIBBES
Gibbes Papers, Library of Congress

Princeton Dec 6th 1843

My Dear Sir

Professor Bache late president of Girard College is a candidate for the vacant office of superintendant of the Coast Survey and his friends are desirous of procuring as many testimonials in his favour from men of science in our country as possible. Will you be so good as to send on to Bache in Phil^d. a letter addressed to the President of the United States or to one of the secretaries giving your opinion of his fitness for the office.[1]

I am sure that there is no person in this country can compare with Bache in qualifications for the successful prosecution of the work. Joined to a range of theoretical knowledge which embraces almost the whole circle of the Physical sciences he possesses practical skill, common sense, good judgement and the power of directing and controlling men in a higher degree than any person with whom I have ever been acquainted. I have little doubt of his election but it will be a source of gratification to him even should he fail to know that his application has been backed by some of the best names in science of which our country can boast. I am sure from your knowledge of his character and your own fitness to judge in such matters that you will not hesitate to give him a warm letter.

I have now by me a copy of the proceedings of the American Phil. Society at their hundredth anniversary which I would be pleased to send you did I know of an opportunity. It is about the size of one of the usual numbers of Silliman's journal and therefore I fear too large to be sent by mail. I am much obliged to you for the papers you sent me. I read the controversy with considerable interest. You had by far the best of the dispute but your opponent was one of those happy men who never know when they are beaten.[2]

[1] Before Gibbes could react to Henry's request, he read of the selection of Bache in the newspaper. Gibbes to Henry, March 13, 1844, Henry Papers, Smithsonian Archives.

[2] Gibbes had gotten involved in an extended public exchange of letters with Richard Yeadon (1802–1870, *DAB*), editor of the *Charleston Courier*. Initially, the two men had clashed over the genuineness of the "Feejee Mermaid," on exhibit in Charleston during

December 6, 1843

I think I mentioned in my last letter[3] that Bache had informed me that the ingenious instrument you invented for the determination of the height of a cloud was not interely new. I think he informed me that one somewhat similar had been presented for consideration to the Franklin Institute.[4] When you next visit the North I hope you will not forget Princeton.

With much esteem
yours Truly
Joseph Henry

Dr J K Mitchells experiments on magnetism have not yet been published but when they are I will send you a copy.[5] You ask me relative to my experiments on electricity.

January 1843. Yeadon was careful not to claim that the mermaid was authentic, but he did state that he saw no evidence of fraud. Gibbes, on the other hand, was one of a number of Charleston naturalists who rejected the mermaid out-of-hand as a scientific impossibility, arguing that it was probably a combination of a fish body and the head and chest of an ape.

The subject of the exchange rapidly expanded, however, from the specific issue of the authenticity of the mermaid to the more general question of the necessity of society to defer to the expertise of the scientist in scientific matters. Yeadon advanced the thesis that an intelligent and careful observer, even without scientific training, was qualified to pass judgement on issues within the scientific arena, as long as these issues were empirical in nature. Gibbes rejected this notion, asserting that since the trained observer could see much more than the untrained observer, society should defer to the superior credentials of the trained observer. Scientific questions were not decided by simply counting the noses on each side of an issue, but by weighing the scientific competence of each observer. *Charleston Courier*, February 6, 14, 15, 22, 23, March 2, 20, 21 22, 23, 24, 25, 1843.

Charleston was not the only community to see controversy over the mermaid. Purchased from a sailor by Moses Kimball of Boston, the mermaid had been exhibited in New York with considerable publicity by P. T. Barnum in 1842. In response, William McGuigan, a taxidermist at the Philadelphia Museum, exhibited a "Japanese Mermaid," which was advertised as a man-made contrivance and raised questions about the authenticity of the Feejee Mermaid. Charles Coleman Sellers, *Mr. Peale's Museum: Charles Willson Peale and the First Popular Museum of Natural Science and Art* (New York, 1980), pp. 299, 301.

The Charleston debate had long-term consequences for the mermaid. Subsequent exhibitions in the South attracted far fewer patrons than anticipated, and the tour was cut short. When reexhibited in New York, the advertising was considerably toned down; claims of authenticity had been diluted by the admission of some scientific rejection. Neil Harris, *Humbug: The Art of P. T. Barnum* (Boston and Toronto, 1973), pp. 65–67.

[3] Not found.

[4] As Henry made explicit in his letter of February 5, 1844 (Gibbes Papers, Library of Congress), he was referring to an instrument which measured the distance to an object with just one observation by utilizing a fixed and a moveable mirror. Although the Committee on Inventions of the Franklin Institute had given the prototype of this instrument a favorable evaluation, there is no record that the inventor patented it. "On Two Reflecting Instruments for Measuring Distances at a Single Observation; by Nathan Scholfield, of Montville, New London County, Connecticut," *Journal of the Franklin Institute*, 1833, n.s. *11*:152–156.

[5] Henry is probably referring to John Kearsley Mitchell's "An Essay Upon Animal Magnetism, or Vital Induction," which summarizes a series of experiments conducted by Mitchell upon mesmerized subjects, and includes comparisons of the physiological parameters of such subjects compared to individuals naturally asleep. Mitchell did not publish this paper in his lifetime. It does appear in a posthumous publication: John K. Mitchell, *Five Essays*, ed. S. Weir Mitchell (Philadelphia, 1859), pp. 141–274.

Henry and Mitchell had discussed mesmerism during one of Henry's visits to Philadelphia. See above, Henry to Harriet Henry, April 22, 1843.

The most surprising results I have obtained are those relative to induction at a distance.[6] I find that by stretching a wire across the college campus and passing a discharge of electricity through this from a single jar or even from a single spark from the machine I am enable to magnetize needles over the whole college grounds without any connection. The effect is intirely produced by the disturbance of the electricity of space which appears to be commensurate with the disturbance of the luminiferous ether in the transmission of light J. H.

[6] Gibbes's initial reaction upon learning of Henry's first success at long-distance induction (reported in "Contributions V: Induction from Ordinary Electricity; Oscillatory Discharge," p. 195) was awe. He wrote that he thought Henry's work "almost equals clairvoyance." Gibbes to Henry, partial Mary Henry Copy, March 11, 1843, Henry Papers, Smithsonian Archives.

FROM ALEXANDER DALLAS BACHE
Henry Papers, Smithsonian Archives

(Confidential)
Philad. Wednesday Ev͞g
Dec. 6. [1843]

Dear Henry.

M͟r Kane went down to Washington on Tuesday & to night a letter brings the information that the Pres͟t has made up his mind in my favour, but will wait to declare himself until my brother in law R. J. Walker reaches Washington, which by the blessing of Providence will be next week. Still we cannot tell what changes may come over the dream and I feel still uncertain. Pour in all the letters you can. It is strange that a man who stands like Strong should be willing to say he has not attended to the progress of physical science in the country, or should require to *see* a man to *know* him. I beg you write to him & apologize for my having addressed him, on the score of previous correspondence. I feel ashamed to have been taken in. Carlisle. Western Reserve. Middlebury Vt. have come in since I wrote to you.[1]

Kindest regards to Mrs. H. from M͟rs B.

Ever Yours
A. D. Bache

[1] A reference to recommendations from Dickinson College, signed by J. P. Durbin, President, and four other faculty members; from Western Reserve College, signed by Elias Loomis and six colleagues; and from Middlebury College, signed by Alexander C. Twining. Two copies of each are in Box 6, Bache Papers, Smithsonian Archives.

December 13, 1843

FROM ALEXANDER DALLAS BACHE
Henry Papers, Smithsonian Archives

Philad. Dec. 13. 1843.

Dear Henry.

The end has come & I have my letter of appointment in due form. To-morrow or next day I shall go on to Washington to see how matters look. The regulations adopted by the Coast S. Board last winter which I saw for the first time last evening trammel me to any annoying extent, but then they are mere regulations & if I can get Mr Spencer's confidence may be accommodated to *circumstances*.[1] Any hints in furtherance of that object, give me if you possess the arcana. Should you write to Washington inclose to Hon. R. J. Walker U. S. Senate.

The Trustees of the Univ. here would be *so* glad to have you. I have been urged in various quarters to approach you.

I will write to you soon again. Love to Mrs H. from M^{rs} B &

Yours ever truly
A. D. Bache

P. S. When the *official* announcement of my app^{t}ment is made take care that the press do not go off in the wrong direction & abuse the Survey. Pray write to the same effect to Dr. Beck at albany or any one who has influence there & will attend to the matter.[2] Let them send you the papers wh. furnish me with. Yrs.

---

[1] Bache soon realized that the "mere regulations" had the force of law. See his letter to Henry of December 26, below, especially footnote 9.

[2] See Henry's letters to Kinney, December 14, and to Bache, December 16, printed below.

FROM ROBERT M. PATTERSON
Henry Papers, Smithsonian Archives

Philadelphia.
Dec. 13, 1843.

My dear Sir,

Our friend Bache has received his appointment in due form. His professorship in the University will of course become vacant. Have any circumstances occurred to change your determination not to leave Princeton; or can you be persuaded to take Bache's chair?[1] You would unite the voices of the whole Board of Trustees. Let me know your thoughts with regard to this matter.

Ever your friend,
R. M. Patterson

[1] Patterson nominated Henry as a candidate for the Chair of Natural Philosophy and Chemistry at the University of Pennsylvania once before, in July 1836. Henry had then indicated that he would decline if the position were offered to him. *Henry Papers, 3*:80, 82–83, 86–87.

FROM BENJAMIN WOOD RICHARDS[1]
Henry Papers, Smithsonian Archives

Philadª Decʳ 14, 1843

Dear Sir,

It is now ascertained that the place of the late Mr. Hassler will be given to Prof. Dallas Bache, which will result in a vacant Professorship in the University of Pennª. As a Trustee I feel much interest in the subject. From a casual conversation after the last meeting of the board of Trustees I feel confident of the preference & wishes of a large number of the board & know of no conflicting preference. That preference would be for yourself.

The suggestion has been made that if elected you would decline the appointment. The importance of the subject to the University & its pupils, must justify me in writing you and in asking if we may not hope for your acceptance, if the invitation should be made by the board. I am aware of the delicacy to be observed in the matter & write under the impression that any slight intimation would determine the board in the case. I need not add my own wishes. I am

very respʸ & truly yrs
B. W. Richards

[1] Richards (1797–1851) was a graduate of Princeton (1815), a former Mayor of Philadelphia, a member of the American Philosophical Society, and a Trustee of the University of Pennsylvania from 1836 to 1851. Stephen N. Winslow, *Biographies of Successful Merchants of Philadelphia* (Philadelphia, 1864), pp. 209–211.

TO WILLIAM B. KINNEY
Kinney Family Papers, New Jersey Historical Society

Princeton Dec 14th 1843

My Dear Sir

My friend Professor A D Bache has been appointed to the office of super-intendant of the coast survey and you will much oblige me when the announcement is officially made by giving the appointment such a notice as the scientific and general character of Bache in your opinion may deserve.[1] There were a number of applicants for the office and consequently there are now several disappointed individuals among whom there may be one who would not scruple to speak disparagingly of the appointment of Bache.

The office in a scientific point of view is by far the most important our government could be called on to fill and I think the selection is the very best that could have been made. Bache not only possesses profound theoretical knowledge but also practical skill and the talents of an executive kind so necessary to carry on this extensive and complicated work. The announcement of his appointment will be received with pleasure by every man of scientific reputation in our country.

With my kind regards to your son and compliments to Mrs Kinney whose acquaintance I hope to have the pleasure of forming at some future time permit me to subscribe myself

Most sincerely yours &c.

Joseph Henry

This letter was written in the early part of last evening and when the Daily was received I found an article copied from the American in it of precisely the character <*which was*> anticipated.[2]

The coast survey is a work in which the scientific character of our country is more involved than in any other ever attempted on this side of the atlantic and the superintendence of it should be intrusted to no one but a man of well established scientific reputation. It should be given to one who has much to lose by failure and who seeks the office not on account of its emolument in a pecuniary point of view but as an object worthy of his

---

[1] Henry's request was fulfilled in the December 18, 1843, issue of the *Newark Daily Advertiser* under the heading "The Coast Survey." Sandwiched between excerpts from extremely favorable commentaries on Bache's selection from other newspapers was a revised version of part of the postscript of this letter (the first two sentences of the second paragraph), without attribution.

[2] The December 14, 1843, issue of the *Newark Daily Advertiser* carried an article originally printed in the *New York American* accusing Bache of inexperience in the manipulation of instruments, a necessary skill in the Coast Survey, and pleading that Hassler's assistants, who combined scientific attainment and practical skill, be considered for the position.

ambition and to which he may devote all the energies of his mind with an eye single to <*the*> its completion <*of the works*> in such a manner as to merit the approbation of the whole scientific world. I am well acquainted with Mr. Ferguson and Mr Blunt and on their account personally I am sorry that Bache has received the appointment but for the cause of the scientific reputation of the country I rejoice that he has been selected. But one of these gentlemen could have been appointed and it is no desparagement of their characters to be superceeded by [such] a man as Bache. There is no danger that they will resign or that the government will be deprived of the skill in their respective departments.

TO ALEXANDER DALLAS BACHE
Mary Henry Copy, Henry Papers, Smithsonian Archives

Princeton Dec. 16. 1843

My dear Bache. Permit me to offer you my most sincere and heartfelt congratulations on the success of your application and to express the hope that the situation will prove all your friends think it is and that it may offer you even more facilities for promoting and advancing science than has yet been anticipated. I do not doubt that you will have many difficulties to contend with but I have full faith in your ability to overcome them and that under your direction the coast survey will assume an entirely new aspect and become a work of which our country with good reason will be proud.

I have written to Dr. Beck,[1] thanking him for the favorable sentiments expressed in his letters relative to you and asking him to put the newspapers of Albany on the right track relative to your appointment.[2] I have also written to the Editor of the Newark Daily requesting him when your appointment is officially announced to give it a proper notice.[3]

I have had two letters from Philadelphia on the subject of the University,[4] which I have not yet had time to answer. I have no thought at present of accepting the office but at the same time if the salary were such as to more than compensate for the pains and difficulties of leaving Princeton I would go. The only objection to my present situation is that I am obliged to spend from two to three hundred dollars more than my salary annually.

Yours as ever
Joseph Henry

[1] Not found.
[2] The December 18, 1843, issue of the *Albany Evening Journal* contained a short notice of Bache's appointment.
[3] See immediately above.
[4] Robert M. Patterson's letter of December 13, 1843, and Benjamin W. Richards's letter of December 14, 1843, printed above.

TO [BENJAMIN WOOD RICHARDS]
Draft, Henry Papers, Smithsonian Archives

Princeton Dec 18th 1843

My Dear Sir

Your kind letter of the 14th was received on the 16th but such have been my engagements that I could not find time to give the subject a serious consideration until yesterday.[1] The inducements to accept the chair in the university of Penn^a are very great. I am very partial to your city and feel much indebted to my many friends in the Philosophical society for their kind support and sympathy in my scientific labours. I am also on terms of intimacy and friendship with several of the officers of the university and I am confident that I would harmonize with them in my views of education and <*the duties of the office*> discipline. On the other hand I am very much attached to Princeton and to my colleagues in this co[l]lege.[2] The years I have spent in this p[la]ce have been the smoothest and by far the happiest of my Life. I have the confidence and good feeling of the Trustees and know that there is a disposition on their part to make me as comfortable as the circumstances of the institution will permit. The only cause I have for dissatisfaction is the smallness of my salary (15 hundred and a free hous) but I have been assured since the receipt of your letter that efforts will be made to diminish this objection.

I have had a confidential conversation with the President and Professor Maclean and they both assure me that if the college continues prosperous my salary will be increased.[3] I have therefore concluded not to become a candidate for the chair in the university and should not accept if I were elected. Your letter and one I received from Dr Pat[terson] have induced me to consider my posit[ion] at Princeton and have been the occas[ion] of the conversation I mentioned above. I hope the result will be[4]

---

[1] Richards's letter is printed above.

[2] Here, and below, tears in the page have obliterated some letters.

[3] Although Princeton did not increase Henry's salary, during the next year the college purchased a $3,000 life insurance policy for him. The annual premium was $200. Trustees' Minutes, December 20, 1844 (3:448).

[4] The draft breaks off here.

FROM WILLIAM C. REDFIELD

Henry Papers, Smithsonian Archives[1]

New York December 21st 1843

Dear Sir,

Your letter[2] relating to the appointment of Prof. Bache to the Coast Survey was duly received, but illness and other causes prevented me from acknowledging it at that time. I had, however, previously received and answered a letter from Profr. Bache on this subject.

As he is now placed at the head of the survey it seems desirable that the opportunity should be taken to introduce a new feature into the work of the topographical parties, (if indeed it should prove to be new,) viz: the delineation of the *geological* features and outlines belonging to the topography. This might perhaps be accomplished without adding to the numerical strength or the aggregate expence of the topographical parties; provided that they will attend properly to the subject and seek, if necessary, proper guidance. The results which might thus be obtained seem too important to be overlooked, whether as viewed in their relations to practical agriculture, to geological science, or to the requisite basis for military operations and works, of a defensive character.

It has heretofore been deemed necessary to distinguish the topographical surface by its varying features of woodlands and meadow, sands and marshes, &c.: and how much *more enduring* and important are the geological characters, positions, and boundaries of the erupted rocks & the stratified formations, as well as the distinguishing peculiarities of the great deposits of *drift*, the sands, and the alluvions? Doubtless there is reason to fear that any public proposition to unite a geological corps with the survey might frighten our Congress from its propriety. But I am willing to believe that much may be done toward securing these delineations in the topography under so accomplished a superintendant as Prof. Bache; without disturbing, or affecting injuriously the established order of the survey.[3]

[1] Redfield's retained copy is in the Redfield Papers, Beinecke Library, Yale University.

[2] Of December 4, 1843, printed above.

[3] Henry's file note, written after receipt of the letter in 1844, reads: "Redfield on the importance of connecting Geological notations with the coast survey." Although no reply of Henry's survives, there is evidence of his awareness of the desirability of combining the various kinds of surveys sponsored by the federal government. For example, see Henry's letter to Elias Loomis of April 22, 1847, in N. Reingold, ed., *Science in Nineteenth-Century America: A Documentary History* (New York, 1964), pp. 155–156.

Redfield's suggestion (and Henry's later one) clearly relate to federal policy on the settlement and use of the lands within the borders of the United States. They also raise the question of the relations of particular intellectual traditions, in this case natural history and geophysics. Bache did not include geology within the work of the Coast Survey. For a discussion of these issues, even noting this particular letter, see N. Reingold, "Alexander Dallas Bache: Science and Technology in the American Idiom," *Technology and Culture,* 1970, *11*:163–177.

I cannot however suppose that this subject has escaped your own attention and that of Profr. Bache, and if, through your friendly relations with him, you can strengthen his hands in any wise for the accomplishment of this end, you will assist in earning for him the gratitude of future generations.

I am Dear Sir
very truly yours
Wm C. Redfield

FROM ALEXANDER DALLAS BACHE
Henry Papers, Smithsonian Archives

Washington. Dec. 26. 1843.

My dear friend

I have waited to answer your very kind letter[1] until I could discern something of the signs of the times, but they show themselves slowly. At first every thing was so new & strange that I felt a good deal isolated, since then so many difficulties of the minor sort have been disposed of that I feel as if the greater ones would in their turn yield. Ferguson came on here full of mortification & of wrath, but after talking with his friends & seeing the Secretary, he came to see me: if I had seen him then I might further have soothed him & as it is will go to his house at Wilmington during my visit to Philad. Mr Spencer appears very cordial & is a real man of business. So far he has shown a disposition to take my views & except that he holds back the Weights & Measures which absolutely require my control & that speedily he has been all I could have asked in a Secretary.[2] The work is in a state of disorganization & what is worse is trammeled by bad legislation.[3] All va-

[1] Henry's letter of December 16 is printed above. Bache's letter is postmarked January 6 and was sent under the frank of J. C. Spencer.

[2] Although the Constitution gave the federal government the power to establish standard weights and measures, Congress had never passed legislation establishing an office for the work. Responsibility for the construction and verification of standard weights and measures had been given to Hassler but was not officially part of his duties as Superintendent of the Coast Survey and therefore did not pass automatically to Bache. A letter from Spencer to Bache of December 28, 1843 (Box 3, Bache Papers, Smithsonian Archives) promised Bache the additional authority. Weights and mea-

sures remained under the supervision of the head of the Coast Survey until the establishment of the National Bureau of Standards in 1901. Gustavus A. Weber, *The Bureau of Standards: Its History, Activities and Organization* (Baltimore, 1925), pp. 1–36. Rexmond C. Cochrane, *Measures for Progress: A History of the National Bureau of Standards* (Washington, 1966), pp. 16–47. Arthur H. Frazier, *United States Standards of Weights and Measures: Their Creation and Creators*, Smithsonian Studies in History and Technology no. 40 (Washington, 1978).

[3] Hassler's numerous deficiencies in management and public relations finally led to Congressional investigations in 1842. An act of

cancies in the field work on land are required to be filled up by topographical officers & their chief will not spare them.[4] It is no get off so but actual *law*.[5] I sent young Boutelle to Mr. Spencer, the other day, & with Jno. Q. Adams to back him & Mr S. went so far as to hint that perhaps Congress might make the military character of the work even stronger than it is.[6] Up to a certain point I agree to this, but to go too far would injure the Survey. The assistants have of course no claim upon me & I suppose will as they appear from their correspondence to have done in regard to my predecessor, worry me. Some of them have not kept their chagrin within decent bounds. They judge me as men are wont to judge of others by themselves & having much requiring to be covered up they imagine that I will be disposed to

---

March 3, 1843, called for a board composed of Hassler, his two principal assistants (Blunt and Ferguson), two naval officers, and four topographical engineers, to draw up a plan of reorganization. Approved by President Tyler on April 29, 1843, the plan gave considerable autonomy to the assistants and chiefs of the surveying parties and allowed them to report directly to the Treasury Department. When Bache became Superintendent, he found himself bound by a plan which had been designed expressly to restrict the authority of the idiosyncratic Hassler.

The plan of reorganization is printed in *Laws Relating to the Survey of the Coast of the United States; With the Plan of Reorganization of 1843, and Regulations by the Treasury Department* (Washington, 1858), pp. 9–14. For Hassler's problems with his superiors and with Congress, see Florian Cajori, *The Chequered Career of Ferdinand Rudolph Hassler* (1929; reprint ed., New York, 1980), especially chapter 13.

[4] The Topographical Engineers, under J. J. Abert, were heavily engaged in western exploration and mapping. William H. Goetzmann, *Army Exploration in the American West, 1803–1863* (New Haven, 1959).

[5] According to the plan of reorganization (article 20): "All vacancies which may occur hereafter in the scientific department of the coast survey, shall be supplied from the army, if having reference to the operations upon land; and from the navy, if in reference to the operations upon the water. . . ."

Adherents of the use of army and navy personnel on the Coast Survey feared that the Survey, with its own civilian staff, might become a permanent scientific establishment. They also argued the economy of employing men already on the government payroll.

The problem of civilian versus military control and personnel had always plagued Hassler. It was in fact an 1818 act outlawing civilian participation that caused a fourteen-year suspension of the Survey just as it was getting started.

Bache was successful in keeping the Coast Survey a civilian establishment that relied heavily on military personnel. The Mexican War gave him dramatic proof that civilians were necessary to keep the Survey in operation. See, for example, the *Annual Report of the Superintendent of the Coast Survey . . . 1851* (Washington, 1852), pp. 6–7, 9. See also A. Hunter Dupree, *Science in the Federal Government* (1957; reprint ed., New York, 1980), pp. 29–33, 52–56, 100–103.

[6] Adams recorded the visit in his diary for December 23:

. . . Mr Charles Boutelle brought me a Letter of introduction from judge John Davis of Boston. Mr Boutelle is a young civil engineer who has been employed in the survey of the Northeastern Boundary, and wishes now employment on the Coast Survey. I went with him and introduced him to the Secretary of the Treasury John C. Spencer who gave him no encouragement to expect employment for the present or approaching Season. Microfilm reel 47, Adams Papers, Massachusetts Historical Society.

Charles O. Boutelle (1813–1890) was a native of Lexington, Massachusetts, and a college graduate. By the spring of 1844, he was working for the Coast Survey. Except for Civil War service, Boutelle remained actively employed as an assistant on the Survey until shortly before his death in 1890. Obituary in the *Norfolk Landmark*, June 24, 1890. *Report of the Superintendent of the U.S. Coast and Geodetic Survey* (Washington, 1891), p. 84.

bring it up in judgment against them. How the Survey has gone on is to me a marvel, for the time that has been lost in quarreling is immense & the results of the quarrels prevented co operation & superintendence. The present sec. has been indoctrinated by the assistants on the Survey, fully. He thinks its exclusiveness is right, that it employs the best talents in the country, that the science in it is far greater than that out of it &c. His general feeling is aided by the locality from which Blunt & Ferguson hail.[7] Rumour says that he will be translated to the bench of the Supreme Court[8] in which case a gentleman not bound to this car may take his place. The absolute obstacle put by the present law for the rules have that force, renders it highly desirable that the provisions should be set aside by a different act: the assistants are quite independent except by the courtesy of the Sec. & have the nomination of *their* assistants. The usages are of a kind wholly unscientific. I hope in time to get the better of these formidable obstacles, but time will be necessary, especially as *the Corps* have reconsidered their resolution to resign en-masse.[9]

---

[7] Blunt and Ferguson were New Yorkers, as was Spencer. Robert Post points out that New York City was the center of opposition to Bache. "Science, Public Policy, and Popular Precepts: Alexander Dallas Bache and Alfred Beach as Symbolic Adversaries," in *The Sciences in the American Context: New Perspectives*, ed. Nathan Reingold (Washington, 1979), p. 84.

[8] The death of Justice Smith Thompson on December 19, 1843, left vacant the Second Circuit seat on the Supreme Court. Tyler did send Spencer's name to the Senate but his nomination was rejected. Carl B. Swisher, *History of the Supreme Court of the United States*, volume 5, *The Taney Period, 1836-64* (New York and London, 1974), pp. 213-215.

[9] After President Tyler approved the plan of reorganization in April 1843 (footnote 3, above), the Coast Survey operated under regulations issued by Spencer on June 3, 1843. Bache may be objecting specifically to these regulations in addition to the plan of reorganization itself. In April 1844, undoubtedly in response to Bache, Spencer issued new regulations which gave the Superintendent much more control, particularly over the senior assistants. For instance, whereas the June 1843 regulations required that monthly reports of the chiefs of surveying parties be submitted directly to the Treasury Department, those of April 15, 1844, stipulated that they be addressed to the Superintendent, who would present a summary to the Department.

One of the April 1844 rules exemplified the Superintendent's increased authority: "All communications, including reports, estimates, and applications, between the persons employed in the survey of the coast and the Treasury Department, and all directions to said persons, will pass through the superintendent."

The June 3, 1843, regulations, apparently never printed, are entitled "Arrangements and directions for executing the coast survey according to the plan submitted by the Board lately organised to the President and approved by him" and are in the National Archives, RG 23, Records of the Coast and Geodetic Survey, Letters Sent by the Treasury Department Regarding the Coast Survey, volume 1, pp. 201-207. The 1844 regulations, entitled "Arrangements and directions for executing the survey of the coast, according to the plan approved by the President on the 29th of April, 1843," are printed in *Laws Relating to the Survey of the Coast of the United States; With the Plan of Reorganization of 1843, and Regulations by the Treasury Department* (Washington, 1858), pp. 15-20.

Besides maneuvering internally for more control over his subordinates, and organizing to make the Survey more efficient and productive, Bache had to gain support for the Survey in Congress. As an expensive and supposedly temporary activity, the Survey was always vulnerable at appropriation time. Unlike Hassler, whose relations with Congress were hos-

I expect to be in Philad. by the close of this week. Kind regards to Mrs. Henry.

Yours truly
A. D. Bache.

---

tile, Bache consciously built support for the Survey. He lined up the scientific community behind him, put survey parties in more areas (and congressional districts), began publishing maps and charts, and explained coherently and in great detail exactly what the Survey accomplished in annual reports that grew from 22 pages in 1844 (compared to Hassler's last report of 8 pages) to 561 in 1851.

As future volumes of the *Henry Papers* will show, Henry and Bache remained confidants and allies after one and then the other moved to Washington to head a national scientific organization. Henry was able to benefit from Bache's Washington experience when he became head of the Smithsonian Institution in 1846.

Bache's stewardship of the Coast Survey is concisely evaluated in A. Hunter Dupree, *Science in the Federal Government*, pp. 100–105. See also Merle M. Odgers, *Alexander Dallas Bache: Scientist and Educator, 1806–1867* (Philadelphia, 1947), especially chapter 12.

RECOMMENDATION[1] FOR JOHN F. FRAZER[2]
Archives, University of Pennsylvania

Princeton Dec 26ᵗʰ 1843

I am informed that Mr. John Frazer is a candidate for the chair of Natural Philosophy and chemistry in the University of Penn\ᵃ and I beg leave to recommend him as a person in my opinion peculiarly well qualified for the situation. I have been intimately acquainted with him for some years and have formed a high opinion of his talents and scientific acquirements.

I have had an opportunity of hearing him lecture on several occasions and I am free to say that he possesses the faculty of imparting knowledge in this way superior to almost any person with whom I am acquainted. As a graduate of the institution, an assistant of Professor Bache, a native of Philᵈ and a gentleman of acknowledged ability as a teacher and a man of science I should think he would be the most prominent candidate for the chair.

Joseph Henry

---

[1] Henry presented this letter to Frazer to use as necessary. Henry to Robley Dunglison, February 10, 1844, Retained Copy, Henry Papers, Smithsonian Archives.

[2] A scientist whose reputation was based on his skills as a teacher, editor, and critic, rather than as a researcher, John Fries Frazer (1812–1872) studied science with Bache while a student at the University of Pennsylvania, graduating in 1830. Prior to his successful candidacy to succeed his former teacher in the Chair of Chemistry and Natural Philosophy at Pennsylvania, he practiced law, worked for the Pennsylvania Geological Survey, and taught the physical sciences at Philadelphia's Central High School. He remained at Pennsylvania until his death. Also active in the Franklin Institute, Frazer edited its *Journal* from 1850 until 1866. *Elliott.*

FROM A STUDENT
Henry Papers, Smithsonian Archives

Thursday Morning [ca. 1843]

Dear Sir

As you are the friend to one of the parties that are going to be engaged in a duel, I think myself bound to inform you of it. They are Petigru & McWhorter.[1] If you wish to be of any service, act speedily.

A Student

[1] Dan Petigru of Charleston, South Carolina, and George Gray McWhorter of Augusta, Georgia, were in the Class of 1843. Both show up frequently as disciplinary problems in the faculty minutes.

The laws of the College expressly forbade any involvement in a duel:

Any student convicted of sending or receiving a challenge to fight a duel, who shall carry such challenge, or be a second in a duel, or in any wise aid or abet it, shall immediately be dismissed by the faculty, and as soon as practicable expelled by the trustees. *Laws of the College of New Jersey* (Princeton, 1839).

Henry noted on the bottom: "attended to this matter had the difficulty settled."

Under a name, "letter from" signifies a letter from that person to Henry, while "letter to" indicates a letter from Henry to that person. When Henry is neither sender nor recipient, the names of both parties are given. In the case of Henry, "letters from," followed by a list of names, indicates letters to Henry; "letters to," Henry's letters to various recipients. Subentries are so arranged that letters and documents precede the customary alphabetical listing.

Index

Atkinson, Joseph M., 44
Atmospheric phenomena, 3, 22, 24, 25n, 42–43, 257, 405
  electricity, 66n–67n, 82, 257, 392n
    apparatus, 292n–293n
  See also Meteorology.
Atwood Machine, 135, 157, 162n
Audubon, John James, 305n
Aurora borealis, 24, 25n, 121
Autographs, collecting of, 357n
Aycrigg, John Bancker, 462

Babbage, Charles, xxv, 130
Babinet, Jacques, 32, 33n, 35, 48, 351
Bache, Alexander Dallas, xiii, xxvi, 19, 21, 30n, 75, 97n, 120, 148, 152, 238, 239, 241n, 242, 263, 269, 280n, 283, 363, 365, 390n
  letters from, 23–25, 128–131, 226–227, 255, 258–259, 303, 326–327, 352–353, 447, 454, 455, 462, 468, 469, 475–478
  letters to, 76–78, 123–124, 229–230, 254, 448–450, 455–456, 464–466, 472
  Michael Faraday to Bache, 118–119

  and American Philosophical Society, 303n, 318, 324, 353, 363, 444n
  and Coast Survey
    appointment as Superintendent of the Coast Survey, 254n, 259n, 469, 470, 471, 472, 474, 475–477
    hostility to, 471n, 477
    impact on scientific work, 456
    candidacy for Superintendent of the Coast Survey, xiv, 365n, 450–451, 452–454, 455, 457–459, 459–460, 461n, 462, 463, 464–465, 466, 468
    Congressional support for, 477n–478n
    reaction to 1843 reorganization, 476n, 477n
  European trip, 118
  and Girard College, 128–130, 137, 258n–259n, 451, 453, 466
  and natural philosophy text, 449
  as scientist
    meteorology, 24, 90, 235, 353
    terrestrial magnetism, 75, 76–78, 120, 130, 281n, 282, 285, 353, 423n, 447
  and *Silliman's Journal*, xvi, 306, 447, 448–449
  and University of Pennsylvania, xiv, 254, 255, 259n, 454n
  and University of Virginia, 258, 269, 273n
Bache, Franklin, 134n, 303, 458
Bache, George M., 226, 227n
Bache, Nancy Clarke Fowler (Mrs. A. D.), 75, 78, 118, 130, 226, 229, 230, 255, 263, 303n, 447, 456, 462, 466, 468, 469
Backus, John Chester, 74
Baconianism, 415

Bailey, Jacob Whitman, xiv, 259n, 273n, 305, 461n
  Bailey to John Torrey, 268–272
Bailey, Maria Slaughter (Mrs. J. W.), 269, 272
Baily, Francis, 142
Baird, Charles Washington, 157, 162
Baird, Fermine Du Buisson (Mrs. Robert), 157, 162
Baird, Robert, 119n, 124
  letters from, 156–157, 161–162
  letter to, 135
Baldwin, C. C., Jr., 44
Baldwin, Matthias William, 458
Ballard, William Henry, 360, 370n
Ballistic pendulum, 295n
Ballistics, 294–297
  application of electricity to, xxix, 295–297, 301, 346, 353, 358, 411
Baltimore, terrestrial magnetic observations at, 281n, 282–283
Bancker, Charles N., 33n
  letter to, 104–105
Bank of New York, 222, 223n
Bank of Princeton, 223n
Bank of the United States, Second, 5n, 223n
Banking system, United States, 145
Banks, Joseph, 143n
Banks, Philadelphia, 160–161
Bard, William, 356
Barnum, P. T., 467n
Barometer, 24, 25n
Bartlett, W. H. C., 135, 156, 281n, 282–283, 321n
  letter from, 226–227
Bartlett, Mrs. W. H. C., 227
Barton, Isaac, 83
Bates, Ralph S., cited, 3n, 318n
Bathe, Dorothy, cited, 63n, 66n
Bathe, Greville, cited, 63n, 66n
Battery, Henry's large galvanic, article on. *See* Electromagnetism, Henry articles, "Contributions I: Battery."
Bayard, Samuel, 132, 377
Bayard estate, 137
Beatty, John, 263
Beaufort, Francis, 285–286
Beaumont, Élie de, 271n
Beck, Charles F., 324
Beck, John Brodhead, 356
Beck, Paul, Jr., 324
Beck, Theodric Romeyn, 23, 28, 30, 128, 235, 236, 241, 245, 465, 469, 472
  letter from, 89–91
Becquerel, Antoine-César, 11–12, 14, 18n, 20n, 26–27, 67n, 75, 307n, 312n, 316, 350
Becquerel, Edmond, 307n, 308n, 348n
Beelzebub, 261
Beeson, Henry White, 232n
Behmen (Böhm), Jacob, 261–262

Index

485

Index

East India Company, 439, 440n, 445n
Easton's interior safety valve, 65n
Eaton, Amos, 149
Eclipses, solar, 324n, 347, 354n
École des mines, 143n
École polytechniques, 80n, 143n
Economic conditions
  Pennsylvania, 160n
  Philadelphia, 160–161
  United States, xiii, 59, 77n, 115n, 132, 145–146, 222, 223n, 285, 377
Edgehill School, 132n
Edinburgh Encyclopaedia, 28
Edinburgh New Philosophical Journal, 28
Edinburgh Philosophical Journal, 253
Edinburgh University, 23n, 87n, 237n, 393n
Edmonds, Franklin Spencer, cited, 21n, 130n
Edomites, 138n
Education, 80n, 247, 248, 254, 267
  of women, 188, 247–249
Electric eel, 109
Electrical fish, 88
Electricity
  analogy with light, xxvi, 387–388, 416
  animal electricity, 84, 85n, 86–87, 88, 109
  applications, 87n, 150–151
    to determine velocity of projectiles, xxix, 295–297, 301, 346, 353, 358, 411
  atmospheric electricity, 66n–67n, 82, 257, 392n
    apparatus, 292n–293n
  batteries
    Bunsen's, 133–134, 147, 154–155
    constant (Daniell's, sustaining), 47, 93n, 104n, 107, 108, 126–128, 154, 250, 397, 406
      use of paper in, 39–40, 42–43, 54
    Franklin's, 97, 101, 166, 169n, 395, 414, 427, 433, 434
    Grove's, 134, 374n
    Henry's, 4–5, 9n
    ignition of wires by, 410, 416
  conduction, xx, 102, 103n, 393n, 394, 401, 406–407, 438, 446n
  consecutive points, xxiii, 207, 208, 211, 215
  earth, as part of circuit, 283–284, 301n, 322n, 412
  free, xxvi, xxviii, 197, 402n, 405
  French discharger, 395
  Henry articles, xxix, 67n, 224n, 230n, 352n, 439n, 440n
  identity of static and galvanic, 246–247, 323
  insulating stool, 314n
  insulation, 321–323
  lateral discharge, xxi, xxiii–xxiv, xxv, xxvi–xxix, 66n, 67n, 130n, 215–216, 322–323, 352n, 395–396, 397, 398–401, 402, 405–406, 439n–440n, 441–445

light, electrical, 334, 339–340, 402, 437–438, 446n
  and phosphorescence, 11–12, 26–27, 334, 349–350, 358–359
  mechanical production of, 99, 407
  motions of mercury, 41–42
  non-conductors, role of, in discharge, 393n
  photography and, 38–39
  plenum, xxi, xxvi, 189, 274, 395, 415–416, 446n, 468
  polarization, xxvi, 333, 409
  static
    distribution of charge, 393, 401n
    induction from, xxi, xxiii–xxiv, 14n, 163n, 164–167, 168–171, 173–175, 176–179, 180–181, 182–183, 184, 186–187, 190–191, 193, 198–205, 206–211, 214–217, 218–221, 224–226, 228–229, 277–278, 394–395, 405–406, 419–422, 424–427, 428, 429–431, 432, 434–437, 440n, 446n, 461
    compared with galvanic induction, xxiii, xxv, 117–118, 164–165, 168–171, 397
    distance effects, 14–15, 97–98, 175–180, 181, 184–187, 198–203, 206–211, 212–214, 434–437
    higher order, 167, 168–172, 208, 433
    lateral induction, xxvii–xxix, 394–395, 398–401, 403–405, 437, 441
    over long distances, xxiii, xxv–xxvi, 88n, 215n, 238, 268, 273–274, 277–278, 279, 283–284, 411, 416–418, 468
    open secondary circuit, xxiii, 184, 196–197
    pierced cards determine direction of, xxi, xxiv, 419–420, 424–428, 429–431, 432
    return stroke, 194–195, 228–229
    vacuum, effects of, 93n, 105
    water, in circuit, effects of, 178, 181, 185–186, 201–203
  oscillatory discharge, xx, xxiii, xxiv–xxv, xxviii, 216–217, 221, 304, 395, 406, 422, 438–439, 446n
  screening, 163n, 166, 171, 205
  standard discharge, 93n, 96–97, 164–165
  from steam, 164
  theory of, 14–15, 105n–106n, 189n, 406, 409, 415, 416n, 438–439
  induction, xxvi–xxviii, 15n, 168, 172–173, 179, 204, 422, 437–438
  velocity of, 33n, 371, 374, 389, 411–412
  See also Electrometer; Lightning; Lightning rods; Thermoelectricity.
Electroacoustics, 33n, 40–41, 93–95, 99, 101–102, 109, 283
Electrochemistry, 42, 54, 317, 439

Index

Faculties, mental, xix, 249
Faith healing, 86n
Faraday, Michael, 22, 357n
   Faraday to A. D. Bache, 118–119

   and electric motor, 81, 82n, 122
   and Robert Hare, 9, 32, 82, 189, 401n, 409, 410
   opinion of Henry, 235n
   on lightning rods, 439–441, 446n
   research, xxix, 163n, 401, 409n
Faraday, Sarah Barnard (Mrs. Michael), 357n
Farr, Ellen R., cited, 270n
Farrar, John, 461n
Fausset, John, 83
Faust, A. B., cited, 30n
Fénelon (François de Salignac de la Mothe), 8n
Ferguson, James, 462, 465n, 472, 475, 476n, 477
Field, Richard Stockton, 132
Fiji Islands, 286
Filler, Louis, cited, 146n
Fincher, Joseph, 118–119
First Presbyterian Church, Baltimore, 74n
First Presbyterian Church, Brooklyn (Old School), 372n
Fish, Hamilton, 356
Fisher, James Cogswell, 374n
   letter from, 321–322
   letter to, 322–323
Fitch, Walter Hood, 305
Fitton, William Henry, 142n
Fizeau, Hippolyte Louis, 347n
Flora of North America, 240, 243, 273, 347n
Fluids, compressibility of, 28
Folsom, Charles, 23
   letter to, 390–391
Forbes, James David, 22n, 23–24, 237n, 241
   letter to, 235–236
Forces, correlation of, xiv, 106–107, 387, 416
Foreign Evangelical Society, 449n
Fourier's thermoscope of contact, 353
Fourth of July, 58, 59
Fowler, Maria, 118
Fox's dip circle, 282
Fraley, Frederick, 318, 458, 459n
France
   instrument makers, 236
   social status of scientists in, 80n
Franklin, Benjamin, 141, 151, 154, 318n, 354n, 450
   electrical equipment, 97, 101, 164, 166, 169n, 395, 414, 427, 433, 434, 443, 446n
   electrical theory, 409, 415, 416n
   Henry compared to, 140, 159–160, 235n, 354n
Franklin Institute, 61n, 280, 318n, 451, 462, 467

Journal, 133n, 465, 478n
   and steam boiler explosions, 65n
Frazer, G., 376
Frazer, John Fries, xiv, 130n, 353n, 458, 459n
   "Recommendation for," 478
Frazier, Arthur H., cited, 475n
Free electricity, xxvi, xxviii, 197, 402n, 405
Freeman, John Edgar, 375n
Frémont, J. C., 306
Frémont Expedition, 305n, 306n
French (language), 8, 18
French Revolution, 80n
Fresnel, Augustin Jean, 33n
Friedrich Wilhelm IV (King of Prussia), 142n
Froissart, John, 378
Fugitive Slave Law, 379n
Fulgurites, 311–312, 316–317, 366
Fuller, Robert C., cited, 313n
Fulminary tubes. *See* Fulgurites.
Fulton, Robert, 8n
Fusible metal, 63n, 64, 65n, 152–153

Gale, Leonard Dunnell, 322, 374n
Galvanometers, 107, 329, 407
   human, 40, 96, 164–165
   Melloni's, 327, 328
   See also Clarke, E. M., galvanometer.
Gardner, Daniel Pereira, 272–273
Garland of the West, 381
Gassiot, John P., xv, 323n
   letter to, 246–247
Gay-Lussac, Joseph Louis, 48, 461n
Gearand, M., 351
Geneva, University of, 143n
Geodesy, 124n
Geography, 381
Geological Society of London, 123n
Geology, 77, 120, 130n, 149, 271, 283, 474
   Henry's glossary of terms, 45n
   illustrations, 61, 361
   and religion, 44n–45n
   theories, 45n, 77n–78n, 79, 240n, 271–272, 361
   See also Henry, Joseph, teaching, geology.
Geophysics, 66n, 474n
George Heriot's Hospital (Edinburgh), 290n
German (language), 18n, 30, 134n
German philosophy, xviii, 259n, 262
Gerstner, Patsy A., cited, 271n, 361n
Gibbes, Lewis Reeve, 465n
   letter to, 466–468
Gibbes, Robert W., 86n
Gibbs, Oliver Wolcott, 356n, 366n
Gibson, J. Breckenridge, 44
Gibson, John, 386
Gibson, Margaret T., 132
Gibson, William J., 386
Giger, Frederick S., 8n, 44

Index

Potter, Alonzo, 352n, 353
Potter, Ludlow D., 44
Potter, Richard, 103n
Pouillet, Claude-Servais-Mathias, 32, 33n, 34, 48
Powder magazines, protection from lightning, 439, 440n, 441, 446
Powell, Baden, xvi, 238, 239, 240n
Powell, Hugh, 325n
Powell and Lealand, microscope, 324–326
Presbyterian Church, xviii, 105n, 187, 239n, 354, 372n, 375n
Presl, K. B., 305
Prevost, Jean-Louis, 86, 123
Prevost, Pierre, 86n, 123
Prevost, Theodosia Ann Mary, 379
Priestley, Joseph, xxviii, 102, 402
Princeton (college), xiii, xix, 131, 140n, 148n
  botany, 78, 84, 136, 243n
  calendar, 58, 93n, 392, 448, 450
  campus, 278, 279, 411, 468
  catalogue, 29n, 240n, 320, 377, 379
  chemistry, 39, 140n, 243
  East College, 278
  enrollment, 58–59, 132, 377, 448, 450
  examinations, 78, 381, 382, 385, 386, 448
  faculty, xiv, 7–8, 18n, 38, 39, 43n, 84, 105n, 132, 139, 158n, 160n, 222n, 237n, 240, 243, 259–261, 291, 319, 354, 356n, 377, 459–460
    Members of the Faculty of the College of New Jersey to President Tyler, 459–460
  finances, xiii, 132, 136, 148, 222, 223n, 377
  French, 8
  geography, 381
  geology, 8n, 43–44, 45n, 59, 61, 76, 78–79, 85, 149, 379
  German, 30n
  honorary degrees, 237, 251n, 289–290
  Library, 136, 276–277, 411n, 416
  literary societies, 278n, 279, 383
  missionary society, 375
  moral philosophy, 8
  museum, 89, 136, 184, 185
  Nassau Hall, 276–277, 278, 378n, 411
  Nassau Hall Education Society, 17n
  Nassau Monthly, 261
  philosophical apparatus, 33n, 89, 133, 135, 156, 161–162, 236, 241, 273. *See also* Henry, Joseph, European trip, purchases, apparatus.
  Philosophical Hall, xxiii, 133, 184n, 185, 276–277, 411, 416
  students, 17n–18n, 31n, 43–44, 45n, 58, 84, 137, 138n, 160, 259–263, 290–291, 292n, 360n, 365, 378n, 383, 384n, 386
    letter from senior class, 43–45
    discipline, 139, 259n, 260–261, 290–291, 319–320, 365
    graduates, 17n, 38n, 49n, 63n, 75, 105n,

129n, 138n, 158n, 225n, 235n, 237, 246, 288n, 293n, 303n, 320n, 337n, 372n, 375n, 383, 470n
    Henry's relations with, 7–8, 15–16, 139, 260–262, 291, 293–294, 465, 479
  Trustees, xix, 8n, 17n, 74n, 105n, 135, 148n, 223n, 289, 290, 291, 319–320, 381n, 462n, 473
    "Minutes," 89
  tuition, 89, 135, 223n
  West College, 278
Princeton (ship), 294n, 297n
Princeton (town), 137, 138, 258, 281n, 367, 371, 380
Princeton Academy, 124n
Princeton Blues (militia), 137n
Princeton Theological Seminary, 267, 378
  faculty, 105n, 287n
  Lenox Hall, 378
  students, 74n, 75n, 124n, 130n, 235n, 287n, 293n, 368n, 372n, 375n, 449n
    financial aid, 287
  Trustees, 74n, 381n
Princeton Whig, 137n, 138n, 381, 423n
Priority disputes
  Henry, 14, 28, 81, 82n, 122, 229–230, 444n
  Melloni, heat, 125
  Moser-Draper, 347n
  Saxton-Fizeau, 347n
Pritchard polarizer, 33n
Professionalization of science, 87–88, 258n, 467n
Progress, Henry on, xix
Projectiles, velocity of, 294–297
  application of electricity to, xxix, 295–297, 301, 411
  Henry paper on, xxix, 295n, 297n, 301n, 346, 353, 358, 411n
Protestantism, 238n–239n
Proudfit, David L., 10, 11
Providence, R. I., 281n
Prussia, meteorology in, 24n–25n
Prussian Institute of Meteorology, 24n
Pseudo-science. *See* Charlatanism.
Psychrometer, 25n
Pumpelly, Harmon, 77
Pusey, Edward, 238n
Putnam, Wiley &, 256n, 265, 384, 448

Quackery. *See* Charlatanism.
Quarterly Journal of Pure and Applied Mathematics, 92n
Quebec (city), 282
Quebec (province), 281n
Queen's College, Cork, 407n
Quetelet, Lambert-Adolphe-Jacques, 237n, 295n
  letter to, 241–242
Quimby, A. M., 130, 131n, 304